To Mustafa,

With best regards,

Art Palmer   May 1, 2008

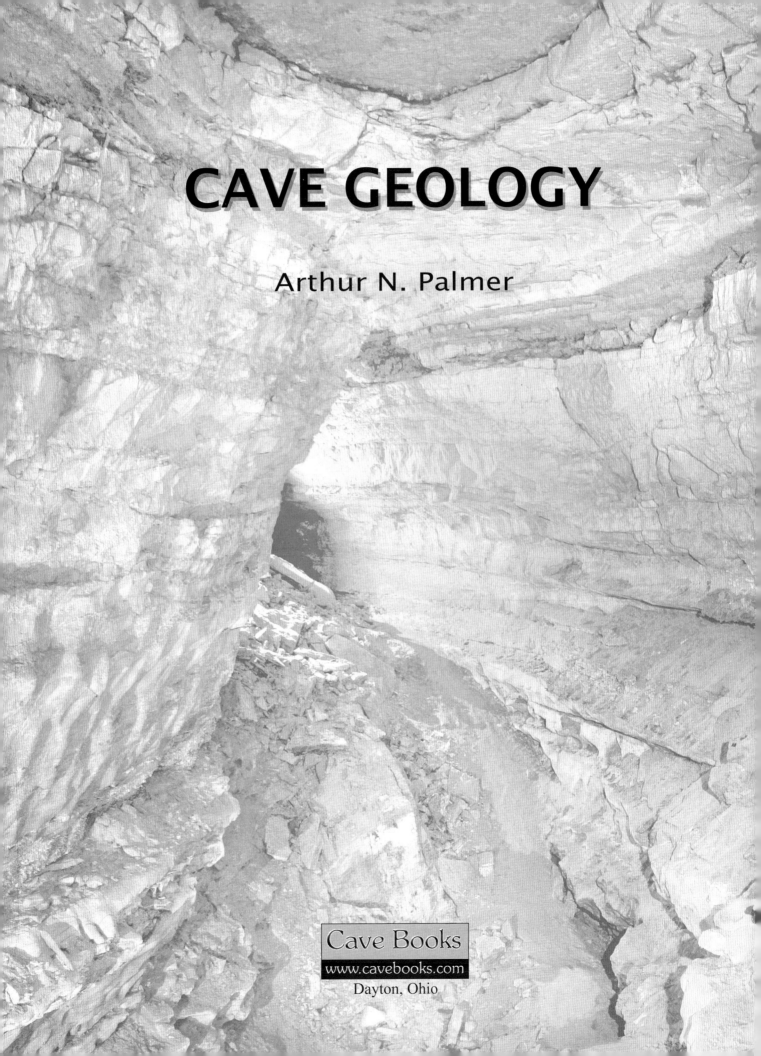

CAVE GEOLOGY

Arthur N. Palmer

Cave Books
www.cavebooks.com
Dayton, Ohio

Published by CAVE BOOKS, 4700 Amberwood Drive, Dayton, OH 45424-4602, U.S.A.

CAVE BOOKS is the publications affiliate of the Cave Research Foundation.

Editor: Richard A. Watson
Publishers: Roger E. McClure, Paul J. Steward
Layout and Graphics: A. N. Palmer

Library of Congress Cataloging-in-Publication Data

Palmer, Arthur N.
  Cave geology / Arthur N. Palmer.
    p. cm.
  ISBN-13: 978-0-939748-66-2 (hardback : alk. paper)
  ISBN-10: 0-939748-66-5 (hardback : alk. paper)
1. Speleology. 2. Caves. I. Title.
  GB601.P35 2006
  551.44'7--dc22
                        2006036330

Printed in the United States of America by Allen Press, Lawrence, Kansas

Contents

Front cover: View from the entrance of Grotte de la Diau, in the Parmelan Plateau of eastern France.

Back cover: Clockwise from top left: Flowstone in Tower Place, Lechuguilla Cave, Carlsbad Caverns National Park, New Mexico. Descending a vertical shaft in McFail's Cave, New York. Main stream passage in Blue Spring Cave, Indiana.

Title page: View in Mammoth Cave, Mammoth Cave National Park, Kentucky.

Photographs in this book are by the author, except where indicated otherwise.

Preface

CAVE GEOLOGY, as treated in this book, concerns not only the geology and origin of caves, but also related aspects such as hydrology, geochemistry, and microbiology. All cave sciences are combined in the field of *speleology*. More than any other science, speleology is closely tied to exploration and adventure. Anyone can participate in it. For that reason, I have tried to make this book accessible to non-scientists, but at the same time provide details that will be useful at all levels. My main concern is to introduce topics that can be applied in the field, in hopes that this book will serve as a bridge between exploration and science, and between observation and interpretation.

There are many books with strong coverage of surface karst — the distinctive landscape that forms on soluble rock. This one focuses specifically on the underlying caves. Surface processes and landscapes are described here too, but mainly in terms of how they influence the subsurface features.

There are several reasons for this emphasis. To understand surface karst, it is necessary to have a thorough knowledge of the underlying cave-forming processes. Familiarity with caves is also important if we are to deal effectively with groundwater supply, contaminant transport, and land stability in karst regions, and to understand the origin and distribution of certain petroleum reservoirs and ore deposits. Most researchers in these fields prefer not to venture into caves, and this book can provide background to support their work.

Cave geology is a science, so the metric system is used throughout this book. A few American equivalents are inserted where appropriate. A guide to conversion of units between the two systems is shown on the final page.

Other books on cave science include those by Jennings (1985), Trudgill (1985), Dreybrodt (1988), White (1988), Ford and Williams (1989), Gillieson (1996), Moore and Sullivan (1997), and an international volume edited by Klimchouk and others (2000). Two encyclopedias of cave and karst science have recently appeared, edited by Gunn (2004a) and by Culver and White (2005). For further references, see *A Guide to Speleological Literature of the English Language, 1794–1996* (Northup and others, 1998), and a recent synopsis of the important literature in cave science (Proudlove, 2006). A new book by Ford and Williams (2007) is now the professional standard in karst hydrology and geomorphology. I strongly recommend it for all advanced researchers in those fields.

Some cave-related topics that are mentioned only briefly in this book are covered thoroughly elsewhere. These include cave biology (Culver, 1982), archeology (Watson, 1998), cave management and protection (Hildreth-Werker and Werker, 2006), history (Shaw, 1992), and exploration techniques (for example, Marbach and Tourte, 2002).

Speleology has a rich international flavor, and I have included as much important work from non-English sources as possible. Still, the main sources and field examples are American. Uncredited statements in this book are based either on personal observation or what I consider to be general knowledge.

I have tried to answer the many questions posed over the years by students and colleagues. For field examples, I have relied on my own experience wherever possible, while still covering alternative ideas of others. As a result, certain caves are used repeatedly to illustrate concepts. This is not a drawback, because they include some of the world's finest caves. Most are easily accessible to others and are also well supervised and protected.

This book will eventually have a companion: *Cave Biology*, by Kathleen Lavoie. We originally planned to be co-authors of a single book, *Introduction to Speleology*, but it grew too big and is now two volumes. Readers are encouraged to consult Kathy's book too, because the link between biology and geology is significant.

Because of its varied history, this book contains some elementary sections that seem at odds with the technical parts. I decided to keep the parts on exploration and personal impressions, such as those that begin and end the book, for three reasons: First, these topics provide comfortable ground for explorers who are making their first acquaintance with cave geology. Second, many people step laterally into cave science from advanced positions in other fields, and they may welcome the chance to fill in the background information that they lack. Finally, I still feel that science is an adventure.

Some readers will wish I had omitted the equations. Skip over them if you like, because their meanings are explained in the text. But be aware that the equations are intended for real use. They are powerful tools.

Our two books on geology and biology came about because of the inspiration of Richard A. "Red" Watson, the presently retired editor-in-chief of Cave Books. He not only saw the need for easily accessible books on cave science, but also provided the necessary badgering for us to see these projects through. His editorial suggestions were invaluable.

I am also indebted to the following people for their contributions: Roger McClure and Paul Steward of Cave Books helped with the logistics of production. Paul also served as copy-editor. John Andersland of Western Kentucky University reviewed the technical chapters and added many new questions to answer. Richard Zopf of Yellow Springs, Ohio, reviewed the semi-final version of the book, and William R. Halliday of Nashville, Tennessee, reviewed the first draft of Chapter 10. Penny Boston tested preliminary versions of the book in her classes at New Mexico Tech. Andrei Filippov of Toronto provided helpful information about the karst regions of eastern Russia (Chapter 2). Many photographers and mappers contributed generously to this book and are credited individually in the figure captions. Uncredited photos and diagrams are my own.

Most of all, thanks to Margaret (Peggy) Palmer, my wife and companion, who provided so much editing, personal insight, and encouragement. I dedicate this book to her. She, however, prefers the following dedication:

Our lives have been greatly enriched by the many people who share a passion for caves. Our appreciation and thanks to you all.

A.N. Palmer
2007

THE *mountain stream tumbled over a ledge of New England marble and disappeared under a low arch. We two teenage brothers ducked inside and aimed our flashlights into the dark passage beyond. Our first cave — and only a few miles from home! Crawling on hands and knees, then climbing down through waterfalls that cut deeply into the banded marble, we followed the underground stream for half an hour and finally stood in a high room where the ceiling was lost in shadow. The stream gurgled into a narrow impenetrable crack, which by our reckoning must have fed the cold spring we had passed on our way up the mountain.*

We were not alone. By chance our visit coincided with an expedition by some of the country's top cave scientists. They showed us their headlamps and protective helmets, and recommended that we leave behind the rope we had brought as a handline. We shared their dismay at seeing a name thoughtlessly scratched in the cave wall by a previous visitor.

The scientists' goal was to make a plaster cast of the ripple-like hollows dissolved in the marble by the underground stream. When the plaster had set, they gently nudged the cast to peel it from the wall. It did not move. Then they pried at it with a knife without success. Finally, one of them hung from the cast with both hands, while another hauled on his legs. The plaster still did not budge. A later trip with a chisel and soft scrub brush was needed to remove it.

For us, though, it was a wildly successful trip. It introduced us to what caves are like, how they form, and how to explore them. We learned about proper equipment, caving ethics, and cave science. We made lasting friends. We will never forget the echo of our voices in that stream-carved tunnel, or the shadows playing across the walls as our lights probed the darkness. The magic of that experience is still a vivid memory. And now, many years later, one of us would like to describe where a little adventure like this can lead.

1

Speleology: The science of caves

A CAVE is a natural void beneath the land surface that is large enough to admit humans. Nearly all caves extend into total darkness. Many underground openings are too small to enter, and some of them have the same origin as caves, but these tiny pores and fissures are not defined as true caves because we cannot explore them ourselves. A cave provides a first-hand view of the subsurface, and this is what makes the exploration and science of caves such an intimate experience. The same urge to take a personal look is what sent humans to the Moon.

Perhaps no other natural features evoke such a broad range of images in the public mind as do caves. To some people they mean adventure, beauty, or mystery. In others they arouse anxiety or even fear. The impression among scientists is just as varied. Most feel that crawling underground, with only a portable light to ward off total darkness, does not fit their image of scientific research. But scientists who venture into caves are rewarded with greatly enhanced insight into their specialties. For example, what better place is there to study underground water and rock structure? Where else can one find such stable biological habitats? Even solutional openings that are too small to enter are important, because they have a great effect on subsurface water, biology, and oil and mineral distribution.

Figure 1.1: Cave entrances in marble, White Chief, California.

The study of caves is the science of *speleology* (from the Greek *spelaion* = cave). Its most fundamental aspect is geology. As treated in this book, cave geology includes a large dose of hydrology and chemistry, and even a little meteorology and microbiology. It also concerns the distinctive landscapes known as *karst*, which result from the dissolving of bedrock, the same process that forms most large caves (Figure 1.1).

Caves have played an important part in human history. Their importance to prehistoric cultures is shown by the many artifacts unearthed in caves throughout the world, and by the exquisite cave paintings of southwestern Europe, some of which date as far back as 30,000 years.

The earliest systematic cave studies date from the 16th and 17th centuries in Europe and China. As an independent science, speleology can be traced most directly to the work of Edouard-Alfred Martel in France near the beginning of the 20th century. It was a late-blooming science, and most of its fundamental concepts have been established only in the past half century. The main reason for this slow progress is that caves cannot be studied without exploration and mapping, and until a large number had been documented throughout the world it was impossible to come to sound conclusions about their features and origins.

Speleology is often considered as much a sport as a science. This book focuses on science, but most speleologists enjoy both. In the popular media, cave explorers are often called *spelunkers* (from the Latin *spelunca* = cave). This word was devised by New England cavers in the 1930s, but today it implies amateurism and experienced cavers avoid it.

A great deal of important speleological field work is done by non-scientists, whose exploration and mapping make the science possible. Hundreds of thousands of caves are known throughout the world, and discoveries continue at a greater rate than ever before. Many of the world's most significant caves have been documented only within the past few decades. Caves are among the last geographic frontiers on Earth, and their scientific value is just beginning to be appreciated.

Cave types

There are many varieties of caves that differ greatly in origin and appearance. Their classification is informal and flexible. Caves are most often grouped by *origin* — whether they formed by dissolution, volcanic activity, mechanical erosion, melting of glacial ice, physical stress within the Earth, or accumulation of boulders at the base of a slope. One complexity is that many caves have a composite origin, or their origin may be uncertain. Artificial tunnels and mines are not considered caves, but they can contain many natural deposits similar to those of true caves.

Caves can also be grouped according to the *type of host rock* — for example, limestone, lava, granite, etc. (see Chapter 3). In some situations a cave's *shape* is the most appropriate aspect. Some are best described as crevice or shelter caves, regardless of their origin or rock type. Archeologists often

a

b

Figure 1.2: Common cave types: (**a**) *solution cave*: Križna jama, Slovenia; (**b**) *volcanic cave*: a Hawaiian lava-tube cave (photo by Bern Szukalski); (**c**) *glacier cave*: Bering Glacier, Alaska (Mark Tracy); (**d**) *stream-cut cave* in granite: Millerton Lakes Cave System, California (Dave Bunnell); (**e**) *wave-cut cave*: Lady's Harbor Cave, California (Dave Bunnell); (**f**) *shelter cave* in sandy limestone, Arizona, containing the pre-Columbian "Montezuma's Castle," built by members of the Sinagua culture; (**g**) *crevice cave*: Big Long Porcupine Sea Cave, Maine, modified by wave action (Steve Higham); (**h**) *talus cave*: Lucky Seven Cave, Massachusetts; (**i**) *framework cave* in a stream-deposited tufa mound, Van Hornesville, New York.

d

c

e

f

g

h

i

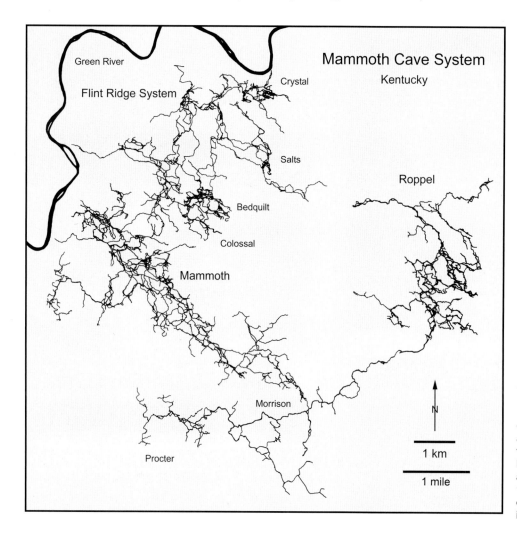

Figure 1.3: Map of the Mammoth Cave System, Kentucky. This cave consists of several different sections that were explored separately. Later discoveries linked the different parts together. The various names (Salts Cave, etc.) were given to those sections before they were connected. The combined length is currently almost 600 km. All active passages drain to the Green River, as did all presently inactive ones. Simplified from map by Cave Research Foundation (Roppel section by Central Kentucky Karst Coalition). Fisher Ridge Cave, with 177 km of mapped passages, lies to the northeast and reaches to within a few hundred meters of Roppel Cave. (See Brucker and Watson, 1976; Bean, 1987; Borden and Brucker, 2000).

Note: At this small scale, the cave passages appear only as dark lines. This applies to most cave maps in this book, except for a few such as those in Figures 1.7 and 1.18, which show both walls of the passages and some internal detail.

use this approach because it relates most directly to how caves have been used by humans. Any or all of these classification schemes can be used in the way that best suits the purpose.

The term *cave system* refers to a group of interconnected or related caves. The best example is the Mammoth Cave System, in Kentucky, which consists of several nearly independent sections that were explored separately and later found to be connected. Caves that consist of highly integrated passages explored from a single entrance, or from two or more entrances already known to lead into the same cave, are not often called cave systems. To a geologist, caves that are unconnected by exploration can still be considered part of a single cave system if the individual caves are, or once were, linked by underground streams. Either approach is valid as long as the context is clear.

What is the difference between a *cave* and a *cavern*? *Cavern* implies grandeur, which is appropriate only for caves with large rooms or spacious corridors. Carlsbad Cavern of New Mexico is a worthy example. Not surprisingly, a cave may suddenly undergo a name change to cavern when it is opened for public tours.

The major cave types are introduced here, grouped primarily by origin. Examples are shown in Figure 1.2.

Solution caves

Solution caves are formed by the dissolving action of underground water as it passes through pores and fissures in soluble bedrock such as limestone. The water chemically enlarges the openings and carries away the dissolved material. The process is called *dissolution*, and the fluid that does the dissolving is the *solution*. The term *dissolution cave* is more appropriate but is not so widely used.

Most of this book is concerned with solution caves, so they are described here only in general terms. They hold the greatest interest to scientists and explorers because they are the largest, most common, and most varied, and they provide much information about local geologic history. They are intimately related to the movement of underground water, and a knowledge of their patterns is essential to understanding water supplies and groundwater contamination in soluble rocks.

A typical solution cave has a branching pattern like that of a river. This pattern is usually complicated by several levels of development, some of which may be dry today. This complexity is illustrated by the map of Mammoth Cave, Kentucky (Figure 1.3), which shows hundreds of kilometers of passages that cross one another on many levels. Some solution caves have maze-like patterns of intersecting passages or of irregular rooms like the holes in a sponge.

Volcanic caves

Volcanic caves (or *lava caves*) are formed by molten lava that solidifies at the Earth's surface. The lava originates beneath the surface and erupts through fissures or vents. Most volcanic caves are produced when the outer surface of the lava solidifies to form a crust, while the remaining liquid flows out from beneath it. Fissures and pockets can also form in the solidifying mass. The volcanic vents that spew the lava, once they become inactive, may also be accessible to explorers for short distances. Volcanic caves are most common on the flanks of volcanic peaks that are continually or periodically still active, or which ceased to be active within the past few thousand years.

Examples include nearly all the caves of Hawai'i. By far the longest and deepest known volcanic cave is Kazumura Cave on Mt. Kilauea. It is 65.5 km long and spans a vertical range of 1102 meters. The deepest vertical drop in any cave in the United States is the volcanic pit Na One, at 263 m, on the flanks of Mt. Hualalai.

Volcanic caves are described in detail in Chapter 11.

Glacier caves

Glacier caves form by the melting of channels inside glacial ice. Although not technically under the *ground*, they are widely considered to be caves. They are sometimes called *ice caves*, but this name has long been applied to caves that simply *contain* ice (Balch, 1900). Glacier caves and their origin are described in detail by Eraso and Pulina (1992) and summarized by Fountain (2005).

Meltwater descends along fissures in a glacier surface or along its edges. Vertical pits in a glacier where water enters are called *moulins*. The flowing water extends the melting process deep into the ice mass, where it widens narrow crevices into caves. The openings are enlarged further by the scouring action of rocks carried by the water and by the circulation of warm air from the surface. Most glacier caves are tubular or canyon-like, and some contain vertical pits. A few join one another as underground tributaries or split apart in the downstream direction (Figure 1.4). Streams typically reach terminal pools, but some water eventually reaches the glacier's base, where it flows along the underlying rock or sediment. Most glacier caves are dry during the winter, but many are inaccessible during the summer because of the large flow of meltwater. The caves originate as water-filled tubes, but eventually tend to have narrow slots carved in their floors by streams. Summer deepening of passage floors can be as much as one meter per week.

Although glaciers move slowly by their own weight, moulins and crevasses tend to form at the same places year after year, despite the fact that the ice has moved downhill. This is because the sink points and fractures are influenced mainly by the shape of the ice surface and its underlying rock bed, which do not change much from year to year (Badino, 2001). While new caves form at favorable sites, old ones are carried downhill by the moving glaciers and are gradually destroyed by melting or crushing. Glacier caves do not often form beneath swarms of crevasses in the ice surface, because meltwater is dispersed among too many openings.

Studies in Nepal show that many glacier caves form along favorable zones, which consist of formerly sediment-filled crevasses that were later closed tight by glacial movement (Benn and Gulley, 2006). Water moves easily through the sand and gravel fill and melts the surrounding ice to form caves. In a similar manner, most caves in Alaska's Matanuska Glacier have formed along *crevasse traces*, which are veins of clear ice formed along zones of fracturing and recrystallization (Gulley, 2006).

Paradise Ice Cave, in the Paradise-Stevens Glacier on Mt. Rainier, Washington, was once the largest known glacier cave, with 13 km of mapped passages (Figure 1.4), but in recent years it has melted away almost entirely. The Greenland ice cap contains many spectacular shafts, including some that descend more than 150 meters. Beyond that depth the flow of ice caused by its own weight tends to seal any openings.

Glacier caves can also form by the melting action of volcanic emissions. Near the top of Mt. Baker in Washington, volcanic heat has enlarged fissures in ice into small caves. Their appeal is diminished by low oxygen, sulfurous gases, boiling water, falling ice blocks, and quicksand. Another type of glacier cave is produced where ice moves over a bedrock projection or boulder and leaves a pocket in its base in the downflow direction.

Some meltwater tunnels can form in snow and non-glacial ice, but most people consider them too transient to be true caves.

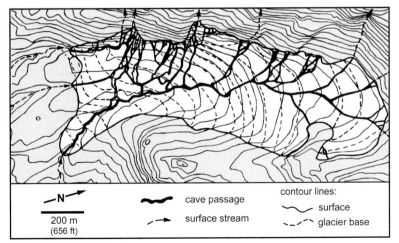

Figure 1.4: Map of Paradise Ice Cave, Mt. Rainier, Washington, showing the size of the cave in 1988. The extent of the ice at that time is shown in white. Since then the glacier has melted and the cave has disappeared. From a map by Charles Anderson and Mark Vining (Anderson and others, 1994).

Erosion caves

Erosion caves are the result of mechanical scouring by moving water. They are rare, and most are small. They can be grouped according to the specific process involved:

Stream-cut caves are formed by water that flows through fissures in bedrock and widens them by mechanical erosion. Most of the erosion is caused by sediment grains carried by the moving water. Enlargement is aided by weathering of the bedrock into loose grains that are carried away by the underground stream. Solution caves are not included in this group, even though erosion may account for some of their enlargement.

The Greenhorn Cave System, California, is one of the largest examples at 1.4 km long and 152 m deep. Figure 1.2d shows the nearby Millerton Lakes Cave. Both are formed in granite and have roofs composed of boulder bridges and offset bedrock slabs. The National Speleological Society's *NSS News* of April, 1986, contains several articles on these caves. Pike's Peak, Colorado, also contains a stream-cut cave, 770-meter-long Hurricane Cave (Luiszer and Frazier, 1997).

Wave-cut caves develop along fractures or weak rock layers by the impact of waves on shoreline cliffs that border the ocean or, less commonly, a large lake. They are also known as ***sea caves*** or ***littoral caves***. Most are located where waves converge, so that their erosive force is concentrated on small areas of the shore. For this reason, projecting headlands are favorable for caves. Waves diverge as they enter broad coves and inlets, so the erosive force is dissipated over a wide shoreline and is less likely to form caves. Once a cave opening has formed, the percussive effect of incoming waves can be enormous, especially during storms. Some wave-cut caves are enlarged further by the boring action of marine animals.

The best known wave-cut cave is Fingal's Cave, on the Island of Staffa, in western Scotland. Its dramatic setting inspired one of Mendelssohn's finest orchestral works. Wave-cut caves are spectacularly developed along the southern California coast and in the nearby Channel Islands (Bunnell, 1995). The longest known wave-cut cave is Painted Cave, on Santa Cruz Island, California, with a mapped length of 374 m. Riko Riko Cave in New Zealand is perhaps the world's largest wave-cut cave, with a volume of 221,500 cubic meters (Bunnell, 2004).

Piping caves form where loose soil or sediment subsides into zones of rapid underground water flow and is carried out to the surface at lower elevations (Halliday, 2004a). The piping process is also known as ***suffosion***. Small tubular or pipe-like openings can be formed in this way. A few piping caves reach lengths of several hundred meters. The Anvil Points Claystone Caves of western Colorado have branching patterns like those of many solution caves, with roofs up to 20 m thick (Davis, 1999). Piping caves are thought to originate when fine particles are flushed out by groundwater seepage along poorly consolidated zones in the sediment. Eventu-

ally the openings grow large enough to carry considerable streamflow, which enlarges the caves further by erosion (Clausen, 1970; Rogers, 1981). In dry climates the roofs of many piping caves are strengthened by mineral deposits that accumulate when moisture evaporates.

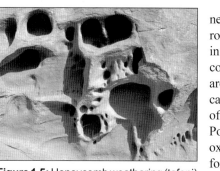

Figure 1.5: Honeycomb weathering (tafoni) in sandstone, near Moab, Utah (width of photo is 1.5 m).

Honeycomb weathering consists of networks of small holes in poorly soluble rocks (Figure 1.5). It is most common in dry climates. Massive sandstone, consolidated volcanic ash, and granite are most susceptible. The holes (also called ***tafoni***) enlarge by crystallization of minerals carried by seeping water. Poorly soluble minerals such as iron oxides harden the outer rock surfaces, to form lip-like rims around the individual holes. Few of the openings are of cave size. Most are tens of centimeters in diameter and rarely more than a meter.

Shelter caves

Shelter caves are produced by the selective weathering of weak rocks overlain by more resistant ones. They can also form along fracture zones in otherwise uniform rocks. Most shelter caves are simply recessed niches in cliff faces. They tend to be broad and shallow and follow the exposed outlines of the weak rock. The exact rock type and cave-forming process do not have to be considered.

Some shelter caves are formed by turbulence and splashing at the bases of waterfalls. Weathering of these kinds can also widen the mouths of other cave types, regardless of their origin. A few curious shelter caves are excavated by large animals, such as elephants, which gouge and lick soluble rock exposures for their salt content (Lundberg and McFarlane, 2006; Lundquist and Varnedoe, 2006).

Many shelter caves serve as homes for animals. Some were used as shelters by early humans, and the practice continues even today for a few people in various parts of the world. The most renowned shelter caves are those of Mesa Verde National Park in Colorado, which contain well-preserved 13th century stone buildings of the Ancestral Pueblo people. The most popular human habitats were high in the walls of stream canyons, where they could provide shelter, strong defensive positions, and access to fertile strips of land in the valleys below.

Crevice caves

Crevice caves, or ***fissure caves***, are widened cracks, or networks of cracks, produced by stresses in Earth's crust or by gravitational sliding of near-surface rock masses on steep mountainsides. They are sometimes called ***tectonic caves***, although not all are formed by tectonic processes (widespread deformation of bedrock by internal stress). Many crevice caves result from a combination of processes. Dissolution is not the major agent in forming caves, but it can help to enlarge crevices that originally formed by mechanical processes. Although crevices in bedrock are common, traversable crevice caves are fairly rare. Most are located in hard, competent rock, but any type of rock that undergoes sufficient tensional stress is suitable.

The guiding fractures are typically steeply inclined or almost vertical. Most crevice caves have long narrow passages with nearly parallel walls (Figure 1.6). They have irregular floors formed by fallen rocks, soil, and perhaps vegetal debris. With depth, many crevice caves pinch out downward or become too narrow to follow. Some are roofed as the result of differing slip rates between slabs, where the roof blocks move more rapidly (or, rarely, more slowly) than those beneath. Some crevice caves are roofed by soil held together by vegetation. The spectacular "earth cracks" in northern Arizona, near the Grand Canyon, are fault-guided crevice caves as much as 165 m deep (Halliday, 2004b).

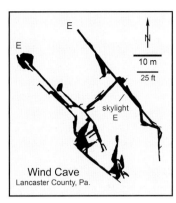

Figure 1.6: Map of a crevice cave formed along fractures by gravitational sliding of blocks of insoluble schist along a river bank. The passages are roofed by slabs that did not move when the fissures opened. The rooms were widened by collapse. E = entrance. Note the small scale. Map by Bernard Smeltzer, from Stone (1953.)

Talus caves

Talus caves, or *boulder caves*, consist of voids between boulders in the talus piles that accumulate at the bases of cliffs or steep slopes. They are roofed by overlapping blocks, as well as by soil mats held in place by vegetation. Their internal spaces interconnect in complex three-dimensional labyrinths. Their maps look confusing because the accessible parts are bounded by a jumble of rock (Figure 1.7). Talus caves can form in all rock types, but massive, competent rock that breaks cleanly along fractures is most likely to form the large boulders necessary for this kind of cave. There is debate as to which is the largest talus cave, but some have several

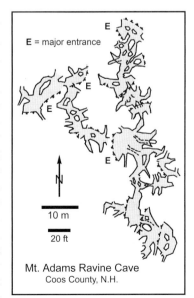

Figure 1.7: Map of a typical talus cave. The accessible cave is shown in gray. It is composed of the spaces between blocks of schist and quartzite (Chapter 3). From map by Robert W. Carroll, Jr. (Higham, 2002).

Figure 1.8: Exploration of a stream passage in a solution cave. The water is still enlarging the cave. (Cueva del Agua, Spain.)

kilometers of explorable openings. Significant talus caves are rare, but in regions of steep topography and little soluble rock or volcanic rock, they may be the dominant type.

Framework caves

Framework caves are produced by *accumulation* of material, rather than its removal. For example, many reefs contain internal voids surrounded by irregular coral growth. Surface streams fed by limestone springs can deposit calcium carbonate as *tufa*, a highly porous type of limestone that forms in fresh water, and at waterfalls the tufa may grow outward as shelves or canopies to form caves (Figure 1.2i).

Some geologists speak of *primary* and *secondary* caves. Framework caves, and most caves in lava, are considered primary, because they formed at the same time as the host rock. Other types of caves are secondary, as they formed later than the rock. These terms are too broad for any but the most general use, because many primary caves have also been modified by secondary processes.

Cave exploration

Even the most scientifically oriented speleologist must learn the basic techniques of cave exploration. Some research can be pursued in easily accessible caves, perhaps along public tour routes, but a full understanding of speleology comes only from exposure to the entire range of cave conditions.

Figure 1.9: Most caves require a great deal of scrambling, climbing, and crawling. Many are warm and dry enough that they can be explored with traditional field clothes. (Clover Hollow Cave, Virginia.)

Nationwide speleological organizations in the U.S.

National Speleological Society
2813 Cave Avenue
Huntsville, AL 35810-4431
(256) 852-1300
www.caves.org

National Cave and Karst Research Institute
1400 University Drive,
Carlsbad, NM 88220
www2.nature.nps.gov/nckri

Cave Research Foundation
177 Hamilton Valley Road
Cave City, KY 42127
www.cave-research.org

Karst Waters Institute
P.O. Box 4142
Leesburg, VA 20177
www.karstwaters.org

American Cave Conservation Association
P.O. Box 409
Horse Cave, KY 42749
(270) 786-1466
www.cavern.org

Those who venture into "wild" caves, which have not been developed for the public, should follow a few common-sense guidelines:

- Never explore alone. A party of 4 or 5 usually offers the ideal balance between safety and efficiency.
- Ask the cave owners or managers for permission and treat them courteously.
- For head protection, wear a helmet approved specifically for climbing or caving. It should have a chin strap with a 4-point suspension and a mount for a headlamp.
- In addition to a primary light source, each person needs to carry at least two spare lights and to be familiar with the operation and repair of them all. Each should provide enough light for getting out of the cave. Electric lamps are usually preferred for their intensity and ease of use. They are typically powered by batteries mounted on the helmet or waist. LED lamps are popular because they are long lasting and require only small battery packs. Carbide lamps are also used for caving, although their popularity is rapidly waning. They run on calcium carbide and water, which combine to form acetylene, a combustible gas. A small flame from the burning gas provides a bright cheery light.
- Move carefully through the cave, stay in contact with the rest of your party, and be willing to lend a hand to your companions at difficult places.

- Notify someone of your destination, when you expect to return, and whom to contact if you are late. If problems arise, the appropriate contact is one of the regional cave rescue groups of the National Speleological Society (see address above), rather than the local police or fire department, who are rarely trained in cave rescue.
- Do not disturb the cave or its contents, and as much as possible leave no trace of your visit.

Caving gear should be selected according to local conditions. Buy it only from specialty suppliers whose products have been designed and tested specifically for caving. The photographs in this book show a wide variety of clothing and equipment. Casual clothing and minimal equipment are appropriate only in caves that pose little hazard, such as those with tour trails open to the public.

The most popular caving attire consists of an abrasion-resistant one-piece oversuit and a warm undersuit, both of synthetic material (Figure 1.8). In wet or cold caves a hood or balaclava and neoprene socks and offer additional protection. Cotton work clothes are acceptable in warm dry caves (Figure 1.9). Synthetic fabrics are preferred because they are warmer, more durable for their weight, and easier

Figure 1.10: Typical equipment for exploring cold or wet caves: synthetic suit, rubber boots and gloves, climbing gear for vertical ascent and descent. (Preparing to ascend a rope in the Siebenhengste Cave System, Switzerland.)

to clean. They also shed less lint, which is a subtle form of contamination. In cold caves, especially where the level of activity is expected to vary, layered clothing can provide adjustable protection. In very warm caves, the best clothing may be only shorts and a T-shirt. In caves that are highly vulnerable to damage or degradation, Lycra clothing and non-marking boots are advised, and soft-soled neoprene socks are worn where delicate floor features might be scuffed by normal footwear.

Boots of medium height provide the best ankle support, although some cavers prefer calf-high rubber boots for their ruggedness and resistance to water and mud. Lugged soles usually work best, although some boots have soles that are dangerously slick, having been designed only for show. Knee pads offer protection where crawling or awkward scrambling is required. Heavy reinforced kneepads are best for extensive crawling, but otherwise the soft flexible variety will do. Elbow pads are appreciated in rough, jagged caves. Gloves provide both warmth and protection. They can be an impediment in technical vertical caving but are essential in cold and wet caves, where rubber and neoprene are the favored materials (Figure 1.10). A life jacket or

other flotation device is appropriate for underground rivers or lakes, even for skilled swimmers. The power of rapidly flowing water should not be underestimated.

Caves present such a wide range of unpredictable conditions that the skills required to explore them must be learned only from experienced cavers. Vertical pitches require specialized rope techniques, which are best learned gradually over time (Figure 1.11). Falls and dislodged rocks are the most common dangers in vertical caving.

Some caves flood to the ceiling during periods of heavy runoff. Caves fed by surface streams that sink underground, or which contain telltale vegetal debris lodged high on their walls, should be avoided when there is any chance of intense rain or snowmelt.

Exposure to severe cold can lead to hypothermia. Even brief immersion in cold water can be dangerous. Proper exposure gear, such as diving wetsuits, polypropylene pile suits, or waterproof dry suits, are needed for wet caves, even in warm climates.

Cave diving in water-filled caves is necessary for some speleological studies, but it is risky. Even some of the most experienced cave divers have lost their lives in this way, despite the use of sophisticated self-contained breathing

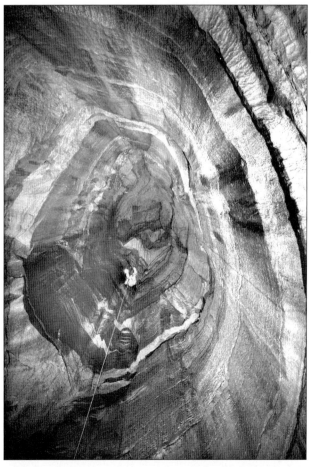

Figure 1.11: Vertical caving requires special techniques and training. This view is looking straight up a 26-m shaft (86 ft) as a person descends on a rope with a seat harness and friction device, in the Silvertip Cave System, Montana.

Figure 1.12: Entrances to solution caves are most common where surface drainage converges from a large drainage area, for example in the gullies between peaks. The peaks themselves are less favorable because they have limited sources of water. (Bob Marshall Wilderness, Montana.)

equipment. Cave diving should *never* be undertaken without considerable training, even by those who are competent open-water divers (Prosser and Gray, 1992).

A detailed description of caving techniques is beyond the scope of this book. Aspiring cave explorers will want to consider joining a local or national caving group, such as the National Speleological Society (see address on page 8). The NSS includes many local chapters whose members hold meetings, lead trips and training sessions, and publish newsletters about their activities.

Good general references to cave exploration are provided by Rea (1992), McClurg (1996), and Burger (2006), and advanced caving techniques are described by Padgett and Smith (1987), Warild (1994), Sparrow (1997), and Marbach and Tourte (2002). A cavers' discussion group is available at *www.caves.com*.

Several nationwide groups are dedicated to specific aspects of cave exploration. The Association for Mexican Cave Studies (Austin, Texas) promotes exploration and science south of the border and publishes extensive reports on their activities. The Alpine Karst Foundation (Missoula, Montana) is concerned with caving in mountainous regions, with emphasis on the American Northwest. Its members produce the occasional publication *Alpine Karst*.

Searching for caves

Explorers who wish to find new caves should first keep in mind how caves relate to their geologic setting. Appropriate information is shown on geologic maps such as those published by the United States Geological Survey or state geological surveys. Solution caves are most abundant where soluble rocks are exposed at or near the surface, and lie above the level of local rivers. Caves in volcanic rocks are most likely to be found in recently active lava flows on the lower flanks of volcanic cones.

To find solution caves, first consider the relationship between surface karst features and underground drainage. Caves are most likely to be negotiable if a large amount of water has flowed through them. In their search for deep caves, explorers often climb too high on ridges or mountain peaks. Caves are rarely found in these areas, even where soluble rock is present, because there is not enough water to form them. It is more fruitful to search in upland valleys, which concentrate large volumes of water (Figure 1.12). This statement can be misleading, though, because some caves have had much of their catchment areas removed by erosion, so their entrances appear in unlikely places such as the middle of a cliff. This is especially common in alpine regions where there has been a great deal of erosion by glaciers.

Where soluble rocks underlie insoluble ones on the eroded flanks of ridges and plateaus, many cave entrances are located at the contact between the rock types, where runoff first encounters the soluble rock. Deep sinkholes (surface depressions) usually indicate the presence of underlying cave streams, which are able to erode away the soil that subsides into them from above. Small sinkholes may offer less strenuous access to caves than large ones, because they are less likely to be choked with large collapse blocks.

Air movement through openings at the surface can reveal the presence of caves. Several well-known caves, such as Jewel Cave, Lechuguilla Cave, and Wind Cave, were discovered by explorers who followed air drafts. On cold winter days it is possible to detect cave entrances from plumes of condensed moisture in rising air. During the winter when there is a contrast between cave and surface temperatures, infrared mapping (thermal imagery) can reveal potential cave entrances as zones of relatively high temperature (Brown, 1972; Campbell and others, 1996; Thompson and Marvin, 2005).

Potential cave entrances are often blocked by sediment and rocks, and digging at likely sites is often productive. Many caves have been discovered in this way, including some very large ones. Regrettably, trash-filled sinkholes are also likely sites for cave entrances, because they are typically the open and rapidly subsiding kind that landowners try to fill, to prevent them from swallowing livestock or family members.

During any digging operation, keep a careful watch for deposits of archeological, paleontological, or historic value. Finds of this type should be left undisturbed and reported to an appropriate specialist. At any dig site, apply proper shoring techniques where appropriate.

Geophysical methods can be used to detect caves that are both large and shallow. As an example, in favorable locations, mapping the gravitational field over suspected caves can identify underlying passages by relatively low values in the measurements. Electrical measurements are also well suited to cave and karst studies. These and other geophysical techniques are described in Chapter 14.

Figure 1.13: Mapping a cave with a tripod-mounted Brunton compass and fiberglass tape. Ceiling heights and passage widths can be measured with a laser rangefinder. Above, a note-taker records the data and sketches passage details.

Figure 1.14: A Suunto compass is preferred by most cave mappers. It is small, light, and easy to read, but it is more difficult to position over the survey station and is more susceptible to deflection by metal in helmets, lamps, and eyeglasses. A separate inclinometer is used for vertical angles.

Dowsing (divining) for caves, for example with a forked stick, is a controversial method with a few avid adherents and occasional success stories (Wilcock, 2002). Although it may relate to irregularities in natural electromagnetic fields, dowsing has no known scientific basis.

Cave entrances and techniques for finding entranceless caves are discussed in Chapters 6 and 14, and in several entries in *Encyclopedia of Caves*, by Culver and White (2005).

Cave mapping

Even if a cave is fully explored, its length and relation to the land surface remain unknown until it is mapped. Nearly all cave maps are produced by explorers or cave scientists, rather than by professional surveyors. Mapping is an essential skill for any speleologist and is the first step in obtaining quantitative data about caves (Figures 1.13–1.14). With care, sufficiently accurate maps can be produced even with inexpensive equipment. Exploration and mapping are often carried out simultaneously, especially during large cave projects that involve many groups. In that way explorers are not tempted to charge ahead into unexplored territory and leave the job of mapping to others. On the other hand, such first-generation maps usually must be redone later in more detail.

Most cave surveys are made with a compass, inclinometer, and tape. The direction, slope, and distance are measured for each segment of passage, so that their orientations can be reconstructed on paper. A sketch is made in the cave, and the details are transferred to the map to portray the way the cave looks in map view and in profile. Cave mapping techniques are described by Dasher (1994) and are summarized on pages 12–13.

For a description of some of the latest techniques in computer-based cave surveying and cartography, see Passerby (2005). Ruggedized computers can be brought into the cave

to enter data, and scalable vector graphics allow morphing of wall contours on the cave map to fit updated survey lines.

In studies of geology and water, vertical accuracy is far more significant than horizontal accuracy. A vertical error of only a few meters can disrupt the interpretation of a cave's origin and geologic relationships, but that is rarely the case for similar horizontal errors. Once the initial map is available as a base, it is often worthwhile to resurvey the cave's vertical profile with a high-precision instrument, such as a tripod-mounted surveyor's level, while taking the opportunity to map geologic details that tend to be overlooked during the original survey (see Chapter 14). Many of the concepts discussed in later chapters are based on surveys of this type.

Volcanic rock is slightly magnetic, and in some caves in this rock type it is difficult to obtain accurate compass readings. This is rarely a serious problem, although discrepancies as much as $10°$ or more have been noted (Green, 2003). These can be minimized by keeping the compass as far away from solid surfaces as possible and checking for significant discrepancies with backsights. If backsights show large errors, it is best to re-run the survey with a transit, which relies on differences in angle between sights, rather than on magnetics (Chapter 14).

Occasionally it is necessary to locate the exact position of a spot in a cave by identifying the point on the surface directly above it. This procedure uses a "cave radio" (Mixon, 1966; Pease, 1997; Gibson, 2004). The technique is useful when drilling a new entrance or checking the accuracy of a normal cave survey. In the cave, a magnetic field is generated by passing a low-frequency alternating current through a horizontal loop of wire. With a receiver coil, a crew on the surface can detect the field. By measuring the orientation of the field it is possible to locate the magnetic axis, which is the point directly above the transmitter. At

Preparation of a cave map

The most common way to map a cave is to measure the direction and length of its passages with a compass and tape. From a point at the entrance, a sighting is made with the compass to a second point farther down the passage. This may be at the most distant visible spot, or a closer point of interest such as a passage intersection. The distance between points is measured with a non-stretching tape (usually made of synthetic fiber), or with a laser rangefinder. The vertical angle between the points is measured with an inclinometer. The compass bearing and vertical angle are then checked by making a backsight from the second station back to the first.

Meanwhile, a note-taker records the measurements and sketches the cave in both plan view and profile. Passage widths, ceiling heights, cross sections, and internal details are included in the notes. To facilitate drawing the final map, some sketchers use a ruler and protractor in the cave to draw each segment of the survey at its proper scale and orientation.

This procedure is then repeated between the second point and a new point farther into the cave, and so on until either the cave or the stamina of the mapping team comes to an end. Surveys of large caves require many trips spanning years or even decades. Each survey point is identified in the cave with an unobtrusive marker that can be left permanently, or at least until the survey is competed. Markers may consist of small plastic tabs or flagging tape labeled with the station numbers.

Figure 1.15 shows typical notes from a cave survey. This is based on a real survey but has been altered to show more variety than the original. The notes are a bit crude, as they were made under cold alpine cave conditions. The important thing is for them to be clear and easily understood by people other than just the note-taker.

After each trip the survey line is plotted at a reduced scale, usually with the aid of a computer, although a simple ruler and protractor will do for small caves. Several versatile cave-survey software packages have been written by speleologists and are available free or at small

cost. Try a Web search for "cave survey software." These programs convert the survey measurements to Cartesian (X-Y-Z) coordinates and allow the plot to be displayed or printed. Some show a 3-dimensional view of the passage outlines.

Using the sketch made in the cave, the cartographer draws the passage walls and other details around a horizontal plot of the survey line (Figure 1.16). This produces a *plan view* of the cave. It is highly recommended that those who take the original notes should also draw the cave map, or at least the preliminary versions of those parts that they personally sketched.

It is also useful to draw a profile of the cave to show its vertical layout as viewed from the side. A *projected profile* is a side view from any chosen direction. It has the same shape as the shadow of a 3-D model projected onto a wall. If the cave passages are oriented mainly in the north-south direction, for example, the most appropriate projected profile is a view from either the east or west. A view from the north or south would be foreshortened so that the passage pattern would look distorted, but even this view can help to clarify passage relationships.

An *extended profile* is drawn by stretching the passages out from beginning to end, maintaining their vertical relationships but forcing all passages to extend in a single direction. Extended profiles are useful for showing passage gradients. They are well suited to individual passages, but complex passage relationships can be confusing when the all the passages in the cave are

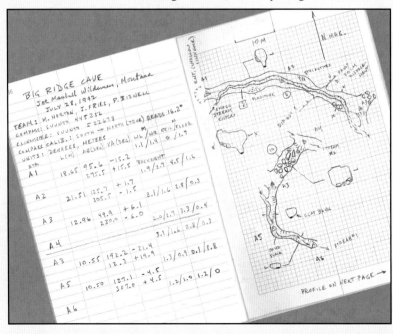

Figure 1.15: Survey notes include all measurements as well as a sketch of the cave in plan view and profile.

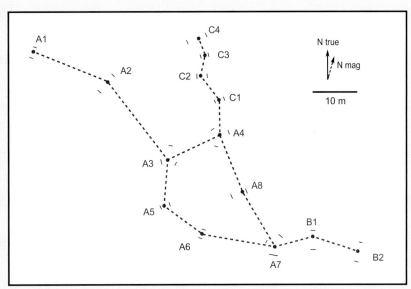

Figure 1.16: A reconstructed line plot of the cave survey, showing survey stations and ticks to show the location of walls.

extended in a single direction. In either type of profile it is common to exaggerate the vertical scale, to show the gradients and vertical relationships clearly.

The map is completed by adding labels, title, north arrow, scale, and a list of personnel. Although some people still prefer to draw their maps by hand, graphics software is now the standard tool (Figure 1.17). The map is drawn right on the computer display, perhaps in color, or with photo inserts. Lines, patterns, and labels are clean and uniform, and the map can be printed at any desired scale. Revisions can easily be made. Different categories of information can be entered as separate layers in the digital file, and various combinations of layers can be included in the printout according to the specific purpose of the map. With any computer drawing routine it is much easier to use a graphics tablet than a mouse.

Figure 1.18 shows a completed cave map with internal detail and profile. Although this map has been fabricated to show a large variety of features, it is identical in style to maps of real caves. Nearly all other cave maps in this book show only the passage outlines (as dark irregular lines), because the scales are too small to show individual walls and internal detail.

Some of the standard symbols for cave maps are shown on the example in Figure 1.18. For further information on map symbols, consult the Web site of the Survey and Cartography Section of the National Speleological Society (*www.caves.org*), and Dasher (1994). Additional symbols can be devised if necessary, as long as the map contains a key that explains them.

Cave geologists often need more information than is shown on a typical cave map. Advanced techniques for mapping and presenting geologic data are described in Chapter 14.

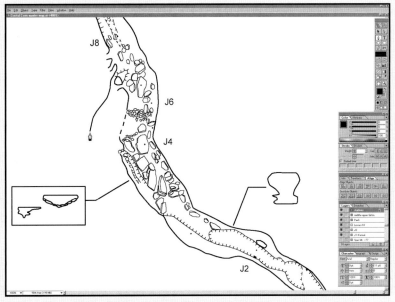

Figure 1.17: Computer-aided drafting is the standard for cave maps.

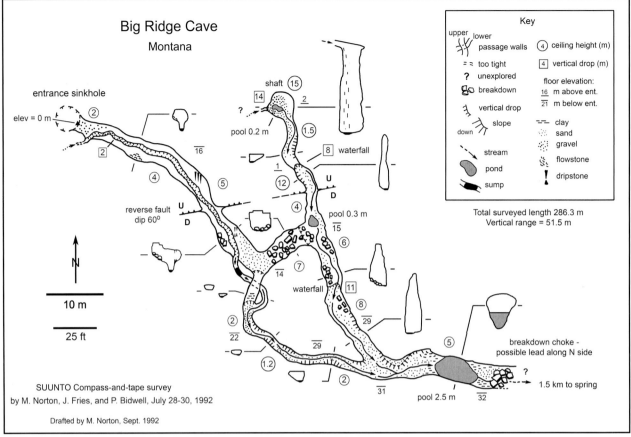

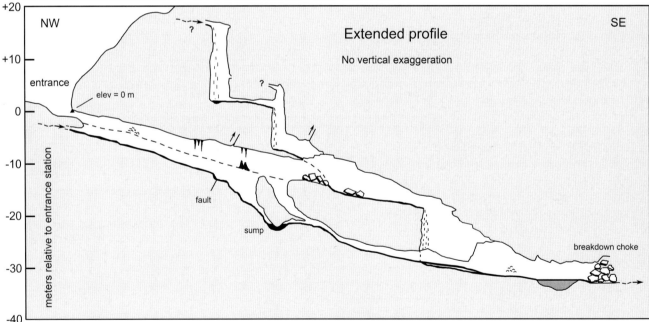

Figure 1.18: Example of a completed cave map, with cross sections and extended profile.

Comments: This is an imaginary cave map designed to show typical characteristics. Items shown in the key may differ between cartographers. Passages and cave features are usually given names by the mappers for convenience in describing locations, but usually not in small caves like this unless there is sufficient inspiration. Extended profiles of interconnecting passages are difficult to portray and may require several diagrams and additional labeling. The cave map will require updating if additional exploration takes place. The original survey notes should be kept for future reference. More geologic detail can be added, but usually at a later date on trips dedicated to this purpose (see Chapter 14). Profiles are sometimes enhanced with wall details such as those shown in Figure 9.60.

that point a vertically oriented receiver will have a zero reading, because it lies parallel to the magnetic field. If the receiver is tilted 45°, a zero reading is obtained where the depth of the transmitter is 1.78 times the horizontal distance to the magnetic axis (Figure 1.19).

For example, if a 45° receiver has a zero reading at a point 14 m away from the magnetic axis, the depth of the transmitter is about 14 x 1.78 = 24.9 m below the receiver. This procedure is repeated in several directions from the magnetic axis to check for consistency. There is a choice of several other methods with the cave radio. Locations and depths determined with this equipment typically have errors within about 5%. The effective depth limit depends on the magnetic properties of the surrounding rock.

With the aid of known points of this kind, three-dimensional computer images of cave passages can be produced by data from a moving sonar device equipped with an inertial positioning unit, a technique developed by covers for underwater surveys (am Ende, 2000, 2005). Similar mapping techniques using a programmed automatic laser rangefinder have been developed for air-filled caves. A three-dimensional image is produced by projecting numerous radiating laser shots onto walls, floor, and ceiling, and then displaying the results with computer software. The equipment is costly and delicate, so its utility for typical cave surveys is limited, but this approach is likely to become more popular as the cost drops and portability increases.

Geographic information systems (GIS) have revolutionized the mapping and graphic portrayal of karst and caves. With the aid of GIS, it is possible with little effort to show caves in three dimensions in relation to their geologic and topographic setting (Szukalski, 2002). Three-dimensional color graphics of caves and their surrounding landscapes can be produced with digital elevation models (DEMs), which consist of data typically supplied by government agencies such as the U.S. Geological Survey (http://data.geocomm.com/dem/). Figure 1.20 shows a monochrome example.

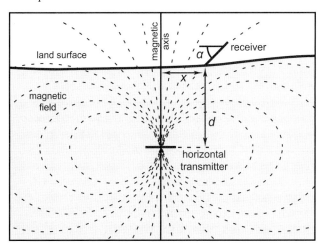

Figure 1.19: The cave radio. When the receiver reads zero at α = 45°, the depth (*d*) = 1.78 times the distance (*x*) from the magnetic axis. At the magnetic axis the field is vertical.

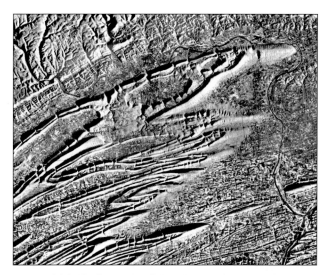

Figure 1.20: Example of a digital elevation model (DEM). This shows some details of the land surface in the Appalachian Mountains in northeastern Pennsylvania. Width of the area is about 65 km (40 mi). Data from U.S. Department of Agriculture.

Global positioning systems (GPS units) provide the spatial coordinates of surface features to a fair degree of accuracy without the need for laborious overland surveys. Because they rely on direct-line satellite signals, GPS units do not work in caves.

Cave science

Few people make their living exclusively as cave scientists, but many professional geologists, biologists, and environmentalists started as cave explorers who wanted to know more about their hobby. For many of them, speleology remains an important part of their professional activity. For example, cave science is a powerful tool in the study of underground water. A person having no knowledge of caves and their water flow patterns cannot properly assess water supply and water quality in soluble rocks. It is impossible to monitor, predict, or remedy groundwater contamination in such rocks without information about caves. Caves are ideal places to study geology, and they provide much information about the developmental history of the surrounding landscapes. Environmental studies, land-use management, structural engineering, and petroleum exploration also benefit from a knowledge of caves (Chapter 15).

Certain organisms related to those on the surface have adapted to the absence of light in caves, and others have evolved entirely within underground habitats. Biologists find that caves are natural laboratories in which they can study these life forms and their habitats. Today there is great interest in the new and challenging field of cave microbiology. Some bacteria and other microbes obtain their energy from chemical processes within caves. They not only facilitate cave-forming processes but also provide clues to past and present geologic conditions (Chapter 12).

Several nationwide organizations are concerned with cave science. Addresses and Web sites are listed in the sidebar

Underground photography

Photography is an important part of almost any cave study, but several difficulties must be overcome. Except near entrances, caves are totally dark, and strong sources of artificial light are required. Carrying delicate camera equipment through a cave requires sturdy containers and great care, but the results are worth the effort. Thorough discussions of the topic are given by Howes (1997), Woods (2004), and Thompson and Van Swearingen (2005).

Most cave photography today is digital. The great advantage of a digital camera is that images can be checked right in the cave. Although film has been matched in quality by advanced digital cameras, print film still excels in tonal range (gradation from dark to light), and large-format film can deliver detail beyond the capability of today's digital cameras. Projected transparencies (slides) eclipse the quality of digitally projected images. Film also provides a more tangible record, as digital files are more easily corrupted or lost than film.

And yet none of the advantages of film can outweigh the convenience and overall success rate of digital photography. Newcomers to cave photography will almost certainly prefer this medium. Point-and-shoot cameras are fine for souvenir snapshots, but their built-in flash units have a short range and produce bland lighting unless augmented by other sources. A capacity of at least 5 megapixels is preferred for high-quality work, including publishing, and at least 6–10 Mpx is preferred. Most digital cameras have electronic viewfinders that are adequate for general purposes, but in caves their view may be so dark that framing is difficult. A digital single-lens reflex (DSLR) camera provides a clear view directly through the lens. It is better suited to cave photography because of its ease in focusing and framing and the choice of many interchangeable lenses. DSLRs also provide a wide range of sensitivity (ISO values up to 1600 or 3200), and their image quality at high ISO settings (>400) is far better than with point-and-shoot cameras. On the other hand, DSLRs are larger, heavier, and more expensive.

On a computer, digital photos can be easily adjusted for tonal balance, color cast, and other variables. Computer-generated prints can rival custom laboratory prints

in quality. Film can be scanned to produce digital files, but the results may not be as clear as on a file of similar size from a digital camera.

Artificial lighting is usually provided by electronic flashes (Figure 1.21). Flashbulbs produce more light and broader coverage and are preferred for photos of large rooms, but the bulbs are expensive, cannot be re-used, and are difficult to obtain. Electronic flashes emit a very short burst of light, so waterfalls look frozen. With the longer pulse of a flashbulb (about 0.02 sec), moving water has a more realistic wispy appearance. At least two flashes are normally required to avoid black featureless shadows, but a single flash can be effective in simple compositions.

Figure 1.21: Typical gear for cave photography: camera, tripod, flashbulb unit, electronic flash, slave unit (connects to either type of flash unit), and water-tight box with internal padding.

The angle of the flashes relative to the subject is important. For example, sidelighting and backlighting can be used to enhance texture, form, or impact. It is helpful to preview each scene with headlamps to determine the most effective lighting arrangement.

If more than one flash is used for a photo, there are three choices: (1) synchronize the flashes with the camera shutter by using slave units that fire when triggered by the light from an on-camera flash; (2) open the shutter for about a second and set off several slaved flashes during that interval; or (3) place the camera on a tripod, open the shutter with a cable release or self timer, and have helpers fire the flashes independently. Direct light from headlamps should be kept out of the picture while using techniques 2 or 3. Low-level, indirect light is not a problem during the short time the shutter is open.

Some on-camera flashes send out one or more pre-flashes to avoid red reflections from eyes or to predict the output needed by the main flash. Most slaved flash units are triggered by the first pulse and are unlikely to recycle in time for the main flash, when the lens is open. Some slave units are designed to trigger on the second light pulse. If the problem persists, choose option 2 above.

With an ISO setting of 100 (or film of the same sensitivity), an electronic flash in typical cave conditions has a guide number of about 15 to 30, depending on the strength of its light output. The required lens aperture (f-stop) is found by dividing the guide number by the flash-to-subject distance in meters. Practice will reveal the best guide numbers.

Low ISO settings (or low-speed films) offer the sharpest resolution of details and greatest color fidelity, but large cave rooms and passages usually demand higher settings. The best compromise between sensitivity and resolution is usually about ISO 200. ISO 400 or more is needed in large caves or where light output is low, but there is increasing loss of quality as ISO increases. On a digital camera the result is uneven edges and erratic color and texture, rather than a reduction in the number of pixels.

The choice of lens aperture (f-stop) is important. At large apertures (such as f/4) more light is admitted, but the depth of field is small, so that a narrower range of objects will be in focus. Depth of field is larger at small apertures (such as f/16), so that a broader range of objects will be in focus, but more light is needed to make the correct exposure. Most lenses yield their sharpest images at openings of about f/5.6 to f/8. This is also a convenient range in caves, because it combines sufficient depth of field with a fair amount of light coverage. Close-up shots require a narrower opening (at least f/16) to keep the entire subject in focus. Large rooms usually require a wide aperture.

Most cave walls reflect light poorly, and much more flash power is needed than in a typical indoor shot. Narrowing the aperture by one f-stop (e.g., from f/4 to f/5.6) requires twice as much light. This can be accomplished by doubling the number of flash guns or by moving the flash closer to the subject (to 70% of the original distance). Doubling the ISO (e.g., from 100 to 200) has the same effect as doubling the light intensity.

Digital photographers can avoid some of these complexities by simply firing away at various settings until things look right. But this easy approach can lead to sloppy technique, because less attention is given to composition and image quality. Also, the full quality of a photo cannot be evaluated from the small LCD display on a digital camera. The guidelines for lens settings are still valid.

Focusing is difficult in caves. Manual focusing is often preferred. Focus on the most important feature in the photo, or at a point about 1/3 of the way into the scene. Unfortunately, most low-level digital cameras are equipped only with autofocus. With them it is best to focus with the aid of a light aimed at a person's face (not aimed directly into the camera). Once the focus is achieved, it can be maintained on most cameras by keeping the shutter release half depressed until you are ready to shoot. Check the result carefully, because the focus is easily lost during this procedure.

A moderately wide-angle lens, such as 28 or 35 mm on a full-frame 35-mm camera, is a ideal for most cave photos. Lenses with narrower fields of view are better for close-ups or for recording details at a distance. Ultra-wide lenses (less than about 24 mm) can produce dramatic panoramas, but lighting is more difficult, and their wide perspective may make the image look distorted. Zoom lenses are handy but are bulkier than those with fixed focal lengths.

Broad panoramas can be obtained by stitching together several shots taken in different directions. This is easy to do with digital files on a computer, although merging the images seamlessly can be tricky. When covering a large area with multiple shots, keep the center of the lens fixed at the same point while the camera angle changes. Normally the same lighting pattern should be used for each shot.

Composition and lighting can be adjusted so that the subject is clearly defined and has few distracting elements. Everyone laughs at the family photo of Uncle Ned with a tree growing from the top of his head. The chances of unexpected distractions are much greater in cave photos, and the camera position and lighting angles should be chosen to avoid them. Attention is naturally drawn to the main subject if it is the brightest and most contrasty part of the photo, and where directional indicators (such as a person's gaze) point toward it. People who appear in cave photos should avoid very dark or very light clothing, to avoid underexposure or overexposure relative to the cave features.

Photos for scientific use require some indication of scale. A person in the photo conveys the feeling of being there, although there is risk of a distracting pose, and bright clothing may draw attention from the main subject. A small standard-size item such as a pencil is convenient for small subjects and is less impersonal than a ruler. Many photos in this book have no scale at all where it would have endangered delicate features, or if the site lay beyond reach. For these the width of the scene is specified.

The photos in this book show various styles of composition and lighting, and you can examine them to see which approaches are best for your purpose. Most are intended simply to illustrate cave features as clearly as possible, regardless of artistic merit. The cutting edge of creative techniques in cave photography is on view in the photo salons of speleological conventions and in published caving calendars. Some fine examples are posted on the Web at a variety of sites that come and go frequently.

For the photos in this book I mainly used a rangefinder camera for general shots and a single-lens reflex camera for close-ups. Light sources were typically flashbulbs for general shots and electronic flashes for close-ups. I used a cheap point-and-shoot camera in the corrosive environment of Cueva de Villa Luz, Mexico. Most photos were made with slide film of ISO 25 to 125, and black-and-white films of ISO 25 to 400. About 15% were made with 5 to 16 megapixel digital cameras (e.g., Figures 1.21 and 2.20) and they will certainly dominate my future photography. Differences in resolution among most digital cameras are not visible in small images such as these.

on page 8. The National Speleological Society (NSS) is
the largest, with about 12,000 members. It hosts an annual
meeting that draws speleologists from throughout the country and around the world. Besides cave science, its goals
include the exploration and protection of caves. It contains
sections that specialize in various aspects of speleology.
The Cave Research Foundation promotes cave studies in
certain areas of the country, particularly in national parks.
The Karst Waters Institute sponsors scientific conferences
and research programs. All three organizations offer grants
for graduate-student research.

At the federal level, the National Cave and Karst Research
Institute was established by Congress in 1998. The NCKRI
headquarters is located in Carlsbad, New Mexico. The goal
of the Institute is to promote scientific speleology, public
education, and sound cave and karst management. Its staff
collaborates with cave and karst research groups, universities, and government agencies. The U.S. Geological Survey,
as part of its geologic mapping program, is constructing a
national karst map to show the distribution and nature of
karst throughout the country.

The International Speleological Union was formed in
1965 to provide a global forum for karst. It hosts meetings
every four years in various countries, to give speleologists
throughout the world a chance to compare ideas, techniques,
and discoveries.

Several publications deal exclusively with cave science. The *Journal of Cave and Karst Studies*, published
by the National Speleological Society, is the main outlet
for reports on cave research in North America. Several foreign journals are also dedicated to cave and karst science.
The *International Journal of Speleology*, published by the
Speleological Society of Italy, is the official bulletin of the
International Speleological Union. See *www.ijs.speleo.it* for
on-line archives. *Cave and Karst Science* is the scientific
journal of the British Cave Research Association. Its future
is uncertain, and it may continue in digital format. Also
written mainly in English are *Acta Carsologica*, published
by the Karst Research Institute in Slovenia, and *Theoretical
and Applied Karstology*, published in Romania by the Emil
Racoviţă Institute of Speleology. Karst studies in Australia
and surrounding regions are described in the semiannual
journal *Helictite*, which is published by the Australian Speleological Federation. The attractively illustrated *Karstologia*,
published jointly by the Fédération Française de Spéléologie
and l'Association Française de Karstologie, is almost entirely
in French, with English abstracts, but it has an international
scope. There are also many regional journals and newsletters concerned with caves. The most significant articles in
American caving newsletters are compiled by the NSS in
their annual *Speleo Digest*. Information on society member-
ship and journal subscriptions can be obtained on the Web.

Further information about cave science can be obtained
from books by Ford and Cullingford (1976), Jennings (1985),
Dreybrodt (1988), White (1988), Ford and Williams (2007,
2007), Gillieson (1996), Moore and Sullivan (1997), Klim-

Figure 1.22: Tour in Jewel Cave, Jewel Cave National Monument, South Dakota.

chouk and others (2000), Gunn (2004a), and Culver and White
(2005). See Northup and others (1998) for a bibliography of
cave-related books in the English language.

There are ample educational opportunities in speleology,
although no college degrees in North America are offered
specifically in that subject. Cave studies are best included
with a more traditional subject such as geology or biology, for a broader and more marketable scientific training.
Several colleges and universities offer courses, specializa-
tions, and research opportunities in cave and karst science.
Information can be obtained from Web sites or catalogs.
Another approach to selecting university programs is to
search scientific journals for appealing articles and then
contact the authors.

The Internet provides a growing number of cave-related
Web sites, many of them highly informative and well illustrated. Site addresses for the major American speleological
organizations are listed on page 8. The international on-line
journal *Speleogenesis and Evolution of Karst Aquifers*
(*www.speleogenesis.info*) provides articles and a discussion
forum for all topics related to cave origin. For access to
other sites, a simple word search is the best pathway into
this steaming jungle of information.

Figure 1.23: Delicate crystals in Jewel Cave, South Dakota. A single touch would damage them permanently. Width of photo is about 20 cm.

Show caves

Many caves throughout the world are open to visitors on a commercial basis. They are popularly known as show caves. Guided tours usually follow maintained trails (Figure 1.22), although a few include special off-trail caving excursions. A description of American caves open to the public is provided by Gurnee and Gurnee (1990) and by various Web sites. Cigna (2005a) describes the history, procedures and responsibilities of presenting caves to the public.

The National Caves Association is an organization of show-cave operators. They hold annual meetings to discuss guidelines for managing and protecting caves, and for presenting them to visitors. It also emphasizes the need for training of guides to ensure safe tours complemented by accurate and informative presentations. Their Web site *www.cavern.com* includes a directory of American show caves.

Three American national parks are devoted primarily to caves: Mammoth Cave, Wind Cave, and Carlsbad Cavern. These and their surrounding areas are on the must-see list of any serious speleologist, not only because they are impressive, but because they illustrate widely diverse cave types, origins, and geologic settings (see Chapter 8). A few other national parks contain caves open to the public, as do several national monuments, state parks, and national forests. Most show caves are under private management, and they include some of the most attractive in the country.

Cave preservation and stewardship

Most natural processes operate very slowly in caves. Once damaged, a cave may never recover, and scars and litter left by careless visitors will remain indefinitely. Some mineral deposits in caves are so delicate that the slightest touch would destroy them (Figures 1.23–1.24). Broken cave formations look pathetically out of place when taken outside. Even the bare bedrock is part of a cave's attraction, and it looks shabby if marked. Biological habitats in caves are easily disturbed, in part because their energy balances are so delicate.

When you visit a cave, try to cause as little disturbance as possible. Consider even your slightest impact on the cave, then multiply it by the number of people who are likely to pass through during the cave's lifespan, and the cumulative effect will be clear.

Protecting, preserving, and restoring caves, as well as maintaining access to them, are essential parts of *cave stewardship*. Given the pressures of land development, landowner liability, and use of caves by explorers and scientists, comprehensive measures are needed to prevent speleology from becoming a victim of its own popularity.

Cave stewardship has evolved to the point where many speleologists volunteer weeks of their time each year to restoring damaged caves to a semblance of their original condition. Graffiti are removed from walls, broken cave features are repaired, and trash is removed (Elliott, 2005; Hildreth-Werker and Werker, 2006). But although much improved, such caves never fully regain their pristine appearance, which a few simple precautions could have preserved intact.

Education, limited access, and secrecy are three different aspects of cave protection. The American Cave Conservation Association, founded in 1981, has the goal of introducing caves and their vulnerability to the public. Its headquarters in Horse Cave, Kentucky, features a museum, cave information, and a cave tour. Annual cave-management symposia are sponsored by various speleological organizations in cooperation with federal and state agencies. Their central theme is how to reconcile the valid use of caves with the desire to preserve them.

Landowners can protect their caves by allowing access only to those with appropriate background and legitimate goals. Caves on federal or state land have restricted access, and some are off limits to recreational cavers. A variety of federal and state laws prohibit removal of cave features, even on private property (Jones and others, 2003). Some caves are closed to visitors during winter months to avoid disturbing hibernating bats. Secrecy about cave locations is another facet of conservation. It is not surprising that those who discover attractive caves are reluctant to publicize their location.

Finally, for better or worse, conservation can be achieved simply by closing a cave entirely, either physically or by denying all access. Most caves are on private property, and a visit to such a cave requires careful respect toward the rights and sensitivities of the landowner. Fear of liability

is leading to the closure of an increasing number of caves. This situation is worsened by discourtesy toward landowners, mostly by casual fun-seekers rather than by dedicated cavers. With increasing frequency, caving organizations are buying or leasing property with cave entrances to preserve the caves and to keep them accessible to those with a serious interest. These groups have established a number of karst conservancies dedicated to this purpose.

In many show caves, visitors are asked not to touch the cave walls, to avoid leaving oily stains. This advice applies to caves in general, although it is difficult to apply in narrow passages or where climbing is necessary (Figure 1.9). Some of the photos in this book use gentle touches to emphasize texture or highlight significant features. Fortunately, many caves are fairly resistant to damage by normal traffic, thanks to vigorous streams or a lack of delicate features. Such caves may show almost no adverse effect even from thousands of unsupervised visitors each year. Even so, an occasional clean-up by volunteers from caving organizations may be needed to keep them tidy.

For many years the unofficial motto of American cave explorers has been "Take nothing but pictures, leave nothing but footprints, kill nothing but time." But what about those footprints? Even the most agile caver cannot avoid touching the floor, but *where* we step is important. It is dismaying to see prints of muddy hands and feet on otherwise pristine surfaces. Wide passages may invite indiscriminate wandering, but it is better to follow a single narrow trail through the passage and leave undisturbed floors on either side, just as they were when the cave was first discovered. Flagging tape is often used to mark sensitive areas or to delineate preferred trails. Even the most conscientious visitor cannot help but leave some stirred-up dust, lint from clothes, and unseen microbes. Biologists are finding unique microbial communities in certain recently discovered caves where the exchange of air and moisture from the surface is limited, and care should be taken to avoid contaminating them.

Given the vulnerability of caves, the idea of simply "killing time" in them is not appropriate. When visited, a cave deserves our full attention and respect, whether the aim is adventure or science. An increasingly popular guideline is simply "Cave softly — leave no trace." Perhaps this is overly optimistic, but it is an ideal worth bearing in mind.

Most cave science requires sampling of some kind, but even a scientist cannot justify damaging caves. It is not appropriate to remove material, except for systematic studies that will result in widely available publications. If possible, only loose fragments should be sampled, and only a small fraction of the available material should be removed. Each researcher should ask: Do I have the proper qualifications for this study? Might future scientists have better methods to interpret these samples? If a cave feature must be destroyed simply to understand its origin, isn't it better to leave it intact and preserve a bit of its mystery?

Figure 1.24: Rare crystal growth on a stalactite in a New Mexico cave. It has since been destroyed, perhaps by accident. Width of photo = 15 cm.

2

Cave country

ONE OF THE FIRST STEPS toward understanding a cave is to look at the landscape around it, because they have both experienced the same geologic history. This relationship is clearest for solution caves. Very few of them originate so far below the surface that they show no relation to it at all.

The dissolution of most soluble rocks, including limestone, dolomite, and marble, is greatly enhanced by the presence of acid. The most abundant acid in surface water and shallow groundwater is carbonic acid, which is produced when water reacts with carbon dioxide gas absorbed from the atmosphere and soil (Chapter 5).

Besides forming caves, the dissolution of soluble rocks has a great impact on the land surface, where it produces a variety of distinctive features such as fissures, rock pinnacles, closed depressions, and sinking streams. A landscape that contains these features is called **karst**. This is the German name for a plateau in western Slovenia, locally called *Kras*, in which solution features reach grand proportions. Some of the first detailed studies of karst were made in that region near the end of the 19th century. Since then, karst has become an international term for the topography that develops on soluble rocks anywhere in the world, and the mechanisms for its origin are known as karst processes. Fields such as karst hydrology and karst geology are now widely recognized.

Mechanical processes, such as erosion and gravitational movement of weathered material, also play an important role in modifying karst features. But the main agent responsible for karst is dissolution, and other processes have only a secondary effect.

Geologic time

Most solution caves have required hundreds of thousands of years to reach their present size. Many are millions of years old, and a few date back as far as several hundred million years. Of course the rock that contains a cave must be still older. Clearly, any discussion of cave origin and cave-bearing rocks must make reference to past periods of geologic time.

Geologists have divided Earth's history into several eras, which are further partitioned into periods. All eras, periods, and smaller time units are named either for their relative ages or for the geographic region where rocks of that age were first studied. The geologic time scale is shown in Figure 2.1. The numerical dates shown on the time scale are based mainly on how much radioactive decay has occurred in the rocks since they formed (Chapter 13). When distinctive fossils from a dated rock layer are recognized in another layer elsewhere, the two rocks are likely to have the same age.

Most caves and karst date from the late Cenozoic Era (Neogene Period) and represent less than 0.1% of Earth's history. But the rocks that contain the caves can be of almost any greater age. The oldest rocks that contain large solution caves are Precambrian, with ages up to about 2.3 billion years. The caves themselves are much younger.

Landscape development

The continents and ocean floors that constitute Earth's crust are composed of rocky material that varies from about 5 to 50 km thick. Beneath the crust the material is hot enough to move in slow convection cells as heat escapes from the deeper interior, like the overturn in a heated liquid. This movement deforms the overlying crust in several ways, as

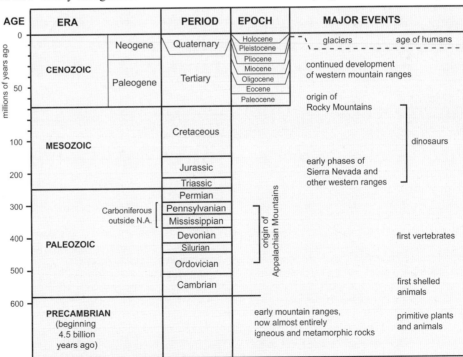

Figure 2.1: The geologic time scale. The Paleogene and Neogene, which partition the Cenozoic, are increasingly used instead of the traditional Tertiary and Quaternary. Outside of North America, Mississippian and Pennsylvanian are grouped as the Carboniferous Period. The Holocene represents the approximately 10,000 years since the last major glaciation.

shown in Figure 2.2. One result is that the continents shift
their position on the globe by drifting slowly in various
directions, as though on conveyor belts. The driving force is
supplied by a combination of convection in the mantle and
the sinking of dense slabs of crust into the mantle.

This movement accounts for the major irregularities in
the land surface, such as mountain chains. Where slabs of
crust converge, compression produces upwarped mountain
chains such as the Rockies, Alps, and Himalayas. Volcanoes
erupt along the contacts between slabs of crust where heat
escapes from the interior. Examples include Mt. Rainier in
Washington, and Fujiyama in Japan. Some mountain chains
such as the Appalachians formed hundreds of millions of
years ago, but persistent stream erosion since then has worn
them down greatly from their original height.

Where continents are pulled apart by the rise and
spreading of convection cells, massive blocks of rock are
uplifted, dropped downward, or tilted to produce isolated
mountain blocks surrounded by low basins. Streams erode
the mountains and bury the lowlands beneath thick covers
of sediment. The Great Basin of Nevada and nearby states
is an example. In areas of crustal tension, lava can seep
upward along fractures and flow outward to solidify into
broad plateaus, such as those that stretch across large parts
of Idaho, Washington, and Oregon.

Internal stress may bow parts of a continent upward to
form high plateaus that are then deeply dissected by stream
erosion. An example is the Colorado Plateau, in which the
Grand Canyon is located. In comparatively stable parts of
the continents, where there is little compression or tension,
movement of the crust is usually limited to broad, gentle
uplifts and downwarps. The resulting landscapes consist of
low plateaus cut by shallow stream valleys, such as those in
the central parts of North America.

Stream erosion carves land surfaces into complex patterns
of valleys with intervening mountains or plateaus. At high
latitudes and elevations, erosion and sediment deposition
by glaciers can alter or even obliterate the features formed
by streams. Wind is a less powerful agent of erosion than
either streams or glaciers, and its effects are usually limited
to minor abrasion of the surface and transport of loose sand
and smaller particles.

Where rocks of varied resistance are eroded, the resistant
ones project as ridges and the weak ones form valleys. Ridges
and valleys are usually arranged parallel to one another like
the grain in the surface of a board. Soluble rocks such as
limestone and dolomite tend to form valleys where they
are surrounded by resistant rocks such as sandstone, but
where they are surrounded by weak rocks such as shale
they stand as cliffs and ridges (Chapter 3). In dry climates,
where chemical weathering is slight, soluble rocks are more
resistant than in humid regions. In soluble rock, regardless
of climate, water easily drains underground, so some of the
water's power to erode and dissolve the surface is expended
instead on forming caves.

The erosion cycle

A simple but convenient way to describe how river
erosion shapes the land surface is to compare the rate of
downward erosion to the rate of uplift of the land caused by
Earth's internal forces. Davis (1922) envisioned episodes of
uplift interrupted by periods of relatively static landscapes.
In contrast, several others, including Hack (1960), suggested
a more dynamic model of continuous uplift and erosion.

Elements of both viewpoints are combined
in the following outline (Figure 2.3).

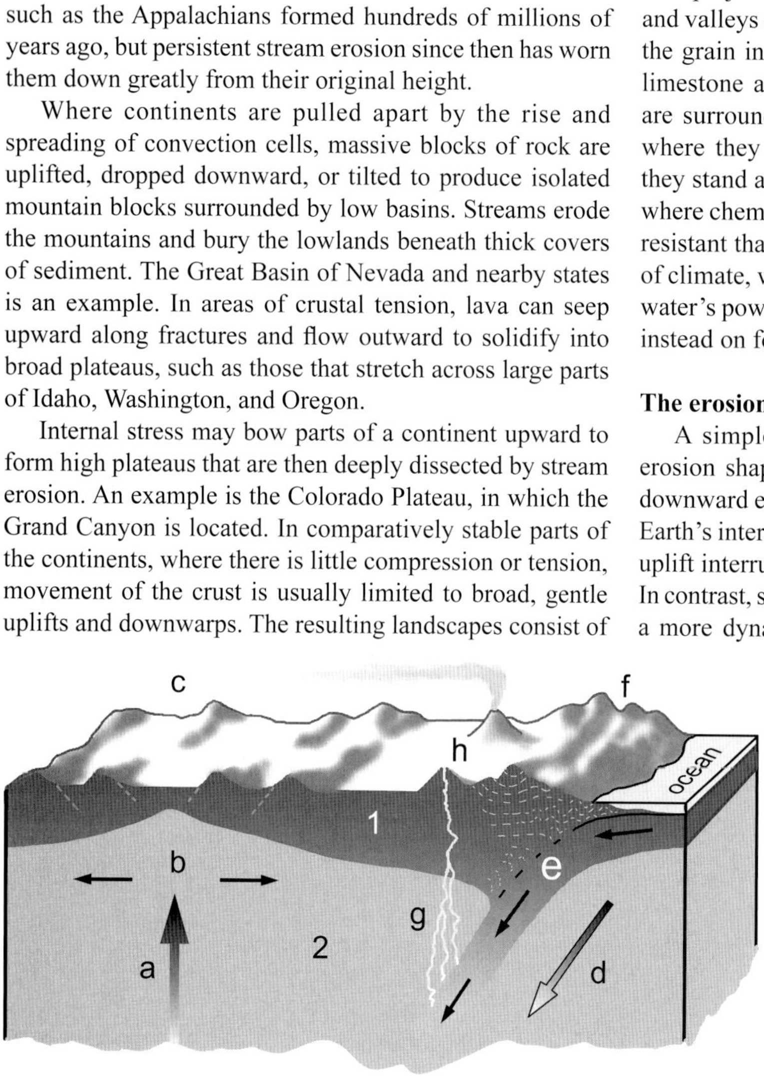

When a region is rapidly uplifted, streams
erode vigorously to form steep valleys with
V-shaped cross sections and with profiles
punctuated by rapids and waterfalls. This
is the *youthful stage* of erosion. It is most
common in actively rising mountain chains
or plateaus.

If uplift is slow enough that erosion can
keep pace, or even exceed the uplift rate,
rivers eventually erode down to a *base level*
below which further deepening is impossible.
The elevation of base level varies from place
to place and with time, as it is controlled by a
variety of factors such as the position of sea
level, distance from the ocean, rate of stream
flow, and amount of sediment load carried by
the water. Once a stream has eroded down
to its local base level it begins to meander
back and forth, widening its valley by lateral
erosion. A nearly flat *floodplain* develops
and broadens with time. The landscape is
then in the *mature stage* of erosion.

Figure 2.2: Patterns of stress and movement in the Earth's crust, and some of
the landscapes they produce on continents: **1** = crust (rocky, brittle); **2** = upper
mantle (solid, but able to flow under stress, like putty); **a** = rising mantle
caused by heating from the interior; **b** = spreading at and just below the crust; **c** = block-
fault mountains and lava flows caused by tension; **d** = descending, cooling mantle
material in the neighboring convection cell; **e** = edge of crustal plate dragged down
into the mantle, metamorphosing and melting at depth; **f** = folded mountain chains
caused by compression in the crust; **g** = molten crust and mantle rock, with low
density, rises to produce volcanoes (= **h**). Beneath ocean basins, rising mantle
material produces ocean-floor rifts, lava flows, and small volcanoes (Iceland is
a result), while convergence of plates produces volcanic island chains, like the
Aleutian Islands of Alaska.

Meanwhile the uplands continue to wear downward in a gradual transition to the ***old-age stage*** of erosion, which is characterized by wide floodplains with only low hills rising between valleys. Unless this stage is interrupted by further uplift, the landscape may eventually be eroded to a nearly flat plain. Earth's surface is dynamic enough that such erosional plains are rare.

At any time during maturity or old age, renewed uplift can push the erosional stage back to youth (***rejuvenation***). If the entire sequence continues from youth through maturity to old age, and then back to youth by rejuvenation, a complete ***erosion cycle*** has taken place.

Occasionally a stream's base level may rise instead of drop, with an effect opposite to that of rejuvenation. The stream valley becomes partly filled with river-deposited sediment, a process called ***alluviation***. Most often this is caused by a rise in sea level, for example when glaciers melt or there is a change in the shape of ocean basins. Local depression of the crust by the weight of glaciers can produce a similar result. A decrease in the flow of a stream, or an increase in its sediment load, can also cause its valley to fill partly with sediment. Figure 2.3 shows an alluviated mature valley. Alluviation of an old-age surface may leave only a few low hills completely surrounded by sediment.

The terms *youth*, *maturity*, and *old age* are a bit out of fashion today, because they give the misleading impression of relative age and of an inevitable sequence of events. Yet these simple graphic words are still useful for describing landscapes in an informal way, and the concepts on which they are based are helpful in explaining cave patterns (Chapter 9).

Effects of glaciers

In cold climates, snow may build up from year to year and eventually turn to ice. If the ice becomes thick enough it spreads over the land surface, driven by its own weight, like a highly viscous fluid. For at least 8 to 12 times during the past two million years (the Quaternary Period), and occasionally during earlier periods, glacial ice sheets up to several kilometers thick extended across much of the land surface. Glacial episodes are caused by a combination of several events, including periodic changes in Earth's orbit, changes in the intensity of solar radiation, and variations

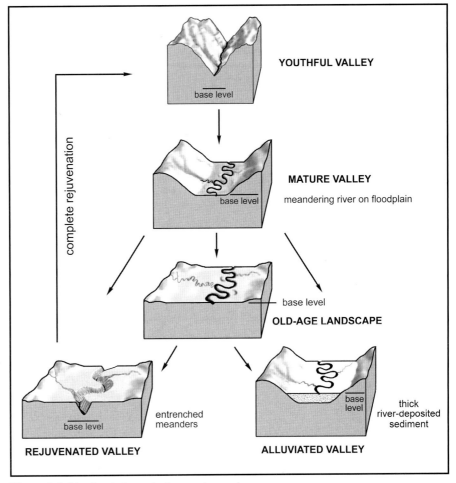

Figure 2.3: Idealized stages in the erosion cycle.

in ocean currents. Clustering of continents at high latitudes can provide large cold land surfaces on which glaciers can grow. Quaternary glaciers covered much of North America, northern Europe and Asia, and parts of the southern hemisphere. The latest glacial episode reached its peak more than 20,000 years ago. In North America the ice covered most of Canada and reached as far south as the Ohio and Missouri Rivers. Only remnants of glaciers remain today, and they are still gradually melting away. The largest remaining glacial masses are in Antarctica, Greenland, and Iceland. In the first two regions, ice is more than 5 km thick in places.

Continental glaciers cover entire landscapes, although high mountains may project through them. At their downflow ends the glaciers extend as fingers into valleys. Where the ice accumulates and spreads, it causes intense mechanical erosion (Figure 2.4). A good example is in east-central Canada, where the land surface has been scoured, rounded, and smoothed by repeated continental glaciations.

Alpine glaciers are tongues of ice that concentrate in the valleys of high mountain chains. They are much smaller than continental glaciers. Alpine glaciers extend down valleys and erode them to produce U-shaped cross sections with steep intervening sawtoothed ridges (Figures 2.5–2.6). The largest alpine glaciers extend onto lowland plains and coalesce into ice sheets.

Figure 2.4: Continental glaciation tends to round uplands by erosion and to fill the intervening valleys with sediment. This valley in eastern New York State was filled by glacial sediments to more than half its original depth about 100,000 to 14,000 years ago. Karst drainage was disrupted as a result (Chapter 9).

Erosion by glaciers is most intense where the base of the ice is frozen to the underlying surface. Fragments of rock and soil are plucked up and carried off by the ice, to be deposited at the downflow end where melting equals or exceeds the glacial flow rate. Much of this sediment comes from nearby sources, but large continental glaciers have moved some sediment hundreds of kilometers. It piles up at the ends of the glaciers, forming ridges called ***moraines***. Similar deposits accumulate at the ends and along the sides of alpine glaciers.

The sediment in a moraine is called ***glacial till***. It is deposited directly by the ice and consists of a jumble of fragments of various size with little or no layering. Meanwhile, meltwater from the ice carries sediment into

lower-elevation valleys and plains, where it is deposited as ***outwash***. In outwash, various particle sizes (e.g., gravel, sand, and clay) are deposited separately in layers according to how fast the water is moving. Gravel is moved and deposited only by rapidly moving water, while fine-grained material such as clay (mud) can settle only from slow-moving water. The broad fertile plains of the north-central United States were built by sheets of Quaternary glacial till and outwash that entirely buried the older bedrock hills and valleys to depths of more than 100 m in places.

Glaciation has considerable effect on sea level, because the ice masses trap large amounts of water that would otherwise drain back into the oceans. At the peaks of major continental glaciations, sea level dropped as much as 200 m compared to its its position today. During the intervening warm periods, sea level rose above its present position as much as 6 m, and possibly more. These fluctuations have affected erosional base levels throughout the world. In seacoast areas remote from glaciers, rivers entrench their valleys during glacial advances, and the valleys are filled with sediment during interglacial times. In regions directly overridden by glacial ice, the crust is depressed by the weight of the ice. As the glaciers melt, lowlands and valleys tend to fill partly with sediment carried in by streams or deposited in lakes and oceanic bays.

When glaciers extend over karst areas, much surface karst tends to be destroyed by erosion or buried by sediment. Some caves are filled by till and outwash, but others may be enlarged by glacial meltwater. Caves in such regions can provide clues to the history and patterns of past glaciations (Chapters 9 and 13).

Surface karst features

Most caves and surface karst features grow in close association with one another. Much of the water that forms caves is fed to them through karst depressions and sinking streams, and this water emerges at springs. These and other surface features are clues to the presence and patterns of caves, and they may also serve as cave entrances.

Figure 2.5: An active alpine glacier on Mt. Shuksan, Washington. Note the sharpening of ridges by glacial erosion of their slopes.

Figure 2.6: Effects of alpine glaciation: a valley in Colorado with a U-shaped cross section and glacially deposited sediment.

Karren

Where bare soluble bedrock is exposed to weathering, it is deeply etched by runoff from rain and snowmelt. The result is most striking in alpine regions, where soil is thin or absent. Exposed fractures enlarge into fissures, while the intervening rock stands in relief. Fairly straight rills form on steep slopes, and sinuous channels form on gentle slopes. These and other solution features on bedrock surfaces are called *karren**, and the resulting landscape is known as *karren topography* (Figure 2.7). Rills, channels, and fissures in the bedrock walls of caves are subsurface forms of karren. The many varieties of karren and their complex international terminology are described by Bögli (1980), Ford and Williams (1989), and Lundberg (2005).

Where highly developed, karren can form a nearly impenetrable terrain of deep clefts separated by towering blades of rock. At the other extreme, nearly flat *limestone pavements* are interrupted only by minor fissures. Pavements are most common on glaciated surfaces that have been stripped of their soil. A good example is the 360 km² Burren of western Ireland (Daly and others, 2000; see Figure 3.29).

Solution pans are shallow basins dissolved by standing water on exposed bedrock surfaces (Figure 2.7c). The water

source is usually rainwater or snow-melt, although in some places floodwater from nearby streams can be the primary dissolving agent. The lower end of a solution pan typically has a narrow outlet that drains to the edge of the bedrock block, or into other pans at lower elevations.

Karren can also form beneath soil, where they are usually more rounded and subdued than those that form on bare bedrock (Figure 2.7d). The soil holds moisture like a sponge and allows dissolution to take place rather uniformly over the bedrock surface. If the overlying soil is eroded away or disappears underground, rounded karren indicate their subsoil origin, until they are eventually carved into sharper relief by running water.

Solution corridors (also known as *karst canyons* or *zanjones*) are elongate trenches in karst surfaces. Most are the collapsed remains of caves. Rudimentary examples may consist of linear zones of sinkholes. Some solution corridors are solutionally widened fractures that intersect in an angular grid, like city streets, to form *labyrinth karst*. Solution corridors are most common in the tropics (Monroe, 1968) but are not limited to those climates. Spectacular labyrinth karst also occurs in the remote subarctic Nahanni region of the Mackenzie Mountains, Northwest Territories, Canada, in prominently fractured limestone that has been exposed to lengthy weathering (Brook and Ford, 1978).

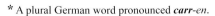

* A plural German word pronounced *carr-en*.

Figure 2.7: A few examples of karren: **(a)** fissures with intervening blades (above Hölloch, Switzerland), **(b)** sinuous channels, (Montana; width of photo = 1.5 m), **(c)** rounded karren once covered by soil (Yorkshire, England), **(d)** solution pans, Haute Savoie, France.

Seacoast karst consists of an intricately etched rock surface resulting from dissolution by mixing of fresh and salt water, which is often aided by the corrosive and burrowing action of organisms (***bioerosion***). It is most common along tropical beaches composed of young limestones (Figure 2.8). Where bioerosion dominates, the landscape is sometimes called ***biokarst*** or ***phytokarst*** (Folk and others, 1973). Horizontal notches form in the tidal range along seacoasts by the combined action of waves and bioerosion. Biokarst pits aligned with narrow sunbeams can also form inside cave entrances, usually in tropical climates (pages 154–155).

Karst pinnacles

As karst develops, variations in land elevation tend to become accentuated (Gams, 1965). Thick soil accumulates in lowlands and depressions, while steep slopes and hills are stripped of much soil by erosion. The thick lowland soil is a rich source of carbonic acid, and the bases of hills and cliffs in contact with the soil are rapidly dissolved, so that they become steeper or even overhung. A typical result is a high-relief karst that contains deep sinkholes bounded by steep residual hills. Such landscapes can form in any climate, but they are best developed in the humid tropics, where bacterial production of carbon dioxide in the soil is most active.

Karst pinnacles and intervening depressions can form broad plateaus whose surfaces look like the bottom of an egg carton. They are known as ***cone karst*** or ***cockpit karst*** (Figure 2.9). Isolated, rounded limestone hills rising from surrounding lowlands are called ***mogotes*** (Monroe, 1968). They are well developed in the limestones of northern Puerto Rico and in Cuba, where the name originated. ***Tower***

Figure 2.9: Aerial view of cone karst in northern Puerto Rico. Aerial photograph by José A. Colón.

karst consists of steep isolated peaks. It is best developed in the almost surreal landscape of southern China, where dramatic finger-like pinnacles rise from the surrounding plains (Zhang, 1980; Yuan, 1991; Figure 2.10). Most karst towers are surrounded by nearly flat erosion surfaces or river sediment. Where moist soil or floodwaters come in contact with the limestone at the tower bases, rapid dissolution produces horizontal notches (***swamp slots***) and swarms of small intricate ***foot caves***. In coastal karst, many towers develop wave-cut notches (Figure 2.11). Remnants of old caves perforate the walls of many towers. Small closely spaced towers of bare bedrock are sometimes called ***stone forests***. This term is used mostly in China, where Yunnan Province contains some of the best examples.

In China, landscapes composed of karst pinnacles are classified by their relation to the erosional base level, rather than by pinnacle shape. ***Fengcong*** karst consists of a hilly surface that lies far above the water table and erosional base level (similar to that in Figure 2.9). Its karst hills consist mostly of cones, because there is little or no flattening of the land at their bases. ***Fenglin*** karst* consists of isolated

---

* Pronunciations: *fengcong* = ***foong-soong***, *fenglin* = ***foong-leen***.

Figure 2.8: Seacoast karst in Bermuda.

Figure 2.10: Tower karst (funglin type), Guilin, China.

Figure 2.11: Wave-cut notch at the base of a karst tower along the southern seacoast of Thailand. Photo by Kevin Downey.

Figure 2.13: Origin of a sinkhole by the collapse of a soil arch, Kentucky.

residual hills, or small groups of hills, surrounded by nearly flat plains composed either of eroded bedrock or of broad sediment-covered floodplains. Figure 2.10 shows the karst towers in a fenglin landscape.

The epikarst

Fissures and pores below a surface of soluble rock, whether or not the surface is covered by soil, become deeply etched to form a network of solutionally enlarged openings (Figure 2.12). This is the *epikarst*. It typically extends a few meters or tens of meters into the bedrock and is essentially a subsurface extension of karren. Many fissures in the epikarst pinch downward, so descending water is unable to follow them very far vertically. Instead the water is forced to drain laterally toward the few large fissures that penetrate deeply into the underlying bedrock (Williams, 1983; Bakalowicz, 2005). These major drains are the openings that enlarge into cave passages or feed

actively growing caves farther down. Soil-filled openings in the epikarst store a large volume of water that accumulates during wet periods and then leaks out slowly, and this water helps to keep underlying cave streams running even during dry periods. Details of epikarst origin and function are described in a symposium volume edited by Jones and others (2004).

Karst depressions

The widest openings at the bottom of the epikarst carry the most water and enlarge most rapidly. Eventually the overlying soil subsides or collapses into them (Figure 2.13). If the flow of water is great enough it carries the soil into underlying caves, where subsurface streams transport the debris to springs.

As subsidence continues, the land surface eventually becomes pockmarked by closed depressions. These are called *sinkholes* in America and *dolines* nearly everywhere else

Figure 2.12: Sawed face of an Indiana limestone quarry, showing a cross section of the epikarst.

Figure 2.14: A typical mature sinkhole (Slovenia).

Figure 2.15: Sinkhole in bare marble, Mineral King, California.

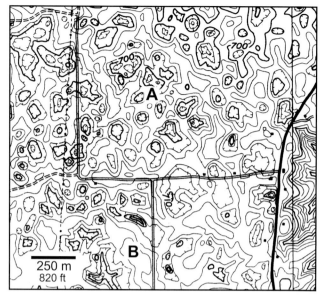

Figure 2.17: Sinkholes can be recognized on a topographic map by their depression contours (indicated with prong-like hachures). A = area of dense sinkholes. B = remnants of upland that has not yet acquired sinkholes. (Part of the Oolitic Quadrangle, Indiana. Elevations in feet; north is upward; contour interval = 10 ft ~3 m).

(Figures 2.14–2.16). A sinkhole has no surface outlet for runoff. Its sloping walls converge toward a low point where the collected runoff drains underground. Many sinkholes are shallow basins nearly filled with soil (Figure 2.14). Water drains out of them slowly by percolating through the soil into one or more solutionally enlarged drains in the underlying bedrock. Other sinkholes have steep walls composed of exposed bedrock (Figure 2.15). Some open directly into caves or vertical shafts. Types of sinkholes and other karst depressions are described by Sauro (2005).

Most sinkholes are located where soluble rock is exposed at the surface, either as bare bedrock or beneath a soil cover. They tend to cluster along contacts with insoluble rock where there is much surface runoff feed them. Some are located in insoluble rock that has collapsed into underlying caves in the soluble rock.

Sinkholes appear on topographic maps as closed depressions delineated by hachured contour lines (Figure 2.17). Typically only about 10–25% of sinkholes are large enough to appear on maps. Whether a given sinkhole appears on a topographic map depends on the depression size, map scale, and contour interval.

Underlying cave streams contribute to sinkhole enlargement in several ways. They

Figure 2.16: World's smallest sinkhole? Beginning stages of soil piping into an underlying conduit (Ontario, Canada).

dissolve the supporting bedrock, as well as blocks of rock that fall in from the sinkhole bottoms, and they also carry away the soil that subsides into them (Beck, 2005). A sinkhole floored partly or entirely by an underground stream is sometimes called a ***karst window***. Large sinkholes are good indicators of underlying active caves.

Some sinkholes form by sudden collapse lasting only minutes or hours, to the dismay of landowners. Such collapses are usually the climax of a long period of subsidence and erosion, which leaves an unstable soil bridge that can abruptly drop away (Figures 2.13 and 2.16). Many collapses are triggered by a lowering of the water table by drought or by pumping of wells, which reduces the buoyancy exerted on the overlying rocks by the groundwater. This process is common in Florida, where the surface rock includes weak impure limestone that is unable to support its own weight across large underground voids. This material tends to collapse with little warning. In most other karst regions, however, rapid sinkhole collapse is usually triggered by *high* water during floods. In this case, the floor of an incipient sinkhole consists of bedrock blocks loosely cemented by soil. Moistening and erosion of this plug by underground water, especially during floods, can cause sudden collapse. Over time the hole becomes more funnel shaped as the loose wall material slumps downward and collects at the bottom.

Sinkhole plains are broad, low-relief plateaus that contain extensive arrays of sinkholes. Some of the best examples are the plains of nearly horizontal limestone in the east-central U.S., which cover tens of thousands of square kilometers (Figures 2.17–2.18).

Sinkhole ponds are sinkholes that contain standing water. In most of them the downward migration of water is impeded by tight clay-rich soil, so that the pond is perched

Figure 2.18: Sinkhole plain of southern Indiana. The sinkhole ponds in the foreground are perched above the water table by thick clay-rich soil.

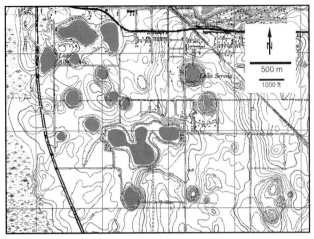

Figure 2.19: Many sinkholes in the Florida karst extend below the water table. Sinkhole ponds (dark gray) stand at nearly similar elevations and at roughly the same level as water in nearby wells. (Part of the Lake Wales Quadrangle, with a contour interval of 5 ft = 1.52 m.)

above the level of the underlying water table (Figure 2.18). In low areas such as Florida, however, sinkhole ponds usually coincide with the water table, and divers have shown that many of them are interconnected by water-filled caves (Figure 2.19).

Cenotes (pronounced *sen-o-tays)* are sinkholes rimmed by steep or overhung bedrock walls, and which extend down to ponded water, usually at the water table (Figure 2.20). They are most common in the Yucatán Peninsula of Mexico, where they provide access to large underwater caves that drain fresh water from the interior of the peninsula to the Gulf of Mexico.

Poljes (*pole-yehs*) are large depressions with nearly flat floors covered by stream-deposited sediment (Figure 2.21). Water enters a typical polje from one or more cave springs at its base, flows across the flat polje floor, and

sinks underground again on another side. Most of the floor sediment is deposited by this water during floods. Poljes are most common in the western Balkan karst, where the name originated. Some cover several square kilometers each. Their origin relies on dissolution, but stream erosion and deposition also take part. The flat polje floors typically lie near the local erosional base level, and, like mature river valleys, they grow mainly by lateral wall retreat. Many poljes are located along large structural features such as faults, or at the border between soluble and insoluble rocks, where dissolution is intense. In America the terms *gulf* and *cove* are used for features that resemble poljes, although there is some dissent as to whether they qualify as true poljes. Grassy

Figure 2.20: A cenote in Tamaulipas, Mexico (El Zacatón), located in Cretaceous limestone. This is a wide shaft 100 m in diameter and more than 360 m deep. Water rises through the shaft and flows through an underwater cave to a nearby spring. The circular grassy islands float on the water and drift in the wind. This wide-angle view gives the false impression that the background falls below the level of the cenote.

Figure 2.21: A polje in Croatia partly rimmed by karst pinnacles. Flat polje bottoms are typically used as farmland.

sink points are called ***swallow holes*** (or ***swallets*** in Britain, ***ponors*** elsewhere in most of the world). Some sinking streams do not disappear into visible openings but instead seep through a bed of sediment that behaves like a sieve. In America, swallow holes are sometimes called *insurgences* (to contrast with *resurgences*, where water emerges at springs), but this term is discouraged (see Glossary). The abandoned surface channel beyond the final sink point is called a ***karst valley***. Examples of sinking streams and the development of karst valleys are described by Ray (2005).

The earliest cave passages

Cove in Tennessee and Wesley Chapel Gulf in Indiana are well-known examples. Grassy Cove is more than 10 km long and 400 m deep, so it is as large as many poljes, but its floor is not flat and it does not flood significantly.

Uvalas are compound sinkholes containing multiple depressions. The term *uvala* is used in a variety of ways and is sometimes applied to youthful poljes or to dry valleys floored by sinkholes. This term needs to be more clearly defined or abandoned entirely.

Tiankengs (pronounced *tyan-koongs*) are very large, steep-walled karst depressions that are most clearly developed in southern China (Zhu and Zhang, 1995; Zhu and Chen, 2005). They are formed by collapse into large caves that contain active rivers. Depths and diameters of more than 100 m are typical (Figure 2.22). They are limited to upland karst areas (fengcong karst) where the land surface stands at least several hundred meters above base level. A few examples are also known outside of China (Figure 6.7; see also Waltham, 2005). There are apparently no sinkholes large enough in the U.S. to qualify as tiankengs. Devil's Sinkhole in southwestern Texas bears some resemblance, at 100 m in mean diameter and 42 to 80 m deep, but its entrance diameter is only about 15 m.

in a karst area are usually formed by sinking streams. For a long time afterward, occasional floodwaters reoccupy the abandoned surface channels, but with time the caves can eventually grow large enough to transmit even the highest flow. As openings continue to develop beneath the still-active upstream parts of the surface channel, the terminal swallow hole may migrate farther upstream until only a few ephemeral streams are left in the headwaters of the drainage basin. Where drainage from a non-karst area sinks at the contact

Figure 2.22: Dashiwei Tiankeng in Guanxi Province, China, is one of the largest tiankengs in the world. It is 613 m deep, 600 m long, and 420 m wide. The entrance of a dry cave is visible in the far wall.

Sinking streams

Streams that lie above the water table lose water through openings in the underlying rock. The water table is the level below which all openings are completely water-filled. If the rock is soluble, the infiltrating water gradually enlarges the openings, allowing progressively more water to leak underground. Entire streams can eventually be captured by underground openings to form ***sinking streams*** (Figure 2.23) The

Figure 2.23: A sinking stream entering Rowten Pot, Yorkshire, England.

with soluble rocks, headward migration of underground drainage is impossible, and the active parts of the surface channel tend to be eroded downward to form a ***blind valley*** that terminates abruptly at the swallow hole.

One of the largest sinking streams is the upper 50 km of the Danube River in Germany, which is in the process of being pirated underground to a tributary of the Rhine River. During low flow the entire headwaters of the Danube sink underground and emerge 12 km away and 175 m lower at a large water-filled cave spring (Kempe, 1987). Instead of following its original course to the Black Sea, this water now follows the Rhine to the North Sea, at the very opposite end of Europe from its former destination.

Most major surface rivers are able to cross a karst area without sinking underground, even in highly cavernous areas. This is because they have eroded their valleys deep enough that they serve as outlets for groundwater, rather than as inputs. Water flows through caves into these valleys from the surrounding uplands, because the surface rivers are the lowest available discharge points. These rivers lose some water to their adjacent banks during floods, when their water levels rise rapidly and reverse the flow of groundwater, but as the floodwaters subside, the water in the stream banks drains back into the rivers.

Subsurface meander cutoffs can form along meandering rivers that have entrenched into soluble rock (Figure 2.24). The groundwater gradient through the narrow neck of a meander is steeper than the stream gradient along the entire meander, and if this condition persists, the surface stream may eventually divert through the neck and abandon the

rest of the meander (Malott, 1922). The steep gradient and abundant supply of solutionally aggressive water allow rapid dissolution to take place, and maze caves are typical (Chapter 8). Eventually the meander neck is breached by collapse and the cutoff becomes part of the surface stream channel. Several subsurface cutoffs in western Kentucky with accessible caves are described by Mylroie and Dyas (1985).

Natural bridges are caves that are short enough that it is possible to see all the way through from one end to the other. Some are the surviving remnants of larger caves (Figure 2.25). A well-known example is Natural Bridge in western Virginia, which has an arch about 46 m high with U.S. Highway 11 crossing over the top. Many natural bridges are not karst features, but instead form in thin blades of insoluble bedrock (often sandstone) that are bounded by fractures. Natural bridges form in them when the rock in the center falls away by weathering (Figure 2.26).

Karst springs

In a karst area, most underground water eventually reappears at the surface as ***springs***. Each karst spring is fed by a cave, or at least an incipient one, and water typically emerges from the ground as a discrete stream. Many karst springs serve as cave entrances (Figure 2.27). In non-cavernous regions, nearly all groundwater emerges at the surface by seeping inconspicuously out of the ground through many tiny openings in and adjacent to stream channels. Even in karst, some water emerges from the ground in this way. Smart and Worthington (2004) give a detailed summary of karst spring types and their geologic controls.

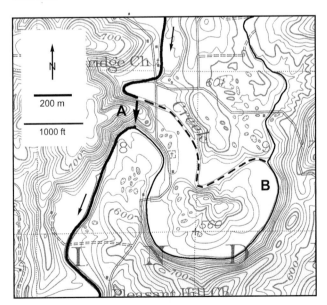

Figure 2.24: Underground meander cutoff on Indian Creek, southern Indiana. The 150 m subsurface route (**A**) cuts through the neck of a 4.5 km meander (**B**). Water sinks at one or two points, depending on the flow rate, and emerges at several springs at the southern end. The cutoff has a gradient of about 1.3 degrees. The dashed line indicates an intermittent stream that is active only during high flow. (Modified from Malott, 1922.)

Figure 2.25: Many natural bridges, such as this one in Slovenia, are the remnants of originally longer caves. Some still contain the original streams that formed the caves.

Most of the world's largest springs are in karst, but there is no consensus as to which is the largest karst spring. The question is complicated by the fact that spring flow, like that of a surface stream, varies greatly between dry and wet weather. On the island of New Britain, Papua New Guinea, two springs each have average flows estimated at more than 90 m³/sec (~3200 ft³/sec; Maire, 1990). Dunmanli Spring in southern Turkey, which is actually a cluster of related springs,

Figure 2.27: A base-level cave spring (Old Town Spring, Indiana).

has a combined total of 125−130 m³/sec (Ford and Williams, 1989). Tisu Spring, which rises through collapse boulders in the karst region near Bama, China, has a high flow of about 200 m³/sec.* The largest single karst spring in the United States is Silver Spring, in Florida, which has a mean flow of 23 m³/sec and a drainage area of almost 2000 km².

The most likely location for a karst spring is at the level of the surface river into which it flows. These are ***base-level springs*** (Figure 2.27). In places, insoluble rocks intercept descending water and guide it to nearby hillsides to form ***perched springs*** (or ***contact springs***) above river level, as shown in Figure 2.28.

Artesian springs are fed by water that rises from depth under pressure (Figure 2.29). Some artesian springs

---

* Communication from Andy Eavis, Hessle, U.K., 2005.

Figure 2.26: Delicate Arch, Utah, in sandstone, hardly qualifies as a cave, but it has some aspects in common with shelter caves. For scale, note the person standing by the left-hand pillar.

Figure 2.28: A limestone spring perched on underlying shale (Bob Marshall Wilderness, Montana).

Figure 2.29: An artesian spring produced by blockage of a former base-level spring by glacial deposits and river sediment (Doc Shaul's Spring, New York).

originated as cave springs at river level, but partial filling of valleys by sediment has forced the water to rise upward through the sediment to the new river level. These ***alluviated springs*** usually form distinctive round pools along the river banks or on floodplains. Their throats are partly choked with sediment and organic debris, and there may be no accessible route into the feeder cave, even for divers.

At the seacoast, some springs are located along the shoreline at sea level. Many, however, emerge into deep seawater, some of them far from shore. The main origin for these submarine springs is a rise of sea level since the last major glaciation. ***Blue holes*** are round springs or spring-like openings in limestone islands such as those of the Caribbean. Most blue holes lead directly to underwater caves. Seawater moves in and out of the openings with the tides. Some blue holes are located inland from the coast and show tidal fluctuations in water level. Most caves that communicate with blue holes were formed during glacial periods when sea level was lower than today. The term *blue hole* is also used informally to refer to any deep, roughly circular spring,

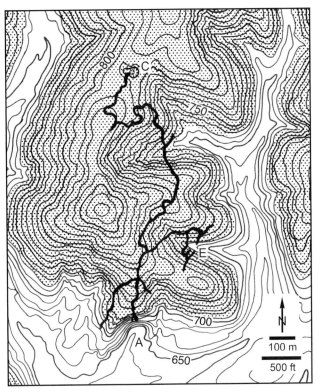

Figure 2.31: Topographic map showing a spring alcove at the collapsed termination of the main stream passage of Popcorn Spring Cave, Indiana. Its downstream (southern) end is blocked by collapse material. The cave is shown by the heavy lines. The dotted pattern shows the extent of a sandstone cap that overlies the cavernous limestone. E = cave entrance, C = collapse sinkhole, A = spring alcove. Contour interval = 10 ft (3 m). Elevations are shown in feet. Cave map by A. and M. Palmer and others.

whether or not it is located on a limestone island. The spring in Figure 2.29 is a potential candidate.

Karst springs can easily become blocked by fallen rocks and surface debris. The cave water that feeds them tends to bypass these impediments, especially during floods. In this way, ***overflow springs*** are formed that may be active only during high flow (Figure 2.30). Collapse at a spring can be so prolonged and intense that it forms a steep-walled bay in the hillside called a ***spring alcove*** (Figure 2.31). Many spring alcoves have been abandoned by diversion of their flow elsewhere, but they may remain for a long time as indicators of former spring outlets.

The larger the karst spring, especially if it is accompanied by a spring alcove, the more likely it is to drain a large cave. Some big springs are fed by cave passages that seem inappropriately small for the amount of flow that they carry. These passages are usually young diversion routes (often called ***underdrains*** or ***tapoffs***), and persevering explorers may follow them upstream to the original larger passages farther upstream.

Thermal springs have temperatures at least several degrees Celsius higher than the

Figure 2.30: An overflow spring during high water (Humpleu Mare, Romania).

Chapter 2: Cave country

Figure 2.32: Mammoth Hot Springs, Yellowstone National Park, Wyoming. Heated at depth, the water reaches the surface at temperatures as high as 73°C. Rapid loss of carbon dioxide allows calcium carbonate to precipitate (see Chapter 5).

mean annual surface temperature of the region. Schoeller (1962) suggests 4°C as the cutoff. These springs are fed by groundwater that follows deep paths or encounters hot igneous rocks. A typical location for thermal springs is at the base of a mountain or plateau, where fissures in bedrock are

likely to extend to great depth. Many thermal springs contain highly mineralized water (Figure 2.32). They are thought by some people to possess healing properties, but enthusiasm for this idea has waned in the past century.

All springs vary in flow rate in response to rainfall and snowmelt. However, a few karst springs have pulsing or intermittent flow that is unrelated to weather. These are **ebb-and-flow springs**, or **intermittent springs**. The spring at Fontestorbes, France, has perhaps the most spectacular rhythmic fluctuations. It pulses with about an hourly cycle, varying from low flow to a high flow that is hundreds of times greater. The most likely cause is a **siphon** (an outlet with an inverted **U** profile), but the repeated priming and breaking of the siphon that is necessary to make the process work requires a system more complex than the kind demonstrated in classrooms with a flexible tube. The exact configuration is still uncertain.

Some intermittent springs are partly blocked by coarse-grained sediment that accumulates in the low points of cave passages. When enough water pressure builds up to clear the blockage, a pulse of water escapes. As the pulse dies away, the sediment settles back to the low point and the cycle repeats.

An **estavelle** is a curious feature that normally serves as a swallow hole but at other times as a spring. During low flow, surface water drains into an underlying cave. During high flow, enough water enters the cave from upstream sources that the lower end of the cave cannot carry it all, and some water overflows onto the surface (Figures 2.33–2.34). At those times, the water that would otherwise enter the estavelle simply joins

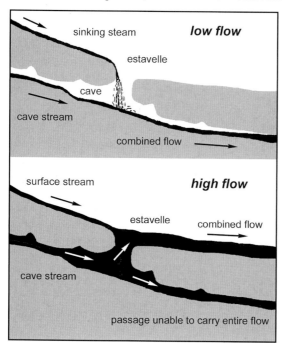

Figure 2.33: An estavelle during low flow and high flow.

Figure 2.34: The entrance of an estavelle in Huntsville, Alabama. A small sinking stream (dry at this time) drains into the opening, but water shoots out during high flow, as shown by the upward orientation of solution scallops on the rock (see Chapter 6).

the overflow from the cave and continues downstream on the surface. Springs at or near valley bottoms may temporarily receive overflow from rivers during floods, but they do not qualify as estavelles, because they normally function as outlets for water, rather than as swallow holes.

Water spouts are intermittent jets of water that squirt from the land surface through narrow openings. Some are produced by the impact of waves as they crash into underlying wave-cut caves. Water spouts are occasionally seen in karst surfaces during floods. They can form in two ways. Shallow caves, if fed by higher passages upslope, may fill with water under pressure during floods and produce jets that spurt upward along fractures in the overlying rock. This is most common just upstream from a partial blockage by sediment or collapse material. Another type of water spout is produced when water fills part of a conduit above the water table and is then blasted out of the ground by air that is compressed in underlying caves by rising floodwater (Veni and Crawford, 1986).

Paleokarst

A karst surface that is buried by later rocks is called *paleokarst* (James and Choquette, 1988; Bosák and others, 1989). Burial may be by sedimentary layers that are deposited during a rise in sea level, or, less commonly, by lava flows. Sinkholes and fissures are completely filled, as are most (but not necessarily all) caves. Soil may be preserved as an irregular granular zone that is typically colored brown or gray by organic material. Paleokarst may eventually be exposed at the surface by uplift and erosion. Caves that are part of the paleokarst can enlarge further if fresh groundwater circulates through them again.

The two most extensive paleokarst zones in North America are at the top of Lower Ordovician limestones and

Figure 2.35: Paleokarst in Bighorn Canyon, Wyoming-Montana. The caves shown here are of Mississippian age (about 300 million years old) and are almost completely filled with slightly younger Pennsylvanian sediment.

Figure 2.36: Paleokarst breccia in Jewel Cave, South Dakota, composed of limestone and dolomite broken into fragments by dissolution and recrystallization of gypsum. The remaining gypsum has since been replaced by calcite (Chapters 5 and 8).

dolomites in southeastern North America, and at the top of the Mississippian limestones in the west (M. Palmer and A. Palmer, 1989; Ford, 1989a; see Chapter 13). Caves can offer evidence for the original conditions in which the karst formed. Inactive caves that are part of the present stage in the erosion cycle are not considered paleokarst.

Although most caves are completely filled during burial of a karst surface, some isolated paleo-caves have remained partly or completely open since they formed. In the Mississippian paleokarst in the northwestern U.S., many small pockets and caves survived intact without filling, although they were once buried as much as 2 km deep by younger sedimentary rocks. In addition, many openings that were completely or nearly filled by sediment have been excavated by surface weathering and erosion after re-exposure at the surface (Figure 2.35).

Widespread bedrock collapse is common in and above paleokarst zones. When the fragments are cemented together by later mineral deposits, the result is a *breccia* (Figure 2.36). Some paleokarst breccias extend laterally for many kilometers. Vertical *breccia pipes* can extend upward from these zones as much as several hundred meters (Wenrich, 1985; Huntoon, 1996; Troutman, 2004). Simple collapse of karst features is the most common explanation, but several other causes are more likely. Many breccias coincide with former gypsum or anhydrite beds that have dissolved and recrystallized below the land surface and caused the surrounding rock to break into fragments (Stanton, 1966; Sando, 1988; Palmer and Palmer, 1995a). Alternatively, at great depth, the bedrock partitions between passages in large cave systems can shatter to produce breccia (Loucks and Handford, 1992). Some paleokarst breccias may have been produced or expanded by dissolution and collapse caused by rising thermal water.

Pseudokarst

Pseudokarst consists of karst-like features that form either by processes other than dissolution, or by slow, lengthy dissolution of rocks that are ordinarily not soluble enough to form karst (Figure 2.37). Examples are given by Halliday (1960a, 2004c). Most caves that do not have a solutional origin are considered pseudokarst. Pseudokarstic surface depressions, widened fissures, caves, and features that resemble those in karst are common in many kinds of rock, especially volcanic rocks. Local melting of glacial ice or permafrost can produce similar results.

In warm, humid climates, lengthy weathering of rocks such as quartzite and granite can form caves and surface depressions that almost qualify as true karst, because dissolution plays an important role in their origin (Wray, 1997; Grimes, 1998). Some pseudokarst is produced by purely mechanical processes such as gravitational sliding, piping, and the differential compaction of sediment. Lava caves are discussed in detail in Chapter 11. Other non-solutional caves are described briefly in Chapters 1, 3, and 5.

The processes described here for pseudokarst can also be important in enlarging or modifying true karst features, so the distinction between karst and pseudokarst is hazy. The term *pseudokarst* is best used only as a broad generality. It is preferable to describe the true nature of a phenomenon than to refer to what it is not.

Figure 2.37: Pseudokarst includes fissures and caves produced by non-solutional processes, such as these in Arizona sandstone.

The scale of karst features

This book contains frequent references to the world's largest known caves and karst features. This is not simply to impress the reader, but to illustrate the size range of these features. The greatest cave lengths and depths in a given area can also be a crude indicator of the intensity of local karst development. But length and depth alone are not good indicators of the inherent value of a cave for geologic study.

Small karst features are generally more numerous than large ones (White and White, 1995). For caves, this fractal size distribution has been quantified by Curl (1986). Curl points out that there is no geological justification for limiting the term *cave* to openings of explorable size. He suggests the term ***proper caves*** for those that are large enough to admit humans, to distinguish them from inaccessibly small ones. On the other hand, there must be some lower limit to the size of a cave, or all the minuscule pores in the ground would also qualify as caves. Because they all interconnect, they would presumably constitute a single huge cave of global scale. Speleology involves the direct observation of caves, so it is natural to consider human size as the lower limit. For karst hydrology, an appropriate criterion is that solutional openings be large enough to carry turbulent flow (Chapter 4).

For most geologic features, the tendency for smaller ones to be more numerous extends down only to a certain size. Some natural processes have a minimum scale below which they do not operate effectively. The features they produce may actually become fewer at very small scales. In solution caves, for example, most of their length might be expected to consist of passages barely large enough to explore, with walls perforated by numerous openings too small to enter. But this is rarely the case. Instead the passage frequency decreases sharply at a point well above the explorable size limit. The reason is that only a few original cracks and pores enlarge into caves, and they do so rather quickly, geologically speaking (Chapter 7). In most solution caves this selective process leaves a considerable size gap between explorable cave passages and the surrounding small openings.

So it is not valid to extrapolate cave observations to scales much smaller or larger than those that have been mapped. The porosity encountered in a well, for instance, may have little relation to caves. This discrepancy must be kept in mind whenever speleology is applied to other branches of geology or hydrology, as described in Chapter 15.

Distribution of karst and caves

About 10–15% of Earth's land area consists of well developed karst, and this figure is much greater if it includes minor karst, buried paleokarst, and solution porosity formed by deep-seated processes. Figure 2.38 (pages 38–39) shows the distribution of major karst and cave areas. Linear patterns on the map generally represent soluble rocks exposed along the flanks of mountain chains. Broad karst areas with irregular boundaries are located mainly in dissected plateaus of nearly horizontal rocks. Some boundaries on the map are arbitrary where the conditions that favor karst and caves terminate gradually. Many small isolated cave areas are grouped together on the map. Some parts of the world with large exposures of soluble rock have climates too arid or too cold for significant karst to develop. These areas are not shown in Figure 2.38.

Boundaries of karst areas

The boundaries of a karst area can include any of the following, and perhaps more than one:

Erosional truncation: Where the soluble rock has been removed by erosion, the boundary of the karst is usually sharp and can be delineated precisely. An example is the eroded edge of the limestones and dolomites around the Black Hills, South Dakota.

Burial beneath insoluble rocks: Where soluble rocks extend beneath insoluble rocks, caves and karst are usually absent beyond where the soluble rock drops below the elevation of local rivers. Dissolution can take place in soluble rock that lies entirely below local river levels, but it is rare. Up to that limit, caves may form beneath the cap-rock, and large collapse depressions triggered by dissolution of the soluble rock may extend upward to the surface through the cap-rock. Caves and karst diminish as the thickness of the cap-rock increases. This type of karst boundary is ragged, with islands of karst surrounded by non-karst areas, and vice versa. An example is the northwestern boundary of the Mammoth Cave karst, Kentucky.

Gradation to low-relief topography: Karst tends to be most common in soluble rocks that have a high relief above local river levels. If such a region grades into a low-relief area, where erosion has nearly flattened the landscape, the intensity of karst diminishes. The boundary around what is considered distinct karst may be unclear. For example, karst is well developed in the thick Cambrian-Ordovician limestones and dolomites of western Virginia, where they form high ridges. But to the southeast the rocks have been eroded to a low plain, where sinkholes and caves are still present, but most are small and choked with sediment.

Gradation to impure rock: Karst is favored by pure soluble rocks. If they grade into impure rock the karst gradually diminishes. The shaly Devonian Kalkberg Limestone of New York State contains a few solution caves and fissures. Karst water can pass entirely through it into more cavernous rocks below. But toward the east the Kalkberg grades into limy shale of the New Scotland Formation, which contains no significant solution features.

Transition to an unfavorable climate: Karst is best developed in humid regions. If an otherwise favorable rock extends into arid or permanently frozen land (permafrost), karst diminishes to where it may be essentially absent. Some of the broad limestone areas of Canada extend into arctic permafrost regions where there is no karst. In arid regions it is possible to have karst surviving from former wet periods or from deep-seated dissolution processes.

The world's longest and deepest caves

The world's longest and deepest known caves are listed on page 40. All those on the list are solution caves. Behind these statistics lies a glimmer of friendly rivalry. Cave length and depth depend strongly on the persistence of explorers and mappers. Undoubtedly there are other caves that do not appear on this list only because they have not yet been found. A cave's length is considered to be the total length of its mapped passages. Its depth is traditionally reckoned to be the total vertical range between its highest and lowest points, rather than its depth below the overlying land surface. A compilation of cave *volumes* would also be useful, but reliable measurements are scant. Although in general there is only a weak correlation between the size of a cave and its geologic significance, most of the largest are also of great scientific interest.

The length and depth rankings change frequently as new discoveries are made (Minton, 2004). In 1950 the record cave depth was little more than 600 m, and the record length was about 70 km. As recently as 1980 only ten caves had been explored to a depth of more than 1000 m. By 2005 there were 83. During the preparation of this book the record holder for deepest cave has changed from Jean Bernard to Lamprechtsofen to Krubera. In 2004, Krubera Cave, in the Republic of Georgia, was explored past the once undreamed-of depth of 2000 m. On the list of longest caves, Mammoth Cave has remained in first place for many decades, but those lower on the list have undergone considerable shuffling in rank.

The world's longest caves are remarkably diverse. Mammoth Cave and Fisher Ridge Cave, in Kentucky, lie in a low plateau of nearly horizontal limestones and drain a broad region of sinking streams and sinkholes. They are close neighbors, and future exploration will almost certainly reveal a connection between them. They consist of several levels of low-gradient stream passages, many of which are now inactive. Jewel Cave and Wind Cave are complex multi-story mazes in the flanks of the Black Hills, South Dakota. They are relics of very old cavities later enlarged by the mixing of several water sources. Optymistychna, in Ukraine, is an essentially single-level labyrinth in gypsum and was formed by water rising from underlying limestone. Hölloch and Siebenhengste-Hohgant are deep and extensive caves in the Swiss Alps that are fed by runoff from mountain uplands. Lechuguilla Cave, in the Guadalupe Mountains of New Mexico, is a dense maze of fissures, galleries, rooms, and sponge-like openings, which was formed by sulfuric acid produced by the oxidation of rising hydrogen sulfide. Sistema Sac Actun, in the Yucatán Peninsula, Mexico, is a complex of tubular, water-filled passages just below sea level. It has been explored by scuba divers. Clearwater Cave, in Sarawak, Malaysia, is a system of huge stream passages in a tropical setting and may have the largest volume of any cave in the world.

At present, Mammoth Cave is a statistical enigma. With well over twice the surveyed length of its nearest competi-

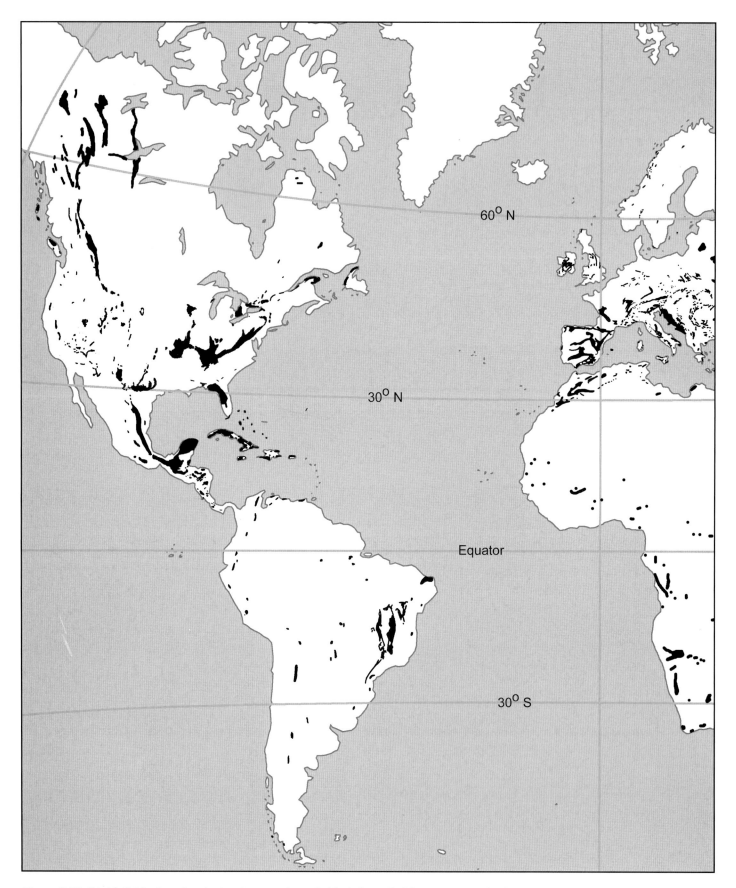

Figure 2.38: World distribution of major karst areas, shown in black (compiled from many sources). The relative sizes of the areas portrayed here are misleading, because some large ones contain only modest karst. The distorted map projection makes high-latitude karst areas look

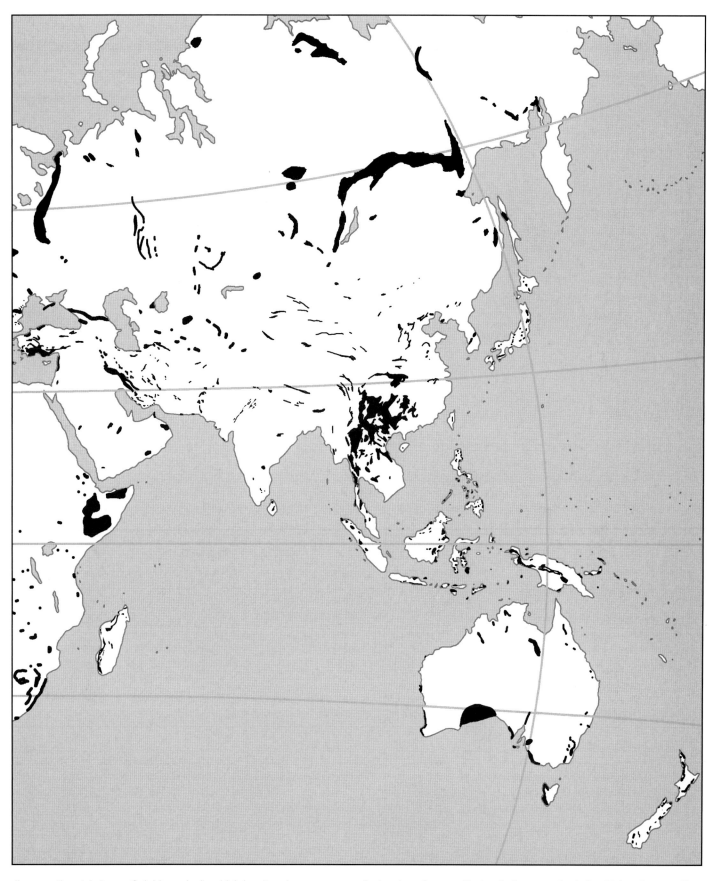

disproportionately large. Soluble rocks in which karst and caves are poorly developed are omitted entirely, as are buried paleokarst zones. See Gunn (2004a) for additional details.

The longest and deepest known caves (2007)

Longest caves	Location	Total surveyed length	
1. Mammoth Cave System	Kentucky, USA	591 km	367 mi
2 Jewel Cave	South Dakota, USA	218	136
3. Optymistychna (Optimisticheskaja)	Podoliya, Ukraine	215	134
4. Wind Cave	South Dakota, USA	199	124
5. Hölloch	Schwyz, Switzerland	194	120
6. Lechuguilla Cave	New Mexico, USA	193	120
7. Fisher Ridge Cave System	Kentucky, USA	177	110
8. Sistema Sac Actun	Quintana Roo, Mexico	155	97
9. Siebenhengste-Hohgant System	Bern, Switzerland	154	96
10. Gua Air Jernih (Clearwater Cave)	Sarawak, Malaysia	151	94

Deepest caves	Location	Total vertical extent	
1. Krubera (Voronja) Cave	Abkhazia, Georgia	2170 m	7119 ft
2. Lamprechtsofen	Salzburg, Austria	1632	5354
3. Gouffre Mirolda - Lucien Bouclier	Haute Savoie, France	1626	5335
4. Réseau Jean Bernard	Haute Savoie, France	1602	5256
5. Torca del Cerro	Picos de Europa, Spain	1589	5213
6. Sarma	Abkhazia, Georgia	1543	5062
7. Shakta Vjacheslav Pantjukhina	Abkhazia, Georgia	1508	4948
8. Čehi 2	Kanin Plateau, Slovenia	1502	4928
9. Sistema Cheve	Oaxaca, Mexico	1484	4869
10. Sistema Huautla	Oaxaca, Mexico	1475	4839

Compiled from data supplied by the individual mappers, 2007. All on this list are solution caves. Exploration continues in all of them, and their surveyed lengths and depths are frequently revised. For updates, see *www.caves. org* (National Speleological Society, Geology and Geography Section; statistics maintained by Bob Gulden).

tor, it defies probability. In a plot of rank of long caves against their surveyed lengths, Ford and Williams (1989) showed that statistically Mammoth Cave should be less than 250 km long. At that time it had exceeded 500 km. It is now almost 600 km and is still being explored.

Mammoth Cave benefits from the coincidence of several favorable conditions — a large karst drainage basin, slow and intermittent dissection by surface rivers, which produced many distinct levels, and a cap of insoluble rock that pre-serves many old passages. Also, the prominent bedding of the local limestone promotes diversion of cave streams to new routes, rather than entrenchment of old ones. The result is a tangle of passages on many levels (Figure 1.3).

In contrast to the longest caves, the world's deepest caves all have similar origins and geologic settings, despite their wide geographic range. They are located in high mountain chains of uplifted limestone, such as the Caucasus, Alps, and eastern ranges of Mexico. In several of these regions the vertical relief between water inputs and springs is more than two kilometers. The caves descend steeply as shafts and canyon passages with active streams.

Significant cave areas of the world are briefly described on the following pages.* A few small areas are included because of their historic or geologic interest. America is emphasized to match the likely readership and the author's experience (see Figure 2.39). Maps and descriptions of major caves are available in books by Waltham (1974a), Middleton and Waltham (1986), Courbon and others (1989), Gunn (2004a), and Culver and White (2005). Caves in rocks other than limestone and dolomite are described by Chabert and Courbon (1997). The scales of Figures 2.38 and 2.39 are too small for each region to be accurately identified, so in the following descriptions a world atlas is useful for pinpointing locations.

North America

North America (U.S. and Canada) contains a wide variety of soluble rocks, karst, and caves. These countries are endowed with many long caves but few deep ones, because most of their high mountain chains are composed of insoluble rocks. The deepest caves are lava tubes in the flanks of active and dormant Hawaiian volcanoes.

* This information is based on personal experience, discussions with others in the field, and a wide literature search. More details are provided by the various authors in the *Encyclopedia of Caves and Karst Science* (Gunn, 2004a).

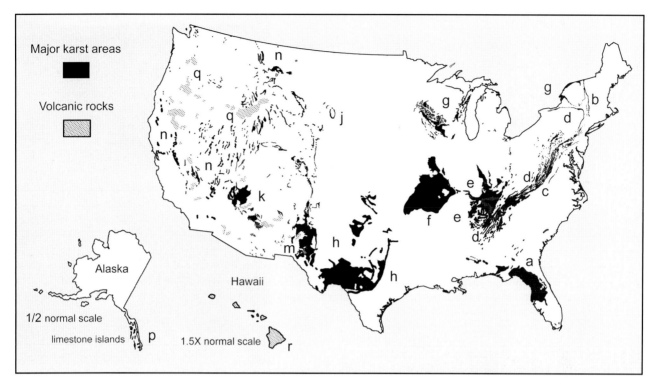

Figure 2.39 : Major cave regions of the United States, including those in soluble rock and lava. **a** = southeastern Coastal Plain, **b** = marble belt in the eastern Appalachian Mountains; **c** = folded Appalachian Mountains; **d** = Appalachian Plateaus; **e** = Interior Low Plateaus; **f** = Ozark Plateau; **g** = glaciated lowlands; **h** = southern Great Plains; **j** = Black Hills; **k** = Colorado Plateau; **m** = Guadalupe Mountains; **n** = western mountain ranges; **p** = Alaskan islands; **q** = western lava flows; **r** = Hawaii, in particular the largest island. Boundaries of cave areas are generalized. See Veni and others (2001) for further details.

In the ***Coastal Plain*** of the southeastern U.S., porous Tertiary limestones are exposed in low plateaus throughout much of Florida and parts of neighboring states. The main cavernous limestones have a thickness of about 700 m and in places more than a kilometer. Most of the large caves of Florida lie almost completely underwater and are still forming (Figures 2.40–2.41). Some caves are complex fissure labyrinths, but most are rambling tubular passages that extend as far as 100 m below sea level. These conduits carry a great deal of water toward outlets in river valleys

Figure 2.40: A typical Florida spring. Springs and most sinkhole ponds connect to water-filled conduits.

or along the seacoast. It is common for water-filled caves to extend beneath surface rivers, with complex exchanges of water between them (Figure 2.41). Most of the conduit water is fresh, as it is recharged by infiltration over broad areas of exposed limestone. A few springs in central Florida are rich in sulfide, and some near the coast contain high salinity. The Leon Sinks Cave System in northwestern Florida is the longest known underwater cave in the U.S., with a surveyed length of more than 30 km. Deep wells in southern Florida encounter cavernous voids at a wide range of depths averaging about 350 m below the surface. These may represent a paleokarst zone unrelated to near-surface caves.

The ***Appalachian Mountains*** contain significant caves in Paleozoic limestone and dolomite. These rocks have been metamorphosed along their eastern margin, especially in New England, and small but attractive caves are located in isolated patches of banded marble. The Adirondack Mountains of New York are surrounded by cavernous marbles more than 1.2 billion years old (Figure 2.42), although most of the caves are well adjusted to the present landscape and are therefore less than about a million years old. In nearby eastern Canada, New Brunswick and Nova Scotia contain some stream caves in gypsum, a rarity in the humid eastern part of the continent.

West of the marble belt the rocks of the Appalachians are strongly folded, but not metamorphosed, and they have been eroded to form long narrow ridges and valleys. Most caves in

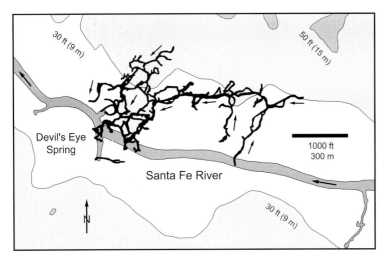

Figure 2.41: Map of the Devil's Eye Cave System, High Springs, Florida, showing the pattern of water-filled caves (black) beneath the level of the Santa Fe River. Flow patterns are shown by arrows. Contour lines show elevation above sea level. From map by Todd Kincaid (1998).

this region are stream passages parallel to these topographic trends (Figures 2.43–2.44). Some are complex network mazes. The deepest caves in the eastern part of the continent are also located in this region. The Omega Cave System in Virginia is the deepest cave (384 m), and Ellison Cave in Georgia contains the deepest vertical shaft in the "lower 48" states,

Figure 2.43: Clover Hollow Cave, Virginia, a typical cave influenced by the trend of the tilted and fractured rocks of the Appalachian Mountains.

at more than 180 m. The most abundant cavernous rocks are Cambrian and Ordovician limestones and dolomites, which have a nearly uninterrupted thickness of up to 4 km. These rocks form massive ridges along the western border of

Figure 2.42: Cave in 1.2-billion-year-old Grenville Marble, Adirondack Mountains, New York (Crane Mt. Cave).

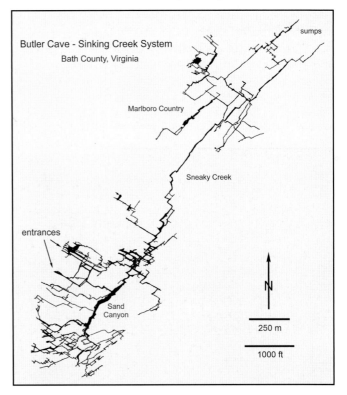

Figure 2.44: Map of the Butler Cave - Sinking Creek Cave System, Virginia. From map by the Butler Cave Conservation Society.

Figure 2.45: Main stream passage in Rumbling Falls Cave, in the Cumberland Plateau of eastern Tennessee. Note the flat bedding of the limestone and the banks of gravel and sand deposited by the cave stream.

the folded Appalachians, but farther east they have been weathered downward to a low, hilly plain with few large caves. When these rocks stood higher, in the early days of the Appalachians, they must have contained some remarkable karst.

Farther west in the Appalachians the strata are less deformed, and soluble rocks form broad, high plateaus. Their most extensive caves consist of stream passages on multiple levels. Friar's Hole and Organ Cave in West Virginia are each more than 60 km long. The dissected western edge of the Appalachians includes the Cumberland Plateau, which extends from eastern Kentucky and Tennessee into northern Alabama. This area is noted for its deep shafts and large cave passages (Figure 2.45). In Tennessee this region contains the largest cave rooms in the eastern U.S., thanks in part to a thick cap of resistant rock over the limestone.

The **Interior Low Plateaus** of Kentucky, Tennessee, and neighboring states include Paleozoic limestones and dolomites only about 100–200 m thick, but because of their nearly horizontal structure they are exposed over very large areas. The tens of thousands of caves in this region are nearly all composed of active and abandoned stream passages with various closely spaced levels. Mammoth Cave, Kentucky (Figure 2.46), is the most celebrated cave in the region because of its great size, but it occupies only a small part of a karst drainage basin that extends for several hundred square kilometers.

The **Ozark Plateau** of Missouri and Arkansas appears superficially to be an extension of the Interior Low Plateaus, but in detail it is quite distinct. It is rich in caves, but surface karst is subdued over much of the area by a thick mantle of residual gravel, which consists of insoluble chert left behind from weathering of the limestones. In places the residual soils are more than 100 m thick. In the U.S., Missouri is second only to Florida in its number of large karst springs (Figure 2.47). Most of them are fed by regional groundwater systems in which caves extend deep beneath the water table, many as much as 100 m. This deep cave development contrasts

Figure 2.46: A dry middle-level passage in Mammoth Cave, Kentucky (Kaemper Avenue).

Figure 2.47: Big Spring, on the Current River, Missouri, is one of the largest karst springs in the U.S., with a mean flow of 12.5 m³/sec. Dye traces have been made to the spring from as far away as 60 km.

Figure 2.49: Caverns of Sonora, Texas, is a show cave noted for its delicate speleothems (cave formations). This is the cave's celebrated "Butterfly," part of which was tragically carried off by a tourist in 2006. Width of photo = 15 cm.

with the shallow depths of most caves in the Interior Low Plateaus.

The **Glaciated Lowlands** of central North America contain a few isolated areas of early Paleozoic limestones and dolomites overlain by thin, patchy glacial sediment. Caves are scattered through much of the upper Mississippi River basin, northwestern New York, and eastern Canada. There are

three varieties: simple stream caves, such as Coldwater Cave, Iowa; network mazes formed by floodwaters invading from nearby rivers, such as Moira Cave, Ontario, and Mystery Cave, Minnesota (Figure 2.48); and small mineralized caves that appear to have formed deep below the surface.

The **Great Plains** of west-central North America are almost devoid of karst, except in the southern part, where there are exposures of nearly horizontal Cretaceous limestones, folded Ordovician limestones, and broad plains of Permian

Figure 2.48: Mystery Cave, Forestville State Park, Minnesota, is a labyrinth of intersecting linear passages along fractures in Ordovician limestone and dolomite.

Figure 2.50: Entrance of Parks Ranch Cave, in the gypsum plain of southeastern New Mexico.

Figure 2.51: Map of Jewel Cave, South Dakota, as of 2003. Recent extensions have been mainly to the southeast. Map courtesy of National Park Service.

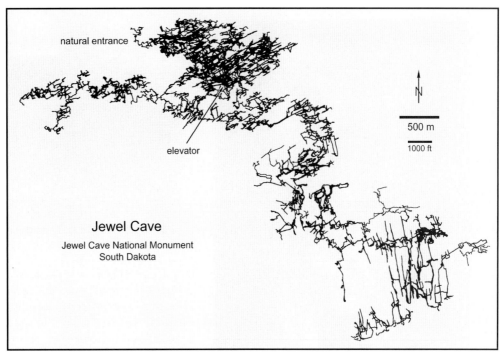

natural entrance

elevator

N

500 m
1000 ft

Jewel Cave
Jewel Cave National Monument
South Dakota

gypsum. Limestone forms a broad band that extends through central and southern Texas. The Cretaceous Edwards Limestone provides most of the region's water supply (page 394). Faults allow water to emerge at large springs that are fed by cavities down to a kilometer below the surface. Mixing of fresh water with water that is rich in hydrogen sulfide produces solutionally aggressive solutions that have formed much of the deep porosity (Chapter 5). This area contains some of the most attractive caves in North America, such as the finely decorated Caverns of Sonora (Figure 2.49). Farther west and north, the Permian gypsum extends across large parts of Texas, New Mexico, Oklahoma, and Kansas (Figure 2.50). The continent's largest cave in gypsum is Jester Cave in Oklahoma, which is about 10 km long. Exploration for caves in the gypsum plain is still in its infancy.

Caves of the **Black Hills**, South Dakota, are among the world's oldest and most complex. Nearly all are in Mississippian carbonate rocks about 100–200 m thick, which were first exposed to dissolution soon after they were deposited. Early caves were buried by later rocks and then enlarged during uplift of the Black Hills in the early Tertiary Period. Jewel Cave and Wind Cave are the largest, with 218 km and 199 km of mapped passages to date (Figure 2.51). Many of their passages are lined by a thick coating of calcite crystals deposited by warm water when the caves were filled with static water late in their development (Figure 1.22).

The **southwestern U.S.** consists of arid plateaus and mountains, many of them composed of Paleozoic limestones and dolomites. Surface karst is sparse because of the dry climate, but caves have formed mainly by deep-seated processes such as mixing between deep and shallow groundwater, and oxidation of hydrogen sulfide to sulfuric acid. Caves are abundant in the Permian rocks of the Guadalupe Mountains of New Mexico (e.g., Carlsbad Cavern, Figure 2.52) and in Mississippian limestone exposed in walls of the Grand Canyon and its tributaries. The Guadalupes include some of the world's most unusual caves. Lechuguilla Cave, whose entrance was excavated only in 1986, is now more than 190 km long. With a depth

of 478 m it is the deepest known solution cave in the U.S. Because of its profuse and colorful mineral deposits, it is widely considered by cavers throughout the world to be the most beautiful cave yet discovered. It is described in later chapters.

The **western mountain ranges** of the U.S. and Canada are studded with hundreds of moderate-sized exposures of Paleozoic limestone and dolomite, most of which form alpine karst that is noted for deep, cold stream caves. They are located along the flanks of the Rocky Mountains and Sierra Nevada, as well as in peaks of the Marble Mountains of California, Vancouver Island, and Prince of Wales Island and Dall Island in Alaska. Although many caves are located high above nearby valley bottoms, their host rocks are rarely

Figure 2.52: Caves in the Guadalupe Mountains of New Mexico formed by sulfuric acid dissolution, but most of their speleothems were deposited by fresh water from the overlying surface. Photo by A. Palmer, J. Michael Queen, and Jack Soman.

Figure 2.53: Big Brush Creek Cave, in the Uinta Mountains of Utah, cuts through a Mississippian-age conglomerate of limestone cobbles. By following the gentle dip of the limestone, the cave reaches a depth of about 260 m with only a few modest vertical pitches.

more than a few hundred meters thick. Thus deep caves are rare except where they follow the dip of the strata for long distances (Figure 2.53). Columbine Crawl and Great Expectations ("Great X") Cave in Wyoming each once held the U.S. depth record. Lilburn Cave and Bigfoot Cave in California are the largest marble caves in North America (Figure 2.54).

In a few places between mountain ranges, limestone and dolomite contain deep groundwater flow that acquires high concentrations of hydrogen sulfide. Where this water discharges into river valleys, caves can form where the

Figure 2.54: The Marble Mountains of northern California contain broad expanses of alpine karst.

Figure 2.55: Alpine karst on a coastal island of Alaska. Photo by Jim Baichtal.

sulfide oxidizes to sulfuric acid. This process can form caves of various patterns. The Kane Caves of Wyoming are simple linear tubes (Chapter 8). In the Bighorn Mountains along the Montana-Wyoming Border, the same kind of water followed more complex flow patterns and produced maze caves, now mostly inactive, such as the Bighorn-Horsethief System.

Several large islands along the coast of *southeastern Alaska* contain thick limestones with abundant caves. Because of the complex local geology, karst is scattered in many irregular patches. Deep fissures partly obscured by forest and patchy soil cover make the terrain difficult to traverse (Figure 2.55). The region is mountainous, and many caves contain shafts and steep passages. El Capitan Pit, on Prince of Wales Island, is one of the deepest known solution shafts in the U.S., at 182 m.

Lava caves occur throughout the relatively recent volcanic areas of the western U.S., particularly in California, Oregon, Washington, Idaho, New Mexico, and Hawai'i (see Chapter 11 for details). Lava flows on the largest Hawaiian island are riddled with large caves, including the two caves with the greatest vertical range in the U.S.: Kazumura (1102 m) and the Umi'i Manu System (570 m).

The largest caves in *Canada* are in the Rocky Mountains. Arctomys Cave is the deepest, at 536 m, and the deepest single shaft is the 254 m entrance pit of Close to the Edge. Castleguard Cave partly underlies the Columbia Icefield (Figure 2.56), and meltwaters periodically surge through the cave. One of its passages terminates upstream in an ice plug at the base of the glacier. It is Canada's longest cave, with 20 km of mapped passages. Along the border between Alberta and British Columbia, Yorkshire Pot and Gargantua cross beneath the continental divide. The Maligne River is the largest sinking stream in Canada, with a catchment area of 2300 km^2 and a mean flow of 13 m^3/sec, but no caves are presently accessible along its underground course.

The labyrinth karst of the Nahanni, Northwest Territories, is some of the most extensive in the world. Much of north-central Canada contains vast areas of soluble rock, but most has little stream entrenchment, is covered by thick glacial

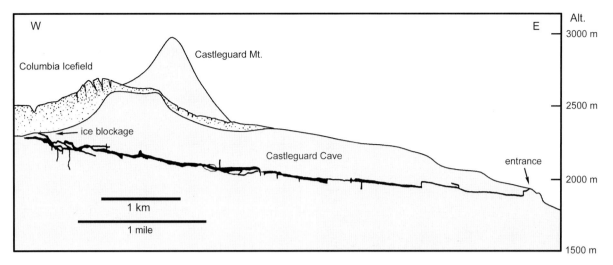

Figure 2.56: Castleguard Cave, in Alberta, partly underlies the Columbia Icefield (after Ford and others, 1983). Vertical exaggeration = 1.8X.

sediment, or is permanently frozen. Thus caves are few or absent, and these areas are omitted from the map in Figure 2.38. If all soluble rocks at or near the surface are included, Canada would contain more than a million km² of potential karst, which would rival that of any other country (Ford, 2004).

Central America and the Caribbean

The eastern mountains and plateaus of Central America contain a great many caves in thick Cretaceous limestone. Some very large and deep caves are located in this region. Although they have been explored mainly by American cavers, expeditions by European and local cavers are increasingly common. Deep caves in Mexico include Sistema Huautla (1475 m deep), and Sistema Cheve (1484 m deep) with a potential range of 2540 m between its highest entrance and its spring. El Sótano del Barro, Sótano de las Golondrinas, and Sótano de la Culebra are vertical shafts more than 330 m deep (Figure 2.57).

Figure 2.58: Sponge-like pattern of a typical Caribbean cave (Lighthouse Cave, San Salvador). Photo by Joan Mylroie.

El Zacatón, in northeastern Mexico, is one of the largest known underwater shafts (Figure 2.20). It is a sulfur spring that extends straight downward more than 300 m to a depth far below sea level. It is the site of a former record-breaking scuba dive of 284 m. Sistema Purificación, in the highlands farther west, is the longest known above-water cave in Mexico, with a surveyed length of nearly 100 km.

The Yucatán Peninsula is a partly submerged plateau of Cenozoic limestone that drains fresh water to the Gulf of Mexico. Cenotes and coastal springs provide access to most of the caves. Underwater cave systems, explored by divers, include the Sac Actun and Ox Bel Ha Systems, each about 150 km long. Caves in the area are still rapidly being explored and mapped, and several other underwater caves nearby have recently been pushed for impressive distances. If they are all eventually linked, their combined length might challenge Mammoth Cave for the title of world's longest cave.

Figure 2.57: Sótano de las Golondrinas, Mexico, a free drop of 376 m (1234 ft). Note the person descending on rope. Photo by Bernard Jackson.

Figure 2.59: The radio telescope at the Arecibo Observatory in Puerto Rico was built inside a natural karst depression to minimize construction costs.

Belize and Guatemala contain large river caves in Cretaceous and Tertiary limestones. Many are significant archeological sites because of their use by the Maya Indians, whose heyday was about A.D. 1000. The Chiquibul System, 39 km long, is fed by recharge from the southern highlands of Belize and extends westward across the border into Guatemala. The massive limestone of the area supports large rooms with roof spans up to 200 m wide.

Most Caribbean islands are located in porous limestones of Tertiary and Quaternary age. In small islands such as San Salvador and Isla de Mona, caves are formed by solutionally aggressive mixtures between fresh water and seawater (Figure 2.58). Larger islands, such as Cuba, Jamaica, Hispaniola, and Puerto Rico, have broad enough catchments to contain river caves. The main stream passage of Río Encantado, in northern Puerto Rico, has been mapped for nearly 17 km. The surrounding karst extends across most of the northern part of the island (Figures 2.9 and 2.59). Cuba contains a variety of caves that range from highly decorated ones along the coast to deep systems in mountain ranges. Cuba's largest cave is Gran Caverna de Palmarito, with 48 km of mapped passages on three levels. Of comparable size is Gran Caverna de Santo Tomás, which contains six or seven distinct passage levels.

South America

Although only a small percentage of South America contains soluble rock, the continent has some impressive local concentrations of karst and caves. The main karst areas are in Brazil, Venezuela, Colombia, Ecuador, Peru, and Chile. Brazil alone contains 200,000 km^2 of karst. Some caves in Brazil and Venezuela are spectacularly large, and new discoveries are being made at a rapid rate. Brazil's Toca da Boa Vista is a maze in Precambrian dolomite with more than 100 km of mapped passages (Figure 2.60). It is currently the longest known cave on the continent and still contains hundreds of unmapped leads. More than 2000 caves are known in the low plateaus of Brazil's Bambuí karst. Some, such as Gruta do Janelão, contain passages up to 100 m high. Figure 2.61 shows an example.

High plateaus (***tepuis***) of Precambrian quartzite in southern Venezuela and eastern Brazil are pierced by some remarkable sinkholes, shafts, and caves that formed during more than 60 million years of slow weathering in a tropical climate (Figure 2.62). An example is Sima Aonda, which is located in southeastern Venezuela near Salto Angel, the world's highest waterfall. The cave is 363 m deep, with large rooms and a mapped length of 2 km. Nearby Cueva Roraima Sur was already known as the world's longest known quartzite cave, at 5.5 km but has recently been linked with others into an 11 km system. Part of the system consists of a large river passage averaging 50 m wide and 15−20 m high. These dimensions are remarkable for caves in supposedly insoluble rock. Brazil contains a similar type of karst in quartz sandstone, but with smaller caves and at lower altitudes.

Caves in the Andes of Peru and Chile lie at elevations as high as 4800 m. The Peruvian Andes contain the Sima Pumacocha, 638 m deep, which is so far the deepest cave on the continent, and other caves with shafts up to 200 m deep.

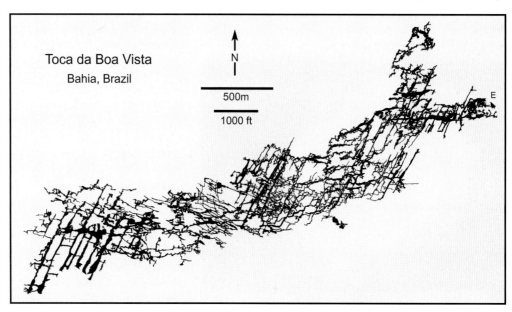

Toca da Boa Vista
Bahia, Brazil

N

500m
1000 ft

E

Figure 2.60: Map of Toca da Boa Vista, in Brazil, South America's longest known cave, mapped by Grupo Bambuí de Pesquisas Espeleológicas. The mapped length is more than 100 km. The vertical range is about 60 m. E = main entrance. Map courtesy of Augusto Auler.

Figure 2.62: Auyan tepui, one of Venezuela's many high plateaus of quartzite. Water pours out of unexplored cave entrances in the plateau walls. Photo by Ken Davis.

Figure 2.61: The 100-meter-high entrance of Brejões Cave, Brazil. Note the tiny white figure of a person in the gap between the trees at the lower right. Photo by Ezio Rubbioli.

The Atacama Desert in Chile, perhaps the driest place on Earth, has hundreds of caves in salt, only a few of which have been explored (see Chapter 9). Recent French expeditions to the rainy windswept islands off the coast of southwestern Patagonia have revealed a spectacular marble karst with challenging river caves. The Galápagos Islands off the western coast of South America contain lava tubes up to 3 km long.

Europe

Modern speleology had its beginnings in Europe, where it is still pursued at a high intensity and level of sophistication. The continent contains many extensive and varied karst regions. It is the home of the classic karst region of western Slovenia, the Kras Plateau, from which the international word *karst* got its name (Figure 2.63). Europe has several internationally prominent karst research centers, such as those in Slovenia, Romania, Hungary, France, Switzerland, and Ukraine. Slovenia's Postojnska jama and Škocjanske jama* are among Europe's most celebrated show caves.

---

* The Slovenian word for cave, *jama*, which appears often in this book, is pronounced *ya-ma*.

Figure 2.63: Planinska jama, one of the major caves of the classic karst of Slovenia.

The largest and most challenging caves in Europe are in the Alpine chains that extend from France in the west, through Switzerland, Italy, and Austria, to the Balkans in the east. In addition there are the Caucasus Mountains between the Caspian and Black Seas, the Pyrenees along the French-Spanish border, and the Cantabrians of northwestern Spain. The deepest caves in the world are located in these regions, mainly in thick Mesozoic limestones.

The Swiss Alps contain some very large and complex caves, such as Hölloch and Siebenhengste-Hohgant (Figure 2.64). Caves like this pose a serious challenge because of their great length and depth, combined with cold and wet conditions. The greatest known volumes of cave ice are located in the Alps and Carpathian Mountains (Chapter 12). The largest cave passages in the Alps are of late Miocene age and are thought to represent prolonged cave development at or near local base levels. Later mountain uplift has raised these passages hundreds of meters above the present valley floors (Figure 2.65).

Figure 2.64: One of many steep canyon passages in the Siebenhengste-Hohgant System, Switzerland.

Figure 2.65: The limestone plateaus along the northern border of the Austrian Alps contain ancient caves well above the valley bottoms, with younger systems that extend to greater depth.

Fine examples of alpine karst are also located in the Pyrenees of France and Spain (Figure 2.66). For many years the Gouffre de la Pierre St. Martin, in the Pyrenees, was the world's deepest known cave. In the past few decades, exploration in the Picos de Europa and Matienzo regions of the Cantabrians has yielded many deep caves. Just to the south is Spain's longest cave, 90-km Ojo Guareña. The High Sierras of southern Spain are in a semiarid climate, but they contain some impressive caves such as 1098-meter-deep Sima GESM. Gypsum karst and caves are common throughout the eastern part of the country. The island of Mallorca, in the Mediterranean Sea, is well known for its coastal karst, which has been formed at least partly by mixing of seawater and freshwater.

Besides alpine karst, France also contains cavernous limestone plateaus in its south and east. These include the Causses, Vercors Plateau, and Grand Chartreuse, which are the sites of many early speleological studies (see cover photograph). Réseau de la Dent de Crolles, in the Chartreuse, and Gouffre Berger, in the Vercors, each held the world's depth record at one time. The Dordogne region of southwestern France is world renowned for its paleolithic cave art, such as the uniquely delicate paintings of Lascaux Cave.

The Jura Mountains along the France-Switzerland border are structurally folded like the Appalachians of North America and consist of parallel ridges and valleys. Long, low-gradient caves are typical, with an elongation along the trends of ridges.

Figure 2.66: The Pyrenees along the France-Spain border, the scene of some of the earliest alpine caving.

Figure 2.67: Antro del Corchia, in the intensely deformed Carrara Marble of the Apuan Alps, is one of Italy's major alpine caves. This is a traverse around a 100-m pit along intersecting fractures.

Italy has a rich variety of karst that ranges from alpine caves in the north to thermal systems farther south. The Apuan Alps, a southern outlier of the true Alps, are composed of Carrara Marble, which has long been valued by sculptors such as Michelangelo. It is also host to Italy's longest cave, the Antro del Corchia (Figure 2.67), as well as its three deepest caves. The Apennine Mountain chain, which extends along the axis of the Italian peninsula, contains some remarkable examples of active sulfuric acid cave development, such as the Frasassi Caves (see Chapter 8). The Merro Well, near Rome, is perhaps the world's deepest water-filled shaft. It has been explored to a depth of 392 m by a remotely operated vehicle. The Apennines also contain a belt of cavernous gypsum.

Karst and caves are less abundant in northwestern Europe but still show great variety. Belgium contains low karst plateaus with paleokarst and active caves. Germany possesses some gypsum karst, and limestone plateaus with small but intricate caves. Iceland is constructed of volcanic plateaus with many lava caves. Narrow bands of marble in Norway contain caves up to 20 km long (Figure 2.68). In Spitzbergen (northern Norway), karst and glacier caves are located within 1000 km of the North Pole.

The British Isles contain several small but intensively explored cave areas in Paleozoic limestone. Despite their thin low-relief limestones and glacial sediment, areas such as the Dales of northern England and the low plateaus of Wales and County Clare, Ireland, contain some long and dynamic caves

(Figure 2.69). The Lancaster-Easegill System (Dales) and Ogof Draenen and Ogof Ffynnon Ddu (southern Wales), have mapped lengths of 50–70 km.

Several extremely deep vertical shafts have recently been discovered in the Kanin Plateau in Slovenia and in the Velebit Mountains of Croatia (see page 228). Slovenia's Vrtiglavica is 643 m (2110 ft) deep, and nearby Brezno pod Velbom has an entrance shaft 501 m deep. Their entrances had been known previously, but exploration was blocked by ice. Although they are not perfect free-fall drops, rocks can fall from top to bottom with only a few bounces. Croatia's Velebita Cave contains an internal 513-meter-deep shaft that is currently the world's deepest known perfectly vertical shaft. Patkov Gust, in the same mountain range, consists of a single nearly vertical shaft 553 m deep. The marble karst of Greece includes some deep shafts such as Provatina, with a 389 m free fall.

Many of the plateaus and mountain ranges of central Europe are rich in soluble rocks, most of which are Paleozoic-Mesozoic in age. There are well-studied karst areas in the Czech Republic, Slovakia, Poland, Hungary, and Romania. Their geologic settings are complex, as are the patterns of the caves that form in them. The largest karst areas of the region are in southern Poland

Figure 2.68: Storbekgrotta is a typical Norwegian cave near the Arctic circle. It is located in a thin band of steeply dipping marble and is fed by a sinking stream.

and in Slovakia. Paleokarst and related lead-zinc ores are common in the Mesozoic carbonates, especially in southern Poland. The longest caves in the region are Amaterska-Punkva Cave in the Czech Republic, and Demänová Cave in Slovakia (Figure 6.20), both of which are more than 30 km long. Many caves in central Europe have been formed partly by rising thermal water, most notably those in and near Budapest, Hungary. Movile Cave in Romania has attracted attention in recent years as the site of an isolated ecosystem in which the energy is supplied by oxidation reactions in rising waters rich in hydrogen sulfide. Some central and eastern European caves are illustrated in Figures 2.70–2.72.

The world's longest caves in gypsum are dense networks such as Optymistychna (or Optimisticeskaja), which is located in Miocene rocks of western Ukraine (Figure 2.72). There are many similar caves in the area, all apparently formed by water rising from underlying limestone (Chapter 8).

Russia contains dozens of large karst and cave areas, especially in the Carpathian and Ural Mountains and in Siberia. In the eastern lowlands the largest caves are in gypsum. The area also includes some of the very few known caves in anhydrite. Karst in the north-south-trending Ural Mountains is strongly controlled by folding, as in the Appalachian and Jura Mountains. In Asian Russia, Siberia contains many large, scattered karst areas in highly varied rock types. Caves include the rambling maze Bol'shaya Oreshnaja, which at 47 km is the longest known cave in conglomerate (Figure 2.73).

Currently the world's deepest known cave is Krubera (Voronja) Cave, in the Caucasus Mountains of Abkhazia, Republic of Georgia. It was explored by a Ukrainian group to a record 1710 m in 2001, and since then they have pushed the cave to the impressive depth of 2170 m (7119 ft). The map and profile are shown in Figure 2.74. This depth record vaults past the runner-up by an unprecedented 526 m. Dye traces in the area have vertical ranges up to 2300 m, and submarine springs emerge at depths as much as 400 m below sea level. The technical difficulties of exploring this cold, wet, and deep cave testify to the dedication and endurance of the explorers.

Many European caves cross national boundaries. The Baradla-Domica Cave System extends beneath the Slovakia-Hungary border and has entrances in both countries (Figure 2.70). The entrance to Zoluška, a sprawling maze in gypsum, is in Moldova, but most of the cave is located in Ukraine. In the Pyrenees, the Pierre St. Martin System zigzags across the French-Spanish border in several places.

Figure 2.69: A wet trip through Ogof Ffynnon Ddu, south Wales. Photo by Chris Howes and Judith Calford.

Asia

Some of the most striking developments in speleology today are in Asia. China alone contains more than a 500,000 km² of spectacular karst, mainly in the provinces of Guangxi, Guizhou, Hunan, and Yunnan in southeastern China. Karst research is conducted at several centers such as the Institute of Karst Geology in Guilin.

The famous Chinese paintings of tall finger-like spires towering over fertile plains may look like the product of a fevered imagination, but they portray the landscape quite accurately (Figures 2.10, 2.75–2.76). Caves and karst have long been held in high regard by the Chinese, and many caves and forests of limestone pinnacles have been developed for tourism. China's karst is developed on a broad range of carbonate rocks, mostly of Paleozoic age, which reach thicknesses as great as 6–7 km. It extends from the humid tropics in the south to the high arid plateaus in the northwest. Toward the northwest the climate becomes more arid and the

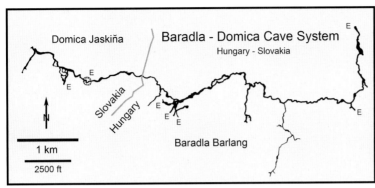

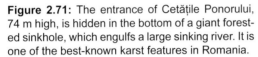

Figure 2.70: The Baradla-Domica (Aggtelek) Cave crosses the Slovakia-Hungary border. Tours are conducted in large parts of the cave in both countries, but a barrier in the cave prevents unauthorized border crossings. E = entrance. Map by Vörös Meteor Club.

Figure 2.71: The entrance of Cetățile Ponorului, 74 m high, is hidden in the bottom of a giant forested sinkhole, which engulfs a large sinking river. It is one of the best-known karst features in Romania.

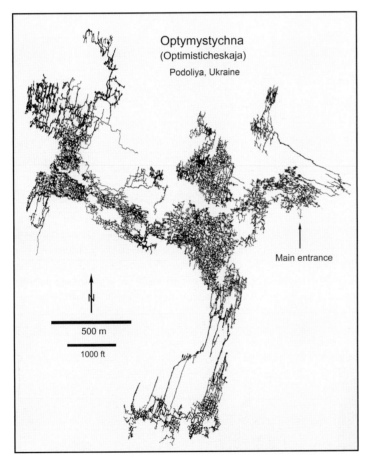

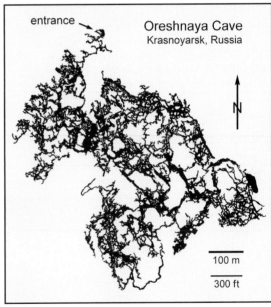

Figure 2.73: Map of Bol'shaya Oreshnaja, in the East Sayan Plateau of Siberia, Russia, from a survey by the Speleo Club of Divnogorsky. This is the largest known cave in a limestone conglomerate (Filippov, 2004).

Figure 2.72: Map of Optymystychna (Optimisticheskaja), in the Ternopol District of Ukraine. With more than 215 km of mapped passages, this is the world's longest known cave in gypsum. This network maze was formed below the water table by seepage of water through a thin gypsum bed from underlying limestone (Klimchouk, 1992). From map by Tsyklop and Bat'kivshchina Cave Clubs, Lvov.

soluble rocks become less pure, and as a result the intensity of karst development decreases sharply in that direction.

Several types of karst landscapes are recognized in China (see page 26). The *fengcong* type consists of mature cone karst with steep hills and surrounding sinkholes (Figure 2.75). The *fenglin* type is composed of tower karst with isolated

Figure 2.74: Krubera (Voronja) Cave, in the Republic of Georgia, is currently the world's deepest cave. In 2005 it was explored further, to a depth of 2170 m (7119 ft). Letters A–N show the relationship between features on the plan-view map and the profile. K = depth in January 2001. M = depth in August 2004. N = depth in October 2004. Map by Ukrainian Speleological Association, courtesy of Alexander Klimchouk. See Klimchouk (2005a).

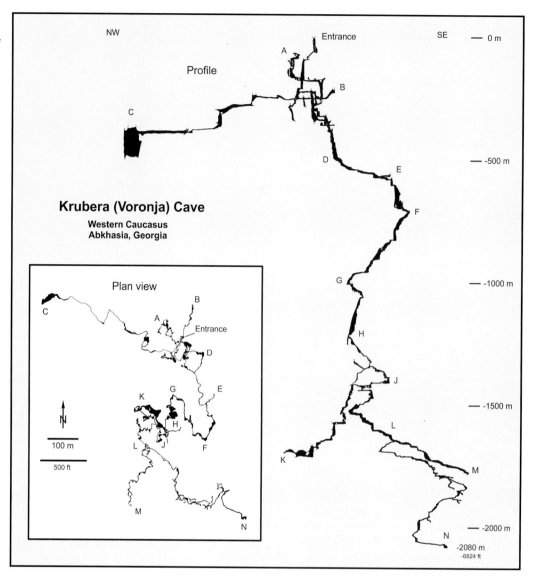

steep-walled peaks that rise from nearly flat erosional or sediment-covered plains (Figure 2.76).

Many Chinese caves are spectacular (Figure 2.77). Some have ceiling heights of more than 100 m. Gebihe Dong, in Guizhou Province, is a huge river cave with a dome reaching 370 m to a skylight entrance. Shuanghedong, also in Guizhou, is the longest cave in the country, with a mapped length of more than 100 km. In places, high karst plateaus rise up to 2500 m above the local valleys and show promise of exceptional cave depths. In 2003, in Baiyudong,

Figure 2.75: Fengcong karst, Guangxi Province, China.

Figure 2.76: Fenglin karst, Guizhou Province, China.

Figure 2.77: Entrance canyon and natural bridge, Zhujin River Cave, Guizhou Province, China. Photo by Kevin Downey.

Guizhou Province, a French team explored China's deepest known vertical shaft, a 424 m free fall (Figures 2.78–2.80). Systematic exploration of Chinese caves has barely begun, and impressive discoveries are certain to follow in the next few decades.

Japan and Korea contain only small areas of karst but some significant lava caves (see Chapter 11). Japan's largest solution cave is Akka-do, with 24 km of passages. South Korea's largest caves are lava tubes on the island of Chejudo, off the southern tip of the Korean peninsula. These are up to 5 km long and include some of the largest cross sections of any known caves in volcanic rock.

In the past decade there have been significant cave discoveries in the humid tropical regions of southeastern Asia, particularly in eastern India, Thailand, Laos, Vietnam, and Burma (Myanmar). Large, low-gradient river caves are common in Paleozoic, Mesozoic, and Cenozoic carbonate rocks. The longest known are Nam Non Cave in Laos and Krem Kotsati-Umlawan in Meghalaya (eastern India), each with mapped lengths of more than 20 km, and also the Phong Nha system in Vietnam with at total of about 45 km in several unconnected segments. Sinking

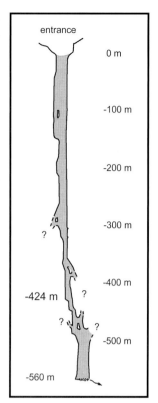

Figure 2.78: Profile of Baiyudong, Guizhou Province, China, from Maire and others (2004). See Figures 2.79–2.80. The total depth of 560 m is equivalent to about 1840 feet.

Figure 2.79: The 424-meter-deep entrance shaft of Baiyudong, Guizhou Province, China, viewed from a depth of 100 m. It was first explored during the Chinese-French expedition of 2003. (Maire and others, 2004; photo by Eric Sanson.)

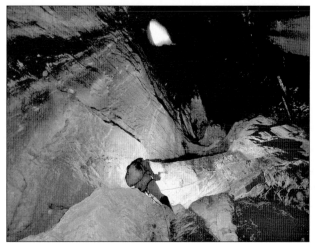

Figure 2.80: Looking up the Baiyudong shaft from a depth of 300 m — still more than 100 m above the floor. The entrance is visible in the top center. Although this is a free-fall pit, explorers have paused on wall ledges. Photo by Richard Maire.

Figure 2.81: Partly submerged tower karst along the seacoast in Phang Na Bay, Thailand. Photo by Kevin Downey.

streams in Laos feed caves that reach 100 m wide in places. Xé Bang Fai Cave in Laos contains a river that flows for 6.5 km through a passage 40 m in diameter with a mean discharge of more than 60 m³/sec. Karst is less abundant in Myanmar, but its highly metamorphosed marble contains some small caves with gem-quality minerals in their sediments.

Some of the coastal karst in southeast Asia has been partly drowned by a combination of land subsidence and sea-level rise. Cave-rich karst towers project from the sea along the coasts of Vietnam and Thailand (Figures 2.11 and 2.81).

The arid plateaus and mountain ranges of south-central Asia contain vast regions of carbonate rocks that are virtually unexplored for karst and caves. In this dry climate many of the caves were formed by deep dissolution processes similar to those of the Guadalupe Mountains of New Mexico. For example, the Kap-Kutan (Cup-Coutunn) System in Turkmenistan is a three-dimensional labyrinth that contains perhaps the most diverse array of minerals of any cave in the world. The vast Tien Shan Plateau and neighboring plains, which stretch across nearly a million square kilometers of Uzbekistan, Tajikistan, Kyrgyzstan, Kazakhstan, and northern China, contain faulted blocks of mainly Paleozoic carbonate rocks. This region is nearly unknown to cavers, so only small parts are shown on the world karst map (Figure 2.38). The more humid mountain ranges of the region contain some fairly deep caves, such as Boj-Bulok in Uzbekistan, which is Asia's deepest at 1415 m. Cenozoic salt and gypsum farther south contain many caves of modest size.

Soluble limestones and dolomites stretch throughout the Himalayas and related mountain chains, right up to the top of Mt. Everest itself. But most of the soluble rocks are impure or dolomitic, and the climate is so cold that the rocks are highly shattered by frost action. So far only a few small caves have been found in them.

Southwestern Asia, which includes the major oil-producing regions of the world, contains widespread soluble rocks. Caves are sparse where the climate is arid, as in the

Arabian Peninsula, and most are relics either of former wetter periods or of deep-seated cave development. Much of the region's petroleum comes from voids in Mesozoic-Cenozoic carbonate rocks.

Significant caves and karst are located in mountainous regions of Turkey, Lebanon, and Iran. The Taurus Mountains of Turkey contain large underground rivers and caves up to 1400 m deep, with potential depths of more than 2000 m. The world's longest underground dye trace (75 km) was performed in this area. Lebanon contains some excellent karst in Mesozoic limestone, with river caves, submarine karst springs, and high-mountain caves up to 620 m deep. The Ghar Ali Sadr of Iran is one of the finest show caves in the region, with a total of 12 km of passages, profuse mineral deposits, and a two-kilometer underground boat ride. Caves in salt, which are rare in most other parts of the world, are common in parts of Israel and Iran. Iran contains the world's longest known salt cave (6600 m). In Oman, several yawning rifts in the flat desert of Cenozoic limestone drop into enormous rooms (Figure 2.82). Syria contains widespread carbonate aquifers with large springs but few known caves, although its Cenozoic gypsum contains caves up to 8 km long.

Western Pacific islands

For such a small percentage of the world's land area, the western Pacific islands have a disproportionate number of large and dynamic caves, thanks to thick limestone and

Figure 2.82: Entrance shaft in a cave in Oman. The scale is given by the white-clad person descending a rope just left of the sunbeam. Photo by Kevin Downey.

intense tropical rainfall. This is an area of rapidly rising Mesozoic and Cenozoic carbonate rocks that receives up to 11 m of rainfall a year.

Papua New Guinea contains some impressive caves with great potential for further discovery. On the island of New Britain (part of Papua New Guinea), roaring cave rivers, reached through giant collapse sinkholes, pose challenges to exploration. The largest of these caves are Minye, Nare, and Muruk (Figure 2.83). The entrance shaft of Minye, perhaps the largest on the island, is more than 400 m in both depth and diameter (see Figure 6.7).

Sarawak, in northern Borneo, Malaysia, contains extensive karst landscapes with the world's largest known cave passages and cave rooms. The astonishing Sarawak Chamber, in Lubang Nasib Bagus (Good Luck Cave), has a floor area of 162,700 square meters (see Figures 3.37 and 6.18). Nearby Gua Payau (Deer Cave) consists mainly of a single solution tube that has a cross section up to 170 m wide and 120 m high (Figure 2.84). Between these two caves is Gua Air Jernih - Lubang Batau Padeng (Clearwater Cave), with a surveyed length of about 130 km, much of it enormous river passages (Figure 2.85).

Indonesia and the Philippine Islands also contain notable karst areas that have so far seen little exploration. The 6-km-long St. Paul's River Cave in the Philippines may contain the world's longest tidally influenced cave stream. Iryan Jaya, the northwestern half of the island of New Guinea, contains karst that is nearly unexplored, but with potential for large and very deep caves. Small carbonate islands in the Pacific, such as Guam and Saipan contain caves formed by mixing between fresh water and seawater, similar to those in the Caribbean.

Figure 2.83: Muruk is one of several huge river caves on the island of New Britain, Papua New Guinea. Photo by Jean-Paul Sounier.

Figure 2.84: The vastness of Deer Cave (Gua Payau), in Gunong Mulu National Park, Sarawak, Malaysia. Photo by Tony Waltham.

Figure 2.85: Clearwater Cave (Gua Air Jernih - Lubang Batau Padeng), in Sarawak, may have the greatest volume of any known cave. Note the person on the right bank. Photo by Tony Waltham.

Africa

Karst is scattered sparsely throughout this vast continent. In the northwest, the folded and faulted Atlas Mountains of Morocco and Algeria contain some large caves in Mesozoic carbonate rocks. Examples are Algeria's Rhar Bou Maza, 19 km long, and Anou Ifflis, 1170 m deep. A few stream caves serve as important water sources. Gypsum and rock salt are exposed in the foothills, and some gypsum caves have vertical ranges up to 200 m, which is unusual for caves in that rock type.

Limestone, dolomite, and gypsum are widespread across much of Tunisia, Libya and Egypt, but karst and caves are sparse because of the dry climate. An exception is an area of gypsum karst in Libya, where caves up to 4 km long have been mapped. Carbonate rocks extend across half of Egypt, and although there are some important karst-fed oases, known caves are few and small.

In eastern Africa, Ethiopia contains many short and shallow caves, as well as the world-class Sof Omar, a 15-km-long network of passages formed as a subterranean cutoff through a meander of a large surface river (Figure 2.86). Somalia contains some small areas of gypsum and anhydrite karst. Kenya contains numerous caves

in volcanic rock, with lengths up to 13 km, and Zimbabwe contains some impressive caves in quartzite up to 300 m deep. Crocodiles lurk in some of the caves of western Madagascar.

South Africa has the greatest variety of caves on the continent. Many are complex network mazes, such as 12-km-long Apocalypse Pothole. They are thought to have been formed by rising thermal water. Bushmansgat contains an underwater room 250 m long, 70 m wide, and more than 260 m deep. Drachenrauchloch in Namibia contains perhaps the largest known underground lake, 207 m by 107 m at the water

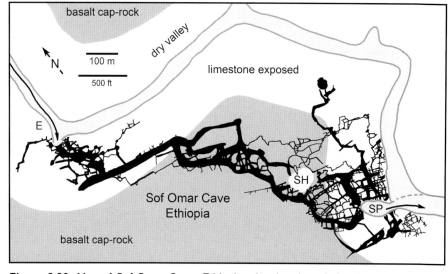

Figure 2.86: Map of Sof Omar Cave, Ethiopia, showing the relationship to the sinking stream, the River Web (modified from Catlin, 1973). E = sinking stream entrance, SP = spring entrances, SH = collapse sinkhole.

Figure 2.87: The Nullarbor Plain, along the southern coast of Australia, is one of the world's largest but flattest karst areas. Photo by Ken Grimes.

surface and belling out to even larger size underwater. There are many other exposures of soluble rock throughout Africa, but their extent is poorly known and their karst potential is uncertain.

Australia and New Zealand

These two countries provide great contrasts in karst types. Australia has been structurally stable for about the past 100 million years, so many old landscapes and karst features are preserved. Sediments in certain caves in the cave-rich southeastern part of Australia have been dated to more than 300 million years old (Chapter 13).

The arid Nullarbor Plain along the southern coast of Australia is a vast, featureless plateau of Tertiary limestone that covers more than 200,000 km^2 (Figure 2.87). This is one of the most extensive continuous karst areas in the world. Its remote location, impression of emptiness, and hostile, dry climate leave a lasting impression on explorers. The plateau is pocketed by collapse sinkholes that lead to caves up to 40 m in diameter, and innumerable small solution holes extend down from the surface, most of them too small to enter. Many openings, including inaccessibly small ones, have great amounts of air movement.

Some Nullarbor caves intersect the water table, which forms static, slightly saline lakes. The arid climate is not conducive to cave development, and the caves may be relics of previous wetter conditions. Evaporative cave deposits of gypsum and salt are common. Nullarbor caves include 10-km-long Mullamullang Cave (Figure 2.88) and slightly smaller Cocklebiddy Cave. Most of Cocklebiddy can be explored only by diving.

There seems to be great potential for further discovery in this plateau.

Australia's longest known cave is the Bullita Cave System in the arid north. This is a multi-entrance network maze with more than 100 km of mapped passages in Precambrian dolomite (page 204). The western coast of Australia contains caves in very young dune limestones. The Kimberly labyrinth karst of northwestern Australia and the Chilligoe tower karst of the northeast are also noteworthy. Lava caves up to a kilometer long are also present in the northeast. The island of Tasmania, off the southeastern tip of Australia, contains glacially modified alpine karst with caves up to 375 m deep and 23 km long.

The karst of New Zealand is concentrated in Cenozoic limestone on the North Island and both Cenozoic limestone and Paleozoic marble on the South Island. Geologically the region is very active, with volcanoes, major faulting, and rapid uplift. The marble of the South Island contains the best examples of glaciated karst in the Southern Hemisphere and some inspiring alpine caves. Many are well decorated with delicate speleothems. Bulmer Cave is New Zealand's longest cave, with 50 km of known passages, and Nettlebed Cave is the deepest, at 889 meters. Bohemia Cave, recently discovered by a Czech team, contains rooms more than 100 m in diameter and up to 50 m high, with some of the world's most extensive aragonite deposits. Glow-worms cover the walls and ceilings of some New Zealand caves and emit an eerie light. Waitomo Cave, which is open to the public, is the most famous glow-worm site.

Figure 2.88: Mullamullang Cave, in the Nullarbor Plain of southwestern Australia. The large "dune" of sand has accumulated by weathering of the overlying cave ceiling by the wedging action of salt-crystal growth. Photo by Alan Warild.

3

Cavernous rocks

A CAVE'S ORIGIN AND CHARACTER depend strongly on the type of rock in which it is situated. This chapter contains a brief summary of rocks and their structure, with emphasis on those aspects that apply to caves. Chapter 4 concerns how these rocks control the flow of underground water, and Chapter 5 describes how water dissolves them to form caves.

Rock types

Rock is the solid material that forms Earth's hard outer crust. It is often called ***bedrock***, even where it has no layering. The largest caves are in highly soluble rock or in lava. Smaller caves, and even a few fairly large ones, can be found in *any* kind of rock. Each rock type is composed of a variety of ***minerals***. Minerals are the basic components of rocks, in the way that bricks and mortar are the materials used to build a house. Each type of mineral has a specific chemical composition. When minerals grow without interference, they display various ***crystal*** shapes determined by the internal arrangement of their atoms (Figure 3.1a).

Rocks form in several different ways, as described below. For further details, see any introductory geology textbook.

Igneous rocks

Igneous rocks solidify from molten material (***magma***), which originates deep beneath the surface by melting of preexisting rocks. This process is most common in actively growing mountain chains and rifts (Figure 2.2). Because magma is less dense than the surrounding rocks, it tends to migrate upward and, aided by the pressure of escaping gases, it may eventually flow onto the surface through volcanoes and fissures (Chapter 11). The most common igneous rock types are illustrated in Figure 3.1.

Intrusive igneous rocks

When magma solidifies before reaching the surface, it forms ***intrusive igneous rocks***. Most of them are massive bodies many kilometers in all dimensions, although some are thin slabs (***dikes***) that intrude along fractures in the surrounding rock. Intrusive igneous rocks are composed of visible crystals, typically about 1–10 mm in average size, which are assembled tightly together like the pieces in a mosaic. The large crystal size is caused by slow cooling at depth, which provides ample time for growth. These rocks are exposed at the surface only where the overlying rock material has been removed by erosion, as in the central parts of mountain ranges.

Igneous minerals are composed mainly of silicon and oxygen combined with other elements. Those that are rich in iron and magnesium are mostly black or dark green. Lighter-colored minerals, which are usually white, pink, or gray, contain more calcium, sodium, potassium, and aluminum.

The most abundant intrusive igneous rock is ***granite***. Minerals in granite include white or icy-looking ***quartz*** (which consists only of silicon and oxygen in the form silicon dioxide, SiO_2), opaque white or pink ***feldspar***, flaky black or clear ***mica***, and blocky, black ***amphibole***. This combination of light and dark minerals gives granite a distinctive salt-and-pepper appearance (Figure 3.1b). Less-common varieties of intrusive igneous rock are composed of different mixtures of dark and light minerals.

Most caves in intrusive igneous rocks consist of fractures widened by weathering or erosion. All igneous minerals except quartz decompose slowly in groundwater that is charged with carbonic acid. Quartz dissolves in water, but very slowly. The main byproduct is clay mixed with sand from the resistant quartz grains. These loose materials are easily eroded by flowing water. In this way, the fractures may enlarge into caves. Some acquire enough water flow to form stream-cut caves (Figure 1.2d). Tectonic stresses or gravity sliding in these rocks can also produce crevice caves and talus caves (Figure 1.2g and h). The overall bedrock contours in caves in intrusive igneous rocks are somewhat smooth, with local sharp offsets. Projecting crystals give the rocks a rough texture.

Volcanic rocks

Where magma erupts onto the land surface it is called ***lava***, both before and after it solidifies. Cooling is rapid, and because there is so little time for elements to arrange themselves into regular patterns, nearly all of the crystals in lava are microscopically small. Thick, viscous lava forms volcanic peaks, while the more fluid, less viscous variety spreads out as layers that can form broad plateaus. Solidified lava is known as ***volcanic rock***. The most common type is ***basalt***, which is composed mainly of dark minerals (Figure 3.1d). Fresh basalt is dark gray or black, but when it is exposed to weathering its outer surfaces may turn slightly red, yellow, or brown with iron oxides. Lighter-colored lava contains greater proportions of feldspar and quartz. Some volcanic rock is riddled with holes left by gas bubbles. This is especially true for ***pyroclastic*** rocks that form when blobs of liquid lava are ejected during a volcanic eruption and solidify before they hit the ground (Figure 3.1e).

Large caves can form in volcanic rock, especially basalt. They are most commonly produced by the flow of liquid lava from beneath a solidified crust (Chapter 11).

Sedimentary rocks

Sedimentary rocks are formed by accumulations of either weathered material or chemical deposits, which have been compacted by the weight of overlying sediment or cemented together by crystal growth. Nearly all sedimentary rocks have distinct layering (***bedding***) caused by variations

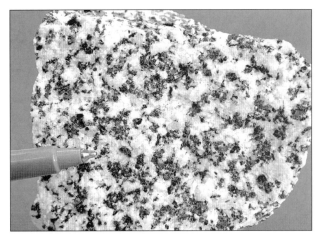

a: The crystal shape of a mineral is best revealed when it forms without interference from surrounding minerals. On the left is a quartz crystal that grew in a water-filled pocket. The quartz in granite (right) does not show this crystal shape because of competition for space with adjacent crystals. Width of photo is about 8 cm.

b: A sample of the igneous rock granite. The dark minerals are mainly amphibole and the light ones are mainly feldspar and quartz. The large crystal size shows that the rock solidified deep beneath the surface.

c: Granite forms the cores of many mountain chains and is exposed where the overlying rocks have been eroded away.

d: Basalt contains crystals that are microscopically small, because it solidifies rapidly at or near the surface.

e: Pyroclastic rocks form when globs of lava are shot out of a volcano and solidify in mid-air.

f: Lava that spreads onto the surface can form extensive plateaus. These are the San Juan Mountains of southwestern Colorado, a plateau of volcanic fissure flows that have been deeply eroded into peaks and canyons.

Figure 3.1: Characteristics of common igneous rocks and minerals. The tip of a ball-point pen provides the scale in some photos.

in composition or rate of accumulation (Figure 3.2). Most of these rocks also contain *fossils*, which are the hard parts, imprints, or casts of plants and animals that lived in the neighborhood when the sediment was being deposited.

Detrital sedimentary rocks

Loose particles are produced by the weathering of preexisting rocks at the land surface, mainly through chemical decomposition and the wedging effects of freeze-thaw cycles. This material is eroded away by streams, wind, and occasionally glacial ice, and is eventually deposited as sediment wherever the transporting medium loses its carrying capacity. Small streams deliver weathered material to larger rivers, which ultimately deposit it in the oceans where it settles on the sea floor. Some sediment also accumulates in lakes and river valleys. In arid climates it may partly fill closed basins that have no surface drainage outlets.

Figure 3.2: Bedded sedimentary rock (mainly limestone). The original bedding was essentially horizontal, but the rocks were later tilted by faulting and folding.

Compaction and mineral precipitation eventually convert these sediments into *detrital sedimentary rocks* (Figure 3.3). These are classified according to their dominant grain size. *Conglomerate* consists of pebbles or cobbles cemented together by mineral deposits. *Sandstone* and *siltstone* are composed of cemented grains of sand and silt. Silt is gritty material finer than sand, but its grains are still barely visible to the unaided eye. Most deposits of sand and silt are composed of quartz, and the cementing agent is usually quartz as well. *Shale* consists of microscopic particles composed mostly of clay, which are compacted and cemented together. *Clay* is the main ingredient of mud. It includes a variety of complex flaky, sheet-like minerals composed of silicon and oxygen combined with other elements such as potassium and aluminum.

The size ranges for the grain types in these rocks are: *boulders* > 256 mm > *cobbles* > 64 mm > *gravel* > 2 mm > *sand* > 0.06 mm > *silt* > 0.004 mm > *clay*. In this scheme, *clay* is used as a size range, rather than as a mineral group.

Nearly all detrital sedimentary rocks are very poorly soluble. Their caves are few and usually small, and they consist mainly of crevice, shelter, talus, and erosion caves. With enough time, caves can form in quartz-rich rocks by slow dissolution aided by erosion. Dissolution takes place along grain boundaries, and the residual sand can be carried away by flowing water. The remarkable sandstone and quartzite caves of Venezuela and Brazil were formed in this way (Chapter 2; Urbani, 2005). The walls of such caves tend to have smooth contours interrupted by fractures and loose blocks. Weathered rock surfaces are granular and slightly abrasive to the touch.

Shale does not dissolve perceptibly, but it erodes easily. Its main contribution to speleology is to form shelter caves capped by more resistant rocks. Piping caves are also common in poorly consolidated shale and siltstone, or in the mud and silt produced by weathering of these rocks. Bedrock surfaces in shale are soft and crumbly.

Chemical sedimentary rocks

Chemical deposits accumulate on ocean floors, as well as in lagoons and evaporating lakes, by crystallization of material dissolved in the water. They include the same kinds of minerals that cement detrital rocks together, but where chemical deposits account for most of the sediment they produce *chemical sedimentary rocks* (Figure 3.4). These rocks are classified according to their mineral composition. The most common are *limestone* (calcium carbonate), *dolomite* (calcium-magnesium carbonate), *gypsum* (hydrated calcium sulfate), and *rock salt* (for example, sodium chloride). All four are highly soluble in fresh water, so they are ideal hosts for cave origin. For that reason they are described in detail later in this chapter.

Chert is a chemical sedimentary rock composed of microcrystalline silicon dioxide (Figure 3.4f). It is poorly soluble and typically forms nodules and beds in other rock types. It is commonly known as *flint*.

Metamorphic rocks

When preexisting rocks are exposed to extreme heat and pressure they are converted to *metamorphic rocks* (Figure 3.5). Some of the original minerals change to new ones that are stable under these extreme conditions. Clay is the most liable to change. It produces a variety of colorful and distinctive metamorphic minerals, including some that are prized as gems. Typical metamorphic minerals include flaky varieties such as *mica* (white, brown, or black) and *chlorite* (soft and greenish); knob-shaped ones like *garnet* (hard and usually red or black); blade-like minerals such as *tourmaline* (hard and usually green); and fibrous or needle-like ones such as *serpentine* (soft and greenish) and *sillimanite* (hard, clear, and sharp-ended). In general, the size of a metamorphic crystal increases with the length of time it is exposed to the specific range of temperatures in which it is stable.

Flaky, bladed, and needle-like minerals line up perpendicular to the major direction of pressure, to form *foliated* rocks, which peel apart easily along planes of weakness. *Slate* is a foliated metamorphic rock composed of microscopic crystals. If the crystals are readily visible,

a: Conglomerate is composed of pebbles cemented into a solid mass, usually by later mineral deposition. In this sample, quartz grains are bound together by a later quartz cement.

b: Sandstone consists of sand grains cemented by later mineral deposits. The most typical kind of sandstone, shown here, is composed of quartz grains with quartz cement.

c: Shale consists of microscopic grains cemented or compacted together. The grains are typically composed of clay minerals, although microscopic chips of quartz are also common ingredients. This crumbly shale bed is sandwiched between more competent limestone beds.

d: Sandstone (above) is more resistant to weathering than shale and siltstone (below).

Figure 3.3: Common types of detrital sedimentary rocks.

the rock is called *schist*. An intermediate form between slate and schist is *phyllite*, which commonly has a greenish cast from chlorite. Minerals may also segregate into light and dark bands to form *gneiss*.* Slate, schist, and gneiss are usually poorly soluble, but they weather and erode easily to produce small crevice and shelter caves that have slabby, splintery rock surfaces.

---

* Some rock pronunciations: basalt = *ba-salt*, phyllite = *fill-ite*, gneiss = *nice*.

During metamorphism, some minerals do not change chemically but simply grow in crystal size. The most common are calcite ($CaCO_3$) and quartz (SiO_2). *Marble* is formed by the metamorphism of limestone and similar rocks. Caves are common in marble, so this rock is described in more detail later in this chapter. Metamorphism of quartz-rich rocks such as sandstone produces *quartzite*, a very resistant material. Because of its feeble solubility at normal groundwater temperatures, prolonged weathering and erosion along fractures is necessary to produce solution caves in quartzite.

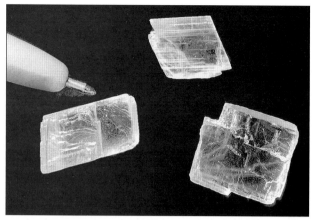

a: Common minerals precipitated in water bodies from dissolved materials. These are the main ingredients of chemical sedimentary rocks. Left to right: calcite ($CaCO_3$), gypsum ($CaSO_4 \cdot 2H_2O$), and halite (NaCl). Where they form bedrock, these crystals are much smaller and their crystal shapes are indistinct.

b: Limestone is composed mainly of calcite. Dissolution of this cave wall has produced scallops (Chapter 6) with protruding fossil fragments. Scale: width of battery pack on lamp = 6 cm.

c: Dolomite (or dolostone) containing a solution pocket lined with dolomite crystals. The composition is $CaMg(CO_3)_2$.

d: Gypsum with a dissolved surface containing solution pits along small fractures.

e: Anhydrite ($CaSO_4$) commonly has a "chicken-wire" texture composed of nodules surrounded by clay impurities. Anhydrite often alters to gypsum but may retain much of its original appearance.

f: Chert (flint) is composed of microcrystalline silicon dioxide (SiO_2), the same material as in quartz. The fractured face of this nodule shows the typical smooth texture and sharp edges.

Figure 3.4: Common chemical sedimentary minerals and rocks.

a: Slate consists of metamorphic minerals with microscopic crystal size. They are aligned parallel to each other to produce a rock that splits easily into sheets (***foliation***).

b: Schist is composed of visible crystals that typically align in sheets. This gives the rock a shiny appearance like fish scales. Rock hammer for scale.

c: Mica and garnet crystals in schist. (Mica is flaky and shiny; garnet is knobby.)

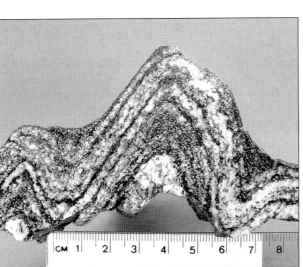

d: In gneiss the minerals have segregated into light and dark bands. It is common for the rock to be highly distorted.

e: Marble (top) and quartzite are composed mainly of single minerals (calcite and quartz, respectively). Impurities tend to segregate into dark bands.

Figure 3.5: Common metamorphic rock types.

Soil and sediments

At the land surface, most bedrock is covered by *soil*. Soil is unconsolidated granular material composed of weathered minerals derived from the underlying bedrock, combined with decaying organic material from the surface. Airborne particles carried by wind can contribute. The typical thickness of soil is one or two meters, although it varies from dozens of meters in some moist lowlands to almost nothing on many steep mountains and in deserts exposed to wind scouring.

Because of the dual source of its material, soil contains distinct zones more or less parallel to the surface. Organic-rich topsoil is underlain by highly weathered material, usually clay-rich, which is derived from the bedrock. Weathering decreases downward through a rubbly zone of partly disintegrated bedrock fragments to an irregular bedrock surface. Some soil contains chemical precipitates deposited from water that evaporates at the surface. In dry climates, calcium carbonate often accumulates in the soil as hard masses called *calcrete*.

Soil contributes to the origin of solution caves and surface karst in several ways. Carbon dioxide from decomposition of organic material is the most abundant source of acid, which is significant in dissolving limestone, dolomite, and marble. As openings develop in the underlying bedrock, the soil tends to subside to form sinkholes, which funnel water to caves. Soil also stores much of the water that infiltrates during wet periods, and some of this water drains slowly downward to feed underlying cave streams, even during dry periods.

Sediment, in contrast to soil, consists of unconsolidated material that has been eroded, transported, and deposited elsewhere by water, wind, or glacial ice. It may also be precipitated from material dissolved in water. If sediment remains in place long enough, especially if buried, the material eventually consolidates to form sedimentary rocks.

Large sediment grains can often be traced to their original bedrock sources. Continental glaciers are able to move them across the divides that separate individual basins, but streams cannot. Exotic rock fragments that contrast with the bedrock in the local drainage basin have probably been transported by glaciers, unless non-geologic agents are responsible.

Stratigraphy

Stratigraphy is the study of stratified (layered) rocks. In particular it concerns the conditions in which each layer was deposited and the geologic history that it represents. This field applies mainly to sedimentary rocks, and since most caves occur in them, stratigraphy is a helpful tool in cave interpretation. Individual strata (*beds*) in a sedimentary rock can be distinguished by differences in composition, texture, and color. The contacts between beds (*bedding planes*) are zones of weakness along which the beds can separate when they are exposed to weathering.

A sequence of beds with fairly uniform characteristics is known as a *formation*. It is usually named for the area where it was first studied (e.g., the St. Louis Limestone). Most sedimentary rock formations are composed of many individual beds, and their upper and lower boundaries are located at major breaks in rock type. For example, a limestone formation may be sandwiched between shale or sandstone formations, each having a separate name. Some rock formations are subdivided into *members*, each of which consists of one or more beds of uniform character.

Caves in the Mammoth Cave region of Kentucky are located in three distinct formations, the St. Louis Limestone, the Ste. Genevieve Limestone, and the Girkin Formation. (The Girkin includes several shale beds, so it cannot simply be called the Girkin Limestone.) Each of these formations is subdivided into several members, and most members contain several even thinner stratigraphic sub-units composed of one or more beds having their own individual characteristics. Mammoth Cave extends through more than 100 sub-units that can be traced throughout the entire region, and each has a unique expression in the cave walls. Figure 3.6 shows the *stratigraphic column* measured in Mammoth Cave, and Figure 3.7 shows how the various rock units can affect the appearance of the passages.

Each rock formation gradually changes in character from one location to another. It eventually pinches out entirely where it has been eroded away or was never deposited in the first place. A formation may also change to a different rock type because of variations in the environment in which the original sediment was deposited. These differences help to account for why caves and karst change character from one place to another, even if they have formed in rocks of identical age.

Periods of rock accumulation are occasionally interrupted by erosion. This may be caused by uplift of the land, by a drop in sea level, or both. If new rocks are later deposited on top of the eroded surface, an *unconformity* is produced. The surface beneath an unconformity usually contains small humps and hollows left by the earlier erosion, and which were buried by the later rocks (Figures 3.8–3.9). If the underlying rocks were tilted or folded, as well as eroded, their beds meet the erosion surface at an angle. Where the underlying rock is soluble, it may contain caves and other karst features that are filled partly or completely with the overlying material (Figure 3.10). The paleokarst surfaces described in Chapters 2 and 13 are examples of unconformities.

Highly soluble rocks

From the standpoint of caves, the most important rocks are those that dissolve readily in water. These are described in detail here.

Limestone

Limestone is the most common cavernous rock. It is so intimately associated with karst that terms such as *limestone caves* and *limestone hydrology* are often applied, even in dolomite and marble regions. These rocks are all composed of calcium and magnesium carbonates, so for convenience they can be grouped as **carbonate rocks**.

The main ingredient of limestone is calcium carbonate ($CaCO_3$), which is deposited as fragments of shells and other hard parts of animals and plants. These are gradually cemented together by additional calcium carbonate precipitated from dissolved components in the water. The various types of limestone are shown in Figures 3.11–3.16.

Calcium carbonate forms two common minerals, **calcite** and **aragonite**, which differ in crystal structure (see Figure 3.53 and Chapter 10). Calcite has a great variety of crystal shapes. The most typical are skewed blocks with parallelogram-shaped sides, and columns with pointed ends. Calcite accounts for the majority of mineral deposits in limestone caves. Aragonite usually forms needle-like crystals and is slightly more soluble than calcite. It is deposited in seawater more often than in fresh water.

If limestone is deposited in shallow water that is agitated by wave action or currents, the rock consists mainly of grains the size of coarse sand (Figure 3.11a-b). Many of these grains are shells that are broken into small pieces or which start out small enough to remain unbroken. Some may be **ooids**, which are round balls that are rolled by waves or currents as they form. They contain concentric layers of calcium carbonate around a tiny central particle. An **oolitic limestone** is a rock in which the dominant grains are ooids. **Pisoliths** are round ball-shaped bodies that contain concentric layers, like ooids, but are typically much larger — about a centimeter in diameter. Their origin is not certain, but they are thought to form in soft sediment above the

Figure 3.6: Stratigraphic column in the Mammoth Cave region, Kentucky. (For details, see Palmer, 1981a.)

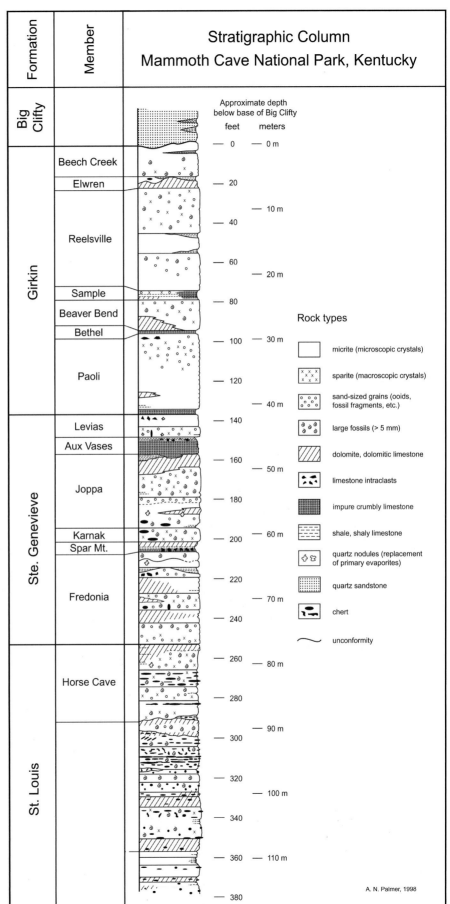

Figure 3.7: Effect of various strata on the wall character in Crystal Cave, Mammoth Cave National Park, Kentucky. Almost the entire Joppa Member of the Ste. Genevieve Limestone is exposed here, at the bottom of so-called Bottomless Pit. The Aux Vases Member appears at the very top. The solution rills in the lower left walls are in the oolitic bed shown at −180 ft (−55 m) in Figure 3.6.

Figure 3.8: An unconformity between sandstone and underlying shale in Utah. The old erosion surface on the shale is indicated by the wavy white dashed line.

water table by accumulation of calcium carbonate around grains by evaporation. Pisoliths are generally rare, except in a few areas such as the Guadalupe Mountains of New Mexico. In addition, some particles in limestone are microscopically small.

Intraclasts are fragments produced by erosion of the rock or sediment surface and then incorporated in the next bed that is deposited on top. They are most commonly ripped up by severe storm waves and deposited along with other sediment, which may entirely surround the fragments. Intraclasts have about the same composition as the material that surrounds them. The underlying material is often still soft when the erosion takes place, so that the intraclasts are rounded, like globs of putty (Figure 3.11d). The fragments

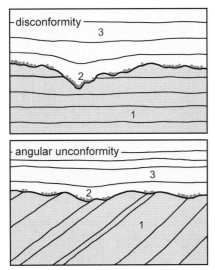

Figure 3.9: Two common types of unconformities: A *disconformity* is produced in the following way: First, erosion takes place on an early sequence of rocks (1). Then a younger rock sequence (3) is deposited on top, burying the former erosion surface (2). An *angular unconformity* is produced in the same way, except that the earlier rocks are folded or tilted before or during erosion, so that the older rocks meet the overlying younger ones at an angle. In both, the erosion surfaces (2) may be covered by eroded fragments or remnants of soil. The horizontal scale in these diagrams can vary from a few meters to about a kilometer, with the smaller scale much more common.

along the unconformities in Figure 3.9 are not strictly intraclasts, because the rock that surrounds them represents an entirely different phase of deposition and probably a different composition as well.

The calcium carbonate cement between grains is called the *matrix*. This can be deposited directly from the original seawater, but some (often most) of it accumulates when the sedimentary grains are exposed to fresh groundwater flow. The fresh water eventually dissolves any original aragonite and redeposits it as less-soluble calcite, which is the most common matrix in limestone.

If the main mass of limestone consists of grains that are sand-size or larger, the rock shows visible crystal faces in freshly broken pieces. This kind of limestone is called *sparite** (short for *sparry limestone*). In caves, sparite produces rough abrasive surfaces like coarse sandpaper (Figure 3.12a).

In quiet-water deposits the hard parts of animals and plants remain more or less intact. The surrounding matrix consists of very finely crystalline aragonite and calcite that precipitate directly from the seawater, along with tiny bits of broken material wafted in by currents. Nearly all individual particles in the matrix are microscopic. This type of limestone is called *micrite* (short for *microcrystalline limestone*). Fossil shapes are well preserved. In caves, micrite may form smooth surfaces that resemble polished wood (Figure 3.12b). More commonly, though, the fossils protrude from weathered surfaces and make the micrite even more abrasive to skin and clothing than is sparite.

The *sparite* and *micrite* designations are part of a classification by Folk (1962) that describes limestone composition. It is convenient in studies of past depositional environments. An alternate classification by Dunham (1962) concerns the packing of grains and the porosity between them. The Dunham classification is favored by many geologists, but Folk's is handier for most cave studies.

Some limestone accumulates as *reefs*, which are massive ridges built in shallow seawater by communities of coral

---

* Pronunciations: sparite = *sparr-ite;* micrite = *mick-rite.*

Figure 3.10: A well-preserved soil zone (*paleosol*) between Mississippian limestone beds in southern Indiana. The soil filled solution pockets in the underlying rock and was later buried by the overlying limestone. Such clear preservation is rare, because soil is usually eroded away by waves before limestone is deposited.

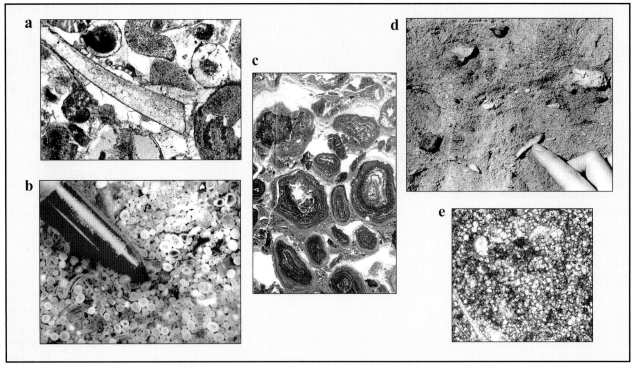

Figure 3.11: Some typical grain types in limestone and dolomite: **a** = fossil fragments (width of photo = 5 mm, **b** = ooids (ball-point pen tip for scale), **c** = pisoliths (width of photo = 2 cm), **d** = intraclasts in a cave wall (Spar Mt. unit in Figure 3.6), **e** = silt-size dolomite crystals in dolomite bedrock, with partly dissolved calcite fossils remaining from original limestone (width of photo ~1 mm). Photos **a**, **c**, and **e** are microscopic views of thin sections (see page 86). In photo **b** the rock sample has been cut and polished, to display the internal structure more clearly. See Scholle and Ulmer-Scholle (2003) for a well-illustrated guide to textures in carbonate rocks.

or other organisms. Reef rock is usually rough and highly porous, with little or no bedding. Rock surfaces tend to display large pores (Figure 3.13). Actively forming reefs can be seen in the Caribbean Sea, Pacific atolls, and the Great Barrier Reef off the northeastern coast of Australia. Small Pleistocene reefs have accumulated around the Hawaiian Islands, and some contain small caves (Halliday, 1998). A more ancient example is the Capitan Limestone of New Mexico, about 250 million years old, in which most of Carlsbad Cavern is developed.

Young limestone composed of poorly cemented sand-size carbonate grains is called **calcarenite**. It is common in coastal areas, especially along beaches and in wind-blown dune deposits (**eolianites**). The exposed surface of a calcarenite is the first part to be cemented into hard rock because of its contact with infiltrating and evaporating water (Figure 3.14). Caves in calcarenite form mostly in freshwater-seawater mixing zones along seacoasts. Their surfaces are sandy and crumbly. Most of the beds in eolianites are steeply inclined. In contrast, most marine limestones are deposited on the sea floor as nearly horizontal beds. But some marine sparites contain **cross-beds**, which look similar to those in Figure 3.14, but which are at a conspicuous angle to the majority of other beds in the formation (Figure 3.15). Most cross-beds are deposited in deltas and sediment banks, where shallow, rapidly moving water drops off into deeper water.

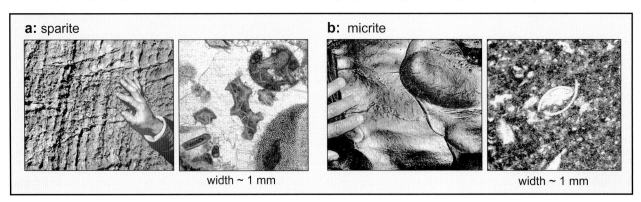

Figure 3.12: The two most common limestone types (sparite and micrite), shown in cave walls and in microscopic view. Note the contrast between the rough sparite surface and the smooth micrite surface. In the microscopic views, note the clear calcite cement between shell fragments in the sparite, and the fine-grained muddy texture and nearly intact fossils in the micrite.

Figure 3.13: Eroded fragments of porous coral reef limestone along the Hawaiian coast. Width of photo is about 20 cm.

Chalk is a soft, porous, white variety of limestone composed of the tiny shells of microorganisms (Figure 3.16). It forms the celebrated White Cliffs that border the English Channel. Because chalk is so porous, water seeping through it becomes saturated with dissolved calcite very quickly. As a result, explorable caves in chalk are few and small. Nevertheless, some chalk formations contain well-developed sinking streams and springs, which indicate lengthy and continuous solution conduits.*

Marl is soft clay-rich limestone. Because of its high insoluble content it is not a favorable host for solution caves. Marl is deposited either in lakes or in muddy marine waters. Some cavernous limestones of the western Alps are underlain by marl, which limits the downward extent of cave development. Many springs in that area are perched at the contact between the marl and overlying purer limestone.

Most limestone is neutral gray, although it can range from very light gray, white, or tan to almost black, depending on the type of impurities and their percentage in the rock. Chalk and calcarenite are the whitest varieties. Although these two rock types tend to crumble easily, most other kinds of limestone are structurally competent and resist breaking. Nevertheless, they are all too soft to scratch glass. All limestone reacts vigorously with acid, and a good test for this rock is to drop dilute hydrochloric acid (~10% solution) on its surface. This produces a distinctive fizz of carbon dioxide, like what is produced when a can of soda is opened.

Nearly all limestone contains ***fossils*** of various kinds and sizes. Individual rock formations and time periods can be identified by their distinctive fossil assemblage. Some fossils can be recognized easily by eye, whereas many others are barely visible or even microscopic. Fossils are well preserved in the rocks exposed in caves and often project

* Communication from Steve Worthington, Hamilton, Ontario, 2003.

Figure 3.14: Dune calcarenite (eolianite) of Pleistocene age, Bermuda. The outer surface is first to recrystallize into hard rock because it is exposed to rainfall and evaporation, while the interior remains longer as soft, crumbly carbonate sand.

Figure 3.15: Cross-beds in granular limestone (sparite) in the Ste. Genevieve Limestone, Kentucky. Note the angle of the cross-beds to the overlying beds. This contact appears to be a minor angular unconformity. Width of photo = 2 m.

from the surfaces almost intact. Figure 3.17 shows some easily recognizable fossils that are common in limestone.

The most common fossils in limestone include the following: ***Brachiopods*** and ***pelecypods*** are two-shelled organisms. The two shells of a brachiopod differ in shape but are symmetrical left to right. A pelecypod shell is asymmetrical (as in clams), but the two halves may be mirror images of each other. ***Cephalopods*** are squid-like creatures with shells that are either coiled like a cinnamon bun, or straight and tapered like a long cone. ***Gastropods***,

Figure 3.16: Chalk and the white streak it produces when rubbed across a rough surface.

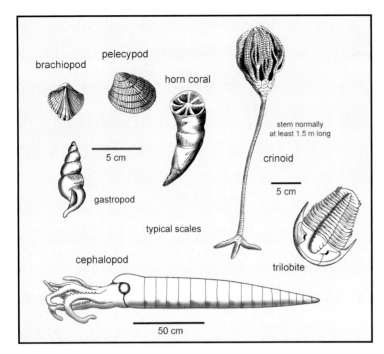

Figure 3.17: Above: Some typical animals whose large fossils are preserved in limestone. Sketches by M.V. Palmer. **Right:** Some fossils in limestone. **a** = fragments of Mississippian crinoid stems (round) and shell fragments of other animals in a polished rock sample; **b** = exceptionally well-preserved interior of a Permian brachiopod shell in a cave wall (width of shell = 4 cm); the shell contains remnants of ribbon-shaped supports for internal organs; **c** = gastropod and pelecypod, Tertiary (width of photo = 10 cm); **d** = Mississippian colonial coral, intersected by calcite veins in a cave (width of photo = 20 cm); **e** = part of an Ordovician cephalopod shell (average diameter = 15 cm).

which include snails, have coiled shells that grow in a tapered spiral. ***Crinoids*** look like lilies, with what seem to be roots, stems, and fronds, but they are actually animals. Most often only fragments of their stems survive; they look like buttons stacked together into rods. ***Corals*** include colonial types, which cluster in stick-like bunches, and individual horn corals shaped like short, stubby cow horns. Corals contain tiny chambers separated by thin-walled partitions. All of these animal types have living representatives today, although brachiopods and crinoids are rare. ***Trilobites*** ** were segmented, shelled animals that once scuttled around on the sea floor. They are now extinct but resemble the modern chiton.

Fossils in other chemical sedimentary rocks are similar to those in limestone, but they are much rarer. They are virtually absent in gypsum and rock salt, which accumulate in highly saline environments that are hostile to most forms of life.

Dolomite

Dolomite has the composition $CaMg(CO_3)_2$. The name applies both to the rock and to the mineral that composes it. The rock is sometimes called *dolostone* to distinguish it from the mineral. Dolomite closely resembles limestone, and there is a continuous gradation in composition between them. Names such as limy dolomite

---

** Some fossil pronunciations: *brachiopod* = **brack**-*ee-o-pod*, *pelecypod* = *pel-**ess**-a-pod*, *cephalopod* = **seff**-*a-lo-pod*, *crinoid* = **cry**-*noid*, *trilobite* = **try**-*lo-bite*.

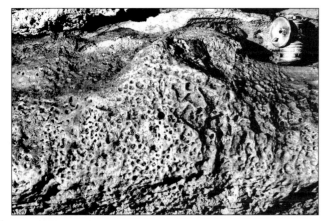

Figure 3.18: Dolomite exposed in a cave wall. It sometimes weathers with a porous surface. This texture can be caused by variations in the rock composition or by weathering of pyrite crystals scattered through the rock (see Chapter 5). A miner's carbide lamp, 12 cm high, is shown for scale.

and dolomitic limestone are often appropriate. Dolomite can form in several ways, and there is controversy over which is the dominant process. Some originates at and near the surface in dry, evaporative conditions along seacoasts. Other dolomites replace existing limestone where magnesium-rich groundwater passes through. Most dolomite is dull gray, but it can also be yellowish or brown. Dolomite is either smooth and compact or has a sugary texture consisting of tiny silt-size crystals. Fossils are far less common in dolomite than in limestone. Not only is dolomite deposited in environments unfavorable to fossil preservation, but fossils can also be destroyed by the recrystallization from limestone to dolomite.

Most dolomite is more brittle than limestone and breaks apart more easily. Where there is no soil cover it may form rubbly surfaces. In caves, dolomite typically forms resistant ledges, rough, fractured walls, or porous zones (Figure 3.18). Like limestone, dolomite is softer than glass. It reacts very slowly with acid, and usually only if the rock surface has been scratched or powdered. It is best identified by laboratory analysis.

Marble

Marble is metamorphosed limestone or dolomite. It is usually massive, with white and gray banding. It can be recognized by its large crystals of opaque white calcite. Non-$CaCO_3$ impurities in the original rock tend to segregate into bands during metamorphism. The darker bands contain insoluble metamorphic minerals such as chlorite and mica. The walls of many marble caves are attractively banded (Figure 3.19). Like limestone, marble reacts with acid and its bands of pure calcite are softer than glass. Marble is highly soluble and contains some very significant caves. The Antro del Corchia, Italy's longest cave, is located mainly in marble (Piccini and others, 2003), as are California's largest caves (Despain, 2003). But most marble outcrops are fairly small compared to those of limestone. Many of the marble caves of California and Oregon are located in narrow isolated

Figure 3.19: Banded marble in Lilburn Cave, California.

pods of metamorphic rock surrounded by granite. In places, dissolution has removed so much of the marble that the local cave walls are composed only of the surrounding insoluble metamorphic or igneous rock. Marble is ideal for building-stone, monuments, and sculptures. The only drawback is that it is soluble in water, especially acidic water, and many marble structures have been damaged irreversibly by exposure to humid climates and acid rain.

Gypsum and anhydrite

Gypsum and anhydrite are the most common varieties of calcium sulfate. They are usually deposited in shallow lagoons and inlets of seas where there is a great deal of evaporation. Anhydrite is pure calcium sulfate ($CaSO_4$). In gypsum the calcium sulfate is combined with water ($CaSO_4 \cdot 2H_2O$). Gypsum is more stable than anhydrite at the land surface, except under very dry conditions, and anhydrite is more stable at high pressures and at temperatures above roughly 60°C. Gypsum is the major ingredient of the sheet-rock used in interior walls. It is so soft that it can easily be scratched with a fingernail. It is usually milky white but may have bands of darker gray impurities (Figure 3.20).

Anhydrite is harder and more resistant than gypsum. Its popular name is ***alabaster***. In places it consists of nodules

Figure 3.20: Gypsum exposed in a road cut in west Texas.

that stack together in a pattern like that of a chicken-wire fence (Figure 3.4e). Some anhydrite is deposited beneath the surface by high-temperature fluids that rise from igneous sources. These deposits usually form the matrix between breccia fragments and may be accompanied by ore minerals.

Gypsum and anhydrite are so soluble that rapidly circulating groundwater in humid regions may remove them entirely, even before the overlying rock or sediment is eroded away. Gypsum karst is most common where the climate is fairly dry, and in humid climates it is usually limited to places where rapid erosion has exposed the gypsum quickly. Anhydrite karst is much rarer.

Gypsum and anhydrite readily convert from one to the other as the physical and chemical conditions change. Gypsum is less dense than anhydrite, so when anhydrite is converted to gypsum in freely flowing groundwater there may be a volume increase that causes the surrounding rocks to buckle and fracture. Deep below the surface, when gypsum is converted to anhydrite the release of water may build pressure that can disrupt surrounding rocks. Gypsum and anhydrite can also play an important role in the development of porosity deep beneath the surface by interacting with other rock types (see pages 121–122).

Rock salt

Rock salt is a collective term for a group of minerals that precipitate in water that is undergoing rapid evaporation. They usually form only in closed basins in arid climates, or in seawater lagoons that have little exchange with the less saline water of the open ocean. Together with gypsum and anhydrite, they are called ***evaporite rocks***. The most common types of rock salt are sodium chloride (NaCl, the mineral

halite) and potassium chloride (KCl, the mineral ***sylvite***). A mixture of various mineral types is common. Gypsum and anhydrite are usually not grouped with rock salt, even though they are chemically true salts.

Rock salt is easily recognized by its light gray or white appearance, combined with its taste and softness. Most salts are easily scratched by a fingernail. Under high pressure it flows easily, like putty. In places it pushes its way upward through soft overlying rocks to form dome-like structures called ***diapirs***. These structures can bring rock salt close to the surface where it is susceptible to cave development. Large openings in salt, such as mines, eventually close up by rock subsidence unless they continue to be excavated. Rock salt is so soluble that it rarely occurs at the surface except in arid climates or where it has been rapidly exposed by erosion or quarrying (Figure 3.21). Widespread salt deposits surround Great Salt Lake in Utah (Figure 3.22). Most salt contains too little fresh groundwater flow to form caves. Nevertheless, many salt caves have formed in parts of Chile, Spain, Romania, Israel, Iran, Algeria, Libya, and central Asia (Frumkin, 1994; Chabert and Courbon, 1997). Many of them carry water only during rare floods. In caves the surfaces of rock salt tend to be rough and abrasive because of deep pitting by dissolution.

Related rock types

Insoluble rocks in contact with soluble rocks can influence the development of solution caves and karst. Streams running off surfaces of resistant, poorly soluble material can disappear underground where they cross onto adjacent soluble rocks, so that cave development is concentrated along the contact. Even thin insoluble beds in cavernous rock can control patterns of water flow, passage elevations, and wall texture.

Chert is a nearly insoluble rock that forms nodules or irregular beds in other sedimentary rocks, especially limestone (Figure 3.23). It is a very finely crystalline form of SiO_2, the same material as quartz, and has a texture almost as smooth as glass. Most chert is dark gray or nearly black, and less commonly lighter gray, buff, or almost white.

Figure 3.21: Sinkholes and caves have developed rapidly in this rock salt exposed by quarrying in northeastern Spain.

Figure 3.22: The Bonneville Salt Flats of Utah.

Figure 3.24: Bedded chert in the Onondaga Limestone, Onesquethaw Cave, New York.

Colorful varieties (red, green, etc.) are rare and are known by different names, such as *jasper*. Chert is very hard and easily scratches glass. It can be chipped into sharp edges and is archeologically important as one of the most favored materials for early tools. In this context, chert is usually called *flint*.

Some chert is a replacement of gypsum and anhydrite bodies, and it mimics their original shapes as nodules, fissure fillings, or irregular beds. Chert can also replace limestone and retain fossils diagnostic of the original rock. It is also possible for chert to accumulate directly in water that has a high content of dissolved SiO_2, for example in the vicinity of nearby volcanic activity.

Figure 3.23: Chert nodules in the St. Louis Limestone, Indiana.

In cave walls, chert projects as knobs and ledges (Figure 3.24). It is wise to avoid using these projections as footholds, because they are brittle and break easily. Chert can include a mixture of carbonate minerals, and as these minerals weather away the chert becomes soft and porous and breaks even more easily. The chert beds in Figure 3.24 are unusually robust.

Soft insoluble rocks, such as siltstone and shale, tend to crumble and form recessed niches in cave walls (Figure 3.25). They also transmit water poorly and act as barriers to water flow. Perching of underground water on shale or siltstone beds, even thin ones, can affect cave development to a degree quite disproportionate to their thickness. The origin of certain passages is governed by perching of water flow on such beds (Chapter 9). Thin sandstone, however, may transmit enough water that it is possible for networks of fissures to develop in underlying or overlying soluble rocks (Chapter 8).

Rock relationships

Sedimentary rocks are not distributed randomly, but instead reflect the local conditions at the time the original sediment was deposited. Each sedimentary formation has a systematic relationship to those around it of the same age. Also, the sequence of sedimentary beds in any area reflects the changes that have taken place at the surface over time. Each bed is like a page in a history book. Because caves are strongly influenced by the rocks in which they occur, even a brief acquaintance with rock relationships can help to explain or anticipate cave patterns.

The character of a chemical sedimentary rock depends on the nature of the water in which it was deposited —

Figure 3.25: Influence of various rock types on passage character (Mammoth Cave, Kentucky). The narrow top and bottom canyons are in limestone. The resistant mound-shaped bodies in the middle are dolomite, and the thin recessed bed is poorly resistant shaly limestone at the top of the Joppa unit in Figure 3.6). The top of the dolomite is a local unconformity.

specifically its chemistry, temperature, depth, and amount of wave disturbance — as well as the local climate. Most limestone is deposited in warm marine water, which easily precipitates aragonite and calcite (Chapter 5). Aragonite is usually deposited in relatively warm shallow water and calcite in deeper, cooler water.

The sparite variety of limestone accumulates where the water is shallow enough for the sediment to be agitated by wave action, mainly along the shoreline. Fine-grained sediment is swept into deeper water by waves and currents, and large particles (such as shells) that remain tend to be broken apart by abrasion. The result is a sandy deposit with fairly uniform grain size. Micrite is deposited in quiet water, either offshore where the water is too deep for wave action to penetrate, or in shallow lagoons where waves are insignificant.

Reefs form in warm, clear, agitated seawater where nutrients are available and there is little suspended sediment to clog the feeding mechanisms of corals and similar animals. Reefs build up as long ridges just below the water surface, while bedded, quiet-water limestone and dolomite may accumulate as ***back-reef beds*** in shoreward lagoons. In the quiet lagoons, most of the back-reef beds are micrite. On the steeper seaward side of the reef, blocks of broken reef

material accumulate at the base to form a breccia known as ***fore-reef talus***. From there, progressively finer-grained limestones extend seaward into deeper water. Carlsbad Cavern, in New Mexico, extends through a Permian-age reef, as well as through its back-reef beds and fore-reef talus.

Calcarenite forms mainly around the shores of tropical oceanic islands composed of young limestone. A drop in sea level favors the build-up of eolianite dunes (Figure 3.14), because broad expanses of beach sand are exposed to wind as the water recedes.

Gypsum and rock salt are deposited in isolated lagoons and basins where the climate is dry enough for evaporation to bring these highly soluble minerals to saturation. This requires an occasional influx of water, from either the open ocean or incoming streams, that is great enough to supply dissolved minerals but not so much as to prevent the minerals from precipitating. As evaporation proceeds, the calcium carbonate minerals are the first to crystallize, because they are the least soluble of the common chemical precipitates. Dolomite may also form, but the process is very slow. Gypsum is next to precipitate, followed by a variety of rock salts such as halite.

Detrital sedimentary rocks have an entirely different distribution. Streams carry relatively insoluble sediment into bodies of water such as the ocean, lakes, or closed basins on the continent. Deltas are formed at these points because of the abrupt drop in water velocity. Where the lake or ocean water is shallow, streams deposit sand and gravel in long fingers that extend outward from the shore. Silt and clay accumulate between these channel sands, where the water velocity is low. These fine-grained materials also accumulate in deeper water beyond the deltas. Some of the sand and gravel is moved by longshore currents and wave action to form beaches. Beach sediment is also contributed by wave erosion of headlands, which can also supply the ingredients for conglomerate. If sea level rises, a continuous bed of sand tends to accumulate as the shoreline moves across the land. If sea level drops, progressively more land area is exposed to weathering and erosion, although dunes may accumulate in narrow bands along the shore where sand is redistributed by wind.

By reducing the concentration of dissolved minerals, the influx of freshwater streams into the ocean tends to prevent local accumulation of chemical sedimentary rocks. Also, detrital sediment makes up nearly all of the deposits contributed by the streams. Chemical deposits are dominant only in areas remote from large sources of detrital sediment. Detrital rocks and chemical rocks therefore grade into one another in a systematic way.

Rock structure

Mineral composition is not the only rock characteristic that affects cave origin. Equally important is the rock structure, which includes warps, tilts, and folds in the rock, the fractures and planes of weakness that cut across it, and the pores between its grains.

Pre-solutional openings

When forming a solution cave, water cannot simply bore its way through a solid mass of rock like a termite eating through wood. Instead it follows preexisting openings in the rock and gradually enlarges them by dissolution. By guiding the original groundwater flow, these initial openings have a profound influence on the pattern of the resulting caves.

All rocks contain several types of internal openings. At the smallest scale are ***intergranular pores***, which form what sedimentary geologists call ***matrix porosity***. They are the openings between the grains or crystals in the rock. Even rocks that appear to be entirely solid contain microscopic pores that can transmit water in small quantities. Intergranular porosity can be fairly high in young limestones, especially calcarenites (more than 25% in places), but it is very low in most old and well-consolidated limestone because the pore space has been almost completely filled with cementing minerals (Figure 3.26). In most soluble rocks the intergranular pores cannot conduct enough water to produce caves. As a result, caves form mainly along fractures and partings (see pages 78–79).

Reef rock and calcarenite are two limestone types that have a high enough intergranular porosity to influence cave patterns. Another type that can have substantial pore size is ***breccia***, a form of conglomerate that consists of fragments of rock broken apart by wave action, collapse, or other disturbances, which are later cemented together without being transported elsewhere. Many caves in the Rocky Mountains and Black Hills have formed at least partly in brecciated limestone and dolomite (Figure 3.27).

Change in rock character with time

Sedimentary rocks begin as soft sediments with a large amount of pore space between their grains. Eventually most sediments are converted to rock, which becomes progressively harder with time (a process called ***diagenesis***). The porosity decreases because of compaction by the weight of overlying sediments, as well as by filling of the pores with secondary minerals that cement the surrounding grains together.

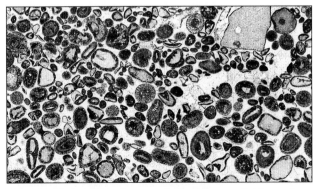

Figure 3.26: Intergranular porosity (matrix porosity) in a microscopic view of the Girkin Formation of Kentucky (see Figure 3.6). The grains (dark) are mostly sand-size fossils or fossil fragments broken apart by currents and waves. The intervening pore space, which appears white, is mostly filled with clear calcite, which reduces the porosity considerably. Width of photo = 1.2 cm.

Figure 3.27: Limestone breccia in Jewel Cave, South Dakota. Brecciation was caused by dissolution and recrystallization of gypsum, which was later replaced by calcite (the dark matrix between the fragments).

Some of the cementing minerals are deposited from through-flowing water and may have an entirely different composition from the original grains. But most of the cement is simply redistributed by partial dissolution of grains and reprecipitation in nearby pores — a process called ***recrystallization***.

As compaction and recrystallization take place, the rock character changes from soft and porous to hard and dense. These changes are proportional to the thickness of overlying rocks and sediment, the amount of groundwater flow that passes through, and the intensity of deformation and metamorphism of the rock by stresses within the crust. These effects are cumulative over the age of the rock. Compare, for example, the soft, crumbly nature of the young dune limestone in Figure 3.14 to the compact, hard, and competent marble of Figure 3.19. These effects are accompanied by a gradual change in composition from aragonite to calcite, and in porosity type from intergranular pores to secondary porosity such as fractures. These characteristics can have a strong effect on cave patterns (Chapter 9).

Many cave descriptions in this book include the age and rock formation in which they are located. These details help to explain the nature of the caves and to relate them to caves elsewhere.

Figure 3.28: Solutionally enlarged joints and bedding-plane partings in limestone.

Figure 3.29: Two intersecting joint sets in nearly horizontal limestone pavement in western Ireland. Photo by Derek Ford.

Fractures

Planar cracks in bedrock caused by stress in the Earth's crust are known as *fractures*. They can be formed by tectonic movements, by release of confining pressure during the erosional removal of overlying rocks, by glacial advances and retreats, and by minor shifts (earth tides) caused by the oscillating gravitational pull of the Moon and Sun. Fractures are the chief forerunners of caves, because they transmit water much more rapidly than do intergranular pores. Major fracture types include bedding-plane partings, joints, and faults.

Bedding-plane partings are cracks that form between beds (Figure 3.28). The original bedding planes in a sedimentary rock are just the contacts between adjacent beds, with no discrete openings. When the rock is exposed at or near the surface, or is deformed by compression or tension, the individual beds tend to shift by different amounts and to separate slightly from each other. The resulting partings are irregular and discontinuous. Each bed is still obviously in contact with those above and below, so the partings represent the narrow irregular gaps that surround the points of contact. Many partings are too narrow to detect by eye, but as anyone with a leaky basement can testify, water is able to seep through even narrow cracks with ease.

Partings are most abundant in thin-bedded strata. Thick beds, which are produced by rapid or very uniform sedimentation, contain few partings. In some rocks the individual beds may be so tightly bonded to each other that a large sequence of them — perhaps the entire rock formation — behaves as a single structural unit with no partings that transmit water. Some geologists do not consider bedding-plane partings to be true fractures, because they follow preexisting planes of weakness. The term *fissures* is a suitable generic term for both partings and fractures, as long as there is no confusion with fissure-shaped cave passages (Chapter 6).

Joints are fractures along which there has been no significant movement, and which cut discordantly across the bedding, if any. There may be a small amount of separation between the opposing blocks of rock, but they do not slide past each other perceptibly as they form. Most joints are nearly perpendicular to the beds (Figure 3.28), although some joints cut diagonally across them. The most conspicuous joints are in thick-bedded, structurally competent rocks of uniform composition. Thinner beds have more numerous joints, but they are less prominent and are typically narrower than those in thick beds. Any single joint may extend through an entire rock formation, or it may be limited to a few beds or even a single bed.

At any given location, the great majority of joints cluster in only a few dominant compass directions. Each group with a uniform trend is called a *joint set*. In plateaus where the rocks are nearly flat-lying, there are usually only two or three joint sets. Typically the two major sets are roughly at right angles to each other (Figure 3.29), but that is not the case everywhere. The joint pattern is more complex in highly deformed rocks, especially those that have experienced more than one episode of mountain uplift.

Regional joint patterns can have a strong effect on cave patterns, especially in thick beds. The influence of joints on caves is readily apparent in fissure-shaped passages, such as

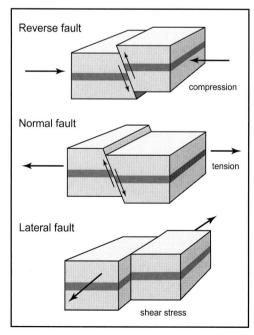

Figure 3.30: Major fault types.

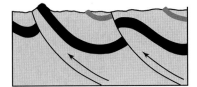

Figure 3.31: Thrust faults (low-angle reverse faults) are common in folded mountains.

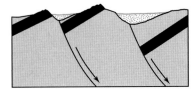

Figure 3.32: Widespread normal faulting produces fault-block mountains separated by broad basins that are partly filled with detrital sediments.

Figure 3.33: Basin and range topography (Nevada) resulting from erosion of fault-block mountains (see Figure 3.32).

Figure 3.34: Thrust fault in Helictite Cave, Virginia, showing slickensides in the roof. The block beneath the fault dropped into a lower passage to form this narrow slot. Slickensides on the floor have been coated by later mud.

those that intersect to form network cave patterns (see, for example, Figure 2.60). On a worldwide basis, partings and joints have roughly equal influence on cave patterns.

Faults are fractures along which the opposing blocks have slid past one another, so the rocks on either side no longer match (Figure 3.30). They are most common in mountainous regions. The largest are caused by the relative motion between plates of crust during continental drift (Chapter 2). Most faults are not vertical, so the rock on one side overlies the fault, while on the other side the rock underlies it. A *reverse fault* is produced by compression where two parts of the crust converge, so that the block overlying the fault is shifted upward relative to the other. Low-angle faults of this type are called *thrust faults* (Figure 3.31). Many of the mountains in Glacier National Park, Montana, are composed of eroded remnants of the upper block of a huge thrust fault.

A *normal fault* is produced by tension, where two parts of the crust are pulled apart. The block overlying the fault slips downward relative to the other. Mountains of the Great Basin in and around Nevada are bounded mainly by normal faults (Figures 3.32–3.33). The basins between them are down-dropped blocks, rather than valleys carved by rivers.

Where two blocks of crust slide past one another more or less horizontally, *lateral faults* (or *strike-slip faults*) are produced. They include the well-known San Andreas Fault and its branches in southwestern California, which are still periodically active and are responsible for occasional earthquakes.

The bedrock walls that border a fault are usually grooved by *slickensides* caused by the friction of the moving blocks (Figure 3.34). The rock faces may also be shattered and recrystallized. In soluble rocks, many fault zones are filled or lined with veins of white calcite or dolomite (Figure 3.35).

Figure 3.35: A lateral fault in Ellison Cave, Georgia, which contains a thick zone of recrystallized calcite. The steps in the slickensides show that the right-hand block has moved away from the viewer. Part of the left-hand block has fallen away. The miner's lamp to the right of the calcite vein is 12 cm tall.

Figure 3.36: The main passage of Sistema Cheve, Mexico, follows an extensive fault zone. Here a person is descending a fault-guided shaft by rope. Note the highly fractured wall. Photo by Ken Davis.

Mexico's deepest known cave (Figure 3.36). In Wind and Jewel Caves, South Dakota, calcite wall crust has been shattered by later faulting, and in some passages there has been displacement between the two bedrock walls, as shown by rock bridges that are offset along fracture planes. The lower levels of Ellison Cave, Georgia, and several deep shafts leading to them, are located along a prominent lateral fault that is periodically active (Figure 3.35). Piles of freshly powdered rock testify to friction between blocks, and small earthquakes are occasionally traced to the area, and yet this activity has disrupted the cave passages only slightly.

Earthquakes seldom have a noticeable effect on caves because the shock-wave intensity decreases sharply with depth below the surface. The local bedrock usually moves almost as a single coherent block that is fairly resistant to damage. People who have experienced earthquakes while in caves report low rumbling sounds, oscillation of water surfaces, and occasionally a few loose rocks sliding down slopes, but rarely anything more dramatic. The great New Madrid earthquakes of 1811–1812 in the Mississippi Valley, among the largest in U.S. history, had only a modest effect on Mammoth Cave, about 250 km away. Saltpeter works were disrupted and some blocks dropped, but there was no major damage (George and O'Dell, 1992). Lava caves are more susceptible to agitation because they lie close to the surface. Werner and Werner (1992) give a vivid first-hand account of a 6.1-magnitude earthquake in a Hawaiian lava cave. There was an alarming rolling motion for 15 seconds, but aside from dust spouts and movement of a loose rock there was no visible damage either to cave or party. No severe earthquake damage has been witnessed in caves, but piles of naturally broken stalagmites and stalactites in some caves may indicate such events in the past.

A few other types of fractures have only small effects on caves and karst. Release of stress in rock faces can produce **sheet fractures** (or **pressure-release joints**), which cause thin slabs to peel away in concentric slabs (Powell, 1977).

Vertical offset between the beds on opposite sides of a fault does not necessarily mean that the movement was entirely vertical. It is common for the slippage to be diagonal or even horizontal and still show some vertical offset. For example, where the contact between two beds is irregular or already dipping, even a perfectly horizontal shift will produce local vertical offsets in the beds. Slickensides help to distinguish the direction of movement by the orientation of small steps in their surfaces (Figure 3.35). Sometimes successive episodes of faulting have a variety of slip directions, and multiple sheets of recrystallized rock along the fault may contain slickensides with several different orientations.

Faults are less common than joints but are much larger. Although faults tend to form in roughly parallel swarms, their patterns are far less regular than those of joints. Large faults can have smaller faults emanating from them in a complex pattern (pages 213 and 240). Faults tend to be reactivated periodically as stresses build up, so it is often difficult to assign a specific date to fault displacement.

Faults are visible in many caves but are not commonly the main controls over cave orientation. An example of strong fault control is the main passage of Sistema Cheve,

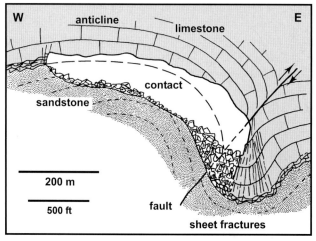

Figure 3.37: Sheet fracturing in the huge Sarawak Chamber of Lubang Nasib Bagus (Good Luck Cave), Malaysia. From Gilli (1993). See also Figure 6.18.

on cave patterns in some marble formations can be similar to that of bedding-plane partings.

Stylolites are irregular surfaces along which the rocks on either side have interpenetrated (Figure 3.39). Nearly all are parallel to the bedding and usually result from dissolution along bedding planes from the pressure of overlying rocks. Meanwhile, insoluble material from the rock accumulates along the contact and accentuates the stylolite outlines. It is not clear why only a few contacts develop stylolites. They very rarely serve as the guiding structures for cave passages.

Fractures are often the hosts for ***mineral veins***. These are thin sheets that completely fill the fractures. Fractures and partings that acquire veins are likely to be relatively old and to have served as pathways for deep groundwater flow. At depth, fractures provide favorable avenues for warm water that is supersaturated with various minerals. Faults are the structures most likely to be filled with minerals, and bedding-plane partings least likely. In places the veins partly replace the bedrock. Most veins exposed in caves are composed of white calcite, dolomite, or quartz. Dolomite and quartz are typical of high-temperature deposits. Some calcite and quartz have replaced former gypsum veins (Chapter 12).

Veins are usually visible as bright streaks in cave walls. They may project into cave passages because some are more resistant than the surrounding bedrock. Quartz or dolomite veins, which are relatively resistant, may cause slight jogs in passages, but they rarely influence the overall cave pattern.

A massive vein is shown along the fault in Figure 3.35. It includes much recrystallization of the host limestone, especially of the shattered rock along the fault. Joint-guided veins tend to be discontinuous and offset from one another. Where one vein pinches out, another parallel vein usually begins only a few centimeters away, with a short section of overlap where the thinning of one is matched by the thickening of the other. Much more irregular are ***gash veins***, which consist of jagged mineral-filled ruptures in rock caused by local stress around faults or folds (Figure 3.40).

Joints and faults commonly occur in swarms that can be loosely grouped as ***fracture zones***. They transmit water more

Figure 3.38: Sheet fractures in the Réseau Jean Bernard, Haute Savoie, France.

They are most common around the perimeters of rooms or passages with broad ceiling spans (Figure 3.37), or in thin rock pillars or buttresses that bear much of the weight of the ceiling rock (Figure 3.38). Massive rocks are the most susceptible to sheet fracturing.

Foliation consists of the alignment of platy minerals or grains, or the segregation of mineral types. It is most common in metamorphic rocks. Partings are common along the resulting planes of weakness (Figure 3.5a) and their effect

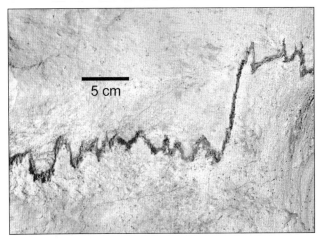

Figure 3.39: Stylolites in massive limestone, Wind Cave, South Dakota. Note the small scale typical of stylolites. These stand out more clearly than most because of iron oxide staining.

Figure 3.40: Gash veins of calcite, Butler Cave, Virginia.

readily than the less-densely fractured limestone around them. Some caves and other karst features tend to concentrate along them, but in other places the intense shattering and recrystallization of the rock can inhibit groundwater flow.

Lineaments are large-scale linear features that are visible on aerial photos or topographic maps, and which presumably indicate major fracture zones (see page 393). They can include straight valley segments, cliff lines, and contrasts in vegetation or soil type, as well as linear patterns of karst features, such as sinkholes. In many areas such patterns are clearly visible on digital images of the land surface (Florea, 2005). On aerial photos it is possible to misidentify as lineaments such non-geologic features as fence lines and boundaries between different kinds of land use. At the land surface, most lineaments are difficult to identify at close range because their details may be masked by deep weathering.

Some fracture-oriented passages in caves coincide with visible lineaments at the land surface, or extend parallel to them (Ogden, 1974), but others show no obvious relationship (George, 1984). Water wells have a better chance of high yield if drilled along lineaments, especially where two or more lineaments intersect (Lattman and Parizek, 1964).

Folds

Where two plates of the Earth's crust converge, their forward edges are crumpled into mountain chains in which rocks are folded, fractured, and metamorphosed. Folding is most noticeable in sedimentary rocks, where the original bedding has been wrinkled like a rug pushed against a wall. The Appalachian Mountains of the eastern U.S. contain excellent examples.

Folds that are bowed upward are called *anticlines*, and those that are bowed downward are called *synclines* (Figures 3.41–3.42). The *axis* of a fold is the trend of its midline. For example, the folds shown in cross section in Figure 3.41 are viewed in the direction of their axes (perpendicular to the page). As erosion of folded rocks exposes a variety of rock types, resistant ones such as sandstone project as ridges, while softer rocks such as shale are worn down rapidly to form valleys. Ridges and valleys follow the axes of the folds and therefore tend to be parallel to one another. Limestone and dolomite usually stand out as ridges if they are surrounded by shale, but where the neighboring rocks are resistant, such as sandstone, the carbonate rocks form valleys or the lower flanks of ridges.

The axis of a fold can also have a dip, which is called the *plunge*. Where plunging folds are intersected by the eroding land surface, the ridges and valleys formed by rocks of contrasting resistance are not parallel but instead form a zig-zag pattern. The folded Appalachian Mountains of eastern Pennsylvania show this pattern well (Figure 1.20). An example of a cave influenced by plunging folds is described in Chapter 14.

Folds and reverse faults are both produced by compressive forces. As compression proceeds, sharply deformed folds may rupture so that one flank is thrust up over the other (Figure

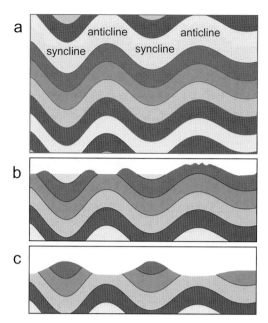

Figure 3.41: Effect of folded rock structure on an eroded land surface: **(a)** Folding in stratified rocks produces a sequence of anticlines and synclines. **(b)** Long, slow erosion intersects the folds and produces a low-relief surface with low ridges of resistant strata that stand above the others. Rapid erosion produces prominent ridges and valleys. **(c)** Resistant rocks exposed at the surface form ridges, even if they are in synclines.

3.31). With intense compression, folded blocks can be thrust over one another in such a chaotic pile that the original position of the beds is difficult to reconstruct. Some beds can even be overturned so their original tops are now on the bottom. Massive rocks that are intensely deformed are shot through with fractures that intersect in complex ways, and there may be little indication of the original bedding attitude. Given enough pressure and heat, metamorphic rocks are produced.

Figure 3.42: A small anticline in limestone beds in southwestern Virginia (rock hammer for scale, 30 cm long).

Where tectonic disturbance is minor, as in much of the central U.S., sedimentary rocks are warped into broad **domes** and **basins**. Where a dome or basin is exposed to surface erosion, plateaus and escarpments form concentric rings around the center of the structure. An example is the Nashville Dome, a structural upwarp on which the city of Nashville, Tennessee, was built. Erosion of the upper beds in the dome has exposed poorly resistant underlying rocks that weather rapidly, so that the uplifted soft center of the dome is actually a lowland. A similar and more familiar process is where pavement has been warped upward by freezing of moisture, and erosion produces a pothole that exposes the soft underlying soil in the center with the hard pavement rimming it.

Dip and strike

No sedimentary rock layers are perfectly horizontal. They tilt at various angles from a fraction of a degree in relatively undisturbed areas to very steep angles in folded mountains. The tilt of the beds is called the **dip** (Figure 3.43). The term includes both the direction and angle of tilt (for example, 12 degrees to the southwest). Rock strata dip away from the centers of anticlines and domes, and they dip inward toward the centers of synclines and structural basins. Intensely folded rocks can have local dips that are vertical or even overturned. Dip can also refer to the inclination of fractures, but unless indicated otherwise it is assumed to refer only to strata. Since most joints are perpendicular to the bedding, joints in dipping beds also dip at a variety of angles.

The **strike** of the beds or fractures is the direction perpendicular to the dip direction. A rock formation that dips to the southeast has a strike that is northeast-southwest. This may seem like unnecessary duplication, but the term *strike* is handy for several reasons. The eroded edges of dipping rock strata form ridges and valleys that are parallel to the strike (Figures 3.43–3.44). Both the dip and the strike have considerable control over the pattern of water movement through the rock, and therefore on cave patterns (Chapter 9). Many cave passages that form along the water table are nearly parallel to the strike.

On geologic maps the strike and dip are shown in various places to augment the information on cross sections. This is

Figure 3.44: Ridge of resistant Cambrian dolomite in the Bob Marshall Wilderness, Montana. The rocks dip toward the right at about 40 degrees. The ridge extends along the strike.

Figure 3.45 The symbol for strike and dip on a geologic map. It can be used on cave maps as well. The dip direction is shown by the stem of the T and the dip angle is indicated. The strike is the direction of the crossbar. In this example, if north is straight up, the dip is to the southeast at 15° and the strike is NE-SW.

also useful on cave maps to help explain the relation of the cave pattern to the local rock structure. The strike and dip are indicated with a T-shaped symbol, with the crossbar of the T representing the strike direction and the leg representing the dip direction (see Figure 3.45). The angle of dip is indicated numerically.

Effect of geologic structure on caves

Most caves are enlargements of partings and fractures, and as the caves grow, their outlines continue to be influenced by the local geology. The structural setting also helps in anticipating the distribution of caves and karst (Figure 3.46). Fracture patterns are determined by the nature of the stresses that have operated on the host rocks, and as a result it is possible to predict, or at least to explain, the patterns of fracture-guided caves. The same is true of prominently bedded rocks, in which the dip and strike of the strata have a strong influence on the trends of cave passages. These topics are discussed in detail in Chapter 9.

Rocks of low dip form many of the most extensive karst regions in the U.S. (Chapter 2). Dips in many regions average less than a degree, which allows even thin formations to be exposed over large areas. Even there, the geologic structure is much more complex that it might seem at first. Superposed on the gentle regional dips are smaller warps resulting from local stresses. Also, all rock strata contain variations in dip caused by differences in bed thickness. The orderly arrangements of beds may also be disrupted by differential compaction of the original sediments and by irregular erosion surfaces.

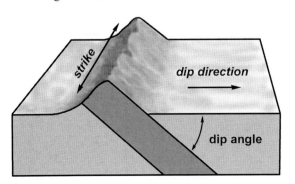
Figure 3.43: The concept of strike and dip in stratified rocks. Resistant rocks usually form strike-oriented ridges, and erosionally weak rocks form valleys.

Figure 3.46: Geologic cross section through the Chartreuse region of the French pre-Alps, showing the effects of stratigraphy, folding, and faulting on the landscape and on the location of soluble rocks. The mid-late Cretaceous limestone (dark gray pattern) is the most cavernous. (Modified from Arnaud, 1978.)

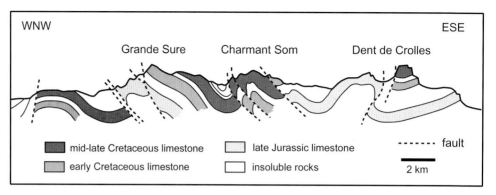

It is in low-dip regions that these small variations in dip and strike have the greatest effect on groundwater flow direction and cave patterns. Passages that form above the water table may follow the steepest available dip (Figure 3.47). In gently dipping strata, the local dip direction can vary a great deal from place to place and give passages a sinuous pattern (for example, the passage shown in Figure 3.25). In contrast, small irregularities in steeply dipping rocks have only a minor influence on groundwater flow, because they do not tend to disrupt the dip pattern.

In rocks that dip no more than a few degrees, the most common joint pattern is a rectangular grid in which the major joints are roughly parallel to the dip and strike of the beds. The dip joints tend to be dominant, even where the overall trend of groundwater flow is not in that direction. Faults are fewer and most of them follow roughly the same trends as joints. There may be a third fracture trend, but it is rarely significant in gently dipping rocks.

In folded rocks, the most prominent joints and faults extend along the strike of the beds and tend to cluster along the axes of the folds. Less dominant fractures may be parallel to the dip, or they may form couples at 60° angles to the dip direction along shear zones produced by regional compression. Most large faults have strikes roughly parallel to the regional fold axes.

In zones of extensive karst collapse, as in the vicinity of large sinkholes, the fracture pattern may be different from that of surrounding rocks. Typically there are three or four joint sets, often with two that intersect at relatively acute angles of about 20° (page 254).

By compiling the compass directions of joints or faults, or the cumulative length of passages that follow them, one can construct a ***rose diagram*** that sums all the measurements in each sector of a circle (Figure 3.48). The typical sector size is 10°, although other angles may be used if they portray the relationships more clearly. A rose diagram of passage trends can show the relative importance of fractures and structural dip in controlling cave development. The relationship of caves to the regional stress pattern is clearly revealed.

Cave mappers find it useful to recognize the influence of geology and hydrology on passage details. Otherwise their maps can look formless, to the point where the interpretation of the cave's genesis is obscured (Figure 3.49). A skilled note-taker first tries to recognize the overall geologic control of the passage, so that it can serve as a guide to drawing the sketch. There should be no irrational wiggles added in an attempt to make the map look more cave-like.

On the other hand, most caves contain some irregularities that seem to make no geologic sense. These should not be omitted from the map just because their geologic context is not clear. Fissures may not line up as perfectly as they do in Figure 3.49a. Groups of joint-guided fissures that superficially appear to be parallel may actually have subtly different trends. After making certain that the scatter is not caused by compass errors, the mapper should portray the fissures, or other cave features, in their exact orientations.

Rock and mineral analysis

Major rock types can usually be determined in the field with no special equipment. A hand lens is helpful for examining fine details. The rock hammer, the traditional symbol of the geologist, is used to supply small samples for close inspection, and to provide fresh surfaces that can be contrasted with weathered surfaces. Fresh surfaces are best for determining color and relationships between minerals or grains, and they are necessary if the sample is to be tested

Figure 3.47: Entrance to a dip-oriented stream passage in Bärenhöhle, Salzburg, Austria (dark slot at lower right). The beds dip at 30°. For much of its 220-meter depth the passage follows the slightly steeper dip of a thrust fault (planar fracture at upper left).

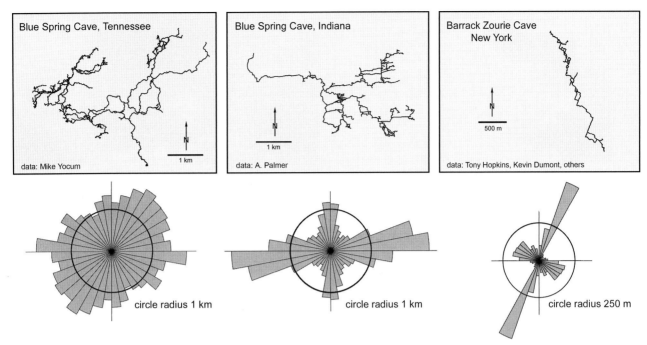

Figure 3.48: Rose diagrams of passage trends in several caves: Blue Spring Cave, Tennessee, is located in well-bedded Monteagle Limestone (Mississippian). Identically named Blue Spring Cave, Indiana, is mainly in the prominently jointed Salem Limestone (Mississippian). Barrack Zourie Cave, New York, is in the prominently jointed Helderberg Group (Silurian-Devonian). For each passage segment, the trend is determined from survey data and grouped into 10° sectors. Passage lengths in each sector are summed, and the sums are represented by the shaded length of each sector. Each segment extends both ways (i.e. a south-trending passage is also north-trending if viewed in the other direction), so the length of each bar is averaged with the one opposite, to balance the diagram. The strong joint influence of the two caves on the right is clear in their rose diagrams. In Barrack Zourie Cave, New York, note how the dominant joint trend is revealed by the rose diagram, even though the overall cave trend is not in that direction. Passage trends are more uniformly distributed in well-bedded rocks (as on the left), but some directions may dominate as the result of dip or strike influence. **Note:** Because the top and bottom of a rose diagram are mirror images, the bottom half is often omitted. Rose diagrams can also be drawn by plotting the peak values as points in the middle of each sector, and the points are then connected by lines to give the diagram sharp-pointed arms. See Figure 9.46 for an example of both approaches.

for carbonate content by its reaction with dilute acid. A small dropper bottle containing 10% hydrochloric acid is helpful for this purpose (see page 87). Weathered surfaces, by their irregularities, reveal more clearly the internal structure and subtle differences in composition. Rock hammers are over-used even on surface outcrops. In caves they should be used sparingly, if at all, and in a way that does not leave visible scars. A more refined tool, such as a putty knife, may be more appropriate in some cases both at the surface and underground.

There are many useful laboratory techniques for detailed rock and mineral analysis. Although the equipment is beyond the budget of most individuals, it is available for professional or student research

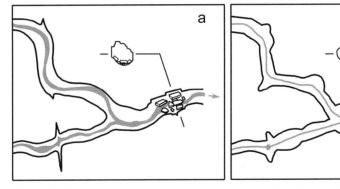

Figure 3.49: A cave map is most useful and convincing if it reveals the influence of geologic structure. Sketches **a** and **b** both show the same passage pattern and details from a cave survey. Sketch **a** clearly shows the influence of jointing and stream flow on the cave outline, but sketch **b** portrays the details as random and amorphous. Any hint of what controls the passage outline is absent in sketch **b**. Attention to the geology (fracture patterns, bedding), as well as stream dynamics, helps to guide the sketcher in preparing the map. There are several causes for the problem in sketch **b**: Many people find it difficult to visualize the cave as viewed from above. There is also a tendency to sketch each survey segment and cave feature as though it were independent, with no relation to its neighbors. At first, one should visualize the entire passage segment and how it relates to those on either end, and then work downward in scale to progressively smaller features. This comparison is based on actual field notes by different parties.

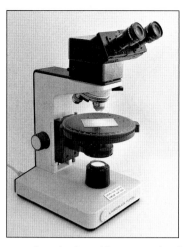

Figure 3.50: Polarizing microscope with a thin section on its stage.

Figure 3.52: Scanning electron microscope (SEM).

at most universities. Samples can also be sent to commercial laboratories for analysis. A few of the common techniques are described below, and their use is referred to in later chapters.

One of the most fundamental approaches to rock and mineral interpretation is to prepare ***thin sections***. Small slabs are made with a rock saw and mounted on glass slides with clear adhesive. They are then ground down with abrasives to a thickness of about 0.03 mm — so thin that light easily passes through them. The slide is examined with a polarizing microscope (Figure 3.50), which allows the internal structure of the rock to be seen. Thin sections are ideal for showing the relationships among the various minerals and grains (see Figures 3.11, 3.12, and 3.26). Photos can be made with a camera attached to the microscope, or the thin sections can be scanned directly on a film scanner.

X-ray diffraction (XRD) can be used to identify specific minerals (Figure 3.51). A rock or mineral is powdered and exposed to an X-ray beam. The pattern of X-ray scattering is unique to each mineral. Analysis may be difficult if more than about two minerals are present. ***Raman spectroscopy*** is a similar method in which the sample is targeted with an intense single-color light beam, such as a laser. The emitted energy produces a distinctive banding pattern, from which the general composition of the sample can be determined. Raman spectroscopy is a non-destructive method of mineral analysis, and recent compact models are well suited to field work (White, 2006).

The ***scanning electron microscope*** (SEM) produces detailed images of small structures (Figures 3.52–3.53). One limitation is that only the surfaces are visible. A ***microprobe*** is a variety of SEM that can be used to make quantitative

0.05 mm

Figure 3.53: SEM image of calcite and aragonite crystals grown in the laboratory. The blocky crystals are calcite and the needles and blades are aragonite. Defects in the surfaces are due to rapid crystal growth.

Figure 3.51: X-ray diffractometer.

analyses of elements within very small spots on the sample or in automated scans that cover larger areas. The transmission electron microscope (TEM) provides greater enlargement and the ability to see internal structure, but the difficulty in sample preparation limits its use among geologists.

Analysis of the elements on the surface of a sample can be made with an ***energy-dispersive X-ray*** unit, which accompanies most SEMs. When targeted with an electron beam, the sample emits X-rays whose energy varies with the material at the surface of the sample. Exact mineral types are not revealed, but they can usually be interpreted from the elemental analysis.

Identification of certain isotopes in a sample may help to determine its age and geologic history, as described in Chapters 5 and 13. A ***mass spectrometer*** is used for this purpose.

A brief guide to rock identification

When identifying rocks, it is important not only to obtain an overall view of large-scale rock features, but also to take a close look, preferably with a hand lens or microscope. It is also helpful to identify neighboring rock types, because rocks tend to occur in logical associations according to their origin. For more complete information, refer to any introductory geology book.

Igneous rocks: In mountains or in areas of ancient former mountains.

Solidified below the surface: Massive, with visible interlocking crystals of different types. Most are light-colored with intermixed black crystals. *Granite* is the most common example.

Solidified at the surface: Typically have crude layering, irregular thickness, and gas-bubbles holes. Most are dark, almost black, with microscopic crystals. *Basalt* is the most common. Some, such as *rhyolite*, are light gray or pink.

Metamorphic rocks: In same regions as igneous rocks.

Foliated: Split easily into sheets, with shiny surfaces in which crystals are aligned with each other. *Slate* has microscopic crystals and smooth planar foliation; *schist* has crystals visible to the unaided eye; *gneiss* has alternating light and dark bands.

Non-foliated: Massive, somewhat uniform, light color, usually with colored bands and with visible interlocking crystals. *Marble* does not scratch glass; it effervesces (fizzes) readily in dilute acid. *Quartzite* scratches glass and does not effervesce in acid.

Sedimentary rocks: Most contain prominent beds and fossils.

Detrital: Almost all sand or gravel grains scratch glass. *Sandstone* consists of visible grains of sand cemented together by quartz or other minerals. *Conglomerate* consists of cemented gravel. **Shale** (composed mainly of clay) is soft, flaky, and dull, with microscopic grains.

Chemical: Dissolve easily in water (look for evidence on exposed surfaces). None except chert can scratch glass. Impurities in the rock may be much harder, so avoid demonstrating with valuable glassware.

        Limestone: Neutral gray, usually rich in fossils, effervesces in acid (see below).

        Dolomite: Neutral gray, fossils rare, fizzes in dilute acid only if pulverized.

        Gypsum: White or light gray, scratches with a fingernail, dissolves readily in water.

        Rock salt: Same as gypsum, but dissolves very rapidly and has salty taste.

        Chert: Scratches glass, chips are smooth and have sharp edges (see below).

Figure 3.54: "Fizz" test for limestone with 10% hydrochloric acid.

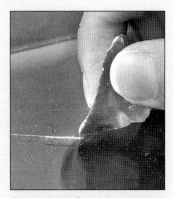

Figure 3.55: Scratch test, chert on glass.

4

Underground water in karst

$\mathbb{S}$OLUTION CAVES are formed by the flow of under-ground water, and knowledge of how this water moves is essential to interpreting cave origin, patterns, and mineral growth. In addition, the broad field of **karst hydrology** includes many practical aspects, including water supply, environmental issues, contaminant studies, aquifer tests, and groundwater modeling. These topics are well covered in other books, such as Ford and Williams (1989, 2007), White (1988), and Bögli (1980). General karst hydrology, with only occasional reference to caves, is presented by Bonacci (1987), and Milanović (1981). Detailed information on groundwater, but with little reference to karst, is given in books by Freeze and Cherry (1979), Domenico and Schwartz (1990), Fetter (2001), and Fitts (2002). A few of the practical aspects of karst hydrology are outlined in Chapter 15.

Types of underground water

Nearly all underground water starts at the surface as rain and snowmelt. This **meteoric water** seeps through the soil (if any) into the underlying bedrock, and finally emerges at lower elevations such as stream valleys (Figure 4.1). In its subsurface travels it follows narrow fissures and pores, and, if the rock is soluble, the openings include solutionally enlarged openings such as caves. In places, small amounts of underground water are contributed by volcanic sources (**juvenile water**) or by the leakage of seawater trapped in sedimentary rocks (**connate water**). These latter two do not necessarily increase the total amount of water at the surface, because water is also absorbed during the origin of certain rocks.

Of all the water that falls as rain and snow, most returns to the atmosphere by evaporation, and by transpiration from plants, before it has a chance to penetrate through the soil. During heavy rainstorms or snowmelt, some water runs off directly on the land surface as overland flow into streams.

Seepage or flow of water into the ground is called **infiltration**. It moves under the combined influence of capillarity and gravity. **Capillarity** is the effect of the adhesion between water and solid surfaces, combined with the cohesion between neighboring water molecules. It controls the movement and storage of water only in narrow openings that are not completely filled with water. A sponge holds water by capillarity, and, like a sponge, soil traps some of the infiltrating water. This water helps to sustain plant growth. Some capillary water is also held by the pores and narrow fissures in underlying bedrock. Capillary water is drawn toward relatively dry parts of the ground, and into zones of relatively small pores. By itself capillary water is too diffuse and slow-moving to form caves, but it can enlarge pores near the surface and is also significant in the deposition of cave minerals (Chapters 10 and 12).

Any excess water in the soil, beyond what can be held by capillarity, is drawn downward by gravity. Where its flow is great enough, this **gravitational water** can form caves. The zone through which water descends by gravity or is held by capillarity is the **vadose zone** (Figure 4.1) Water in this zone does not fill all the openings, nor does it build up any significant pressure.

As water infiltrates into the soil, it displaces much of the capillary water that was left behind during the last infiltration event. Therefore the water that drips into a cave is usually not the same water that has most recently seeped into the ground. This often-overlooked process has an impact on vadose-zone chemistry. The same process operates in the epikarst and in narrow fissures below it.

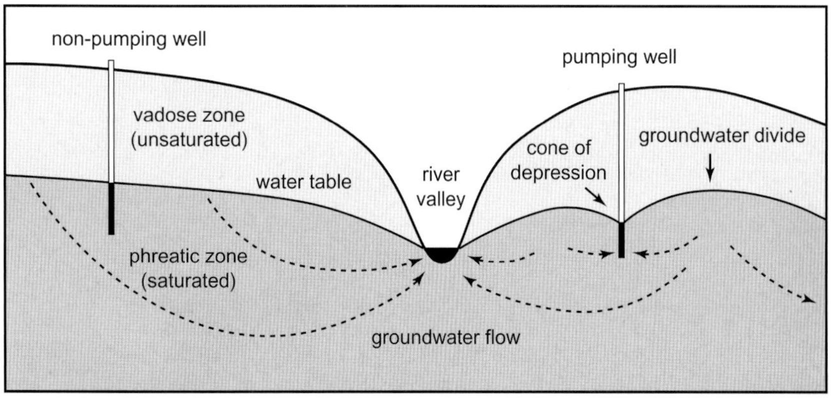

Eventually the gravitational water reaches a deeper zone where all openings are completely water-filled. This is the **phreatic zone** (Figure 4.1). Here the water pressure increases downward, as in a lake, and water moves by a combination of gravity and pressure. The downward pull of gravity is offset to varying degrees by the downward increase in pressure. As a result, phreatic water has a strong horizontal component and eventually reappears at the surface at lower elevations, such as river valleys. This is the water that feeds most springs and keeps surface streams running during dry periods. The term **groundwater** traditionally means only water in the

Figure 4.1: Idealized patterns of groundwater flow. The water table is roughly the level of water that stands in a shallow non-pumping well. Virtually all openings below the water table are filled with water (phreatic zone), and the water flows in the direction of water-table slope toward the nearest valleys. In the overlying vadose zone, air and water are mixed and water drains downward by gravity. Because of geologic irregularities, the actual flow patterns are more complex than those shown here, especially in karst.

phreatic zone, but it is often used to refer to *all* underground water.

The upper surface of the phreatic zone is the ***water table***, which coincides approximately with the water levels observed in shallow wells that are not being pumped. Pumping a well depresses the local water table around it to form a ***cone of depression***. The amount of drop in the water table at any point in the cone is the ***drawdown***. Groundwater generally moves in the direction that the water table slopes, although some deep groundwater can pass beneath local reversals in water-table slope (as in the lower right in Figure 4.1). All infiltration into the cone of depression moves as groundwater toward the well.

Most groundwater scientists consider the long-established terms *vadose*, *phreatic*, and *water table* to be out of fashion, and instead favor ***unsaturated zone***, ***saturated zone***, and ***potentiometric surface***. But for several reasons most geologists still prefer the older terms. Although these older ones have been misused at times, they are unambiguous. *Saturated* can imply *chemical* saturation, as well as saturation with water — a distinction that is especially important in karst studies. Also, *vadose* and *phreatic* can be used as convenient adjectives (as in *vadose caves*). But *potentiometric surface* is more valid term than *water table* for the level at which water stands in wells, especially if the wells penetrate into water-bearing layers confined by rocks that do not transmit water easily (see page 93).

The ***hydraulic head*** at any given point in a groundwater system is essentially the elevation of standing water in a well that penetrates to that point, measured with respect to sea level. At the water table, or in a stream, the head at any point is simply the elevation of that point. It is the *difference* in head from place to place that makes the water move. For example, if descending vadose water reaches the water table at an elevation of 1200 m above sea level and exits at a spring at 900 m, the head difference in the phreatic water is −300 m. Water moves in the direction of decreasing head, and that is why it nearly always moves in the same direction that the table slopes (Figure 4.1). The ***hydraulic gradient*** between the two points is the head difference divided by the total flow distance, which includes all the curves along the way (*not* the straight-line distance).

The catchment area for the water that feeds a spring is the ***groundwater basin*** for that spring. In cavernous rock the ***drainage divides*** (boundaries) between groundwater basins are difficult to determine, even with extensive water-tracing experiments and information from wells. Groundwater flow is three-dimensional, so the divides can overlap, with water at different elevations draining to different springs. Divides can also shift as flow rates change. During floods it is common for otherwise dry cave passages to be temporarily reactivated, making it possible for water to cross over low-flow divides. These characteristics are valid in any groundwater setting, but they are most significant in karst (Chapters 9 and 15).

Caves are formed by water that enters soluble bedrock, either by infiltrating through the soil or by flowing directly

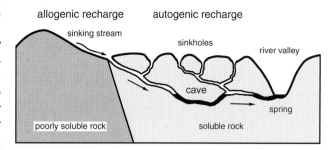

Figure 4.2: Allogenic and autogenic recharge to a cave.

into karst depressions and open fissures. As shown in Figure 4.2, cave water can come from rain and snow that falls on the karst area itself (***autogenic*** recharge) or it can accumulate on adjacent regions of relatively insoluble rocks and then flow into the karst as sinking streams (***allogenic*** recharge). The distinction between the two is not always clear, because many sinking streams collect water from thick soil or insoluble rock that overlies cavernous rock. Allogenic recharge is more variable in flow rate and in caves it is usually more solutionally aggressive than autogenic recharge. The effects of these two types of recharge on caves are described in Chapter 8.

The amount of flow at a karst spring can be used to estimate the size of its catchment area. In a karst upland draining to several springs, the low-flow discharge of each can be compared to the combined flow of all springs in the upland. The percentage of flow from any one spring is roughly the percentage of the area that it drains.

In the popular imagination, underground water follows discrete veins that must be tapped if a well is to be successful. This is usually incorrect. Most groundwater is widely dispersed in a network of tiny fractures or pores, as in wet sand on a beach. The popular view is faintly valid in karst, because cave streams account for most of the water flow. But even in cavernous rock the small openings around the caves contain a much greater water volume than the cave streams. The stream water just moves faster. Most wells obtain their water only from small non-cave openings.

The water table fluctuates up and down with time, according to the amount of groundwater flow. During the periods of high water that follow heavy rains or snowmelt, the water table rises. At other times, when groundwater recharge is slight, the water table drops. The zone of water-table fluctuation is often called the ***epiphreatic zone***. Regarding caves, however, it is often appropriate to call it the ***floodwater zone***, to emphasize its dynamic character. The slow rise and fall of the water table in non-karst settings is nothing like the rapid and severe fluctuations in karst.

The amount of groundwater that moves through a cave depends on the nature of the water source. If there is enough water to keep the cave completely filled throughout the year, the amount of flow depends only on the physical characteristics of the cave itself (length, diameter, sinuosity, roughness). This represents ***hydraulic control*** of the flow rate. An example is the flow contributed by a surface stream that loses only part of its water to an underlying water-filled conduit. The water supply exceeds the capacity of the conduit, and the excess runs off through the surface channel (Figure 4.3). This condition is usually limited to small underground flow routes that have not yet reached cave size, although it also applies to caves that are completely flooded during occasional periods of intense runoff.

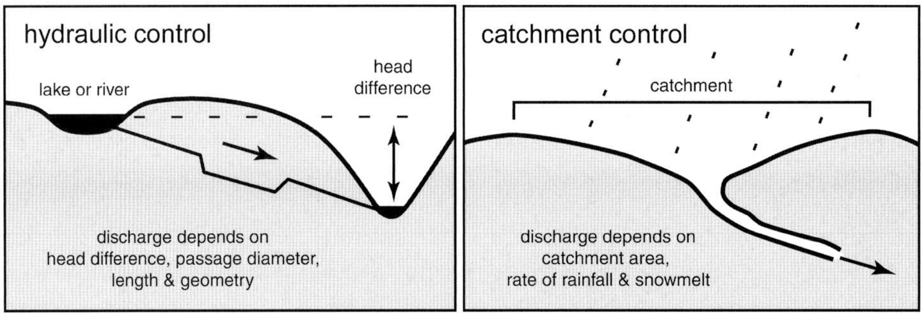

Figure 4.3: Hydraulic control and catchment control of water flow through caves.

(diagram labels) hydraulic control — lake or river — head difference — discharge depends on head difference, passage diameter, length & geometry. catchment control — catchment — discharge depends on catchment area, rate of rainfall & snowmelt.

The amount of flow through a cave is more often controlled by the size of its catchment area and by the rate of rainfall and snowmelt within it. This represents **catchment control** of the flow rate. Examples include caves that are fed by autogenic recharge through soil or sinkholes, or by streams that disappear entirely into swallow holes. In nearly all accessible caves the flow is determined in this way. The water level in the cave adjusts to the amount of flow, rising during floods and dropping during low flow. Although the largest passages also tend to have the largest streams, their flow volume is not determined by passage size.

Figure 4.4: A vadose stream in Norman Cave, West Virginia. Waterfalls such as this are often used erroneously as evidence against the water-table concept in karst.

Vadose flow patterns

In the vadose zone, gravitational water flows downward along the steepest available openings. Caves formed by this water have profiles that descend continuously. They have no segments that rise in the direction of flow, except where local (and usually temporary) phreatic conditions are perched within the vadose zone by poorly transmissive beds.

Vertical openings are clearly the most favorable routes for gravitational water. But if these openings are narrow, the amount of incoming vadose water can easily overwhelm them, so that excess water must overflow along less steeply inclined openings. A narrow vertical fissure may transmit all the water fed to it during dry periods, but it may overflow during wet periods. Thus a great deal of water can be deflected along gently inclined openings such as bedding-plane partings, to form sloping passages. Meanwhile the steeper openings continue to grow and may eventually capture all the water from the inclined passages (pages 265–267). Many caves contain remnants of vadose passages that have been abandoned in favor of steeper routes. Throughout this sequence of development, the typical vadose passage consists of an irregular step-like series of inclined canyons interspersed with vertical drops (Figure 4.4).

Because gravity is the major driving force in the vadose zone, the vadose streams that form cave passages do not tend to converge toward each other, except where they are forced to by the geologic structure, such as fissure intersections or synclinal troughs. Neighboring vadose streams generally remain independent. They flow down the dip through passages that roughly parallel one another other for long distances without intersecting. In pattern they may resemble the independent dribbles of rainwater that run down a windshield. Because of their independence, vadose streams, and the passages they form, can cross over one another (see Figure 2.74). Crossing and divergence of vadose water have been documented by dye tracing in the Austrian and Swiss Alps by Zötl (1961) and Häuselmann (2005).

Most vadose water eventually reaches the underlying phreatic zone. But where water is perched on poorly transmissive beds, some may drain along those beds to springs in hillsides without ever reaching the water table.

A **sump** is a section of water-filled passage between air-filled portions. Sumps are located where passages descend below the water table, or where there is local ponding in the

Figure 4.5: A sump perched in the vadose zone in Big Brush Creek Cave, Utah. The passage ceiling abruptly drops below the pool surface.

Figure 4.6: A water-table passage in Blue Spring Cave, Indiana. The water level lies at exactly the same elevation as the spring along the East Fork of White River. The passage is more than half full of water. Water levels in wells to either side are higher than this cave stream.

vadose zone. Two sumps of the water-table type are shown in black on the profile in Figure 4.2. A vadose sump is shown in Figure 4.5, but to an explorer it looks no different from the water-table type. The cave survey verifies that it lies well above the spring elevation. Sumps are often indiscriminately called **siphons**, but this term is appropriate only for those rare sumps that have the shape of an inverted **U** (Chapter 2).

Sumps can occur in vadose passages where structural conditions cause water to pond locally and spill over a threshold. These are **perched sumps** (or **vadose sumps**). A common form of perched sump is a downward loop in an abandoned phreatic passage that has its water replenished during occasional high flow. A method for determining whether a sump is perched in the vadose zone is described on pages 110–111.

Phreatic flow patterns

Phreatic water, in contrast to gravitational vadose water, has no inherent tendency to follow the steepest openings. Instead it eventually returns to the surface at lower elevations by following the most efficient routes — those that transmit the water with the least amount of energy loss. The widest and shortest openings are the most efficient and can carry the greatest amount of water at a given hydraulic gradient. A cave passage that forms in the phreatic zone can rise and fall along its length, with a profile that is irregular and undulatory. In general the rate and amount of karst groundwater flow diminishes with increasing depth below the water table, because fractures in bedrock tend to become narrower downward, and the flow paths are longer. In most places, caves are concentrated at shallow depths at or just below the water table, where water flow is greatest.

Phreatic passages with large cross-sectional areas tend to carry the most water. They transmit water so efficiently that the water table in or above them is lower than in the narrower openings around them (Figure 4.6). In a large solution conduit, the head is not much greater than that of the spring that the conduit feeds. As a result, water flows into the large openings from the surrounding smaller ones. For this reason, most phreatic water tends to converge, at least during low flow, and the resulting caves develop a branching pattern. This is certainly not the only phreatic cave pattern, as shown in Chapter 8. Branching of phreatic flow in the downstream direction is rare, except near spring outlets where water is partly diverted to overflow springs by collapse or sediment fill at the main spring.

During floods, water rises in surface rivers and percolates into the adjacent river banks. This water is known as **bank storage**. In karst areas, a great deal of this water enters caves. As surface floodwaters rise and force water into karst springs, cave streams may temporarily reverse direction so that they flow in what is normally the upstream direction (Figure 4.7). In a similar way, some cave streams occasionally fill their passages under pressure during floods (Figure 4.8) and deliver bank storage to the surrounding bedrock. As the flood recedes, this water drains back into the cave streams.

Figure 4.7: Backflooding in Eyeless Fish Trail, Mammoth Cave, Kentucky. As floodwaters rise in the nearby Green River, water pours into the cave. In this photo the stream is running in what is normally the upstream direction (left to right). Thick mud banks have been deposited by this kind of flow.

Figure 4.8: Floodwater in Onesquethaw Cave, New York. Water occasionally fills the entire cave to the ceiling. There is normally no waterfall at this point. Care must be taken to avoid being trapped by floods in caves. This photo was taken only a few meters from the entrance.

This kind of flooding has a great effect on the character and pattern of caves (Chapter 8).

The movement of phreatic water through bedrock can be compared to traffic flow on a network of highways. Most of the traffic follows the main roads, those that are widest and most direct. Meanwhile, fewer vehicles follow the narrow, winding secondary roads, and they move more slowly. This is the most efficient overall pattern. If everyone were to follow the main highways there would be a traffic jam. In a similar way, groundwater flow is distributed throughout the available space as it moves from high to low head, in such a way that it requires the least amount of head build-up. Most of the water follows short paths and wide openings, while smaller amounts follow the less efficient routes.

If part of a main highway is closed, a tangle of traffic is forced to follow inefficient detours around the closed segment. Irate drivers follow all possible routes in an effort to find the most convenient bypass. When a cave passage is blocked, for example by collapse, water is forced around the blockage along a great variety of paths and can form maze caves (Chapter 8).

Complex flow patterns in karst can sometimes be clarified by constructing *pipe diagrams* (Meiman and Ryan, 1999). These are drawings that portray the hydraulic function of a cave system in a simplified way. Cave passages and even unexplored conduits are shown as interconnecting pipes, so

that complex relationships, such as periodic flow reversals, overflows, and intermittent drains, are easily shown. Figure 4.9 shows a pipe diagram constructed by Smart (1983) to clarify the intricate flow patterns in the karst aquifer that includes Castleguard Cave, Alberta (see also Figure 2.56).

Aquifers

Underground water moves through openings in rock, sediment, or soil. These openings are collectively called the material's *porosity*. As described in Chapter 3, porosity includes *fractures* and *partings* in rock, as well as the spaces between solid particles (*intergranular pores*). Any of these may be enlarged by dissolution to produce *solution pores* or *solution conduits*. Porosity can also be expressed numerically as the *percentage* of open space in the rock, sediment, or soil. The greater the porosity, the more water the material can hold.

Typical porosities in soluble rock range from less than one percent in old, well-consolidated rock to more than 20% in young, poorly cemented granular limestones. In most consolidated carbonate rocks the 1% porosity includes only the intergranular pores and non-solutional fissures. Solution conduits typically raise this percentage only to about 2–5%. Caves may look large when we are in them, but they rarely account for much of the total volume of a karst aquifer (Worthington, 1999).

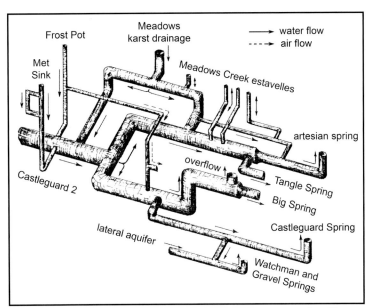

Figure 4.9: Pipe diagram of the Castleguard Valley karst aquifer, Alberta, based on dye tracing and cave observations (Smart, 1983).

Permeability is a measure of the ability of a material to transmit fluid. In reference to groundwater, the term ***hydraulic conductivity*** is often preferred, but *permeability* is a more versatile term because it applies to all fluids at any temperature (see footnote on page 98). Permeability is controlled by the *size* of pores rather than the percentage. The yield of water to a well depends more on permeability than porosity. Permeability can be measured in the laboratory, but a more meaningful estimate is obtained by pumping water from wells and analyzing the rate at which the water levels drop in other nearby wells. These techniques are described in the groundwater textbooks listed at the beginning of this chapter.

Aquifers are bodies of rock or sediment with high enough permeability that they can transmit large quantities of water. The usual criterion is whether the material can supply adequate water to wells. Even a material with fairly low permeability can be considered an aquifer if it is able to supply the small amount of water required for domestic use. Cavernous rocks are the most permeable of all, and gravel and most volcanic rocks are second. Sand, sandstone, and prominently fractured bedrock are moderately permeable. Shale and poorly fractured bedrock of most kinds have low permeability, and clay is almost impermeable. These low-permeability materials are rarely able to sustain adequate water supplies.

In karst hydrology it is appropriate to refer to ***conduits*** rather than to caves, except when caves are the specific topic of interest. Conduits include all solution passages whether or not they are of cave size, as long as they are capable of transmitting turbulent flow (pages 96–97). Some conduits are only partly or temporarily water-filled. Many have been abandoned entirely by their flow and are essentially dry.

The hydrology of a karst aquifer is complicated by the fact that it contains several different kinds of porosity. In a small fragment of limestone the permeability is provided only by intergranular pores, which may be microscopically small. The average permeability of the entire aquifer is much greater, because fractures and conduits transmit most of the flow. The permeability measured by well tests is usually provided by intersecting fissures of various sizes. This permeability is greater than that of small rock samples measured in the laboratory. Conduits have the highest permeabilities of all, but few wells intersect them. The complex interrelationship among these three different porosity and permeability types makes it difficult to predict water supply and flow patterns in karst (Chapter 15).

Despite its high permeability, a water-filled conduit has little effect on well yield unless the well intersects the conduit or connects to it by wide fissures. Vadose channels have no effect at all on well yield unless the well directly intersects them. Vadose passages are the main sources of rapid recharge to karst aquifers.

The nature of the porosity in a typical limestone changes with time (Vacher and Mylroie, 2002). In immature, poorly cemented limestones the porosity consists mainly of interconnected solution pockets surrounded by primary pores, but in older limestones, especially those that have previously undergone deep burial, most of the porosity consists of solution conduits surrounded by fractures.

Aquifers are classified according to their relation to the low-permeability materials that bound them (Figure 4.10). An ***unconfined aquifer*** is one that contains a water table. Whether the aquifer extends all the way to the land surface or is overlain by less permeable rocks, the top of the aquifer lies above the water table. In a ***confined aquifer*** the water table is located in or above an overlying low-permeability rock. Water levels in wells stand higher than the top of the

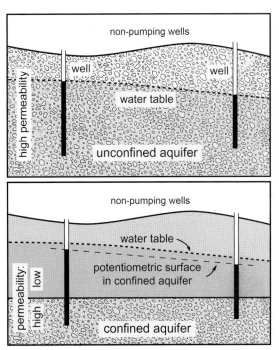

Figure 4.10: Unconfined and confined aquifers.

aquifer. They rarely coincide with the local water table in the low-permeability cover. Water levels in wells that penetrate a confined aquifer define the ***potentiometric surface*** of the aquifer. Contrary to the popular view, confined aquifers do not have totally impermeable boundaries. Water is able to seep in or out across the boundaries. But because the aquifer has the greatest permeability, most of the water flow takes place through it, just as a highway is the preferred route for traffic. Flow across the boundaries is greatest in recharge and discharge areas, where water infiltrates into uplands or discharges upward toward valleys. The impact of permeability boundaries on cave development is discussed in Chapter 8.

If the hydraulic pressure in a confined aquifer is great enough, water can flow out of wells onto the surface. Such an aquifer is called ***artesian***. Artesian conditions may diminish with time as the pumping of water increases. At the other extreme, a ***perched aquifer*** is an isolated phreatic body suspended in the vadose zone, where the underlying material has too low a permeability to transmit the infiltrating water without ponding.

As usual, karst aquifers thwart any attempt at a simple classification. For example, a cave filled to the roof with water under pressure might be considered a kind of confined aquifer. To avoid confusion, the distinction between confined and unconfined should be applied to the entire thickness of the aquifer and not just to the caves within it.

Nature of the karst water table

To produce a miniature version of the vadose zone, phreatic zone, and water table, fill a jar with gravel, then fill it part-way with water. The water level in the jar represents the water table. Most textbook diagrams show the water table as a smooth surface, as in the jar or in Figure 4.1. In bedrock, however, it is irregular and discontinuous, because the water occupies only the open spaces in the rock.

The water table is most irregular in karst. In a cluster of closely neighboring wells, their water levels may differ a great deal. Head values in different strata are rarely identical. The head in a water-filled cave is usually lower than in the small openings around it. During wet periods certain openings receive infiltrating water more rapidly than others, and water may temporarily rise in them to higher elevations than in other nearby openings.

In a karst aquifer the conduits behave like an elaborate leaky plumbing system, in which some of the pipes are water-filled, while others are only partly filled or temporarily dry. Water leaks into some conduits and out of others. In some conduits the water leaks both in and out at different times or at different places.

A few researchers take the pipe analogy so far as to deny the existence of a true water table in karst. A common argument against a continuous karst water table is the presence of underground waterfalls, and cave streams that cross over air-filled passages. But these are simply examples of vadose water on its downward journey to the water table

(Figure 4.4). They do not represent steps or discontinuities in the water table.

Phreatic cave passages form zones of low head, with the water table sloping downward toward them from both sides, just as it does around a surface stream (Figure 4.11). By measuring water levels in wells over a large area, the approximate locations of caves can often be determined by identifying zones of low head (Quinlan and Ray, 1981). Much scatter should be expected in the data.

During low flow, between floods, water slowly drains into conduits from the soil, epikarst, and minor fissures. Heavy rain or snowmelt causes a rapid increase of flow into sinkholes and sinking streams. At the onset of a flood, cave streams rise rapidly in comparison with the water in surrounding less-permeable parts of the aquifer. As a result, water is temporarily forced from the conduits into the surrounding smaller openings. The flow of springs also increases sharply during a flood, and temporary overflow springs may become active. As a flood subsides, the aquifer gradually reverts back to its low-flow status.

Johnson and Meiman (1994) measured the effects of flood pulses in seven drillholes located near Mill Hole, a karst window floored by a large stream in south-central Kentucky. Most wells showed rapid rises and falls in water level in exact phase with the stream in Mill Hole, which were clearly caused by interconnecting solution conduits. In some wells the water levels rose sooner than in Mill Hole, apparently because of efficient vadose recharge from the overlying surface. In some of these the well water rose several meters in a few minutes, to levels higher than the subsequent flood peak in Mill Hole. In the remaining wells, water rose and dropped more slowly than in Mill Hole. The flood peak in these wells was lower than that in Mill Hole, but during the flood recession the Mill Hole level dropped past the levels of the well water. These wells are apparently connected to the underground river by narrow fissures and possibly also by tiny solution conduits.

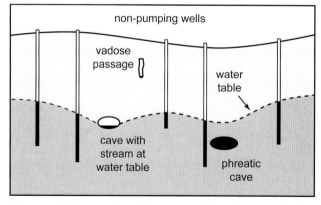

Figure 4.11: The position of the water table detected in shallow wells can indicate the approximate location of active phreatic caves. Caves tend to draw down the water table because they drain the water so efficiently to springs. Zones of low water table can be used to infer the presence of phreatic caves, even if the wells do not intersect the caves. Vadose caves are not detected in wells unless the wells physically intersect them.

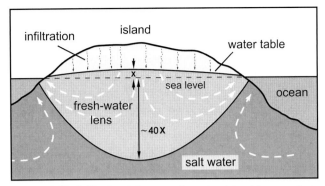

Figure 4.12: Infiltration into a small marine island forms a lens of fresh water that floats on underlying denser salt water. The thickness of the lens below sea level is about 40 times the height of the water table above sea level. Fresh water is constantly recharged from the surface, so the bottom of the lens remains fairly intact despite diffusion of salt water across it. Flow paths are shown in white.

At close range, at the scale of a cave or a group of closely spaced wells, the water table can be difficult to identify because it is so irregular and variable with time. Only at a broader scale can the presence and position of the water table be recognized. Nevertheless, the general concept of a water table is useful for distinguishing between vadose and phreatic conditions, and any valid interpretation of caves, groundwater, and water supply in karst relies on this distinction. Chapter 7 includes discussions of how the water-table concept has guided interpretations of cave origin.

The freshwater-seawater interface

Along the seacoast, water at considerable depth below the surface has roughly the same salinity as seawater. Infiltrating fresh water forms a lower-density lens that floats on the salty water the way a blob of oil floats on water (Figure 4.12). The interface between the two water types, called the ***halocline***, is kept distinct by the constant inflow of fresh water.

The depth of the halocline is determined mainly by the contrast between the two water densities. For comparison, a wooden log with 75% of the density of water will float in water with 75% of its volume submerged. The density of seawater is about 1.025 times greater than that of fresh water, so the freshwater lens has a density 97.6% of that of seawater. Therefore, 97.6% (40/41) of the freshwater lens extends below sea level. For every meter that the freshwater surface stands above sea level, the halocline will lie 40 times that distance below sea level. This is known as the Ghyben-Herzberg relationship.

This idealized relationship is disrupted by the flow of fresh water toward the sea. The white arrows in Figure 4.12 show this flow pattern, as well as the movement of salt water as it is dragged slowly toward the coast by the fresh water. If the lens pinched to zero thickness at the shoreline, outflow of fresh water would be impossible. Instead, the top and bottom of the lens meet the shore slightly above and below sea level, to produce a seepage face through which water can escape, as shown in Figure 4.12 (Hubbert, 1940).

This idealized view of the freshwater lens is disrupted still further by tidal flushing. In caves that drain to the sea, as in Yucatán Peninsula and Florida, rising tides can temporarily reverse the flow direction. As the tides ebb, this water is released with a discharge greater than the average. Along the coast of the Yucatán Peninsula, Beddows (2003) measured tidal effects in caves more than 5 km inland. She estimated that conduits account for only about 3% of the aquifer storage but about 99% of the flow.

When wells in the freshwater lens are pumped, the resulting drawdown causes the underlying halocline to rise. With sustained pumping the amount of rise eventually approaches 40 times the drawdown. In most aquifers this response is very slow. Likewise, once part of the aquifer is contaminated with salt water, recovery of the freshwater lens requires considerable time after pumping has ceased. The response is faster in high-permeability karst aquifers.

In seacoast carbonate rocks, the permeability increases as dissolution progresses. Because water moves more easily through the aquifer, the water table drops with time and the freshwater lens gets thinner (Vacher, 1988). If this process continues long enough, the freshwater lens eventually dwindles to a thin zone of brackish water at sea level. Evidence for this sequence is clearest in small islands of recently deposited limestone (Figure 4.13). Mixing along the halocline enhances dissolution and is a major agent in forming caves in these rocks. The shape of the freshwater lens, and how it changes with time, have an important influence over the location of caves (pages 209–212).

In some caves at the halocline there is a layer rich in hydrogen sulfide caused by reduction of dissolved sulfate in the sea water in contact with organic materials (Whitaker and Smart, 1994). The position of this layer is determined by its intermediate density between those of fresh water and seawater. It appears dark because of clouds of microscopic sulfide minerals. This can be a dangerous zone for divers because at high concentrations hydrogen sulfide is toxic and also corrodes equipment.

Figure 4.13: Sea-level pool in Lighthouse Cave, San Salvador, Bahamas. Note the high-tide marks on the rocks and walls.

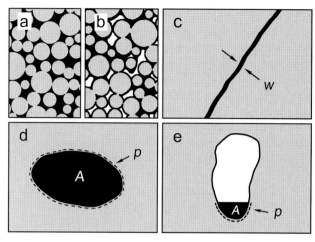

Figure 4.14: Types of openings through which underground water flows. (**a**) = laminar flow through intergranular pores below the water table; (**b**) = capillary seepage through intergranular pores above the water table; (**c**) = laminar flow through narrow fissures; (**d**) = turbulent flow in water-filled caves (closed conduits); (**e**) = turbulent open-channel flow. Cross sections (**a**), (**b**), and (**c**) are greatly magnified; (**d**) and (**e**) are of cave size. A = cross-sectional area, p = wetted perimeter, w = fissure width. In (**a**) the cross-sectional area includes both the pores and the grains, and is designated A_{total} in Eqs. 4.4 and 4.5.

Groundwater hydraulics

An acquaintance with the mechanics of water flow through aquifers and caves is helpful in the interpretation of cave origin and patterns. The most important characteristics of water flow are its **velocity** (distance of flow per time) and **discharge** (volume per time). Discharge (Q) is related to the average flow velocity (v) and the cross-sectional area of flow (A) in the following way:

$$Q = vA \qquad (4.1)$$

If a cave stream has a width of 1.2 m and an average depth of 0.35 m, its cross-sectional area is 1.2 m x 0.35 m = 0.42 square meters. If the average velocity in the channel is 0.88 m/sec, the discharge (Q) is 0.88 m/sec x 0.42 m² = 0.37 m³/sec. This is equivalent to 370 liters/sec or 370,000 cm³/sec. One cubic meter per second equals 35.3 cubic feet per second (cfs), so in this example Q also equals 13 cfs. Note that the answers are rounded to the same number of significant figures (two) as in the field data, to avoid the impression that the answer is more precise than the original data.

Types of water flow

Figure 4.14 shows cross sections of the various kinds of openings encountered by underground water. Each has a different flow character. In every application of Eq. 4.1 the area (A) must be perpendicular to the flow direction.

In Figure 4.14a, water saturates the sample and flows through all available pores in the direction of the local hydraulic gradient. The cross-sectional area is chosen arbitrarily. For example it may be chosen as one square

meter, or the entire cross section of the aquifer. The amount of flow through such an aquifer obviously depends on the size of the chosen area. Water flows only through the pores, so the true area is the total area (A_{total}) times the porosity. In Figure 4.14b the water does not saturate the sample. In this case, capillary water moves from moist to dry areas and from large to small pores (which have greater surface areas in contact with the water), while gravity pulls excess moisture downward.

In narrow water-filled fissures, A is the average fissure width (w) times the long dimension of the fissure cross section (Figure 4.14c). Measuring A is difficult, because the width varies from place to place, and the long dimension may be hard to determine.

A water-filled cave (Figure 4.14d) is an example of **closed-conduit flow** (or **pipe flow**). In water-filled conduits the cross-sectional area (A) is well defined and does not change with the rate of discharge.

A stream that fills only part of its channel is an example of **open-channel flow**. The water surface is in contact with air and changes with the amount of flow. Underground streams behave differently from those on the surface. A surface stream remains in its channel only during low to moderate discharge and overflows onto the surrounding land during floods, but a cave stream is constrained by its passage walls (Figure 4.14e). During floods the water depth increases more abruptly than in a surface stream, and if there is enough flow the water fills the entire passage.

In a water-filled passage, as the discharge increases, the velocity must increase proportionally, because the cross-sectional area remains constant. So if the discharge doubles, the velocity must also double (Eq. 4.1). In passages that are only partly filled by their streams, the increase in discharge is accommodated in the following way: the water gets deeper, and the slope of the water surface also increases. For both reasons the water moves more swiftly. But because the cross-sectional area (A) increases with water depth, the velocity (v) does not increase nearly as much as in a water-filled passage.

Water in small or narrow openings moves slowly, and the individual flow paths are very stable, with no swirling eddies. This is called **laminar flow**. In large openings, such as caves,

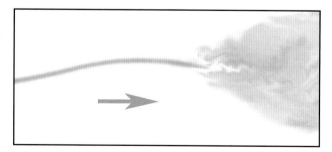

Figure 4.15: Difference between laminar flow on left (smooth, non-mixing) and turbulent flow on right (irregular flow patterns, eddies, rapid mixing). This pattern can be illustrated by carefully injecting dye into flowing water. The water has been artificially disturbed on the right to produce turbulence.

pipes, and streams, the water moves in irregular swirling paths with many unstable eddies that change with time. This is ***turbulent flow***. Narrow fissures in bedrock contain laminar flow, but if they widen by dissolution the flow gradually becomes turbulent. The transition takes place at fissure widths of about 0.5–1 cm, depending on the hydraulic gradient and temperature. As turbulent eddies develop, the water's ability to carry sediment increases, and there may also be an increase in dissolution rate (Chapters 5 and 7). The onset of turbulent flow is often considered the beginning of true cave development and karst groundwater conditions. Turbulent flow is rare in non-karst aquifers.

One way to distinguish between laminar and turbulent flow is to inject a thin jet of dye into the water. If the flow is laminar, the dye is carried downstream in a thin line that does not swirl into the surrounding water. In turbulent flow the dye quickly mixes and disperses throughout the flow (Figure 4.15). The status of flow can also be estimated by the Reynolds Number (**R**):

$$\mathbf{R} = \rho v \, (A/p) \, / \mu \qquad (4.2)$$

where ρ, v, and μ = fluid density, velocity, and viscosity, A = cross-sectional area of flow, and p = wetted perimeter. In any given cross section, the wetted perimeter is the length of the contact between the fluid and the walls (Figure 4.14d and e). A/p = ***hydraulic radius***. Viscosity varies significantly with temperature (Table 4.1). Water density is 1.00 g/cm^3 at 4°C and slightly decreases above and below that temperature.

If **R** is less than about 500, the flow is laminar. If **R** is greater than roughly 1000, the flow is turbulent. In the transition between 500 and 1000 the flow has intermediate characteristics. Laminar flow can be disrupted even at **R** < 500 if the pathways are rough and devious. In Figure 4.14d, if v = 125 cm/sec, A = 1400 cm^2, p = 185 cm, and temperature = 10°C, is the flow laminar or turbulent? At 10° the viscosity (μ) is 0.013, so the Reynolds Number = (1)(125)(1400/185)/0.013 = 72,000. This flow is clearly turbulent.

Open-channel cave streams, like all other streams, vary in velocity as the channel slope changes from place to place. It is easy to distinguish two types of stream flow: ***supercritical flow***, in which the water is shallow and rapid, and ***subcritical flow***, in which the water is deep and slow. Supercritical flow has a shimmering surface that is cross-hatched with small standing waves. Subcritical flow has a smooth and glassy surface, although it usually contains broad ripples and waves. Along its length, nearly every stream alternates many times between the two types.

Temp. (°C)	Viscosity μ (cgs)
0	0.0179
5	0.0152
10	0.0131
15	0.0114
20	0.0100
25	0.00894
30	0.00801
40	0.00656
50	0.00549

Table 4.1: Viscosity (μ) of water at various temperatures. Units of viscosity are dyne-sec/cm².

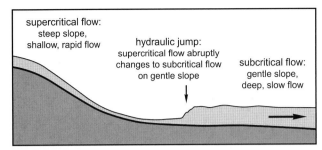

Figure 4.16: Supercritical and subcritical flow in a stream. Where supercritical flow is forced to flow onto a slope that is too gentle to sustain it, the flow slows down and eventually becomes subcritical by forming a hydraulic jump.

These two flow types have fundamental differences in their energy distribution. Supercritical flow is erosive, but subcritical flow is often slow enough to allow sediment to accumulate. If there is a small submerged body on the stream floor, it produces a hump in the water surface of supercritical flow but a hollow in the surface of subcritical flow. If a pebble is dropped into subcritical flow, waves on the upstream side can move against the current and progress upstream. In supercritical flow, all waves are swept downstream. Standing waves on the upstream side, which move neither upstream nor downstream, indicate ***critical flow***.

These flow types can be distinguished by the Froude Number (**F**):

$$\mathbf{F} = \frac{v}{\sqrt{gy}} \qquad (4.3)$$

where v = mean flow velocity, y = mean water depth, and g = gravitational field strength (980 dynes/gram).* The term $\sqrt{gy}$ is equivalent to the velocity of waves in shallow water, as in a stream. These characteristics apply only to turbulent flow. **F** is greater than 1 in supercritical flow and less than 1 in subcritical flow. If **F** = 1 the flow is critical, and the flow velocity equals the wave velocity. That is why standing waves on the upstream side of an impact are characteristic of critical flow.

Where supercritical flow shoots onto a slope that is too gentle to sustain supercritical conditions, the water surface rises abruptly in a turbulent standing wave called a ***hydraulic jump*** (Figure 4.16). Hydraulic jumps are highly erosive and can also increase local dissolution rates.

These aspects of open-channel flow have only minor application to cave development, but they help to explain the behavior of cave streams. As shown on page 101, they also provide a way of estimating stream discharge.

Flow equations

The velocity of water through any conduit, channel, or porous material can be estimated from flow equations, each of which is designed for a specific kind of opening. In all of the following relationships the units are assumed to be in the centimeter-gram-second (cgs) system.

---

* On steep slopes, y is measured perpendicular to the channel floor and is multiplied by the cosine of the slope angle (Chow, 1959). In waterfalls the slope is 90°, and **F** is undefined because cos (90°) = 0.

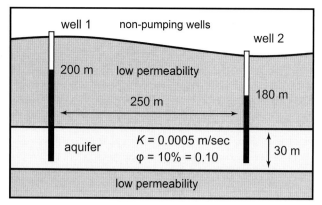

Figure 4.17: Use of Darcy's Law to interpret flow through an aquifer. Assume laminar flow through intergranular pores or a dense network of narrow fissures. The cross section is drawn parallel to the groundwater flow direction. The steps are as follows: (1) The aquifer is confined, because the water levels in the wells lie above the aquifer top. (2) The head is lower in well 2 (by 20 m), so the flow is toward the right. (3) The discharge through each meter of aquifer width (measured perpendicular to page) = $K (\Delta h/L) A_{total}$ = 0.0005 (20/250) (30)(1) = 0.0012 m³/sec. (4) Flow velocity = $Q/\varphi A_{total}$ = 0.0012 / [(0.1) (30)(1)] = 0.0004 m/sec. (5) Contaminants would move from well 1 to well 2 in about 250/0.0004 = 625,000 sec (7.2 days). These estimates are only as good as the field data. Steps 1 and 2 are valid in karst aquifers, and 3 is valid in most non-cavernous, fissured aquifers. Steps 4 and 5 give crude results and apply only to aquifers with homogeneous porosity, such as gravel.

In water-saturated material with intergranular pores, such as sediment, or in bedrock with a fine network of fractures, the flow is almost always laminar. The flow rate is determined by Darcy's Law:

$$Q = K (\Delta h/L) A_{total} \qquad (4.4)$$

where Q = discharge, K = hydraulic conductivity*, Δh = head difference between two points of measurement**, L = distance between the two points, and A_{total} = total cross-sectional area of the aquifer under consideration (including both grains and pores). The combined term $\Delta h/L$ represents the hydraulic gradient. Figure 4.17 gives an example of how Darcy's Law can be applied. Usually K is first calculated from Eq. 4.4 under controlled conditions in the field, for example by pumping a well, and then the result is used to predict the flow elsewhere in the same aquifer. Flow velocity can be estimated by

$$v = Q/(\varphi A_{total}) \qquad (4.5)$$

where φ = porosity in decimal percent (e.g., 25% porosity = 0.25).

Although Eqs. 4 and 5 do not apply to caves, they are useful for estimating flow through related bedrock or sediment, as long as the flow is laminar and the material has a fairly uniform permeability.

For laminar flow in a single narrow tube or fissure (Figure 4.14c), the mean flow velocity is given by the Hagen-Poiseuille Equation:

in fissures: $v = w^2 (\gamma/12\mu) (\Delta h/L)$ (4.6a)

in tubes: $v = r^2 (\gamma/8\mu) (\Delta h/L)$ (4.6b)

where w = fissure width (distance between walls), r = tube radius, and γ = specific weight of the fluid, which is its density x gravitational field strength. (For fresh water at normal groundwater temperatures, γ = 980 dynes/cm³. γ is higher in saline water and slightly lower in hot water). In bedrock fissures Eq. 4.6a tends to become inaccurate at Reynolds Numbers well below 500, because wall irregularities force the water to follow sinuous paths. Those paths with the greatest flow enlarge preferentially, so fissures grow in a non-uniform way (Hanna and Rajaram, 1998).

For turbulent flow in a closed conduit (Figure 4.14d), the mean velocity can be estimated with the Darcy-Weisbach Equation:

$$v = \sqrt{\frac{4rg \, \Delta h}{f \, L}} \qquad (4.7)$$

where f is a friction factor that depends on the wall roughness and is typically about 0.05–0.1 in caves. In conduits with fully turbulent flow, the friction factor can be estimated by the von Kármán Equation:

$$f = [1.74 + 2 \log (r/\varepsilon)]^{-2} \qquad (4.8)$$

where ε = roughness height (cm), which is the distance that the average wall irregularities project into the passage. In a typical cave a good approximation of ε is the scallop relief. For example, in a passage 50 cm in radius with roughness projections of 1.5 cm, r/ε = 33 and f = 0.044.

If the cross section is not circular, the radius (r) in Eqs. 4.7 and 4.8 can be replaced by twice the hydraulic radius ($2A/p$). If the conduit is shaped more like a fissure than a tube, the friction factor has to be adjusted slightly (Castillo and others, 1972).

Over long distances (for example, the length of an entire passage), the effective f value can be estimated from Eq. 4.7 by measuring all the other variables. The calculated f is invariably higher than that calculated by Eq. 4.8 because of energy losses in the passage caused by sinuosity, breakdown, and changes in cross section. In that case, values of f may exceed 1, or, in breakdown, even 100. Ideally all such energy losses should be calculated individually, because some do not behave like roughness, but the overall results are similar.

---

* *Hydraulic conductivity* and *permeability* are used interchangeably in this book. **Intrinsic permeability** (*k*) is a more versatile term, which takes into account the type of fluid at any temperature: $k = K\mu/\gamma$, where μ = viscosity of any fluid (see Table 4.1 for water) and γ = specific weight of the fluid. The units for k are cm².

** Hydraulic head is equivalent to energy per unit weight of fluid.

Use of flow equations in cave interpretation

Concepts of water flow can be used in many cave studies, for example to interpret what is happening in inaccessible parts of a cave and to help explain the origin of solution conduits and their patterns.

Example 1: The main stream passage of a cave contains a water-filled section that is accessible at both ends but seems too narrow to admit divers. The difference in water level between the upstream and downstream end is surveyed to be 0.25 meter. The flow rate is measured to be 0.32 cubic meters per second. The length of the sump appears to be about 17 meters. How large is the water-filled section?

Rearrange Eq. 4.7 to read $r = (v^2 f L) / (4g\Delta h)$. Since $Q = vA$, therefore $r = [(Q/A)^2 f L] / (4g\Delta h)$. Assume that the passage cross section is roughly circular (the error is small even if it is not), and replace A with πr^2. Combine the r terms to get $r^5 = [(Q/\pi)^2 f L] / (4g\Delta h)$. Solve for r by raising both sides to the 1/5 power. This is a simple operation with a calculator. If the passage walls have typical roughness, assume that f is about 0.05. The scale is in meters, rather than centimeters, so $g = 9.8$ m/sec^2. Now $r = [(0.32/3.14)^2 (0.05)(17) \div (4)(9.8)(0.25)]^{1/5} = 0.25$ meter.

Diving is not an option. Not only is the average radius very small, but the velocity is dangerously high. Velocity $= Q/A$, which is about $[0.32] / [\pi (0.25)^2] = 1.63$ m/sec, or 5.3 ft/sec. It would be impossible to fight such a current, especially in this small tube.

Example 2: This is a conceptual problem related to cave origin. Groundwater splits into two separate paths (1 and 2) that have not yet been enlarged by dissolution. They are both planar openings along bedding-plane partings:

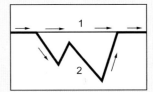

Path 2 is twice as long as path 1, but the fissure along path 2 is twice as wide. In other aspects they are similar. They have the same beginning and end points, so Δh is identical in both. They are each narrow enough to carry laminar flow, so Eq. 4.6a applies. A small amount of energy is lost at the bends, but this is insignificant in slow-moving water. Which path will carry more water and therefore be more likely to grow into a cave?

Note that $v = w^2 (\gamma/12\mu) (\Delta h/L)$ in each fissure. Take the ratio of v in path 1 to that in path 2. They differ only in w and L, so all other factors cancel out. The exact widths and lengths are not specified, but the ratios are known. So $v_1/v_2 = (w^2/L)_1 / (w^2/L)_2 = 1^2/1 \div 2^2/2 = 0.5$. So the velocity along path 2 will be twice as great as in path 1. Again because path 2 is twice as wide, the discharge along path 2 will be *4 times* as great as in path 1, despite having to travel twice as far. This example shows how it is possible for long, sinuous cave passages to form, even when more direct routes are available.

Turbulent stream flow in an open channel (Figure 4.14e) can be estimated with the Manning Equation:

$$v = \frac{4.64 \, (A/p)^{0.67}}{n} \sqrt{S} \quad \text{cm/sec} \quad (4.9)$$

where S = channel slope (drop in elevation ÷ distance of flow) and n = Manning friction factor (about 0.03–0.08 in most cave streams; see Table 4.2). As before, A/p is the

Nature of channel	Manning n
glass, smooth metal	0.01
smooth concrete	0.015
rough concrete	0.02
typical rivers	0.03
channels in bedrock	0.04
rough, rocky channels	0.05–0.1

Table 4.2: Some typical Manning friction factors (n).

hydraulic radius. Eq. 4.9 is based on experiments, rather than derived, and that is why its units do not balance from one side of the equation to the other. A must be measured in square centimeters and p in centimeters to obtain the mean velocity in cm/sec. If the measurements are in meters, replace 4.64 with 1.0 to obtain m/sec. If in feet, use 1.49 to obtain ft/sec. The discharge (Q) can then be determined with Eq. 4.1.

Any of these flow equations (4.4–4.9) can be handy for estimating flow rates in the field. They also show the various factors that control water movement and which openings are likely to carry the most flow. This kind of approach can also help to explain the origin of cave patterns (Chapters 7–9). Two examples of how these equations can apply to caves are given in the shaded box above.

In laminar flow the velocity increases in direct proportion to the hydraulic gradient. If the gradient doubles, the flow velocity also doubles. In turbulent flow the velocity increases with the square root of the gradient. Doubling the gradient increases the velocity only 1.4 times. If water flows through a narrow water-filled passage segment, the head rises at the upstream end. The flow is turbulent, so if

Figure 4.18: Some typical equipment for measuring stream flow. **Above:** V-notch weir; the "bird house" contains an automatic stage recorder. **Right:** pressure sensor (foreground) with programmable data logger. **Below: a** standard (Price-type) current meter with rotating cups. **Below right:** Pitot tube designed for cave use.

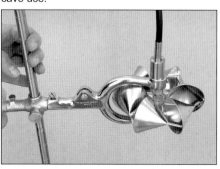

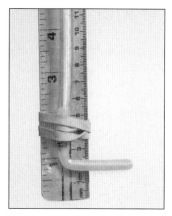

the discharge increases 10 times, the head difference across the water-filled segment must increase 100 times. It is easy to see why many caves fill to the ceiling during floods (see page 199).

To calculate the flow in an aquifer, conduit, or channel that varies in size or shape along its length, it must be divided into segments of fairly uniform character so the equations can be strung together to solve for the overall head difference (for an example, see Palmer, 2000a).

Flow measurements

Discharge measurements are helpful in many karst studies. A few examples: Comparing the discharges of springs or cave streams during low flow can indicate the relative sizes of the drainage basins that feed them. Multiplying discharge by the concentration of dissolved minerals gives the rate at which the water is removing dissolved bedrock. Comparing discharges between two different points in a cave stream can show whether a hidden tributary has come in somewhere between them. Several methods for measuring the discharge in caves, springs, and streams are described here briefly and are illustrated with examples on pages 102–103.

The ***volumetric method*** is the most accurate. Find a place where the stream runs over a waterfall and catch the flow in a container. Measure the volume of water in the container and the time required to collect it. Discharge = volume/time, so the calculation is simple. Drip rates from a cave ceiling or speleothem can also be measured in this way.

Suitable waterfalls are scarce in streams. Sometimes a large waterfall can be measured in parts where the water splits into several jets, so that the discharge of each can be measured independently and added together. A single wide waterfall can sometimes be measured by repeatedly holding the container under various parts of it and calculating each partial discharge until the entire width has been accounted for.

The ***float method*** is also simple, but it is less accurate than the other methods described here. It is best suited to the steep, high-velocity parts of a stream. Measure the length of a fairly uniform section of channel, and calculate the average cross-sectional area by multiplying the stream width by its average depth (see page 102). Find the time required for a floating object to be carried the length of the stream segment. Repeat the float measurement several times and average the results. The stream velocity is the distance divided by the time, and the discharge is calculated with Eq. 4.1. The result is usually an overestimate, because the float tends to follow the most rapid part of the stream.

A ***weir**** is a dam with a sharp-edged notch or orifice for the water to flow through (Figure 4.18). It is placed across the stream, and when the flow has stabilized, the elevation of the ponded water is measured above the bottom of the notch (or middle of the orifice). The discharge is calculated by using an equation that fits the specific weir design. The weir must be high enough to pond the water to a very low velocity, and care should be taken to prevent leakage around or under it. A popular type is the version with a 90° V-shaped notch. Measure the height of the ponded water surface above the bottom of the notch, and calculate the discharge as follows:

$$Q = 13.8 \, H^{2.5} \text{ cm}^3/\text{sec} \qquad (4.10)$$

where H is the height of water above the bottom of the notch, in centimeters. The result is most accurate if H is more than about 10 cm.

A ***Pitot tube**** is a transparent L-shaped tube that is open at both ends. Place the short end of the tube in the stream so that its opening faces upstream (Figure 4.18). Hold the long end vertically so that it projects above the water surface. The pressure of the flowing water on the short end forces the water level in the vertical part to rise above the surface of the stream. In the tube, measure the height (H) of water above the stream surface, and calculate the stream velocity with

$$v = \sqrt{2 \, g \, H} \qquad (4.11)$$

* Pronunciations: *weir* = **weer**, *Pitot* = pee-**toe**.

To keep the tube steady, brace it against a rigid support, such as a metal meter stick held vertically and placed on the stream bed, with its thin edge facing into the flow. If the water level in the tube fluctuates, measure both the low and high water levels, calculate the velocity of each, and then average the two. (This is more accurate than averaging the water levels and then calculating the velocity, but the difference is slight.) A small correction factor is sometimes added, but it is insignificant. The error caused by the water-level fluctuation is not large, because the square root in Eq. 4.11 diminishes its numerical effect.

The tube's internal diameter should be at least 5 mm to minimize capillary rise. The tube can be made by making a right-angle bend in glass tubing held over a propane torch and cutting the ends to the desired length. Round the tip of the short end over the flame to make the hole as small as possible without sealing it entirely. This small aperture acts as a governor to reduce the water-level fluctuations in the tube. If glass is not suitable for field work, make a short L of plastic or metal tubing and attach a clear vinyl tube for the vertical extension as in Figure 4.18.

To make the discharge measurement, find a cross section with smooth contours where the flow is fast enough to raise the water level in the tube at least a couple of centimeters. This requires supercritical flow with a moderately steep slope. Measure the stream depth at small intervals across its width (as described on page 102 for the float method), and at each point measure the velocity with the tube. Because the velocity at any location increases upward from the stream floor, the average velocity is found by placing the mouth of the Pitot tube above the floor at a height 40% of the water depth. For example, if the stream depth is 20 cm, hold the opening of the tube 8 cm above the channel floor. Alternatively, measure the velocity at 0.2 and 0.8 times the water depth and take the average. With Eq. 4.11, calculate the velocity at each point where the depth is measured. Water depth is zero at both edges of the stream, and the velocity may be difficult to measure there. Often the velocity at each shore is assumed to be half the velocity that is measured at the points closest to the shore. Calculate the discharge between each pair of measurement points, and sum them all to obtain the total discharge (see pages 102–103). Practice is needed to master this technique, but with care it is possible to keep the error below 5%.

Commercial *flow meters* (*current meters*) are also available, many of which operate like small turbines or windmills (Figure 4.18). The water velocity is proportional to the rate of rotation and is determined from a calibration table. Otherwise the procedure for obtaining discharge is similar to that with the Pitot tube.

The *Manning Equation* (Eq. 4.9) is most useful for estimating discharges that occurred in the past, or which may occur in the future. An example is given on page 103. In a cave stream, the Manning friction factor (n) should be about 0.03 if the cave walls are fairly smooth or the bed consists of fine-grained sediment, about 0.04–0.6 if the channel is rough (as in artificially cut bedrock or a bed of cobbles), and up to

about 0.1 if the channel is highly irregular (see Table 4.2). Determine the mean velocity with Eq. 4.9 and the discharge from Eq. 4.1. This method is less accurate than most because of the uncertainty in estimating the friction factor.

The *critical-flow method* involves ponding a stream with a flat-topped dam. Water flows over the top of the dam at critical flow. Because $\mathbf{F} = 1$ (Eq. 4.3), $v = \sqrt{gy}$ in this water. Measure the water depth (y) over the dam and estimate its discharge in the following way:

$$Q = w\sqrt{g}\ y^{1.5} \qquad (4.12)$$

where w = bank-to-bank width of the water over the dam.

The accuracy of any discharge measurement depends on the method, the nature of the field site, and the experience of the user. In the field, discharge may be difficult to measure accurately, but it varies so much with time and place that errors as high as 10% are acceptable for most projects.

The most accurate methods are, in approximate order: volumetric method, current meter, weir, Pitot tube, and critical-flow method. The Pitot tube is ideal for small streams where current meters are too bulky. Least accurate are the Manning Equation, float method, and the dye-concentration method described on page 105, all of which have uncertainties that usually exceed 20%. For methods that require measuring conditions over a length of channel, the accuracy is greatest in straight segments with uniform slopes and well-defined boundaries. Accuracy is poorest in channels with gravel beds, irregular floor contours, and shallow flow that is dispersed among many channels. It is best to obtain an average of several discharges measured at the same point, or, preferably, at a few different closely spaced locations, as long as there is no significant gain or loss of water between the points.

Long-term flow monitoring

Long-term records of water flow can be obtained with electronic data-loggers (Figure 4.18). The simplest method is to measure the water level with a pressure sensor and then convert the readings to discharge. The sensor is placed beneath the water surface, and the record of pressure variations can be automatically converted to changes in water level or discharge. This can be done in any stream channel but is easiest where the water is ponded by a weir or dam, where either Eq. 4.10 or 4.12 applies. In an unponded stream, use of a data-logger with Eq. 4.9 is valid, but it is important first to measure the discharge at several different times at a variety of flow depths and to plot a graph of discharge vs. water level. This *rating curve* can then be used to convert the data-logger measurements directly to discharge.

Data-loggers can also record flow-meter velocities, temperature, and a few chemical variables. They can also record rainfall or drip rates by measuring how frequently a small tipping bucket fills and empties, or by counting the impacts of falling drops. Any event that can be converted into a voltage pulse can be recorded (see Kranjc, 2002).

Measuring the flow of streams and springs

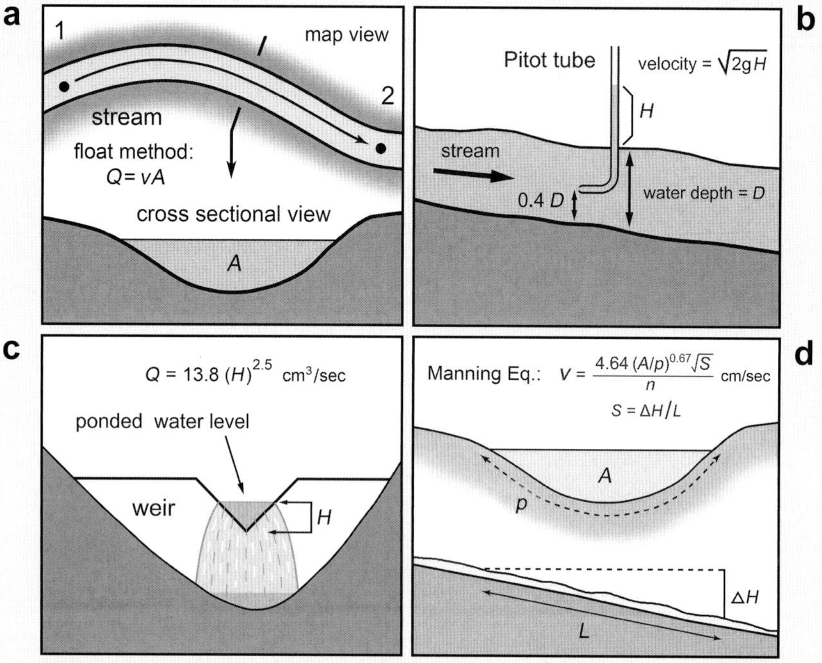

Figure 4.19: Some common methods of measuring stream flow: (**a**) float method, (**b**) Pitot tube, (**c**) weir, (**d**) Manning Equation. See text for details.

Volumetric method: At a waterfall, collect the water in a bucket and measure the time it takes to fill the bucket nearly to the top. Measure the volume of water in the bucket and divide it by the time. If 25 cm of water is collected in a cylindrical container that has a cross-sectional area of 1100 cm^2, the volume is 27,500 cm^3. If the collection time is 14.3 seconds, the discharge is 1920 cm^3/sec (1.92 liters/sec). Repeat several times and take the average.

Float method: In a fairly straight and uniform length of stream, measure the distance between two points (1 and 2). Say the distance is 42 meters (4200 cm). At point 1, drop a wood chip into the water and measure its travel time to point 2. Repeat several times. If the average time is 35 seconds, the approximate velocity (v) is 4200/35 = 120 cm/sec. Measure the width of a typical cross section (say 172 cm), and also the depths at uniform intervals across the width. Include a value of zero for one shore, but not for the other. For example, if the average of these depths is 16.7 cm, $A = 172 \times 16.7 \approx 2870$ cm^2. Discharge (Q) = vA = 120 × 2870 = 344,000 cm^3/sec = 344 liters/sec. Because the measured velocity is likely to be too high, so is the calculated Q. A crude way to correct it is to divide by 1.5, so about 200–250 liters/sec is a more reasonable estimate.

Pitot tube: Find a narrow part of the stream where the flow is rapid. Extend an aluminum meter stick across the width of the stream and weight it down so that it stays in place. On it, note the position of both shorelines. At frequent intervals across the width of the stream, measure the water depth with a second meter stick. To do so, first measure down from the horizontal ruler to the water surface, then from the horizontal ruler to the stream bottom, and calculate the difference. (Measuring the depth by simply inserting the ruler into the water is difficult because of the standing wave that results.) Hold the Pitot tube against the vertical ruler so that its lower opening is above the floor at a height 0.4 times the water depth. The tube opening should project forward into the flow, away from any interference from the ruler. Read the height of the water in the tube on the vertical ruler. Note the location of this site on the horizontal ruler. At each point, the velocity is found in the following way: Subtract the stream depth from the water level in the tube, call the result H, and then apply Eq. 4.11. If the stream depth = 2.3 cm and the height of water in the tube (above the stream floor) = 5.1 cm, $H = 5.1 - 2.3 = 2.8$ cm. From Eq. 4.11, with $g = 980$ cm/sec^2, $v = 74$ cm/sec.

Do the same at each measurement point across the width of the stream. Between each pair of measure-

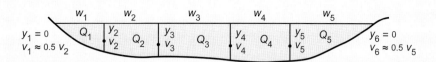

ment points, the discharge (Q) = (width) x (average depth) x (average velocity), as shown in the diagram above. Add all Q values to obtain the total discharge. The velocity at each shore is estimated to be half of what is calculated at the nearest Pitot tube site. Thus if one shore is at 12 cm on the horizontal meter stick, and the nearest Pitot tube reading is located at 17 cm, the width of this section is 5.0 cm. If the Pitot tube reading gives v = 48 cm/sec, assume that $v \approx 24$ cm/sec at the shore. The average velocity in this cross section will be 36 cm/sec. Suppose that the water depth at the Pitot tube site = 6.6 cm and the depth at the stream edge = 0, so the average depth in this cross section = 3.3 cm. The discharge in this segment = 5.0 cm x 3.3 cm x 36 cm/sec = 594 cm³/sec (round to 590). Repeat at other points across the width of the stream. Add the Q values of all segments to obtain the total discharge ($Q_{total} = Q_1 + Q_2 + Q_3 + Q_4$ ....).

Current meter: The meter is positioned in the stream as in the Pitot-tube method, and once the velocity measurements have been made the calculation of discharge is also the same. With a properly calibrated commercial flow meter, this is the most accurate method for large streams.

Weir: Install a sturdy dam of reinforced wood, sheet metal, or concrete, with a 90° notch in the top. The V should have a sharp metal edge. Suppose that the water level (H) above the bottom of the notch is 12.9 cm. From Eq. 4.10, Q = 13.8 x $(12.9)^{2.5}$ = 8250 cm³/sec. This is one of the most accurate methods for measuring discharge, and once the weir is installed it is also the easiest.

Manning Equation: Find a fairly straight and uniform segment of stream. Suppose that the channel floor consists of smooth sand. The friction factor (n) is approximately 0.03. With a hand level, measure the amount of drop in the stream surface (ΔH) over a given length of stream (L). Slope = $\Delta H/L$. An alternative is to measure the slope angle with an inclinometer: the slope equals the sine of the angle. As with the float method, measure the width of the stream at a typical cross section, and measure the water depth at uniform intervals across its width (including a zero for one shore). Find the average depth. A = width x average depth. Now measure the wetted perimeter (p) by holding a tape across the bottom of the stream and measuring from shore to shore. Estimate the velocity with Eq. 4.9 and discharge with Eq. 4.1. If ΔH is 22.3 cm over an L of 598 cm, S = 22.3/598 = 0.037. If the width is 44 cm and the average depth = 8.9 cm, A = 44 x 8.9 = 390 cm². Suppose that p = 51 cm. According to the Manning equation, v = [4.64 x $(390/51)^{0.67}$ x $(0.037)^{0.5}$] ÷ 0.03 = 116 cm/sec. Q = vA = 116 cm/sec x 390 cm² = 45,240 cm³/sec = 45 liters/sec. The estimate of n is the weak link, so rounding the estimate to two significant figures (or even one) is appropriate, unless the accuracy of n has been verified in this stream or similar ones with other flow-measuring techniques.

With this method, flood discharge can sometimes be estimated even after the flood has subsided. Suppose a past flood in a canyon passage 125 cm wide reached an average depth of 350 cm, as shown by a line of vegetal debris. The cross-sectional area of flow (A) was roughly 43,750 cm². Suppose that the wetted perimeter (p) is measured to be 820 cm by draping a tape from the flood level down one wall, across the floor, and up the other side to the flood level again. A/p = 53.4 cm, and $(53.4)^{0.67}$ = 14.4. An inclinometer reading along the flood line gives an angle of 4.6 degrees (channel slope would probably suffice). Slope = sin(4.6) = 0.080. Its square root is 0.28. A reasonable n value is 0.04. Then calculate the velocity: v = (4.64)(14.4)(0.28)/(0.04) = 470 cm/sec. From Q = vA, the flood discharge is estimated to be about 20 million cm³/sec, or 20 cubic meters per second. One cubic meter per second = 35.3 cubic feet per second, so the flood peak reached about 700 ft³/sec (cfs). An interesting study would be to compare flood velocities to those calculated from solutional scallops (see Chapter 6).

Critical flow over a flat-topped dam: A flat-topped dam is constructed across a stream so that the water is ponded and flows over at a uniform depth. The velocity and discharge can be calculated from Eq. 4.12. Measure the depth where the water surface is flattest. For example, if the water depth over the dam is 4.1 cm and the wall-to-wall width of the dam is 125 cm, the discharge is 125 x square root of (980) x $(4.1)^{1.5}$ = 32,400 cm³/sec = 32 liters/sec. This method is usually more accurate than methods B and F but less accurate than the other methods.

Groundwater tracing

To determine paths of groundwater flow that are not accessible by exploration, a dye or other tracer can be injected at an upstream point, while downstream points such as springs are monitored for the appearance of the tracer. Only the basic concept of dye tracing is described here. Field and laboratory techniques are described in detail by Smart (1988), Käss (1998), Aley (2002), Field (2002a), and Jones (2005). Tracer tests should not be attempted unless they are part of a systematic project, and, even then, not without advice from someone with considerable experience. It is also wise to inquire whether anyone else is conducting traces in the same area. Use of dyes in contaminant studies should be left to professionals.

Most traces are done only to verify a connection between two points, but if water sampling is done frequently enough it is possible to calculate the travel time and approximate groundwater velocities as well. Published results show that water in solution conduits moves at velocities typically between ten and several hundreds of meters per hour (Ford and Williams, 1989). Local velocities occasionally exceed one kilometer per hour. Open-channel streams in caves flow as fast as comparable surface streams. In contrast, velocities in the phreatic zones of non-karst aquifers rarely exceed a few centimeters per hour.

The most popular tracers are dyes such as *fluorescein* (bright yellow-green) and *rhodamine WT* (red). They are available either as pre-mixed solutions or as dry powder. Both are visible by eye down to roughly 0.1 part per million, but with a fluorometer they can be detected down to a few tens of parts per trillion. If several different dyes are injected simultaneously at different points, they can be distinguished from each other with a scanning spectrofluorophotometer, which graphs the wave lengths emitted by the sample over a range of incoming light frequencies.

In comparison to rhodamine WT, fluorescein is detectable in smaller concentrations and adheres less readily to solid surfaces. Rhodamine degrades faster with time, losing its potency and drifting slightly into the emission spectrum of fluorescein. But background levels of fluorescein in natural water are usually higher than for rhodamine because fluorescein is more common in commercial products such as antifreeze. Tracing with particles such as plant spores or artificial micrometer-sized spheres can determine the capacity of an aquifer to transmit microbial contaminants.

Qualitative tracing

The goal of qualitative tracing is mainly to verify connections between upstream and downstream sites. Approximate travel times can also be determined if sampling is frequent enough.

Dye is introduced at a discrete inlet, such as a sinking stream, while potential outlets are monitored with packets of activated charcoal ("bugs"). Activated charcoal, which is available commercially, is made by heating wood in the absence of air to drive off volatiles, which increases its porosity and adsorptive properties. In a dye bug, several grams of charcoal are enclosed in an envelope of plastic screen and held in the water by a wire or cord. If dye is present, it is adsorbed onto the charcoal.

The charcoal is sampled periodically and tested for dye. Fluorescein is released from the charcoal by immersing it in a 5% solution of potassium hydroxide dissolved in ethanol. Rhodamine WT is released by a warm solution of 10% ammonium hydroxide in 50% aqueous 1-propanol. The dye can then be detected visually or with a fluorometer. Visual detection is best done in a dark room by shining a small flashlight through the sample at a right-angle to the line of sight. See Smart and Laidlaw (1977) and Smart and Simpson (2001) for a further discussion of laboratory techniques.

Quantitative tracing

In quantitative tracing a known mass of tracer is injected, while samples are taken at frequent intervals with automated samplers at potential outlets (see pages 106–107). Each sample is then analyzed for tracer concentration. For each spring with a positive trace it is possible to calculate the elapsed times for the initial arrival, the peak concentration, center of mass, and percentage of dye recovered. The background level of tracer in the stream must be checked before running the trace, and this amount, if any, is subtracted from the measured concentrations. The shape of the dye recovery curve (**breakthrough curve**) provides the travel times, as well as information about the nature of the conduits and the storage characteristics of the aquifer.

The entire mass of dye is rarely recovered. Some adheres to bedrock or sediment surfaces, and it may break down chemically, especially in bright light. Some tracer may emerge at outlets that are not monitored. Some may be trapped in standing pools or in narrow fissures and pores, from which it leaks out over a long time in small concentrations.

It is rare that automated samplers can be installed at every potential outlet during a dye trace. Instead they are usually placed at the most likely springs, while other potential outlets are monitored with charcoal bugs. If dye is detected with the charcoal, another trace may be warranted with an automated sampler at that site. Sufficient time should be allowed for water to emerge at potential outlets, even unlikely ones, and charcoal is ideal for this kind of long-term monitoring. Charcoal accumulates dye over time, so it is more sensitive than direct water analysis.

Estimating the ideal amount of dye involves many uncertainties. In an analysis of hundreds of traces through simple conduits, Worthington and Smart (2003) find a good fit to the data with

$$m = 19 \, (LQC)^{0.95} \qquad (4.13)$$

where m = mass of dye (grams), L = distance (meters), Q = spring discharge (m^3/sec), and C = dye concentration desired at the outlet (mg/liter). It is usually appropriate to keep tracer concentrations below visible detection levels.

First-timers often use far too much. The dyes described here are non-toxic, but the consequences of coloring someone's water supply can be serious. On the other hand, too small a quantity of dye may go undetected, which gives the false impression that the test has been negative. Studies of contaminant dispersion usually involve much more dye than those designed simply to verify major connections, because the goal is to identify all possible flow paths.

With any kind of tracing it is essential to avoid contamination of field sites or samples. Scrupulous cleaning of equipment is needed, and every attempt should be made to keep the dye from coming into contact with anything other than the water that is being traced. Fortunately the dyes are very soluble and can be cleaned fairly easily from non-absorbant materials.

Estimating stream discharge with tracers

Dye tracing provides one more way to estimate stream discharge (Kilpatrick and Cobb, 1985). There must be close to 100% dye recovery, which requires a trace over a fairly short distance, yet long enough to allow full mixing of dye in the water. The mass of injected dye is measured first. Then, as shown on page 107, the dye breakthrough curve is divided into small time increments. For each increment, the average dye concentration (C, grams/liter) is multiplied by the time interval (Δt, sec), to give gram-sec/liter ($C\Delta t$) for that interval. The discharge of the stream (Q, liters/sec), is the total mass of dye (m, grams) divided by the sum of all the $C\Delta t$ values from the breakthrough curve:

$$Q = m / \Sigma(C\Delta t) \qquad (4.14)$$

The symbol Σ means to add up all the individual values for the item that follows it (in this case, $C\Delta t$).

Interpreting groundwater character from tracer tests and flood pulses

Sinking streams and springs indicate the presence of caves, but the caves themselves may be inaccessible. The character of these caves can sometimes be interpreted from dye traces and flow variations.

Estimating cave size

If a dye trace is conducted and the average discharge (Q) and travel time (t) between the sink and spring are measured, it is possible to estimate the average size of the conduit that carried the dye. The volume of water (V) that passed through during the trace is found by $V = Qt$. This is roughly equal to the conduit volume. For this to be valid, t should be the time to the centroid of the dye arrival at the spring (see page 107). If the passage is not completely filled with water, the result will underestimate the passage volume. Dividing the volume by the assumed length of the conduit gives an estimate of its cross-sectional area. From this it is possible to calculate its approximate radius or diameter.

Consider a dye trace from a sinking stream to a spring with a travel time of 21 hours and a mean discharge of 95 liters/sec (= 0.095 m³/sec). The straight-line distance between the points is 2300 m. The travel time = (21 hrs) x (3600 sec/hr) = 75,600 sec. So V = (0.095 m³/sec) x (75,600 sec) $\approx$ 7200 m³ for the water-filled part of the conduit. The total flow length is estimated from the straight-line distance multiplied by a sinuosity factor. Suppose that local cave maps show an average passage length of 1.3 km for each kilometer of straight-line distance. The sinuosity factor is about 1.3, so the estimated flow distance for the dye trace is 2300 m x 1.3 $\approx$ 3000 m.

The cross-sectional area of the water can be estimated at 7200 m³/ 3000 m = 2.4 m². For a water-filled conduit this would suggest a mean diameter of about 1.75 m. The actual passage size is larger if the water does not fill it completely. The result is only approximate, especially if the sinking stream and the spring have different discharges. At least this example suggests a cave of traversable size, perhaps only for divers.

Interpreting cave geometry

Tracer tests can show whether an unexplored cave is an open channel or closed conduit. If the cave is a combination of the two, the approximate percentage of each can be estimated. Several dye traces are required at different discharges. The following example is valid only for a simple conduit with no branches, although the approach can be extended to more complex settings.

In a water-filled cave, $v = Q/A$ (from Eq. 4.1) and the flow velocity increases in direct proportion to the discharge. Suppose that a dye trace is performed through a closed conduit at low flow, with an initial dye arrival of 30 hours. If at a later date the discharge is 10 times greater, then the velocity should also be 10 times greater, and the dye would ideally be recovered in only 3 hours.

The relationship between discharge and velocity is different in an open-channel stream passage. As the discharge increases, so does the velocity, but not in direct proportion. Much of the increase in flow is accommodated by a rise in water level, which increases the cross-sectional area. A ten-fold increase in discharge will decrease the dye recovery time, but by much less than ten times. The open-channel flow equation (Eq. 4.9) is complex enough that it is easiest to solve this problem by trial and error, by choosing a variety of water depths and calculating the velocity and discharge for each.

Consider a canyon passage one meter wide and 1000 m long, with a slope (S) of 0.01 and a friction factor (n) of 0.05. As the discharge increases, the water depth and velocity increase, and the travel time decreases, according to Eqs. 4.1 and 4.9, in the following way:

Q (liters/sec)	depth (m)	velocity (m/sec)	time (sec)
10	0.04	0.23	4400
100	0.19	0.53	1890
1000	1.03	0.97	1030
10,000	8.26	1.21	826

(Discussion continues at bottom of page 107.)

Quantitative dye tracing

Dye tracing is most useful when it is done quantitatively, with dye concentrations measured frequently while dye is passing through the karst system. With this technique the travel times and percentage of dye recovered at each spring are determined. In complex flow systems it may first be convenient to delineate the major flow paths with a simple qualitative trace. The following example shows how to perform a quantitative dye trace. The exact numbers will vary with the local conditions.

1. A 180-gram sample of liquid rhodamine WT dye is injected into a sinking stream (Figure 4.20). The manufacturer states that the dye is a 20% solution, so the actual mass is 36 grams. Care is taken to avoid contamination of field sites or equipment.
2. Prior to the dye injection a water sampler (Figure 4.21) is set up at each possible spring outlet. Each is programmed to sample the spring water at 15-minute intervals. If it is not feasible to install a sampler at each possible outlet, charcoal bugs are used at potential recovery sites to test for the presence of dye, and quantitative tracing to the successful sites can be done at a later date.

Figure 4.20: Injecting dye into a sinking stream. Photo by Kristin Johannessen.

3. Before the dye is injected, water samples are taken so that any background level of dye can be determined.

This concentration can be subtracted from each measurement in the dye breakthrough curve.
4. After a few days the samples are retrieved and their dye concentrations are measured in the laboratory with a fluorometer (Figure 4.22). The background level of dye, if any, is subtracted from the total.
5. In this example, dye is detected in only one spring. Flow measurements show that this spring maintained an essentially uniform discharge of 9.5 L/sec during the dye trace.
6. Dye concentration vs. time is graphed, as in Figure 4.23. This is the dye breakthrough graph.
7. The first dye arrival was at about 12.5 hours (= ***breakthrough time***), and the maximum dye concentration was at about 16 hours (= ***peak time***). This gives information about how fast the water was flowing through the system, and also the rate at which soluble contaminants might travel.
8. To determine the total mass of dye recovered, the graph is divided into small time increments (Figure 4.23), say half an hour. In each increment, the average dye concentration ($\overline{C}$) is multiplied by the time interval (1800 seconds) and by the discharge (9.5 liters/sec).

For example, in the half-hour interval shown in Figure 4.23, the average dye concentration was 75.2 micrograms per liter (= parts per billion, ppb),

Figure 4.21: An automatic water sampler, disassembled. The timing and sampling mechanism is at right, the sample bottles are in the compartment in center (= the bottom third of the sampler), and the top cover is at left.

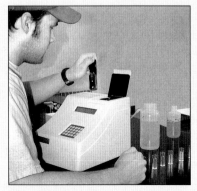

Figure 4.22: Measuring dye concentrations with a fluorometer.

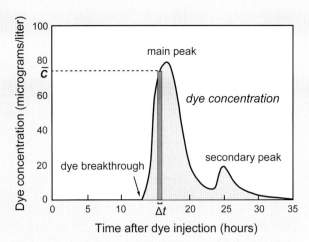

Figure 4.23: Dye breakthrough curve. Concentrations are in micrograms/liter (= parts per billion). The curve is divided into small time intervals, Δt (30 minutes is appropriate for this lengthy curve) and the mass of dye in each interval is calculated. The total dye recovery is the sum of all the individual masses. Secondary peaks may be caused by loops in the stream passage or by dye released from ponded water as a flood pulse passes through.

which is equivalent to 7.52×10^{-5} gram/liter. So, during this interval, the mass of dye that emerged from the spring was 7.52×10^{-5} gram/ liter x 1800 sec x 9.5 liters/sec = 1.29 grams.

10. If the discharge varied during the dye recovery, the calculation of dye mass for each interval would include the discharge measured at that time.

11. This procedure is repeated for all the other time increments. Summing the dye masses for all of the increments gives a total of about 25.5 grams. Therefore about 71% of the dye was recovered from this single spring. The rest can be accounted for in several ways: (a) dye was still emerging in small concentrations when the sampling ended; (b) some of the dye may have degraded, adsorbed onto solid surfaces, or escaped undetected through

other springs; and (c) there is always some error inherent in the measurements. Still, it is clear that most of the dye has been recovered and that this is the major outlet for the sinking stream.

12. This calculation is greatly simplified if the time increment (Δt) is a multiple of the sampling frequency. In this case, Δt = 30 minutes, which is twice the sampling frequency. The mean concentration in each time increment can be found by simply averaging each pair of measurements, beginning with the first two that show a measurable increase in dye concentration above the background value. Plotting the breakthrough curve is still important, though, to show the pattern of recovery and for the following steps.

13. The mean travel time is determined from the *center of mass* (centroid) on the breakthrough curve. The simplest way to calculate it is to use step 8 to find the mass for each time interval and add them together, beginning with the first, until the sum equals half of the total mass determined in step 9. This works best if the time intervals are short. Because most breakthrough curves rise rapidly and taper off gently, the mean travel time is almost always greater than the peak arrival time. Often only the arrival time or peak time is reported in the literature. Mean travel time is given less often. Because each conveys different information, it is appropriate to report all three.

14. Computer software from the Environmental Protection Agency (Field, 2002a) can be used to predict the mass of dye more accurately by smoothing the data, extrapolating the shape of the tail end of the dye breakthrough, and calculating the breakthrough, peak, and centroid. It also estimates mean velocity and rates of dye dispersion in the underground conduits.

In this example (page 105) the discharge increases 1000 times, but the travel time decreases by only 5.3 times. The reason is as follows: As the water rises in a narrow canyon, the contact between the water and cave walls (wetted perimeter) increases at almost the same rate as the cross-sectional area, so the ratio A/p in Eq. 4.9 increases slowly. As a result, the velocity increases only slightly as discharge increases.

Most conduits include a combination of open-channel flow and conduit flow, so the relationship is more complex than in these idealized examples. Furthermore, as discharge increases, parts of a passage are likely to change from open-channel to closed-conduit flow. Still, it is easy to calculate the relationship between discharge and travel time for any combination of idealized conduits. The difficulty is in working the problem backward, from discharge and travel

time to an interpretation of passage geometry. This can be done, but not with great precision.

To interpret the passage character, dye breakthrough times are plotted for a variety of discharges and plotted on a logarithmic scale, which accommodates a broad range of values (Figure 4.24). If the conduit is mainly filled with water, the plot will have a slope of -1.0 (i.e., the slope will be 45° downward to the right), as in examples *a* and *b*. If the conduit contains mainly open-channel flow, the slope of the graph will be gentler and will also decrease in slope as discharge increases (examples **c** and **d**).

In a cave that contains significant lengths of both types of flow, the water-filled section is likely to dominate the discharge-time relationship at low discharges. Water runs rapidly through the vadose channel to the filled section, where

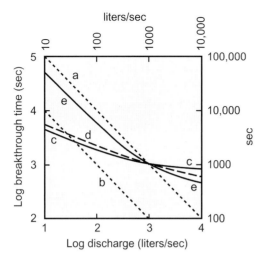

Figure 4.24: Plot of travel time vs. discharge in tubes and canyons. Length = 1000 m. (**a**) closed conduit 1 m^2 in cross section, (**b**) closed conduit 0.1 m^2 in cross section, (**c**) open channel 1 m wide, with slope = 0.01 and n = 0.05, (**d**) similar open channel 2 m wide, (**e**) 500 m open channel, like that of **c**, leading to 500 m of closed conduit 1 m^2 in cross section.

it slows down. In this case, the direct relationship between discharge and velocity in the water-filled section exerts the main control over total travel time. The slope of the graph will be close to −1 during low flow. But during high flow, the water shoots rapidly through the filled section, while in the open channel it moves only a little faster than it did during low flow. The slower open-channel flow accounts for most of the travel time, so the slope of the plot decreases with discharge (example *e* in Figure 4.24). The point where the 45° slope on the graph first begins to decrease depends on the discharge at which the travel time in the open channel begins to exceed the travel time in the closed conduit. This in turn depends on the relative sizes and lengths of the two sections of cave. This approach has been used by Woodell (2004) and Siemion (2006) to interpret flow conditions in New York karst aquifers.

Analysis of spring discharge

Natural discharge variations in a karst spring can reveal many of the characteristics of the groundwater basin and caves that feed it. The best approach is to measure its discharge, preferably with the aid of a continuous water-level recorder (Figure 4.18). The study should extend over a period when there are significant flow variations. A spring *hydrograph* can be drawn that shows the variation in discharge with time. Figure 4.25 shows a typical hydrograph for a single flood. A continuous record of several years is most useful, but few researchers have this luxury.

During dry periods, cave streams and springs are at *base flow*, which is the flow supplied only by leakage of water from storage in the ground. The base flow decreases gradually as the dry period progresses. It is supplied almost entirely by seepage from small pores and fractures. Soil-filled fissures in the epikarst can contribute much of the water at these times. Base flow is large in aquifers that are highly porous and only moderately permeable. Thin karst aquifers that drain rapidly

through caves have very low base flows, especially if the aquifers are perched above the normal water table. The base flow in most karst aquifers falls between these extremes.

Comparing spring hydrographs with rainfall records will show the elapsed time between rainfall events and the first response at the spring, as well as the rise time to the flood peak (crest) and how rapidly the aquifer drains afterward. Multiple peaks are common where several tributaries respond to rainfall at different times, or where the rainfall is not uniform. Melting snow can complicate these relationships.

A typical flood hydrograph (Figure 4.25) rises abruptly, reaches a peak, and then tapers off at a gradual rate. The hydrograph usually begins to rise within half an hour of a local heavy rainfall. If the rainfall takes place in a remote part of the drainage basin, several hours may elapse before the discharge begins to rise. The height of the flood crest depends on the size of the catchment area, the intensity and duration of the rainfall or snowmelt, the distance to the spring, and the permeability of the materials in the basin. All of these relationships apply as well to stream flow in caves.

In a karst aquifer, flood peaks are supplied by rapid flow that travels more or less directly through conduits from surface inputs. As a peak subsides, an increasing percentage of water is delivered by laminar flow through narrow non-solutional openings. The hydrograph usually drops rapidly at first and then at a decreasing rate.

If the discharge during the recessional part of a flood is plotted logarithmically, the hydrograph eventually tends to become a straight line (Figure 4.26). This straight line represents the time when the spring is fed mainly by slow drainage out of the minor fissures and pores around the cave passage (Atkinson, 1977b; Milanović, 1981; Padilla and others, 1994). Of course the cave that feeds the spring still contains turbulent flow, but the rate at which the flow is supplied to the cave is governed by laminar seepage into it. The logarithmic relationship is characteristic of laminar outflow from a system that is no longer receiving recharge from the surface. Prior to that time, much of the spring flow is still contributed by inflowing turbulent streams, which account for the curved part of the graph. Transitional states between the two types of drainage may cause additional breaks in slope prior to the final straight line, but these tend to be minor and difficult to interpret. The beginning of the straight line in Figure 4.26 is the beginning of base flow.

Over any given time period, the ***volume*** of flow equals the area under the hydrograph during that period. In Figure 4.25, for example, the total volume of water discharged by the spring or stream can be estimated by dividing the hydrograph into small time increments, as in the dye breakthrough curve in Figure 4.23. For each increment, the volume of water is the discharge (volume/time) during that time interval multiplied by the length of the interval. For example, if the average discharge during a ten-minute interval was 1.4 cubic meters per second, the total volume that passed through during that ten minutes was (1.4 m^3/sec) x (10 minutes) x (60 sec/minute) = 840 cubic meters. Adding the volumes for each time increment during a flood will give the total volume of runoff for that flood. The

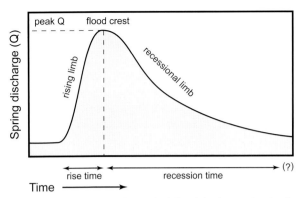

Figure 4.25: Example of a typical flood hydrograph at a karst spring.

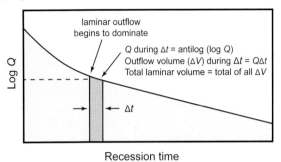

Figure 4.26: If the recessional limb of the flood hydrograph is plotted with log Q, the point where laminar outflow begins to dominate can be recognized by a fairly straight line. The volume of laminar outflow can be estimated as shown.

same approach can be used to obtain a rough estimate of the total volume of laminar seepage from the aquifer over any time period (Figure 4.26).

In a spring or cave stream the ratio of annual maximum to minimum discharge (Q_{max}/Q_{min}) can help to reveal the hydraulic character of the karst system that it drains. A large ratio shows that the water is delivered mainly as rapid flow through solution conduits, with a relatively small base flow contributed by seepage from small openings. A small ratio is typical of aquifers with high intergranular porosity, such as those in poorly consolidated limestones, where most of the infiltration is diffuse and little runoff drains directly into solution conduits. This technique is not appropriate for overflow springs that have zero base flow. Climatic variations also affect the ratio, so it is best to compare systems that are in the same climatic region. Q_{max}/Q_{min} values are most representative if the measurements are averaged over a year or more, because for any single flood the rainfall depth and intensity are likely to vary between drainage basins.

Karst springs that are fed rapidly through sinkholes and sinking streams typically have Q_{max}/Q_{min} values in the range of 100–10,000. In contrast, most springs in young porous limestones, such as the Tertiary limestones of Florida, have ratios less than 10 (Wilson, 2002).

In a karst aquifer with well-developed conduits, spring hydrographs respond rapidly to rainfall and snowmelt. Aquifers that are dominated by diffuse flow through pores and narrow fissures have broader and more subdued flood peaks. In the Tertiary limestones of Florida, the non-conduit permeability (from pores and narrow fissures) is more than 10,000 times that of typical Paleozoic limestones (Florea and Vacher, 2004). The Florida springs have broad hydrograph peaks with little relation to individual rainfall events, except for the most intense. The springs respond mainly to seasonal or even longer-term variations in recharge.

See Ford and Williams (1989, p. 193–203) for descriptions of other ways in which aquifer properties can be interpreted from spring hydrographs.

Pulse-train analysis

This technique involves releasing a water pulse into a karst depression and measuring its effect on spring flow (Ashton, 1966). One method is to dam a sinking stream and then release it suddenly. Another is to empty a large water tank into an open sinkhole or fissure. Springs are then monitored for changes in water level or discharge. Various ways of interpreting the data are described in the following section on flood tracking.

Pulse-train analysis is most useful where dye traces are not feasible, or where they would require inconveniently long travel times. Tracers are greatly slowed by ponded or water-filled passages, but a pulse of water travels through them almost instantaneously as a pressure wave. In New Zealand, Williams (1977) used pulses triggered by periodic releases from a reservoir to trace groundwater leakage from a river bed, through an artesian marble aquifer, to a spring 15 km away. The pulses traveled that distance in only 10 hours. Williams estimates that dye would have taken several years to travel the same distance.

Flood tracking through caves

Where an inaccessible cave lies between a sinking stream and a spring, the nature of the intervening passage can be interpreted by comparing the patterns of inflow and outflow during floods. The approach is also valid for artificial pulses, if they are large enough to provide the necessary detail. It can augment the information from quantitative dye traces.

One more hydrologic relationship is helpful: the **water balance**, which is based on the conservation of mass:

$$Q_{in} - Q_{out} = \Delta\text{Storage} / \Delta\text{time} \qquad (4.15)$$

It states that any difference between the inflow and outflow from a system is balanced by a change in storage within the system. For example, if all the flow inputs to a cave at a given time have a combined discharge higher than the discharge at all the springs, water must be rising somewhere in the cave. If Q_{in} = 1500 liters/sec and Q_{out} = 900 liters/sec, the water volume in the cave is increasing at a rate of 600 liters/sec. If $Q_{in} < Q_{out}$ the storage is decreasing with time.

To apply flood tracking, discharge must be monitored continuously at both the main swallow hole and spring during a flood. Weirs equipped with stage recorders are most convenient for providing the data. If a large flood overtops the weirs, the stream depth can be converted to discharge

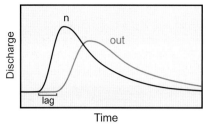

Figure 4.27: Comparison between a flood hydrograph at a sinking stream (**in**) and at the karst spring that it feeds (**out**). If there is a measurable lag time between the two rises, at least part of the cave between the sink and spring contains air-filled passages. As shown in Eq. 4.15, any difference between Q_{in} and Q_{out} is balanced by changes in storage in the cave. See text for details.

Figure 4.28: If the spring hydrograph begins to rise at approximately the same time (**a**) as the sinking stream, most of the intervening cave is water-filled. See text for details.

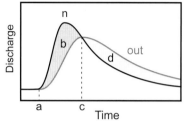

with the Manning Equation (Eq. 4.9) at the expense of some accuracy. The analysis is easiest if the flood consists of a single pulse. A few examples are given here:

- During low flow, compare the discharges of the spring and sinking stream. If the two are roughly equal, there are no significant gains from tributaries or from laminar seepage. If $Q_{spring} > Q_{sink}$ there are tributary inputs, and if $Q_{sink} > Q_{spring}$ there is some loss by overflow to another outlet.
- During floods of various magnitudes, compare the flood volume at the sink to that in the spring (total areas under the two curves in Figure 4.27). Calculate the flood volume (V), as described on pages 108–109. If the ratio V_{sink} / V_{spring} varies with flood severity, there is likely to be an increasing amount of overflow across low-flow divides either into or out of the system being measured. Separating the spring flow into laminar and turbulent components (Figure 4.26) will help to determine how much of the variation is caused by each type of flow.
- If there is a measurable time lag between the rise of the inflow and the rise of the outflow (Figure 4.27), the flood has traveled mainly through an open channel, such as a canyon passage. The flood pulse also becomes broader and lower with distance. This is partly because the forward part of the flood pulse has a steeper water surface than the trailing part, so the forward part moves faster. The amount of delay between the inflow peak and outflow peak depends on the passage length, size, slope, and frictional resistance.
- The approximate flow velocity through the cave can be determined by dividing the estimated channel length by the lag time. A result less than about one meter per second confirms that the channel is mainly vadose. If this calculation gives an apparent velocity greater than about one or two meters per second, most of the cave length

is water-filled. This is not the true flow velocity, but the velocity of a pressure pulse through water-filled passages. An open cave stream cannot have such a high velocity unless its gradient is unusually steep. If the cave is almost entirely water-filled, the rise in spring outflow will coincide almost exactly with the rise in the inflow at the sinking stream (so the lag time in Figure 4.27 will be negligible).
- During a flood, water may overflow into adjacent rooms, blind passages, or fissures that are normally air-filled, either entirely or partly. The result is a local rise in water table around the cave. The water then drains back into the main conduit as the flood subsides. In this situation the spring hydrograph will be broader, with flattened peaks, in comparison with the inflow hydrograph (Figure 4.28).
- In Figure 4.28, the outflow begins to rise soon after the inflow (at time **a**). The outflow does not rise as rapidly, so at first there is more water entering the cave than is exiting. The shaded area (**b**) represents the volume of water that is filling the cave and the openings around it (see Eq. 4.15). The inflow reaches its peak and begins to drop, but as long as the discharge in is greater than the discharge out, the build-up of stored water continues, and the outflow continues to rise. But at point **c**, where the in and out hydrographs cross, the outflow begins to decrease because more water is draining out of the cave than is flowing in. The volume of released storage is represented by the shaded area (**d**), and at the end of the flood its volume should be roughly the same as area (**b**). Any discrepancy is caused by scatter in measurements and by unmeasured inputs or springs.

Using these and similar techniques in a karst basin in southern France, Mangin (1975) and Bakalowicz (1979) developed the concept of ***karst annexes***, which are subsidiary voids connected to the main underground drainage lines. Karst annexes fill with overflow water during floods and drain out as the floods subside.

Identifying perched sumps

When explorers reach a sump, they may wonder if the entire cave beyond is water-filled, or if the sump is perched in the vadose zone with air-filled passages beyond. The answer may determine whether diving is worthwhile. If there is little flow through the sump the answer should be obvious, but it may not be so clear if even the minimum flow is large.

The distinction can be made by measuring how the water level at the sump varies with discharge. In turbulent flow, the hydraulic gradient increases with the square of the discharge (Eqs. 4.7 and 4.1). Therefore, a graph that relates Q^2 to the elevation of water at the upstream end of the sump should be a straight line. The relationship is not exact because the water level over the threshold increases as well, but this effect is comparatively minor.

Two or more measurements are needed at significantly different discharges. In Figure 4.29, suppose that the water elevation (H) is noted on a day when the discharge (Q) is 214 liters/sec and $Q^2 = 45,800$. Consider this H to be zero,

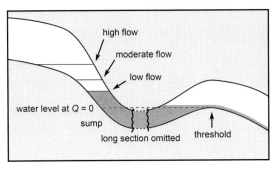

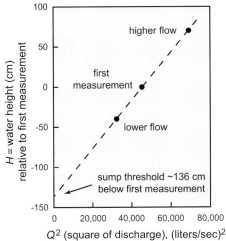

Figure 4.29: A perched sump and interpretative procedure. The first water-level measurement is considered zero, and other measurements at different discharges are made relative to it. Projecting the best-fit line down to $Q^2 = 0$ provides the elevation of the threshold of the sump at the downstream end. Some scatter should be expected in the data points.

so it can be used as a standard of comparison. On another occasion, when $Q = 265$ liters/sec ($Q^2 = 70,200$), $H = +71$ cm relative to the first measurement. On a third occasion, when $Q = 179$ liters/sec ($Q^2 = 32,000$), $H = -40$ cm relative to the first. All three points are plotted on the graph of H vs. Q^2.

Although only two points are necessary, the addition of a third gives an idea of how reliable the measurements are. Ideally they should plot on a straight or slightly curved line. When this line is drawn through the points and extended to $Q^2 = 0$, this point is the elevation of the threshold at the downstream end of the sump. In other words, this would be the elevation of the water surface when there is no flow at all. In this example, that elevation is 136 cm below the first reading. If the elevation of the point at $Q^2 = 0$ lies significantly above the elevation of the surface spring, the sump is perched, and there are passages beyond that are not water-filled (Palmer, 1987). A careful survey from the sump to the spring is needed; see Chapter 14 for techniques. The length and diameter of the sumped section cannot be determined exactly, but with a combination of Eqs. 4.1 and 4.7 it is possible to narrow the range of possibilities.

The approach described here helped in planning the exploration of Mexico's Sistema Huautla, when there was concern that a particular sump might represent the beginning of a water-filled cave reaching all the way to

the spring. The elevation difference was 550 m, but the sump was a full 9 km in a straight line from the spring. Anecdotal information about variations in water level with discharge was enough to show that the sump was perched and that much air-filled cave lay beyond. This interpretation was later validated by the discovery of extensions that led to a Western Hemisphere depth record (Stone and am Ende, 2002; see Figures 8.8–8.10).

Where there is little change in elevation with discharge, the graphical approach is unnecessary. The elevation of the threshold will be essentially that of the lowest water level. Most sumps require no more analysis than this.

Estimating groundwater age

The age of groundwater — i.e., how long it has been in the ground — can sometimes be estimated from dissolved radioactive isotopes. One of the most suitable for this purpose is ***tritium*** (^3H), which consists of hydrogen with three neutrons instead of the usual one. It is measured in tritium units (TU), where one TU represents one tritium atom per 10^{18} hydrogen atoms. The natural background level was once about 5–10 TU, but during atmospheric hydrogen-bomb tests in the 1950s and 1960s the tritium level in the atmosphere increased to as much as 5000 TU. The peak was reached in the mid-1960s and has since dwindled to about 20. Its graph with time is irregular and varies from place to place (Kehew, 2001).

Rain and snow absorb tritium from the atmosphere, so the tritium concentration in groundwater provides a rough estimate of how long ago it infiltrated. It takes 12.43 years for half of any remaining tritium to decay. This is its ***half life*** (see pages 347–348). So, for example, if precipitation fell in 1963, when the tritium value was about 1000 TU, by the year 2000 the groundwater that it fed would have gone through 3 half-lives, and the concentration would have diminished to 125 TU. Mixing with water of different ages can complicate the interpretation.

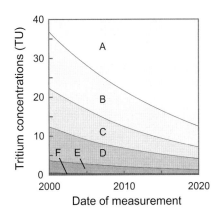

Figure 4.30: Approximate tritium concentrations in groundwater and springs (calculated from data in Clark and Fritz, 1997). As tritium decays, the concentrations decrease with time. The timing of infiltration is as follows: A = dominantly 1960s; B = much from 1960s and 1970s; C = some from 1950s–1970s; D = recent (up to about 10 years old); E = mixture of pre-1952 and recent; F = pre-1952.

Tritium concentrations in groundwater and springs can be interpreted roughly as shown in Figure 4.30. Most cave water passes through the ground so rapidly that tritium levels remain essentially unchanged during their transit. In karst, tritium dating is most appropriate for springs that are fed by deep groundwater, or in arid climates where infiltration rates are low. Many thermal springs have very low tritium values, which indicate that all or most of their

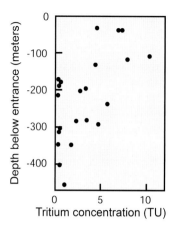

Figure 4.31: Variation in tritium concentration (TU) in pool water with depth below the entrance in Lechuguilla Cave, New Mexico (Turin and Plummer, 1995).

water infiltrated prior to 1952 (Ţenu and David-escu, 1995). Turin and Plummer (1995) used tritium measurements in Lechuguilla Cave, New Mexico, to show that the mean rate of vadose seepage is about 4–5 m/yr, with much mixing between waters of varied age. Pools more than about 300 m below the surface contain mostly pre-1952 tritium levels (Figure 4.31). One hopes that tritium levels will continue to decrease in the future, but if so, the usefulness of this technique will gradually diminish.

Chemical tracers

Non-toxic salts can be added to pools to determine rates of dilution or concentration. Soluble halides that are not likely to react with other components in the water are preferred. A decrease in concentration with time indicates that the pool water is being diluted by recharge. An increase in concentration shows that evaporation exceeds inflow. Combining this information with changes in pool volume makes it possible to estimate rates of leakage, inflow, and evaporation. Forbes (2000) gives an example in which sodium bromide (NaBr) was added to pools in Carlsbad Cavern, New Mexico. Monitoring of the bromide concentrations showed long-term slow leakage from the pools, with bursts of recharge during unusually rainy periods.

Measurements of natural chloride can complement the interpretation of the artificial tracers. Chloride minerals such as halite (NaCl) are highly soluble and do not tend to precipitate in normal cave water. Thus variation in chloride level can be used to distinguish different water sources and to track patterns of dilution, evaporation, and mixing.

The chemical mass balance

The mass of a particular material in solution is its concentration (C) in grams/liter times the water volume (V) in liters. Discharge (Q) = volume/time, and therefore the mass of dissolved material that passes through a stream in a given time = QC. If two streams join to form a third, the combined

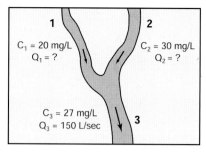

Figure 4.32: Use of the mass balance to determine flow rates or chemical concentrations in cave streams. For details, see text and Eqs. 4.15–4.17.

mass/time in the tributaries must equal the mass/time in the main stream. This is an example of the ***mass balance***.

In Figure 4.32 the discharges of two tributaries are Q_1 and Q_2, and the discharge of the main stream is Q_3. So

$$Q_3 = Q_1 + Q_2 \qquad (4.15)$$

In the same streams, the concentrations of any dissolved material (e.g., chloride) are C_1, C_2, and C_3. Over any time period, the combined mass of chloride that passes through streams 1 and 2 equals the mass of chloride that passes through stream 3:

$$Q_3 C_3 = Q_1 C_1 + Q_2 C_2 \qquad (4.16)$$

This relationship can be used in various ways. For example, if C_1, C_2, C_3, and Q_3 are measured, the discharge in each branch can be calculated. This would be handy where the discharges of the branches are difficult to measure. Eqs. 15 and 16 can be combined as

$$Q_1 = Q_3 \, [(C_3 - C_2)/(C_1 - C_2)] \qquad (4.17)$$

Concentrations are usually measured in milligrams/liter, rather than grams/liter (one mg/L = 0.001 g/L). But in Eq. 4.17 the concentration units cancel out, so this conversion is not necessary. In Figure 4.32, $Q_1 = 150 \, [(27 - 30)/(20 - 30)] = (150)(0.30) = 45$ liters/sec, and $Q_2 = 150 - 45 = 105$ liters/sec. Because Q_2 is about 2.3 times greater than Q_1, it is likely that the catchment area for tributary 2 is about 2.3 times larger than that of tributary 1.

Any two unknowns in Eq. 4.16 can be determined in a similar way. In the Sierra de El Abra karst in Mexico, Fish (1977) used a similar approach to determine seasonal variations in the percentage of deep water (rich in magnesium and sulfate) relative to shallow karst water that contained little sulfate or magnesium.

The principles and character of underground water flow discussed in this chapter reappear elsewhere in this book, (e.g., Chapters 5, 7 and 15), but mainly in reference to cave origin and chemistry. Details of aquifer tests, basin analysis, and groundwater modeling are presented more thoroughly in books by Milanović (1981), Bonacci (1987), Palmer and others (1999), Beck and Herring (2001), Harmon and Wicks (2006), and Ford and Williams (2007).

5

Chemistry of karst water

AN UNDERSTANDING OF CHEMISTRY is essential for determining the origin of solution caves and cave minerals, and that is the focus of this chapter. Broader information on natural water chemistry is available on-line at *http://water.usgs.gov/pubs/wsp/wsp2254/html/pdf.html*).

Dissolution and precipitation

A grain of salt quickly dissolves in water. The solid salt, consisting of sodium chloride (NaCl), simply breaks apart (***dissociates***) into two charged ions, Na^+ and Cl^-, which go their separate ways as dissolved particles in the water. They are invisible, even under a microscope, but their concentrations can be measured by laboratory analysis. Dissolved salt can also be detected by taste.

Gypsum and anhydrite dissolve in the same way as salt (Figure 5.1), but more slowly and in smaller amounts:

$$\text{gypsum:} \quad CaSO_4 \cdot 2H_2O \rightleftharpoons Ca^{2+} + SO_4^{2-} + 2H_2O \quad (5.1)$$

$$\text{anhydrite:} \quad CaSO_4 \rightleftharpoons Ca^{2+} + SO_4^{2-} \quad (5.2)$$

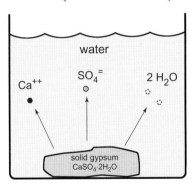

Figure 5.1: Dissolution of gypsum. Solid gypsum dissociates into ions of calcium (Ca^{2+}) and sulfate (SO_4^{2-}), plus two water molecules that cannot be distinguished from the main body of water. When the water becomes saturated with dissolved gypsum, the reaction stops.

Water that is able to dissolve a mineral is said to be ***undersaturated*** with that mineral, or ***solutionally aggressive*** toward it. As the solid mineral dissolves, the concentration of its dissolved components increases, and the solution rate slows down. Eventually the water can hold no more of these particular dissolved materials and the process stops. At this point the water has become ***saturated*** with the mineral. The volume of dissolved mineral that can be held in solution depends on the mineral type, quantity of water available, temperature, and the presence of other materials in solution. For example, pure water at 25°C can hold about 2500 parts per million (ppm) of gypsum.* This is the ***saturation concentration*** for gypsum at that temperature.

Note that many chemical reactions have double-ended arrows — they can go either forward or backward. To precipitate solid gypsum, Reaction 5.1 must be reversed in one or more of the following ways: by evaporation, a change in temperature, or interaction with other dissolved materials. Suppose that a sample of water is saturated with gypsum. Then if 20% of the water evaporates, the same amount of dissolved gypsum is held by only 80% of the original water volume. The concentration of dissolved gypsum increases to 1.25 times the saturation value (i.e., $1 \div 0.80$). The water has become ***supersaturated*** with respect to gypsum. Solid gypsum is forced to precipitate, and the solution approaches gypsum saturation again. It does not quite reach saturation, because a small threshold amount of supersaturation must be present for a mineral to precipitate. So slightly less than 20% of the dissolved gypsum will precipitate.

Dissolution of limestone and dolomite

Most large caves are located in limestone, which consists mainly of the mineral calcite ($CaCO_3$). Calcite hardly dissolves at all in pure water. Distilled water that contains no dissolved gases will hold only about 12 ppm of dissolved calcite at 25°C, which is only about twice the solubility of quartz. Calcite dissociates in the same way as gypsum and anhydrite:

$$CaCO_3 \rightleftharpoons Ca^{2+} + CO_3^{2-} \quad (5.3)$$

In most natural water the process does not stop there. Carbonate ions (CO_3^{2-}) react rapidly with acids (which supply H^+ ions), and acids are available from many sources. So a more complete way of expressing calcite dissolution is:

$$CaCO_3 + H^+ \rightleftharpoons Ca^{2+} + HCO_3^- \quad (5.4)$$

where $HCO_3^- = $ ***bicarbonate*** (also known as *hydrogen carbonate*). Even water itself supplies small amounts of H^+, but there are other more potent natural acids. The most common is ***carbonic acid*** produced by dissolved carbon dioxide (CO_2) supplied by the atmosphere and from biological activity in the soil:

$$CO_2 \text{ gas in air} \rightleftharpoons CO_2 \text{ dissolved in water} \quad (5.5)$$

The concentration of a gas is usually measured as ***partial pressure***. In an open container of water, this is the

---

* This water would contain about 740 ppm of Ca^{2+} and 1760 ppm SO_4^{2-}. There are equal numbers of Ca^{2+} and SO_4^{2-} ions, but SO_4^{2-} is about 2.4 times denser than Ca^{2+}.

pressure that the gas exerts on the water surface. The total air pressure at sea level is one atmosphere, and because CO_2 today accounts for about 0.038% of the air mass, its partial pressure (P_{CO_2}) is 0.00038 atm. If the water absorbs as much of the CO_2 as it can, so that it is in equilibrium, the CO_2 concentration *in the water* is also considered to be 0.00038 atm. The P_{CO_2} of our atmosphere diminishes with increasing altitude and at present is increasing with time.

In the soil, the P_{CO_2} of water usually ranges between 0.01 and 0.1 atm (Brook and others, 1983). It is greatest during the growing season (warm months), when microbial activity is at its peak. Dense, clay-rich soils tend to have higher values than loose, well-aerated soils, because their smaller pore sizes inhibit the escape of gases. In general, about 90% of the CO_2 generated in the soil is lost to the outside atmosphere. The rest is retained or carried downward by infiltrating water.

The greater the P_{CO_2} in the atmosphere, the more CO_2 is absorbed by any water in contact with it. Below the water table, where there is no gas in contact with the water, the dissolved CO_2 concentration is still usually expressed as P_{CO_2}. It can either be measured directly or calculated from an analysis of other components in the water. The more CO_2 in the water, the more limestone or dolomite can dissolve.

The process works like this: In solution, some of the CO_2 reacts with water to produce carbonic acid:

$$CO_2 + H_2O \; \rightleftharpoons \; H_2CO_3 \qquad (5.6)$$

The carbonic acid dissociates to produce hydrogen ions and bicarbonate ions:

$$H_2CO_3 \; \rightleftharpoons \; H^+ + HCO_3^- \qquad (5.7)$$

Bicarbonate can dissociate *very* slightly in water:

$$HCO_3^- \; \rightleftharpoons \; H^+ + CO_3^{2-} \qquad (5.8)$$

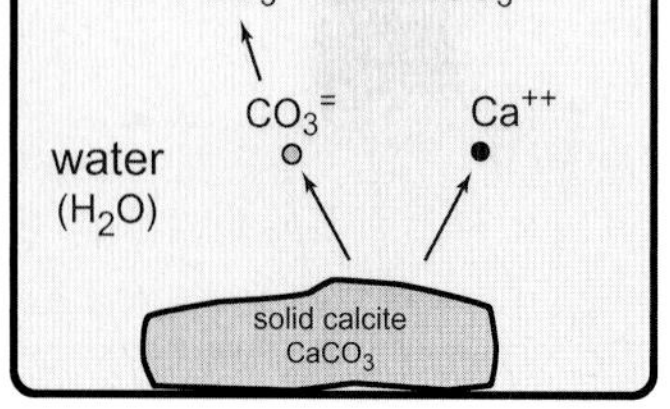

but because of the large number of carbonate ions produced by limestone and dolomite, the reaction is usually forced toward the left. The amount of calcite that can dissolve is limited by the concentration of Ca^{2+} and CO_3^{2-} ions in the water. And so, as CO_3^{2-} is used up by its interaction with acid, more calcite can dissolve to replace it (Figure 5.2). As a result, acidic water can dissolve much more limestone than pure water can. If it were not for this reaction, this book would probably not have been written.

The solubilities of calcite and dolomite at various P_{CO_2} values and temperatures are shown in Figure 5.3. Water in contact with the outside atmosphere, with P_{CO_2} ~0.00038 atm, can dissolve about 50–70 ppm of calcite (depending on the temperature). This is equivalent to 0.018–0.026 cm³ of dissolved solid in each liter of water. On bare limestone, the origin of surface channels, rills, and fissures relies mostly on this kind of dissolution. But in the soil, biological processes drive the P_{CO_2} to values about 100 times greater than in the outside air. Water passing through the soil acquires a P_{CO_2} of 0.01–0.1 atm, which allows it to dissolve about 200–450 ppm of calcite (about 0.07–0.17 cm³/liter). That is the main reason why groundwater forms caves so readily.

In most caves the CO_2 content of the air is about ten times less than that in the soil, and about ten times greater than that of the outside air. If water acquires a high P_{CO_2} in the soil and then seeps downward through narrow fractures in limestone, it dissolves some of the rock. If this water

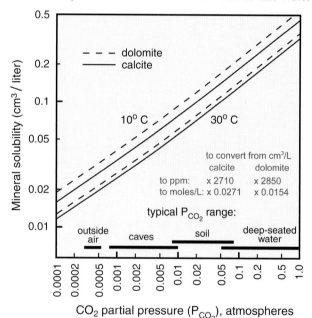

Figure 5.3: Solubility of calcite and dolomite in carbonic acid solutions, in terms of volume of dissolved mineral. Dolomite is more soluble than calcite in volume and in ppm, but not in number of molecules dissolved. Both minerals become less soluble with increasing temperature. The effect of hydraulic pressure on calcite solubility (and probably dolomite as well) is negligible at less than 200 atm, equivalent to about 2000 m of water depth (Sippal and Glover, 1964). Compare with Figure 5.14. Except where noted otherwise, all graphs in this chapter are based on computer-aided calculations by the author (see page 136). All pertinent reactions and adjustments for activity are included.

Figure 5.2: Dissolution of limestone (calcite) by carbonic acid. Carbon dioxide in air is absorbed by water and reacts with it to form carbonic acid. The H^+ in the acid reacts with CO_3^{2-} from the calcite to form HCO_3^-, which allows more calcite to dissolve. For every Ca^{2+} ion in solution there are about two HCO_3^- ions.

How much rock has dissolved?

Most soluble rocks consist almost entirely of a single mineral. In limestone, that mineral is calcite. The amount of dissolved limestone in a water sample is measured by how much calcite is present in solution. Distinguishing it from other types of dissolved rock is described in **Chemical field studies** on page 135.

Published lists of chemical data are usually stated in parts per million (**ppm**), i.e., milligrams of dissolved material per kilogram of water. One kilogram of water is essentially the same as one liter (except at high temperatures, when the density is lower), so ppm is closely equivalent to milligrams/liter (**mg/L**). All of these units represent **mass** per kilogram or liter.

But mass is not always the most convenient unit. For example, seawater contains more Mg^{2+} ions than SO_4^{2-} ions, but on lists that show seawater composition in ppm, sulfate is listed above magnesium because sulfate has a greater mass.

For the interpretation of chemical processes, it is easier to consider **number of ions or molecules** per liter. The appropriate units are **moles/L**. A mole of a particular substance is a certain number of molecules of that substance (6.022×10^{23} to be exact). To convert from mg/L to moles/L, simply divide mg/L by the molar mass (atomic weight) of the element involved. For a list of molar masses, see any chemistry book.

Geologists are often concerned with the **volume of mineral** that has been dissolved, because it is a measure of how much has been removed by the enlargement of pores or caves. In this case, cubic centimeters per liter

(cm^3/L) is the most appropriate unit. To convert from mg/L to cm^3/L, divide by the density of the mineral (refer to any mineralogy book).

Example: Calcite ($CaCO_3$) dissolves to produce Ca^{2+} ions and CO_3^{2-} ions. Because most of the CO_3^{2-} converts to HCO_3^-, Ca^{2+} is the more stable ion to measure.

Suppose that a water analysis gives a Ca concentration of **85 mg/L** (or ppm). This includes all dissolved calcium, even though some may have linked temporarily with other ions to form complexes such as $CaHCO_3^+$. If calcite is the only likely source, the interpretation will be as follows:

The molar mass of Ca = 40.08 g/mole = 40,080 mg/mole. So Ca = 85 mg/L ÷ 40,080 mg/mole = **0.0021 moles/L**. Conveniently, this is also the number of moles/L of dissolved calcite, because it requires one molecule of calcite to produces one Ca ion.

The concentration of **dissolved calcite** in mg/L indicates the milligrams of calcite dissolved by each liter of water. The molar mass of CO_3 is 60.01 g/mole (12.01 for carbon plus 16.00 for each of the three oxygens). So the total molar mass of calcite = 40.08 + 60.01 = 100.09 g/mole, and Ca represents 40% of it. The total concentration of dissolved calcite in this sample is therefore 85 mg/L ÷ 0.40 = **213 mg/L of $CaCO_3$**.

The density of calcite is 2.71 g/cm³, which is 2710 mg/cm³. So the **volume** of dissolved calcite per liter is 213 mg/L ÷ 2710 mg/cm³ = **0.079 cm³/liter**. Inverting this number shows that one cubic centimeter of dissolved calcite is contained in 12.7 liters of this water.

---

then enters an air-filled cave, some of the CO_2 escapes into the cave atmosphere by a reversal of Reactions 5.5–5.7. As a result, the water cannot hold as much Ca^{2+} and CO_3^{2-} and may become supersaturated with calcite. If so, some of the dissolved calcite precipitates as stalactites and other speleothems in a reversal of Reaction 5.4. So the process that forms many mineral deposits in caves is the opposite of what dissolves the caves in the first place.

Dolomite dissolves in nearly the same way as calcite:

$$CaMg(CO_3)_2 + 2H^+ \rightleftharpoons Ca^{2+} + Mg^{2+} + 2HCO_3^- \quad (5.9)$$

Dolomite is less soluble than calcite in concentration of dissolved molecules, but at temperatures below about 50°C it is slightly *more* soluble than calcite in terms of rock *volume* and parts per million (Figure 5.3). The solubilities of rock salt and gypsum increase with temperature, but calcite, dolomite, and anhydrite are *less* soluble as the temperature rises. Water that is rich in dissolved limestone and dolomite is popularly known as **hard water**. Heating

it causes calcium carbonate to precipitate, which can eventually clog pipes and water heaters.

pH

The **pH** of water is a measure of its H^+ concentration*, which indicates the amount of acidity (Figure 5.4). More precisely, pH indicates the H^+ *activity*, or *effective* concentration, which is slightly less than the true concentration. A pH of 7 at 25° C indicates neutral conditions, neither acid nor basic. At that pH, the H^+ activity is 0.0000001, or 10^{-7} moles/liter. At a pH of 4, $H^+ = 10^{-4}$ moles/liter, and so on. So a *decrease* of one pH unit indicates a ten-fold *increase* in acidity. As carbonate rocks dissolve, the pH rises, because H^+ is consumed by Reactions 5.4 and 5.9.

Pure rainwater has a pH of about 5.6. It is slightly acidic because of the carbon dioxide picked up from the atmosphere. As water passes through the soil it absorbs enough additional

---

* Most of the H^+ ions combine with water to produce H_3O^+ (hydronium ion), but for simplicity nearly everyone assumes that they are all H^+.

Figure 5.4: Measuring the pH of karst spring water.

CO_2 to bring the pH down to about 4.5–4.8. Such acidic water attacks limestone and dolomite vigorously. But as the concentration of dissolved rock increases, acid is consumed and the pH rises. One might expect the process to stop when the pH reaches the neutral value of 7, but the attraction between H^+ and CO_3^{2-} in Reaction 5.8 is so strong that, in most water, H^+ continues to be used up until the pH rises well above 7, into the alkaline (basic) realm. Most karst water, even if it is not yet saturated with dissolved carbonate minerals, has pH values between 7 and 8. The exact pH depends mainly on the concentrations of carbon dioxide and dissolved calcite and dolomite in the water.

Dissolution of carbonate minerals by Reactions 5.4 and 5.9 releases bicarbonate (HCO_3^-). Meanwhile, Reactions 5.5–5.7 provide a second source of bicarbonate. Therefore, in most karst water, the concentration of bicarbonate is roughly twice the amount of dissolved calcite, plus four times the amount of dissolved dolomite (all in moles/liter).

During the first 10–15% of limestone or dolomite dissolution, the pH rises rapidly to around 6.5 or 7 (Figure 5.5). From there on the pH rises much more slowly. Near saturation, as H^+ continues to be consumed by rock dissolution, additional H^+ is released by the breakdown of bicarbonate (Reaction 5.8). Under these conditions bicarbonate is thousands of times more abundant than either H^+ or CO_3^{2-}, so the slight loss of bicarbonate is nearly unmeasurable. Still, this tiny release of H^+ is enough to limit the rise in pH.

In this way, bicarbonate in high concentration acts as a ***buffer*** that resists changes in pH. Addition of acid (H^+) converts some of the bicarbonate to H_2CO_3. Addition of a base (OH^-) causes some of the bicarbonate to break down into CO_3^{2-} and H_2O. As a result, neither the acid nor the base has much effect on changing the pH. Thus it is necessary to measure pH very precisely in karst waters if accurate calculations of P_{CO_2} and saturation levels are to be made. An error of 0.05 pH unit gives an error of roughly 10% in calculating either of these variables.

Undersaturation and supersaturation

To tell whether water is able to dissolve or precipitate a mineral, it is necessary to find whether the water is undersaturated or supersaturated with that mineral. It is also helpful to know exactly how undersaturated or supersaturated the water is. Then it is possible to estimate how much more mineral the water can dissolve, or, if the water is supersaturated, roughly how much it can precipitate. Because limestone is composed mainly of calcite, the amount of calcite undersaturation is a measure of the water's potential for forming caves in that rock.

Rates of dissolution or precipitation can also be estimated from this kind of information. The more undersaturated the water is with a mineral, the faster the mineral can dissolve. The greater the supersaturation, the faster it can precipitate. These topics are discussed later in this chapter, and in Chapters 7 and 10.

Concentration and activity

Before the amount of saturation can be estimated, it is necessary to examine the idea of chemical activity in more detail (see section on ***pH***). The ***concentration*** of a dissolved substance refers to the actual amount in solution. This is what is measured by a chemical analysis. The ***activity*** of that substance refers to how concentrated it *behaves*.

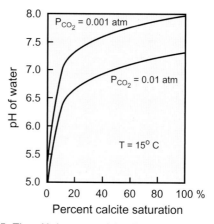

Figure 5.5: The pH rises as calcite dissolves. Note the abrupt slowing of the rise as the solution exceeds about 10% saturation, and also how much of the dissolution takes place at pH > 7. At 15°C, calcite saturation = 86 ppm at P_{CO_2} = 0.001 atm (typical of well-aerated caves), and 195 ppm at P_{CO_2} = 0.01 atm (typical of poorly aerated caves). The graph is approximately the same for dolomite dissolution.

A 5-person basketball team is very effective. A 10-person team would be more effective, but certainly not twice as much. The players would interfere with each other. The same is true in a solution. As more calcite dissolves in water, the calcite behaves as though it were less concentrated than it really is. For that reason, more calcite can dissolve than one would calculate on the basis of concentration alone. This is true for any mineral that produces ions when it dissolves.

Some materials, such as quartz, produce mainly uncharged molecules when they dissolve. Most gases behave in the same way. As ions are added from other sources, the solubilities of quartz and gases *decrease* slightly.

Mineral solubility

To determine the tendency for calcite to dissolve or precipitate, it is necessary to refer to Reaction 5.3. At equilibrium, where calcite has reached perfect saturation, the amount of dissolved calcite can be expressed by

$$(Ca^{2+})(CO_3^{2-}) = K_{calcite} \qquad (5.10)$$

where (Ca^{2+}) = calcium ion activity, (CO_3^{2-}) = carbonate ion activity, and $K_{calcite}$ is the equilibrium constant for the reaction. (Ca^{2+}) x (CO_3^{2-}) is the *ion activity product*, abbreviated *IAP*. The K for any dissolved substance varies with temperature. For example, $K_{calcite}$ = 5.5 x 10^{-9} at 10°C and 3.3 x 10^{-9} at 25°C (note the decrease with temperature). Typical K values for minerals, and the methods for calculating them, are given by Drever (1997) and Faure (1998).

If IAP is less than K, the mineral is undersaturated. Dissolution stops when IAP = K. If IAP is greater than K, the mineral is supersaturated. The same is true for any other mineral, although the ions and K values are almost always different. Aragonite, another form of $CaCO_3$, is slightly more soluble than calcite and has a higher K value.

In typical groundwater, calcite must be more than about 110–120% saturated for it to precipitate. Smaller amounts of supersaturation can persist without causing calcite to precipitate. The required amount of supersaturation decreases with temperature.

Reactions 5.3 and 5.5–5.8 and many related ones also take part in the equilibrium, and each has its own equilibrium constant. All of these items are interdependent and rely on calculations of ion activities, so the resulting tangle is best unraveled with computer software (see section on *Chemical field studies*, pages 135–136). Even without calculations, the concepts can still be applied to the interpretation of caves.

The saturation index

In Eq. 5.10, if IAP < K, the solution is undersaturated, so IAP/K < 1. Likewise, if the solution is supersaturated, IAP/K > 1, and in a solution exactly at saturation, IAP/K = 1. This relationship can be applied to the solubility of any mineral by multiplying together the activities of all the ions

it produces (= IAP) and dividing by the appropriate K value. This gives the *saturation index* (**SI**) for the mineral:

$$SI = IAP/K \qquad (5.11a)$$

where IAP = ion activity product. The solution is saturated at SI = 1. SI < 1 indicates undersaturation and SI > 1 indicates supersaturation. This is the simplest form of SI, but it is more often calculated by

$$SI = \log(IAP/K) \qquad (5.11b)$$

In this case, a saturated solution is indicated by SI = 0. Negative SI indicates undersaturation, and positive SI indicates supersaturation. This way the SI values can more conveniently span a large numerical range. Also, in tables of data it is easier to distinguish between + and − values than between numbers greater or less than 1.

If a mineral produces more than two ions, it is appropriate to adjust the SI in Eq. 5.11b by multiplying it by $2/n$, where n is the number of ions released by each molecule. The calculation of SI becomes

$$SI = (2/n) \log (IAP/K) \qquad (5.11c)$$

For example, when dolomite dissolves, each molecule breaks into 4 ions (Reaction 5.9). The interpretation of SI from Eq. 5.11a or 11b is still valid, but with n = 4 in Eq. 5.11c the SI value for dolomite will be more comparable with that of calcite. This is how the SI values were calculated for the list of typical cave waters at the end of this chapter (page 137). Without this correction, water that is 50% saturated with calcite would have a calcite SI of roughly −0.8 (Eq. 5.11b), but if the solution also happens to be 50% saturated with dolomite, the dolomite SI would be roughly −1.6. This gives the false impression that dolomite is far more undersaturated than calcite. Eq. 5.11c gives SI = −0.8 for both calcite and dolomite. Whenever SI is reported, it is important to specify how it was calculated.

The saturation ratio

In a solution that is undersaturated with calcite, the percentage of calcite saturation can be estimated in a crude but simple way by measuring the calcium concentration in the solution, adding powdered calcite, and then leaving the container open to the local atmosphere for a couple of weeks. The new Ca concentration is then measured to see how much more has dissolved (Ca concentration = calcite concentration in moles/L). The ratio of original to final calcium concentration is the approximate *saturation ratio*:

$$\text{Saturation ratio} = C/C_s \qquad (5.12)$$

where C is the concentration of the mineral in solution, and C_s is its saturation concentration. A similar relationship applies to any mineral, although most (like dolomite and quartz) react too slowly to be measured in the way described for calcite. Measurement of C/C_s may be inaccurate because of other components and interactions in the solution. It also does not work for supersaturated solutions because of the residual supersaturation that persists after precipitation has ceased. Undersaturation and supersaturation are more easily quantified by the saturation index.

Despite the virtues of the saturation index (SI), the saturation ratio of Statement 5.12 is an easier concept to grasp and is usually preferred for describing measurements of dissolution rate. For this purpose the saturation ratio is usually calculated by comparing measured concentrations to calculated equilibrium values, rather than by the powder method. For calcite, C/C_s is approximately related to SI by

$$C/C_s \approx (IAP/K)^{0.35} \qquad (5.13)$$

where IAP/K is the simplest form of SI, from Eq. 5.11a. For dolomite, the exponent is 0.175 (i.e., 0.35 ÷ 2).

Epigenic and hypogenic acids

Carbonic acid from soil CO_2 is an example of an *epigenic* acid — one that is derived from a source at or near the land surface. What makes soil CO_2 especially effective in forming caves in underlying limestone or dolomite is that the gas is constantly being replenished by microbial activity, so it is not used up as the rock dissolves. *Epigenic caves* are formed by the underground movement of CO_2-rich water from the land surface to springs in nearby valleys. On a worldwide basis they account for roughly 80–85% of all explored caves, although this percentage varies with location.

Organic acids in the soil are also epigenic. They contribute to cave origin, especially in warm climates, but their overall effect is not well known (see page 124). Acids from bat and bird droppings can also dissolve bedrock if they are sufficiently concentrated. Other epigenic acids include sulfuric and nitric acids from the atmosphere. In the past century they have increased greatly as the result of industry and traffic. They also contribute slightly to bedrock dissolution, but their additional effect beyond that of soil CO_2 is usually small.

Hypogenic acids originate deep beneath the surface, and they too can form caves. For example, volcanic gases often include CO_2 and hydrogen sulfide (H_2S). If carbonate rocks are heated above several hundred degrees Celsius, high concentrations of CO_2 and carbonic acid are produced. The same result can occur when carbonate rocks are metamorphosed in the presence of other rock types. Carbon dioxide and organic acids can be generated at high temperature by conversion of organic material into petroleum. These processes can increase the porosity of limestone and dolomite in oilfields (Kharaka and others, 1986). Hypogenic P_{CO_2} can be as high as several atmospheres, which is much greater than epigenic P_{CO_2}.

Hydrogen sulfide and its byproducts are the most potent agents in producing hypogenic caves. H_2S is the gas responsible for what is popularly known as *sulfur water*. It tastes and smells terrible but is rarely concentrated enough to be harmful. Even in small quantities H_2S has the distinctive smell of rotten eggs. At high concentrations it is a deadly poison. Most of it forms below the surface in rocks or sediments that contain sulfur or sulfates (such as gypsum) in combination with organic carbon compounds. The most common deep subsurface source of carbon is petroleum. There is some evidence that methane (CH_4) can also serve as a carbon source (Kirkland and Evans, 1976). H_2S is generated only where oxygen is very sparse. The sulfur compounds are reduced to hydrogen sulfide, while the carbon oxidizes to bicarbonate or carbonic acid. *Reduction* of a substance is the transfer of electrons to that material. *Oxidation* of a substance is the removal of electrons from it. The two processes occur simultaneously, so the exchange is balanced. These are known as *redox* reactions.

Reduction of sulfate typically takes place as follows:

$$\boxed{\begin{array}{l}\text{dissolved gypsum} \\ \text{or anhydrite + carbon} \\ \text{compounds } + \text{ H}_2\text{O}\end{array}} \longrightarrow H_2S + Ca^{2+} + HCO_3^-$$

$$(5.14)$$

H_2S production can be observed at close range in gypsum caves that contain stagnant pools replenished periodically by organic-rich streams.

Dissolved hydrogen sulfide is a mild acid:

$$H_2S \rightleftharpoons H^+ + HS^- \qquad (5.15)$$

and by itself it can dissolve almost as much limestone and dolomite as can carbonic acid. But H_2S forms in an environment where water is already likely to be saturated with calcite and dolomite. To dissolve these minerals further, hydrogen sulfide must usually migrate elsewhere.

Minor porosity can be produced by the acid released when H_2S reacts with dissolved metals, as in

$$H_2S + Fe^{2+} \longrightarrow 2H^+ + FeS \qquad (5.16)$$

FeS eventually recrystallizes to FeS_2 (the mineral pyrite, popularly known as "fool's gold"). In deep, highly mineralized groundwater, the highest concentrations of dissolved metals are often present as soluble complexes in combination with chloride (Hanor, 1996).

Iron sulfide also forms when iron oxide is reduced by organic compounds in the presence of sulfate. Instead of acid, this produces an alkaline solution that tends to be supersaturated with carbonate minerals (Surdam and others, 1993).

H_2S is abundant deep beneath the surface, but it forms caves mainly in the few places where it is brought to the surface by rising water. This highly focused style of cave development is quite unlike the widespread action of epigenic carbonic acid. Hypogenic acids may rise at erratic rates as a result of tectonic disturbances or by squeezing of sediments in deep basins by the weight of overlying strata.

In some places these acids leak to the surface slowly and continuously, for example where circulating groundwater follows deep paths and carries the acids upward to springs.

At depth, most hypogenic gases are carried in solution, rather than as bubbles. As the transporting water rises toward the water table, the confining pressure decreases and some of the dissolved gases can bubble out of solution, in the same way that carbon dioxide does from a carbonated beverage. The depth at which bubbles can form depends on the concentration of the dissolved gas and its solubility in water (page 217).

If dissolved hydrogen sulfide comes in contact with oxygen, these two gases react to form sulfuric acid. This is an extremely powerful cave-forming agent. Sulfuric acid is almost entirely in the form $(2H^+ + SO_4^{2-})$ or, at very low pH, $(H^+ + HSO_4^-)$. The conversion from hydrogen sulfide takes place in one or more steps:

$$2H_2S + O_2 \longrightarrow 2S + 2H_2O \qquad (5.17)$$

$$2S + 3O_2 + 2H_2O \longrightarrow 4H^+ + 2SO_4^{2-} \qquad (5.18)$$

or in the following way where certain sulfur-oxidizing bacteria facilitate the process:

$$H_2S + 2O_2 \longrightarrow 2H^+ + SO_4^{2-} \qquad (5.19)$$

H_2S can also oxidize partially to SO_2, which eventually oxidizes further to SO_3 and still further to sulfuric acid.

In the H_2S-rich Cueva de Villa Luz, Mexico, the water and air compositions vary widely and often rapidly. The water contains up to 700 ppm H_2S and P_{CO_2} up to 0.3 atm. In the cave atmosphere as much as 210 ppm of H_2S and 0.035 atm of CO_2 have been measured (Hose and others, 2000). These are minimum values, as both exceeded the limit of the instruments. The gases sulfur dioxide (SO_2) and carbon monoxide (CO) have been measured at around 35 and 85 ppm respectively.

Most of these processes can also be observed at sulfur springs, where H_2S-rich water encounters oxygen at the surface. These reactions form caves only where oxygen is able to mix with the sulfide-rich water inside a carbonate aquifer, before the water emerges at springs. Although many are shallow, caves of this sort are considered hypogenic because they depend on H_2S, which forms at depth and has little relation to the overlying surface.

Several minerals are byproducts of sulfuric acid cave origin. Gypsum is by far the most common. It forms where the acid is fairly concentrated, especially if the water already contains some dissolved gypsum. The most common reaction is:

$$CaCO_3 + H^+ + SO_4^{2-} + 2H_2O \rightleftharpoons$$
$$CaSO_4 \cdot 2H_2O + HCO_3^- \quad (5.20)$$

Dolomite reacts in a similar way. The resulting gypsum often forms a crust that replaces the original bedrock (Figure 5.6).

Figure 5.6: Gypsum crystals growing on a limestone surface, Grotta del Fiume, Italy, as described by Reaction 5.20. The droplets on the crystal tips are sulfuric acid with a pH of about 1.0.

Gypsum can precipitate even in fairly acidic water, but at pH below about 2, sulfate is consumed in the following way:

$$SO_4^{2-} + H^+ \rightleftharpoons HSO_4^- \qquad (5.21)$$

and, as a result, more gypsum may dissolve to replace it. Anhydrite $(CaSO_4)$ is affected in a similar way but is not often exposed to such high acidity.

Local reduction takes place in the organic-rich mud that floors the streams of some sulfide caves, to produce fine-grained FeS and FeS$_2$. This process is active in the sediment of the main stream passage in Cueva de Villa Luz. When the sediment is exposed to air while it is still moist, the production of gypsum can be viewed in action right under the microscope.

When sulfuric acid attacks the clay in shaly beds, several rare but significant minerals are produced (Polyak and Provencio, 2001). **Alunite** $(KAl_3(SO_4)_2(OH)_6)$ is the most important, because it can be used to determine the age of sulfuric acid cave development (Chapter 13). ***Hydrated halloysite***, also known as ***endellite*** $(Al_2Si_2O_5(OH)_4 \cdot 2H_2O)$, is a distinctive waxy clay that is brilliant white or light blue, and less commonly other colors. It also provides evidence of former sulfuric acid. Other common byproducts of clay breakdown in strong acid are quartz (crystalline SiO_2), chert (microcrystalline SiO_2) and non-crystalline opal $(SiO_2 \cdot nH_2O$, where n = several possible numbers). They tend to accumulate in the pore spaces of surrounding bedrock.

Incomplete oxidation of hydrogen sulfide (Reaction 5.17) can produce sulfur. Sulfur is most stable in acidic solutions, and because acid is easily neutralized by limestone or dolomite, sulfur tends to concentrate on non-carbonate materials such as gypsum.

Sulfuric acid can also be produced by oxidation of iron sulfides. One of several possible reactions is

$$4FeS_2 + 15O_2 + 14H_2O \longrightarrow 4Fe(OH)_3 + 16H^+ + 8SO_4^{2-} \quad (5.22)$$

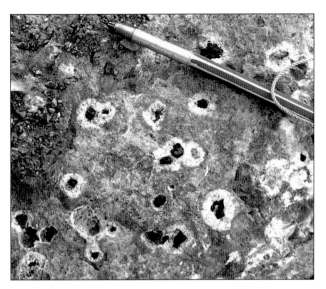

Figure 5.7: Pyrite crystals have oxidized to iron oxides in this weathered limestone in Indiana. Sulfuric acid released by the reaction has bleached the surrounding limestone. In a drier environment, gypsum would grow in the reaction zone.

A field example is shown in Figure 5.7. Although the oxygen comes from the surface, the resulting sulfuric acid may be considered hypogenic because, like H_2S, the pyrite forms in oxygen-poor zones below the surface. This source of sulfuric acid rarely produces more than scattered porosity, although some significant caves have been attributed to this process (Morehouse, 1968). Brazil's largest cave, Toca da Boa Vista, is thought to have formed, at least partly, in this way (Auler and Smart, 2003).

A related topic is ***acid mine drainage***, which is caused by the speading of pyrite-rich mining wastes on the land surface. The pyrite rapidly oxidizes to sulfuric acid and iron hydroxides, which contaminate surface streams with acidic water and yellow or red bacterial slime. The acidic water can quickly form or enlarge karst features in carbonate rocks. These rocks in turn help to neutralize the acid.

The mineral ***siderite*** ($FeCO_3$) also forms in oxygen-poor environments. When exposed to shallow groundwater it produces carbonic acid, which can form caves in surrounding carbonate rocks (Kempe, 1982):

$$4FeCO_3 + O_2 + 4H_2O \longrightarrow 4H^+ + 4HCO_3^- + 2Fe_2O_3 \quad (5.23)$$

Hypogenic caves are most common in arid regions, where dissolution is not dominated by acids from the surface. But there are excellent examples of hypogenic caves in humid regions as well, and it is likely that many others have been later enlarged and modified by epigenic carbonic acid. Certain caves have clearly been formed by a combination of acids from both sources (see page 226). The distinction is complicated by the fact that carbonic acid is produced both at the surface and at depth. Where the exact source is unclear, it is appropriate simply to describe the local details rather than force the caves into artificial categories.

Chemical interactions

The chemical reactions described in this chapter rarely take place alone. When a rock or mineral dissolves, it affects all other dissolved materials in the water. Some of these interactions can have a major influence on cave origin.

Open and closed systems

Where carbonic acid from the soil dissolves underlying limestone or dolomite, the CO_2 consumed by this process is readily replaced from the nearby soil. This is an ***open system*** with respect to the carbon dioxide. Even where bedrock dissolution extends to considerable depth, the open fissures that connect with the soil still allow enough CO_2 transfer to keep the water more or less replenished (Atkinson, 1977a). Oxidation of organic material carried down from the surface can also sustain carbonic acid levels (Wood and Petraitis, 1984).

But after water enters the phreatic zone, there is no longer a nearby source of CO_2 and any that is lost by bedrock dissolution is not readily replaced. This is an example of a ***closed system*** with respect to CO_2. There is actually a continuous range between open and closed systems, and as water moves through the ground the conditions are frequently shifting between the two extremes.

In an open system, water can dissolve more limestone or dolomite than in a closed system (Figure 5.8). But in most karst areas the water first dissolves bedrock under essentially open conditions above the water table and then continues dissolving under essentially closed conditions below the water table. There is no abrupt decrease in either the solubility or the solution rate when water passes from vadose to phreatic conditions, because most water entering the phreatic zone carries with it a high level of CO_2, which is used up slowly from then on. An example is given in ***A chemical cave tour*** on pages 131–134.

If infiltrating water first seeps through insoluble rock (such as quartz sandstone) it may become isolated from

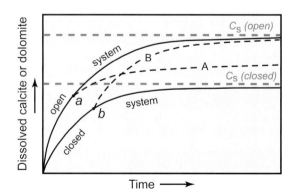

Figure 5.8: Contrast between open and closed systems for dissolution of calcite or dolomite in a carbonic acid solution. Both paths start at the same P_{CO_2} and follow the solid lines if there is no change in the status of the system. Variants: At ***a***, the open system becomes closed to further CO_2 uptake and follows path **A**. At ***b***, the closed system becomes open to the CO_2-rich atmosphere of the open system and follows path **B**.

the CO_2 supply in the soil before it reaches limestone or dolomite. If so, dissolution of the soluble rock takes place in an essentially closed system from the very start. This causes the CO_2 level to drop sharply and the pH to rise. If this water continues on into an air-filled cave, CO_2 is rapidly absorbed and the pH drops, which causes a burst of solutional activity that can deeply etch the cave walls (Chapter 12).

Effect of concentration of dissolved components

If salt is added to water, limestone and dolomite become *more* soluble. The increase in the number of ions causes the activities of all ions to fall well below their concentrations. According to Eqs. 5.11a–5.11c, the SI values for all minerals in the water will decrease, except for the salt that is being added to the solution. Any ions in the water will have this effect on any mineral, as long as there are no ions in common. For example, the Na^+ and Cl^- from salt do not match the Ca^{2+} and CO_3^{2-} from calcite. The sodium and chloride ions interfere with the ability of calcium and carbonate to link together to form calcite, so that more calcite can dissolve than in fresh water (Figure 5.9).

The common-ion effect

If two dissolved minerals each produce one or more of the same ions, the solubility of each mineral *decreases*. This is the ***common-ion effect***.

For example, limestone ($CaCO_3$) and gypsum ($CaSO_4 \cdot 2H_2O$) both release Ca^{2+} when they dissolve. As a result, each becomes less soluble than if it were alone. If groundwater first passes through limestone, approaches saturation with calcite, and then encounters gypsum, the water rapidly dissolves the gypsum, which is about 10 times more soluble than calcite in typical groundwater. The influx of Ca^{2+} from the gypsum drives the water to supersaturation with calcite, and some of the calcite is forced to precipitate (Figure 5.10). Deposits of calcite are common at springs fed by this kind of water (Figure 5.11). If the sequence is reversed, where calcite is added to a gypsum-rich solution, the process is similar but subdued. Very little calcite can dissolve because of the high Ca^{2+} already in the water, and the effect on gypsum is very small.

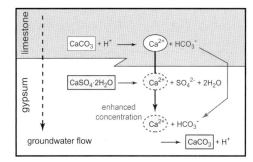

Figure 5.10: An example of the common-ion effect. As the water moves downward, limestone first dissolves to produce a solution nearly saturated with calcite. When the water encounters gypsum, the gypsum rapidly dissolves, and the addition of more calcium forces some calcite to precipitate.

The common-ion effect between calcite ($CaCO_3$) and dolomite ($CaMg(CO_3)_2$) is more complex than in the previous example, because each mineral releases both Ca^{2+} and CO_3^{2-}. In fact, the dissolution of dolomite alone can bring the water roughly to saturation with calcite. If the water already contains dissolved calcite, adding dolomite may force some of the calcite to precipitate.

The same is true for the dissolution of anhydrite at low temperatures (below about 60°C). It and gypsum both produce Ca^{2+} and SO_4^{2-} when they dissolve, but gypsum is less soluble. As anhydrite approaches saturation, gypsum becomes supersaturated and tends to precipitate.

Perhaps the most extreme example of the common-ion effect in cave origin is the interaction among limestone,

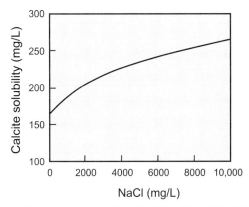

Figure 5.9: Increase in calcite solubility with salinity (NaCl concentration), at 25°C and $P_{CO_2} = 0.01$ atm. Note that the vertical scale begins at 100 mg/L, not zero.

Figure 5.11: Deposits of limestone (travertine) in a surface stream fed by a sulfate-rich spring, Chiapas, Mexico.

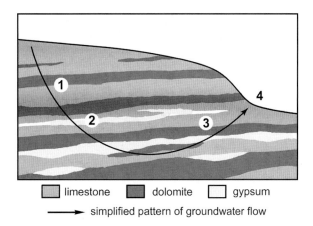

limestone   dolomite   gypsum

⟶ simplified pattern of groundwater flow

Figure 5.12: Where groundwater moves through interbedded limestone, dolomite, and gypsum (or anhydrite), the following reactions take place: (1) Calcite dissolves rapidly and approaches saturation. Dolomite dissolves more slowly. (2) Water encounters gypsum and dissolves it very rapidly, forcing calcite to supersaturation by the common-ion effect. Calcite begins to precipitate, which allows more dolomite to dissolve. (3) Dolomite and gypsum continue to dissolve along the entire remaining flow route, while calcite precipitates. (4) At springs the water is still supersaturated with calcite, so calcite tends to precipitate as tufa or travertine. Precipitation is speeded by CO_2 loss to the air. These processes are most significant where sulfate rocks are the last of the three to be encountered (typical of humid regions).

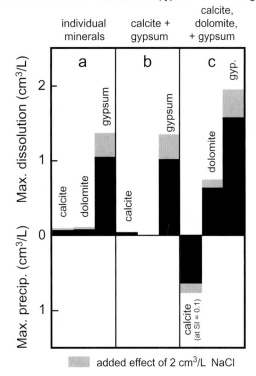

added effect of 2 cm³/L NaCl

Figure 5.13: Solubilities of calcite, dolomite, and gypsum: (**a**) as individual minerals at 15°C and $P_{CO_2} = 0.01$ atm; (**b**) in a mixture of calcite and gypsum (both become less soluble); (**c**) where water first encounters calcite and dolomite, and then gypsum (both dolomite and gypsum become more soluble as calcite is forced to precipitate). Shaded areas show the effect of 2 cm³/liter (0.074 moles/L) of dissolved NaCl. In **c**, calcite is held at SI = 0.1 to account for the supersaturation required to precipitate it. (From Palmer and Palmer, 2004.)

dolomite, and sulfate rocks (Figures 5.12–5.13). The sulfates can include either gypsum or anhydrite. Gypsum is used in the following example, but anhydrite can serve just as well. The process operates like this:

As water infiltrates from the surface, calcite ($CaCO_3$) is usually the first mineral to approach saturation. Dolomite ($CaMg(CO_3)_2$) dissolves more slowly. If gypsum ($CaSO_4 \cdot 2H_2O$) is then encountered, its dissolution adds a great deal of calcium to the solution because gypsum is much more soluble than either calcite or dolomite. Calcite is forced to precipitate by the common-ion effect. But this is only the beginning.

As calcite precipitates, it removes some calcium and bicarbonate from solution. This reduces the saturation ratios of *both* dolomite and gypsum and allows more of them to dissolve. Compared to the solubilities of gypsum and dolomite alone, up to 1.5 times more gypsum can dissolve, and up to 7 *times* more dolomite. The effect is even greater if the water is also saline. Figure 5.13 shows the combined effects of mixing limestone, dolomite, and gypsum in typical groundwater conditions.

Because dolomite dissolves very slowly as it nears saturation, these solutional processes are drawn out over long flow distances. None of them rely on the production of acid. The only requirement is for groundwater to remain in contact with both dolomite and gypsum, at least intermittently. If dolomite becomes nearly saturated before the water encounters gypsum, these processes will still take place even if limestone is not present.

The precipitated calcite is composed mainly of the calcium and carbonate produced by gypsum and dolomite, which are greater than the amounts produced by the original calcite dissolution. This calcite occupies less than one third of the volume of the dissolved gypsum and dolomite, so there can be considerable porosity as a byproduct. The remaining water is enriched in both magnesium and sulfate.

This little-known process may have a profound effect on the earliest stages of cave development. It has been documented in only a few areas (e.g., around the Black Hills in South Dakota by Back and others, 1983; in Spain by Bischoff and others, 1994; in Oklahoma by Dewars, 1997; and in New York State by Taylor, 2000), but it appears to be much more widespread than originally thought. Interbedded limestone and dolomite are common in many gypsum areas, such as the plains of eastern New Mexico. This process may allow gypsum caves in these areas to reach greater lengths than would otherwise be possible. It can also help to initiate cave development along deep flow systems in carbonate rocks by enhancing the original permeability over long and continuous paths. It is interesting to note that high sulfate levels are present in a large percentage of karst springs that drain extensive regional aquifers (Worthington, 1994).

Mixing dissolution

The greater the amount of carbon dioxide in water, the more dissolved calcite or dolomite the water can hold. But this

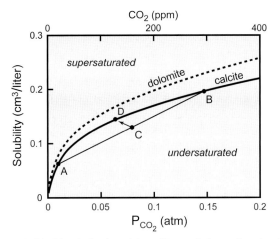

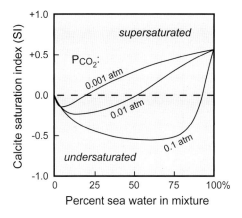

Figure 5.14: Dissolution by mixing of two solutions of contrasting CO_2 content for calcite and dolomite at a typical groundwater temperature of 15°C. Because the curves are convex upward, mixing of two waters of contrasting P_{CO_2} reduces the saturation index of either mineral. For example, A and B are each saturated with calcite, but at different CO_2 levels. A mixture of the two falls below the saturation line and produces an undersaturated solution. A 1:1 mixture of A and B produces C. The resulting dissolution progresses toward D along a sloping line because CO_2 is consumed as the mineral dissolves.

Figure 5.15: Variation in calcite saturation where fresh water mixes with sea water. Both initial solutions are assumed to be saturated with calcite. Calcite becomes undersaturated when mixed with a small proportion of sea water but becomes supersaturated with larger proportions of sea water. P_{CO_2} values apply only to the fresh water. Temperature = 15°C. Zones of undersaturation diminish with increasing temperature. The effect on dolomite is similar, although the curves differ in shape. (After Plummer, 1975.)

is not a straight-line relationship. In Figure 5.3 the solubility plot is logarithmic, to allow it to span a wide range of values, and that makes the graph look almost straight. On a plot with linear scales (Figure 5.14), the slopes of the saturation curves for both calcite and dolomite clearly decrease as CO_2 content increases. When mixing takes place between two saturated waters that fall on different parts of the curve, the resulting mixture is able to dissolve more limestone or dolomite than either of the original solutions (Laptev, 1939; Bögli, 1964). Aragonite has a similar solubility curve, but it has little significance for cave origin.

In Figure 5.14, consider two different solutions, each near saturation with dissolved calcite, but with contrasting CO_2 values (e.g., A and B). A mixture of the two waters must fall somewhere on the line A–B, which lies *below* the saturation curve. The resulting solution can dissolve additional calcite.

If equal portions of the two waters mix, the mixture would fall on point C in Figure 5.14. If the system is closed, dissolution of each molecule of calcite consumes a molecule of CO_2. On the graph, further progress toward saturation is not vertically upward. Instead, as the aggressiveness is used up, the calcite concentration follows the sloping line from **C** and reaches saturation at point D.

The mixing effect is greatest if the two initial solutions span the steep part of the saturation curve. The effect is diminished if either solution (or both) is supersaturated.

In closed systems this process also applies to differences in H_2S concentration. It does not work in gypsum or rock salt, because their solubilities do not depend on dissolved gases.

Mixing between fresh water and sea water has a more complex result. A mixture of fresh water with a small

amount of seawater usually reduces the saturation levels of calcite, aragonite, and dolomite, making them dissolve more readily; but large proportions of seawater drive the mixture to supersaturation (Figure 5.15). Mixing of fresh water and sea water often involves a contrast in CO_2 content as well as in salinity. CO_2 is usually more abundant in fresh groundwater than in seawater. Figure 5.15 suggests that the CO_2 content may have as great an effect as salinity in controlling freshwater-seawater mixing dissolution.

Two water sources rarely mix in equal proportion. Usually one is much less abundant, and its rate of inflow is what controls the dissolution rate. In small openings that support only laminar flow, mixing takes place mainly by diffusion of chemical components through the water, rather than by physical mixing of the two water types. As the openings grow larger, mixing may be enhanced by turbulence and convection. The rates of mixing and dissolution often vary with time according to fluctuating inflow rates of the initial solutions.

Figure 5.14 shows that the boost in aggressiveness caused by mixing is usually small. But the amount of dissolution is not as important as *where* it takes place. In many places, dissolution caused by mixing occurs well beneath the surface, where its effect is concentrated on forming caves and solutional pores, instead of on lowering the bedrock surface. Because the renewal of aggressiveness is unrelated to the overlying land surface, many people view mixing-zone caves as hypogenic, even if the original acid source is epigenic CO_2 (page 209).

Mixing of waters of different *temperature* has a *negative* effect on dissolution. The saturation concentrations of dissolved carbonate minerals *increase* because their relation to temperature follows curves that are convex downward (Figure 5.16). Even so, water sources of different temperature usually differ in chemistry as well (e.g., in CO_2 content), and this difference frequently overwhelms the negative

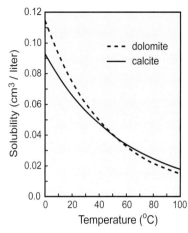

Figure 5.16: Variation in calcite and dolomite solubility with temperature.

temperature effect and makes the mixture aggressive. On the other hand, if hot water is rich in organic acids, mixing with cooler water may force calcite to precipitate, as shown in the following section.

Cave origin by mixing of different water sources is described in detail in Chapter 8.

Influence of organic acids

Organic acids are present in the soil and are also produced at depth by the reaction of oxides or sulfates with organic compounds such as those in petroleum (Surdam and others, 1984; Kharaka and others, 1986). Among the most common products are *acetic acid* and *formic acid*, which can greatly enhance the solubility of carbonate rocks (Trudgill, 1976; Meshri, 1986). Calcium and magnesium can also form complexes with organic compounds, which tends to lower the saturation index of calcite and dolomite. Analysis of total Ca and Mg in solution may overestimate the saturation indices unless these complexes are taken into account.

At temperatures below about 80°C, concentrations of organic acids are limited because bacteria readily metabolize them to carbon dioxide (Carothers and Kharaka, 1978). Under these conditions the net effect of organic compounds on karst and caves is uncertain. At higher temperatures the organic acids tend not to be metabolized by bacteria and appear to have great influence on both carbonate dissolution and precipitation. The origin and mineralization of certain hypogenic caves may be affected in this way.

Dissolution of calcite by acetic acid (CH_3COOH) takes place as follows:

$$CH_3COOH + CaCO_3 \rightleftharpoons CaCH_3COO^+ + HCO_3^- \quad (5.24)$$

At temperatures above ~120°C, organic acids become chemically unstable and break down to CO_2 and CH_4 (methane). High hydrostatic pressure at great depth can prevent this water from boiling. The following reactions for acetic acid are typical (Surdam and others, 1984):

$$CH_3COOH \longrightarrow CO_2 + CH_4 \quad (5.25)$$

$$CaCH_3COO^+ + H_2O \longrightarrow Ca^{2+} + HCO_3^- + CH_4 \quad (5.26)$$

Production of CO_2 by Reaction 5.25 has the potential to form carbonic acid and to dissolve more carbonate rock. Where $CaCH_3COO^+$ is present, however, it acts as a pH buffer that partly neutralizes the carbonic acid:

$$CaCH_3COO^+ + H^+ \rightleftharpoons Ca^{2+} + CH_3COOH \quad (5.27)$$

In addition, $CaCH_3COO^+$ partly dissociates to Ca^{2+} and CH_3COO^-, and the CH_3COO^- also helps to neutralize acid. The consumption of H^+ and release of Ca^{2+} (Reaction 5.27) force calcite to precipitate (a reversal of Reaction 5.4).

As organic acids continue to break down at temperatures above ~120°C, they become less concentrated and their buffering activity diminishes. The pH is lowered by further production of CO_2 by Reactions such as 5.25, and carbonate rocks begin to dissolve once more (Surdam and others, 1984).

So, when petroleum is progressively heated at depth, the probable sequence is (1) an increase in carbonate solubility as organic acids are produced, (2) precipitation of calcite as organic acids break down, and (3) further carbonate dissolution as the organic acids are depleted and no longer serve as pH buffers. Dissolution and precipitation can take place simultaneously in different areas depending on temperature distribution. Certain ore minerals can precipitate during these steps, even while the bedrock is dissolving (Chapter 15). If hot organic-rich waters rise from depth and mix with cold fresh water, calcite may precipitate because of bacterial degradation of organic acids as the temperature drops (MacGowan and others, 1994).

Dissolution rates

Cave origin depends not only on the *amount* of rock that can dissolve in water, but also the *rate* at which it dissolves. This topic is covered in Chapter 7, and only a brief outline is given here.

In general the most soluble rocks dissolve fastest. For example, gypsum is far more soluble than limestone and it also dissolves much more rapidly. Dolomite is an exception. At typical groundwater temperatures dolomite is slightly more soluble than limestone (at least in terms of volume). And yet in water that contains no previously dissolved carbonate rock, pure dolomite dissolves about 2.5–7.5 times more slowly than limestone, with the greatest differences at low CO_2 values (Liu and Dreybrodt, 2001). As dolomite saturation increases beyond about 20–30%, its dissolution rate drops even farther below that of limestone, and from there the approach to dolomite saturation is extremely slow (Herman and White, 1985). Likewise, although anhydrite is more soluble than gypsum at typical groundwater temperatures, anhydrite dissolves more slowly (Jeschke and others, 2001).

The rate at which rock dissolves is controlled by the reaction rate between rock and water, and also by how rapidly the dissolved material is transferred through the water away from the solid surface. In rocks of low or moderate solubility, including limestone and dolomite, the dissolution rate is controlled mainly by the rock-water interaction. Dissolved material can migrate away from the surface rapidly enough that the reaction rate is usually the limiting factor, except in acidic solutions with pH less than about 6 (Plummer and Wigley, 1976). In highly soluble rocks such as gypsum, the reaction is rapid enough that the limiting factor is the rate at which the dissolved material can migrate away from the rock surface.

Transport of dissolved materials away from the bedrock surface is controlled mainly by diffusion and turbulence. Diffusion takes place from areas of high concentration toward areas of low concentration, in a manner similar to the flow of heat from high to low temperatures. Water at the bedrock surface is at or near saturation with the products of bedrock dissolution, and they diffuse into surrounding water that contains a lower concentration of these materials. Diffusion rates increase with temperature and they vary with the type of dissolved material. In a porous medium, such as sediment, the diffusion rate is also affected by the size, shape, and percentage of the pores.

Mixing by turbulent eddies in the water greatly increases the rate of mass transfer. This process is absent in laminar flow. Turbulence increases with flow velocity, conduit size, and (slightly) with increasing temperature (Chapter 4). Even in turbulent flow there is a thin boundary layer of essentially laminar flow through which diffusion of ions must take place without the benefit of transport by turbulent eddies. If the flow velocity doubles, the boundary layer diminishes by almost exactly one-half. As the boundary layer becomes thinner, the diffusion rate of dissolved material across it increases proportionally. This accounts for the rise in dissolution rate in most rocks, especially gypsum and rock salt, as flow velocity increases.

The reaction rate at the bedrock surface increases with the solutional aggressiveness of the water, and also with temperature (Sjöberg and Rickard, 1984). An increase in CO_2 content (or other acid source) increases both the amount and rate at which limestone and dolomite dissolve, but it has almost no effect on dissolution of rock salt or sulfate rocks.

Maximum dissolution rates occur where aggressive water first encounters soluble rock. As water acquires more dissolved components from the rock, the dissolution rate of the rock decreases. This decrease is not uniform. The dissolution rate of limestone drops sharply beyond about 60–90% saturation (Berner and Morse, 1974; Plummer and Wigley, 1976; Plummer and others, 1978). The decrease is even greater in dolomite. Gypsum dissolution slows considerably at roughly 95% saturation (Jeschke and others, 2001). The decrease in dissolution rate of soluble rocks as the solution nears saturation is extremely important to cave origin, as shown in Chapter 7.

The rapid decrease of dissolution rates at high saturation ratios is apparently caused mainly by accumulation of insoluble grains on the surface (Eisenlohr and Dreybrodt, 1999). Fast-moving water removes most of them by erosion, but those remaining can form a rind that slows further dissolution. This effect is severe if the insoluble content is more than about 20–30%. If the rock is mainly insoluble, dissolution is limited to removing soluble grains from a continuous matrix of insoluble material. The solubility of this kind of rock drops rapidly with time, even if the solutional aggressiveness of the water remains high.

Variation in dolomite dissolution rate from rapid to very slow is caused by a similar process. Pure dolomite, with a 1:1 ratio of Ca to Mg, dissolves more slowly than poorly structured dolomite, in which the Ca does not balance the Mg. The most soluble (poorly structured), grains are removed first, leaving a shield of purer dolomite behind.

The dissolution rate of rocks also decreases with increasing crystal size. Coarsely crystalline limestone (sparite) dissolves less rapidly than fine-grained limestone (micrite). Marble, because of its large crystals, has a still smaller dissolution rate. In limestone it also decreases with dolomite content. Percentage of insoluble material or dolomite has a greater effect on dissolution rate than does grain size. The effects of rock composition and texture in limestone can be seen in the differential solution of cave walls (Chapter 6).

Adhesion of certain ions to the bedrock surface can also decrease the dissolution rate (Terjesen and others, 1961). Solution-inhibiting materials include phosphate, lead, copper, zinc, manganese, and magnesium.

Dissolution of poorly soluble rocks

Dissolution of detrital sedimentary rocks and non-carbonate igneous and metamorphic rocks, though feeble, is fastest where conditions are warm, wet, and acidic — most specifically in the humid tropics. They dissolve and decompose most rapidly along crystal boundaries, and the remaining loose granular material is easily eroded away. These rocks also break down to a variety of alteration minerals such as clay and metal oxides.

Quartz is a common mineral in many rocks and is the main ingredient in quartzite and most types of sandstone. Its solubility is controlled by reaction with water (hydration):

$$SiO_2 + 2H_2O \;\rightleftharpoons\; H_4SiO_4 \qquad (5.28)$$

H_4SiO_4 is silicic acid, which behaves as a true (though feeble) acid only at high pH. It is also produced by the decomposition of other silicon-rich rocks, such as igneous rocks, most metamorphic rocks, and shale. H_4SiO_4 may later re-precipitate as quartz, opal, or chert.

At pH less than 9, quartz and other varieties of SiO_2 have low solubilities. But as the pH rises above 9, silicic acid increasingly breaks down to H^+ and $H_3SiO_4^-$ so that much more SiO_2 can dissolve (Figure 5.17). Such high pH values are rare, except, for example, in highly evaporative waters, or

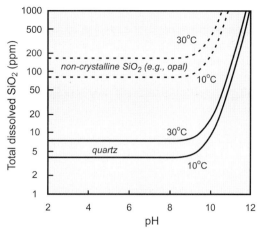

Figure 5.17: Effect of pH and temperature on the solubility of quartz and non-crystalline SiO_2. The lines for non-crystalline SiO_2 are approximate. To convert quartz solubility to cm^3/liter, multiply ppm by 3.77×10^{-4}. The conversion factor is slightly larger for non-crystalline SiO_2, depending on the exact mineral involved. For further information see Drever (1997) and Faure (1998).

in groundwater that dissolves carbonate rock in the absence of carbon dioxide. Strong acids have no effect on quartz solubility. The only common exception is hydrofluoric acid (HF), which reacts with quartz to produce ionic complexes of silicon fluoride. That is why HF should not be stored in glass containers. HF production is rare in caves, but a notable exception has been documented in the Kap-Kutan Cave in Turkmenistan, as discussed on pages 339–340.

Quartz becomes more soluble as the temperature rises. Calcite solubility decreases with temperature, and the two solubilities cross at roughly 100°C (Wood, 1986). Deep high-temperature groundwater can dissolve cavities in sandstone and quartzite if the water is not already saturated with H_4SiO_4. In Russia, hot, high-pH water has dissolved large cavities in quartzite, one of which, discovered by drilling, is 25 m wide and 350 m deep (Tsykin, 1989).

At surface temperatures, quartz dissolves very slowly and requires several years to reach equilibrium in pure water (Bennett, 1991). Although salinity or organic compounds can increase the dissolution rate (Martini, 2000), it is clear that, near the surface, dissolution alone cannot form caves in quartz sandstone or quartzite without the help of mechanical erosion and a great deal of time.

Clay and similar minerals decompose at both high and low pH (Drever, 1997). They are most stable at a pH of about 6 and most liable to break down in strong acids. In sulfuric acid caves, breakdown of clay produces a variety of alteration minerals and SiO_2 (Chapter 12).

Microbial effects on karst chemistry

It has long been recognized that carbon dioxide production in the soil, so important to cave origin, is largely the result of microbial processes. Microbiology also plays other roles in cave origin that have been recognized only recently. Many microbes obtain their energy directly from chemical processes that take place in their vicinity. They also help

to speed up these reactions. Their most conspicuous contribution is in reduction and oxidation ("redox") reactions that involve various combinations of oxygen, carbon, sulfur, iron, manganese, and a few other elements (Ehrlich, 1996; Banfield and Nealson, 1997; Chapelle, 2001). Geomicrobiologists have barely begun to sort out their complex effects on geologic processes (Taylor, 1999).

Microbes are present everywhere at and near the Earth's surface, to depths of at least several kilometers, and even in highly acid conditions and at temperatures above the boiling point of water. They multiply rapidly wherever their special dietary needs are met. In general they do not generate widespread chemical environments that otherwise would not exist, but they can speed up certain processes as much as thousands of times.

Microbes tend to form symbiotic communities (***consortia***), in which each species contributes only a single step in complex chemical processes. For example, in organic films on rock surfaces, microbes that promote oxidation may form only the outer zones of the films, while those that promote reduction lie underneath in contact with the rock (Ehrlich, 1996).

It is not certain to what extent microbes act as protagonists or opportunists — whether they cause reactions to take place or merely take advantage of processes that would occur anyway, without their participation. Apparently they do both, according to environmental conditions. They can cause reactions that would otherwise appear to violate the laws of classical thermodynamics. Within a narrow range of chemical conditions, certain organic structures and compounds, such as enzymes, are able to trap specific molecules and release them as the chemical environment changes. For example, some organisms can precipitate minerals for use in shell construction even from water that is greatly undersaturated with those minerals. Microbial processes like these show great promise for future energy production, decontamination, and materials science (Gillett, 2006).

Reduction of sulfates to hydrogen sulfide, as in Reaction 5.14, takes place spontaneously at temperatures around 100–180°C (Machel, 2001). Below about 80°C this process requires the intervention of sulfate-reducing bacteria, which accomplish the job metabolically. Oxidation of hydrogen sulfide to sulfur and sulfuric acid (Reactions 5.17–5.19) is speeded greatly by the activity of sulfur-oxidizing bacteria (Figure 5.18).

Some of these microbes thrive in intense acids with pH levels as low as zero, and even at negative pH. In H_2S-rich caves they serve as the base of a long and complex food chain. Examples of this biodiversity have been described in many caves, including Parker Cave in Kentucky (Thompson and Olson, 1988; Olson and Thompson, 1988), Movile Cave in Romania (Sarbu and others, 1996), Frasassi Cave in Italy (Galdenzi and others, 1999), Cueva de Villa Luz in Mexico (Hose and others, 2000), and Lower Kane Cave in Wyoming (Engel and others, 2004).

Even in air-filled caves, reducing conditions can persist where water is rich in organic material. If sulfate is also

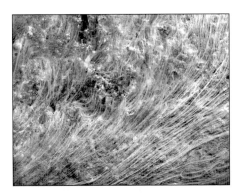

Figure 5.18: Filaments of sulfur-oxidizing bacteria grow in an H₂S-rich water inlet to Lower Kane Cave, Wyoming. Width of photo is about 25 cm.

present it is reduced to H_2S and iron sulfides to within a few centimeters of an air supply. The effects of bacterially mediated sulfur reactions have been measured in H_2S-rich Lower Kane Cave, Wyoming, by Engel and others (2004). Although the cave stream is saturated or slightly supersaturated with calcite, the carbonate bedrock surfaces are etched by sulfuric acid dissolution where they are in contact with mats of sulfur-oxidizing bacteria. Thus the local chemical environment generated by bacteria can contrast with that of the surrounding water.

Bedrock exposed to moist cave air can weather to a variety of hues such as red, yellow, and black. Most of these colors are produced by iron oxide from oxidation of iron compounds such as pyrite. Manganese oxides generally form black deposits (Moore, 1981; Hill, 1982). Many cave and paleokarst deposits contain microscopic fossil filaments that provide evidence for past redox processes (Figure 5.19).

Iron and manganese are moderately soluble in oxygen-depleted water, which is common at depth. If this water rises into caves or springs where oxygen is abundant, the dissolved metals precipitate rapidly as hydroxides and oxides. These reactions provide a microbial feast, as shown by the concen-

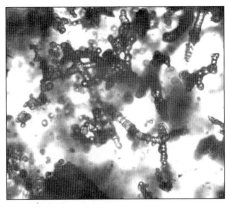

Figure 5.19: Photomicrograph of bacterial filaments in a thin section of quartz crystals in a Mississippian-age paleokarst deposit, Wind Cave, South Dakota. They are red and appear to represent iron-oxidizing bacteria. The filaments are about 2 micrometers (μm) in diameter. Preservation is excellent in quartz, and Individual cells seem to be visible. Photo by Margaret Palmer.

tration of filaments of bacteria, fungi, etc., in the vicinity. The reddish-yellow goo that is conspicuous in some springs is composed of the filaments of iron-fixing bacteria coated by iron hydroxides and oxides. The biological aspects of iron and manganese deposition in caves have been described by Peck (1986), Cunningham and others (1995), and Northup and others (2003).

The various aspects of karst geomicrobiology are described in the proceedings of a multi-disciplinary symposium sponsored by the Karst Waters Institute (Sasowsky and M. Palmer, 1994). Recent reviews of the subject are given by Northup and Lavoie (2001), Engel and others (2004), and Barton (2006). The microbial influence on the accumulation of surface travertine, as in Figure 5.11, is described by Chafetz and Folk (1984) and Viles (1984).

Isotopes and their use

Most atoms of carbon have 6 protons and 6 neutrons, so they have an atomic mass of 12. Carbon-12 provides an arbitrary standard by which the masses of all other elements are compared. Similarly, most oxygen atoms have an atomic mass of 16 (8 protons + 8 neutrons). But these and many other elements have variants that contain more than the typical number of neutrons. They are still the same elements, but their masses are slightly different. These variants are called *isotopes*. They can be distinguished in the laboratory with a mass spectrometer.

Some isotopes are radioactive and eventually decay to stable elements. An example is the decay of uranium-238 (radioactive) to lead (stable) by way of intermediate radioactive byproducts such as uranium-235. Radioactive isotopes are useful for determining the ages of the rocks and other materials that contain them (Chapter 13).

Stable isotopes are non-radioactive, so their individual percentages remain constant within a given system. The ratio of the two most common stable isotopes of an element can be used to interpret the conditions in which the host material formed. In cave studies the stable isotopes of carbon, oxygen, and sulfur are most useful. Although carbon-12 (^{12}C) is the most abundant form of carbon, about 1.1% of all carbon contains an extra neutron and forms the stable isotope ^{13}C. A much smaller percentage contains yet another neutron. This is radioactive ^{14}C, which is used for dating organic material such as wood or bone. Oxygen includes three isotopes: ^{16}O is the common form, ^{18}O accounts for 0.2% of all oxygen, and there are also negligible amounts of ^{17}O. The common isotope of sulfur is ^{32}S (95%), and less-common isotopes include ^{34}S (4.2%) and the rare ^{33}S and ^{36}S. For further details see Faure and Mensing (2005).

In geologic studies of carbonate minerals the ratios of ^{13}C to ^{12}C and of ^{18}O to ^{16}O are frequently used. In sulfur-bearing materials, such as gypsum, anhydrite, and sulfides, the ratio of ^{34}S to ^{32}S is most pertinent. In each sample the ratio of "heavy" to "light" isotopes is compared to that of a universally accepted standard. This comparison is expressed as follows, with carbon as the example:

$$\delta^{13}C\ (‰)\ =\ \frac{R_{sample} - R_{std}}{R_{std}}\ x\ 1000 \qquad (5.29)$$

where R = isotopic ratio ($^{13}C/^{12}C$), R_{sample} is the ratio in the sample, and R_{std} is the ratio in the standard. The variable $\delta^{13}C$ is pronounced "del 13-C" or "del C-13." Its values are expressed in parts per thousand (i.e., per mil, or ‰), which is a more sensitive measure than percent. In the same way, $\delta^{18}O$ indicates the $^{18}O/^{16}O$ ratio in the sample compared to that in the standard.

For carbon, the standard ratio ($^{13}C/^{12}C$) is from a calcite belemnite fossil (a cigar-shaped cephalopod) in the Pee Dee Formation in South Carolina, so $\delta^{13}C$ is measured in ‰ PDB (= Pee Dee belemnite). For oxygen, the standard can be either PDB or standard mean ocean water (SMOW), where $\delta^{18}O$ SMOW = 1.03 x ($\delta^{18}O$ PDB) + 30.86. For sulfur, the standard is a sample of troilite, an iron sulfide, from Cañon Diablo, Mexico, and ratios are expressed in ‰ CDT. Measurement of isotopic ratios does not require a visit to South Carolina or Mexico, because the standards have long been established by early laboratory measurements (see Brownlow, 1996, for a list of standards).

In cave geology, a few of the many applications of stable isotopes are described below. First, a few concepts should be kept in mind:

• If two water types mix, and they start with different isotopic ratios (R_1 and R_2), the isotopic ratio in the final mixture (R_{final}) is a weighted average that depends on the proportion of each water type. If V_1/V_{total} is the proportion of source 1 in the mixture, then

$$V_1/V_{total} = (R_{final} - R_1) / (R_2 - R_1) \qquad (5.30)$$

For example, if soil water with $\delta^{18}O = -12.4‰$ mixes with cave water with $\delta^{18}O = -9.1‰$, and the final $\delta^{18}O$ is $-11.8‰$, the proportion of soil water is $[-11.8 - (-12.4)]$ / $[-9.1 - (-12.4)] = 0.18 = 18\%$ of the mixture. This is a variant of the chemical mass-balance approach described on page 112.

• Isotopic ratios in the products of a chemical reaction must be compatible with those of the reactants. If water dissolves carbon dioxide from soil air to produce carbonic acid (Reactions 5.5–5.67), and then the acid dissolves limestone bedrock (Reaction 5.4), any calcite that is deposited from this water is expected to have $\delta^{13}C$ and $\delta^{18}O$ values roughly midway between those of the soil CO_2 and the dissolved limestone. The exact values depend on the ratio of water volume to rock volume involved. In addition, any of the following processes may alter this relationship:

• When there is a chemical reaction or a change of phase (e.g., evaporation, condensation, precipitation of solids from solution), the isotopic ratios of the products differ from those in the remaining source. This phenomenon is called **fractionation**. Each reaction has a different fractionation factor, which decreases as temperature rises. For example,

when sulfate is reduced to hydrogen sulfide by bacteria, the $\delta^{34}S$ of the sulfide is lower than that of the original sulfate. Differences in the isotopic ratios of reactants and products increase with the rate of the reaction.

• When evaporation and condensation take place, the denser phase acquires a greater proportion of the heavier isotopes. Water vapor from evaporation has a lower ("lighter") $\delta^{18}O$ than the water that remains. When the vapor condenses as rainwater, the ratio shifts back toward higher $\delta^{18}O$ values, but not as high as those in the original water. The $\delta^{18}O$ in rainwater decreases toward the poles and inland away from the oceans, in response to successive cycles of evaporation and condensation. $\delta^{18}O$ is also lower (more negative) during cold seasons.

• As a reaction proceeds, there is a decrease in the isotopic contrast between the source and product materials. For example, when gypsum is reduced to H_2S, the earliest H_2S has a very light $\delta^{34}S$. Later H_2S is heavier (less negative) as ^{32}S in the remaining sulfate is depleted. Both the remaining sulfate and the H_2S derived from it become isotopically heavier. In a closed system, if *all* the sulfate is eventually used up, the *total* H_2S would have the same number of light and heavy isotopes as the original sulfate.

• As water remains in contact with rock, the isotopes of the liquid and solid tend toward equilibrium with each other. For example, if water with a certain $\delta^{18}O$ is in contact with rock having a different $\delta^{18}O$, the two will slowly exchange isotopes so that their ratios approach one another. Whether or not equilibrium is achieved, there can be a significant shift in the isotopic signature of both the water and the solid carbonate.

• It is common for isotopes to be influenced by several of the above factors at the same time, so that they show considerable scatter. Isotopic boundaries between different types of mineral deposits are rarely sharp. Thus it may not be appropriate to interpret past conditions from isotope data alone without other supporting evidence.

Several applications of isotopes to cave geology are described here:

Interpretation of chemical processes

Isotopes can provide information about past or present chemical processes. See Figure 5.20 for typical ranges of $\delta^{13}C$ and $\delta^{18}O$, and their interpretation, for a variety of carbonate rocks and cave minerals. Unaltered limestone and dolomite have slightly positive $\delta^{13}C$ values. Isotopes in speleothems have a wide range of isotopes depending on the materials that contributed to their origin, as well as the environmental conditions in which they were deposited.

CO_2 in soil air has a low $\delta^{13}C$. Carbonate minerals deposited by dripwater have isotopic ratios between those of soil and the carbonate of the local bedrock. Cave air has a higher $\delta^{13}C$ than soil air, and minerals that precipitate in and around pools that have equilibrated with cave air have isotopic ratios between those of the cave CO_2 and the bedrock.

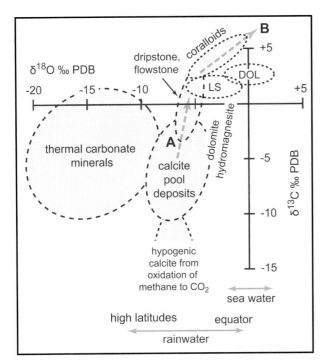

Figure 5.20: Typical ranges of carbon and oxygen isotopes in carbonate cave deposits and bedrock. As CO_2 is lost from the water, the position of carbonate minerals on the graph rises steeply at first (line **A**), and then more gently if evaporation begins to dominate (line **B**). Dolomite and evaporative Mg carbonates (hydromagnesite, etc.) follow the same trend, but in positions slightly to the right of calcite. Carbonate minerals deposited at high temperature have light oxygen isotopic ratios. LS, DOL = typical limestone and dolomite bedrock. Data shown here are from caves of the western U.S. At higher latitudes they shift toward the left, and toward the equator they shift toward the right. See also Bakalowicz and others (1987), Lohmann (1988), González and Lohmann (1988), and Moore (1989).

Sulfur isotopes are helpful in tracing the source of gypsum in caves. For example, in Carlsbad Cavern, New Mexico, gypsum has highly negative $\delta^{34}S$ compared with that of Permian-age gypsum beds in the nearby lowlands (Figures 5.21, 8.66). The relatively light $\delta^{34}S$ of the cave gypsum shows that it has been influenced by microbial processes and is not derived from primary marine gypsum (Hill, 1987). At Carlsbad the specific reactions include reduction of the original sulfate to hydrogen sulfide, oxidation of the hydrogen sulfide to sulfuric acid, and production of secondary gypsum when the sulfuric acid reacted with the limestone. The gypsum inherited the light isotopic signature of the sulfuric acid. Sulfate produced by the oxidation of pyrite usually has a negative $\delta^{34}S$ as well. In contrast, dissolved sulfate derived from marine gypsum and anhydrite usually has a positive $\delta^{34}S$.

Values of $\delta^{13}C$ in most calcite cave deposits reflect the nature of the overlying soil. CO_2 derived from forest soils is about 7‰ lighter than that from grassland soil (Dorale and others, 1998). Carbonate minerals deposited from CO_2 generated by oxidation of hypogenic carbon compounds such as methane have a lower $\delta^{13}C$ than those from soil CO_2.

Isotopic signatures can be used to track the sources of dissolved material in water samples. If the sulfate in spring water has an unusually heavy $\delta^{34}S$, it is likely that the light isotopes have been depleted by conversion of some of the sulfate to hydrogen sulfide, which is no longer present in the water. Sulfur in the H_2S may have precipitated as a solid sulfide (as in Reaction 5.16) or it may have escaped as a gas by an independent route.

Estimating temperatures of mineral deposition

The $\delta^{18}O$ in mineral deposits becomes lower (more negative) as the temperature rises. Variations in $\delta^{18}O$ in calcite speleothems can be used to interpret the relative temperatures of various cave deposits, or between laminations in individual deposits. Thermal deposits can be distinguished from those that formed at normal groundwater temperatures by the lighter $\delta^{18}O$ in high-temperature calcite (Figure 5.20; Bakalowicz and others, 1987). There are limitations to this method that make it difficult to determine exact temperatures (see Schwarcz, 1986).

Calcite dripstone in caves is often close to isotopic equilibrium with the vadose drips from which they form (Hendy and Wilson, 1968). In a deposit that has accumulated fairly continuously under uniform chemical conditions, variations in $\delta^{18}O$ can indicate changes in the regional temperature with time (page 351).

Interpreting groundwater sources and flow paths

Deuterium (^2H, or D) is an isotope of hydrogen that has twice the mass of the common variety of hydrogen (^1H). The concentration of deuterium relative to ^1H is expressed as δ^2H or δD. Its standard is mean ocean water. At the equator, δD and $\delta^{18}O$ in seawater are both approximately zero on

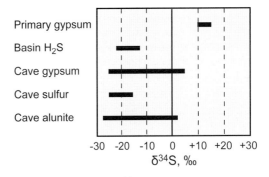

Figure 5.21: Contrast in $\delta^{34}S$ values (‰ CDT) between marine gypsum and sulfur-bearing materials derived from them by reduction-oxidation reactions, Guadalupe Mountains area, New Mexico. **Primary gypsum** = marine Castile Formation, Delaware Basin, adjacent to Guadalupe Mountains (28 samples). **Basin H_2S** = hydrogen sulfide in Delaware Basin from reduction of gypsum (33 samples). **Cave gypsum** = deposits in Guadalupe caves (17 samples). **Cave sulfur** = similar locations (6 samples). **Cave alunite** = alunite and natroalunite (a sodium-rich variant) in Guadalupe caves (13 samples). After Hill (2000) except for alunite-natroalunite values from Polyak and Güven (1996). See Figure 8.66 for the geologic setting.

the SMOW scale. In rain or snow, both isotopic ratios become increasingly negative with latitude, altitude, and distance inland (Faure, 1998; Faure and Mensing, 2005). A graph of the two ratios in fresh water derived from rain or snow describes an approximately straight line (the **meteoric water line**), with an equation of roughly $\delta D = 10 + 8(\delta^{18}O)$. There is some deviation according to local meteorological conditions, and the exact line should be based on measurements in the study area. There is also a seasonal effect. Snow and cold rainfall in a given area generally have lighter (more negative) δD and $\delta^{18}O$ than warm rainfall. The response of springs to seasonal variations can sometimes be determined from this information.

Figure 5.22 shows some typical δD and $\delta^{18}O$ values in a karst region. Surface streams generally have isotopic signatures that reflect the current season, as do springs fed by rapidly transmitted water. In cold rain or snowmelt both isotopic ratios are relatively light (A at lower left of Figure 5.22). During warm weather the ratios in surface streams are relatively heavy (N, P). The same relationship holds for rapid flow through caves (compare D, F, and G, which show the effect of progressively warmer temperature). Minor seeps into caves have a delayed response to season (C, H–L). Lack of correlation with season may represent a delay of more than a single season, so verifying the delay time requires measurements over several years.

In springs fed by slow, deep flow in which there is considerable mixing between waters of different seasons, the isotopes tend to fall between the cold and warm extremes, regardless of season (Figure 5.22, E). Lengthy contact with carbonate rocks by deep, slow groundwater tends to shift the points slightly toward the right, toward heavier $\delta^{18}O$ values, also possibly shown by the points at E. Many thermal springs show this trend.

Evaporation from lakes or swamps selectively depletes the water of its lighter isotopes, which shifts the data away from the meteoric water line toward heavier $\delta^{18}O$ and δD values (Figure 5.22, M, N, P). It is possible for cave springs recharged by lakes or swamps to be recognized in this way.

Cave drips from seepage through soil may show a similar but smaller shift as the result of summer evapotranspiration of soil moisture (triangular points: B, C, H, J, L). The same trend is shown by point K, which represents a cave stream fed by local seepage through soil. These interpretations are uncertain because the amount of shift toward the right in Figure 5.22 is small.

Evaluations of δD and $\delta^{18}O$ must be based on many data points of varied hydrology and weather patterns. Minor scatter in the data should be expected. To calibrate the field data, the isotopic values of precipitation in the area should be measured at least once each season.

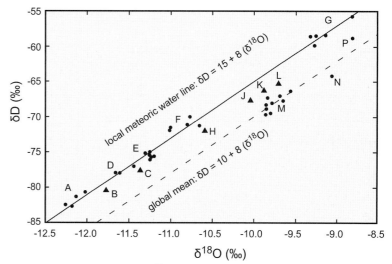

Figure 5.22: Plot of δD vs. $\delta^{18}O$ (both in ‰ SMOW) for representative water samples in the karst of east-central New York State. A = surface streams during early spring snowmelt. B = cave drip, late spring. C = same cave drip, summer. D = cave streams, late spring. E = springs fed by deep groundwater, summer. F = sinking streams and their outlets, late spring. G = same as F, but in fall. H = stalactite drip beneath 60 m cover, partly of low permeability, fall. J = vadose seep into cave beneath 40 m of permeable cover, fall. K = cave stream, fall. L = slow stalactite drip beneath 30 m of permeable cover, late fall. M = surface lake, summer. N = river draining lake, fall. P = surface stream draining swamp, summer. Compiled from Siemion and others (2005), Terrell and others (2005), Moskal and others, (2005). The local meteoric water line is based on local rainfall measurements (not shown).

Water that rises from the Earth's mantle (**juvenile water**) can be recognized by its high ratios of the helium isotopes $^3He/^4He$. This is typical in spring water where there is tectonic activity and a partially molten mantle, as shown by low seismic velocities. In such areas of the western U.S., many springs, both hot and cold, have helium isotopes that indicate mixing between shallow groundwater and juvenile water (Newell and others, 2005). These springs are depositing travertine. Compared to the shallow groundwater, the deep component has a high CO_2 and salinity, as well as high levels of trace elements. A $^3He/^4He$ ratio of more than 0.1 is typical where there is considerable water from the mantle. Spilde and others (2005) have used this approach in the H_2S-rich Cueva de Villa Luz, Mexico (see page 221).

Isotopes as geologic fingerprints

Isotopic data can be used to show the affinity among samples of similar origin, even where that origin is uncertain. Clustering of samples in Figures 5.20–5.21 helps to group the deposits into genetic types, regardless of their interpretation.

In a similar way it is possible to trace the origin of dissolved material in water by relating the isotopes to those of possible source rocks. For example, in Figure 5.23 the $\delta^{34}S$ of sulfate in certain mineralized springs is compared to that of regional beds of Silurian anhydrite and gypsum that occur at depth but are not present at the surface. The $\delta^{34}S$ ratio in marine sulfates has varied with time, and the average $\delta^{34}S$ of sulfate in the spring water exactly matches that of Silurian sulfates. Not all correlations are this clear.

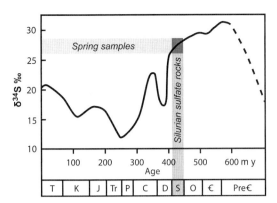

Figure 5.23: Use of sulfur isotopes to identify the source of dissolved sulfate in karst spring water, Sharon Springs, NY. The variation of $\delta^{34}S$ in marine sulfate rocks with time is from Claypool and others (1980). $\delta^{34}S$ values in the spring water match those of deep-seated beds of anhydrite and gypsum of Silurian age, which lie below the surface at the field site. $\delta^{34}S$ in hydrogen sulfide is highly negative (−29 to −30‰), indicating microbial reduction of sulfate. For correlation of time periods, see Figure 2.1. Water data from Terrell and others, 2005.

Analysis of spring chemistry

The nature of a karst aquifer can be inferred from chemical measurements at the springs that drain it. These measurements are best plotted as **chemographs**, which show chemical variations with time. During low flow, water temporarily stored in the soil, epikarst, and narrow fissures approaches saturation with the minerals in which it is in contact. During storms or snowmelt it is displaced by fresh inflow, which releases an initial burst of water having high chemical concentrations. At the onset of a flood, the concentration of dissolved solids in many springs increases at first, and then drops with time, often to levels below those of the prior low flow. Chemical analysis of springs in western Kentucky-Tennessee by Vesper and White (2006) shows that the highest aggressiveness (lowest SI) may occur after the flood peak, when high-CO_2 seepage through soil contributes a large proportion of the recharge.

Shuster and White (1971) noted that springs fed by conduits tend to have a greater variation in chemistry and temperature than those where much of the flow is contributed by narrow fissures. They distinguished between the two types of flow by the fact that conduits tend to have greater

fluctuations in discharge. This subject is also discussed by White (1988) and Ford and Williams (1989).

Spring chemistry also reflects the nature of the recharge area that feeds the spring. Concentration of dissolved solids, saturation ratios of calcite and dolomite, and P_{CO_2} all tend to be greater in springs fed by autogenic recharge through a karst surface than those with a large proportion of allogenic recharge from sinking streams. In humid climates, where sulfate and chloride levels are sparse in surface strata, high concentrations of these ions usually indicate deep groundwater flow. Hydrogen sulfide, methane, or high iron or manganese content indicate water from oxygen-poor zones that typically (but not everywhere) lie at considerable depth. Bacterial mats and filaments of iron-oxidizing or sulfur-oxidizing bacteria are common at such springs.

A chemical cave tour

To illustrate the chemical behavior of cave water, an example is given for an idealized cave system (Figure 5.24). The cave is imaginary but typical of most epigenic caves in limestone regions. Numerical values are based on measurements in a variety of real caves. The description of how the water chemistry changes through the cave system is fairly representative. This generic model can serve as a basis for comparison with those from other studies. See Hess and White (1993) for a description of chemical conditions in a similar setting in central Kentucky. Descriptions of chemical conditions in hypogenic caves are included in Chapter 8. For further details see **Chemical Field Studies** on pages 135−137.

Cave description

The cave in Figure 5.24 is a typical solution cave in limestone and contains active streams that join as tributaries. The main passage (labeled C on the profile) is fed by a sinking stream (A) that drains impure limestone covered by thick low-permeability soil. The stream has a large discharge, especially during floods, and it has formed a substantial conduit. The downstream half (D) is water-filled, except for a short aerated section (E) at the very end, beyond which the stream emerges at a spring (F).

Smaller tributaries (such as H) drain sinkholes in the relatively pure limestone in which the cave is located.

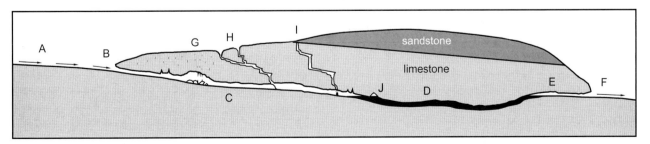

Figure 5.24: Cross section through the idealized cave used in the "chemical cave tour" (see text for details). A = surface stream flowing across impure limestone; B = sink point = cave entrance; C = air-filled stream passage; D = water-filled section of stream passage; E = short aerated section; F = spring; G = region of dispersed infiltration; H = sinkhole inputs; I = recharge at edge of, and through, quartz sandstone; J = air bell.

Water also seeps through the soil into the cave as infiltration dispersed among narrow fissures (G).

Quartz sandstone overlies part of the cave but has been eroded away in many areas. Some water (at I) runs off the sandsone into sinkholes and some seeps through the thin edge of the sandstone into the underlying limestone. Both eventually reach the cave through canyons and shafts. Where the sandstone is thick, water enters the underlying limestone only as small amounts of diffuse seepage.

Rainfall

Rainfall in the area normally has a pH of about 5.1, which is maintained by the normal atmospheric CO_2 plus a small amount of acid derived from the sulfur and nitrogen oxides of industrial and automotive emissions. The P_{CO_2} of the rainwater is roughly 0.00038 atm.

Soil moisture

Rainwater infiltrates into the soil, where the P_{CO_2} is 0.02–0.05 atm — around 100 times greater than in the outside air. As the water adjusts to the high CO_2, the pH drops to about 4.5–4.7. In comparison to soil CO_2, the "acid rain" contribution of nitrates and sulfates has only a minor effect (about 1%). The average underground temperature in this area is about 10°C.

Today the amount of runoff is small because there has been little recent rain. The sinking stream is fed only by water that has seeped through the soil. Some has followed narrow openings through the limestone but is too diffuse to form caves. By the time it emerges into the stream, the water contains an average of 100 ppm of dissolved calcite. The saturation concentration (C_s) of calcite in this water is about 300 ppm, so the present saturation ratio (C/C_s) is about 0.33 (33%). This is enough to raise the average pH to about 6.5.

Carbon dioxide production in the soil is greatest in the summer. This does not automatically translate into greater dissolution rates, because the inflow of water to the cave is less than during the wetter seasons, at least in this local climate.

Seepage into the sinking stream

As it emerges into the sinking stream (Figure 5.25), the soil water loses much of its CO_2 to the outside atmosphere. The typical P_{CO_2} drops to roughly 0.002 atm. CO_2 in the stream never reaches equilibrium with the outside air because of the constant inflow of water from the soil and the production of CO_2 by oxidation of organics in the water. Still, the amount of CO_2 loss is enough to raise the pH to about 7.7, and to drop the saturation concentration to about 120 ppm. In the stream the calcite saturation ratio has risen to

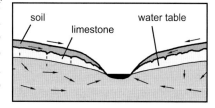
Figure 5.25: Cross section showing recharge to the sinking stream. Groundwater seeps into the cave in a similar way.

more than 80%, and this level rises as limestone continues to be dissolved from the stream bed.

During dry periods the soil moisture moves very slowly and has prolonged contact with the limestone. This brings the water close to calcite saturation, and when the water emerges into the stream, loss of CO_2 causes it to become supersaturated. Under those conditions the sinking stream has no aggressiveness at all. Local deposits of calcite may accumulate in places, but they are easily removed during higher flow.

Streamflow into the cave

Today, however, as the sinking stream enters the cave it is undersaturated with calcite and has the potential to dissolve an additional 20 ppm. The cave grows slowly under these low-flow conditions. CO_2 in the cave is less than that of the soil air because of exchange of air through entrances to the surface. Today the CO_2 level in the cave is about the same as that of the sinking stream — about 0.002 atm, roughly 5 times that of the outside atmosphere.

Sinkhole inputs

During low flow the recharge through sinkhole entrances (Figure 5.26) is similar in chemistry to the water that seeps into the sinking stream. By the time it enters the cave the sinkhole water has already had enough contact with limestone to be near saturation. Still, it is able to dissolve a little more limestone inside the cave. Because the discharge is small, this water forms a narrow passage. Where the water joins the main

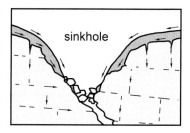
Figure 5.26: Cross section of sinkhole entrance to cave, showing paths of runoff and seepage.

stream there is almost no mixing effect because the two streams are fairly similar in chemistry. Aggressiveness is much greater during high flow.

Dispersed infiltration through limestone

Meanwhile, a great deal of water infiltrates through the soil into narrow limestone fissures. Any single opening receives only a small amount of seepage, but together they produce an extensive epikarst of solutionally enlarged fissures and pores.

Although the P_{CO_2} is high in the fissures (about 0.02–0.05 atm), the water has such intimate contact with the limestone that it rapidly reaches calcite saturation at an average of roughly 300 ppm. Some of this water reaches the water table adjacent to the cave and eventually drains laterally into the cave stream in the same manner as the recharge to the surface stream shown in Figure 5.25. Thus there is mixing between high-CO_2 water that is fully saturated with dissolved calcite and low-CO_2 cave water that is not quite saturated with calcite. Where fissure seepage enters the section of cave that is water-filled (D on the cave profile), the two waters produce a mixture that is more undersaturated than the original cave water. In this closed environment the mixing can boost the rate of cave enlargement slightly by the process shown in Figure 5.14.

Some infiltrating water drips or flows into air-filled parts of the stream passage (C) and eventually into the stream. The drip water rapidly loses most of its CO_2 and its ability to hold calcite drops from roughly 300 ppm to much lower values. Calcite starts to precipitate almost as soon as the CO_2 begins to escape. Roughly half of the dissolved calcite in the dripwater can precipitate in this way. This is the source of calcite or aragonite speleothems (stalactites and stalagmites, for example). Precipitation stops when the dissolved calcite is at roughly 150 ppm and the pH is about 7.8. The remaining calcite is retained in solution at slight supersaturation, and as it mixes with the cave streams the water shifts closer to saturation.

Vadose inputs with large discharge are more likely to be solutionally aggressive than small seeps, which tend to precipitate speleothems. These chemical properties are not controlled by the discharge itself, but by the fact that rapidly moving water does not have time to become saturated with calcite as it descends to a cave. Measurements of seepage into Kentucky caves by Thrailkill and Robl (1981) show that the threshold between these two types of vadose water is typically about 1 cm^3/sec. This threshold is only a broad trend and varies a great deal with time and physical setting.

Runoff and seepage from the sandstone

Runoff from the quartz sandstone forms small streams that sink into the limestone along the contact between the two rock types (I). This water produces passages similar to those of the sinkhole inputs at H. Runoff from the sandstone is more aggressive, even though its P_{CO_2} is lower (about 0.002 atm, with a pH of about 5.2), and it has a larger catchment area. The passages that it forms tend to grow more rapidly than those at H. Where the sandstone is thin, water that passes through it has a lower P_{CO_2} than that in the soil over the limestone. Weathering of sandstone produces a loose, sandy soil that does not retain CO_2 as well as the clay-rich soils elsewhere. P_{CO_2} in the sandy soil is typically about 0.005 atm, and the pH is about 5.0.

As this water passes through the sandstone it tends to keep the same P_{CO_2} and pH that were acquired in the soil. Only about 5 ppm of quartz can dissolve (as H_4SiO_4), and this has no measurable effect on limestone dissolution. So when this water eventually reaches the limestone it dissolves that rock vigorously, just as the direct surface runoff does, except that the diffuse seepage may not be so abundant. Fissures, pores, and conduits are enlarged along and below the sandstone contact, especially where the water flow is greatest. The amount of limestone that can be dissolved is no greater than that of other water sources, but this dissolution is expended almost entirely on cave enlargement rather than being wasted (as speleologists might view it) at the soil-bedrock contact. Where there is sufficient water from the sandstone to form a continuous flow, it retains its aggressiveness and forms shafts and canyons, as described in Chapter 6.

Where only small amounts of this seepage are available, openings in the limestone remain small and there is little or no exchange of air through entrances. Because of the sandstone beds between the limestone and the overlying soil, there is no nearby source of CO_2 to replenish what is used up by dissolution. The P_{CO_2} drops to very low values, often below 0.0001 atm (far less than that of the outside atmosphere), and the pH rises to more than 8 and in places more than 9. At this low P_{CO_2} the water can hold only about 20–40 ppm of dissolved calcite.

If this water enters a cave stream or water-filled conduit, mixing with the high-P_{CO_2} cave water slightly boosts the aggressiveness of the resulting mixture, but the seepage rate is so small that there is little effect on cave development. If instead the seepage emerges through the walls or ceiling of an air-filled passage, the water rapidly absorbs CO_2 from the cave air and becomes highly aggressive. Over a short distance it is able to corrode the nearby bedrock surfaces and forms a zigzag pattern of small solution rills (see pages 345–346).

Tracking the chemistry of the main cave stream

The surface stream that feeds the main cave passage during low to moderate flow is already at least 80% saturated with calcite. As this water is joined by other cave streams its chemistry changes only slightly. Most tributaries are slightly closer to calcite saturation than the main stream because of their slower flow and greater area of contact with the limestone. Organic materials, both dissolved and solid, tend to oxidize in the cave streams. This boosts the CO_2 in both the water and cave air and helps to sustain the stream's aggressiveness.

Sinkhole entrances part way through the cave allow air to be exchanged between the cave and the surface (as at H on the cave profile). Both the P_{CO_2} and aggressiveness of the cave streams decrease as a result. During low flow the cave water may become supersaturated with calcite, and during exceptionally dry periods it may precipitate a thin film of calcite on the stream floor. In this cave any deposits of this kind are removed during the next episode of high flow, but in some caves they may continue to accumulate and eventually build rimstone dams.

Today, during moderately low flow, the water is more than 95% saturated by the time it reaches the sump part of the way through the cave. In the water-filled section (D) it is no longer possible for CO_2 to be absorbed from the cave air. As dissolution proceeds, the P_{CO_2} decreases, but because the water is already near saturation at a high P_{CO_2}, the effect is insignificant.

Part of the way through the water-filled section is an air bell (J). Air and water exchange CO_2 and other gases, which keeps the composition of the air in the bell essentially in equilibrium with the dissolved gases in the cave water. The gas content of the water is, in turn, adjusted to that of the cave air upstream from the sump. For that reason, divers who enter an air bell may expect to find fresh air to breathe. Unfortunately this is often not true where oxidation of organic material has depleted the oxygen and built up CO_2.

Spring outflow

The final segment of the cave, which lies beyond the water-filled conduit, has a low atmospheric CO_2 because of air exchange through the large spring opening. The cave stream loses CO_2 to the air and the P_{CO_2} of the water drops to about the same level as that of the surface stream that feeds the cave. The water loses most or all of its remaining aggressiveness. In some springs this process may cause calcite to precipitate as travertine or tufa. In this one, however, calcite is not deposited because the water has already been aerated for most of its travel through the cave and its CO_2 level is too low. This is typical of most springs fed by shallow cave water.

The cave in flood

The sky darkens and a storm drops heavy rainfall on the cave's drainage basin. Some of the water runs off as overland flow directly into the sinking stream and sinkholes. The rest drains slowly through the soil but eventually reaches the same destinations. The P_{CO_2} of the soil water is less than in low flow because of the shorter flow-through time, but it also contains less dissolved limestone for the same reason.

The sinking stream becomes a raging torrent that is turbid with suspended sediment. Its dissolved calcite content is fairly low, about 50 ppm, which is less than 50% of saturation. The P_{CO_2} is about 0.003 atm and the pH about 7.3. This water is highly aggressive. Streams that enter through sinkholes have similar behavior, but their flow and aggressiveness are less than that of the main stream.

Water begins to fill the cave. The gradient of the surrounding groundwater is toward the cave during low flow (as in Figure 5.25), but during high flow it is reversed so that solutionally aggressive water is forced into many of the surrounding fractures and partings. These openings are rapidly enlarged, as is the entire passage.

The flood begins to subside and water drains out of the minor openings that surround the cave passages. Gradually the flow recedes to the low-flow level described earlier. But this flood, and others like it, have a significant impact on the cave growth. In caves such as this, fed mainly by a sinking stream and sinkholes, most of the enlargement takes place during floods (see Chapter 8).

Summary

The wide range of conditions in this example is illustrated in Figure 5.27. This idealized example illustrates the character and evolution of water in many real karst aquifers. It is a dynamic system in which the chemistry of the water and air are constantly adjusting to local conditions. To account for this variability, it is important to measure the chemistry during all seasons, in many parts of the flow system, and under the entire spectrum of flow stages.

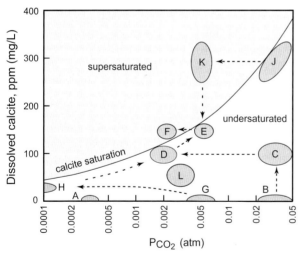

Figure 5.27: Chemical character of typical cave water (a summary of conditions in the ideal cave of Figure 5.24). T ~10°C.
A = rainwater
B = soil water
C = seepage into sinking stream
D = sinking stream
E = cave stream
F = spring
G = water infiltrating through sandstone
H = seepage in limestone, fed by water through sandstone
J = seepage through fissures in limestone
K = vadose seepage into cave (deposits speleothems)
L = floodwater in cave (little change with distance)

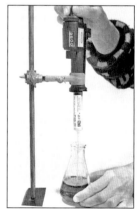

Figure 5.28: A digital titrator for analysis of major ions in water (except for sodium). With care, the results are accurate to within a few percent. This method is fairly accurate yet well suited to field work or for those on a modest budget.

Figure 5.29: The inductively coupled plasma spectrometer (ICP) can analyze nearly all dissolved elements.

Chemical field studies

How much rock has a cave stream dissolved? Is the water able to dissolve more? What minerals can it deposit? These are a few of the questions that can be answered by analyzing the chemistry of cave water. Major dissolved components can be measured with simple and inexpensive titration (Figure 5.28), and the results are adequate to answer all the questions above. More elaborate equipment is required for a full water analysis (Figure 5.29). The appropriate steps are described here:

Sample and analyze the water at a variety of places, such as flow inputs, cave streams, pools, drips, and springs. Try not to disturb the natural character of the water. Water that drips or seeps into a cave or emerges from a water-filled passage must be sampled as close to the source as possible. Half-liter samples are adequate for general purposes. Use plastic bottles that have been cleaned in distilled water, and, where possible, rinsed a couple of times with the same water that is being collected. Each sample should fill the entire bottle, so that no air bubbles are present. If observations suggest that the water might be depositing calcite, take two samples and add a drop of 10% hydrochloric acid to one of them to prevent mineral precipitation in the bottle.

Measure the water temperature and pH at the sample site, again disturbing the water as little as possible. The pH meter must be carefully calibrated with at least two buffers that bracket the expected sample pH. Most cave water has a pH between 7 and 8.5, so buffers of 7.00 and 10.00 are usually appropriate. Gently stir the water with the probe at first, but make the final measurement in unagitated water. Rapidly flowing water will give incorrect pH measurements, so this water should be collected in a container first (Sasowsky and Dalton, 2005). For drips, measure the pH where the water first appears, by collecting the sample in a small plastic cup held right at the drip site to minimize the escape of carbon dioxide. The pH of a water drip can rise several tenths over just a meter of fall. An error as small as 0.05 pH unit can produce a 10% error in the later interpretation. If the meter drifts slowly or is erratic, the probe must be replaced or cleared of air bubbles. Typical probe life is only about a year.

Major dissolved components can be analyzed in the laboratory or with portable field equipment (Figure 5.28). Instructions are available in manuals such as *Standard Methods for the Examination of Water and Wastewater* (Clescerl and others, 1999). Filter the samples first to remove solid particles. The major components to be analyzed are described below. Chloride and alkalinity must be measured in the non-acidified sample, and alkalinity should be measured as soon as possible. Keep the samples cool prior to analysis, preferably at temperatures no warmer than that of the cave.

Alkalinity is a measure of how much acid the dissolved components can neutralize. It is the sum of HCO_3^-, CO_3^{2-}, and OH^-. In most cave water the alkalinity consists almost entirely of bicarbonate (HCO_3^-). In moles per liter, it is usually about twice the amount of limestone and dolomite that has dissolved, because it is supplied by both the dissolved carbonate rock and the carbonic acid that normally does the dissolving.

Calcium comes mainly from limestone, dolomite, and gypsum. Each molecule of the minerals in these rocks releases one calcium ion. In a typical karst area, *magnesium* is released mainly by dolomite, which produces magnesium and calcium in roughly equal amounts (in moles/liter). In this case, the magnesium concentration is roughly equal to the amount of dissolved dolomite (again in moles/liter).

Sulfate is usually supplied by gypsum or anhydrite. It also comes from the oxidation of sulfides such as pyrite or H_2S. It may be possible to distinguish the exact source from sulfur isotopes, but usually the source can be guessed simply from field evidence.

Sodium and *chloride* are derived mostly from salts. Except in arid regions or at the outlets of deep groundwater flow systems, the most common source is salt that is spread on roads to remove ice. Calcium chloride or magnesium compounds are sometimes used for de-icing, and these may complicate the interpretation of karst chemistry.

Measurements of these six components, plus pH and temperature, are sufficient for a simple interpretation of typical karst water. Other ingredients may also be significant, even though their concentrations are usually low. Potassium, nitrate, phosphate, H_4SiO_4, iron, manganese, strontium, dissolved oxygen, and sulfide (usually as dissolved hydrogen sulfide) are among those that may help to determine the nature and flow history of the water, even though their concentrations are low.

If the sources are mainly chemical sedimentary rocks, the *volume* of dissolved minerals can be crudely estimated as follows. All concentrations must be in moles per liter. Dissolved calcite, in cm^3/liter = [total Ca] − [Mg + SO_4] x [36.9]. The factor 36.9 is the molecular weight of calcium carbonate (100.09 grams/mole) divided by the density of calcite (2.71 grams/cm^3). Dissolved dolomite in cm^3/liter = magnesium x [64.8]. Gypsum or anhydrite can be estimated from sulfate in a similar way, but there is often too much uncertainty as to the sulfate source for this interpretation to be accurate. If the estimate of dissolved calcite is negative, it may mean that calcite has precipitated upstream from where the sample was collected.

To obtain a rough estimate of whether the water is undersaturated or supersaturated with respect to a certain mineral, drop pieces of the mineral into the water sample and quickly re-cap the bottle. Keep it at the field temperature. Periodically re-analyze the water to see if the dissolved components of that mineral have increased. If so, the water was originally undersaturated. If they decrease, it is possible that some of the mineral has precipitated from solution. If there is no change, the water is so close to saturation that no measurable dissolution or precipitation has taken place. Figure 5.5 shows the relationship between pH and dissolved calcite content in a simple limestone solution, but the graph is only approximate because other minerals can disrupt the relationship.

The approximate $CaCO_3$ content can be estimated from the specific conductivity (SpC) of the water, which is measured with a conductivity meter. SpC increases with total dissolved solids, which, in typical karst water, is provided mainly by dissolved carbonate minerals. White (1988), from data by Langmuir (1971), gives the following relationship for karst groundwater in Pennsylvania:

$$\text{Dissolved } CaCO_3 \text{ (ppm)} = 0.59 \text{ SpC} - 30 \quad (5.31)$$

where SpC is measured in microsiemens/cm at 25°C. This relationship is valid only for water having low concentrations of dissolved chlorides and sulfates. Adjustments should ideally be made for local conditions. For pure calcite the constants in Eq. 5.31 are 0.77 and −21. Check the instrument instructions to correct for temperature and to adjust the readings to microsiemens/cm. With an electronic data-logger, SpC can be recorded continuously, which is ideal for field studies.

A full and accurate analysis of the water requires the aid of computer software such as WATEQ, which is available from the United States Geological Survey (*http://water.usgs.gov/software/wateq4f.html*). Output includes the saturation index (SI) for minerals in the water, partial pressure of dissolved gases (e.g., P_{CO_2}), and the estimated error in the laboratory analysis. Mineral solubilities shown in this book (as in Figure 5.3) are based on computations with personally developed software, which give the same results as the USGS programs. Eq. 5.13 was determined in the same way.

The P_{CO_2} in rainfall is about 0.00038 atm (= 0.038%), and in soil water it is about 0.01−0.1 atm. The P_{CO_2} of cave streams and pools is usually about 0.001−0.005 atm. Water dripping into caves typically has values close to those of soil. Springs fed by deep groundwater can have P_{CO_2} as high as several atmospheres, although rapid CO_2 loss as the water approaches the surface generally reduces it to about one atmosphere. A comparison of P_{CO_2} in various water types can tell much about the water sources and how they react with their surroundings (pages 131−134).

If the dissolved load is measured in a cave stream at different points separated by a long distance, it may be possible to estimate the dissolution rate over this distance. Unfortunately the results are often flawed. There is usually some leakage of water into (or out of) the cave stream. Inputs of supersaturated drip water are common. Also, many cave streams are close enough to saturation that the difference in concentrations is very small over the length of the stream, and the measured differences are too small to be reliable.

A simple way to check the accuracy of a chemical analysis is to calculate the *charge balance*. This is provided by the software described in the previous column but can also be estimated by hand. The dissolved load in the water is derived from materials that have no net electrical charge, so when they dissolve they produce ions with an equal number of positive and negative charges. The sum of the positive charges should balance the sum of the negative charges. Some ions have multiple charges (for example, Ca^{2+} has two + charges) and these must be accounted for. The *charge-balance error* is the amount by which the positive and negative charges fail to balance. In typical karst water, if only the major ions are considered, the charge-balance error is

$$2[Ca^{2+}]+2[Mg^{2+}]+[Na^+]-[HCO_3^-]-[Cl^-]-2[SO_4^{2-}] \quad (5.32)$$

where [Ca] = calcium ion concentration, etc, in moles/liter. Note that $[H^+]$, which is so important to karst development, has a comparatively tiny concentration, typically less than 10^{-7} moles/L, and is omitted from Eq. 5.32. Charge-balance errors can be caused by mistakes in the chemical analysis or omission of significant ions. Note that even if the charge-balance error is small, this does not guarantee that the analysis is accurate for P_{CO_2} and SI, which depend on pH.

The water chemistry in typical caves is shown on the following page. Only major components are shown. Note the high P_{CO_2} of drip waters (measured at the drip source) even in dry climates, and also that some cave streams are supersaturated during low flow.

Further information on karst water chemistry is given by Bögli (1980), Trudgill (1985), Dreybrodt (1988), White (1988), Ford and Williams (1989, 2007), Langmuir (1997), and Klimchouk and others (2000).

Average chemistry of some typical cave waters

	temp (°C)	pH	P_{CO_2} (atm)	Ca (ppm)	Mg	HCO_3	SO_4	Na	Cl	SI calcite	SI dolomite*
1. McFail's Cave, NY (drips, at source)	9	7.2	0.02	110	15	350	50	60	90	0.0	−0.3
2. McFail's Cave, NY (low-flow streams)	8	7.9	0.002	85	5	230	40	10	15	+0.5	−0.1
3. McFail's Cave, NY (high-flow streams)	10	7.4	0.006	50	5	170	5	2	3	−0.3	−0.7
4. Mystery Cave, MN (standing pools)	9	7.9	0.004	75	40	390	20	10	15	+0.6	+0.5
5. Mammoth Cave, KY (streams)	11	7.9	0.0007	25	1	65	15	1	2	−0.5	−1.1
6. Mammoth Cave (standing pools)	12	8.1	0.0008	35	8	120	15	3	4	+0.1	−0.1
7. Florida cave streams (typical)	23	7.5	0.008	60	20	250	15	10	20	+0.2	+0.1
8. Carlsbad Cavern, NM (drips)	15	7.4	0.01	60	35	330	25	3	5	+0.1	+0.0
9. Carlsbad Cavern (standing pools)	18	8.4	0.0007	20	35	200	20	4	7	+0.5	+0.7
10. Villa Luz, Mexico (H_2S ~500 ppm)	21	6.5	0.07	430	80	360	1100	500	790	−0.2	−0.4

*Calculated with Eq. 5.11c

Interpretation

1–3: Typical cave water, with moderate P_{CO_2}, pH above 7, and high Ca and HCO_3 from dissolution of limestone. Mg, from dolomite, is moderate. Na and Cl are from de-icing salts on nearby road. SO_4 is probably from oxidation of iron sulfide in the bedrock. Slow drips are high in dissolved load and are calcite-saturated where they emerge into the cave. Streams have a lower P_{CO_2} and higher pH because of loss of CO_2 from entrances. They are calcite-saturated at low flow and aggressive at high flow, when inflow is rapid and there is little time for the water to reach equilibrium with the bedrock.

4: Compatible with 1–3, with high Mg from dolomite. Supersaturation caused by CO_2 loss from drips.

5–6: Very low P_{CO_2}, and therefore high pH, caused by many low-CO_2 inputs through a sandstone cap. Pools are near saturation with calcite and dolomite. Many streams are perched on low-solubility beds and are aggressive toward calcite and dolomite year-round.

7: Typical Florida cave water seems to resemble that of New York caves, except in temperature. Some Florida groundwater contains high Na, Cl, Mg, and SO_4 from sea-water mixing. Hydrogen sulfide is abundant in a few caves as the result of sulfate reduction.

8–9: Drips show a fairly high P_{CO_2} despite the semi-arid climate, but rapid CO_2 loss to the well-aerated cave atmosphere produces supersaturated pools with very low P_{CO_2}, high pH, and calcite supersaturation.

10: An active sulfuric acid cave. Very high H_2S, high P_{CO_2}, and low pH, with high dissolved load, indicate a deep-basinal water source, with sulfate reduction. Water is aggressive toward both calcite and dolomite.

6

Characteristics of solution caves

TO DETERMINE a cave's origin, one must examine its overall pattern, the nature of its passages, and the individual details that make each passage unique. The characteristic features of solution caves are introduced here, and their interpretation is discussed further in the next few chapters. Cave minerals and weathering products are described in Chapters 10 and 12. Although most of the features described here are limited to solution caves, or are most abundant in them, some (such as sediments) are common in caves of all kinds.

Cave entrances

Natural cave entrances include swallow holes, springs, holes in the bottoms of sinkholes, and openings formed by the erosional intersection of caves (Figure 6.1). Entrances are exposed to subsiding soil or collapse debris, and many have been blocked by these processes. Some caves, especially those formed by deep-seated processes, have no natural entrances. Many caves have been discovered by excavation (Chapter 1). Ardent cave diggers believe that any sinkhole will eventually lead to a cave, given enough effort.

Figure 6.1: Common entrance types in solution caves: (**a**) sinkhole, McClung's Cave, West Virginia; (**b**) vertical shaft along a fracture, McFail's Hole, New York; (**c**) collapse entrance, Cirque Cave, California; (**d**) spring, Planinska jama, Slovenia; (**e**) shaft with waterfall, Stephens Gap Cave, Alabama; (**f**) sinking stream, Stephens Gap Cave; (**g**) erosional intersection of a cave, entrance to Hicks Cave, New Mexico, about 50 cm in diameter; (**h**) artificial excavation in a sinkhole, Czech Republic.

Cave entrances are usually small in comparison to the caves to which they lead, although their presence can usually be anticipated by their location in sinkholes or at springs. Some entrances are huge. The entrance of Brazil's Gruta Casa de Pedra, reputedly the world's tallest, is 215 m high. Tantalizing holes are visible in many cliff faces, but most are merely rock shelters that lead nowhere (Figure 6.2).

Passage types

Most solution caves consist of an array of interconnected passages of various types. They are also occasionally called *galleries*, *corridors*, and similar terms. In reference to turbulent groundwater flow, the term **solution conduits** is most appropriate, since it applies not only to traversable passages but also to those too small to explore. Each passage reflects the nature and flow pattern of the water that formed it, so the various passage types and their interconnections provide direct clues to a cave's origin.

Figure 6.2: Many inviting holes in cliffs are mere pockets that lead nowhere. These are in the Guadalupe Mountains of Texas.

Shafts are well-like voids that are vertical, or nearly so (Figure 6.3). Most are formed by vadose water flowing downward along fractures and are simply the vertical components of vadose passages. Many cave entrances consist of shafts (Figure 6.1b, e, and f).

A shaft may follow intersecting small fractures that allow it to develop a rounded cross section (Figure 6.4), or it may follow a single large fracture that enlarges with a lens-shaped cross section (Figure 6.5). In poorly fractured rock, shafts tend to deepen with time, bed by bed, as the descending water dissolves the floor and exits through a sequence of drains at progressively lower elevations (Figure 6.4). It is common for a shaft to be fed by a stream that is perched on an insoluble or resistant bed. The water usually begins its descent where the bed is breached by a fracture. Some shafts are formed instead by the convergence of several small infeeders at the base of the epikarst (Chapter 2). Many shaft drains are perched on resistant beds, as in Figure 6.6.

When explorers discover a shaft from the bottom, they peer upward into what looks like a *dome*, and they sometimes give it that name. When viewed from the top it may be called a *pit*. For this reason, shafts are sometimes inappropriately called *domepits*.

During high flow, a typical shaft contains a roaring waterfall that bathes the walls with a highly aggressive spray. During low flow the water is closer to saturation. It moves down the shaft walls as a thin film that still assures a large

Figure 6.3: Enlargement of a vertical shaft by a waterfall, McFail's Cave, New York.

area of contact with the soluble bedrock. The infeeder and drain are low-gradient channels that enlarge more slowly than the shaft, especially if they are perched on resistant beds or floored with sediment. As a result, shafts tend to be much larger in diameter than the passages that feed or drain them.

Figure 6.4: A sequence of abandoned drains (on right) in the wall of Keller Well, a vertical shaft in Mammoth Cave, Kentucky. Water enters through a low bedding-plane crawl at the top. The shaft diameter is about 2.5 m.

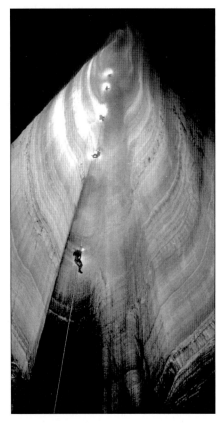

Figure 6.5: Upward view into a vertical shaft developed along a fault zone (Fantastic Pit, Ellison Cave, Georgia). The shaft spans a vertical range of more than 200 m, and its lowest tie-off point for descent is 155 m (510 ft). Flashes were fired at intervals by a single person descending the rope.

Where cavernous rocks are overlain by insoluble rocks, shafts are concentrated beneath the eroded edges of the insoluble cap, especially where perched streams have cut into the flanks of ridges (Figure 6.1f). The growth of shafts accelerates the erosional retreat of the cap-rock by undermining its edges. Caves in the plateaus of the eastern U.S. contain many fine examples of this kind of shaft development.

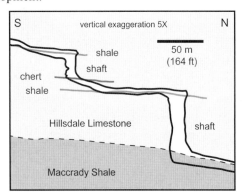

Figure 6.6: The Polar Passage in Ludington Cave, West Virginia, has a typical vadose profile with a series of shafts interspersed with passages that are (or once were) perched on insoluble shale and chert beds. Like most vadose passages, this one extends down the dip of the beds, except where it is deflected along joints and faults. (Data from Palmer, 1974.)

Figure 6.7: Aerial view of the collapse sinkhole entrance of Minye, on the island of New Britain, Papua New Guinea. The sinkhole is a vertical-walled shaft 500 m in diameter and 417 m deep. A large river flows across the floor from the cave opening in the center of the photo. Photo by Jean-Paul Sounier.

A few shafts are not formed by descending water at all. In hypogenic caves, such as those formed by sulfuric acid, shafts are usually formed by rising phreatic water. Well-known examples punctuate the entrance passages of several caves in the Guadalupe Mountains of New Mexico. Much of their growth may take place above the water table by sulfuric acid that is generated where hydrogen sulfide and oxygen are absorbed by droplets and films of vadose water. Shafts in such caves have smooth, rounded, profiles that step upward in gentle arcs (Chapter 8, Figures 8.70–8.71). They rarely contain vadose solution features.

Some shafts are formed by collapse and upward migration of cave ceilings. One of the largest is the colossal entrance sinkhole of Minye, in Papua New Guinea (Figure 6.7; Audra and others, 2001). Mexico's Sótano de las Golondrinas is a well-known example (Figure 6.8; Raines, 1968). Shafts formed in this way, or by hypogenic processes, can be modified later by descending water, which may obscure their primary origin.

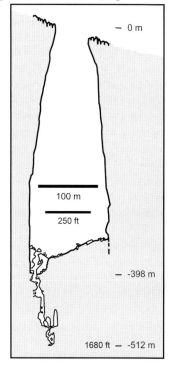

Figure 6.8: Profile through Sótano de las Golondrinas, San Luis Potosí, Mexico, a shaft formed by collapse generated by dissolution below. The shaft floor is obscured by rubble of unknown depth. The narrow lower section is located in bedrock adjacent to the rubble. (Association for Mexican Cave Studies.)

Figure 6.10: Splitting of a canyon passage into two levels along bedding-plane partings. As shown here, it is common for the two levels to diverge and then combine again into a single passage.

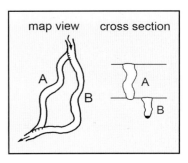

The width of a canyon is usually proportional to the discharge of the stream that forms it, although the spray of a retreating waterfall produces a wider passage than a low-gradient stream. Differences in rock solubility and competence can cause local widening and narrowing of passage cross sections (Figure 3.25). Accumulation of sediment may encourage widening at the floor level. As a vadose stream cuts down through stratified rock, it may be deflected laterally to new routes along bedding-plane partings, so that the canyon splits into a variety of levels. The branches may converge downstream to form a single passage, as in Figure 6.10, or they may remain independent and lead to different destinations.

Tubes (or *tubular passages*) are tunnels with cross sections that are lenticular, elliptical, or nearly circular (Figure 6.11). Most tubes originate at or below the water table, where they are entirely water-filled, either continually or periodically. Unlike canyons, which enlarge mainly downward, tubes enlarge around their entire perimeters. Many tubes are formed and enlarged above the normal water-

Figure 6.9: Canyon passage in McFail's Cave, New York, the result of dissolution by a still-active vadose stream.

Canyons (or *canyon passages*) are formed by vadose water that follows inclined paths where vertical openings are not available (Figure 6.9). Bedding-plane partings are the most common routes for the initial water flow. Inclined faults serve the same function in some caves. When the initial openings acquire enough flow, their floors are dissolved and eroded downward so that the passage heights are almost always greater than their widths. Most canyons are high, narrow, and sinuous. Many are interrupted along their length by shafts.

Vadose streams in canyons may cut their bedrock floors downward almost uniformly to produce profiles that are interrupted only by small waterfalls and rapids (Figure 6.9). Other canyons form by the upstream retreat of one or more large waterfalls (Figure 4.4). In the same way, a shaft may become elongate as its infeeder cuts into the wall on one side, thus blurring the distinction between shaft and canyon.

Most canyons are only a meter or two in width and a few meters to tens of meters high. Some are much larger. The impressive canyon of Škocjanske jama, Slovenia, which carries one of the world's largest underground rivers, is about 90 m high and nearly as wide. Some canyon passages in China are up to 200 m high.

Figure 6.11: Tubular passage in Trou du Glaz, France, formed by phreatic water and enlarged by occasional floodwaters.

Figure 6.12: Tube with a lenticular cross section elongated along prominent bedding, Mammoth Cave, Kentucky. This is a tour route in Cleaveland Avenue.

table level by periodic floodwaters (Chapter 8). Most tubes are less than 10 m in diameter, although a few exceed 100 m (Figures 2.83–2.85). Vadose passages form the tributary infeeders for most tubes.

Where they are guided by gently dipping bedding-plane partings, tubes tend to have sinuous, curving patterns with cross sections that are widened along the bedding (Figure 6.12). Where high-angle fractures are the main control, tubes have angular patterns composed of fairly straight segments that are generally greater in height than in width.

In profile, a typical tube loops up and down along its length, with some segments that rise in the downstream direction. Those parts of a passage that, when forming, extended beneath the water table and then rose to it again are called ***phreatic loops***. The cave profile in Figure 5.24 shows an example at location D. This term can also be applied to downward loops in formerly phreatic passages that are now dry.

Some tubes have a vadose origin. They include ***perched tubes***, which are floored by resistant beds that inhibit downward enlargement (Figure 6.13), as well as incipient canyons that were active for too short a time for their floors to have deepened. A vadose tube can be recognized by its continuous downward gradient and little or no upward ceiling enlargement. Tubes of phreatic origin can be perched in the vadose zone in areas of local ponding,

Figure 6.13: Perched tube floored by resistant shaly, dolomitic limestone, Waterfall Trail, Mammoth Cave, Kentucky. Dating of sediment (Chapter 13) shows that this passage has been actively enlarging above the water table for more than a million years with only the small amount of low-gradient stream entrenchment shown here. Note the earlier canyon in the ceiling.

Figure 6.14: Fissure passage in McFail's Cave, New York.

and they have all the characteristics of true tubes, including irregular profiles. The perched nature of such a tube can usually be shown by the presence of vadose development farther downstream in the same passage.

Fissures (or *fissure passages*) form along vertical or steeply inclined fractures (Figure 6.14). They are straight and narrow, and their typical cross sections are lenticular, narrowing upward and in places downward as well. Fissure widths are usually much less than their heights. Where the bedrock floor of a fissure is obscured by sediment, its cross section may resemble a gothic arch. There is a continuous gradation between fissures and fracture-guided tubes, which have more rounded cross sections than fissures. Dead-end fissures may branch from larger passages as linear ceiling pockets or as spurs at the junctions between passage segments (Figure 3.49).

Most fissures form at or below the water table, or in zones of periodic flooding, so their greatest enlargement takes place while they are completely water-filled. A few originate in the vadose zone as narrow shafts or canyons that are aligned along prominent joints or faults (Figure 6.1b). Some fissure passages along major fractures are perfectly straight for hundreds of meters.

In discussions of cave origin, the term *fissure* is sometimes applied to any pre-solutional fracture or parting, regardless of the passage shape into which it eventually grows (Ford and Ewers, 1978). Because the context is usually clear, this dual application of *fissures* to indicate either initial fractures or fissure-shaped passages is widely accepted.

Some cave passages are composites of more than one type. The most common is the *keyhole passage*, which is a tube with a relatively narrow canyon entrenched in its floor. Together they form a distinctive keyhole-shaped cross section (Figure 6.15). The usual interpretation is that a pre-existing phreatic tube has been deepened by smaller amounts of vadose water. Commonly, however, the vadose flow is no less than the phreatic flow but simply moves more rapidly and occupies a smaller cross section. A passage above the normal water table can also acquire a keyhole shape as the result of periodic flooding, where narrow canyons are cut in the tube floors by trickles of receding floodwater.

Some passages do not fit any of the above descriptions. Caves that are guided by a complex of intersecting fractures or intergranular pores have irregular cross sections and patterns. In passages that flood severely, various solution features can be superposed on the original passage outlines and increase the complexity of the cave. Passages modified by breakdown or sediment fill can acquire a variety of shapes considerably different from their original form.

Phantom passages appear to be openings filled with sediment, except that they were never true caves. Instead they are incipient passages formed in impure sandy limestone, where the limestone between the insoluble grains has been dissolved away, to leave behind only the sand (Schmidt, 1974; Quinif, 1999). The residual sand typically consists of quartz grains. The sand often retains its original sedimentary structures, such as cross beds, which can be traced without a break from the phantom passages into the adjacent bedrock (Figure 6.16). Some excellent examples can be seen in Laurel Caverns, Pennsylvania (Schmidt, 1974). It is located in the impure Loyalhanna Limestone of Mississippian age, which contains up to 50% quartz sand. Phantom passages are most common in caves that are exposed either to slow phreatic flow or to periodic flooding. Rapid water flow is needed to remove the insoluble material from the major flow routes, but the low-velocity water that is injected into dead-end pockets and fissures during floods simply dissolves the carbonate matrix between the sand grains, so that the insoluble material

Figure 6.15: Keyhole passage in the Silvertip Cave System, Montana.

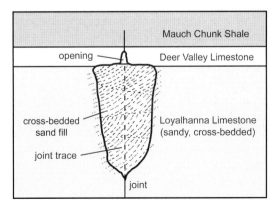

Figure 6.16: Phantom passage in Laurel Caverns, Pennsylvania (after Schmidt, 1974). Quartz sand that fills the passage has cross beds that are more or less continuous with those in the adjacent Loyalhanna Limestone. Scale: the Deer Valley Limestone is about 60 cm thick.

is left behind. Häuselmann and Tognini (2005) describe a cave in Switzerland in which phantom passages have been enlarged by erosional removal of the sand. They suggest that certain characteristics, such as ungraded profiles and abrupt changes in cross-sectional area, may help to distinguish this kind of cave even after its internal sediment has been removed.

Passage terminations

Most cave passages cannot be explored over their entire lengths, from where the water enters the ground to where it discharges at springs or into other passages. On a typical cave map they are shown to terminate where they are filled by sediment or collapse material. Some passages simply become too narrow to follow, especially where the cave branches into progressively smaller tributaries in the upstream direction. A small inlet by itself may produce only a tiny channel, so that a cave-sized passage is produced only after several others have joined it. In contrast, a large inflow of water, for example from a sinking stream, can form a traversable passage right from the input point.

A passage formed by a discrete stream tends to retain approximately the same cross-sectional area for long distances. It is rare for such a passage to pinch down or enlarge abruptly. Irregular cross sections are typical of passages enlarged by flooding, mixing, or deep-seated processes. Nevertheless, the exploration of a stream passage may terminate at a pinch in the downstream direction if the solvent water has lost most of its aggressiveness, or if passage growth has been retarded by resistant rock or accumulation of sediment.

For all of these reasons it is rare for a cave map to show the entire pattern of water flow that formed the cave. A typical cave map shows passages that terminate abruptly, with no indication as to where they continue beyond the impasse (Figure 1.18). A cave's drainage lines usually continue far beyond the upstream ends of the mapped passages. Care should be taken to recognize the limitations of cave maps when interpreting present and former groundwater patterns.

Cave rooms

Most caves broaden here and there into rooms that are conspicuously larger than the passages leading into them.

Some cave rooms are simply the enlargements produced where two or more passages intersect. Others are located in zones of bedrock collapse (Figure 6.17). But collapse alone cannot form a large room, because the resulting rock pile occupies more volume than the original solid bedrock. A large room can form by collapse only if some of the fallen blocks are dissolved or eroded away by cave streams. In this way the ceiling and walls can continue to retreat even if they lie above the highest level reached by the stream. The largest cave rooms are of this type. The most formidable example is Sarawak Chamber in Lubang Nasib Bagus (Good Luck Cave), Malaysia, which has a volume of about 12 million

Figure 6.17: Harbinger Hall, in Sistema Cheve, Mexico, is a large room formed by collapse, with much of the collapse material removed by the cave stream. Photo by Ken Davis.

cubic meters and a floor area of 162,000 square meters, or roughly 40 acres (Figures 6.18 and 3.37).

Truncated remnants of large passages are considered rooms if they are larger than nearby passages. In a large passage nearly filled with sediment or breakdown, local removal of

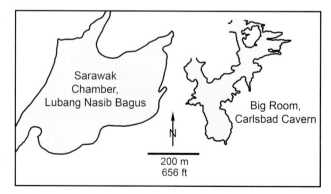

Figure 6.18: Map of Sarawak Chamber in Lubang Nasib Bagus, Sarawak, Malaysia (from Eavis, 1981) compared to that of the Big Room in Carlsbad Cavern, a well-known standard for size (from map by Cave Research Foundation). See also Figure 3.37.

Figure 6.19: The Big Room of Carlsbad Cavern was formed by concentrated dissolution by sulfuric acid (see Chapter 8). This is the narrow northeastern part of the room shown in Figure 6.18, where the ceiling height averages about 25 m.

the fill by an underlying stream can excavate rooms that are connected by the smaller partly filled segments.

Large rooms formed by dissolution alone are uncommon, but they include some world-class examples, such as the Big Room of Carlsbad Cavern (Figures 6.18–6.19). They are formed by intense local dissolution, as where sulfuric acid is produced by oxidation of hydrogen sulfide, or where there is mixing of two water sources with contrasting chemistry. Ponding of solutionally aggressive floodwaters can also enlarge passage segments into rooms where the bedrock is locally more fractured or soluble than in surrounding areas.

Cave levels

The vertical distribution of passages in a solution cave is nearly always related to the evolution of local river valleys (Figure 6.20). Major passages tend to form at or near the elevations of the rivers into which they drain, except where insoluble rocks interfere. As rivers deepen their channels by erosion, the cave streams divert to successively lower levels. In a multi-level cave, the largest passages are typically those

that have been active for the longest time, generally during periods of nearly static base level. Concentrations of passages at certain elevations are known as ***cave levels***. Many formerly phreatic passages, now at elevations higher than the present water table, are ***fossil passages*** that have been abandoned by their streams.

Some caves do not correlate well with local patterns of valley erosion. The vertical distribution of their passages may result instead from perching of vadose water on resistant beds. Rising phreatic water can be confined beneath low-permeability beds to form passages at elevations unrelated to surface drainage. In some phreatic caves the passages are concentrated in favorable strata, as in the Black Hills caves of South Dakota (pages 354–358).

Because few passages are truly level, some karst scientists use the terms ***tier*** or ***story*** in preference to *cave level*. It is appropriate to use *tier* or *story* in referring to the vertical layout of a cave if no relationship to nearby river levels is implied. This topic is covered in more detail in Chapter 9.

Cave patterns

All but the simplest caves contain a variety of passages that interconnect in distinctive patterns (Figure 6.21). Some have a branching pattern, whereas others are mazes with many interconnecting passages and closed loops. In addition to the basic patterns described here, every cave has its own unique passage layout that reflects the local geologic conditions. These topics are discussed in detail in Chapters 8 and 9, so they are introduced only briefly here.

A cave's basic pattern is easily identified from field observation or maps, unless only a small part of the cave is accessible. Different parts of the same cave may have different patterns, and more than one pattern can be superposed at a single location. Some passages are inaccessibly small or blocked by breakdown, and although they are part of the hydrologic picture, their exact trends are usually unknown.

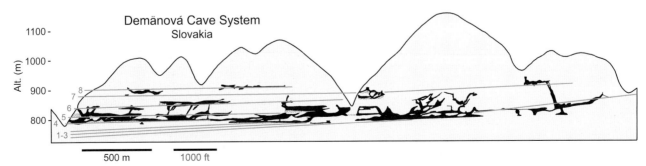

Figure 6.20: Stages of passage development in the Demänová Cave, Slovakia (Droppa, 1966). Cave levels are labeled in ascending order from 1 to 8 (youngest to oldest). Level 1 coincides with the present position of the nearby Demänovska River, which parallels the main trend of the cave. The cave was formed in limestone mainly by subterranean diversion of the river.

Despite these complications, the following cave patterns can be easily recognized (Figure 6.21):

Branchwork caves

Branchwork caves consist of stream passages that converge as tributaries. This kind of drainage is essentially the underground equivalent of surface streams. Each major water source, such as a sinkhole, contributes to a single solution conduit, or occasionally more than one. Passages rarely branch in the downstream direction. Closed loops are rare, except where water abandons its original passage for a new one and rejoins an older route farther downstream.

At least 60% of all known solution caves have branchwork patterns. The examples in Figure 6.21 show the distinctive trend of converging passages, from many small infeeders to progressively larger and fewer trunk passages. The effects of local rock structure are also apparent. In well-bedded rock the passages are sinuous and curving. In prominently fractured rock most of the passages follow angular patterns. Despite these differences, the overall branching style is similar.

The branching character of a cave can be obscured in various ways. If the passages form during several different stages, so that water diverts to progressively lower routes, both the new and old passages contribute to the overall pattern of the cave. Also, as the overlying land surface erodes downward, caves are segmented by breakdown and valley erosion. Some of the segments may become isolated so that their original pattern is unclear. A cave map shows all accessible passages, both active and abandoned, so the overall pattern may appear more complex than that of its presently active streams. The map of a large branchwork cave may resemble a plate of spaghetti (for example, the map of Mammoth Cave, Figure 1.3), but the *active* passages still follow an essentially branching pattern, as they have done during every stage in the cave's evolution.

Maze caves

The following four cave types can be grouped loosely as *maze caves*, which contain many closed loops that originate more or less simultaneously. These contrast with closed loops in branchwork caves, which form sequentially by stream diversion to lower levels, which rejoin the original passages farther downstream.

Anastomotic caves are composed of curving tubes that intersect in braided patterns that have many closed loops. Nearly all are formed by periodic floodwaters fed by sinking streams or by rapid infiltration through a karst surface of

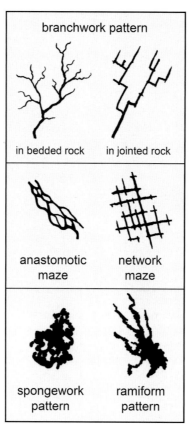

Figure 6.21: Common patterns of solution caves. Single-passage caves are simply rudimentary versions of those shown here. See Chapter 8 for details.

bare bedrock. A typical anastomotic cave forms a two-dimensional array along a single low-angle parting or fracture. There can be a few fracture-controlled fissure passages, but they do not dominate the pattern. Rare three-dimensional examples follow more than one geologic structure. About 5–10% of solution caves are at least partly anastomotic. Although some entire caves have this pattern, it is also common for small anastomotic mazes to serve as local diversion routes around constrictions in flood-prone branchwork caves. Many alpine caves are anastomotic, or at least partly so. Much of the giant Swiss cave Hölloch is a three-dimensional anastomotic maze.

Network caves are angular grids of intersecting fissure passages formed by the widening of nearly all major fractures in local areas. They are produced in several ways: (1) uniform seepage through overlying or underlying insoluble rock, (2) periodic flooding, (3) mixing of waters of different chemistry, or (4) generation of sulfuric from oxidation of hydrogen sulfide. Unlike branching passages, the fissures in a network cave are not fed by individual water sources. Instead they pinch in the direction away from the main parts of the cave. Closed loops are common, and the passages form a pattern like that of city streets. Some crude networks contain mostly dead-end fissures with only a few closed loops. The fissures in a network tend to be roughly uniform in cross section and passage density. Most caves of this type are limited to a single tier, although some large ones are multi-tiered. About 15–20% of all solution caves are networks. The largest are those of the Black Hills (e.g., Jewel and Wind Caves) and the gypsum mazes of Ukraine.

Spongework caves consist of interconnected solution cavities of varied size, which produce a three-dimensional pattern like the pores in a sponge. They form by the growth and coalescing of intergranular pores and other minor openings in rocks that contain no major fractures or partings. Good examples include seacoast caves in young, porous limestone. Caves of Bermuda and the Bahamas are mostly spongework mazes, although partial collapse has obscured this pattern in many places. Local spongework caves, or parts of caves, are common in reef rocks that have large primary porosity. Most spongework caves are produced either by mixing of contrasting water types or by sulfuric acid. A few are formed by floodwaters. About 2–5% of all known solution caves have spongework patterns or include large spongework sections. Spongework also accounts for a great amount of porosity that is less than cave size.

Ramiform caves (or ***ramifying caves***) are composed of irregular rooms and galleries in three-dimensional arrays with branches that extend outward from the central portions. They are most commonly produced by sulfuric acid from the oxidation of rising hydrogen sulfide, less often by mixing processes. In plan view they may resemble ink blots. Passage profiles and cross sections are highly irregular and show abrupt changes over short distances. Closed loops are common. The outward branches usually form as sequential outlets for groundwater at different times and at different elevations. Former inlets for rising water commonly include dead-end rifts that extend downward from the major levels. In shape, but not necessarily in origin, there is a continuous gradation between ramifying caves and mazes of spongework and network pattern.

Ramiform caves account for only about 5% of all solution caves, but they include some spectacular examples. Their baffling layout makes them exciting to explore, because the tiniest hole can lead to large rooms and passages beyond. Lechuguilla Cave, New Mexico, and the Kap-Kutan System of Turkmenistan are renowned for their size, complexity, and variety (Taylor and Widmer, 1991; Maltsev and Korshunov, 1998). Some of the larger caves in the Bahamas have crudely ramifying patterns, although most of the branches appear to be former inlets, rather than outlets (Mylroie and Carew, 1990).

Single-passage caves

Single-passage caves are rudimentary forms of any of the types described above. The few large examples are mainly stream caves fed by sinking streams, or are remnants of what were once more extensive caves. There are many single-passage caves, but most are quite small. It is difficult to tally all the insignificant holes that might qualify. Although they are numerous, single-passage caves probably account for less than 1% of known solution caves in terms of passage length or total volume.

Small-scale solution features in caves

The individual passages of a solution cave are embellished by a variety of solution features that provide clues to the cave's origin. They are sometimes called ***speleogens***, in contrast to ***speleothems***, which are secondary mineral deposits in caves. For additional information on speleogens, see Slabe (1995) and Lauritzen and Lundberg (2000). The erosional bedrock forms in the walls and floors of surface canyons (Richardson and Carling, 2005) can also be found underground.

Scallops are asymmetrical hollows dissolved in soluble bedrock surfaces by turbulent water (Figure 6.22). They indicate both the direction and velocity of the water that formed them. They are especially useful in determining former flow conditions in passages that are now dry. Scallops range in length from about half a centimeter to one or two meters. Many canyons and tubes are lined by a nearly continuous dimpling of scallops. They are poorly developed or absent in rock that is impure, thin bedded, or which

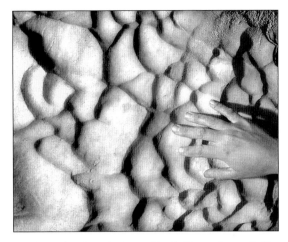

Figure 6.22: Scallops in the walls of Cirque Cave, California. Their asymmetry shows that the flow that formed them was from left to right. Look carefully, because the hollows in the photo may at first look like mounds. The light was from the left (note shadow of hand). The steep sides of the scallops are in shadow.

contains internal structures that interfere with the scallop shapes. In places, scallops have been removed by collapse, mechanical erosion, or dissolution by static, low-velocity floodwaters.

The flow direction of the most recent water to enlarge the cave is shown by the scallop asymmetry (Figure 6.23). The steep sides of the hollows are on the upstream side. The faster the flow, the smaller the scallops. In high-velocity flow, jets of water emerging from the scallops quickly absorb rotational energy from the main body of water and produce small turbulent eddies. The method for analyzing flow velocity from scallop length was developed mainly by Curl (1966, 1974) and Blumberg and Curl (1974). Their observations are summarized in Figure 6.24 and are applied in simplified form on page 149.

Scallops are very sensitive to local flow conditions. For example, where a sharp break in a cave wall causes water to swirl in a reverse eddy, the scallop asymmetry is also reversed. Where high-velocity water invades a passage that formerly contained slower-moving water, small scallops may be superposed on larger ones. It is rare for large scallops to develop over small ones without obliterating the earlier ones. In some places, two sets of scallops are oriented in opposite directions. More often, the most recent flow simply removes all traces of earlier scallops.

Scallops are not formed if the water velocity is less than about 1 cm/sec, because the turbulent eddies are not

Figure 6.23: Profile through a typical scalloped surface, showing relation to flow direction. Scallop length is used to estimate the former flow velocity (Figure 6.24).

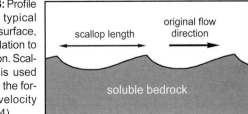

scallop length

original flow direction

soluble bedrock

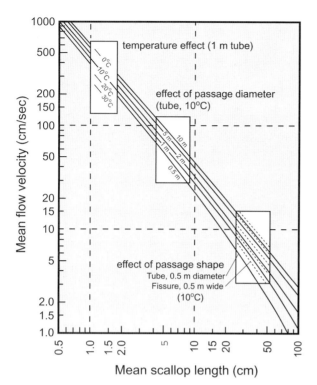

Figure 6.24: Scallop length in relation to flow velocity in water-filled cave passages, based on the equations of Curl (1974). The main (heavy) lines show the results for different tube diameters at 10° C (labeled in central box). The effect of temperature is shown in the upper box for a tube 1 m in diameter. The effect of passage shape (tube vs. fissure) is shown in the lower box at 10° C. In all cases, larger scallops indicate smaller flow velocities. For any given scallop length, higher temperatures decrease the interpreted velocity. The interpreted velocity in a fissure of width *w* will be larger than that in a tube with a diameter equal to *w*. Curl recommends weighting the mean scallop length in favor of the larger scallops: (sum of all L values)^3 / (sum of all L values)^2. Field calculations (M. Palmer, 1976) suggest that a comparable result is obtained from the simple mean length of only the fully-formed scallops, which are not truncated by others. The concepts in this graph are idealized and should be applied to field examples only in a general way.

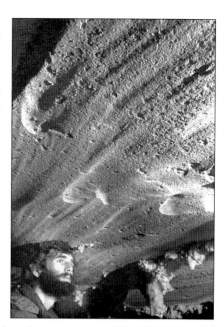

Figure 6.25: Elongate ceiling grooves, which resemble long scallops, appear to form where sediment fills the passage almost to the ceiling. That was the case in this passage in Mammoth Cave, Kentucky (Collins Avenue), but the sediment has been excavated to allow tour access. The original flow was in the direction of the person's gaze.

stable or uniform enough in such slow-moving water. At velocities greater than about 3 m/sec the bedrock surfaces are usually abraded by sediment, which prevents scallops from forming. Lauritzen and others (1985) estimate that the velocity calculated from scallops is roughly equivalent to the highest 5% of the annual flow, or about three times the average flow velocity.

Greatly elongate scallops are sometimes found on the ceilings of passages that were once filled almost to the ceiling with sediment (Figure 6.25). Such scallops are usually very shallow and at least 5 times longer than they are wide. Their shapes are apparently influenced by the abrasive action of suspended sediment. They show the flow direction, but apparently not the flow velocities.

Flutes are parallel vertical grooves dissolved in cave walls by descending vadose water (Figure 6.26). They resemble the flutes in the columns of classical architecture. Fluted walls are most common in shafts, and also in canyons

formed by the headward retreat of waterfalls. Thick-bedded rocks are most easily fluted.

Flutes of a different kind are formed in streams as variants of scallops, where turbulent eddies are unusually stable. Their long dimensions are oriented perpendicular to the flow direction, and, as in scallops, their asymmetry and spacing indicate local flow directions and velocity (Curl, 1966). They are rare and are usually limited to small areas of cave wall.

Rills are vadose channels similar in origin to flutes, except that they form on sloping surfaces. They resemble the rills in karren topography described in Chapter 2. Rills occasionally form in cave walls where water drains out of bedding-plane partings or sediment as floodwaters recede (Figure 6.27). Low-gradient rills, or those formed by thin films of water, may have meandering courses.

Figure 6.26: Vadose flutes in the walls of a vertical shaft in Mammoth Cave, Kentucky (on right side of photo).

Interpreting past flow conditions from scallops

Scallops represent the peak flow rates of the water that most recently enlarged the passage in which they occur. Flow direction is shown by the asymmetry of the scallops (see Figure 6.23). The flow velocity can be estimated from Figure 6.24, which is based on the analysis of Curl (1974).

This graph provides the mean velocities over the entire passage cross section. Curl suggests measuring all scallops and using a weighted mean that favors the larger ones, but it is also satisfactory to take a simple average of only the well-formed ones, which are usually the largest in any group.

The graph is best used by obtaining scallop measurements from a fairly straight section of passage, where the bedrock surfaces are covered uniformly with scallops of roughly equal size. Under these conditions, the passage was probably filled completely with water when the scallops formed, and the discharge can be estimated by multiplying the velocity by the cross-sectional area of the passage (see Eq. 4.1).

The velocity increases away from the cave walls, so its mean value depends on the passage size and shape. The effect of passage size is shown by the four main lines on the graph, one each for passages 0.5, 1, 2, 5, and 10 m in diameter at a water temperature of 10°C. To convert from degrees Fahrenheit, use °C = (°F − 32)/1.8. The larger the diameter, the larger the mean velocity calculated from a given scallop length.

These lines are valid only for tubes of roughly circular cross section. In fissures, the passage width is used instead of the diameter, and the calculated velocity shifts slightly upward, as shown by the dashed lines in the lower box on the graph. The lines for passages of intermediate shape fall somewhere between the two extremes.

The effect of temperature is shown in the upper box for tubes 1 m in diameter. As temperature increases, the velocity calculated for a given scallop length decreases. The amount of temperature offset is the same for all other lines on the graph, regardless of passage size or shape.

This approach also applies to scallops formed in *ice* by water or wind (Figure 1.2c). For air at 0°C, the velocity for ice scallops is ~7.4 times the velocity calculated for similar scallops formed in bedrock by water.

For most cave studies, only a rough estimate of flow velocity is required. It may be enough just to contrast slow, moderate, and fast flows by noting the distribution of large, medium, and small scallops. The following expression provides a quick estimate of flow velocity in the vicinity of the scalloped surface:

$$v \text{ (cm/sec)} \approx X/L \qquad (6.1)$$

where L = mean scallop length in centimeters, and X is a number that depends on the temperature of the water that formed the scallops. $X = 375$ at 0°C, 275 at 10°, 210 at 20°, and 170 at 30°.

Example 1: Scallops are measured in a Wyoming cave where the water temperature is 5°C, so X in Eq. 6.1 is about 325. The average scallop length is 7.5 cm. The flow velocity they represent is 325/7.5 ≈ 43 cm/sec (about 1.4 ft/sec).

Example 2: Scallops are measured in a limestone fissure 50 cm (0.5 m) wide. Their mean length is 3.0 cm. Glacial sediments scattered throughout the passage suggest that the scallops formed by glacial meltwater that was probably about 0°C. From 3.0 cm on the horizontal axis of Figure 6.24, extend a vertical line upward to the 0.5 m line (lowest solid line). To correct for the passage shape, extend your line about 2/3 of the way to the 1-meter line, as shown by the dashed line for 0.5 m wide fissures in the lower box. To correct to 0°C, note the space between the 10° and 0° lines in the upper box, and extend your vertical line further by that same distance. Then extend a horizontal line from this point to the scale on the left. The estimate for mean flow velocity in the fissure is roughly 155 cm/sec. Given the many uncertainties, there is no point in scrutinizing either the graph or the original equations for more precise results. Note that the simplified equation above would give an estimate of 125 cm/sec, but that is only for the flow right at the passage wall. If the passage is 5 m high and its width of 0.5 m is fairly constant, the cross-sectional area is about 2.5 m². The discharge indicated by the scallops is about 2.5 m² x 1.55 m/sec ≈ 3.9 m³/sec.

Example 3: In most passages the scallop length varies from place to place, especially with height above the floor. Thus it is necessary to measure scallops at a variety of heights and interpret them in terms of local flow conditions. For example, if scallops become smaller with height above the floor, they probably indicate that the water did not always fill the passage completely and that the high-level flood flow was faster than the low flow. Scallops lower on the walls represent the more frequent low flows, even though they were also exposed to infrequent high flow. The higher walls, reached only by floodwaters, contain only small scallops. Near the ceiling the scallops may become larger and perhaps disappear entirely. This is often caused by ponding of water upstream from passage constrictions during the highest floods.

Figure 6.27: Rills emanating from bedding-plane anastomoses in the wall of Swinnerton Avenue, Mammoth Cave.

Flutes and rills have a complex international classification that is beyond the scope of this book. Ford and Lundberg (1987), Ford and Williams (1989), and Lundberg (2005) offer the most complete guides to the subject.

Anastomoses are small, sinuous tubes that interconnect in a braided, maze-like pattern, normally along bedding-plane partings (Figures 6.27–6.28). They are much less common along fractures, which suggests that they are guided by the internal irregularities typical of bedding contacts. The tubes have roughly semicircular to circular cross sections and range in diameter from about a centimeter to a meter. They are usually dissolved upward into the base of the overlying bed, because their floors tend to be armored by insoluble sediment or thin shale beds. In pattern they resemble anastomotic

Figure 6.28: Anastomoses in Mammoth Cave. They formed along the parting between two beds, and the lower bed has since fallen away, to expose the anastomoses in plan view.

Figure 6.29: Spongework in limestone breccia, Big Brush Creek Cave, Utah.

caves, but the scale of anastomoses is smaller and the passage density is higher. Anastomotic caves transmit large amounts of through-flowing water, but most anastomoses receive only local and temporary injection of water during floods.

Spongework resembles spongework caves in pattern but is smaller in scale. Spongework forms by the enlargement of primary pores or closely spaced fractures, either by local production of acids (e.g., sulfuric acid, or mixing of different waters, as in Figure 2.58) or by periodic injection of floodwaters from neighboring cave passages (Figure 6.29). Spongework is usually limited to small parts of a cave. In floodwater caves it has the same relationship to spongework caves that anastomoses have to anastomotic caves.

Solution pockets are dead-end solutional holes in cave walls or ceilings (Figure 6.30). Most are located along fractures. They occur singly or in linear groups along the guiding fractures. They are rarely confused with scallops because solution pockets are of varied size, are usually deeper than scallops, and are not asymmetrical in the systematic way that scallops are. Solution pockets do not migrate downflow with time, as do scallops, and in stream passages they must have even higher rates of wall retreat than scallops in order to form and survive (Springer and Wohl, 2002).

Solution pockets form in several ways. Most are the result of periodic flooding of the cave when aggressive water is injected into fractures (see pages 202–204 for details). Some

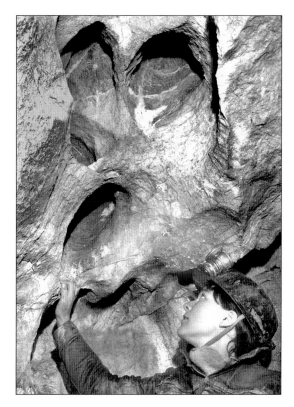

Figure 6.30: Solution pockets in the ceiling of Bergerhöhle, in the Austrian Alps. They are concentrated along minor joints.

Figure 6.31: Cupolas in the ceiling of Reed's Cave, South Dakota. With no other object for reference, it may be difficult to visualize these as rounded solution pockets. Width of photo = 5 m.

cause a local increase in P_{CO_2} in the confining water, which accelerates the dissolution of the cupola perimeters.

In stream passages, solution pockets can intersect and form sharp-edged blades of rock called ***echinoliths*** (Aley, 1964; Figure 6.32). Extreme examples can resemble

pockets are formed by sulfuric acid generated by oxidation of pyrite in the bedrock. The acid etches smooth round holes in the rock. They have abrupt contacts with the cave walls and may contain residual iron oxide. In caves formed entirely by sulfuric acid, solution pockets can be produced by the alteration of limestone or dolomite to gypsum, followed by dissolution of the gypsum. Some pockets that appear superficially to be large scallops are merely artifacts of gypsum replacement of carbonate rock (Chapters 8 and 12).

Solution pockets are sometimes attributed to mixing of two waters — the water in a phreatic passage plus water entering it through a ceiling fracture. This process is far less likely to produce solution pockets than floodwater, because dissolution by mixing requires that the two waters have substantially different water chemistries, which is not typical. Furthermore, mixing would take place only after the seepage from the fracture had already entered the main passage, and it is unlikely that the fissure itself would enlarge. Finally, if seepage enters through the fracture under phreatic conditions, it is likely to continue to do so after the passage becomes vadose, and dripstone deposits would form along the fracture trace. Few solution pockets contain dripstone.

Cupolas are large rounded solution pockets in cave ceilings that generally do not follow visible fractures (Figure 6.31). Most are formed by slow-moving water in hypogenic caves (Chapter 8) or by condensation corrosion in convecting air (Chapter 12). If a cave is only intermittently filled with water, cupolas may retain air pockets under pressure. Lismonde (2000) suggests that the high pressure in the trapped air may

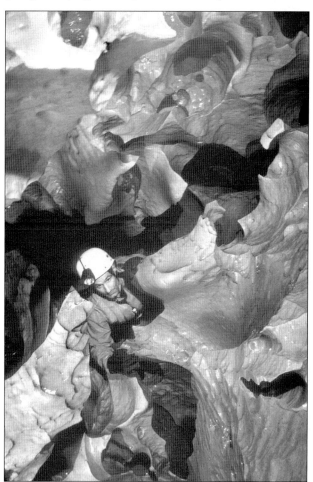

Figure 6.32: Echinoliths surround the author in a rapidly entrenching vadose stream passage, Cueva Zumbo, Puerto Rico. Photo by Kevin Downey.

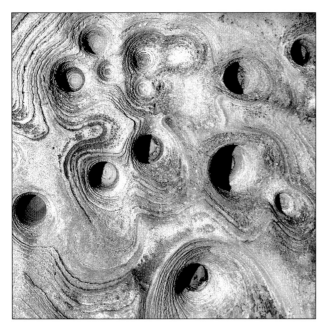

Figure 6.33: Bell holes in the ceiling of Cueva del Indio, Puerto Rico. Width of photo is about one meter. Most bell holes in other caves are deeper and more widely spaced. Note the "contour lines" produced by the intersected thin beds.

spongework, except that echinoliths are superficial forms that do not extend deeply into the bedrock. They are most common in the tropics, especially where the solution rate is enhanced by organic acids. Bird or bat guano can be a major source of corrosion, even above water.

Bell holes are narrow, cylindrical ceiling pockets with round tops, and are generally greater in height than in diameter (Figure 6.33). They are outside the tropics. Some serve as bat roosts, which leads some researchers to suspect that bat urine may help to dissolve them (Miller, 1990). The enhanced aggressiveness of trapped air during periodic flooding may

Figure 6.34: Pothole in Big Brush Creek Cave, Utah, formed by the swirling of quartzite pebbles by turbulent eddies.

Figure 6.35: Ceiling channel in Bluff Cave, Kentucky.

help to enlarge them. Tarhule-Lips and Ford (1998) suggest that at least some bell holes are initiated by local microbial activity and that they are enlarged by water condensing from convecting air currents. Some bell holes are accompanied by small underlying pits in the floors, which are broader than the overlying bell holes (Lauritzen and Lundberg, 2000). Dogwiler (1998) favors an origin by convection currents driven by density in phreatic conditions, but he also points out the limitations to this and all other hypotheses. So far there is no widely accepted explanation for bell holes.

Potholes are pockets in the floors of stream passages that are produced and enlarged by the abrasive action of pebbles rattling around during high flow (Figure 6.34). They are no different from the potholes that form in the bedrock floors of high-gradient surface streams, although in solution caves their origin involves considerable dissolution as well as mechanical erosion. Where large pebbles are swirled around the perimeter, a pothole may contain a central raised boss or pinnacle of rock (Bögli, 1980; Slabe, 1995). Contrary to some interpretations, this boss is not an indicator of open-channel stream flow, because it can also form when a cave is completely filled with water. Remnants of now-inactive potholes can be used as evidence for high-volume flow in the past (Ford, 1965a).

Ceiling channels are sinuous trenches in cave ceilings cut by the upward dissolution of streams (Figure 6.35). Some are remnants of the earliest stage of passage development, but many have formed atop sediment that once filled the passages nearly to the ceiling. A few channels that form above sediment migrate from the ceiling down the walls of the passage, which demonstrates that the passage was sediment-filled at the time the channel developed. The sediment was later excavated, perhaps by the same stream that formed the channel. Ceiling channels are usually more sinuous than the passages they occupy. The sinuosity can be generated by irregularities in the sediment-bedrock contact, but experiments by Lauritzen and Lauritsen (1995) show that it can also be caused by erosion and deposition of the sediment itself. Some broad, shallow channels in cave walls and ceilings are formed by condensation corrosion in rising plumes of warm moist air (page 330).

Figure 6.36: Ceiling pendants and intervening drainage grooves indicate the former presence of sediment fill (Mammoth Cave).

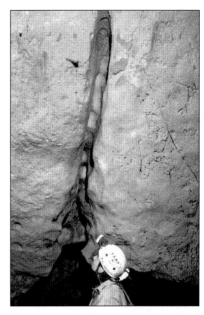

Figure 6.37: Bubble trail in Grotta del Fiume, Italy.

Drainage grooves (or ***inverted rills***) are smooth channels in cave walls formed by water draining downward by gravity between sediment fill and bedrock during periodic floods. They form most easily alongside clay-rich fill that has retracted slightly from the walls during dry intervals. If erosion later removes the sediment, the origin of the grooves may seem puzzling. They are good evidence that the passage was once filled with sediment to at least their level. Drainage grooves may coalesce upward into ceiling pendants (Figure 6.36) and may extend downward into the ceilings of side passages. Their contours are rounded, in contrast to the sharp relief of flutes, and they are rarely perfectly vertical. Most are inclined down the slopes of overhanging walls.

Bubble trails are grooves formed in ceilings and overhanging walls by gas bubbles rich in CO_2 or H_2S that rise from lower passages while a cave is water-filled (Figure 6.37). They are most common where dissolved gases are released from solution as water rises (see pages 216–217). Gas bubbles themselves cannot dissolve bedrock, but they can make the surrounding water aggressive. Bubble trails form isolated narrow grooves interspersed with larger pockets in which escaping gas has concentrated. They may resemble drainage grooves but are more widely spaced. In places the two features are related, because as floodwaters drain along sediment-bedrock contacts to form drainage grooves, high-CO_2 air bubbles can be expelled from below and help to enlarge the channels. Sediment fill is not required for the origin of many bubble trails.

Ceiling pendants are bedrock projections left in a cave ceiling or overhanging wall when the surrounding rock is removed by dissolution. Some are the remnants

of anastomoses, where the underlying bed has dropped away (Figure 6.28). Others form along the sloping walls of cave passages that are nearly filled with sediment (Figure 6.36) and are related to drainage grooves.

Solution notches are horizontal grooves that form at persistent water levels or above former sediment fill (Figure 6.38). They can be incised in cave walls or along the bases of cliffs composed of soluble rock. In the same manner, swamp slots and foot caves may form in towers or cliffs at the level of the alluvial sediment that accumulates around their bases (page 26).

Solution ramps are corrosion notches in cave walls that rise and fall sinuously along the length of a passage (Figure 6.39). They are located above or below former sediment banks that have since been removed by erosion. Dissolution is usually more rapid above the sediment, so the underlying wall juts into the passage. In some cases there is more dissolution below the sediment surface than above.

Figure 6.38: Solution notches in the walls of Clearwater Cave, Malaysia. Photo by Tony Waltham.

Figure 6.39: Solution ramps are notches at the tops of former sediment banks. Here, in Great Saltpeter Cave, Kentucky, the main ramp runs through the center of the photo. Higher notches lie above it, and drainage grooves line the walls below. The ramps cut across nearly horizontal beds.

Where slow-moving floodwaters occasionally rise into an otherwise dry passage and briefly saturate the sediment, the walls in contact with the sediment become corroded over a long period of time, but the walls above are dissolved very little during their brief encounter with the water.

Some solutional cave ceilings are almost perfectly flat, even where they cut across geologic structures (Figure 6.40).

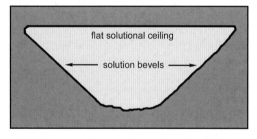

Figure 6.40: Cross section of solution bevels and flat solutional ceilings, typical of caves in highly soluble rock such as gypsum (after Kempe, 1972).

They are most common in gypsum and salt, which dissolve rapidly. They are rare in carbonate rocks, except where very aggressive water is generated in standing pools by oxidation of organic matter or hydrogen sulfide. Usually accompanying these flat ceilings are **solution bevels** (*facets*), which are sections of cave walls that slope uniformly downward toward the center of the passage. Where opposing walls are beveled, the passage cross section may be nearly triangular (Figure 6.40). In highly soluble rock, density gradients can develop in the water. Dissolution is rapid in the low-density, upper, aggressive parts of the water, and diminishes downward in the denser, more saturated water (Kempe, 1972; Kempe and others, 1975). On the other hand, Lange (1963, 1964) and Goodman (1964, 1965) interpret bevels to be the result of solutional widening in areas of contrasting solubility or sediment accumulation, or at the intersection between bedding planes and joints. The hypotheses of Lange and Goodman may account for the few bevels that occur in limestone and dolomite.

Etched surfaces are caused by thin films of aggressive water that move slowly downward while adhering to cave ceilings and walls by surface tension (Figure 6.41). The water is naturally drawn toward small hollows in the rock surface, where the rock-water contact is greatest. Where the flow is greatest the water enlarges the hollows into wiggly channels about 5 mm wide that zigzag back and forth and intersect one another. They are separated by sharp ridges and spikes of rock, from which the excess water drips off. A paste of residual minerals may accumulate on the rock surface. Etched surfaces are most common near vertical shafts where water dribbles down the shaft walls and spreads out along the undersides of ledges.

Phototrophic corrosion is the result of biologically augmented dissolution in the twilight zones of cave entrances, where incoming light is limited to a narrow range of angles. Algae and other photosensitive biota grow in moist hollows that deepen into narrow, parallel pits, while the intervening rock protrudes as rims and fingers.

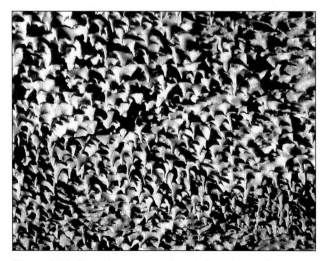

Figure 6.41: Etched bedrock surface in Blue Spring Cave, Indiana. Width of photo is about 20 cm.

Figure 6.42: Phototrophic corrosion in Pleistocene limestone, near the entrance of a cave at St. David's Head, Bermuda. Daylight enters from the upper left. The rock hammer is only for scale (30 cm long).

Figure 6.43: Differential solution in the thin-bedded Manlius Limestone, McFail's Cave, New York. The resistant ledges contain up to 30% insoluble clay and quartz silt.

Figure 6.44: "Velcro" texture formed by resistant dolomitic worm burrows in the Ordovician Stewartville Formation, Mystery Cave, Minnesota. Width of photo is about 40 cm.

Both the pits and fingers are oriented in the direction of the incoming entrance light (Figure 6.42). These features are a variant of phytokarst (page 26). Phototrophic corrosion is most common in warm, humid climates.

Differential solution is the process by which poorly soluble strata or grains project outward in relief from adjacent bedrock surfaces (Figure 6.43). It is most conspicuous in vadose shafts, especially where there has been little or no mechanical erosion. Beds that protrude are mainly either dolomitic, massive, coarse-grained, or contain a large percentage of insoluble material. Beds with the opposite attributes tend to be recessed. Solutional retreat is also common along major bedding planes. Beds of shale or shaly limestone may protrude if they are exposed only to slow-moving water, but more often they are recessed inward because of erosion or crumbling.

Fossils in bedrock usually project from cave walls either because they have a coarser crystal size than the surrounding rock or they have been replaced by nearly insoluble quartz or chert (Chapter 3). Burrows left by worms and other animals usually contain a greater proportion of dolomite or chert than the surrounding material, so they may jut outward as sharp, curving fingers of rock. In caves in the Ordovician-age Bighorn Dolomite of Wyoming, the walls contain sharply protruding fossil burrows that relentlessly snag the clothing of passing cavers, who refer to these surfaces as "velcro." In the Stewartville Formation of Minnesota, burrows project outward where they were formerly buried beneath cave sediment, but they are indented where they have been exposed to the cave air for a long time (Figure 6.44). Pyrite in the recessed burrows has oxidized more vigorously than in the projecting ones, and the resulting sulfuric acid has attacked the dolomite. Where burrows have been replaced by chert, they tend to stand out in bold relief, forming shapes that resemble sausages, hoops, branches, or even dog droppings. Caves in the St. Louis Limestone of Kentucky contain fine examples (Figure 6.45).

Differential solution can cause mineral veins to project from cave walls as resistant fins. Most veins consist of calcite, dolomite, or quartz deposited along fractures prior to cave development. Veins of quartz and dolomite usually form deep beneath the surface at high temperatures. Quartz is poorly soluble. Although dolomite is moderately soluble, it dissolves much more slowly than limestone. Consequently, both quartz and dolomite veins stand in relief as caves form. In contrast, most calcite veins protrude as fins only where the surrounding bedrock is deeply weathered.

A variety of *weathering features* can form on rock and mineral surfaces that are exposed for a long time to cave air. These features vary from thin alteration crusts to bizarre lips and projecting blades. Some are adjusted to currents of moist air or are artifacts of former mineral deposits. In places, intersecting veins form compartment-like structures called *boxwork*, which is best known from caves of the Black Hills, South Dakota, and which occupy former sulfate zones in dolomite. These and other weathering features are discussed in detail on pages 343–344.

Figure 6.45: Fossil shrimp burrows replaced by chert in the St. Louis Limestone in Logsdon River, Mammoth Cave, Kentucky. Flashlight = 15 cm long.

Cave sediments

A variety of sediments accumulate in caves and can be preserved more or less intact for long periods of time. They are reliable indicators of past environmental conditions and are also useful for determining cave ages (Chapter 13). Only mechanical deposits are considered here. Mineral deposits, or **speleothems**, are distinctive enough to deserve their own chapter (Chapter 10).

Detrital sediment consists of granular material produced by the weathering of preexisting rock, and which has been eroded and eventually deposited by water, wind, or ice. In caves the transporting agent is usually flowing water, although in a few places wind and ice movement have contributed. Loose material can also drop into entrances by gravity or be carried in by animals. Detrital particles range in size from boulders down to microscopic specks and can include soluble as well as relatively insoluble materials. Grains that are resistant to chemical decomposition are much more abundant than soluble grains. Most detrital sediment in caves consists of gravel, sand, and clay carried in from the land surface by the same streams that form and enlarge the caves. It is mixed with material that weathers from the cave walls and ceilings. If the cave's catchment area consists only of soluble rock, the volume of detrital sediment may be small.

Sediment types

During transport, rock fragments break into smaller particles and are rounded by abrasion. Rounding is an indication of lengthy transport. Most clay deposits in caves are derived from the mechanical weathering of shale (Chapter 3). Blocks that have fallen from cave walls or ceilings tend to be sharp-edged.

Grain size, composition, and internal structures of sediments provide information about the source and flow character of the water that deposited them. Detailed studies of cave sediment include those by White and White (1968), Bull (1981), Milske and others (1983), Osborne (1984), Gillieson (1986), Springer and others (1997), and by the contributors to a recent volume on cave sediments edited by Sasowsky and Mylroie (2004). Hydraulics of sediment transport are discussed by Graf (1971).

When transported by a stream, most gravel and sand is simply dragged along the stream bottom as **bedload** by the flowing water. If the water is turbulent enough, some is carried in **suspension** within the stream water. Clay is carried almost entirely in suspension. Sediment of silt or clay size can also be carried into or through caves by air currents (Michie, 1997).

The character of a sedimentary deposit is controlled by three variables: **nature of the source material**, **transport mechanics**, and **depositional environment**. Whatever is deposited must have an available source, and its grains must have been loose enough to be carried away. Rapid flow is required to erode and carry large grains. The size of the grains in the final deposit also depends on the velocity of the transporting water. Grains are deposited mainly where the velocity drops below the critical threshold needed to move

Figure 6.46: Sand and gravel deposits indicating rapid water flow, Mammoth Cave, Kentucky. (Flash bulb 4 cm long for scale.) See text for discussion.

them. The shape of the deposit depends on the extent of the water body and its patterns of flow.

As an example, the cave sediment shown in Figure 6.46 indicates (1) an upstream source of coarse sand and gravel; (2) rapid flow velocity to carry the material far into the cave; (3) slowing of the flow enough to deposit the sediment; and (4) fluctuating velocities to favor alternate sand and gravel deposition. Each of these statements need to be clarified. At Mammoth Cave, both sand and gravel are abundant at the surface, but the gravel is present only on high ridges where remnants of Pennsylvanian conglomerate are exposed. Loose grains wash downhill into sinkholes and are eventually carried into the cave by streams, especially during high flow. Much of the sediment may be released in bursts — for example, when sediment slumps into an underlying cave passage. The alternation between gravel and sand in the deposit may indicate variations in flow, perhaps floods vs. normal flow, or, less likely, it may indicate intermittent release of gravel from loose accumulations along the ridge flanks. These deposits extend for hundreds of meters through many passages, so the cave streams did not simply dump the sediment into standing bodies of water.

Several other processes contributed. As floods subside, water velocity slows and much of the sediment ceases to move. Even in a stream with an average velocity rapid enough to carry it, much of the sediment accumulates where the velocity is slowest — on the insides of bends, and at places where the channel widens and causes the water to spread out. Sediment is moved gradually through the channel, especially during high flow, but it is continually replaced by additional sediment from the surface.

To interpret the flow velocity required to erode a sediment grain, the *erosive force* on the grain can be expressed as:

$$F_e = C_d A \,(\rho v^2 / 2) \qquad (6.2)$$

where F_e = erosive force (dynes), A = cross-sectional area of grain exposed to the water flow (cm^2), ρ = water density

(1 g/cm³), v = flow velocity (cm/sec), and C_d = coefficient of drag, which varies with the Reynolds Number of the flow (Eq. 4.2). Experiments show that C_d is typically about 0.2–0.6 for spherical particles (see graphs in any hydraulics handbook). There are 444,800 dynes in a pound.

The *resistance* of a grain to erosion depends mainly on its effective weight in water:

$$F_r = C_b V g \Delta\rho \qquad (6.3)$$

where F_r = resistance to erosion (dynes), V = grain volume (cm³), g = gravitational field strength (980 dynes/gram), $\Delta\rho$ = difference between grain density and water density (typically about 1.6 g/cm³), and C_b is a poorly defined factor that depends on the bed characteristics around the grain (packing, etc.).

Example: The uncertainty of estimating C_b makes it difficult to apply Eq. 6.3 to most field examples. The main exception is where isolated grains are lifted vertically by the force of a current. In this case, $C_b = 1$, and F_e in Eq. 6.2 must be greater than F_r in Eq. 6.3. For a spherical grain, $A = \pi r^2$ and $V = (4/3)\pi r^3$, where r = grain radius. Suppose that cobbles 5 cm in radius have been carried up a vertical pitch by floodwaters. How fast must the water have been moving?

In this case, $F_e > F_r$. Inserting the appropriate values into Eqs. 6.2 and 6.3, and with $C_d = 0.5$ (typical), the result simplifies to

$$v^2 > 8400\, r \quad \text{(cgs units)} \qquad (6.4)$$

With $r = 5$ cm, the velocity (v) that lifted the grains must have been more than 200 cm/sec (6.6 ft/sec).

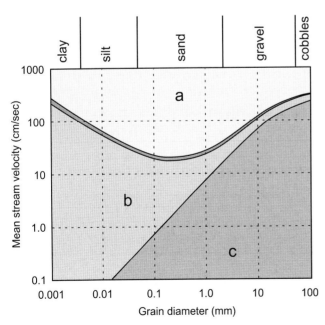

Figure 6.47: Stream velocities required to erode sediment grains of uniform size (zone **a**). In zone **b**, sediment can be transported but not eroded. In zone **c**, the velocity is not sufficient to transport the grains, and they are deposited. Scatter in the data is shown by the thickness of the transition between **a** and **b**. This idealized graph applies only to streams less than a meter deep. (From measurements by Hjulström, 1935.)

Figure 6.48: Rounded cobbles of chert and sandstone at the base of an intermittent 16 m waterfall, Two Second Pit, New York. Width of photo is about 35 cm.

For stream deposits in general, Figure 6.47 shows the velocities needed to erode, transport, and deposit sediment grains of various sizes (from widely accepted experiments by Hjulström, 1935). The exact values depend on additional variables such as channel slope, grain shape, composition, packing, and water temperature, but the graph works well for general purposes. For example, to move gravel (Figure 6.48), a stream must have a velocity of at least 50 cm/sec. Only the severest floods are capable of moving the largest boulders through a cave (Figure 6.49). Sand is eroded by stream velocities greater than about 20 cm/sec. Erosion of clay requires higher velocities, in some cases more than 2 m/sec, because its tiny grains nestle inside a boundary

Figure 6.49: Boulders in Lockridge Aqua Cave, Virginia, have been lifted up from a lower-level passage. They had already been carried deep into the cave from quartz sandstone overlying the cavernous limestone. Blocks of this size can be lifted by water only if the vertical flow exceeds roughly 8–10 meters/sec.

Figure 6.50: Banks of clay and silt deposited by ponded flood-water, Eyeless Fish Trail, Mammoth Cave. Note the surge marks and mud funnels left by rising and falling water. Width of photo = 2.5 m.

Figure 6.51: Sediments in Mammoth Cave, trenched for trail-building, consist of cross-bedded sand and gravel, which were capped by clay deposits from backflooding after the passage was abandoned by its original stream.

layer of laminar flow along the stream bottom. Compacted clay also resists erosion because it is so cohesive. Gravel is deposited if the stream velocity drops only slightly below that required to erode it. Deposition of sand takes place at velocities less than about 10 cm/sec. The velocity must drop nearly to zero for clay to settle out because only a small amount of turbulence will keep it in suspension.

Gravel and sand therefore accumulate in stream channels. Potholes, steep canyons, and shaft bottoms usually contain only cobbles and gravel. Elongate gravel banks pile up where high-velocity water rises out of a small opening into a larger passage. Large grains may be absent in some stream passages simply because there is no source for them in the catchment area, or because the grains have settled in ponded water upstream.

Small grains, such as clay and silt, form mud banks alongside stream channels and are the equivalent of floodplain deposits in river valleys (Figure 6.50). They also accumulate in ponded areas, especially in passages that are normally dry but are periodically filled with slow-moving floodwaters that overflow from nearby streams. The most typical sequence of cave sediments consists of interbedded sand and gravel deposited by swiftly moving streams, and overlain by a cap of fine-grained silt and clay from periodic slow-moving floodwaters after the passage has been abandoned by its original stream (Figure 6.51).

Sediment is well adjusted to the hydrologic environment in which it is deposited, regardless of the geologic setting. In a cave passage there are more physical constraints than at the land surface (Bosch and White, 2004). The velocity of flow in a cave increases with discharge, as it does in a surface stream, but the cave walls limit the extent to which the water can spread out during high flow. If a passage is completely water-filled, the velocity is directly proportional to the discharge. If sediment accumulates in a cave it causes the flow velocity to increase, so that during high flow much of the sediment may be removed by erosion. Sediment accumulation in caves tends to reach an equilibrium that is more rigid than that of surface streams because the cave water cannot spread out onto a floodplain.

Changes in climate may also be recorded in cave sediments, although the sedimentary record is usually incomplete because of periodic interruption by erosion. Examples are described in Chapter 13.

Sediment composition

The catchment area for cave streams, and perhaps also the timing of sediment deposits, can sometimes be inferred from the composition of the grains in cave sediment. For example, pebbles of metamorphic rock in New York caves must have been carried underground after the region was glaciated, because only glaciers could have carried these rocks into the caves' drainage basins from the Adirondack Mountains far to the north.

Cave entrances in river bluffs are receptacles for sediments carried in during floods. Springer and Kite (1997) and Springer and others (1997) used sediments of this type in caves along the Cheat River, West Virginia, to determine the interrelated geologic history of the river canyon and the caves. They show that peak flood stages can be determined from low-velocity sediments and rafted vegetal debris in caves, and that this information is much clearer and better preserved than in comparable sediments on the surface.

Some of the insoluble residue from the dissolution of bedrock can contribute to the detrital sediment in caves. Carbonate grains can be released by the chemical weathering of limestone or dolomite. This is most typical of caves that contain little or no running water, and which are exposed to long-term weathering in air (Chapter 12). Wind Cave and Jewel Cave in South Dakota contain mounds of weathered material more than a meter thick.

Sedimentary structures

Structures in sediment reflect the nature of the water flow that deposited the material, as well as past environmental conditions. ***Cross beds*** are thin, sloping beds that combine to form thicker sedimentary layers, as in a sand dune or delta (page 71). The slope direction of the cross beds indicates the former flow direction (Figure 6.52). On the other hand, flat pebbles stacked against each other in a stream bed tend to slope downward in the upstream direction.

Ripple marks are like small sand dunes that indicate the direction of flow by their asymmetry, just as scallops do. Their steep sides point in the downstream direction (Figure 6.53). Water velocity cannot be interpreted precisely from the ripple size.

If the top of a sediment sequence contains channels that were re-filled at a later time (***cut-and-fill structures***), the sediment was probably deposited in an open-channel stream, rather than in water that completely filled the passage.

Insoluble material such as soil can also infiltrate from the surface through fissures. This material tends to move slowly, especially if it is rich in clay. It can form debris cones in the cave (Figure 6.54) or it may extrude into the cave like toothpaste, forming striated pillars or sheets (Jancin and Clark, 1993). The extruded forms are most typically fed by relatively soft beds of shale. Measurements of banks of this material by Lundquist and Varnadoe (1991) show downslope movements of several millimeters per year, with the greatest rates during wet periods.

Surge marks are grooves in slopes of clay-rich sediment that are formed by fluctuating water levels (Figure 6.50).

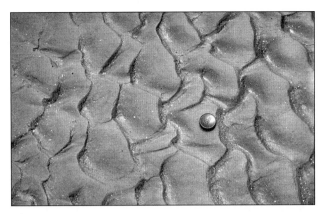

Figure 6.53: Ripple marks in a sandy stream bed. The flow that formed them was toward the right. The lens cap is 5 cm in diameter.

During floods, sediment is deposited on the surface, but as the water level drops, trickles of water and saturated mud drain down the sloping faces to form small gullies about 5–20 cm wide. If a flood subsides very slowly, more sediment may remain on the surface of the band than flows off it. The reverse can be true if the flood subsides rapidly.

In flood zones, banks of silt and clay can form sloping rims around holes in a passage floor that lead to underlying passages. The resulting ***mud funnels*** resemble volcanic craters (Figure 6.50). ***Mud cracks*** are fissures in fine-grained sediment caused by splitting of the deposits into polygonal blocks (Figure 6.55). They indicate deposition of mud by slow-moving water followed by drying of the sediment surface.

Mud stalagmites are usually produced in two stages. Where drips of water fall from the cave ceiling and form a small hole in a bed of fine-grained sediment, calcite may accumulate around the drip hole and make its walls more resistant than the surrounding sediment. Later, if the sediment is partly removed by subsidence or erosion, the resistant mud stalagmites are often left projecting from the new floor.

Vermiculations are deposits of clay and/or organic material on cave walls that form swarms of worm-like

Figure 6.52: Cross-bedded sandstone exposed in a surface canyon wall in Utah. The water that deposited the beds was flowing toward the right. Cave sediments can show similar features. Width of photo is about 5 m.

Figure 6.54: Conical pile of sediment directly beneath a large sinkhole pond, Blue Spring Cave, Indiana. The pond is about 100 m in diameter. Digging to extend this passage has not been attempted.

Figure 6.55: Mud cracks in clay, Fort Stanton Cave, New Mexico. Width of photo is 1.5 m.

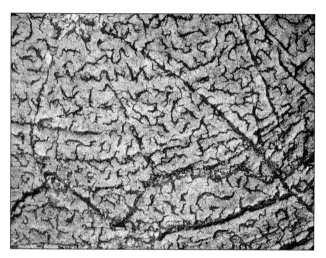

Figure 6.56: Vermiculations composed of organic material and clay on the walls of Clifton Cave, Virginia. These materials also concentrate along fractures, which produce the linear patterns. Width of photo is about 50 cm.

or polygonal patterns (Figure 6.56). Some vermiculated surfaces resemble leopard skin. Most vermiculations are only a couple of millimeters wide, about a millimeter thick, and a few centimeters long. They tend to form on damp, smooth surfaces by periodic wetting and drying, especially when accompanied by microbial processes. The clay usually accumulates either from air-borne dust or is plastered onto solid surfaces by floodwater. Their patterns can change with time, which suggests that they are not related to the texture of the underlying surfaces. It is still not certain why the sediment or organic material concentrates as vermiculations, while the intervening spaces are left bare.

Organic deposits

Organic debris is carried into caves by streams, wind, or animals, or it can fall into open cave entrances. In floodwater caves, the entrances and narrow sections are often partly or completely blocked by rafted logs and other vegetal matter (Figure 6.57). Water also carries dissolved organic compounds

Figure 6.57: Organic debris carried by floodwater into Big Brush Creek Cave, Utah. Oxidation of this material has depleted the oxygen and raised carbon dioxide levels to uncomfortable and potentially dangerous levels in the deeper parts of the cave.

derived from the decomposition of plant and animal matter. As these organic materials oxidize, carbon dioxide is released. This process can help to keep the cave water aggressive even during prolonged underground travel (Bray, 1972). Many fissures and pores deep in the vadose zone have CO_2 levels as high as those in the overlying soil (Atkinson, 1977a; Wood and Petraitis, 1984). Living plant roots can also invade caves (Figure 6.58), and it is possible to examine how they respond to variations in water supply.

Guano in caves consists of the droppings of bats or, less commonly, birds. It is abundant in many caves in warm climates but sparse in other regions. With time it turns into a dry granular material that can be mined for fertilizer (Figure 6.59). Soon after the discovery of Carlsbad Cavern in the early 1900s, a guano-mining operation was established in

Figure 6.58: Roots from overlying trees invade a shallow cave in lava on the island of Hawai'i.

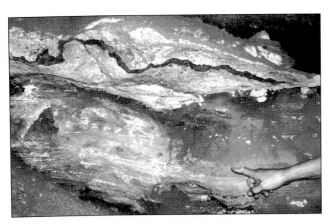

Figure 6.59: Guano deposits of early Pleistocene age in Cueva del Pájaros, Isla de Mona, Puerto Rico. These deposits are rich in phosphate and were mined for fertilizer in the 19th century. They are partly covered by carbonate sediments and breakdown.

Figure 6.61: The skeleton of the extinct Pleistocene cave bear, *Ursus spelaeus*, dwarfs a human. This specimen is housed in the Karst Institute at Postojna, Slovenia.

a branch of the cave still inhabited today by a large bat colony. Guano mining is far less common today than in the past. Most of the large deposits have been depleted.

Animal and plant remains in caves may include bones, tracks, and pollen. These materials can help to date various cave events, such as the deposition of sediments and the opening and closing of entrances. Protected from the harsh exterior conditions, these delicate features can be preserved in caves for many thousands or even millions of years. In places they are preserved by a coating of mineral deposits (Figure 6.60). Certain caves are rich sources of vertebrate fossils and evidence for human occupation (Figures 6.61–6.62; Kowalski, 2005; Watson, 1998).

Fossils in bedrock may weather out of cave walls and become part of the sedimentary material on the floor. They can also be carried in by water. Although as sedimentary grains they post-date the cave, the fossils themselves are older than the cave.

Bedrock collapse

Breakdown is caused by the collapse of cave ceilings or walls. The term applies both to the process and to the fallen pieces that result from it. The process can greatly modify passage shape and make it difficult to determine the original solutional pattern. Breakdown material varies from small chips and flakes to large slabs and blocks. Studies of cave

Figure 6.60: Roots encased in calcium carbonate in a Bermuda cave. Fossilized roots are known as ***rhizoliths***. Width of photo is 60 cm.

Figure 6.62: Archeological excavation of sediments in Salts Cave, Kentucky, supervised by Patty Jo Watson of Washington University. This site provided much information on the Woodland Indian Culture of about 4000 years ago.

Figure 6.63: Slab breakdown in the thin-bedded Paoli Member, Girkin Formation, Mammoth Cave, Kentucky. (See Figure 3.6.)

breakdown include those of Davies (1951), White and White (1969), Jameson (1991), and Gilli (1993).

Piles of breakdown in a cave give the unpleasant impression that an entire ceiling has come down in a single catastrophic failure. In reality, massive failure is very rare, and breakdown usually subsides slowly, one block, or a few blocks, at a time. Breakdown is most likely when a passage is first drained of water, because the slight buoyant effect of the water is removed. Limestone blocks with a density of 2.7 g/cm³ have an effective density of only 1.7 g/cm³ when immersed in water. Periodic flooding can enlarge the fractures between blocks and enable them to drop as the water recedes. Blocks do occasionally fall in dry caves, particularly near entrances, but far less frequently than from cliffs on the surface. Very few visitors to caves have seen an undisturbed rock fall on its own.

A cantilevered bed or a rock beam across a cave ceiling is able to resist gravitational stress in direct proportion to its thickness and inversely proportional to its length (White, 1988). With time, the rock is able to deform slowly and develop microfractures that weaken its strength. Eventually the bedrock may fail and produce breakdown. Thin-bedded rocks produce platy breakdown slabs (Figure 6.63), while massive rocks produce large blocks (Figure 6.64). Failure along minor fractures can bring down chips of various sizes. The maximum size of a breakdown block is obviously limited by the size of the passage into which it falls. In rare situations a single block will fall that spans the entire passage width, leaving only a small gap between the block and the bounding walls, or no gap at all.

In dry caves the breakdown process can be facilitated by crystal wedging caused by the growth of gypsum (pages 342–343). But the gypsum crystals that shatter the bedrock also tend to bind the blocks together, like cement, and delay their fall. Given enough time, thin beds may sag and curve under their own weight before they drop (Figure 6.65). Vadose weathering processes that promote breakdown are described by Osborne (2002).

Where a lower-level passage meanders back and forth beneath a higher-level passage, breakdown rooms may form

Figure 6.64: Breakdown blocks of Coeymans Limestone, McFail's Cave, New York, are more massive than those in Figure 6.63.

at the intersections. Collapse may truncate a cave passage entirely. This **terminal breakdown** may halt exploration and mapping, but the passage generally continues beyond.

As a cave ceiling retreats upward by breakdown, it may stabilize into an arch. In wide sections of passage, or at intersections, the result is usually an oval or circular **breakout dome**. The largest cave rooms in the eastern U.S., located in east-central Tennessee, are breakout domes that developed

Figure 6.65: Sagging and warping of thin-bedded St. Louis Limestone by its own weight, Blue Spring Cave, Indiana.

in bedded limestone that was protected from total collapse by a thick cap of sandstone and shale (Figure 6.66).

Breakdown can progress upward for hundreds of meters, sometimes into relatively insoluble overlying strata. If breakdown reaches the surface, a large steep-walled sinkhole or pit may be produced. A spectacular example is Sótano de las Golondrinas in Mexico (Figures 2.57 and 6.8). Most large sinkholes owe much of their origin to breakdown. The collapse sinkhole at point C in Figure 2.31 extends upward through about 30 m of insoluble sandstone and shale.

Dissolution of subsurface evaporite beds is commonly accompanied by the upward migration of solutional voids. Collapse into dissolving evaporites is thought to account for the origin of certain breccia pipes (Chapters 2, 13, and 15).

The total volume occupied by the jumble of breakdown blocks on a cave floor is greater than that of the original bedrock that produced the breakdown. Unless cave streams dissolve the blocks, breakdown diminishes the volume of open passage. As it progresses upward, the breakdown process may eventually terminate spontaneously when the underlying passage becomes choked with collapse material (Šušteršič, 1984).

During cold weather, crystallization of ice can shatter rock and speleothems in caves, especially near entrances or in caves that serve as blind pockets for cold air (Chapter 12). Glacial episodes have caused widespread breakage of speleothems in some shallow caves. Many old speleothems in the Northern Rockies and in the glaciated central plains of North America show natural shattering. Some of the fragments are re-cemented by later deposits. Radiometric dating shows that nearly all of these shattered speleothems are older than end of the latest glaciation, which ceased about 15,000 years ago. Most of the intact ones are post-glacial (Chapter 13).

Figure 6.66: Breakout dome in Camp's Gulf Cave, Tennessee. The view is diagonally upward at the ceiling, which is about 60–80 m away. The circular pattern is the top of the dome, which is composed of resistant beds of limestone. The silhouetted person near the center of the photo is standing on the pile of breakdown that came from collapse of the ceiling. This is one of the largest cave rooms in the eastern U.S.

Cave biology

The cave environments described in previous chapters support a small and specialized biological community (Figure 6.67). These organisms are delicately adjusted to the local geologic setting, hydrology, and chemistry, and they also contribute to many chemical cave processes. Some biota, like ourselves, are only visitors, while others spend their entire lives underground. For those species that can adapt to total darkness and a limited food supply, a cave can offer a stable and fairly secure habitat.

Most cave organisms have little concern for what kind of cave they inhabit, although some thrive at temperatures and chemical conditions that we consider extreme. Their energy comes from one or more of the following sources: inorganic chemical reactions (such as oxidation of sulfides), organic material carried into the cave by water and air, and organic material supplied by other cave-dwelling organisms. Photosynthesis is a great energy producer at the surface, but except around cave entrances it does not operate underground. Energy sources are scant in most caves, and so the population density of cave animals and plants tends to be low and easily disrupted. Underground habitats are delicate, and care should be taken to avoid disturbing them.

Microbes, such as bacteria, are most common in areas of active oxidation or reduction (Chapters 5 and 12). Filaments of sulfur bacteria (white) and iron bacteria (red) are abundant in certain caves and mineral deposits. Decomposition of organic material is another energy source for bacteria and fungi, as well as for insects and more advanced animals. They too eventually contribute to the organic food supply. Carbon dioxide is the main product of decomposition, and its importance to cave development and speleothem growth is described elsewhere in this book.

Cave animals include the following: *Troglobites* are fully adapted to cave environments. They tend to have little pigmentation and small or vestigial eyes. There are no troglobitic mammals. *Troglophiles* have some adaptation to caves, but they must leave regularly for food. They tend to cluster around entrances, including those too small for human access. *Trogloxenes* visit caves but are not adapted to underground living. They include humans. Many bats use caves for hibernation or to raise offspring, but they have no special cave adaptation and are also trogloxenes. A few common cave animals are described below.

Troglobites

Isopods are small white creatures a few millimeters long. They have flat bodies and many identical legs. They are widely distributed in aquatic cave environments ranging from gravelly or rocky streams to the mud-bottoms of drip pools, and even flowing water on speleothems. *Amphipods* are similar but are flattened side to side and have legs of different shapes. Amphipods are most common in streams, particularly in gravelly riffles or under rocks.

Cave crayfish are white, average about 5–10 cm long, and usually spend more time crawling across surfaces than swimming. They grow very slowly and require decades to mature. Some may live more than 100 years.

There are about 100 known types of troglobitic *cave fish*. Most are slender and small and range from 3 to 15 cm long. In color they vary from pale brown to completely white. Cave fish are usually individualists and rely on chemical sense organs to find food.

Cave beetles do not have the light color favored by other troglobites. The red-brown sand beetle is one of the most abundant and widely distributed troglobites. It prefers moist sandy areas and feeds on cave-cricket eggs and young crickets. Some beetles are scavengers and concentrate under bat roosts.

Troglophiles

Cave crickets are light brown, with long appendages and with body lengths about 2–5 cm. Most are troglophiles or trogloxenes. Some species are true troglobites and spend their entire lives in caves. Some use caves only as a refuge during the day, and lay their eggs outside. Others leave caves only to feed. Some are seen remote from entrances, but they may have access to the outside through small openings that are not negotiable by humans. Crickets lay their eggs in aerated, sandy soil. Closely spaced, random patterns of small holes in sediment are usually cricket-egg holes. Young crickets go through several molts in the cave.

Salamanders in caves range from trogloxenic to troglobitic. Most common are the bright orange variety that cluster in damp locations around entrances. Some salamanders are true troglobites with no eyes, thin appendages, and little pigment.

Trogloxenes

Many species of *bats* do not use caves at all, but others use caves as shelters, winter hibernacula, or maternity roosts. Their guano provides organic material to support the rest of the cave ecosystem. Those that live in caves fly out at night to feed. An estimated 20 million Mexican free-tail bats live in Bracken Bat Cave, Texas. This is the world's largest known bat concentration, and they consume about 200 tons of insects each night. They are brown and range from roughly 5 to 8 cm long. Little brown bats are smaller, usually brown, of course, with a lighter-colored belly. Baby bats cluster to decrease their heat loss. In caves, maternity roosts tend to be located in small ceiling pockets that can be warmed by the bats' bodies. The onset of winter in temperate regions forces bats to become torpid, to hibernate, or to migrate. Hibernating bats require cool locations such as caves.

Bats navigate through caves by echolocation (biosonar). They emit directed high-pitched squeaks far above the range of human hearing, about 100,000–200,000 Hz (cycles/sec). When the sound hits a surface it reflects back to the bat. The sound does not travel far, but it is highly directional and reveals fine details in the target. A bat can detect and identify an insect within about a 2-meter radius. Not all bats have biosonar. Many large species find food by sight or smell. Even bats with sonar use sight for some navigation.

Bats face many threats. Their tendency to cluster in large numbers in only a few places adds to their vulnerability. They have declined mainly because of pesticide contamination and disturbance of habitats. To learn more about bats, and to support their protection, contact Bat Conservation International at *www.batcon.org*.

A variety of trogloxenes may occupy the entrance areas of caves. **Cave rats** (also known as pack rats or woodrats) resemble large mice, with large eyes, furry tails, and large ears. They are fairly solitary, and often only a single individual will nest at a cave entrance. Birds, bears, harvestman spiders, and humans (at least in the past) may inhabit the entrance areas. In the tropics, this assemblage may include some intimidating species such as crabs, alligators, and giant turtles. Some trogloxenes spend the winters in cave entrances. Snakes may hibernate or seek the coolness of an entrance during hot summer months.

Plants cannot grow in the complete darkness of caves, although seeds that are carried underground may sprout if there is sufficient moisture. They extend delicate white tendrils that grow for a short time until they consume the food supply in their seeds. Plants can also grow around the artificial lights in show caves (see *lamp-flora*, pages

344–345). Certain types of algae can metabolize organic compounds and are able to live in caves where these energy sources are available. The entrance zones of caves contain many plants, particularly mosses and algae. Cyanobacteria (blue-green algae) appear as dark green coatings on rocks and walls in the twilight zone.

Cave animals are very sensitive to the local geology, hydrology, and water chemistry. The presence of certain species can indicate the long-term quality or degradation of water. They also have an effect on their surroundings, for example by moving sediment grains (**bioturbation**) and by producing corrosive organic acids (Chapter 12). Distribution of biota can also give information about the interconnectivity and size of pores.

Further information on cave biology is given in books by Culver (1982), Moore and Sullivan (1997), Gunn (2004a), and Culver and White (2005). There is also a forthcoming book on the subject, *Cave Biology*, by Kathleen Lavoie, an early draft of which served as the source for much of the information in this summary.

A troglobitic cave fish, *Amblyopsis*, Donaldson Cave, Indiana. Length is ~6 cm. Photo by Richard L. Powell.

Figure 6.67: Some typical cave animals.

Unpigmented crayfish, Donaldson Cave, Indiana. Length is ~6 cm.

Proteus, a rare troglobitic salamander, in Postojnska jama, Slovenia. Total length is ~40 cm.

Cave cricket in a Kentucky cave. Body length is ~4 cm. Two-thirds of the antenna length extends beyond the frame, as does up to one-third of the length of the near hind leg.

Little brown bat in repose in a New York cave, hanging upside-down from a ledge, with ears protruding downward. The wings are folded. Length ~6 cm.

Salamander in the twilight zone of Onyx Cave, South Dakota; length, nose to hind legs, is ~15 cm.

7

Speleogenesis: the origin of caves

ALL THE CONCEPTS from previous chapters can now be combined to explain how caves form. This is the topic of ***speleogenesis***. Cave origin involves complex interactions among geology, chemistry, and the mechanics of underground water flow, but the basic ideas are easy to grasp. Only solution caves are discussed in this chapter, because most other types have relatively simple origins that are outlined in Chapter 1. Caves in volcanic rocks are covered separately in Chapter 11.

Basic concepts

If a solution cave is to form at all, enough solid material must be removed to produce the cave before it is destroyed by surface erosion. There is a continual race between the destructive surface processes that lower the land surface and the less conspicuous ones that form caves. In areas of rapid uplift and erosion, such as young mountain chains, the time available for caves to form may be less than half a million years. Caves that form deep beneath the surface, or which are located in regions of comparatively stable geology, may continue to develop over many millions of years.

The origin of a solution cave requires an ample flow of underground water, as well as a continuous network of preexisting openings that the water can follow through soluble rock. Fractures and partings are abundant in nearly all rocks, so a lack of caves in soluble rock can usually be traced to limited supplies of water (as in arid or frozen regions) or to insufficient time. In humid regions, solution caves are present in nearly every large body of soluble rock. This shows that cave origin is the rule rather than merely a geologic accident.

Development of ideas about cave origin

A rich literature on cave origin has appeared during the past few hundred years, and it contains many conflicting ideas. There are still many debates about the details, but today most cave scientists agree on the fundamentals. The history of cave science has been summarized by Watson and White (1985), Shaw (1992, 2000), Lowe (2000), and White (2000). The evolution of speleogenetic ideas is briefly outlined below in more or less historical order.

The first descriptive studies

The earliest known scientific cave studies date back as far as the Siu Dynasty in China (581−618 CE), when geologists first began to describe karst and caves in a systematic way (Barbary and Zhang, 2004). Chinese cave exploration began in earnest during the Song Dynasty (960−1279). Shen Kuo (1031−1095) wrote extensively on geology and included a section on caves. He correctly attributed stalactites to

dripping water. Fan Chengda (1126−1193) described karst and caves in Guangxi Province, China, and drew the first known cave map.

During the early decades of the 17th century, the Chinese geographer Xu Hongzu traveled widely through the mountains and karst regions of southern China and recorded his observations (Cai and others, 1993; Barbary and Zhang, 2004; Ravbar, 2003; Figure 7.1). During a single expedition in 1636−1640 he covered 18,000 km, not including his return journey, and mainly by foot. He visited more than 300 caves, and under the pen name Xu Xiake* wrote extensive descriptions of them and their karst landscapes. His work still stands as one of the greatest advances in the field of karst science.

In Europe, extensive studies dealing exclusively with caves and karst began to appear in the 16th and 17th centuries (Shaw, 1992, 2000). The earliest scientific description of the classic Balkan karst was that of Nikola Gučetić in 1585. More thorough was the work of Johann Valvasor, of Ljubljana, who studied the karst in and around

---

* Pronounced, approximately, *Shu Shee-ock-uh*.

Figure 7.1: Statue of Xu Hongzu (Xu Xiake), a pioneer in the exploration and study of the Chinese karst. This monument stands in front of the Institute of Karst Geology in Guilin, China.

Figure 7.3: Jovan Cvijić (1865–1927) was a pioneer in the interpretation of karst landscapes.

Figure 7.4: E.-A. Martel (1859–1938) is considered the founder of scientific speleology.

Figure 7.2: A narrow road winds through limestone pinnacles in the Balkan karst — home of the true Karst, and of the first comprehensive Western karst studies.

what is now Slovenia (Figure 7.2). Among his several publications on karst, a massive 4-volume work on the geography of that region is best known (Valvasor, 1689). He included descriptions of his own cave explorations, cave maps, and interpretive sketches of the internal workings of karst hydrology. His conclusions were based on a combination of observation, surveying, and deduction, and for that reason he is considered by some to be the first truly scientific karst researcher (Shaw, 1992).

In early studies such as these, most authors recognized the importance of water in cave origin. There was no consensus as to whether dissolution or stream abrasion is the main cave-forming agent. By the end of the 18th century, however, scientists had a fair understanding of karst. For example, in his boldly titled book *Theory of the Earth, with Proofs and Illustrations*, James Hutton (1795) clearly attributed the origin of caves to the dissolution of limestone, and the deposition of dripstone to loss of carbon dioxide. Still, most cave studies of that time were descriptive rather than interpretive.

Growth of karst science

The most extensive early analysis of karst landscape evolution was made in the Balkans by Jovan Cvijić* (1893;

* Pronounced *tsvee-yitch*.

Figure 7.3). Meanwhile, the French explorer Edouard-Alfred Martel (1894) concentrated specifically on caves and explored a great many of them throughout the world (Figure 7.4). Though trained in law, Martel was a scientist at heart, and he is widely acknowledged to be the father of scientific speleology. At the time of Cvijić and Martel, caves were explained as merely the underground equivalent of surface streams, and their place in the evolution of karst landscapes seemed fairly simple.

Early controversies

Prior to the 20th century, karst studies tended to be isolated from one another in time and location. But as karst investigations multiplied and became more rigorous, overlapping interests and contradictory observations led to some substantial disagreements.

The exact nature of groundwater flow in karst was one of the first issues to generate controversy. Alfred Grund (1903) viewed it as similar to any other kind of groundwater in porous material, and having a discrete water table. He argued that continuous underground rivers do not exist, and that sinking streams degenerate underground into diffuse flow paths along many narrow fissures, mostly limited to shallow depths below the water table. He considered karst springs to be located where diffuse groundwater flow converges.

Walter Von Knebel (1906), Freidrich Katzer (1909), and E.-A. Martel (1921) disagreed. They viewed subsurface karst as a system of interconnected conduits. Their exploration of lengthy underground rivers from sinks to springs appeared to prove the point. They argued against the presence of a discrete water table in karst by citing the fact that water can stand at greatly different levels in neighboring cave passages.

Although Grund seems to have been less correct, his concept has some validity. Caves do behave like pipes, but water also drains into them from the surrounding network of unenlarged fractures and partings. Karst does in fact contain a water table, but it is irregular and discontinuous (Chapter 4). Today, many traditional groundwater hydrologists whose underground observations are limited to wells, and who have no experience in caves, view karst in the same way that Grund did.

Birth of karst science in America

Although overshadowed by the great speleological advances in Europe, there was much American work on cave geology during the late 19th and early 20th centuries. The widely celebrated authors on cave origin, who are discussed in the next section, did not emerge from a vacuum.

Horace Hovey (1882) described several karst areas of the eastern U.S., with emphasis on Mammoth Cave (Kentucky), Wyandotte Cave (Indiana), and Luray Caverns (Virginia). He noted the subtleties of karst drainage and the importance of both dissolution and abrasion in cave origin. Nathaniel Shaler (1898) noted passages at persistent levels in caves and attributed them to resistant beds. Frank Greene (1909) instead considered the elevations of large cave passages to be controlled by erosional base level in surface streams, and that rapid erosion of surface valleys tends to form narrow canyon passages. Joshua Beede (1911) related cave levels in southern Indiana to erosion levels in nearby surface streams. James Weller (1927) and Armin Lobeck (1928) applied these concepts to Kentucky's Mammoth Cave and attributed the various cave levels to the evolution of the nearby Green River. Although these researchers did not supply detailed cave surveys to back their observations, they had a clear grasp of the link between caves and the evolution of river valleys.

George Matson (1909) noted that caves tend to form in zones of greatest groundwater movement and are therefore most common at shallow depths below the surface. Yet he considered that most of the groundwater that formed caves was fed by diffuse recharge, because water that sinks rapidly to form underground streams contains less carbonic acid than does widespread infiltration through the soil.

R.T. Walker (1928) observed that most caves are formed by cold descending water, whereas hot ascending water normally deposits ores, sometimes in preexisting caves.

Oscar Meinzer (1923), of the U.S. Geological Survey, is considered the founder of American groundwater hydrology. Besides performing a great deal of field work, he developed much of the groundwater terminology that is still in use today. Significantly, his work acknowledged the importance of caves, karst aquifers, and karst springs. The stage was set for promising developments in American karst science.

The great water-table debate

During the short span of time from 1930 to 1942, several prominent American geologists attempted to explain the origin of limestone caves in detail. Their main focus was the relation of caves to the water table. Each had his own interpretation based on somewhat different field observations and assumptions, and the echoes of their debate have still not died away.

Deep-phreatic interpretations

Early researchers in this field included two of the world's greatest geologists: William Morris Davis (Figure 7.5) and J Harlen Bretz (no period after the J). Davis, whose concept of landscape evolution is reviewed in Chapter 2, dealt with caves in some of his final publications (e.g., Davis, 1930). He naturally related cave origin to his own model of the erosion cycle. At 80 years of age, he was able to do only cursory fieldwork in caves. From the few cave maps available in his day, he gained the erroneous impression that most caves are complex three-dimensional mazes of interconnected passages. He concluded that they form deep beneath the water table, mainly during the old-age stage of the erosion cycle, when groundwater flow paths are most likely to remain stable for long periods of time.

Figure 7.5: William Morris Davis, probably the world's most influential authority on the origin of landscapes and a pioneer in speleogenesis.

Bretz supplied abundant field evidence to support Davis's ideas. In his first major publication on caves (Bretz, 1942), he clearly distinguished between vadose and phreatic cave features. But he was convinced that caves form beneath the water table and are merely modified by vadose water at a later time. One of his lines of evidence was that most caves show little relationship to the pattern of local uplands and valleys. (Today we consider this poor relationship to be more apparent than real, as it simply reflects the strong control of groundwater by local geologic structure.) Impressed by the great quantity of mud in the caves he visited, especially those in Missouri, Bretz hypothesized that phreatic cave origin must be followed by a stagnant phase in which caves are filled with sediment, most of which is later removed by vadose water.

Shallow-phreatic and vadose interpretations

Other researchers preferred a shallower origin for caves. Allyn Swinnerton (1932) contended that caves are likely to form where groundwater flow is most vigorous — i.e., at and just below the water table. This origin can account for the low-gradient profiles of many cave passages. He pointed to the zone of water-table fluctuation as most favorable for cave origin.

Clyde Malott (1937) held similar views and stressed the importance of floodwater invasion in the origin of caves. Arthur Piper (1932) compared the evolution of caves to that of surface streams, with youthful channels propagating upstream from springs, enlarging to mature passageways, and eventually decaying by collapse and valley widening — the speleological equivalent of the old-age stage of the erosion cycle. James Gardner (1935) considered that successively lower cave levels are formed as rivers entrench their valleys and expose strata favorable to down-dip water flow. R. Rhoades and M. Sinacori (1941) proposed that cave enlargement is most active where groundwater converges near spring outlets, and that caves enlarge headward with time. Some of the lack of agreement among these authors boils down to minor differences in emphasis and wording. Implicit in all of their viewpoints is the idea that cave origin is well adjusted to the present topography.

Several of the early concepts of speleogenesis are compared in Figure 7.6.

Parting of the ways

Near the end of this classic debate came a minor incident that had disproportionately wide implications. The formidable M. King Hubbert, who helped lay the foundations of modern groundwater hydrology (and is best known

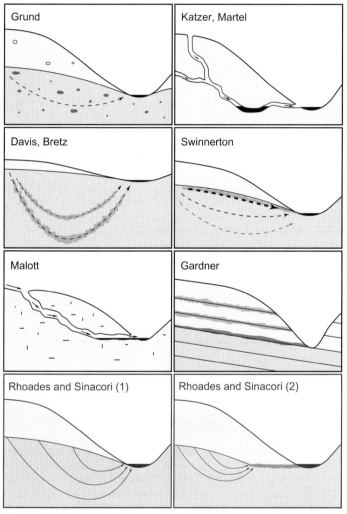

Figure 7.6: Comparison of several early concepts of cave origin: **Grund:** Caves are formed by diffuse groundwater beneath a distinct water table. **Katzer** and **Martel:** Caves are stream conduits, and there is no true water table in karst. **Davis** and **Bretz:** Caves form deep beneath the water table, where groundwater has the greatest time to form them. (Only two of many deep flow routes are shown.) **Swinnerton:** Caves form at or near the water table, where groundwater flow is greatest. **Malott:** Caves are formed by invasion of sinking streams into small, early openings. **Gardner:** Caves form down-dip along favorable beds as the beds are exposed progressively by river erosion. **Rhoades and Sinacori:** Caves form where flow converges at the downstream end of the groundwater system; caves grow headward and distort the flow pattern, so diffuse groundwater continues to converge on the upstream ends of the caves. Ideas are simplified here to emphasize their main points. See the original publications for details.

today for his concept of peak oil production), criticized Swinnerton's view that flow paths in karst could diverge in many directions from points of groundwater input (Hubbert, 1940, p. 927). Hubbert claimed that this idea contradicts the law of conservation of mass and does not fit potential-field theory. This was a rare case where Hubbert was wrong, because he failed to account for the many flow discontinuities in karst aquifers and the plumbing-like nature of caves. Responsibility cannot be placed entirely on this incident, but the attraction of traditional groundwater hydrologists to potential-field theory has led to misinterpretations of karst hydrology that persist even today (see Chapter 15).

Karst scientists continued on their own path, which was still solidly rooted in field observation. During the next few decades, detailed fieldwork appeared to support the shallow-phreatic view of cave origin. Evidence showed that large cave passages tend to lie at the same elevation as terraces in nearby valleys, and that each terrace represents a former river base level (Sweeting, 1950; Davies, 1957, 1960; Ek, 1961; Droppa, 1966; Powell, 1970). The limited vertical range of passages in certain Appalachian caves, even those in steeply dipping strata, was used as evidence that their origin is influenced by the water table (White, 1960).

Light at the end of the tunnel

Progress in understanding cave origin was slowed by the contradictory arguments about the role of the water table. But in the meantime cave exploration and mapping were making great strides, and by the 1960s there were enough detailed cave maps to reveal the true nature and variety of cave types. Growing dissatisfaction with the classical views became apparent during a symposium on cave origin hosted by the National Speleological Society (Moore, 1960). For example, William Halliday (1960b) argued that caves cannot be adequately explained by shoehorning them all into a specific groundwater zone. He urged speleologists to interpret each cave in terms of its local flow characteristics and geologic history. Championing the traditional view, William Davies replied in a later discussion that followed, "I do not agree and feel that there is one way in which most caves are formed, and we must find that way. If not, we will have chaos; there will be 5000 different ways to form caves." Both views have merit, but the new one prevailed, and it is now supported with field evidence far more dramatic than any of the symposium participants had imagined.

Expanding the scope of speleology

Field observation, mapping, and logical deduction can go a long way in supporting ideas on cave origin, but only up to a point. Limestone dissolution and groundwater flow are governed by physical laws that must be considered if any of these ideas is to be validated. Because early cave scientists treated these laws qualitatively and selectively, their ideas had limited application. Further advances required the combined application of hydraulics and chemistry.

Advances in karst chemistry

The foundations of karst chemistry were laid by Schoeller (1962), Roques (1962, 1964), and Garrels and Christ (1965), who applied well-established principles of chemistry and thermodynamics to the problems of limestone dissolution and precipitation. Jacobson and Langmuir (1972) developed the concept of the saturation index (SI), which provided estimates of mineral saturation from measurements of the major dissolved components in water samples (see Chapter 5).

Kaye (1957) and Weyl (1958) measured calcite dissolution rates with cave origin specifically in mind. Using strong acids, they found that dissolution rate increases with flow velocity. They concluded that caves form along the paths of most rapid groundwater movement. Later work by Plummer and Wigley (1976) showed that velocity actually has little effect on dissolution rate except in highly acidic waters such as those used by Kaye and Weyl. Howard (1964a) and Wigley (1975) interpreted cave origin on purely theoretical grounds, although not enough was known about dissolution rates at that time for the results to be applied in a detailed way.

Bögli (1964) noted that most karst water below the water table is saturated with dissolved limestone. He proposed a mechanism to explain phreatic cave origin by the mixing of waters of differing carbon dioxide content. This process of *mixing corrosion* is described on pages 122–123. Its potential role in karst development had been recognized earlier (Laptev, 1939), but Bögli's application of the idea to specific problems in speleogenesis gained widespread appeal. The idea was later expanded to include differences in salinity (Runnells, 1969), sea-water content (Plummer, 1975; Wigley and Plummer, 1976), and H_2S in phreatic systems (Palmer, 1991).

Bögli claimed that dissolution in the phreatic zone was possible only where there is convergence between waters of contrasting CO_2 value. But mixing corrosion is minor in typical phreatic caves, and although it may speed their growth, it is rarely necessary for their development. The best application of the concept is in young porous limestones, especially those along the seacoast, where mixing takes place between waters of considerably different P_{CO_2} and salinity.

Smith and others (1969) estimated rates of cave enlargement by measuring the increases in dissolved calcite with distance in stream passages. The role of oxidation in boosting dissolution rate was found to be substantial (Bray, 1972). The contribution of mechanical abrasion to cave enlargement was examined by Newson (1971) and Smith and Newson (1974). They found that abrasion by solid stream-borne particles was insignificant during low flow but increased rapidly during floods, when mechanical abrasion may even exceed dissolution.

Rates of dissolutional lowering of the land surface (karst denudation) were examined by Corbel (1957) and many others, by measuring the mass of material removed in solution through springs and surface rivers. Calculated rates are generally proportional to the amount of rainfall and reach values up to 20 cm/thousand years, highest in the tropics and lowest in alpine and high-latitude karst (Drake, 1983). These researchers also found that cave enlargement represents only a small percentage of the total karst denudation, because most bedrock dissolution takes at the soil-bedrock interface. Cave enlargement represents a greater percentage of the total in bare karst such as that in alpine regions.

To make direct measurements of bedrock dissolution rates, High and Hanna (1970) developed the *micro-erosion meter*, which consists of a dial micrometer mounted on a triangular base, held in position by bolts in the rock surface (Figure 7.7). Measurements are repeated over a period of years. It can be used in caves or on exposed rock at the surface. Rates of bedrock retreat in active stream caves were found to be as much as 1 mm/yr.

Gams (1965) developed the concept of *accelerated corrosion*, in which carbonate rock beneath the thickest soils dissolves downward most rapidly, owing to greater CO_2 production. Such areas accumulate increasing amounts of soil, so their denudation rates accelerate, and the relief between high and low topography increases with time. To quantify the effect he buried limestone tablets in various soils to compare their rates of dissolution (Gams, 1981).

Thrailkill (1968) interpreted cave origin on the basis of hydraulics and chemical equilibria. He distinguished between vadose flow, which retains its aggressiveness during its travel to the water table (usually more than about one cubic centimeter per second), and vadose seepage, which has a flow small enough to reach saturation, and which deposits speleothems when it enters caves.

Figure 7.7: Micro-erosion meter used for measuring rates of solutional rock retreat. (This particular model was designed and constructed at Western Kentucky University.)

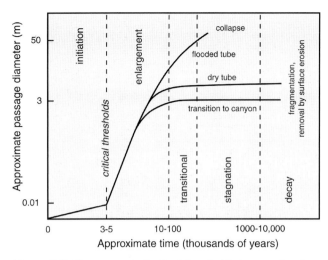

Figure 7.8: The concept of critical thresholds in cave development, as applied to a single passage (after White, 1988). Stages of cave development are approximated from field observations and data on dissolution rates.

Thresholds in cave development

Although the Kaye-Weyl approach was misleading because of the strong acids used (see previous page), it led to a turning point in the history of speleogenesis. Using Weyl's equations, White and Longyear (1962) concluded that the rate of cave enlargement should increase greatly when the solvent water changes from laminar to turbulent flow. Thus was born the concept of a kinetic trigger in cave origin. According to this idea, any pre-cave openings that acquire turbulent flow are able to grow rapidly to cave size, while others stagnate with little or no enlargement. Although turbulence has since been shown to have only a modest effect on dissolution in carbonate rocks, the concept of a kinetic trigger was an important advance in speleogenesis. It became clear that earlier hypotheses that apply only to specific groundwater zones are not valid as general concepts.

Further developing the concept of the kinetic trigger, White (1977a, 1984) noted that as a typical cave passage enlarges, the water emerging from the downstream end becomes more aggressive, gradually at first, and then abruptly. He showed that the sudden rise in aggressiveness takes place at about the same time that the water becomes turbulent. Meanwhile, the growing turbulence allows the cave water to begin transporting sediment. This is an important step in the enlargement of surface depressions such as sinkholes, which funnel increasing amounts of water into growing caves. So the kinetic trigger combines three different processes — turbulence, rapid dissolution, and sediment transport — all of which are related to the flow conditions in the growing cave (Figure 7.8).

White based his model partly on studies of calcite dissolution by Berner and Morse (1974), Plummer and Wigley (1976), and Plummer and others (1978). Their measurements showed that as water reaches about 70–90% saturation with calcite, the dissolution rate suddenly decreases much more rapidly than previously expected

(Chapter 5). Even though these studies have been partly superseded (see Buhmann and Dreybrodt, 1985a, 1985b), they led to new directions in the study of speleogenesis that are still being pursued today.

Hardware models of cave origin

Ewers (1982) modeled cave development by forcing water through blocks of plaster, gypsum, and salt. He mapped the growth of solution conduits by viewing them through a glass plate or transparent bladder pressed upward against the dissolving surface. Despite differences in scale, hydraulic gradient, and solution kinetics between the models and karst aquifers, these carefully designed models clearly showed how conduit growth affects flow patterns (Figure 7.9). The earliest of these experiments contributed greatly to the comprehensive model for cave origin of Ford and Ewers (1978) described on pages 174–175.

Cave origin by sulfuric acid

An important development of the last few decades is the recognition of cave origin by sulfuric acid. This is the acid used in car batteries. In nature it is most often produced by the oxidation of sulfides such as pyrite or hydrogen sulfide. Durov (1956), Morehouse (1968) and Jagnow (1979) described examples of cave development by oxidation of

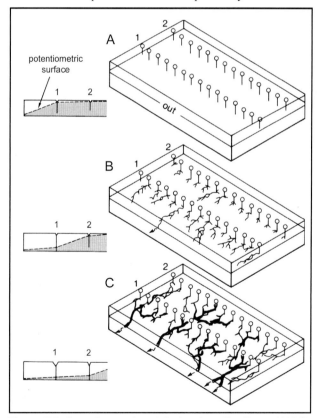

Figure 7.9: One of several models developed by Ewers (1982), based mainly on hardware models, which show how phreatic cave passages link together. Two ranks of water inputs are shown, with outflow along the lower left side. As a passage develops between rank 1 and the outlet, its head decreases so that the passage serves as a target for inputs from rank 2.

pyrite, although most researchers now consider this process to have only a local effect on the overall growth of caves. Egemeier (1973, 1981), Maslyn (1979), Davis (1980), and Hill (1981a, 1987) championed the idea of cave development by the oxidation of hydrogen sulfide, which takes place where rising H$_2$S-rich groundwater encounters oxygen at or near the water table. This idea is also mentioned in earlier but little-known literature from Italy, Hungary, and Mexico. This process has been documented in several actively forming caves. Many caves, especially in dry climates, have odd patterns that defy traditional interpretations, but which are easily explained by the sulfuric acid mechanism.

Thermal cave origin

Thermal karst has received a great deal of attention in recent decades, especially in eastern Europe (Jakucs, 1977; Müller and Sárváry, 1977; Dublyansky, 1980). The caves in and around Budapest, Hungary, are among the best examples of thermal cave origin (Takácsné Bolner and Kraus, 1989). Bakalowicz and others (1987) applied the concept to the Black Hills caves of South Dakota, which had previously been attributed to artesian speleogenesis. The central idea is that rising water becomes more aggressive as it cools, because the solubility of carbonate rocks decreases with temperature. Alone, however, the thermal effect on karst and caves is small. Most of the dissolution is caused by other processes such as mixing of high-CO$_2$ thermal water with shallow low-CO$_2$ water.

Eogenetic karst

One of the most appealing developments in modern cave geology is the study of coastal karst, with emphasis on tropical carbonate islands (Back and others, 1984; Mylroie and Carew, 1990; S. White, 1994; Mylroie and Vacher, 1999). Limestones in such areas are very young, typically less than a million years old, and they tend to be chemically immature. Most of the cave development in these rocks takes place by mixing of fresh water and seawater.

A large portion of freshly deposited marine limestone consists of the mineral aragonite, which is more soluble than

Figure 7.11: Incipient caves along a fracture in limestone exposed by quarrying. What conditions are needed to form them?

calcite (Chapter 3). With time, as groundwater passes through, the aragonite recrystallizes to calcite. This transformation is most rapid when recently deposited limestones are exposed at the surface, either by lowering of sea level or uplift of the land. As fresh water dissolves the aragonite and precipitates calcite, the overall porosity of the limestone decreases. Meanwhile, caves and surface karst features develop along major paths of infiltration and by local dissolution in mixing zones. The linked processes of dissolution and precipitation produce a hard rock that contains larger but fewer pores (Figure 7.10). This rock-forming process is called *early diagenesis*, or *eogenesis* (Choquette and Pray, 1970). Karst formed in this way is called *eogenetic karst* (Mylroie and Vacher, 1999; Vacher and Mylroie, 2002), or *syngenetic karst* (Jennings, 1968; Grimes, 2003). *Eogenetic* refers to processes or features that relate to the depositional environment of a rock. In contrast, *mesogenetic* processes and features are associated with burial beneath younger rocks, when they are isolated from depositional and erosional environments at the surface; and *telogenetic* processes and features are associated with the erosion of rocks when they are exposed at the land surface (with or without intervening burial). Most karst is telogenetic.

Inception horizons

A provocative topic of recent years is the concept of *inception horizons* (Lowe, 1992, Lowe and Gunn, 1997). These are strata, or contacts between strata, in which certain chemical or physical attributes provide favorable conditions for cave development (Figure 7.11). The idea is based on the assumption that groundwater alone cannot initiate caves in carbonate rocks unless certain favorable conditions are met. In particular, if a certain bed or parting contains large concentrations of sulfide minerals such as pyrite, these minerals may oxidize and release sulfuric acid to the groundwater. According to the inception-horizon concept, even a slow release of acid by this process would be sufficient to speed the crucial early stages of cave origin.

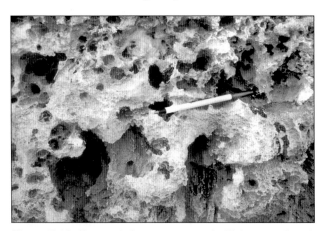

Figure 7.10: Eogenetic karst processes in Pleistocene beach limestone, Isla de Mona, Puerto Rico. Ball-point pen for scale.

Field observations and chemical modeling by Pezdič and others (1998) suggest that CO_2 released by low-temperature metamorphism of dolomite in contact with clay may have a similar effect.

The most enthusiastic proponents of inception horizons suggest that the entire pattern of a cave may be determined by these early deep-seated processes, and that later dissolution by shallow groundwater merely enlarges these patterns (Lowe, 1992). In recent years, many researchers who discuss inception horizons ignore the chemical issue and note only that caves are often initiated along a few favorable geologic contacts.

Earlier work by Davis and Moore (1965) considered earth tides as a mechanism for cave inception. As the Earth rotates, the gravitational force of the Moon and Sun causes shifts in the solid parts of the planet as well as tides in water. Rock deformation is slight because of its rigidity, but back-and-forth motion along favorable fractures can draw water through the openings. The effect on cave origin is limited, because the movement smears the water along the fractures with only a minor tendency for through-flow. Still, the process helps to keep the fractures open. It also accounts for the shapes of certain speleothems (Chapter 10).

Computer modeling

Although the hydraulic and chemical processes that form caves are reasonably well understood, they involve complex interactions that are almost impossible to calculate by hand. This difficulty can be overcome by computer modeling, in which idealized fissures are divided into a large number of small segments, while imaginary water is passed through them. Meanwhile the overall enlargement history is divided into many time steps. This is known as *finite-difference analysis* (Figure 7.12). Its application to cave origin has been developed independently by several people in different countries.

The first computer models of conduit enlargement were devised in England for engineering purposes such as leakage around dams (James and Kirkpatrick, 1980). In

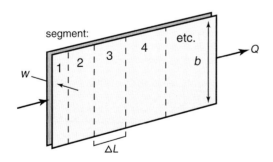

Figure 7.12: Finite-difference modeling of fissure growth. On a computer, an idealized fissure of specified size is divided into small segments, and the effect of water flow of given gradient and chemistry is calculated in each segment. Solutional widening of each segment is calculated at different time steps to estimate the growth history of the fissure. Q = discharge, ΔL = segment length, w = fissure width (increases with time), b = long dimension of fissure cross section.

America, to explain the origin of maze caves in comparison to branchwork or single-passage caves, Palmer (1981b, 1991) used computer modeling to clarify the different rates at which competing cave passages form. In Germany, Dreybrodt (1990, 1996) developed models that drew upon his own detailed investigations of calcite dissolution rates. Also in America, Groves and Howard (1994) and Howard and Groves (1995) expanded the modeling approach to two-dimensional networks. Recent work in Germany has greatly advanced the field (e.g., Clemens and others, 1996; Kaufmann and Braun, 1999; Gabrovšek, 2000; Dreybrodt and Gabrovšek, 2002; Dreybrodt and others, 2005). A comprehensive review of this subject is given by Dreybrodt and others (2005). All of these models converge on similar conclusions and more or less confirm earlier interpretations of cave origin in a quantitative way.

Karst hydrology comes of age

The hydrology of a karst aquifer tells a great deal about the caves within it, even if they are inaccessible. Hydraulic aspects of caves have been examined by Lehmann (1932), Bögli (1980), and Gale (1984). Mangin (1975) and Bakalowicz (1979) used hydraulic and chemical measurements in springs to interpret the nature of the solutional openings in groundwater basins. Williams (1983, 1985) and Smart and Friederich (1986) examined the structure of the epikarst and the pattern of water inputs into the karst system. Shuster and White (1971) showed that variations in flow and water chemistry are greater in springs fed primarily by large turbulent-flow conduits, rather than by diffuse flow through a network of small openings. These and many later approaches have advanced our understanding of water supply and contaminant transport in karst (Chapter 15).

International collaboration

The development of computer modeling of karst is an example of how modern scientific advances tend to take place simultaneously on a worldwide basis. Not long ago, innovations in karst science were fairly isolated. For example, in the mid-20th century one of France's most distinguished speleologists, Bernard Gèze, noted that Americans such as Davis and Bretz were almost totally unaware of the European karst literature, and that they "seem to be reinventing speleology right from square one" (translated loosely from an early book on speleology by Trombe, 1952, p. 366). But at the same time, Trombe appears to have been unaware of the substantial contributions to karst science that were being made in central and eastern Europe. The main difficulty was the language barrier.

Today speleologists in most countries work together closely, often as unified teams. This convergence is due mainly to the establishment of the International Union of Speleology, as well as to increased frequency of international karst conferences and electronic communication. The emergence of an almost universal second language (English) has also helped to close the communication gap. The Web

Flow type	Hydrologic control	Cave type
I. Diffuse	Shaly limestone, crystalline dolomite, or high primary porosity	Caves rare and small, with irregular patterns
II. Free flow	Thick soluble rocks	Integrated conduit systems
A. Perched	Underlying low-permeability rocks at or above base level.	Cave streams perched, often have free air surfaces
1. Open	Soluble rocks extend upward to surface	Sinkhole inputs; large sediment load; channel-type caves
2. Capped	Overlain by low-permeability rocks	Vertical shaft inputs, lateral flow beneath capping beds, long integrated caves
B. Deep	Karst extends deep below base level	Flow through water-filled conduits
1. Open	Soluble rocks extend upward to surface	Short tubular caves, many abandoned, likely to be sediment choked
2. Capped	Overlain by low-permeability rocks	Long integrated conduits under cap. Active caves water-filled
III. Confined	Structural and stratigraphic controls	
A. Artesian	Low-permeability beds force low below regional base level	Inclined 3-D network caves
B. Sandwich	Thin beds of soluble rock between low-permeability beds	Horizontal 2-D network caves

Table 7.1: Cave patterns in various aquifer types, according to White (1969, 1977b).

site *www.speleogenesis.info* provides a forum for discussion of cave origin, as well as reprints of important articles in the field. It is sponsored by the International Speleological Union and International Geographical Union and has a team of editors from around the world. Two recent books on speleogenesis (Klimchouk and others, 2000; Gabrovšek, 2002) draw on authors from many countries to present examples of their field work and current ideas about cave origin. Another outcome of this growing international collaboration is that earlier karst scientists whose influence was limited mainly to their own countries are now gaining global recognition (see Shaw, 1992, 2000; Lowe, 2000).

Comprehensive views of speleogenesis

During the past few decades there have been several attempts to devise a single comprehensive model for the origin of all, or most, solution caves. Five approaches have been taken to explain the various cave types and patterns. They are introduced here in approximately historical sequence and are discussed in greater detail in the following two chapters. The various models complement each other and are not mutually exclusive.

Relationship of caves to aquifer type

White (1969, 1977b) classified karst aquifers according to their hydrogeologic settings and described the types of caves found in each (Table 7.1). Although his model does not apply solely to cave origin, it provides a framework within which different cave types can be placed. He recognized the following aquifer-cave relationships: ***Diffuse-flow aquifers***

include shaly limestone, crystalline dolomite, and soluble rocks of high primary porosity. The few caves that occur in these aquifers are small, with irregular patterns. ***Free-flow aquifers*** include those that are perched on relatively impermeable rocks, as well as deeper aquifers in which any underlying flow barriers lie well below the erosional base level. Both perched and deep types can be either exposed directly at the surface or overlain by a relatively insoluble cap-rock. Sinkholes are the main water inputs in the exposed type, and short caves with high sediment load are common. Capped aquifers are fed by vertical shafts around the eroded perimeters of the cap-rock, and long integrated caves extend beneath the cap-rock. White divides confined aquifers into the artesian type, in which impermeable beds force water to flow below the regional base level, and the "sandwich" type, which are confined between thin impermeable beds. Inclined three-dimensional mazes are common in artesian aquifers and horizontal two-dimensional mazes are typical of sandwich aquifers.

Resolving the water-table debate

Ford (1971), and Ford and Ewers (1978) proposed a model based on the evolution of flow fields and fissure frequency in karst aquifers. In this model, cave patterns depend on the spatial density of partings and fractures (***fissure frequency***). Ideally, the fissure frequency is initially low, but it increases with time as fractures and partings become wider, owing to pressure release resulting from cave development and erosional removal of overlying rocks. Ford (1971) envisioned a four-state model with the following sequence: (1) At the

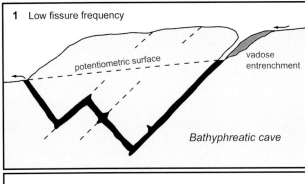

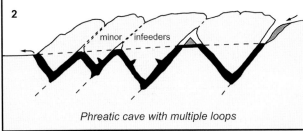

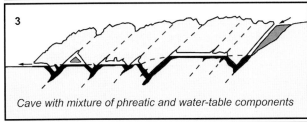

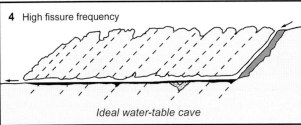

Figure 7.13: Relation between fissure frequency and depth of cave development below the water table (after Ford, 1971; Ford and Ewers, 1978). These patterns tend to develop sequentially, so remnants of older loops are preserved above the younger passages (omitted from diagram).

lowest fissure frequency only a few phreatic loops develop, and possibly only one. These extend deep below the water table and represent ***bathyphreatic*** cave development. (2) As fissure frequency increases, multiple loops develop that are shallower than the first ones, and the water table drops as the permeability increases. (3) As fissures become still more numerous, a mixture of phreatic and water-table cave segments develops. (4) When fissure frequency is so great that phreatic loops cannot form, cave passages develop almost entirely along the water table. This sequence is shown in Figure 7.13.

Many caves exhibit more than one state, or they may bypass one or more of them. Two other conditions are possible (Ford, 1988): state 0, in which no fissures at all are present, which prohibits cave development; and state 5, in which there are so many small openings (e.g., in chalk)

that groundwater is too diffuse to form significant caves. Ford (1971) considers artesian conditions to be a special case in which maze caves are formed by slow, lengthy dissolution.

Studies in the Alps show that many cave passages with high-amplitude loops can form above the water table during floods (Audra, 1994; Häuselmann, 2002; Choppy, 2002). These characteristics are typical of floodwater caves in general (Palmer, 1972), although they are most notable in high-relief mountainous karst.

Worthington (2004, 2005) has expanded the interpretation of cave profiles by recognizing the development of sub-horizontal cave development as much as 100 m below the water table. Depth of cave development is proportional to overall length of flow paths and angle of the stratal dip. Enlargement of deep conduits may be aided by the downward increase in temperature, which reduces the viscosity of the water and provides less resistance to flow. These topics are discussed in Chapter 9.

How cave passages link together

As a phreatic cave passage enlarges, water flows through it more easily. As a result, its hydraulic head decreases to nearly the level of the spring outlet, and water in neighboring openings is attracted toward this passage. Using these relationships and supplementing them with cave observations and hardware models, Ewers (1982) presented a conceptual view of how individual cave passages link together to form a complex cave. Figure 7.9 is an example. Given various inputs at different distances from an outlet, those with the shortest paths are the first to form cave passages. Incipient caves fed by multiple inputs compete for supremacy, and the first to break through to the target surface valley becomes the main conduit. Because the head decreases in the main passage, the flow from more remote inputs is drawn toward the earliest passages to form tributaries. Ewers (1985) gives a detailed field example from eastern Kentucky.

Ewers also applied the linking process to passages that drain along the strike of steeply dipping beds. Water is progressively captured by a developing strike-oriented passage that is fed by increasingly remote water sources. Some of his other models illustrate cave development where the outlet is created by erosional breaching of a low-permeability cap-rock.

Interpretation of cave patterns

Palmer (1975, 1981b, 1991) combined geologic mapping with hydraulics and chemistry to explain the origin of cave patterns (Figure 7.14): (1) In the early stages, the rate of cave enlargement depends almost entirely on the ratio of discharge to flow length (Q/L). Differences in this ratio account for the varied growth rate among the competing flow paths. (2) Along any path, the enlargement rate increases with discharge, but only up to a certain limit. From then on, greater discharge increases the enlargement rate only

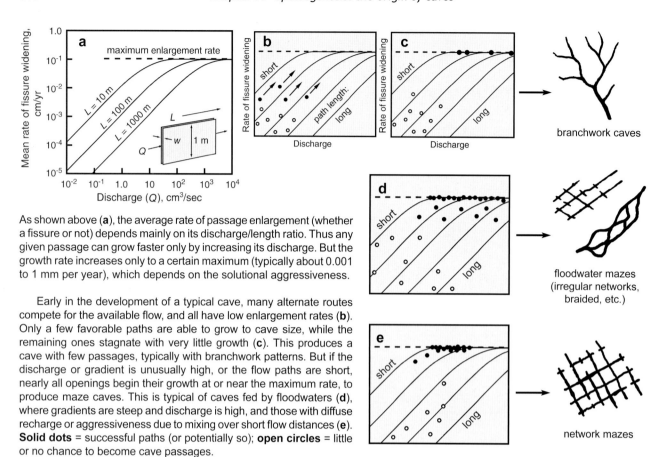

Figure 7.14: Development of cave patterns under various groundwater conditions (after Palmer, 1991, 2002).

As shown above (**a**), the average rate of passage enlargement (whether a fissure or not) depends mainly on its discharge/length ratio. Thus any given passage can grow faster only by increasing its discharge. But the growth rate increases only to a certain maximum (typically about 0.001 to 1 mm per year), which depends on the solutional aggressiveness.

Early in the development of a typical cave, many alternate routes compete for the available flow, and all have low enlargement rates (**b**). Only a few favorable paths are able to grow to cave size, while the remaining ones stagnate with very little growth (**c**). This produces a cave with few passages, typically with branchwork patterns. But if the discharge or gradient is unusually high, or the flow paths are short, nearly all openings begin their growth at or near the maximum rate, to produce maze caves. This is typical of caves fed by floodwaters (**d**), where gradients are steep and discharge is high, and those with diffuse recharge or aggressiveness due to mixing over short flow distances (**e**). **Solid dots** = successful paths (or potentially so); **open circles** = little or no chance to become cave passages.

slightly, if at all. (3) If a flow path is to grow fast enough to become a cave, its discharge must increase with time. This is usually achieved by expansion of its catchment area. Only a few paths reach cave size. Other openings stagnate with little further growth. (4) The only exception to this rule is where openings enlarge at high rates more or less from the start. Maze caves form where the ratio of discharge to flow distance is large along many alternate routes, for example where recharge enters soluble rock through an adjacent permeable but insoluble rock (small *L*), or where periodic floodwaters produce steep hydraulic gradients (large *Q*). Other examples of small flow length include aggressiveness produced by mixing, oxidation of sulfides, or cooling of thermal water.

According to this model, fully confined artesian conditions are not sufficient by themselves to form maze caves. They require other processes such as mixing or diffuse inflow from adjacent permeable rocks. The time required for cave inception increases with flow distance and temperature, and decreases with initial fissure width, hydraulic gradient, and CO_2 concentration. Geologic control of passage trends is also included in the model (Chapter 9).

Relationship of caves to aquifer evolution

Klimchouk (1997, 2000) stressed the evolutionary history of karst aquifers as a major control of cave development. His

model is not limited to cave origin, but instead defines the framework in which caves develop. From the time the soluble rock is deposited it is exposed to a variety of conditions such as early diagenesis, burial, deformation, and uplift, and each stage has an impact on the resulting caves (Figure 7.15).

A typical karst aquifer undergoes the following sequence: (1) eogenetic dissolution soon after the rock is deposited, (2) deep burial, with dissolution or mineralization, often by artesian flow, and (3) exposure of the rock at the surface by erosion of overlying rocks. As soluble rocks are exposed at the surface they go through several stages: (a) *subjacent karst*, where soluble rock is covered by insoluble rock everywhere except for local breaching by valleys, (b) *entrenched karst*, in which valleys extend below the bottom of the karst aquifer, but where the aquifer is still partly covered by insoluble rocks, and (c) *exposed karst*, where the overlying insoluble rocks have been completely removed by erosion. As these stages progress, cave development usually becomes more intense and surface karst features become more numerous.

Karst may bypass stage 2 (deep burial), or it may be re-buried by a covering of younger rocks to form paleokarst and be re-exposed at a later time. Each stage has an effect on the next, although some earlier features may become abandoned relics. Klimchouk emphasized the importance of upward groundwater flow through soluble rocks sandwiched

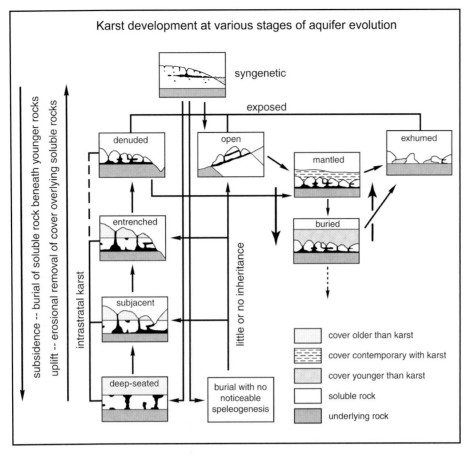

Karst development at various stages of aquifer evolution

Figure 7.15: Types of karst and cave development in relation to the evolutionary stages of a soluble-rock aquifer, according to Klimchouk (2000).

where ΔV = increase in volume during time t, and ρ = bedrock density. Typical units are: ΔV = cm^3, Q = liters/sec, t = sec, ΔC = grams/liter, and ρ = grams/cm^3. ΔC (grams/liter) is expressed as mineral equivalents. For example, the mass of $CaCO_3$ is 2.5 times greater than that of Ca, as shown by a list of atomic weights. Thus if Ca is measured in mg/L and comes only from the dissolution of limestone ($CaCO_3$), the Ca must be multiplied by 2.50 to obtain mg/L of $CaCO_3$.

In the calculation of volume, bedrock density must be adjusted for porosity. For example, the density of calcite is 2.71 g/cm^3. If the bedrock is limestone composed mainly of calcite and with 5% porosity, only 95% of the total volume is solid. The effective density is therefore 2.71 x 0.95 = 2.57 g/cm^3. Densities of other relevant minerals are: aragonite = 2.94, dolomite = 2.85, gypsum = 2.32, halite (NaCl) = 2.16, and quartz = 2.65 g/cm^3.

Q and ΔC vary with time, especially during floods. For a long-term estimate of cave growth, it is necessary to break the total time into small time steps (Δt) and determine the mean Q and ΔC in each. The volume increase during any time interval is expressed as $\Delta V = Q \, \Delta t \, \Delta C / \rho$, and the total increase in volume during the entire project is

$$\Delta V = \Sigma(Q \, \Delta t \, \Delta C)/\rho \qquad (7.3)$$

where $\Sigma(Q \, \Delta t \, \Delta C)$ is the sum of all individual ($Q \, \Delta t \, \Delta C$) values.

In summary, the growth of a solution cave depends on *discharge*, *dissolution rate*, and *time*, all of which are essential and have equal importance. Bedrock density is not a significant factor because it varies only slightly between soluble rock types. In other words, caves form along the paths where groundwater flow and solutional aggressiveness toward the local bedrock are greatest, and where flow patterns are stable for long periods. A solution cave cannot form at all if any of these conditions are small or absent.

As shown in Chapter 4, the *discharge* through any conduit is controlled in two possible ways, or by a combination of both: In a water-filled conduit fed by a large water source,

between insoluble but semi-permeable strata. Maze caves can form in this way, and the extensive gypsum network caves of Ukraine are examples (Chapters 2 and 8).

Rates of cave enlargement

The overall concept of solutional cave origin is simple: the mass removed from the bedrock must be carried away in solution by flowing water. This process involves conservation of mass, or the ***mass balance***. The details are more complicated, but the basic principle remains valid.

Application of the mass balance

The mass balance is most easily demonstrated in a single actively forming cave passage. The mass carried away in solution depends on discharge (Q), concentration of dissolved solids (C), and time (t). Before the water even enters the cave passage there is almost always some dissolved load, so it is more appropriate to consider change of concentration (ΔC) rather than concentration alone. These variables are easily measured in the field. The amount of mass removed is

$$\Delta m = Q \, t \, \Delta C \qquad (7.1)$$

where Δm = mass removed during the time t. Regarding cave growth, it is appropriate to convert mass to volume (V). Mass = density x volume, so the result is

$$\Delta V = Q \, t \, \Delta C / \rho \qquad (7.2)$$

the discharge depends on the hydraulic efficiency of the conduit. But where the inflow is not sufficient to keep the entire passage filled, the discharge depends on the size of the catchment area and the net recharge rate (precipitation minus evapotranspiration).

Dissolution rate depends on several variables: aggressiveness of the solvent water, hydraulic characteristics of the water (mainly turbulence and geometry), rock type and crystal size, and temperature. Carbonate dissolution rates can be maintained at high levels by renewal of aggressiveness, for example, by mixing of waters of contrasting composition, uptake of CO_2 from surrounding air, or by generation of CO_2 by oxidation of organic compounds in the water.

Measurement of overall rates of cave growth requires years of continuous monitoring. A simple approach is to use automatic recorders to monitor stream depths and specific conductance. Stream depths can be converted to discharge (Chapter 4), and specific conductance can be converted to dissolved load (Chapter 5).

A similar approach can be used to estimate the rate at which bedrock is removed by dissolution from an entire drainage basin. In Eq. 7.2, $[Qt]$ can be replaced by the available water volume each year, which is essentially precipitation minus evapotranspiration (both measured as depth) multiplied by the area of the basin.

Basin-wide estimates of dissolution rate should not be confused with rates of cave development. Most groundwater obtains its solutional aggressiveness from CO_2 generated in the soil. As a result, much (and usually most) of the water's solutional potential is expended at the bedrock surface just beneath the soil and does not contribute to cave origin. Farther down, most of the remaining dissolution is likely to take place in narrow fissures and pores that never enlarge to cave size.

Accessible caves account for only a small part of the dissolution. Where water moves rapidly along favorable routes, dissolution can extend over long distances to form conduits. In slow-moving water the dissolution may be concentrated in local areas where mixing or oxidation cause local bursts of aggressiveness (Chapters 5 and 8).

Measurement of dissolution rates

Soluble rock dissolves most rapidly when the solvent water does not yet contain any dissolved material from the rock. As dissolution proceeds, the dissolved load increases and the dissolution rate decreases. In a typical actively enlarging cave the upstream end grows rapidly, while farther downstream the water is closer to saturation and the cave grows more slowly. This tendency can be offset by an increasing discharge in the downstream direction as tributaries enter.

In the initial fissures the flow rates are so low that the water is very close to saturation with dissolved bedrock everywhere but in the first few meters. As conduits develop, the discharge and velocity increase, and water can move through the system while still retaining much of its aggressiveness. As a result the

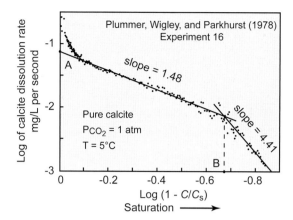

Figure 7.16: Decrease in calcite dissolution rate with saturation ratio in an open system with turbulent flow (from experimental data by Plummer and others, 1978). $(1 - C/C_s)$ represents the degree of undersaturation. The logarithmic scale is used to produce straight lines. **A** = maximum dissolution rate of about 0.066 mg/L/sec at $C/C_s = 0$; log $(1 - C/C_s)$ also = 0. Dissolution rates are less at lower P_{CO_2}. Data points above **A** are ignored, as they disagree with Figure 7.17 and may be an artifact of the experimental method (see Palmer, 1991); but Kaufmann and Dreybrodt (2007) suggest that high rates at $C/C_s < 0.3$ may be valid. The effect on cave origin is negligible. **B** = change in slope at about $C/C_s = 0.8$ (point **B** shifts to the left at lower P_{CO_2} and to the right with increasing temperature). Although the graph slopes to the right, the slopes are positive, because the horizontal scale decreases to the right. Values of k and n, and the transition point from gentle to steep slope, $(C/C_s)_t$, which are derived from these graphs, are summarized in Table 7.2.

dissolution rate increases greatly and remains high while the cave grows.

The initial flow through narrow fissures is almost always laminar (Chapter 4). With time, as the passage enlarges, the flow becomes turbulent. The onset of turbulence depends on the flow velocity, fissure width, and water temperature, but it typically takes place when fissures grow to roughly 0.5–1.0 cm in width. As turbulent flow develops, there is a slight increase in dissolution rate (approximately 2–3 times at low saturation ratios, but much less at high saturation ratios (Plummer and others, 1978; Dreybrodt and Eisenlohr, 2000; see their Table 2).

P_{CO_2}	n_1	5°C		15°C		25°C	
		k_1	$(C/C_s)_t$	k_1	$(C/C_s)_t$	k_1	$(C/C_s)_t$
1.0	1.5	0.07	0.8	0.09	0.85	0.12	0.9
0.3	1.6	0.03	0.65	0.035	0.7	0.04	0.8
0.03	1.7	0.009	0.6	0.015	0.7	0.02	0.8
0.003	2.2	0.006	0.6	0.01	0.7	0.015	0.8

At $C/C_s > (C/C_s)_t$: $n_2 \approx 4$, $k_2 = k_1[(C/C_s)_t]^{(n_1-n_2)}$

Table 7.2: Values of k, n, and $(C/C_s)_t$ for dissolution of limestone (impure calcite) by turbulent flow, from Palmer (1991), calculated from laboratory data of Plummer and others (1978) and Plummer and Wigley (1976). Units for k are mg-cm/L-sec; n and $(C/C_s)_t$ have no units. For applications, refer to Eq. 7.4.

Experiments by Berner and Morse (1974) and Plummer and Wigley (1976) showed that the calcite dissolution rate undergoes a sharp decrease at about 90% saturation. Previous researchers had stopped their experiments prematurely, because they assumed that dissolution had run its full course. Later measurements by Plummer, Wigley, and Parkhurst (1978) show that at lower temperatures and P_{CO_2}, which are typical of most groundwater, the sharp rate decrease takes place at C/C_s as low as 0.60 (60% saturation), so it has a much greater effect on cave development than was originally thought.

Dissolution by turbulent flow

Dissolution by turbulent water is easily measured in the laboratory. The experiments of Plummer, Wigley, and Parkhurst (1978) involved stirred turbulent solutions with grains of pure and impure calcite. They summarized their experiments with an idealized equation. Their goal was mainly to understand the processes of calcite dissolution rather than to apply it to field problems, and their idealized equation deviates from experimental data, including their own. Palmer (1991) recalculated the original PWP data to fit a series of graphs (as in Figure 7.16), which allowed the rate of limestone dissolution to be estimated by the simple equation

$$S = 31.56\ k\ (1 - C/C_s)^n / \rho \quad cm/yr \qquad (7.4)$$

where S = rate of solutional wall retreat (cm/yr), k = reaction coefficient, C/C_s = saturation ratio, n = reaction order, and ρ = bedrock density (about 2.7 g/cm³ for limestone). Eq. 7.4 is valid for any flow conditions, P_{CO_2}, or temperature, as long as the k and n values can be estimated (see Table 7.2 for representative values). The constant 31.56 converts the result to cm/yr.

At C/C_s values less than $(C/C_s)_t$, $n = n_1$ and $k = k_1$. At C/C_s values greater than $(C/C_s)_t$, $n = n_2$ and $k = k_2$. The increase in n beyond $(C/C_s)_t$ causes the dissolution rate to *decrease*, because $(1 - C/C_s)$ is less than 1.0.

On the graphs of cave development shown in Figure 7.14 (Palmer, 1991, 2002), the maximum enlargement rate is determined by Eq. 7.4 with $C/C_s = 0$. The maximum rate of wall retreat (S) is therefore 31.56 k/ρ cm/yr. The sloping lines on the graphs in Figure 7.14 are defined simply by the mass balance (Eq. 7.2), because water emerges from narrow fissures essentially at calcite saturation. The curved parts of the lines that connect the sloping and horizontal segments were determined by computer modeling (see pages 181–183).

Experiments by Rauch and White (1977) show the decrease in dissolution rate in various types of carbonate rock as the percentage of calcite saturation increases in the water (Figure 7.17). These experiments were run in artificial boreholes in rock slabs near the transition from laminar to turbulent flow. The water was collected at the downstream end and recycled. The tube interiors were pre-treated by exposing them to dissolution before the experiments began.

A plot of the equation of Plummer, Wigley, and Parkhurst (1978) is labeled **PWP** in Figure 7.17. A better fit, labeled **P**, is provided by Eq. 7.4. This line is adjusted for impure calcite, which approximates the behavior of natural limestone (data from Plummer and Wigley, 1976). This was a valid choice, because line **P** passes through the middle of the Rauch and White data. Groves (1993) also found that Eq. 7.4 and Table 7.2 gave a closer fit to experimental data than other approaches available at that time.

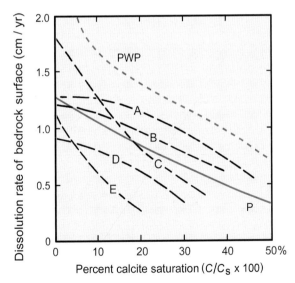

Figure 7.17: Effect of composition and texture on dissolution rates of limestone and dolomite at 23°C and 1 atm P_{CO_2} (adapted from Rauch and White, 1977). **A** = fine-grained limestone with silty interbeds; **B** = pure limestone; **C** = dolomitic limestone; **D** = limestone with detrital impurities; **E** = dolomite with detrital impurities. **PWP** = rate predicted by the model of Plummer, Wigley, and Parkhurst (1978) for pure calcite. **P** = rate predicted by Palmer (1991) for impure calcite, based on recalculation of experimental data from Plummer and Wigley (1976) and Plummer and others (1978).

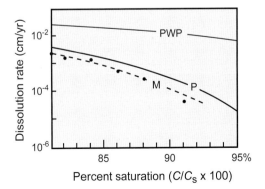

Figure 7.18: An example of limestone dissolution rates near saturation. **M** = experimental data from Morse (1978), with limestone grains in turbulent seawater, P_{CO_2} = 0.003 atm, T = 25°C. **PWP** = equation of Plummer, Wigley, and Parkhurst (1978), **P** = results from Eq. 7.4, with k and n values from Table 7.2.

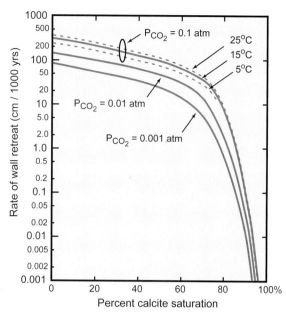

Figure 7.19: Approximate rates of solutional cave enlargement in limestone in carbonic acid systems, based on Eq. 7.4 and Table 7.2. The graphs apply to turbulent flow and represent the rates observed in cave streams, regardless of passage shape. This graph is generalized to show the overall trends. Direct use of Eq. 7.4 provides more precise results.

Figure 7.18 shows dissolution measurements from limestone grains immersed in solutions close to calcite saturation (Morse, 1978). A close fit is again provided by Eq. 7.4. The original PWP equation overestimates the dissolution rate. A summary of dissolution rates predicted by Eq. 7.4 is shown in Figure 7.19, to show the overall trend of cave enlargement rates by turbulent flow.

Example: Measurements in a cave stream show a temperature of 15°C, a saturation ratio (C/C_s) of 0.85, and a

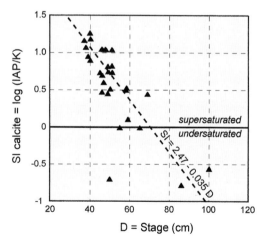

Figure 7.20: Calcite saturation index of water entering Mystery Cave, Minnesota, vs. stage (water level) of South Fork of Root River, which feeds the cave (calculated from data by Grow, 1986). Solutional aggressiveness is greatest at high flow rates. Scatter in the data is caused mainly by seasonal effects. The best-fit line and its equation are shown. Correlation coefficient = −0.80. See Chapters 5 and 14 for details.

P_{CO_2} of 0.01 atm (see Chapter 5 for field and laboratory methods). What is the estimated dissolution rate?

From Table 7.2, $n_1 \approx 1.9$, $k_1 \approx 0.012$, and $(C/C_s)_t \approx 0.7$. But because C/C_s is greater than 0.7, use $n_2 \approx 4$ and $k_2 = k_1[(C/C_s)_t]^{(n_1-n_2)} \approx 0.012 (0.7)^{(1.9-4)} \approx 0.025$. From Eq. 7.4, the dissolution rate $(S) = (31.56) (0.025) (1 - 0.85)^4 /2.7$, which is roughly 1.5×10^{-4} cm/yr. If this rate represents a long-term average, the limestone exposed to the flow would retreat one centimeter in roughly 6500–7000 years. Alternatively, Figure 7.19 can be used.

The calculated dissolution rate is fairly low, and yet it is representative of many cave streams. It is wise to avoid jumping to conclusions from a single measurement, however, because the rates calculated during typical flow conditions probably do not represent long-term averages. More dissolution may take place during a few major floods than in all the intervening periods of low flow combined. An example of how the saturation index of calcite decreases with increasing flow in cave streams is shown in Figure 7.20. In that example the water entering the cave already contains much dissolved limestone, and it is able to dissolve additional limestone *only* during high flow. To obtain a valid average dissolution rate, many measurements at a variety of flow conditions are needed.

Dissolution by laminar flow

In experiments with grains of calcite suspended in stirred water, Plummer and others (1978) showed that increasing stirring rate causes more rapid dissolution, but that the effect becomes negligible as the solution approaches calcite saturation. Thus it appears that turbulence has a small effect on dissolution rates in most cave water, and that the values of n and k in Table 7.2 may be crudely valid for laminar flow as well. This would be convenient, because the initial stages of cave development take place in laminar flow, and almost entirely near calcite saturation.

Recent experiments show the situation to be more complicated than originally thought. The details are beyond the scope of this book, but they are summarized by Dreybrodt and Eisenlohr (2000) and Dreybrodt and others (2005). The most important point is that very near calcite saturation, at which the earliest stages of cave development take place, the reaction rates are so slow that they cannot be reliably measured in the laboratory. So the estimates of n and k near saturation are only approximate and may not apply well to the inception phase of cave development. In some experiments by Dreybrodt and his associates, n_2 values as high as 11 were calculated.

Microscopic examination of dissolved surfaces of soluble rock by Dreybrodt and Eisenlohr (2000) shows a gradual build-up of impurities, and they concluded that the sharp decrease in dissolution rate shown in Figures 7.16 and 7.19 is probably due to this process. These impurities consist mainly of insoluble residue and adsorbed ions such as phosphate, which inhibit the transfer of soluble rock into the water.

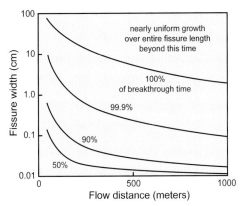

Figure 7.21: Solutional enlargement of a fissure, determined from computer modeling (after Palmer, 1991). The initial fissure width = 0.01 cm, hydraulic gradient = 0.1, initial P_{CO_2} = 0.01 atm, and temperature = 10°C. Breakthrough time in this particular model is 96,000 years. The upstream part of the fissure grows so rapidly that it merges with the general karst landscape. Beyond the breakthrough time, the fissure grows rather uniformly along its entire length, producing a passage with no significant taper in the downstream direction. In a real system, the exact timing varies with many other factors, such as the interaction between neighboring fissures (see Figure 7.23), but the overall growth pattern resembles that shown here.

Insight from computer modeling

The earliest digital models of cave development involved the imaginary flow of water through single fissures (James and Kirkpatrick, 1980; Palmer, 1981b, 1984b; Dreybrodt, 1990). All three models were developed independently, in three different countries (Britain, U.S., and Germany, respectively) but their results are compatible.

Modeling of single fissures

Real groundwater flow is three-dimensional, but modeling a single fissure (or a single series of interconnected fissures) is the most direct way to understand the factors involved in cave development. First the fissure length is defined and is divided into many short segments (Figure 7.12). Then the initial conditions are chosen, such as fissure width, hydraulic gradient, carbon dioxide content, and temperature. The initial discharge through the fissure is then computed, as are the initial n and k values. As the water passes through the first segment, the dissolution rate, change in dissolved load, saturation ratio, loss of CO_2, and rate of fissure enlargement are calculated. The resulting solution, with its new saturation ratio and other variables, is then passed on to the second segment. The calculations are repeated in all remaining segments in their turn. This operation takes a fraction of a second on a computer. Then the new size of each segment is determined for a specified time period (for example, 100 years). A new discharge is calculated and the entire process is repeated for many additional time periods, while the growth of each segment is tracked (Figure 7.21).

James and Kirkpatrick (1980), who were the first to devise computer models of fissure growth, were concerned mainly with the design of dams and foundations. They modeled the early growth of wide fissures under steep hydraulic gradients, which do not apply directly to cave origin, so the results are not described here.

The models of Palmer and Dreybrodt determine the **breakthrough time** needed for a fissure to reach its maximum growth rate (where the graphs in Figure 7.14 reach their maximum height). This is essentially the same as the time required for the water emerging from the downstream end of the fissure to change from slow to high reaction rate, as in Figure 7.16. According to Palmer's model, the breakthrough time can be expressed as

$$t_b = \alpha \ (w_o)^{-3.12} \ (i/L)^{-1.37} \ (P_{CO_2}{}^o)^{-1.0} \ \text{years} \qquad (7.5a)$$

where t_b = breakthrough time, α = temperature-dependent coefficient that converts time to years (= 5×10^{-12} at 10°C), w_o = initial fissure width (cm), i = hydraulic gradient ($\Delta h/L$, no units, because the lengths cancel), L – total fissure length (cm), and $P_{CO_2}{}^o$ = initial P_{CO_2} (atm) where the water first enters the fissure (Palmer, 1988, 1991). Hydraulic gradient (i) and fissure length (L) have exactly opposite effects and can be combined as a single term. The negative exponents indicate an inverse relationship — in other words, if w_o, i/L, and $P_{CO_2}{}^o$ are large, the breakthrough time is short. The breakthrough time is greater along those paths that are relatively long (large L).

Typical fissure width at breakthrough is a few centimeters at the downstream end. From then on, passage growth is fairly uniform over the entire passage length, with only a small amount of narrowing in the downstream direction.

Dreybrodt (1996) derived the following equation, which differs only slightly from Eq. 7.5a:

$$t_b = \alpha \ (w_o)^{-3.0} \ (i/L)^{-1.33} \ (k_2)^{0.33} \ (C_s)^{-1.33} \ \text{years} \qquad (7.5b)$$

where k_2 is the reaction coefficient at saturation ratios greater than $(C/C_s)_t$, and C_s is the closed-system saturation concentration in moles/cm³. Values for α, $k2$, and C_s must be determined experimentally (see Dreybrodt and Eisenlohr, 2000).

Note the close agreement in the effects of w_o and i/L on breakthrough time in Eqs. 7.5a and 7.5b. The chemical variables in the two equations are different and are not easily compared. Breakthrough times for Eqs. 7.5a and 7.5b are compared in Figure 7.22. The main graph is from Palmer (1991), and a single dashed line is added to show how Dreybrodt's results differ. An example is given in the figure caption.

Although the Dreybrodt and Palmer lines in Figure 7.22 have almost identical slopes, those of Dreybrodt indicate breakthrough times about 4 times shorter. The Dreybrodt values are based on experiments that are more appropriate

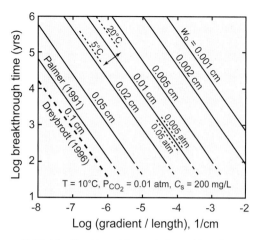

Figure 7.22: Idealized breakthrough times (time for cave inception) according to Palmer (1991) and Dreybrodt (1996). **Example:** Consider a fissure 100 m long (10,000 cm), with a hydraulic gradient of 10 m/km (= 0.01) and initial width (w_o) of 0.02 cm. The temperature is 10°C and P_{CO_2} = 0.01 atm. Gradient ÷ length = 0.01 ÷ 10,000 = 10^{-6}, so the log = −6. Extending a line up from −6 to the 0.02 cm line, then over to the vertical axis, gives a log breakthrough time of about 4.2, i.e., $10^{4.2}$ years, or about 16,500 years. This is the estimate using the Palmer graph. To adjust it to the equation of Dreybrodt (1996), shift the graph downward roughly 0.6 of a log cycle. The estimated breakthrough time then becomes $10^{3.6}$, or about 4000 years. Passage growth beyond that time will follow Eq. 7.4. The Dreybrodt estimates are probably more accurate, but the relationships among variables are essentially the same.

than those of Plummer and others (1978), and for that reason Dreybrodt's results are inherently more sound. But in terms of geologic interpretation, given the many simplifying assumptions, the differences are not great.

Figure 7.22 shows that initial fissures 0.01−0.1 cm wide should require no more than a few thousand or tens of thousands of years to reach their maximum enlargement rates from the time aggressive groundwater first begins to flow through the limestone. For example, in a fissure one kilometer long, with an initial width of 0.015 cm, hydraulic gradient of 0.02 (20 m/km), P_{CO_2} of 0.05 atm, temperature of 10° C, and in a system closed to further uptake of CO_2, the maximum rate of enlargement should be reached in about 20,000−70,000 years. These are probably typical conditions in most karst aquifers. Breakthrough times can also be diminished by acids generated in passages by oxidation of organic compounds in the water or of sulfides in the bedrock.

To obtain the data in Figure 7.22, Palmer (1984a, 1991) used the original laboratory data of Plummer and Wigley (1976), Plummer and others (1978), and Rauch and White (1970, 1977). These measurements were made in open systems, which contrast with the closed systems typical of early cave development. To compensate for this difference, Palmer calculated the decrease in P_{CO_2} with flow distance in the model and adjusted the k and n values accordingly.

Dreybrodt (1990) bypassed this awkward procedure by drawing on experimental data for closed systems obtained by his own research group at University of Bremen (see,

for example, Buhmann and Dreybrodt, 1985a, 1985b). Dreybrodt's work suggests that n_1 should be approximately 1.0 in closed systems.

The most useful results of the modeling are the relationships between breakthrough time, initial width, hydraulic gradient, and flow length. They provide a conceptual basis for explaining why certain passages are favored to become caves, and how the various cave patterns develop (Chapter 8). Also, they appear not to be affected by the uncertainties of the chemical process.

The most sensitive factor in controlling breakthrough time is the initial fissure width. Given two fissures with identical length, gradient, and chemical conditions, if one is twice as wide as the other, the wider one will achieve breakthrough about 8 times faster. Hydraulic gradient and flow length are next in importance. Doubling the gradient reduces the breakthrough time by about 2.5 times, and doubling the fissure length increases it by the same amount. Note that the fissure width and hydraulic gradient in Eqs. 7.5a and 7.5b are also key ingredients in the equations for discharge in laminar-flow conditions (see Chapter 4).

Temperature plays a complex role in breakthrough time. Higher temperatures speed the chemical reactions, but in long flow systems this can *increase* the breakthrough time. If the reactions are rapid, most of the water's solutional capacity is expended near the upstream end, which leaves less for the remaining downstream parts. High temperature can increase the flow velocity by reducing the viscosity of the water, but it also decreases the amount of limestone or dolomite that can be dissolved. The net result is an increase in breakthrough time with rising temperature. Another complication is that in warmer climates CO_2 production in the soil is usually greater, which offsets the effect of temperature and may slightly reduce the breakthrough times compared to those in temperate climates.

In general, the early phase of cave growth takes place in essentially closed systems, either in the phreatic zone or in narrow fissures in the vadose zone. Therefore, CO_2 is used up as dissolution proceeds. Breakthrough time decreases as much as 5 times if the system is open and CO_2 is readily available, as in many vadose fissures.

The equations and graphs of breakthrough time shown here were calculated while holding the hydraulic gradient constant, and with an initial zero concentration of dissolved calcite. Neither is valid in real aquifers, but this procedure serves as a convenient standard. Initial calcite concentration is not of great concern in the calculations, because the concentrations rise very rapidly within a few centimeters of flow during the early stages of cave development so that the initial concentration has a negligible effect on enlargement of the remaining downstream parts.

If fresh sources of acid are introduced along a flow path, fissure enlargement rates increase. Adding CO_2 to water along the path of flow, for example by oxidation of organic compounds, decreases the breakthrough time significantly. Breakthrough times are reduced most if the CO_2 is added to the narrow downstream parts of the fissure. Mixing of waters of varied CO_2 content can decrease the breakthrough time, but large differences in CO_2 concentration are necessary (Gabrovšek, 2000).

The abrupt slowdown of dissolution at high C/C_s values is crucial to cave origin (Palmer, 1984b). If the dissolution rate were to decrease uniformly in the initial narrow fissures, the water would approach saturation after only a few meters of flow, and the vast majority of the remaining fissure network would hardly enlarge at all. Cave origin by dissolution would be possible only in extremely favorable places, such as along the edges of steep plateaus. Instead, the sharp decrease in dissolution rate allows the last 10–40% of dissolution to be drawn out slowly over long distances, so fissures can be enlarged, slowly but fairly uniformly, all the way through to the spring outlets. As these long, narrow openings gradually enlarge, the more aggressive water typical of the upstream areas eventually penetrates all the way through the conduits and enlarges them rapidly over their entire lengths. Without the slow uniform enlargement rate near saturation, the initial fissure widening would be limited to very short distances at the upstream end, and long caves could not form. But without the rapid dissolution that follows, the openings would not enlarge rapidly enough to become caves within a geologically feasible time. The fact that both of these requirements are met is a remarkable coincidence.

The conclusions of Eisenlohr and Dreybrodt (1999), that the build-up of impurities on the rock surface inhibits dissolution rate at high saturation ratios, imply that the dissolution history is drawn out over even longer distances than originally thought. If so, breakthrough times may be shorter than those estimated by the earlier models.

From field evidence, Faulkner (2005) extrapolated the graph in Figure 7.22 to show that the lines bend toward vertical as they approach zero time. He applied these revised curves to the origin of short, high-gradient marble caves in Scandinavia to demonstrate their short development times.

Other cave geometries besides single fissures can be modeled with any desired complexity, but the results are essentially the same as described here. Siemers and Dreybrodt (1998) show that the breakthrough times in two-dimensional networks depend on the same controlling factors as those in single fissures. For further references, see the modeling chapters in the book by Klimchouk and others (2000).

Modeling of multi-dimensional fissure networks

Although the models for individual fissures give an understanding of the relative importance of the controlling factors, it is more appropriate to use a two-dimensional or even three-dimensional grid of intersecting fissures to represent entire aquifers. An example of the output from a two-dimensional model is shown in Figure 7.23.

With a multi-dimensional approach, Clemens and others (1996) used computer models to support the idea that

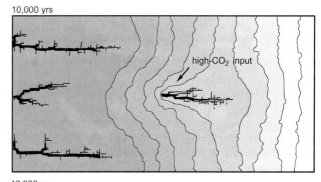

10,000 yrs

high-CO_2 input

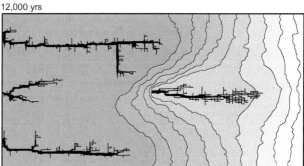

12,000 yrs

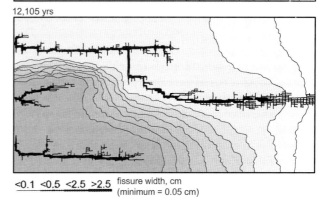

12,105 yrs

<0.1 <0.5 <2.5 >2.5   fissure width, cm
(minimum = 0.05 cm)

Figure 7.23: Example of a two-dimensional computer model of conduit growth (after Dreybrodt and Gabrovšek, 2002). Aggressive water is injected along the left side at a head of 50 m, with outflow along the right side at a head of 0 m. An additional input is located in the center. The hydraulic head decreases at the input points after breakthrough takes place. length of model = 2 km. Black lines are solution conduits. Dark-to-light patterns show the head distribution (high-to-low head). The rapid growth and the many downstream branches are the result of highly aggressive water, sustained high gradient prior to breakthrough, and absence of higher heads in the surrounding bedrock. The result most resembles the development of a cave by sinking streams. For a summary of recent modeling results, see Dreybrodt and others (2005).

network mazes could form by diffuse seepage through a permeable but insoluble cap-rock. This mode of cave origin is described in Chapter 8 and illustrated in Figure 8.27.

Models by Kaufmann and Braun (1999) show that the complexity of the resulting conduit system in a two-dimensional model increases with steeper hydraulic gradient and larger initial width. This supports the concept shown in Figure 7.14**d**. To quantify their results, Kaufmann and Braun devised what they termed the ***maze index***, which is the ratio of the length of the solutionally enlarged fissures to the length of all fissures in their model grid. This concept applies only to computer or laboratory models, because the length of all fissures cannot be determined in the field. Dreybrodt and Siemers (2000) show that if the breakthrough time in a model is decreased, the resulting caves become more complex. This observation also agrees with Figure 7.14 (**d** and **e**).

Dreybrodt and others (2005) summarize the previous 15 years of computer modeling of karst systems. Their book also contains a compact disk with animated examples of the output from the various models. The major conclusions from their highly technical document are condensed here:

- Rates of cave development are greatest if there is a single major path of relatively wide fissures that extends through the general fissure network.
- Inflow of saturated water from narrow fissures surrounding the major flow paths delays the development of caves. This would tend to make the breakthrough times in Figure 7.22 longer than indicated.
- When breakthrough takes place, and turbulent flow develops, adjacent flow systems tend to become integrated, as small conduits join the larger ones as tributaries. This agrees with the models of Ewers (1982).
- Where there is no inflow from neighboring fissures, the resulting cave branches in the downstream direction (see Figure 7.23). But when tributary water is allowed to flow into the main channels from the surrounding fissure network, the resulting caves tend to be limited to single conduits from input to outlet. This result is valid even if the neighboring fissures are too narrow ever to enlarge into caves themselves. This agrees with the model of Palmer (1981b, 1991).
- Mixing corrosion is not essential for cave development. It boosts the dissolution rate most if the mixing takes place about half-way along the conduit length. Breakthrough times decrease in proportion to the contrast in P_{CO_2}.
- Most cave development takes place at the water table. The presence of relatively wide fractures in the initial system can lead to phreatic loops, if they develop prior to those at the water table. This is compatible with the conclusions of Ford (1971) and Worthington (1991, 2001).
- Depth of penetration of solution conduits below the water table is affected very little by the aquifer thickness, because the water at depth is mainly saturated. Although this seems to contradict the concepts of Lowe (1992) and Worthington (1991, 2001), the computer modeling does not consider the deep-seated reactions and temperature variations that are part of the Lowe and Worthington models.

How valid are computer models?

The computer models tend to support earlier conceptual views of cave origin, and this helps to validate both approaches. Computer modeling goes a step farther by quan-

tifying the relationships among the governing variables. In addition, the mere process of devising a model raises other questions for investigation. Still, there is always the question of whether the models are flawed and are simply creating a fantasy world.

Computer models need to be tested in the field. Unfortunately, this approach has serious limitations. The minimum age of a cave can be estimated by dating the deposits in them, as described in Chapter 13, but projecting that time back to the earliest stages of cave inception is still a problem. Most of the evidence for initial field conditions is destroyed by later cave enlargement. Unenlarged fractures and partings can be examined in roadcuts and quarries, but these are not necessarily the ones that eventually form caves.

For example, cosmogenic dating of sediments in Mammoth Cave, Kentucky, show that the lowest major level (D in Figure 9.54) is about 200,000 years younger than that in the next-higher level (Granger and others, 2001). The largest passages at Level D are about 3 m in radius. The time required for turbulent flow to enlarge them to this size can be estimated by Eq. 7.4 with the aid of chemical measurements in the present cave streams. Obtaining a valid enlargement rate is not easy, because the water chemistry varies in response to runoff rates. Rough averages (based on Anthony, 1998) are as follows: saturation ratio $(C/C_s) \approx 0.7$, $P_{CO_2} \approx 0.01$ atm, and temperature = 11°C. At this saturation ratio, n ≈ 4 and k is calculated to be ~0.02 (Table 7.2). The dissolution rate estimated by Eq. 7.4 is roughly 0.002 cm/yr. A passage would require 150,000 years to enlarge to a radius of 3 m. So far the result seems compatible with the sediment dating, but the breakthrough time must be added to give an estimate of the entire time required to form the passages. This is the time from when the passage first began to enlarge to when dissolution reached its maximum rate (essentially at the onset of turbulent flow). This is where computer models enter the picture.

Estimating breakthrough time is not easy. The overall passage length and hydraulic gradient can usually be reconstructed from the regional setting, but initial fissure width is difficult to evaluate. By the time a cave is large enough to explore, the critical evidence has long disappeared.

Initial fissure width is a slippery concept, because the widths increase with time even without dissolution, simply by release of stress as the overlying rocks are eroded away. Field evidence suggests that a fissure must have an initial width of at least 0.01 mm to be widened by dissolution (Böcker, 1969). It is clear, however, that the there is no single minimum fissure width, because the breakthrough time also depends on hydraulic gradient, flow distance, water chemistry, and length of time available for cave inception.

To estimate how large the initial fissures in limestone might be, data can be gathered from relatively insoluble rocks that have the same brittleness as limestone. Crystalline igneous rocks give a close approximation. Water wells in rocks such as granite have fairly small yields, especially at depths of more than 50 m below the surface (Freeze and Cherry, 1979;

Gustafson and Krasny, 1994). But even with conservative estimates for hydraulic gradient and fissure frequency, well tests show that the fissures that deliver the water must have average widths of roughly 0.01–0.05 cm. Only a few of the many fissures are this large, but they are the most important in delivering water. In soluble rock they are the ones that grow into caves. In limestone, solutional enlargement of the widest fissures probably begins long before they reach the size indicated by well tests in granite.

Assume, then, that the initial fissures at Mammoth Cave were between 0.01 and 0.05 cm wide. Conditions in the cave suggest a hydraulic gradient of about 0.01 and flow length of about one kilometer (10^5 cm). At $w_o = 0.01$ cm, Figure 7.22 and Eq. 7.5 indicate a breakthrough time of about 8.7 million years (Palmer) or 2.2 million years (Dreybrodt), neither of which is feasible. But at $w_o = 0.05$ cm, the breakthrough time drops to 22,000 years (Palmer) or 5500 years (Dreybrodt), either of which would fit the available time interval. This single example does not validate the computer models, but it illustrates one method for testing them.

Another way to test the models is to see whether the relationships among the variables in Eqs. 7.5a and 7.5b are compatible with the distribution and pattern of passages of known age. For example, did long, low-gradient passages require more time to develop than shorter, steeper passages? If so, is the difference predicted by the equations?

To date there has been no detailed attempt to validate the breakthrough times or the relationships among controlling variables that are predicted by computer models. This goal may never be achieved to everyone's satisfaction, but a great deal can be learned in the attempt.

Life cycle of a solution cave

All of the complex threads from this chapter can now be drawn together to describe the origin and development of a typical solution cave in limestone.

To form a solution cave, groundwater must circulate in large quantities from surface inputs to spring outlets. In humid climates, caves form nearly everywhere that limestone is exposed over broad areas. No special or unusual conditions are necessary to produce them. They can form in other ways besides the one described here, and in some areas (such as arid regions) these alternative origins may even dominate. But in most parts of the world the simple circulation of meteoric water through the ground is sufficient.

A typical solution cave develops in several stages that grade smoothly from one to the next. At any given time, various passages in the same cave may occupy different stages in this sequence.

1. Initial openings are slowly enlarged by water that is nearly saturated with dissolved bedrock. Flow rates are low, and groundwater follows a network of many alternate routes.
2. As the early routes enlarge, those with the most flow become wide enough that the groundwater retains much

of its solutional aggressiveness all the way through to the springs. This ends the inception phase for these passages.
3. As the discharge increases through these few favored routes, passages begin to grow rapidly over their entire length.
4. Cave passages eventually become air-filled, and secondary mineral deposits such as flowstone may start to grow.
5. Growth of a cave passage is slowed or halted in several ways, for example by diversion of water to different routes.
6. Each passage is eventually destroyed by roof collapse and dissection by surface erosion. Meanwhile, newer ones may form at lower elevations, as long as there is sufficient soluble rock remaining. For a long time the cave remains in a sort of equilibrium between the destruction of old passages and the origin of new ones. Cave origin ceases only when the body of soluble rock is eventually removed entirely by erosion.

Details of this history are described below:

Birth of the cave
A cave has no discrete birth date, so it is difficult to pin down the exact timing of its early phases. Nevertheless, the basic events are easy to interpret. Deep beneath the surface there is very little groundwater flow because the initial openings are narrow and sparse, and hydraulic gradients are feeble. If the land is uplifted by stresses in the Earth's crust, these rocks are gradually exposed at the surface by erosion of the overlying material (Chapter 2). As surface streams carve their valleys deeper, increasing amounts of water move through the ground and emerge in those valleys as springs. The water is recharged by infiltration into the surrounding uplands. It is this flow of underground water that forms most caves.

Soluble rock may be exposed at the surface by erosional removal of overlying insoluble rocks. In this case, flow of water into the soluble rock is focused in those areas where the overlying rock is first breached.

Groundwater follows many thousands of intersecting joints, faults, and bedding-plane partings. At first these openings are all so narrow that no single fissure can transmit more than a tiny amount of water. The water remains in contact with the rocks for such a long time that it loses virtually all of its solutional capacity well before it emerges at the surface.

The amount of flow differs greatly among the many flow paths because of the variety of fissure widths, flow lengths, and hydraulic gradients. Short, direct routes are likely to transmit the most flow. Most important of all is the initial fissure width, because even minor variations in width can cause great differences in flow rate (Chapter 4). Most of these width variations are present even before the rock begins to dissolve, and, therefore, certain routes are favored to become caves right from the beginning of ag-

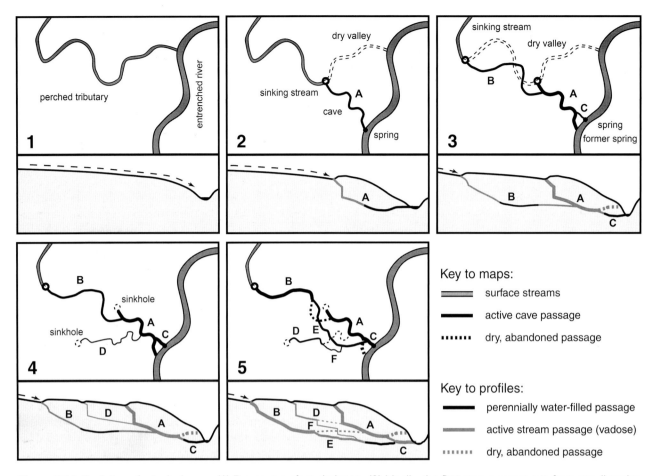

Figure 7.24: Evolution of a typical cave: (**1**) Pre-cave surface drainage. (**2**) Ideally, the first cave passages to form are diversion routes for sinking streams that are perched above the local base level. Passage A is an example. (**3**) Further diversion of stream water takes place by upstream migration of sink points. New passages, such as B, tend to join earlier ones in which the hydraulic head has dropped. Further entrenchment of the surface river allows diversion passages such as C to drain to new springs. (**4**) Drainage from surrounding uplands requires a longer time to develop cave passages, such as D, because their capture zones are small. (**5**) With time, vadose passages divert to lower levels, such as E and F, which link with other passages and complicate the cave pattern. Passages that are fed by sinking streams, such as B, may fill completely with water during floods. Passages fed by sinkholes of limited catchment area (such as D, and eventually A), once they have enlarged to cave size, rarely if ever fill completely with water. The actual passage pattern may be more complex, as shown in Chapters 8 and 9.

gressive groundwater movement through the soluble rock. Those routes with the greatest flow enlarge fastest because more dissolved material is removed from them. At this stage, when all groundwater is essentially saturated with dissolved bedrock by the time it emerges at the surface, if one path carries twice as much water as another, the volume of the high-flow route will increase twice as fast. Differences in water chemistry can also cause some paths to enlarge faster than others, but in most aquifers these differences are slight.

The best measure of passage growth is the rate at which its cross section enlarges. Where all routes are exposed to the same groundwater chemistry, the cross-sectional growth rate depends on both the discharge and the length of the opening. If two routes have the same discharge (and thus the same rate of volume increase), the shorter one will widen more rapidly because the volume increase is spread over a shorter distance. Most growth takes place at the

upstream end because the water becomes less aggressive downstream.

In its effect on enlargement rate, the length of a conduit is exactly as important as discharge, but with the opposite effect. In other words, the rate of early cave enlargement depends on the ratio of discharge to flow length.

At first the flow is so small, even along the most favorable paths, that caves could never form within a geologically feasible time if those conditions remained constant. The only way a flow path can enlarge to cave size is for its discharge to increase. Those routes with the greatest discharge grow fastest, and this allows them to carry ever-increasing amounts of flow. In this way, the early development of most caves involves the runaway growth of just a few favorable paths.

Rapid growth

As the discharge increases in a growing passage, solutional enlargement becomes faster, but only up to a certain limit.

8e888
g8888888

Beyond that point, in limestone at least, a further increase in discharge has little effect on enlargement rate. By that time, water emerges from the downstream end of the conduit while still fairly aggressive, and the enlargement rate is controlled mainly by how fast the limestone can dissolve, rather than by the discharge.

The time required to achieve this maximum dissolution rate is the **breakthrough time** (page 181). This point is reached when Q/rL is greater than about 0.001 cm/sec, where Q = discharge (cm³/sec), r = average passage radius (cm), and L = flow distance (cm). This relationship is shown in Figure 7.14. Passage growth is fairly rapid from there on, at rates of about 0.001 to 0.1 cm/year, depending on the local water chemistry (Figure 7.19).

The earliest phase of cave enlargement, when routes with the greatest discharge grow fastest, determines which flow paths will become caves. Only those openings that reach the maximum solution rate (high on the graphs in Figure 7.14) grow fast enough to become traversable caves. That is why most caves contain just a few passages. As long as the water remains fairly aggressive while passing through them, cave-size passages grow more or less steadily and uniformly over their entire lengths.

Individual fractures and partings in the bedrock may be very extensive, but only their widest parts enlarge into caves. The water flow is concentrated in narrow bands along which the openings enlarge rapidly, while the narrower parts barely grow at all.

If a certain underground flow path is fed by a large supply of water (such as a surface stream with a leaky channel bottom), groundwater discharge increases automatically as the openings become wider and more efficient. For that reason, leakage from sinking streams is most effective in forming the earliest cave passages. This kind of groundwater flow is usually under **hydraulic control** (pages 89–90). The stream eventually sinks entirely at the point where it loses the most water to the subsurface (stage 2 in Figure 7.24).

As an incipient cave reaches its maximum growth rate, several other changes take place at roughly the same time (White, 1977a). The cave water changes from laminar to turbulent, which increases the solution rate slightly. It also gains the ability to transport sediment, which helps to enlarge caves by mechanical abrasion. Flowing water also carries away the soil that subsides into caves through sinkholes, and this allows the sinkholes to grow more rapidly.

Water chemistry and flow rates vary seasonally, but their effects average out over the years. A water-filled cave may increase its diameter as much as a meter in 1000 years. This may seem slow by human standards, but it is extremely fast for a continually active geologic process. Micrometer measurements repeated over several years have verified these rates in caves fed by sinking streams (High, 1970; Coward, 1975; see Figure 7.7).

As passages grow larger and their hydraulic gradients decrease, some areas that were once water-filled become partly air-filled (Figure 7.25). During floods, the dissolution

Figure 7.25: Active cave development above the water table, Sistema Cheve, Mexico. Photo by Ken Davis.

rate increases, not only because the water is more aggressive when it first enters the cave, but also because it retains most of its aggressiveness throughout the cave during its rapid transit. At these times there can also be a substantial amount of mechanical erosion (Newson, 1971). In places, sediment accumulates in thick beds that protect the cave floor from further abrasion, although water in the sediment is often undersaturated and may still dissolve the underlying rock (Vaughan, 1998).

Development of tributaries

Passage A in Figure 7.24 grows rapidly, and it eventually transmits water so efficiently that the head in the passage drops to low values not much higher than the spring. Meanwhile the sinking stream forms another sink point farther upstream (stage 3 in Figure 7.24). Because of the steep hydraulic gradient between the new sink point and passage A, the younger passage (B) between them enlarges rapidly, just as passage A did (stage 3 in Figure 7.24). Deepening of the main river valley may encourage diversion of early passages to lower levels (as at passage C).

With time, additional sink points develop farther upstream, and new passages join the earlier ones. As new routes continue to link with older ones, the overall cave system tends to grow in the upstream direction and to extend its reach progressively farther from its spring outlets (Ford and Ewers, 1978; Ewers, 1982). Eventually the headward migration of the sink point will diverge upstream into the tributaries of the sinking stream, each of which will contribute its own smaller amount of flow to proportionally smaller cave passages.

The cave can enlarge more rapidly in steps like this than if it formed all at once as individual long passages. This step-wise growth is not always possible. For example, many caves extend beneath an insoluble cap-rock, so there is a long interval between the sink points and springs in which no significant inflow can take place. Flow routes such as this require much longer times to reach the stage of rapid growth (pages 181–182). Many caves in the eastern U.S. have formed in this way (Figures 1.3, 7.30, 9.53, and 9.1c).

Meanwhile, the cave stream is joined by diffuse seepage through the soil of the surrounding uplands. This water enlarges openings in the underlying rock, and sinkholes form as the soil subsides into them. As a sinkhole grows, its catchment area increases. Progressively more water is delivered to the incipient cave passage below, so its growth rate increases as well. This is an example of ***catchment control*** of the water flow (page 90). Stage 4 in Figure 7.24 shows the development of a tributary passage by this process (passage D). The flow rate increases rather slowly, so passages fed by sinkholes are also likely to develop at a more leisurely pace than those fed by sinking streams. They will also be narrower. Where sinkholes are small, a cluster of several may be required to deliver the water needed to form a traversable passage. As a result, many caves finger upstream into tiny infeeders that are too small for human access.

As a typical cave grows, a branching pattern develops. As the early routes grow and the water table drops in their vicinity, they draw water from surrounding openings that are fed by progressively more remote sources. Each passage is fed by water from a separate source, such as a sinking stream, sinkhole, or group of sinkholes. Passages generally get larger in the downstream direction as tributaries join and discharge increases. The combined water is usually no more solutionally aggressive than in the individual feeders, but the greater discharges retain their aggressiveness for longer distances and cover a larger surface area of soluble rock. They can also carry more sediment and cause more mechanical erosion.

Cave development to traversable size within about 10,000 years has been documented by Mylroie and Carew (1987) and has also been inferred from the presence of small post-glacial caves throughout the world. At the slow end of the spectrum, many of the long, low-gradient cave passages in the plateaus of Kentucky and Tennessee require at least half a million years to develop (Granger and others, 2001; Anthony and Granger, 2004).

Adjustment of the cave to changes at the surface

It is clear that sinking streams, sinkholes, caves, and springs must evolve simultaneously and interactively. This is a complicated and on-going process. Stage 5 in Figure 7.24 shows further adjustments to the passage pattern as passages form lower levels in response to deepening of the river valley. Meanwhile, older passages tend to stabilize in their growth.

As sinkholes grow they may eventually merge to form a continuous karst surface. Eventually the only surface streams that retain their flow are the main entrenched rivers and the ephemeral upstream ends of sinking streams.

Patterns of groundwater recharge change as the land surface is dissected by erosion. The few large initial water sources may be partitioned into many smaller ones. Vadose water must travel increasingly greater distances to reach the water table, and extensive complexes of vadose canyons and shafts can form. The resulting pattern of active cave streams is much denser than that of the original surface drainage. A larger catchment area for diffuse underground seepage is needed to sustain the upstream ends of a surface stream.

As surface valleys deepen by river erosion, spring outlets migrate to progressively lower elevations. Cave streams that were once adjusted to older levels of a river tend to entrench into the floors of their original channels (Figure 7.25), or (more commonly) they may abandon their original passages entirely to form new ones at lower levels (Figure 7.26).

Limits to passage growth

From Eq. 7.3 it is clear that passage size depends on discharge, solutional aggressiveness, and time. All are of equal importance. In any given cave, the passages with the greatest

Figure 7.26: The upper level of Mystic River, in Mammoth Cave, Kentucky, was long ago abandoned by its original flow but still receives overflow from lower-level stream passages. Thick clay banks and standing pools show the effect of low-velocity floodwaters. Large scallops on the ceiling indicate moderately slow flow and may represent either the floodwater flow or the last phase of enlargement before the passage was abandoned by its original flow.

discharge are generally the largest. But passage A in Figure 7.24 probably has a larger cross-sectional area than passage B, despite the similarity in discharge, simply because A has been active for a longer time.

The rapid growth rates shown in Figure 7.19 do not continue throughout the life of a cave. Although caves have the potential to carry ever-greater amounts of water as they enlarge, there is a limit to the amount of available water. Once a cave passage has the capacity to transmit all the water from its catchment area, its average discharge can increase no further. Instead, the hydraulic head in the passage decreases as the cross section enlarges. If the diameter of a water-filled passage doubles, while its discharge stays the same, the hydraulic gradient drops to only about 3 percent of its former value. Large passages cannot maintain steep hydraulic gradients, so, as they grow, the water table in and around them drops to almost the same elevations as their springs. Much of the upstream part of the cave becomes vadose, and streams may entrench canyons in the passage floors.

As a cave becomes air-filled, it begins to exchange air with the outside atmosphere through open entrances and

Figure 7.27: Calcite precipitation (light gray) in the main stream of McFail's Cave, New York, during the exceptionally dry summer of 1995. The calcite coating is 0.3 mm thick. The stream is supersaturated with calcite most of every typical year, and dissolution takes place only during high flow.

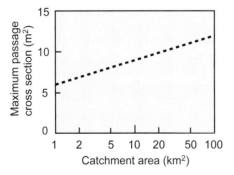

Figure 7.28: Relationship between maximum passage cross section (m²) and catchment area (km²), based on field work in Norway and Sweden by Faulkner (2005). Although the exact figures will not apply to other karst areas where the chemistry, runoff character, and rock type are different, the general relationship should be similar.

Figure 7.29: The main passage of Tantalhöhle, near Salzburg, Austria, is an abandoned upper level high above the current base level (see Figure 2.65).

narrow fissures in the overlying rock. The outside air contains only about 1% as much carbon dioxide as soil air. The P_{CO_2} of the cave air drops to a value somewhere between that of the soil and that of the outside air. The cave water loses CO_2 to the cave air, which diminishes the amount of dissolved limestone or dolomite that the water can hold. Through this process, cave enlargement rates decrease greatly and may completely stall. Secondary mineral deposits such as flowstone may start to grow. Calcite may even be deposited in the cave streams as a thin sheet (Figure 7.27) or as rimstone dams (Chapter 10).

In a study of Scandinavian caves, Faulkner (2005) shows that the maximum cross-sectional area of caves increases with the size of the catchment area, but not in direct proportion. Instead, the relationship is roughly logarithmic, as shown in Figure 7.28. In general, the discharge through a cave is proportional to the catchment area, but the inhibiting effects of vadose conditions, sediment load, and exposure of poorly soluble rock are clearly demonstrated by the low slope on this graph.

Abandonment and decay

New cave passages follow the same evolutionary sequence as the original ones. Abandonment of a passage by its water does not always take place in a single episode. Often the first escape point for water is not at the headwaters of the passage, but at a point part-way along the passage that presents the most favorable combination of large fissure widths, steep hydraulic gradient, and short flow distance to a new outlet. With time, additional diversions may take place farther upstream until the original passage is entirely abandoned by its flow (Chapter 9).

Dry upper-level passages may persist for a long time with little change (Figure 7.29). Evidence for geologic

events can be preserved in them long after weathering and erosion have obliterated from the land surface any trace of these events.

Eventually the soluble rock is eroded from the original site of cave development, and the earliest passages are destroyed. But the cave may live on as newer passages continue to develop where the soluble rock remains. Figure 7.30 shows an example of shifting flow routes and fragmenting of upper levels.

As a cave passage is intersected and fragmented by surface erosion, it may persist for a while as a series of short tunnels and natural bridges (Figure 2.25), but eventually

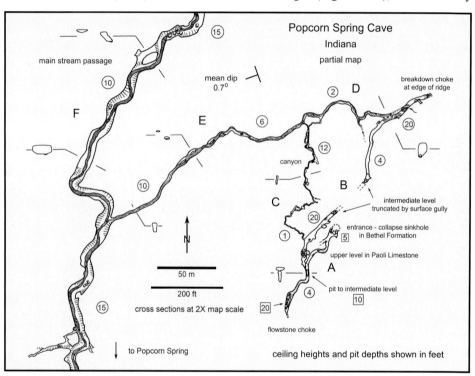

Figure 7.30: Generations of passages in Popcorn Spring Cave, Indiana: partial cave map above and profile below. The uppermost passage (A) is now a fragmented and partly filled relic. The intermediate level (B) has been segmented by valley erosion. Vadose drains from the two segments (C and D) join to form a tributary (E) to the large main level (F), which has a much larger drainage basin than the upper levels ever did. Drain C carries little water and is barely passable. The main passage is blocked by collapse at the spring alcove shown in Figure 2.31. In the profile below, dark gray strata are sandstones and shales. The mean dip is shown on the map, but local dips vary in magnitude and direction. For map symbols see page 14. (From Palmer, 1969).

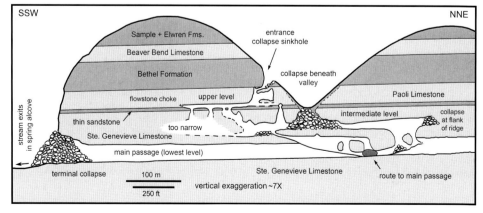

Figure 7.31: A collapsed cave passage in Slovenia forms a shallow trench in the land surface. This highly weathered stalagmite is a relic that survives from the now-unroofed cave.

Figure 7.32: As surface rivers deepen their channels, the zone of active cave development migrates into progressively lower parts of a soluble rock formation, while the upper parts, containing older caves, are removed by erosion. Long periods of erosion at a static base level can also lead to almost complete destruction of caves as the land surface flattens. As caves migrate down through the soluble rock, the new passages are simply the descendents of earlier ones that have disappeared. Eventually the limestone formation in a given area may be removed entirely, and local cave development ceases.

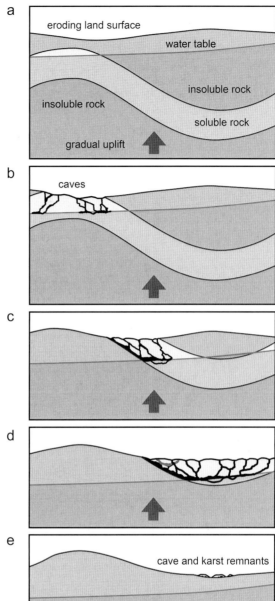

the overlying surface degenerates into an irregular line of sinkholes, or merely a rubble of collapse blocks. In rare cases a shallow unroofed passage may temporarily remain at the surface as a solution corridor (Figure 7.31). This final episode in the life of a cave passage may endure for tens of thousands of years.

In dipping limestone, new areas of rock are uncovered by erosion at about the same rate as it is eroded away in the up-dip areas (Figure 7.32). Many newly formed caves in recently exposed limestone are simply diversion routes for older caves that once occupied parts of the limestone that have since been eroded away. If the drainage pattern is favorable, the entire cavernous zone can migrate down the dip as the land rises and the higher parts of the rock are stripped away. The process ends when the last vestiges of a cave are limited to an isolated block of soluble rock that is then completely eroded away.

Many caves are formed in entirely different ways from the example given here. These topics are explored in the next two chapters.

8

Control of cave patterns by groundwater recharge

CAVE ORIGIN was described in the preceding chapter only in general terms. But each cave has its own unique pattern that cannot be explained by generalities. In this chapter and the next, the patterns of solution caves are explained in terms of their local geology, groundwater characteristics, landscape evolution, and climate. These variables have the following effects:

- The distribution of soluble rocks determines the general location of caves, and to some extent the flow directions of karst groundwater and overall cave trends.
- The nature of groundwater recharge — its chemistry and how it enters the soluble rock — controls overall cave patterns. It determines, for example, whether a cave has a branchwork or maze pattern.
- Geologic structure and stratigraphy control the shape and direction of individual passages, and in some places their vertical distribution.
- Topographic relief and geomorphic history determine much of the vertical layout of a cave, as the active passages respond to adjustments in base level in nearby river valleys.
- Climate affects caves indirectly by influencing the nature and amount of groundwater recharge. By itself, climate has little direct effect on cave patterns.

The main control over the organization of passages in a solution cave is the nature of the groundwater recharge — the way in which water enters the local soluble rock, and how it behaves hydraulically and chemically. Climate is included in this discussion, because it affects the physical and chemical nature of groundwater recharge.

There is a great variety in the types of groundwater inputs to caves. Sinkhole recharge from a typical karst surface is examined first, because it is the most common type and provides a standard to which the others can be compared.

Sinkhole recharge: branchwork caves

Branchwork caves consist of passages that join each other as tributaries (Figure 8.1). They are more numerous, and have a greater sum of lengths, than all other solution caves combined. It is not surprising that they are formed by the most common type of karst recharge, through sinkholes and other small point sources of water in a karst surface. Most caves that consist of single stream passages are included, because nearly all of them contain at least the rudiments of tributaries, and their origin is identical to that of branchwork caves. Simply calling all caves of this origin *stream caves* is not appropriate, because many caves contain streams that differ in their relationships to the passage pattern. Ford

Figure 8.1: Junction of two tributary stream passages in a branchwork cave (Binkley's Cave, Indiana).

(1988) groups all caves formed by streams of meteoric water as ***common caves***.

Where soluble rock is exposed either directly at the surface or beneath a soil cover, infiltrating water follows all available openings. These enlarge rapidly near the surface because the water is highly aggressive, having no prior contact with soluble rock. The result is a network of enlarged fissures and pores (the ***epikarst***). In humid, temperate regions, most epikarst openings are filled with soil (Figure 8.2).

At greater depth, water becomes less aggressive and fissures are narrower. Solutionally enlarged openings lose their maze-like character, and only a few major routes continue to enlarge. The others tend to pinch out, because they transmit little flow, and their water quickly reaches saturation with the minerals in the local bedrock. Most openings in the epikarst become so narrow with depth that incoming water becomes ponded during periods of intense infiltration and overflows laterally into the few wide conduits that penetrate more deeply (Mangin, 1975; Williams, 1983; Gunn, 1983). In the widest openings, water retains some of its aggressiveness because of its high discharge and small time of contact with the bedrock. These routes serve as points of recharge that form branchwork caves. Sinkholes eventually develop where soil subsides into the largest of these drains (Figure 8.2). Sinkhole growth is aided by bedrock collapse and soil erosion. Where soil is absent, rock-walled sinkholes can form (Figure 2.15).

Each point source serves as the feeder for a cave passage, or at least a potential passage. Because the catchment areas are small at first, each has a limited water supply. The resulting passages are narrow at their upstream ends, and most are traversable only downstream from where several tributaries have merged. Nearly all passages in these caves are discrete tubes, canyons, and vertical shafts (Chapter 6). Some sections of passage may be linear fissures guided by

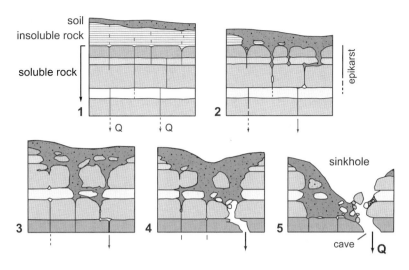

Figure 8.2: Development of a sinkhole as a local point of recharge to a branchwork cave.

major fractures, but the fissures do not intersect in a network pattern, except where the caves have been modified by other types of flow.

Passage origin

Cave patterns can be explained with the help of Figure 8.3, borrowed from Chapter 7. This graph is based on two well-validated principles. The sloping straight lines are calculated from the mass balance (Eq. 7.2), and the

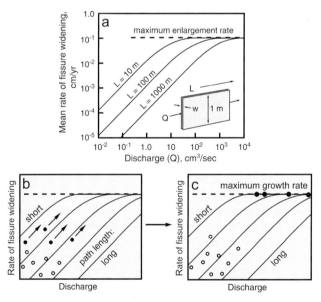

Figure 8.3: Origin of a branchwork cave (from Figure 7.14): (**a**) Rate of fissure enlargement vs. discharge and passage length in limestone. A fissure one meter high is used as an example. (**b**) In a typical limestone aquifer, flow paths are narrow at first. Growth rates are slow but highly variable. The fastest-growing paths (black circles) capture more discharge and grow even more rapidly. (**b**) Only a few favorable routes reach the maximum growth rate (dashed line) and develop into cave passages. All other paths stagnate with only minor flow and enlargement rates.

horizontal dashed line is a plot of Eq. 7.4 for limestone dissolution, combined with data from Table 7.2. The curved parts of the graph are calculated from a combination of the two. Although the dashed line does not account for mechanical abrasion or degree of turbulence, these effects cause only minor deviations from the values shown on the graph.

The rate of fissure widening shown in Figure 8.3a is the average over the entire length of the fissure. This graph shows the relative rates of enlargement among the various fissures but not the local rate at any point in a fissure. That information comes from computer analysis, as described in Chapter 7, but it is not needed for interpreting cave patterns.

Caves formed by sinkhole recharge generally involve long flow distances (L) and many point sources of recharge, each with a small to moderate discharge (Q). Discharge and flow length have equal but opposite effects, so they can be combined as a ratio (Q/L). During the first stages of branchwork cave origin, Q/L ratios are small and passage enlargement is very slow. Lengths do not vary with time, so growth becomes faster *only* if there is an increase in discharge.

Discharge in a cave passage (or an incipient passage) can increase in two ways: (1) A sinking stream can deliver increasing amounts of water as the underground openings enlarge with time, until the entire stream flow is captured. Most sinking streams have enough flow, at least during wet periods, to enlarge all available openings to cave size without assistance from other sources. (2) Passages fed by local sources of infiltration, such as sinkholes, can gain discharge only if the sinkholes expand in size, so that their catchment areas grow. Because there is only a finite amount of water available, any gain in discharge to some passages must be balanced by a loss of flow to others (see Figure 8.2).

Only a few of the many initial flow routes increase their discharge with time and become traversable cave passages. Other openings enlarge very little, if at all. As a result, passages in most branchwork caves are sparse, and they have discrete walls that are not perforated by a maze of smaller holes. Closed loops are rare except where passages intersect on different levels, with the individual segments of the loop having different ages.

Infiltration from the surface feeds vadose streams, which form canyons, shafts, and perched tubes. They eventually reach the water table, unless they emerge as perched springs in valley walls. At and below the water table, phreatic passages are water-filled (either permanently or intermittently) and tend to be tubular in cross section. These conduits extend with a strong horizontal component toward the nearest surface river valley. The water commonly emerges at a single spring, but it may finger into several diverging routes if the main spring is blocked by collapse or by sediment fill.

Figure 8.4: Convergence of tributaries in branchwork caves: (**a**) In general, groundwater converges from broad recharge areas to springs in narrow discharge areas. Because of diminishing space toward the valleys, passages naturally tend to join as tributaries.

In the **vadose zone**, geologic structures may guide water along convergent paths, as in synclines (**b**), where water flows down the local dip of the beds toward the synclinal axis. A few representative structural contours are shown, with flow toward decreasing elevations. Vadose water may also converge because of random intersection of guiding fractures (**c**).

In the **phreatic zone**, water is drawn toward areas of low head. In (**d**), the wide opening (X) transmits more flow, but so efficiently that the heads in it are only slightly higher than those in the outlet river. The narrow opening (Y) has less flow but greater resistance, so its head remains high. Most water follows the more efficient route (Z) toward the low head in the nearby large opening. If Z carries more water than the downstream end of Y, route Z will become a tributary to X, as shown in (**e**). Meanwhile the downstream end of the narrow route stagnates with little enlargement. If the main cave streams entrench into their passage floors, Y may be abandoned entirely, except during floods.

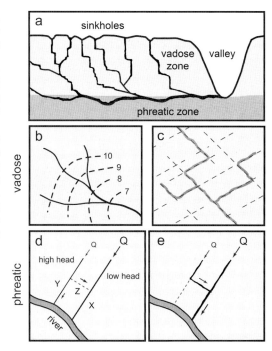

In this chapter, as in all others in this book, most maps show the caves only as black lines, with the surrounding bedrock in white or gray. Exceptions include large-scale maps such as Figures 8.19b, 8.21 and 8.41, which show both walls of the caves with the internal space in white or gray.

Why underground streams form tributaries

The joining of tributaries to form a branchwork pattern can take place in both the vadose and phreatic zones. In the vadose zone, water drains downward along fractures and dipping beds. Any convergence in these structures, such as synclines or fissure intersections, forces the passages to merge as tributaries (Figure 8.4).

In the phreatic zone, passages converge by a different mechanism. As a passage grows large enough to carry all the water from its surface catchment, the hydraulic head in the passage drops sharply. As a result, water is drawn toward the passage from other openings in the surrounding aquifer, where the head is greater. This flow forms secondary passages that join the main route as tributaries. There is also a natural tendency for phreatic passages to converge, because they drain water from a large surface area and deliver it to a narrow discharge zone, such as an entrenched river valley. Passages tend to join one another as the available space diminishes in the direction of flow.

Branchwork caves owe their origin to freely draining water that follows the most favorable paths through the ground. Water is not injected into them under pressure. As a result the typical branchwork pattern is fairly simple. Complexities arise mainly because of diversions of flow with time, or exposure to severe flooding.

Examples of branchwork caves

An ideal example of a branchwork cave is Crevice Cave, Missouri (Figure 8.5). It consists of 46 km of sinuous passages in the well-bedded Joachim Dolomite of Ordovician age, which dips gently toward the northeast.

Vadose canyons are fed by sinkhole recharge and extend mainly in the dip direction. They join passages that are (or once were) phreatic tubes, which trend more or less along the strike to the valley of Cinque Hommes Creek. As the valley deepened, cave passages formed two distinct but closely spaced levels.

Blue Spring Cave, Indiana, is a well-known branchwork cave, with 33 km of mapped passages (Figure 3.48). More than 50 tributaries join to form a single large stream passage that drains to Blue Spring on the entrenched East Fork of White River. An enlarged view of its northeastern section is shown in Figure 8.6. The cave is located in the strongly jointed Mississippian Salem Limestone, which dips about half a degree toward the southwest in this section of the

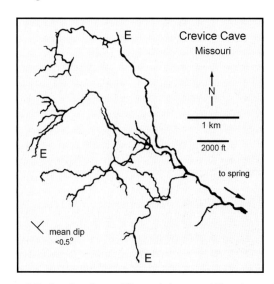

Figure 8.5: Crevice Cave, Missouri, is one of the clearest examples of a branchwork cave. The tree-like pattern and sinuous passages are characteristic of branchwork caves in well-bedded rocks. E = entrance. Mapped by Paul Hauck and others.

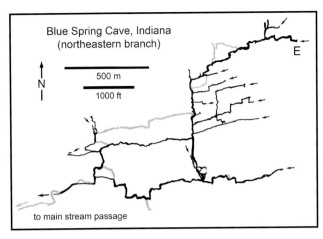

Figure 8.6: Part of Blue Spring Cave, Indiana, a branchwork cave in prominently fractured limestone. **Black** = active stream passages. **Gray** = abandoned upper-level passages, now dry except during extreme high flow. Arrows indicate stream inputs. **E** = entrance. Map from Palmer (1969).

cave. The influence of joints is clearly visible in the linear passage trends, but it does not disrupt the branchwork pattern. Each active stream passage on the map (in black) is fed by a separate inflowing stream. There are two major passage levels. As the river deepened its channel, several of the passages were abandoned in favor of lower routes. Abandoned passages, shown in gray on the map, now carry water only during high flow. Closed loops on the map are formed in this way and are not the result of cave streams splitting and then rejoining downstream. A few minor loops have formed by enlargement of joints during high water, but the effect on the passage pattern is negligible.

Although branchwork caves are common, their branching patterns are obscure on many cave maps. The accessible

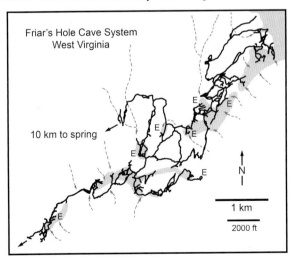

Figure 8.7: Friar's Hole Cave, West Virginia, has a branchwork pattern obscured by multiple tiers, vadose tributaries that cross over lower passages, and structural complexities such as faulting. Water drains into the limestone mainly through erosional windows in an overlying insoluble cap-rock (exposed limestone is shown in gray). E = entrances, or groups of entrances. Map by Douglas Medville and others; see also Worthington (1984), Jameson (1985), and Worthington and Medville (2005).

part of a cave is usually only a small part of its entire flow system, because most of its passages terminate in breakdown or sediment fill or become too narrow to explore. Small caves may have only a few minor tributaries. The cave pattern can also be distorted by structural irregularities that prevent the passages from attaining the open, tree-like pattern shown in Figure 8.5. Structural effects on cave patterns are described in the next chapter.

In many caves the branching pattern is also obscured by multiple levels. The maps of Mammoth Cave, Kentucky (Figure 1.3) and Blue Spring Cave, Tennessee (Figure 3.48) are extreme examples. At any stage in their development, however, the active passages have had a distinct branching pattern. Many dry upper-level passages presently overlie active ones, and in Mammoth Cave there are also many active vadose stream passages that cross over lower levels, some of which are now dry. The resulting complexity is not easy to decipher from the plan-view maps.

The Friar's Hole Cave System, West Virginia, is a good example of a branchwork cave in a complex geologic setting (Figure 8.7). It is located in mildly folded and faulted limestones of the Mississippian Greenbrier Group. Above most of the cave the limestone is overlain by thick sandstone and shale, and nearly all recharge to the cave is focused as small sinking streams into narrow zones where the insoluble cap has been eroded away (shown in gray on the map). The cave's branching pattern is distorted by the limited areas of water input, by structural influences, and by passages that cross one another in multiple tiers. The overall trend is parallel to the axis of folding in this region.

Sistema Huautla, located in a high wet plateau of Cretaceous limestone in Oaxaca, Mexico, is one of the world's deepest known caves (Figures 8.8–8.10; Stone and am Ende, 2002; Steele and Smith, 2005). It is a branchwork cave, but in map view its 56 km of passages seem to interconnect erratically (Figure 8.9). This apparent complexity is caused by the fact that many passages overlap, as in Friar's Hole Cave. At Huautla the limestone dips steeply to the southwest at about 30–40 degrees and is cut by major faults that trend northwest-southeast. The branchwork pattern is shown more clearly in profile (Figure 8.10). Sinkhole-fed passages in the northeastern part of the system extend down the steep dip. They jog laterally and downward in places along faults to form a stair-step pattern of alternating canyons and shafts. These passages converge into several large canyons and tubes that follow the major fault zones to a spring in a deep gorge. Each passage fits clearly into the overall branchwork pattern, even those that have been abandoned by their original flow in favor of deeper and more recent routes.

Despite the great contrasts in geologic setting and climate, the branchwork patterns of Friar's Hole Cave and Sistema Huautla, in deformed strata, are fundamentally no different from those of Crevice Cave and Blue Spring Cave, which are located in nearly undisturbed rocks. The unifying factor is that all four, and others like them, are fed by sinkholes in the overlying karst surfaces.

Many caves in Florida and the Yucatán Peninsula have crude branchwork patterns. The limestones are undeformed, relatively young (Tertiary in Florida, Cretaceous in Yucatán), highly porous, and exposed over large areas. These regions might seem ideal for branchwork caves because they appear to be extensive sinkhole plains. Most of the karst depressions are collapse features into active stream passages, however, and they are not the primary sources of recharge to caves. Most caves have complex anastomotic patterns and distributaries (Figure 2.41; Smart and others, 2006; Florea, 2006). Large tributaries are sparse. Some of these patterns are caused by diversions around collapse zones (Smart and others, 2002), but this cannot account for all of the complexity.

Many Florida caves are formed by sinking streams along the border of a retreating siltstone cap-rock (Kinkaid, 1998). A few conduits are fed by runoff from organic-rich soil into open sinkholes. Otherwise, most groundwater is supplied by diffuse infiltration, in which the solutional potential is nearly exhausted in enlarging near-surface pores. Aggressiveness of the cave streams is kept high by mixing with incoming seepage water, as well as by carbon dioxide produced by

Figure 8.8: This enormous sinkhole, filled with early-morning fog, contains the entrance of Sótano de San Augustín, Mexico. It is the main entrance of Sistema Huautla.

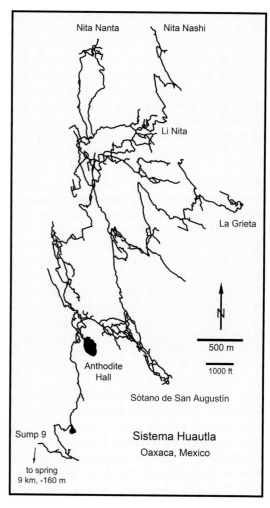

Figure 8.9: Sistema Huautla is a branchwork cave, but its branching character is masked by multiple levels and complex geologic structure. Located in the Sierra Mazateca, Oaxaca, Mexico, it is typical of caves in mountainous regions throughout the world. It resembles alpine caves, except that the local climate is semi-tropical. In the northeastern part of the cave, canyon passages follow a 30–60° WSW dip but are deflected by faults and folds. Many passages in the southwestern section are guided by the strike of the beds and by a system of large faults. From map by Stone and am Ende (1995); see Smith (1994) for a description of the local hydrogeology.

Figure 8.10: When viewed in profile, the branching pattern of Sistema Huautla is much clearer than on the map. This view is toward the direction 135°, roughly along the strike of the beds. Dip-oriented canyons are clearly shown. Río Iglesia is a major tributary not shown on the map in Figure 8.9. From Stone and am Ende (1995).

oxidation of organics. Divers have noted hydrogen sulfide in some caves. Mixing between sulfide-rich water and fresh water may contribute to cave enlargement, and it is likely that oxidation of H_2S to sulfuric acid is a factor as well. Freshwater-seawater mixing aids cave enlargement along the seacoast. Because of the complicated nature of the groundwater, the caves of Florida and the Yucatán Peninsula occupy only the outer fringes of the branchwork domain. See pages 241–242 for additional details.

Loops and downstream branching

It is possible, though not common, for a cave stream to branch in the downstream direction, so that some of the water goes in one direction and some in another. This is normal where an established cave stream is in the process of diverting to a new route (usually at a lower level), or where water overflows into ordinarily inactive routes during high flow. But these are temporary conditions in which one of the branches will eventually become dominant and carry all the base flow. It is rare for a cave stream to diverge into two active channels at the same level and for both to have an equal opportunity to enlarge to cave size.

A closed loop has the same constraint, because the two alternate flow paths must enlarge at the same rate. But closed loops are the essential elements in maze caves, where somehow the two branches in each loop must enlarge at about the same rate. This process is discussed below.

The problem of maze caves

Maze caves are complex arrays of passages that intersect in many closed loops that form simultaneously, or nearly so (Chapter 6). A cave may qualify as a maze even though it contains few loops, or none at all, as long as its passages are not the simple stream courses typical of branchwork caves.

For many intersecting passages to form simultaneously, they must all grow at roughly the same rate. In Figure 8.3, it is clear that maze caves must form at or near the top of the enlargement-rate graph, along the dashed line, where growth rates are fast and uniform. Elsewhere on the graph the growth rates are too diverse.

Uniform growth can be achieved where the discharge (Q) is great, or the flow length (L) is short. A combination of the two is even more favorable. If the Q/L ratio is large enough, *all* openings grow at about the same rate, regardless of their size or flow rate. Unlike branchwork caves, most maze caves do not undergo long, slow enlargement during their early growth, and an increase in discharge is not usually needed to give a boost to those flow paths that are destined to become cave passages. Instead, many alternate flow paths enlarge at or near the maximum growth rate, right from the time they first begin to carry significant amounts of flow. This is the fundamental requirement for a maze cave. The exact Q/L ratio required for uniform growth depends on the passage shape. In a fissure of height b (where $b = 100$ cm in Figure 8.3a), Q/bL must be greater than 0.001 cm/sec (Palmer, 1991).

Maze caves can be formed in any of the following situations, or combinations of them:

- *High discharge along many alternate routes.* This is most common during severe flooding of caves by sinking streams (Figure 8.11).
- *Sustained steep hydraulic gradient.* Leakage through the floor of a river or lake, or around a dam, can maintain a steep hydraulic gradient over a long period of time. Every major opening can enlarge more or less simultaneously.
- *Short flow distances through the soluble rock.* This can be produced in several ways: (a) by uniform infiltration directly into soluble rock, as in the epikarst, (b) by recharge through insoluble but permeable rock that overlies or underlies the soluble rock, or (c) by local production of aggressive conditions in the soluble rock (for example, by mixing of waters of different chemistry). In all three cases the flow distance (L) is the distance from where aggressive water first encounters the soluble rock. In example (c), the aggressiveness is formed right in the soluble rock (for example, by mixing), and L is measured from that approximate location. Most mixing-zone and hypogenic caves are mazes at least partly for this reason.
- *Uniform recharge to all major openings.* Infiltration through a thin insoluble rock, such as sandstone, not only involves short flow distances, but is also an ideal setting for uniform recharge. The insoluble rock acts as a governor to the flow rate by distributing water to many fissures, each of which receives only a small percentage of the total flow.

Figure 8.11: A sinking stream during the peak of a 50-year flood — i.e., with a statistical return period of 50 years (Cave Disappointment, New York).

Finally, for a maze cave to develop, the initial network of fractures, partings, or pores must provide many alternate flow routes. Release of pressure by erosional unloading greatly facilitates the opening of pre-solutional fractures. Tension along the axes of folds has a similar effect. Fractures and partings become less numerous with increasing depth below the surface, so there is some tendency for maze caves to form at shallow depths, typically less than 100 m below the surface. This is not an iron-clad rule, because deep mazes can and do form at considerable depth where fracturing is intense or porosity is unusually high.

On the other hand, the presence of many fractures is not enough to ensure that maze caves will form (e.g., Figure 8.6). Some prominently fractured limestones contain few mazes. Simultaneous enlargement of many fissures requires one or more of the conditions described on the preceding page.

The origin of maze caves and related features is described in greater detail in the following sections.

Floodwater caves

Sinking streams are common where water collects on insoluble, low-permeability material and then flows onto soluble rock. Caves fed by sinking streams are exposed to severe floods during heavy rainfall or snowmelt (Figure 8.11). They can also flood if they receive rapid infiltration from large catchments of bare alpine karst. In addition, rising surface rivers during floods can force water into adjacent bluffs of soluble rock and temporarily fill the caves with water. All of these processes are able to form maze caves.

Sinking streams are less common than sinkholes, and most of the caves produced by them have only a crude branching pattern. Additional passages and solution features are superposed on this pattern by flooding. Floodwater features include overflow routes, mazes, and *injection features* such as solution pockets, dead-end fissures, and anastomoses. At least 10–15% of all caves show significant floodwater effects, and many others have been modified to some extent by flooding. These effects are subdued or absent in caves that drain efficiently, or where the recharge rate does not fluctuate greatly.

Relatively little attention has been given to floodwater in karst (Malott, 1937, 1949) or its role in producing maze caves (Palmer, 1972, 1975, 2001). This type of flow and cave development is often called *epiphreatic*, but the term refers simply to the zone in which the water table periodically rises and falls, and it does not convey the dynamic aspects of karst water during floods (Figure 8.12). Thus the term *floodwater caves* is used here instead. Discharges are higher than in any other natural groundwater setting. Rapid rises in water level can pose a danger for explorers.

During severe floods, water levels can rise several hundred meters in some caves, especially in alpine regions. Flooding to depths of more than 700 m has been documented in Krubera Cave, Republic of Georgia (Figure 2.74).*

* Information from Alexander Klimchouk, Kiev, Ukraine, 2006.

Figure 8.12: Moderately high flow in Ogof Ffynnon Ddu, Wales. A complex floodwater maze surrounds the stream passage. Photo by Chris Howes and Judith Calford.

The water-level rise during a flood can be viewed as a return of phreatic conditions to what are ordinarily vadose domains. But the effects are quite different from those of normal phreatic water. In comparison to typical groundwater, the hydraulic gradients and discharges are much larger, and the water, having been delivered rapidly from the surface, is far more aggressive. In well-drained stream passages, floodwater can easily move large cobbles and boulders (Figure 6.49). Some passages are swept entirely clean of sediment by high-velocity floodwaters, leaving bare bedrock floors. Where the water ponds upstream from constrictions, it tends to deposit banks of fine-grained sediment.

The solutional capacity of a cave stream rises with discharge and is greatest during floods (see example in Figure 7.20). Floodwater also travels rapidly through the main passages of caves so that it remains aggressive even when it is carried deep underground. Although floods occur only during a small part of the year, their intense dissolution and abrasion can form traversable passages in less than 10,000 years in favorable situations. Much of the enlargement is caused by abrasion by water-borne sediment (Newson, 1971).

The effect of floodwater is greatest in caves that are partly air-filled during low flow, especially if the water is supplied by sinking streams. Water levels in the main cave passages rise faster than in surrounding fractures, partings, and pores. Water often fills entire passages at high pressure

Figure 8.13: A fissure passage in Skull Cave, New York, formed by frequent severe flooding from an adjacent stream passage. This fissure extends about 600 m in an almost perfect straight line. Note the drains in the bedrock floor, through which floodwaters rise and subside. (See map in Figure 8.17).

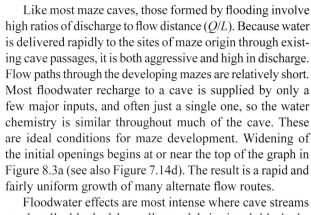

and is injected into all the adjacent openings, which enlarges them rapidly by dissolution.

Most passages formed or modified by floodwater have profiles that loop up and down along their length. They also have large variations in cross-sectional area and shape. Natural rock spans across passages are much more common in floodwater caves than in caves fed by sinkholes. All of these characteristics are usually thought to be evidence for phreatic cave development, but they are at least as common in passages formed in the floodwater zone above the normal water-table level (Palmer, 1972, 1975). The great fluctuations in discharge make it impossible for an individual well-graded passage to remain the stable route. From observations in alpine caves, Audra (1994) and Häuselmann (2005) consider ungraded passages with prominent vertical loops to be diagnostic of epiphreatic cave development.

Bedrock floors in most floodwater passages contain narrow drains that form as water seeps out after floods (Figure 8.13). A few drains are large enough to explore, and it is evident that they convey receding floodwaters back to the water table. Most drains also serve as inputs for rising water from lower stream passages during the onset of flooding.

Floodwater spans the extremes between dynamic, high-velocity water and relatively static water ponded under pressure, and its effects on caves are equally varied. Scallops, boulders, and scoured bedrock floors attest to dynamic flooding, while commonly in the same cave there are sections having no scallops, but solution pockets, fissures, and clay deposits instead, as the result of static flooding.

All caves that are fed by recharge through a karst surface are susceptible to flooding to some extent, and the effects, even if minor, can be discerned in most of these caves. The caves considered in this section are exposed to the severest floods, and the effect on the cave patterns is conspicuous.

Floodwater mazes

Floodwater cave enlargement can produce anastomotic, network, or spongework patterns, depending on whether the original openings in the rock are bedding-plane partings, intersecting fractures, or intergranular pores. Mazes may constitute entire flood-prone caves, but more commonly they are simply superposed on branchwork patterns.

Like most maze caves, those formed by flooding involve high ratios of discharge to flow distance (Q/L). Because water is delivered rapidly to the sites of maze origin through existing cave passages, it is both aggressive and high in discharge. Flow paths through the developing mazes are relatively short. Most floodwater recharge to a cave is supplied by only a few major inputs, and often just a single one, so the water chemistry is similar throughout much of the cave. These are ideal conditions for maze development. Widening of the initial openings begins at or near the top of the graph in Figure 8.3a (see also Figure 7.14d). The result is a rapid and fairly uniform growth of many alternate flow routes.

Floodwater effects are most intense where cave streams are locally blocked by collapse debris, insoluble beds, or sediment fill. Water expends considerable energy in passing through or around obstructions like these. The hydraulic gradient across such a constriction varies with roughly the square of the discharge, which causes sudden and severe ponding upstream from the constriction (Figure 8.14). Because flooding often involves discharges hundreds or even thousands of times greater than the lowest flow, the results can be spectacular. Under these conditions, all openings wider than about 0.05–0.1 mm will enlarge rapidly at about the same rate, without having to endure the usual slow stages of growth typical of early cave development. A maze of intersecting passages may form a bypass around the blockage. Similarly, the partial blockage of a cave spring (for example, by breakdown) can produce a maze of distributary passages that feed overflow springs (Figure 8.15).

Floodwater mazes around constrictions start as minor enlargements of fissures or pores and quickly evolve into

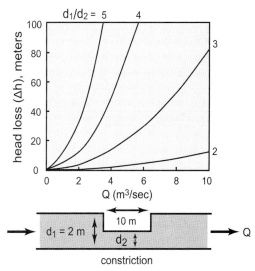

Figure 8.14: Loss of hydraulic head across a constriction in a stream passage (after Palmer, 2001). Head loss is the build-up of head required to force the water through the constriction. The hydraulic gradient is the head loss divided by the length of the constriction (10 m in this example). Head loss and hydraulic gradient increase with the square of the discharge and also with the narrowness of the constriction. In the constriction shown here, if the diameter d_2 is 0.5 m, $d_1/d_2 = 4$. If the discharge rises from 2 to 4 m^3/sec, the head loss will increase from about 10 to almost 50 meters.

through-flow conduits. It might seem that a single bypass route would be enough to transmit the flow. But during floods these bypasses have steep and irregular hydraulic gradients that are highly sensitive to passage size. As a result, there can be large head differences between adjacent conduits so that water is forced to leak between neighboring conduits and produce connecting passages. The pattern is further complicated by injection features such as fissures and pockets, which can eventually grow enough to connect with nearby passages.

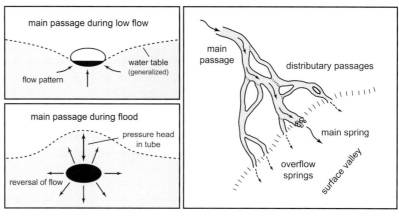

Figure 8.15: Where a karst spring is partly blocked by collapse or landslide material, a distributary pattern of tubes or fissures may develop around it, which lead to overflow springs that are active mainly during high flow (Palmer, 1984b). Laminar groundwater around the cave normally flows into the main passages during low flow, but during high flow the sudden influx of water from sinking streams fills the passages under pressure, which forces water into all surrounding openings. These openings eventually grow into diversion routes. Diversion around blockages in cave streams form in the same way. The ***pressure head*** shown here is the height to which water would rise in a well or other opening that intersects the passage.

About 15−20% of all network caves have a floodwater origin. A fine example is Sof Omar, in Ethiopia (Figure 2.86). Blue Spring Cave, Indiana, contains a major diversion maze (Figure 8.16). Late in the cave's development, collapse at a wide passage junction caused water to pond upstream during floods, to form a network maze that bypassed the blockage. A large compound sinkhole developed at the surface as collapse material was carried away by the cave stream. Floodwater enlargement of the maze allowed further collapse and diversion. The maze consists of intersecting fissures with a total length of almost 2 km and a vertical range of 20 m. Some fissures are partly or completely filled with water year round, and others are filled only during floods. Many passage intersections in the maze have acute and obtuse angles that contrast with the nearly right-angle pattern of fissures elsewhere in the cave. Some of the controlling joints in the maze were apparently produced by release of stress around the growing sinkhole (see Figure 9.46). Such intersections are common in this kind of maze but by themselves do not prove a floodwater origin.

Such diversions and accelerated cave enlargement are also key factors in the development of the giant vertical-walled sinkholes called tiankengs (Chapter 2). Few individual cave passages are large enough by themselves to produce a collapse hundreds of meters in diameter, and this continued diversion-and-collapse mechanism provides an effective substitute for a single massive collapse.

Several unusual networks have developed in Skull Cave, New York, as the result of severe flooding from sinking streams, where the water drains out of the cave through low-permeability strata and glacial sediment that overlie the discharge area (Figure 8.17). The cave is located in prominently jointed limestones of the Silurian-Devonian Helderberg Group. The entire southern end of the cave fills with water on roughly an annual basis. The mazes contain few closed loops but instead consist of parallel fissures that are long, straight, narrow, and high (Figure 8.13). They terminate abruptly in dead ends. In places the maze has enlarged upward into impure limestone that contains no other known caves (see ***paragenesis*** on pages 264−265).

Anastomotic mazes form braided patterns in well-bedded limestones or along low-angle faults. About 5-10% of all caves contain some anastomotic development, and almost every anastomotic maze has a floodwater origin. Some anastomotic mazes ramble in three dimensions along many intersecting openings. Most anastomotic mazes are not bypasses to local constrictions, but instead provide alternate routes for floodwater as it fills the rest of the cave. Scallops are abundant on the majority of solutional surfaces as the result of high-velocity flow. Many alpine caves contain anastomotic floodwater mazes. The largest is Hölloch, in Switzerland, in which anastomotic passages are superposed on the basic levels of cave development (Figure 8.18). The rock is fairly massive but is cut by low-angle thrust faults that serve as the main paths for cave development.

In some anastomotic caves, chert beds constrict the main cave passages and facilitate the development of diversion routes (pages 382−384). A similar anastomotic maze is located at the far southeastern end of Blue Spring Cave (labeled **X** in Figure 8.16a).

Floodwater probably accounts for no more than 5% of all spongework mazes. There are good examples in Big Brush Creek and Little Brush Creek Caves, Utah, which are fed by large flood-prone sinking streams (Figure 8.19). These caves are located mainly in the massive limestone breccia of the Mississippian Humbug Formation, in which the initial openings were mainly pores and seams between adjacent breccia blocks. Their spongework mazes are complex but of limited extent. Most of the passage length in these caves consists instead of three-dimensional anastomotic mazes that twist erratically through the massive bedrock. Blockage of passages by sandstone boulders and pebbles, carried in by the sinking streams, has helped to promote maze development.

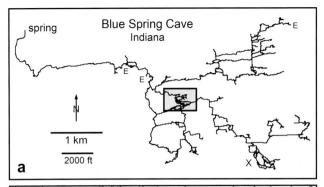

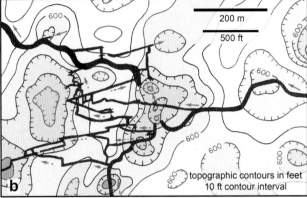

Figure 8.16: The main passage of Blue Spring Cave, Indiana, collapsed at a tributary junction (see shaded rectangle on map **a**). Diversion of water around the collapse has produced a network maze along joints (**b**). The topographic map shows the compound sinkhole above the collapse. The cave lies an average of 25 m below the surface. The maze fills completely with water during high flow (arrows show flow directions). **X** = anastomotic maze in bedded, cherty limestone. **E** = entrance. (From Palmer, 1969).

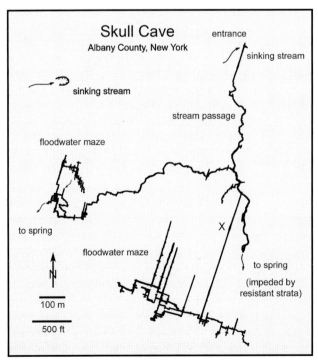

Figure 8.17: Map of Skull Cave, New York, showing floodwater mazes with few closed loops (Palmer, 1975). Figure 8.13 was shot at point X.

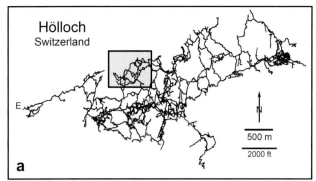

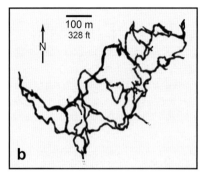

Figure 8.18: Hölloch, in Switzerland, is an alpine cave exposed to severe flooding fed by runoff from a bare karst surface. Much of the cave is developed along low-angle thrust faults and has a roughly anastomotic pattern (**a**). The enlarged view (**b**) shows a representative anastomotic maze. (From Bögli, 1970.)

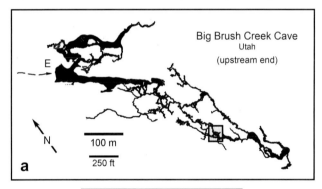

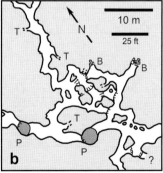

Figure 8.19: Big Brush Creek Cave, in the Uinta Mountains of Utah, is developed mostly in a Mississippian limestone breccia. Big Brush Creek sinks into the cave and fills it entirely during floods. Bedding and joints are limited, so severe flooding has produced spongework mazes along the boundaries between breccia fragments. The area shown in the rectangle on map **a** is enlarged on map **b**, where B = boulder choke, P = pool, and T = too tight to explore. See also Figure 6.29. (From Palmer, 1975.)

Where floodwater enters young, porous limestones or gypsum, it can form network or spongework caves in the vicinity of sink points but then may dissipate into small unexplorable voids in the downflow direction. This pattern is well illustrated by certain caves in the porous Tertiary limestones of Florida and southern Georgia.

Floodwater mazes can also be produced by overflow of surface rivers into adjacent valley walls. The process is similar to the injection and release of **bank storage** (page 91). Bank storage in non-karst regions involves the gradual seepage of water into and back out of the ground adjacent to a river as floods rise and fall. In karst areas the process is more dynamic. Where river gradients are steep, narrow bands of network or anastomotic caves form parallel to the river and contain scallops and coarse-grained sediment. Caves formed in this way can extend hundreds of meters along the river banks and convey much of the flood discharge. Where rivers have low gradients, flooding involves a more gradual rise and fall of low-velocity water. The resulting caves are mostly networks floored in places by thick clay and silt carried in from the river. Some caves formed by low-velocity flooding have undergone inception by other processes such as diffuse seepage from above.

Some maze caves are underground meander cutoffs that connect sink points to downstream outlets. Mystery Cave, in Minnesota, is an example that formed as a cutoff through the well-jointed Stewartville and Dubuque Formations of Ordovician age (Figure 8.20).

In a similar way, mazes can form along the borders of swamps and lakes where the water bodies drain directly into soluble rock. Although flooding may not be severe, the caves are exposed to highly aggressive water over short flow distances (Figure 8.21). Grimes (2003) describes spongework mazes in young, poorly cemented limestones in western Australia that apparently formed by flooding from swampy land. Hills that rise from swamps in Florida

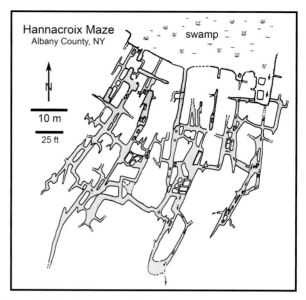

Figure 8.21: Hannacroix Maze, New York, is a network that receives aggressive recharge from an adjacent swamp. Map by William J. Gregg, in Evans and others (1979).

contain many small network caves (Pruitt, 1997). Wave action on bluffs of soluble rock along lake shorelines can have similar effects. Auler (1995) describes network caves that border swamps and lakes in Brazil.

Many residual hills of carbonate rock that rise above lowlands contain intricate floodwater maze caves. These include the **foot caves** at the bases of karst towers (Chapter 2). Many residual hills in the eastern Appalachian Mountains contain maze caves, but the caves are mainly abandoned relics whose origin is uncertain.

Floodwater injection features

Floodwater injection features form in approximately the same way as floodwater mazes but are merely embellishments superposed on the overall cave pattern. During floods, when aggressive water is forced into the small openings around stream passages, the openings enlarge rapidly and eventually form solution pockets and dead-end fissures (Figures 8.22–8.23). The water drains back into the main passages as the floods subside.

Some pockets and fissures are large and intricate, and there is a continuous gradation between them and floodwater mazes. The water that forms them is often either slow-moving or merely swirls around in haphazard eddies, so scallops may be sparse or absent. These openings do not serve as through-flow conduits, as they do in the diversion mazes shown in Figures 8.16 and 8.20. Injection features are most common in cave walls and ceilings, where insoluble sediment is least likely to act as a barrier to water flow and dissolution. Fracture-guided fissures

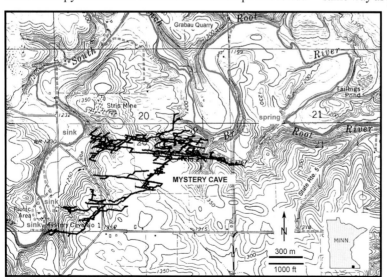

Figure 8.20: Mystery Cave, Minnesota, is a network maze formed by diversion across several river meanders. Elevations are in feet. Contour interval = 10 ft. Map by Minnesota Speleological Survey, courtesy of Forestville State Park.

that extend laterally into passage walls are evident on many cave maps (Figures 8.17 and 8.21). Some floodwater fissures extend upward into cave ceilings more than 20 m. Ceiling pendants are common as residual knobs and blades that remain between adjacent fissures or solution pockets (Figure 8.22).

Floodwater fissures can have a distinct taper — they become narrower away from the stream passage from which they emanate (Figures 8.22 and 8.24). This kind of

Figure 8.22: Ceiling fissures and intervening pendants formed by frequent flooding in Blue Spring Cave, Indiana. These are in the main downstream passage in Figure 8.16a. Note the thick clay deposits.

solution pocket is often attributed merely to dissolution beneath the water table, but this interpretation has weaknesses. A stream passage continually filled with water tends to have the lowest hydraulic head in the area, and the water in adjacent narrow fissures drains *toward* it (Figure 8.24a). This tributary water moves slowly and is in such intimate contact with the bedrock that it is essentially saturated with dissolved carbonate minerals. It is unable to enlarge narrow fractures at all, and certainly not with the taper shown in the figures. But in a cave that is exposed to flooding, adjacent fissures are enlarged as shown in Figure 8.24b. Because the water drains out as the flood subsides, most of the fissures have blind terminations. As the entrance

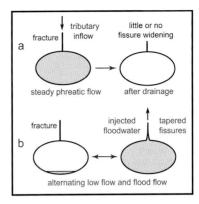

Figure 8.24: Origin of floodwater fissures: (a) In caves that contain fairly steady phreatic flow, water in adjacent fractures is normally tributary to the passage and saturated with carbonate minerals, so the fractures are not enlarged. Even where cupolas form in the ceiling by convection or by later condensation corrosion, adjacent fractures are not enlarged significantly (Figure 8.51). (b) Periodic flooding forces aggressive water into neighboring joints, faults, or partings, and widens them by dissolution.

areas of the fissures widen, injected floodwater can travel farther into the fractures before it loses aggressiveness or drains back out, and with time the fissures grow longer as well as wider.

Where bedding-plane partings are the dominant openings, the most common floodwater injection features are ***anastomoses*** (Figures 6.28 and 8.25). These are small interconnected tubes that diminish in size away from the source passages and are too small to explore. In pattern they resemble anastomotic mazes, but they are much smaller, have denser patterns, and rarely contain rapid-flow features such as scallops or coarse sediment. The lower walls of some passages are covered by rills formed by water draining out of anastomoses after floods (Figure 6.27).

Many cave geologists consider anastomoses to be remnants of the earliest stage of passage development by slow-moving phreatic water (Ewers, 1966). But the simultaneous growth of many alternate channels is produced most effectively by the steep gradients and aggressive flow supplied by flooding. Anastomoses that are relics of early

Figure 8.23: A scene in the Maze of Blue Spring Cave. Note the solution pockets, natural bridges, and irregular passage cross section.

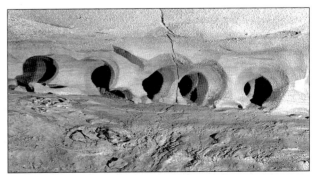

Figure 8.25: Most bedding-plane anastomoses are formed by floodwater injection along bedding-plane partings. Because clay accumulates on their floors, dissolution is directed mainly upward from the initial partings. This example is from Mammoth Cave, Kentucky. Width of photo = 1 m. (See also Chapter 6.)

cave development tend to be concentrated at the upstream ends of passages, where the solvent water was still highly aggressive.

Even a passage that is continually water-filled will experience varying flow rates. As a result, adjoining fractures and partings may be enlarged to some extent as water is alternately forced into and out of them, but the effect is not usually as intense as where floodwaters fill otherwise air-filled passages. This is because most phreatic water is less aggressive than the sudden floodwaters that surge into aerated passages.

In deep phreatic passages, especially those of hypogenic origin, many ceiling pockets are wide, rounded *cupolas* rather than fracture-controlled pockets (compare Figures 6.31 and 8.22). Cupolas can also form in air-filled caves by condensation corrosion (Chapter 12). Fractures that are intersected by cupolas rarely enlarge by dissolution unless the fractures are already unusually wide. Cupolas can also be formed by flooding, but only where fractures are too narrow to accept water, or are not present at all.

Caves formed by diffuse flow

Caves can be formed by diffuse infiltration either through intergranular pores in soluble rock, or through permeable insoluble rock that overlies or underlies the soluble rock. Almost all caves of this type have network or spongework patterns.

Epikarst and related caves

The *epikarst* is the deeply corroded zone of soluble rock at the surface or just below the soil (Chapter 2). Although any single opening receives only a small amount of flow, they all enlarge at comparable rates in the top few meters where the flow length is short and the Q/L ratio is sufficiently large (Figure 7.14e). A network of enlarged fissures and partings is typical (Figure 2.12). Many are filled with soil. Some epikarst fissures are wide and interconnected enough to qualify as caves, although most are too small to have been mapped. Where widening has persisted over a long period of time, the fissures may be separated by tall fins of bedrock.

Where the epikarst is floored by insoluble rock, infiltrating water travels laterally along the contact, which helps to integrate the epikarst fissures into true cave passages. The result is a network maze with many openings to the surface. Australia's

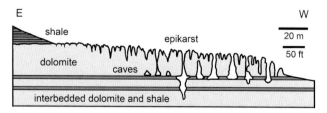

Figure 8.26: Idealized cross section through Bullita Cave, part of an extensive epikarst system in Precambrian dolomite, Northern Territory, Australia (after Bannink and others, 1995). The cave contains more than 100 km of mapped passages in a dense, mainly rectangular network pattern.

Bullita Cave is considered to be an example where dispersed recharge along many epikarst fissures has been perched on a shale base that restricts downward dissolution (Figure 8.26). Some of the cave development was initiated by runoff from a retreating shale cap-rock nearby, but the solution rills that line many of the cave walls show the importance of local infiltration through the overlying epikarst. The cave is now mainly inactive as the result of a drying climate.

Diffuse recharge through a permeable cap-rock

Of all network caves, about 20–30% are located in prominently fractured beds of limestone or dolomite capped by thin, insoluble, but permeable rock such as quartz sandstone. Most are located at or near the top of the soluble beds and receive infiltration during wet periods. Diffuse recharge through the permeable rock is able to form network caves. Where the cap-rock is thick or poorly permeable, less infiltration takes place, and instead of network patterns, most of the underlying caves have branchwork or floodwater patterns fed by sinkholes and sinking streams (Palmer, 1975). In addition, many sandstone-capped networks are formed by processes other than diffuse recharge through the cap.

When diffuse water passes through the porous cap it enters fractures in the underlying soluble beds and enlarges all but the narrowest ones more or less uniformly. This is because the water is highly aggressive and the flow distances from where the water first enters the soluble rock are short. In addition, both the discharge and water chemistry are fairly uniform. Wide fissures receive only slightly more water than narrow ones, because the cap-rock acts as a governor that distributes the water more or less uniformly to the fissures in the underlying rock (Palmer, 2000b).

Fractures in the soluble rock may begin to enlarge while the contact between the two rock types is still below local river level (Figure 8.27). At first the cap-rock may have the greater permeability and transmit most of the groundwater flow, because openings in the soluble rock have not yet enlarged by dissolution. But the small amount of water that does enter the soluble rock is highly aggressive and gradually widens the fractures. Eventually the permeability of the soluble rock exceeds that of the cap-rock, and from then on most of the water flows through the soluble rock. The basic framework of network caves is established during this phase. As the river breaches the cap-rock, the water table drops, and eventually only vadose water passes through the cap. This water is still aggressive and continues to enlarge the network cave. Computer modeling by Clemens and others (1996) have verified that network caves can form in this way.

Many caves with this origin have been enlarged further by backflooding from nearby rivers. Where flooding accounts for most of the enlargement, the widest fissures may lie well below the contact with the overlying cap-rock. Flooding by itself can form mazes, and tightly capped mazes may have little to do with infiltration through the cap-rock.

Figure 8.27: Origin of network caves by infiltration through an insoluble but permeable cap-rock, such as quartz sandstone. **SS** = sandstone; **LS** = limestone. (**a**) At first, the sandstone is more permeable than the underlying limestone. Most groundwater flows through the sandstone, but what little water enters the limestone is aggressive and able to enlarge fractures. (**b**) With time, the fractures enlarge enough to allow most water to pass through the limestone. Network caves develop. (**c**) As surface rivers erode downward, the caves eventually drain. Flooding from the rivers can enlarge the caves further. (From Palmer, 1975.)

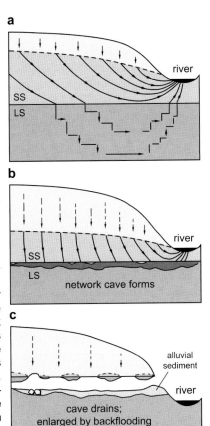

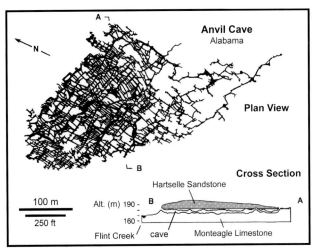

Figure 8.29: Anvil Cave, Alabama, is a network maze in the Monteagle Limestone (Mississippian), formed beneath a thin cap of Hartselle Sandstone. The network pattern was apparently initiated by diffuse recharge through the sandstone, and much of the enlargement was caused by periodic flooding from Flint Creek. (From Varnedoe, 1964.)

enlarged the cave by floodwater invasion. It is likely that both processes have contributed to the cave enlargement.

Crossroads Cave, Virginia, is a maze in Devonian limestone, in which one part was formed by diffuse infiltration through sandstone and another by floodwater (Figures 8.30–8.31). Passages that formed by infiltration through the cap-rock have ceilings at the base of the sandstone, and their walls contain flutes and rills formed by descending water. The floodwater passages are scalloped and lie below the top of the limestone. They intersect at angles that contrast with the right angles of the maze formed by diffuse infiltration. This difference probably has more to do with local structural conditions than with the type of cave origin.

By itself, vadose infiltration through the cap-rock is often enough to produce a network cave. In this case, vertical flutes are abundant, and nearly all passages extend upward to the sandstone contact (Figure 8.28). If the soluble rock is poorly fractured, dissolution concentrates along its upper surface and penetrates into lower beds only in the few places where the water encounters joints, for example near the eroded edges of a plateau. Complex systems of shafts and narrow canyons may form instead of fissures.

Anvil Cave, Alabama, is located beneath a thin cap of permeable Hartselle Sandstone, and it appears to be a fine example of a network maze formed by diffuse recharge from above (Figure 8.29). But the cave is also located in a meander of Flint Creek, which has undoubtedly

Figure 8.28: Fissure passage in a network maze fed by diffuse seepage through an overlying sandstone (James, Cave, Kentucky). The sandstone-limestone contact is shown (S/L). The block of sandstone at left and center has dropped downward slightly.

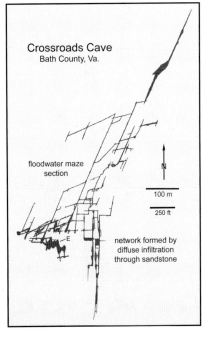

Figure 8.30: Map of Crossroads Cave, Virginia, showing a network maze formed by diffuse recharge through an overlying thin sandstone formation. Other parts of the cave are formed by stream action, including floodwater. The non-rectangular pattern of the floodwater maze is typical for that origin but is not diagnostic. (From map by T. Miller, R. Lutz, L. Slade, and D. Abbott, in Douglas, 1964.)

Figure 8.31: A fissure in the network maze of Crossroads Cave, Virginia, formed by diffuse seepage through thin overlying sandstone. The walls are fluted, especially at junctions.

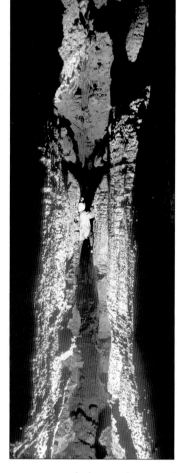

Some network mazes in similar settings show no evidence for diffuse recharge. Cameron Cave and Mark Twain Cave, Missouri, are located in bluffs that overlook the Mississippi River (Bretz, 1956; Dom and Wicks, 2003; Figure 8.32). They developed in dolomitic limestone of Devonian age, which is capped by poorly permeable Mississippian shale. Passages extend upward to the shale in only a few places, and no visible seepage enters from above except near hillsides that intersect the caves. Passages are floored with stream-deposited sediment up to gravel size, and most of them terminate in sediment fill up to 10 m thick. The caves lie at about the same elevation as a broad river terrace. These caves were apparently formed by flooding from the Mississippi River or its local tributaries. The network maze Moestroff Cave, Luxembourg, is a similar example of this kind of origin adjacent to a surface river (Figure 8.32b).

Figure 8.32: Network mazes formed beneath a caprock by static flooding. (**a**) Cameron Cave, Missouri, formed beneath impermeable shale (mapped by P. Herbert, E. DuBois, and C. Johnson; Bretz, 1956). (**b**) Moestroff Cave, Luxembourg, formed beneath soluble but low-permeability marl (mapped by Groupe Speleologique Luxembourgois; Massen, 1997).

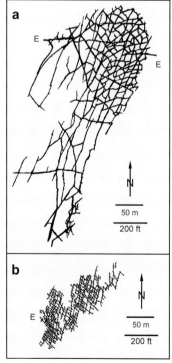
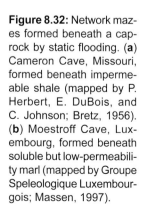

The Pennsylvanian-age Vanport Limestone of western Pennsylvania is a thin, gently dipping unit only 3–6 m thick sandwiched between beds of sandstone and shale. It contains many rectilinear network caves, some of them several kilometers long. Their origin is debated (Christenson, 1999). Diffuse infiltration from above is possible, as the overlying beds are mainly sandstone, which forms the ceilings in places. Aggressive dripwater is abundant (Fawley and Long, 1997). Past backflooding from nearby streams is also a likely agent and probably deposited the copious mud fill (White, 1976). Bodies of limonite iron ore overlie the Vanport in places, and if oxidation of pyrite was involved in its origin, the initial fissure enlargement in the limestone may have been aided by sulfuric acid. Although there no consensus on the cave origin, the alternatives are fairly clear.

Caves formed by rising water, or which have an artesian origin, are almost universally considered *hypogenic*. In this book the term is applied only where the *chemical aggressiveness* is produced below the surface. If groundwater simply descends and rises without gaining aggressiveness in the process, caves formed by this water are not considered hypogenic. Nearly all karst aquifers contain local areas of rising water, but only those that gain aggressiveness from deep-seated processes should be considered hypogenic. The examples on the next two pages are grouped with epigenic caves, but those who disagree are welcome to begin the hypogenic section here.

Diffuse upward recharge

Network caves can also form by diffuse recharge through *underlying* insoluble rocks. To do so, water must first descend below the cavernous zone and then rise through the soluble rock on its way to springs. This is not common, at least in carbonate rocks, because groundwater in sedimentary rocks can rarely travel long distances and remain aggressive toward carbonates, unless the aggressiveness is renewed by deep-seated acids or by mixing of contrasting water types. Filippov (2000) attributes one of the largest limestone maze caves in Russia to diffuse upward flow through sandstone, where the aggressiveness was enhanced by hypogenic acids.

In eastern Missouri, Brod (1964) describes rudimentary fissure mazes formed by water passing through permeable

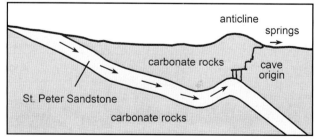

Figure 8.33: Proposed origin of fissure caves by water rising through carbonate rocks from underlying sandstone in eastern Missouri (Brod, 1964). The sandstone is about 30 m thick and the width of the cross section is roughly 100 km. Wide fractures along the crest of the anticline facilitated the upward flow.

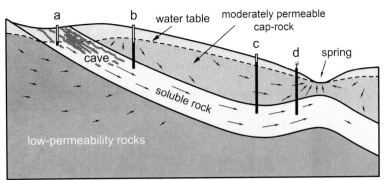

Figure 8.34: Cave origin in an artesian aquifer with outflow through the cap-rock (e.g., in the flanks of the Black Hills, S.D.). Arrows show flow directions. Water levels in non-pumping wells show local head values. The soluble rock provides an efficient path that in the higher areas draws water from adjacent insoluble rocks. Outflow takes place where the cap is thin and fractured. Palmer (1981c) proposed that maze caves might form in the underlying soluble rock because of the restricted outlet. That is unlikely, because the deep slow-moving water has little or no solutional capacity. The level in well **a** approximates the water table. In **b** the head in the aquifer lies below the water table. In **c** and **d** the head lies above the water table. Well **d** is a flowing well, because the head in the aquifer lies above the land surface (water rarely shoots into the air, as shown).

Ordovician sandstone into overlying fractured carbonates (Figure 8.33). No renewed aggressiveness was needed, because the groundwater that formed the caves remained unsaturated during its travel through the sandstone. This may be the earliest account of aggressive meteoric water rising into carbonate rocks through an underlying insoluble rock. The beds underlying the sandstone are also carbonates, but their permeability is apparently too low to allow much water to pass through them. The caves are not actively forming today, so this interpretation is speculative.

Western Australia contains examples of caves formed by upward seepage of water from quartz sand into overlying poorly consolidated granular dune limestones (Bastian, 2003). The contact dips toward the nearby seacoast more steeply than the water table. Caves in the limestone are concentrated in a narrow zone where the water table lies above the contact. No caves have formed farther updip, where the contact lies above the water table. Farther downdip from the caves, where the water table lies high above the contact, solutional permeability is concentrated at the base of limestone. Still further downdip, where the contact extends below sea level, phreatic caves form at and below the water table and appear to be independent of recharge from below.

Artesian cave development

A *confined aquifer* is one that is capped by low-permeability material and is completely water-filled, so that the water table lies above the contact between the two rock types (Figure 4.10). An *artesian aquifer* is not only confined, but contains water under high enough head that it can flow to the surface through wells. Many people consider any confined aquifer to be artesian, which is technically not true.

The surrounding rocks have some permeability, however, and water leaks into and out of the aquifer according to the local head distribution (Figure 8.34). Water from the aquifer

leaks to the surface where the capping beds are thinnest, most permeable, or absent. The amount of leakage depends on the thickness and permeability of the overlying rock, and the amount of head in the aquifer. If the aquifer is exposed at the surface somewhere in the down-flow direction, most, or all, of the water escapes through that route.

Many speleologists have the intuitive impression that most maze caves form in artesian aquifers, or that all artesian karst aquifers contain maze caves, because of the slow and long-term dissolution that persists there. But these conditions are exactly the opposite of the high discharge and/or short flow distances that favor maze caves in all other settings. Many maze caves have formed in confined aquifers, but their maze patterns are not the result of artesian conditions alone.

Maze caves can form in artesian aquifers where ground-water rises from the underlying beds and flows out through the overlying beds (Klimchouk, 1991, 2006). This must take place beneath the discharge area of the aquifer, as shown around well **d** in Figure 8.34. Examples include the world's largest caves in gypsum, which were formed in Ukraine by water rising from underlying limestone (Figures 8.35–8.37; see also Figure 2.72). Most known examples are now inactive. Although the rising water was apparently saturated with dissolved calcite, it was undersaturated with gypsum. The proposed flow pattern is illustrated in Figure 8.36.

Inflow of aggressive water to each point is limited by the low permeability of the underlying rocks, which prevents any single flow path from dominating. This produces extensive two-dimensional network caves confined to the rather thin gypsum strata, which are only 10–40 m thick. This process

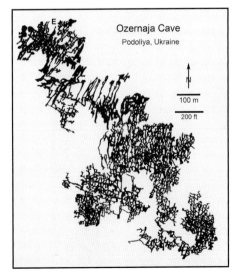

Figure 8.35: Ozernaja Cave, with more than 100 km of passages, is a network formed by water rising across the strata from below (from Klimchouk, 1996b). E = entrance.

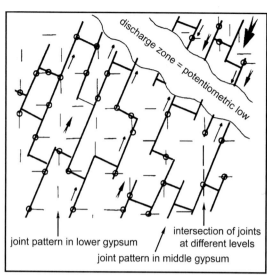

joint pattern in lower gypsum

intersection of joints at different levels

joint pattern in middle gypsum

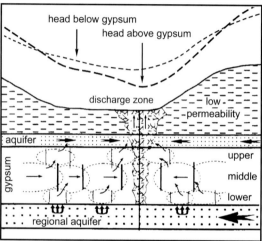

Figure 8.36: Origin of large Ukrainian network mazes in late Tertiary gypsum, according to Klimchouk (1996a, 1996b). Water rose into the gypsum from underlying carbonate beds, flowed toward low-head zones, and discharged upward to the surface.

Figure 8.37: Ceiling channels in Atlantida Cave, an artesian gypsum maze in Ukraine. Photo by Alexander Klimchouk.

would presumably work in carbonate rocks as well, although it is more likely for rising groundwater to be saturated with calcite or dolomite than with gypsum. In some ways this is a variant of the kind of cave development shown in Figure 8.27, where the flow rate and chemistry of the water feeding each fissure are fairly uniform and flow distances are short.

Upward enlargement of early fissures in gypsum may be aided by convection, where water with little dissolved load rises because it is less dense. This process is negligible in carbonate rocks, which in most groundwater are only about 10% as soluble as gypsum, because they do not produce sufficiently dense solutions.

Birk and others (2005) applied computer modeling to the origin of gypsum caves under the conditions described by Klimchouk. They found that maze caves would form, but only if the overlying rock has few enough outlet points that the water in the gypsum is forced to travel a substantial distance horizontally before exiting. Otherwise only single large conduits would form between the largest inlets and outlets. Klimchouk (1996b, 2006) suggests that this flow pattern did in fact exist when the caves formed (Figure 8.36). Ceiling channels in the caves show lateral paths of water through the caves (Figure 8.37).

The groundwater flow that formed these gypsum mazes is not typical of all artesian conditions. Throughout most of an artesian aquifer the flow is roughly parallel to the aquifer boundaries (Figure 8.34). Upward flow across the strata tends to be concentrated in local areas where the hydraulic gradient is largely upward. For the water to cross through an entire soluble formation requires a deeper aquifer to serve as the water source.

Hypogenic acids, which form deep beneath the surface, can also contribute to the origin of artesian maze caves. In addition, some mazes in artesian aquifers are paleokarst relics from older karst episodes that pre-date the present aquifer configuration.

Despite the well-documented mazes in deep-phreatic and artesian settings, most caves in these settings consist of only a few major flow routes, as shown by diving, dye tracing, and examination of formerly deep caves that have been exposed by erosion. For example, many large springs in Missouri are fed by deep conduits that underlie insoluble strata. Some of the conduits extend more than 100 m below the water table, and even below present sea level.* Caves that are confined below sandstone beds, at least those that have been explored by divers, have branchwork patterns with few tributaries (Orndorff and others, 2006). Some air-filled caves that show evidence for deep-phreatic development are also branchworks.

Effect of outflow through insoluble rocks

Some authors have proposed that artesian maze caves owe their patterns to the inefficiency of outflow through insoluble rocks of low or moderate permeability, rather than

* Communication from R. Scott House, Cape Girardeau, Missouri, 2006.

by artesian conditions alone. This idea is based on the fact that the outflow is diffuse and inefficient, so that all passages are limited to a slow and fairly uniform growth. The gypsum mazes of Ukraine may have been influenced by this process (Klimchouk, 2005b, 2006). Palmer (1981c) considered this a possible explanation for maze caves in the Black Hills of South Dakota and presented the diagram in Figure 8.34 to illustrate the idea. He later rejected this idea on the basis of further field evidence: (a) most of the caves are located in the recharge areas and terminate far upstream of the outflow areas; (b) deep inside the aquifer the water is close to saturation with dissolved carbonates, and dissolution rates are too slow to produce cave-size conduits. Maze caves may be favored by an inefficient outlet, but only where groundwater flow distances through the soluble rock are short.

Hypogenic caves

Chemically, the caves described so far are *epigenic* — their origin depends on acids derived from surface or near-surface processes, such as CO_2 production in the soil. In contrast, *hypogenic* caves owe their origin to processes beneath the surface. Worldwide they represent about 10–15% of known caves, but in some regions almost all caves are of this origin. The percentage of hypogenic caves may be underestimated because they tend to have few accessible entrances. They include several types, most of which are maze caves.

Because the solutional aggressiveness is generated at or below the water table, dissolution begins where this water first comes in contact with soluble rock. This can be where water that is already aggressive crosses the boundary from insoluble to soluble rock, but more often the aggressiveness is produced right inside the soluble rock, for example by mixing of different water sources. In either case, the length of flow over which the cave development takes place is fairly short, and the ratio of discharge to flow length (Q/L) is large (see Figure 8.3a). This helps to explain why so many hypogenic caves have maze patterns. Where the flow is slight, the caves may consist merely of isolated fissures or irregular rooms.

Hypogenic caves have several possible origins, but they all have several characteristics in common. Their patterns have no relation to surface karst or recharge. Network, spongework, and single-fissure patterns are typical. Internal features include rounded ceiling pockets such as cupolas. Vadose features such as shafts and canyons are generally absent. Evidence for rapid water flow, such as scallops and coarse-grained sediment, is sparse and local, and may not be present at all. Certain speleothems and mineral types are diagnostic (Chapters 5, 10, and 12). On the other hand, each type of hypogenic cave has distinct characteristics that help to identify its specific mode of origin.

In the past, hypogenic dissolution was not considered a karst process, because it does not contribute to the shaping of karst landscapes. This viewpoint has changed in recent decades, and now hypogenic cave origin and related phenomena are recognized as some of the most challenging targets for karst research.

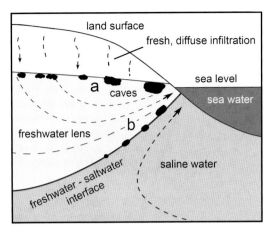

Figure 8.38: Origin of mixing-zone caves in coastal limestone: (**a**) mixing of fresh, high-CO_2 vadose water with fresh phreatic water with a lower CO_2 content; and (**b**) mixing of fresh phreatic water with underlying saline water. There can also be a CO_2 contrast between the fresh and salty water. Oxidation of H_2S can supply local aggressiveness. See also Figure 8.45.

Caves formed in seacoast mixing zones

Solution caves are common in young, porous limestones along the seacoast (Figures 8.38 and 8.39). They are rarely formed by diffuse water that infiltrates directly into soluble rock, because this water loses most of its aggressiveness within a couple of meters of flow, owing to low seepage velocities and a high water-rock contact area, compared to water in fissured bedrock. Whether or not the exposed bedrock is covered with soil, the descending water forms a porous epikarst and some shallow pits, but few caves. Oxidation of organic compounds can prolong the dissolutional capacity of the descending water (Atkinson, 1977a; Wood and Petraitis, 1984), but the flow is usually too diffuse to form caves by itself. Instead, most caves in this kind of rock form at and below the water table where the solutional capacity of the descending water is boosted by mixing with another water source of contrasting chemistry.

Figure 8.39: Sea-level pool in Church Cave, Castle Harbour, Bermuda. Because of the high permeability of the Pleistocene limestone, the freshwater lens is limited to a thin layer of brackish water with a minimum salinity about 30% as concentrated as seawater. The water depth is more than 10 m in places.

Figure 8.40: Spongework formed in the freshwater-saltwater mixing zone in young (late Pleistocene) limestone, Shelley Bay Cave, Bermuda. A carbide lamp 12 cm high shows the scale.

These caves can be considered hypogenic, because the aggressiveness that forms them is generated below the surface, even though most of their water infiltrates from the overlying land surface and most of the CO_2 comes from the soil. There is also little relation between the caves and overlying surface features. The porous epikarst and surface pits formed by vadose water have little to do with the phreatic cave development below. Yet, many people restrict the term *hypogenic* to processes that involve rising water.

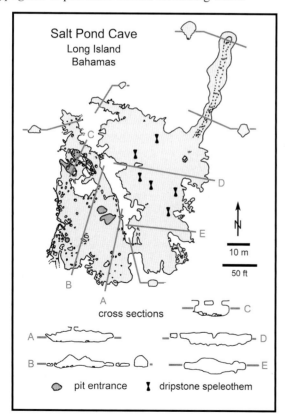

Figure 8.41: Map of a typical flank margin cave in young, porous limestone: Salt Pond Cave, Bahamas (from Mylroie and Carew, 1995). Entrances are shown in the cross sections.

Figure 8.42: Entrances of coastal mixing-zone caves, Isla de Mona, Puerto Rico. The caves formed in bedded, late Tertiary rocks at the contact between two rock formations — dolomite below and limestone above. Since then, the caves have been raised above sea level by uplift of the island and exposed by coastal erosion.

Along seacoasts the infiltrating fresh water forms a phreatic lens that floats on the denser saline water below (Figures 4.12 and 8.38). Mixing between the infiltrating water and the fresh water of the lens can produce an aggressive solution if the two waters have contrasting CO_2 content (Figure 5.14; Laptev, 1939; Bögli, 1964). For example, CO_2 is often higher in the infiltrating water because much of the CO_2 in the phreatic water below has been lost by dissolution of limestone in a closed system, and by escape to the surface through caves or pores.

Mixing along the freshwater/saltwater contact can also produce an aggressive solution (Plummer, 1975; Wigley and Plummer, 1976). This process is illustrated in Figures 5.15 and 8.38. Aggressiveness in this lower zone is caused not only by the salinity contrast, but also by differences in CO_2 and H_2S content. Decay of organics at the halocline can help to produce CO_2 and H_2S. Growth of seacoast caves can be enhanced by oxidation of H_2S. Cave origin by all of these processes has been confirmed in many areas (Back and others, 1984; Smart and others, 1988; Mylroie and Carew, 1990; Whitaker and Smart, 1994; Jenson and others, 2006).

This mode of cave origin is common in the limestone islands of the Caribbean and western Pacific, where the rocks are less than a few million years old, and

Figure 8.43: Entrances to Erickson Cave, a flank margin cave along the coast of Isla de Mona, exposed by coastal erosion. There are two tiers of development, possibly at two successive positions relative to sea level.

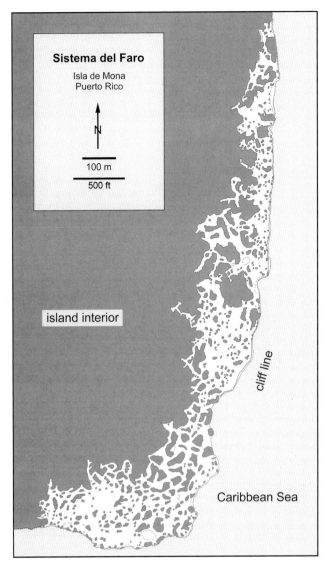

Figure 8.44: Map of Sistema del Faro, Isla de Mona, an example of a flank margin cave intersected by cliff retreat. (Marc Ohms, Isla de Mona Project, National Speleological Society.)

typically much younger (Vacher and Quinn, 1997). Besides producing caves, these processes account for a great deal of porosity that is smaller than cave size.

Caves formed in this way are mainly spongework mazes or irregular rooms, some of which are modified by breakdown (Figures 8.39–8.44). They tend to form sub-horizontal zones limited to the areas of most intense mixing. Fewer than 5% of all known caves have a seacoast mixing origin, but this process is also important in forming and modifying most kinds of early porosity in carbonate rock, not simply accessible caves.

The contact between fresh water and underlying salt water (the *halocline*) is clearly visible in many seacoast caves as a hazy underwater zone that distorts the images of objects viewed through it. Solution caves that form at or near this contact are sometimes called *halo-phreatic caves*.

Cave development is most active along the seaward edge of the freshwater lens, where there is convergence between

the two mixing zones shown in Figure 8.38 and where the flow rates and mixing are greatest. In young porous limestones, most caves form close to the shoreline and subparallel to it. Mylroie and Carew (1990) call these *flank margin caves*, because they develop along the *flanks* of islands at the *margins* of freshwater lenses. Most of the cave origin is concentrated slightly inland from the coast. Wave erosion often exposes the caves in sea cliffs. In cross section the caves may resemble stringed beads, with closely spaced rooms connected by narrow openings at a single level (Figure 8.42).

Most flank margin caves are small and isolated from one another (Figure 8.41), but some extend parallel to shorelines for more than a kilometer with ceiling heights up to 10 m (Figures 8.42–8.44). The most common access to flank margin caves is through collapse sinkholes or random intersections with the coastline.

Meanwhile, as caves enlarge, and the permeability in the mixing zone increases, the freshwater lens becomes thinner. Dissolution is focused essentially at sea level. Tidal flushing can aid the mixing between fresh and saline water, as well as enlarge the caves by erosion. If sea level remains at a single position for a long time, the lens becomes a thin brackish zone. Drips of vadose water into brackish sea-level pools continue to produce mixtures that are undersaturated with respect to calcite (Palmer and others, 1977).

The floors of flank margin caves are locally irregular, but overall they maintain fairly uniform elevations. Cross sections tend to be low and wide because of the sea-level control of their genesis. Rounded ceilings and cupolas are typical. Some flank margin caves are crude branchworks formed by converging water, but their branches terminate headward and cannot be traced all the way to their sources of diffuse water. In map view they may resemble ramiform caves, except that they branch in the upflow rather than downflow direction. Salt Pond Cave in the Bahamas shows this tendency but contains only a single significant branch (Figure 8.41). Sediments are sparse and consist mainly of fine carbonate grains. Calcite speleothems, such as dripstone, are common but irregularly distributed.

The origin of seacoast caves is summarized in the *carbonate island karst model* of Mylroie and Vacher (1999) and Mylroie and others (2001); see Figure 8.45. On small islands the catchment for water is relatively small compared to the length of seacoast. Groundwater is diffuse and moves radially in small amounts toward the island perimeters, where caves are produced in coastal mixing zones. Small spongework caves are the usual result.

The zone of cave development rises and falls with sea-level fluctuations. With increasing island size, the ratio of surface area to shoreline perimeter is greater, because the area increases with the square of the diameter, while the shoreline increases only linearly. If the land slopes gently seaward, changes in sea level cause large variations in catchment area. Caves that form at low sea level receive greater amounts of recharge and may develop more conduit-like passages than caves at higher elevations. This is especially true where

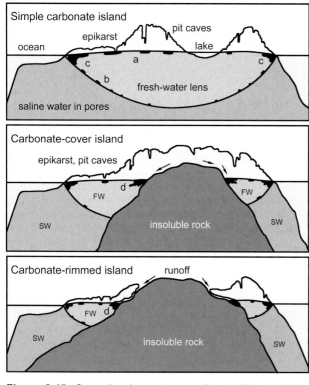

Figure 8.45: Cave development on carbonate islands (after Mylroie and Vacher, 1999). ***Simple carbonate islands*** have only carbonate rock exposed above sea level. All recharge is autogenic and diffuse. In ***carbonate-cover islands***, insoluble rock extends above the water table but is capped by carbonate rocks. Infiltration is autogenic and diffuse, but, below the surface, vadose water runs down along the interface with insoluble rock. In ***carbonate-rimmed islands***, insoluble rock is exposed at the surface with a rim of carbonate rock around it. The carbonates receive allogenic runoff from the insoluble rock, as well as diffuse infiltration. Caves are formed in several ways: **a** = caves formed by mixing of fresh vadose water with water in the freshwater lens; **b** = caves formed by mixing of fresh water with saline water; **c** = flank margin caves, formed by mixing of all types of water; **d** = caves formed by vadose runoff from the insoluble rock. **FW** = fresh water; **SW** = saline water. The status of an island can change with time as sea level rises or falls.

insoluble rocks are exposed by a drop in sea level, because they can collect surface runoff that drains as sinking streams into neighboring soluble rocks. Branchwork caves are the typical result. On large islands such as Puerto Rico, karst areas have drainage basins large enough to produce stream caves that are not affected significantly by seawater mixing. Sea-level fluctuations have little or no influence on caves in the island interiors, so these caves tend to resemble those on continents.

Thermal caves

Temperatures in the Earth increase downward at a rate of about 20–30°C/km. Groundwater that descends along deep paths is warmed by the surrounding rock and reappears as hot springs at the surface or in caves (Figures 2.32 and 8.46). Deep paths of this kind are usually provided by faults or by intensely folded strata. Groundwater can also be heated

by local igneous activity. In addition, warm water can be expelled from deep sedimentary basins by the weight of rapidly deposited sediment or by tectonic stress.

To be classified as ***thermal***, water must be at least several degrees warmer than the normal groundwater temperature of the surrounding region. Schoeller (1962) suggests at least 4°C. The term ***hydrothermal*** refers to processes or features that owe their origin to the high temperature of water. It is usually applied to ore deposits. A cave should be considered hydrothermal only if high temperatures were somehow responsible for its origin.

Thermal water is widely regarded as a potent cave-forming agent, and certain characteristics are considered diagnostic of thermal caves (Takácsné Bolner, 1989; Y. Dublyansky, 2000). The best-documented thermal caves are in eastern and southern Europe, where the concept of thermal cave origin was first developed (Jakucs, 1977).

Because thermal water cools as it approaches the surface, it can dissolve progressively more limestone or dolomite as it rises (Figure 8.47; see also Chapter 5). This is a feasible way for caves to form, provided that these conditions remain stable for a long time. The rising water cools by releasing heat to the surrounding rock. Because the rock becomes warmer with time, the cooling rate of the water must diminish with time, and its gain in solutional capacity diminishes. Eventually the rock temperature stabilizes as it loses heat to the surface, but by that time the effectiveness of cave origin has been greatly diminished by the build-up of heat in the surrounding bedrock. Rising thermal water is guided more easily by paleokarst features than is shallow descending water (Ford, 1995). The rising water is also more capable of breaching impediments to flow, such as igneous dikes (Osborne, 2005a).

Computer modeling verifies that caves can form by the cooling of thermal water as it rises, and that unless the

Figure 8.46: Hot vapor rises from the lowest level of Grotta Nuovo, Acquasanta Terme, Italy. The air and the stream below contain sulfur dioxide and hydrogen sulfide, and their average temperatures are about 40ºC (104ºF). Metal equipment corrodes rapidly. The cave walls in this passage are bright red from oxidation reactions.

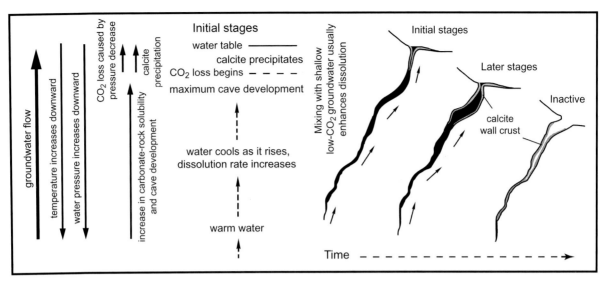

Figure 8.47: The concept of thermal cave origin: Hot groundwater rises toward an outlet and gains aggressiveness as it cools. At low water pressures near the water table, loss of carbon dioxide causes calcite to precipitate on the cave walls.

discharge is very small, the rate of fissure widening is fairly uniform (Palmer, 1991). Network mazes should result. Again a high ratio of discharge to flow length is shown to produce maze caves. Aggressiveness is generated continually as the water rises, so the flow length from where aggressive water first encounters soluble rock is negligible.

A more sophisticated model by Andre and Rajaram (2005) supports the idea that maze caves can form by rising thermal water. These authors also show that in any given fissure the dissolution is initially nearly uniform over the entire flow distance, but that it can increase with distance as thermal convection develops. Under ideal conditions, both models suggest that a fissure can widen about a centimeter in 10,000 years, once there is sufficient flow of thermal water. Ideal conditions are probably rare.

Deep fissures tend to be sparse and scattered, so there are few deep sources of thermal water with enough flow to form caves. Most caves suspected to be thermal consist of irregular arrays of intersecting fissures, with greater variation in cross section and fewer closed loops than in network caves formed by diffuse recharge (compare Figures 8.48 and 8.29).

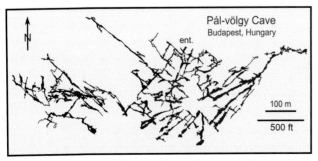

Figure 8.48: Map of Pál-völgy Cave, the largest thermal cave in Hungary (from map by Jósef Kárpát and Katalin Takácsné Bolner). The cave is in highly faulted Eocene limestone. Note the sparse network pattern and few closed loops, in contrast to the dense networks of caves formed by uniform seepage from above or below. Compare also with Figure 8.52.

Some thermal caves probably form along faults and other fractures that branch upward from larger faults deep beneath the surface (*flower structures*; Figure 8.49). The relation of thermal caves to these structures has apparently not yet been investigated. Note the many non-parallel fissures on the map in Figure 8.48 produced by intense and complex fracturing. Similarities in map pattern with certain floodwater caves (e.g., Figure 8.16b) are only superficial.

Igneous activity and metamorphic decomposition of carbonate rocks can raise the CO_2 content of thermal water to as much as several atmospheres. As the water approaches the surface its pressure decreases and much of the CO_2 bubbles out of solution, as in an open soda bottle. This causes calcite to precipitate at and just below the water table (Chapter 10). Dissolution takes place at lower depths, where cooling has made the water aggressive but CO_2 has not yet escaped. As the water table drops, calcite crystals are eventually deposited on the older solutional surfaces (Bakalowicz and others, 1987). Calcite deposited by thermal water has relatively negative $\delta^{18}O$ values (Figure 5.20).

Many characteristics of thermal caves are shared by other hypogenic cave types. Networks are most typical, with dead-end fissures, irregular rooms, solution pockets, and spongework (Figure 8.50). Rounded rooms and cupolas are common, and rooms separated by narrow constrictions give the appearance of clusters of grapes (Figure 8.51). Ceiling and floor profiles are highly irregular, and cross-sectional areas vary a great deal. Breakdown is not as common as in most other cave types. Detrital sediment consists mainly of clay and other fine-grained materials, most of

Figure 8.49: Flower structure produced where large lateral faults at depth are propagated upward as smaller faults in a branching pattern.

Figure 8.50: Passage character of Pál-völgy Cave (Budapest, Hungary), which was formed by rising thermal water. Note the irregular passage profile and cross section.

which are insoluble residue from the bedrock. Caves have no obvious relation to sources of surface recharge. Their relation to stages of surface valley entrenchment may be obscure.

The most common speleothems in thermal caves are calcite wall crusts, folia, rafts, and raft cones, all of which form at or below the water surfaces (Chapter 10). Calcite and aragonite coralloids are also abundant. None of these deposits are diagnostic of thermal conditions, however, as

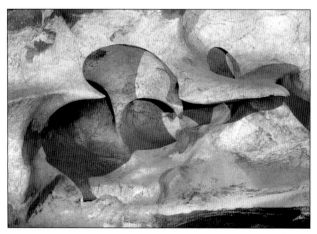

Figure 8.51: Rounded cupola-like rooms and ceiling pockets, like these in Old Man Cave, Nevada, are considered diagnostic of thermal caves. They can also form by other processes. The view is looking upward at about a 20° angle. Width of photo is about 6 m.

they are just as common in sulfuric acid caves and are even well developed in some cold-water epigenic caves.

Certain types of mineralization are limited almost entirely to thermal caves. Rising hot water will sometimes line or replace the bedrock walls with quartz and other forms of silica (SiO_2). Later caves tend to follow the boundaries of these mineralized zones. Because silica is poorly soluble, these caves tend to enlarge preferentially into the more soluble carbonate rock, while the resistant silicified walls remain as flat surfaces (Takácsné Bolner, 1989). Where silica walls are steeply sloping or vertical, the resulting passage cross sections are roughly D-shaped.

Much of the water that rises from depth is rich in dissolved magnesium, and as a result the limestone bedrock around the caves may be partly converted to dolomite. A large percentage of the resulting dolomite will be have a poor internal arrangement of its atoms. This ***poorly ordered*** dolomite is more soluble than the well-ordered kind. Dissolution can dissolve the poorly ordered dolomite and leave the well-ordered variety behind as residual sand. Decomposition of dolomite is not exclusively a thermal process, because it is also well documented in mixed sulfate-carbonate systems (Chapter 5).

Trace elements such as barium, thallium, lead, and arsenic are usually found in rising thermal water, and where they are observed in cave sediments it is likely that thermal water has carried them in. Whether this was the water that formed the caves is not always certain.

Iron and manganese oxides may be abundant in some thermal caves. In reduced form, the metals can be carried in solution from deep below the surface, where there is little oxygen, and precipitate as oxides when they meet oxygen-rich conditions near the surface (Chapters 5 and 10).

Thermal water is often invoked to explain many cave features that seem out of the ordinary. But hot water alone is poorly equipped to form caves, because it can dissolve less limestone or dolomite than cold water can. For example, if water is heated from 10 to 50° C, a six-fold increase in CO_2 is necessary to offset the decrease in limestone solubility caused by the rise in temperature (see Figure 5.16). Also, computer modeling shows that the breakthrough time for cave inception *increases* with temperature (Figure 7.22).

Many features considered diagnostic of thermal caves are more easily explained by processes unrelated to hot water. Convection in rising hot water is a common explanation for the pockets and rooms in thermal caves, such as those in Figure 8.51 (Rudnicki, 1989). The small-scale convection needed to form these small rounded pockets would require very steep temperature gradients, however, and it is not certain that such conditions are present at all, let alone whether they can persist long enough to create these features. Rounded rooms can also be attributed to condensation corrosion, where moist air rises through caves that have been partly drained (Chapter 12).

If a thermal cave forms in the manner of Figure 8.47, one would expect it to contain deep fissures. Although most

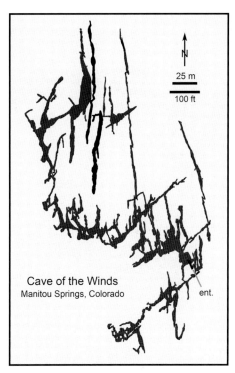

Figure 8.52: Cave of the Winds, Colorado, is a well-documented example of cave origin by mixing of deep and shallow groundwater. From map by Paul Burger.

thermal caves have considerable vertical relief, none are exceptionally deep. Perhaps many infeeders become partly choked with sediment or calcite wall crust. Alternatively, the cave origin may depend more on mixing of deep and shallow water than on simple cooling.

Mixing of deep and shallow waters

Most caves that are considered to be thermal really owe their origin to the mixing of different water sources. The dissolved carbon dioxide content of groundwater normally increases with depth (Lundegard and Land, 1986), and where deep water rises and mixes with near-surface water, there is likely to be a boost in aggressiveness because of the CO_2 contrast. Caves formed in this way have irregular ceiling and floor profiles, abundant cupolas, and no evidence for significant vadose dissolution, so it is probable that their origin was entirely below the water table.

One of the best-documented examples of this kind of cave origin is Cave of the Winds, Colorado, in the eastern flank of the Front Range (Luiszer, 1994). The cave is located in the highly fractured limestones of the Ordovician Manitou Formation and Mississippian Williams Canyon Formation. The cave is now inactive, and evidence for its original spring has been eroded away. But a cluster of mineral-rich springs 1–2 km downhill from the cave provide what appears to be a modern analog of the water that formed it. The P_{CO_2} of the present spring water is about 0.5–1 atm, which is far too high to represent shallow meteoric water, but its high nitrate content also signifies mixing with shallow water. Temperatures at the various springs are in the range of 8–15°C, and most

are clustered in the upper half of that range. The warmest springs are only mildly thermal, but this is appropriate for a mixture of deep and shallow water.

The springs are also depositing abundant iron and manganese oxides similar to those in the cave. Filaments of iron-oxidizing bacteria are common in the oxides in both the cave and the springs. Other cave sediments consist mainly of red clay carried in from the surface, except that the basal bed is composed of residual material left from dissolution of the limestone. The nature of the sediments shows that the cave was not open directly to the surface during its earliest phase of development. Paleomagnetic dating of cave sediments (Chapter 13), and correlation with the local history of mountain uplift, suggests that cave development began about 4–7 million years ago.

The map of Cave of the Winds (Figure 8.52) shows the same kind of irregular fracture-guided pattern as the thermal caves of Budapest, such as the one illustrated in Figure 8.48. Those caves have also been attributed to mixing between deep thermal water and shallow meteoric water (Müller, 1974). That mode of origin can explain the absence of deep fissures that would otherwise be expected in thermal caves. Timpanogos Cave, in the Wasatch Mountains of Utah, is also considered to have formed by this process (Herron, 1998).

Mixing between hot and cold water is sometimes cited as a mechanism for increasing the aggressiveness of water. But this process actually *decreases* the ability of the water to dissolve limestone and dolomite (pages 123–124). If mixtures of hot and cold water are to form caves, there must also be a suitable chemical contrast.

Our understanding of the deep subsurface is limited, and drilling often reveals strange and unexpected features. For example, several boreholes in Precambrian marble in Bulgaria encountered a giant water-filled void more than 1340 m in vertical extent (V. Dublyansky, 2000). The top of the void lies about 600–800 m below the surface. The water is sulfate-rich and increases in temperature with depth from 90°C to 130°C. The deep water is prevented from boiling by its high pressure. There is no evidence that high temperatures alone were responsible for the void.

Dissolution by H₂S-rich water

Most hydrogen sulfide is generated beneath the water table by reduction of sulfate, either from dissolved gypsum or anhydrite, or from sea water trapped in sedimentary pores. Organic carbon is usually necessary to reduce the sulfate, so the process is common in petroleum reservoirs. Reduction can also take place in the sediment deposited on the floors of oceans and lakes. In addition, sulfur and sulfides are produced by the alteration of certain igneous rocks and are common volcanic emissions. Sulfur isotopes can help to distinguish the various H₂S sources (page 129).

When dissolved in water, hydrogen sulfide (H_2S) is a mild acid. But the water in which it forms tends to be already saturated with calcite, so the H₂S-rich water usually starts with no cave-forming potential at all. Nevertheless, if this water flows elsewhere and mixes with water that contains little or no H_2S, the mixture may become undersaturated and dissolve more carbonate rock (Palmer, 1991). This process can take place even if both water sources are initially saturated with calcite or dolomite (Chapter 5), but it requires a closed system that retains any CO_2 generated by the reaction between H_2S and carbonate rocks.

Deep mines and wells sometimes intersect fissures and pockets that release the obnoxious rotten-egg smell of H_2S (Warwick, 1968), and these isolated openings were probably formed by mixing of waters of contrasting H_2S content. The few naturally accessible caves with this origin have almost certainly been enlarged and modified at a later time by other processes at shallow depths.

H_2S can also react with dissolved metals, such as iron, to produce sulfide ores. Acid is released by this reaction, and carbonate rocks can dissolve as a result. Although no significant caves have been attributed to this process, it apparently accounts for much of the porosity encountered by the mining of sulfide ores. Further details are given in Chapter 15.

The greatest cave-forming power of H_2S is achieved when it oxidizes to sulfuric acid, as described below:

Sulfuric acid caves

Of all hypogenic caves, those formed by sulfuric acid are the most spectacular. Probably no more than 5% of all known caves have this origin, but they include Carlsbad Cavern and Lechuguilla Cave in New Mexico (DuChene and Hill, 2000), the Frasassi Cave System in Italy (Galdenzi and Menichetti, 1995), and Kap-Kutan Cave in Turkmenistan (Maltsev and Korshunov, 1998), all of which are known for their size, complexity, and lavish mineral decoration. Most known sulfuric acid caves are now inactive. Few caves of this type are both active and accessible. It is likely that many more caves have been affected by sulfuric acid than have yet been recognized.

Origin of sulfuric acid caves

Nearly all sulfuric acid caves are formed when hydrogen sulfide rises from depth and is oxidized at or near the water table. These caves have a variety of patterns. Many are ramifying and consist of irregular rooms and mazes with passages branching outward from them, commonly in several overlapping tiers (Figure 8.53). Their maps resemble the splatter of raw eggs dropped from a great height. Some passages are horizontal and others are steeply sloping rifts or tubes. Branches do not converge as tributaries, but instead serve as distributary outlets at successively lower elevations as the regional base level drops. Some sulfuric acid caves, or parts of them, have network or spongework patterns or consist simply of a few intersecting fractures widened by dissolution. A few consist of tubes that terminate upstream in narrow inlets that supply H_2S-rich water (Figure 8.54). Irregular passage cross sections and blind terminations are common, as are solution pockets, domed ceilings, and cupolas. In contrast

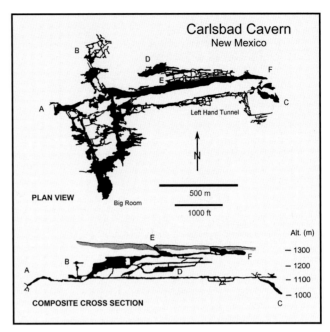

Figure 8.53: Map and profile of Carlsbad Cavern, New Mexico, a cave formed by sulfuric acid. Letters show relation between map and cross section. E = entrance. Courtesy of Cave Research Foundation and National Park Service.

with caves of thermal or mixing origin, many sulfuric acid caves contain passages with roughly horizontal floors in well-defined levels. Like most hypogenic caves, they usually tend to have little or no relation to surface karst features.

Figure 8.55 shows the typical processes and geologic setting for sulfuric acid cave origin. Hydrogen sulfide is generated mainly where sulfate rocks (gypsum or anhydrite) are in contact with sources of organic carbon, such as petroleum. See Chapter 5 for the chemical details. If the surrounding rocks are mainly detrital, especially shale, much of the H_2S is consumed by reactions with metals, such as iron, to produce solid sulfides. Therefore the production of H_2S suitable for cave origin is most effective in chemical sedimentary rocks. H_2S is more soluble in water than most other gases (Figure 8.56), so it normally remains in solution rather than forming bubbles, unless the concentration is high and the water depth is small. Some H_2S can be absorbed by bubbles of other less-soluble gases to form mixtures. These bubbles can rise through water because of their lower density, but

Figure 8.54: Inlet for H_2S-rich water in Lower Kane Cave, Wyoming. White mats of sulfur-oxidizing bacteria line the stream bed.

Figure 8.55: A typical setting for the origin of sulfuric acid caves. Deep flow of oxygen-rich water may be scant or absent, so that nearly all dissolution takes place at or near the water table. Enlargement by sulfuric acid also occurs in air-filled parts of the cave where H_2S and oxygen are absorbed by moisture on bedrock surfaces.

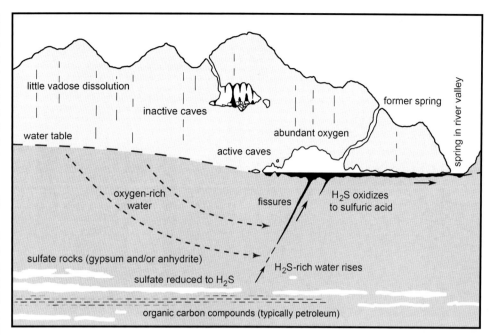

they tend to become trapped where pores are small.

Sulfide-rich water can rise to surface springs where there is an upward hydraulic gradient. This is common where groundwater is fed by recharge areas at higher elevations, flows downward below the water table, and rises beneath river valleys (Figure 4.1). Water can also rise from depth where it is heated by igneous processes, or when it is released from sediments that are under pressure from overlying strata, but contributions from these sources tend to be small.

When this water encounters oxygen, the dissolved H_2S begins to oxidize to sulfuric acid, often with sulfur as an intermediate step (Reactions 5.17–5.19). Certain sulfur-oxidizing bacteria can speed the reactions or bypass the sulfur step. Sulfuric acid attacks limestone, dolomite, and marble, but rock salt is not affected. Gypsum and anhydrite are essentially unaffected by sulfuric acid except at pH values less than about 2 (page 119).

The aggressiveness from sulfuric acid is produced right at the location where the cave is forming, and therefore the flow distances are small. The large ratio of discharge to flow length helps to account for the maze patterns that are common in sulfuric acid caves. In systems with large discharge, rooms with ramifying branches reflect the overall flow pattern.

Oxygen is most abundant in the open air (for example, in the cave atmosphere). The greatest dissolution rate is at or near the water table, as shown by the fact that many cave rooms and passages are widest at the present or former levels of cave

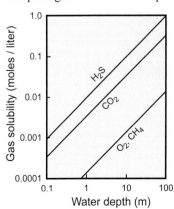

Figure 8.56: Solubility of several gases in water at various depths below the water table, at 25°C (Palmer and Palmer, 2000). **Example:** at a water depth of 10 m the solubilities are: H_2S = 0.1 mole/L, CO_2 = 0.034 mole/L, O_2 and CH_4 (methane) = 0.0013 mole/L. At those concentrations, some of the gas will escape as bubbles as the water rises past a depth of 10 m.

streams. But most of the cave *volume* is produced *above* the water table. H_2S gas escapes from the streams and is absorbed, along with oxygen from the cave air, by water films and droplets on the cave walls. This moisture comes either from infiltration or from condensation on the cave walls. The uptake of oxygen is much faster than in standing or flowing water bodies. The two dissolved gases react to form sulfuric acid, which quickly attacks the limestone or dolomite bedrock.

The build-up of sulfate from the acid, plus the calcium from the carbonate rock, is often great enough to force gypsum to precipitate on the bedrock surface (Figure 8.57). This is often referred to as ***speleogenetic gypsum***. It can even replace the original bedrock so that it inherits the original rock textures (Queen, 1973; Buck, 1994). Sulfuric acid that forms on the gypsum tends to seep by diffusion to the adjacent bedrock surface, where dissolution continues. Meanwhile, blocks and granules of gypsum fall to the floor and may be dissolved by the cave stream. This process is sometimes known as ***replacement solution*** (Egemeier, 1973).

Oxidation of H_2S can also take place beneath the water table where fresh groundwater mixes with sulfide-rich water. As water infiltrates from the surface, it loses much of its dissolved oxygen by reactions with organic compounds in the soil, so the potential for oxidizing H_2S is diminished. In dry climates, however, where the soil is thin and low in organics, the water retains more oxygen than in humid regions (Winograd and Robertson, 1982).

Below the water table, oxidation of H_2S is concentrated along a few major fracture zones. These fractures serve as the most efficient paths for both the rising sulfide-rich water and the shallower fresh water, so it is natural that these two solutions should converge and mix, like traffic merging from several directions into a single lane. The mixing process involves diffusion of H_2S and oxygen throughout the water, from where the concentrations of dissolved gases are highest

Figure 8.57: Scene in the Chandelier Maze, Lechuguilla Cave, New Mexico. Note the spongework pattern and the white gypsum deposits formed by the reaction between sulfuric acid and limestone.

to where they are least concentrated. Any turbulence in the water is an even more powerful mechanism for mixing of the two dissolved gases.

Because dissolved oxygen becomes less abundant with depth, the rate of sulfuric acid production increases upward toward the water table. Where deep mixing has been possible, sulfuric acid caves contain fissures in their floors that become narrower downward. In caves that are now dry, the fissures pinch out several tens of meters below the former water table. They are now partly choked with carbonate minerals and sediment. Good examples can be seen in caves of the Guadalupe Mountains, New Mexico (Figure 8.58).

Sulfide-rich water that enters a cave is already close to saturation with calcite and dolomite. When the H_2S oxidizes to sulfuric acid, there can be a substantial increase in the solubility of these minerals (Figure 8.59). Carbon dioxide is generated when limestone or dolomite is dissolved by sulfuric acid, and dissolution is greatest if the CO_2 is retained in solution. If some of the CO_2 escapes into the atmosphere the capacity for dissolution is less, or even negligible (dashed lines in Figure 8.59). The higher the P_{CO_2} of the cave atmosphere, the less CO_2 is lost. Where the concentration of atmospheric CO_2 is low, for example around entrances, the additional solubility caused by the production of sulfuric acid can be small and perhaps negligible.

Oxygen is most abundant if there is air exchange with the surface through entrances and other openings. But then the CO_2 level will be low and the capacity of sulfuric acid to dissolve carbonate rock decreases. Perhaps the ideal compromise is a cave with no entrances, and with dissolved oxygen carried in by fresh water from the surface. Although oxygen has a low solubility (Figure 8.56), its supply at the surface is essentially unlimited. Water retains much of its dissolved oxygen if it passes through fissures that allow rapid infiltration.

As sulfuric acid caves enlarge, there is an increasing tendency for H_2S to be released into the cave air,

and eventually to be lost to the surface through vadose passages, skylights, and fissures. H_2S is denser than normal air, so it does not convect upward on its own, but it can move by diffusion and by air currents generated by the high temperature and humidity around the cave streams. The most powerful mode of transport, however, is air movement by barometric winds (Chapter 12). Whenever the outside pressure decreases, air moves out of the cave and carries H_2S with it. In passages or fissures that ascend to the surface, any moisture on the walls will absorb H_2S and O_2, which form sulfuric acid. As these openings enlarge, they may eventually become traversable entrances.

When H_2S escapes from cave streams it leaves behind all the dissolved minerals in the water. When it is absorbed by

Figure 8.58: A fissure in the floor of the Left Hand Tunnel, Carlsbad Cavern, New Mexico. This was a former inlet for H_2S-rich water. Oxidation to sulfuric acid at the former water table produced the horizontal passage at the top. This rift is only about 10 m deep, but some in nearby caves reach depths of more than 50 m.

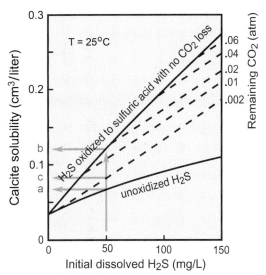

Figure 8.59: Change in calcite solubility when H_2S in solution oxidizes to sulfuric acid (Palmer, 1991). The initial carbon dioxide level in the water is assumed to be 0.001 mole/L (P_{CO_2} ~0.6 atm). Effects of other components are ignored. **Example:** A solution with 50 mg/L H_2S can hold a maximum of 0.065 cm^3/L dissolved calcite (point **a**). If all the H_2S oxidizes to sulfuric acid with no loss of CO_2, the water can hold up to about 0.12 cm^3/L of calcite (point **b**). If the cave air has a P_{CO_2} of 0.002 atm, the water can hold only about 0.08 cm^3/L of calcite (point **c**). See Figure 5.3 for a comparison with dissolution in a simple CO_2 system.

moisture droplets or films above the water table, it is able to expend its full solutional potential on the carbonate rock. As it oxidizes to sulfuric acid, its potential to dissolve increases even more. That is why so much of the volume of a sulfuric acid cave is produced above the water table.

In sulfuric acid caves, passages that discharge water to the surface tend to diminish in cross-sectional area in the downstream direction. Part of the reason is that the water becomes less aggressive as it reacts with the carbonate rock, while the generation of acid decreases as H_2S becomes more dilute in the direction of flow. Another reason is that the atmospheric carbon dioxide may decrease in the same direction because of loss through entrances. Variations in discharge with time are small in most sulfuric acid caves, and there tend to be no floodwater surges to carry water rapidly through the outlet passages and to produce more uniform cross sections.

In H_2S-rich cave streams exposed to air, the water is essentially neutral, with pH values around 7.0 to 7.3. Although sulfuric acid is generated in the water, the reaction with local carbonate rock neutralizes most of it. Where the sulfide-rich water first emerges into the caves the pH tends to be lower (usually about 6.3–6.8) because of the high CO_2 content typical of water from deep sources. CO_2 is less soluble than H_2S (Figure 8.56) and as the water enters an air-filled cave, much of the CO_2 is lost to the cave atmosphere and the pH rises.

The pH can decrease greatly if sulfuric acid is produced in locations that are shielded from carbonate rock by a non-carbonate material, such as gypsum, clay, or chert. Biofilms

on rock surfaces also provide an effective shield, especially where organic filaments hang from the ceiling (Figure 10.72). In water droplets that linger on these surfaces for a long time, hydrogen sulfide and oxygen are absorbed and react to form highly concentrated sulfuric acid. As the gases are consumed by this reaction, more of them are absorbed by the water. Sulfuric acid is extremely soluble, and this process can continue until the pH drops below 1.0 or even to negative values. These solutions are often stronger than battery acid.

Sulfuric acid that forms on or in gypsum may be limited in strength, because at pH values less than about 2, the acid is moderated by Reaction 5.21. Some gypsum crystals show visible rounding in photomicrographs. But organic films may coat the gypsum and shield it from the reaction. As the droplets of water that hang from biofilms or gypsum surfaces become more acidic, the dissolved load increases. Such concentrated solutions allow water vapor from the air to be absorbed more readily, so that the droplets grow with time and eventually fall to the floor. Where the acid drips onto carbonate rock they form rills and potholes (Figure 8.60).

Almost all speleogenetic gypsum forms above the water table. It can also form under water, but much more rarely, and few caves probably contain gypsum that formed in this way. For gypsum to form in a mixture of fresh water and sulfide-rich water, both must already be close to saturation with gypsum. The solubility of oxygen is about 100 times less than that of H_2S, which limits the potential for sulfide oxidation. Production of sulfuric acid would boost the sulfate content of the water, and dissolution of bedrock by the acid would provide more calcium. These additional ingredients could drive gypsum to supersaturation, but even under the best of conditions only a tiny amount of gypsum would precipitate. Still, over a long time, this process might have a cumulative effect. Evaporation from the water surface can speed the process. But most underwater gypsum forms where existing gypsum falls off the cave walls into pools and recrystallizes.

Figure 8.60: Potholes in the Eastern Branch of Lechuguilla Cave, New Mexico, formed by sulfuric acid draining from former gypsum deposits above.

Figure 8.61: Masses of gypsum that accumulated on cave floors during sulfuric acid speleogenesis are readily dissolved by dripping water (Grotta del Vento, Italy). The gypsum is the white corroded mass in the center.

Gypsum can build massive deposits on cave floors. Even after a cave ceases to enlarge by sulfuric acid, its gypsum can be dissolved by vadose water. Incoming seepage, though usually saturated with dissolve calcite, is highly aggressive toward gypsum and dissolves vertical holes through it (Figure 8.61). Gypsum that is dissolved by seepage at one location in a cave can easily be reprecipitated elsewhere by evaporation. The striking gypsum speleothems in certain sulfuric acid caves are formed in this way (see, for example, Figure 10.59).

Sulfuric acid can alter clay minerals to byproducts such as alunite (Chapters 5 and 12). These minerals can be used as evidence for sulfuric acid speleogenesis. The alteration process also releases silicic acid (H_4SiO_4), which precipitates as opal or quartz, either as linings on bedrock or mineral surfaces, or as pore fillings. An abundance of any of these minerals is a clue that sulfuric acid may once have been present.

Sulfur isotopes in water and minerals can be used to interpret the sulfur sources. For example, speleogenetic gypsum tends to have negative $\delta^{34}S$ values, and gypsum that is deposited in seawater has positive values (Chapter 5). If this marine gypsum is dissolved and re-precipitated elsewhere by evaporation, the sulfur isotope ratio will still be positive. Gypsum that is precipitated from oxidation of H_2S or pyrite tends to have negative values because they are byproducts of sulfate reduction. If water contains dissolved sulfate from both a marine source and from sulfide oxidation, the sulfur isotopes will have intermediate values.

A major contrast between sulfuric acid speleogenesis and the epigenic variety, besides their obvious chemical differences, is that the supply of rising H_2S is limited, intermittent, and fairly localized. The CO_2 that drives epigenic cave origin is ubiquitous at the land surface, available to all infiltrating water, and continually renewed. The flow of CO_2-rich water from the surface is abundant enough to sustain cave development over long distances through entire aquifers. Although sulfuric acid caves can be large and complex, they tend to be fairly local.

Stern and others (2002) point out that despite all the documented bacterial activity in sulfuric acid caves, it is still not clear how much of the speleogenesis can be attributed to it, in comparison to oxidation of sulfide with no microbial influence.

Examples of sulfuric acid caves

The first detailed study of active sulfuric acid cave origin was made by Egemeier (1973, 1981) in Lower Kane Cave, Wyoming (Figure 8.54). This is a single large unbranching stream passage fed at the upstream end by several narrow water inlets that contain about 6 ppm H_2S. Oxidization of the dissolved gas to sulfuric acid has formed the cave at the same level as the local Bighorn River, to which it drains. A few earlier authors had written on the subject, in particular Principi (1931) in a work on cave hydrology in Umbria, Italy, but these early works were not very detailed or widely read, so they did not have the impact they deserve.

Among the first caves of this type to be examined by biologists were Parker Cave, Kentucky (Thompson and Olson, 1988) and Movile Cave in southeastern Romania (Sarbu and others, 1996). Sulfur-oxidizing bacteria in H_2S-rich caves serve as the base for a complex food chain that typically includes other microbes, as well as snails, insects, spiders, and, less commonly, cave fish (Hose and others, 2000).

In Lower Kane Cave, Engel and others (2004) show that sulfide-rich cave streams lose H_2S gas most rapidly over bacterial mats. About 8% of the total H_2S escapes into the atmosphere. Although the bulk of the cave water is saturated or slightly supersaturated with calcite, the surfaces of carbonate bedrock are etched by dissolution where they are in contact with the filamentous mats. Barton and Luiszer (2005) show that in sulfide-rich cave streams it is possible to have partial reduction of sulfate and iron, followed by oxidation to sulfuric acid (see Chapter 12).

Among active sulfuric acid caves, Cueva de Villa Luz in Tabasco, Mexico, may best illustrate this kind of cave origin (Figure 8.62; Hose and others, 2000). It is fed by many narrow inlets, some of which contain more than 300 ppm of dissolved H_2S. The cave has a two-dimensional spongework pattern with a faint resemblance to the braided stream character of an anastomotic cave. Hydrogen sulfide gas in the cave air reaches dangerously high levels of up to 200 ppm. The main cave stream is white with suspended

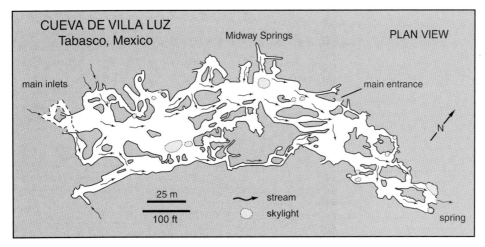

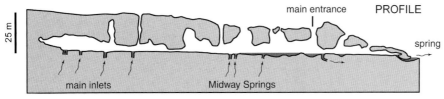

Figure 8.62: Map and profile of Cueva de Villa Luz, Tabasco, Mexico, a sulfuric acid cave with a two-dimensional spongework pattern. Simplified from map by Hose and others (2000).

colloidal sulfur (Figure 8.63). Gas masks are standard equipment in this cave (Figure 8.63).

As in Lower Kane Cave, the strongest sulfuric acid is generated in water droplets on the walls and ceiling. Most of the exposed limestone has acquired a rind of crystalline gypsum, which shields the limestone and prevents the acid from being neutralized. Measurements of water droplets show pH levels as low as zero. Slow drips that linger a long time in this atmosphere become so acidic that they can burn skin and eat holes in clothing. The energy released by the reaction sustains abundant sulfur-oxidizing bacteria, whose filaments coat the streambed and hang from the walls and ceiling. They form flexible, rubbery speleothems with the consistency of mucus (Figure 10.72). Patchy deposits of elemental sulfur

form around the H_2S-rich water inlets (Figure 8.64).

Water that rises from the Earth's mantle contains high helium isotope ratios, $^3He/^4He$ (Newell and others, 2005). By analyzing dissolved helium, argon, and nitrogen gases in the water of Cueva de Villa Luz, Spilde and others (2005) conclude that about 6% of the water comes from this deep source, and that the rest is from shallow meteoric water. Negative $\delta^{34}S$ values show that H_2S in the cave is apparently derived from reduction of sulfate rocks. In contrast, nearby volcanic sources of H_2S have $\delta^{34}S$ values of about +4‰.

The Frasassi Cave System, at the eastern margin of the Apennine Mountains in Italy, is one of Europe's best-known show caves (Figure 8.65; Galdenzi and Menichetti, 1995; Galdenzi and Maruoka, 2003). It contains a stream system with active sulfuric acid enlargement (Grotta del Fiume, or River Cave) connected to nearby higher levels that are no longer actively forming (Grotta del Viento, or Wind Cave). The upper level includes large well-decorated rooms that are open to the public.

The caves are developed in medium-bedded, folded and faulted Jurassic limestone. They are concentrated around the faulted borders of uplifts where hydrogen sulfide is able to rise from depth. Passages have irregular profiles and cross sections but their overall patterns are fairly horizontal. They cut across local geologic structures and are clearly adjusted to present and past levels of the local river. The H_2S concentration in the main cave stream is approximately 18 ppm, and

Figure 8.63: The main stream passage of Cueva de Villa Luz. Although this is an active sulfuric acid cave, this water has a nearly neutral pH because of the reaction with the limestone bedrock.

Figure 8.64: Sulfur deposits line the walls of an H_2S-rich inlet, Cueva de Villa Luz. These include rare sulfur folia in the center of the photo (see Chapter 10).

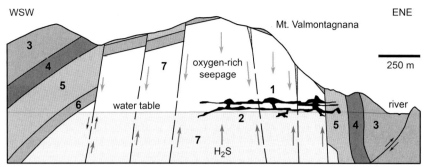

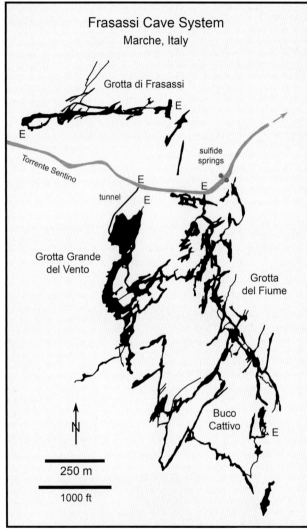

Figure 8.65: Map and profile of the Frasassi Cave System, Italy. Grotta del Fiume is the active stream level, which contains H₂S-rich water. It is connected to Grotta Grande del Vento, an inactive upper-level show cave. The other caves are also dry upper levels. E = major entrance. On profile, 1 = Grotta del Vento, 2 = Grotta del Fiume, 3 and 5 = cherty limestone, 4 = marl, 6 = low-permeability limestones, 7 = highly permeable Massiccio Limestone. (After Galdenzi and Menichetti, 1995).

moisture on bacterial strands above the stream has pH values less than 1.0. Thick masses of gypsum have accumulated in many passages, especially in the upper levels, from the reaction between the acid and carbonate bedrock (Figure 8.61). The H₂S source is apparently reduction of gypsum

beds below the limestone. Vlasceanu and others (2000) have identified sulfur-oxidizing bacteria with RNA analysis.

In a similar geologic setting 90 km to the southeast is the cave system at Acquasanta Terme. It contains a stream with water temperatures up to 40°C that releases H₂S, SO₂, and water vapor into higher levels with temperatures as low as 10°C (Figure 8.46; Galdenzi, 2001).

Some caves contain hydrogen sulfide from sources other than reduction of gypsum or anhydrite. At Cesspool Cave, Virginia, the H₂S is derived from adjacent black shale (Herman and Hubbard, 2002). In the huge water-filled shafts of El Zacatón and similar springs in eastern Tamaulipas, Mexico, the H₂S is derived from nearby volcanic sources (Figure 2.20; Gary, 2002; Gary and Sharp, 2006).

There are many caves no longer forming today that show abundant evidence for a sulfuric acid origin. Caves of the Guadalupe Mountains of New Mexico are the best known (Hill, 1987; Egemeier, 1987; Duchene and Hill, 2000). Their geologic setting is shown in Figure 8.66. Guadalupe caves include Carlsbad Cavern and Lechuguilla Cave (Figures 8.53 and 8.67). The Guadalupes are composed of massive Permian reef limestone that grades northwestward into extensive bedded back-reef limestones and dolomites. The mountains rise above an adjacent lowland (Delaware Basin) that contains thick sulfate rocks and petroleum reservoirs. The basin is considered to be one of several sources for the H₂S that formed the caves (Hill, 1987).

Another possible H₂S source during the early phases of cave development was reduction of sulfate in saline pore water below the freshwater zone (Queen, 1994a). Queen also considers that the initial voids in the Guadalupe caves were formed by mixing at the boundary between the saline water and the shallower fresh water infiltrating into the Guadalupe Mountains, and that sulfuric acid enlargement took place later. This process might offer a mechanism for allowing large amounts of oxygen to enter the system early in its development, so that incoming H₂S could react with it before escaping to springs.

Many of the Guadalupe caves are huge. They stand high above the surrounding plains in a ridge that provides little recharge for oxygen-rich water, and yet there is evidence that acidic water rose hundreds of meters to former springs near the tops of present ridges. DuChene and Cunningham (2006) suggest that the recharge area to the west was once much larger, and that after the caves formed, most of it dropped below the present level of the Guadalupes by faulting (see page 360).

The largest rooms and passages in the Guadalupe caves formed wherever H₂S emerged at the water table. Passage relationships are complex, however, and many large rooms and galleries are connected by narrow constrictions (Figures 8.53 and 8.68). H₂S-rich water rose along different routes at different times and caused intermittent episodes of cave development. Because of this non-uniform history of cave

Figure 8.66: Geologic cross section through the Guadalupe Mountains of New Mexico and Texas. Most of Carlsbad Cavern is located in the massive Capitan reef limestone. Lechuguilla Cave extends mainly through the Seven Rivers, Queen, Capitan, and Goat Seep Formations.

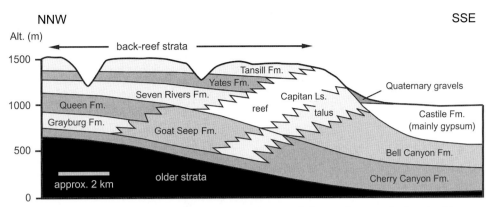

development, many of the major rooms and passages correlate poorly between caves (Palmer and Palmer, 2000).

Spongework and network mazes in Guadalupe caves commonly rim, underlie, or connect rooms Figure 8.57). The mazes were probably formed by highly aggressive water in zones of rapid H_2S oxidation. They may have been enlarged by corrosion where air, rich in H_2S and/or CO_2, was drawn through them by atmospheric pressure differences (Queen, 1994b).

Gypsum is common as massive beds and sheet-like wall coatings in many Guadalupe caves, and some has replaced

the outer surfaces of the carbonate bedrock (Queen, 1973; Buck and others, 1994). The gypsum has negative $\delta^{34}S$ values, which supports the view that the H_2S came from reduction of gypsum or anhydrite beds (Hill, 1987). Unusual minerals in the caves, such as sulfur and rare clay minerals, show the effects of strongly acid environments (Polyak and Provencio, 2001).

Many rooms and passages in the Guadalupe caves have roughly horizontal floors as the result of sulfuric acid

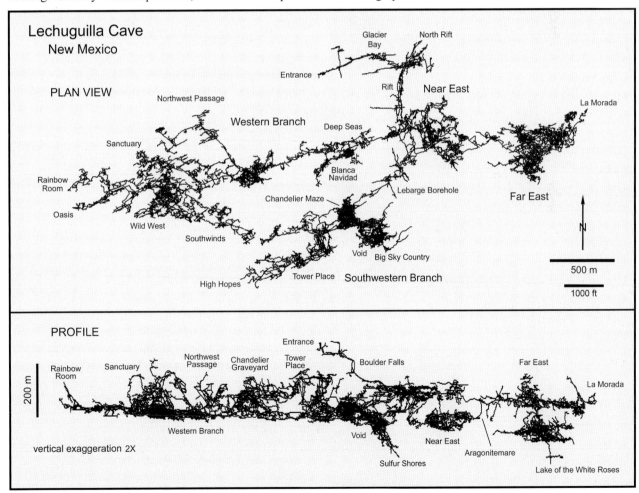

Figure 8.67: Map and profile of Lechuguilla Cave, Carlsbad Caverns National Park, New Mexico. Note rifts in the lower part of the cave, which formerly conveyed H_2S-rich water upward toward the water table; the concentration of maze patterns above them; and the ascending character of higher-level passages toward surface outlets. Map by Lechuguilla Cave Project and Lechuguilla Exploration and Research Network, courtesy of the National Park Service. Only the survey lines are shown here (as in Figure 1.16), because the passage density is so great that even larger parts of the map would be solid black if the full passage widths were shown.

Figure 8.68: The Lebarge Borehole in Lechuguilla Cave is a fairly horizontal tube, but over a distance of about 200 m it pinches to a narrow inlet at one end (originally upstream), and in the other direction it rises as a steep rift that joins a higher passage.

Figure 8.69: Rills in limestone formed by dripping sulfuric acid in the Far East of Lechuguilla Cave. Note the white gypsum rind. This process is no longer active in the cave. Width of photo is about one meter.

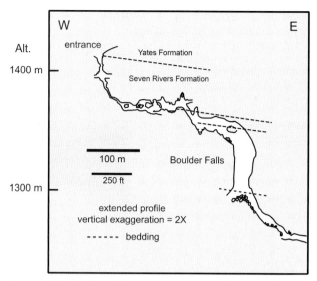

Figure 8.70: Profile of the entrance section of Lechuguilla Cave, which shows the curving, non-vertical walls of shafts formed by ascending water. The passages are roughly concordant to the strata because the rising water was deflected up-dip along the bedding planes. Note the contrast with Figure 6.6.

production at the former water table. In places, deep rills were carved in limestone floors where the acid dripped from gypsum-lined ceilings (Figure 8.69). Although development of the Guadalupe caves by sulfuric acid seems to have ceased, vadose water continues to enlarge them by dissolving the speleogenetic gypsum.

The great vertical relief and many ascending passages of the Guadalupe caves suggest that oxidation of H_2S in the rising water began as much as 200 m below the water table. This required convergence of the rising H_2S-rich water with deeply circulating fresh water that infiltrated from recharge areas at higher elevations. Some ascending passages serve as cave entrances today. Their steep gradients give the false impression that they were formed by vadose streams, but they show no evidence of stream entrenchment, and they contain no scallops, vadose flutes, or coarse detrital sediment. Truly vertical shafts are rare. Instead, at shafts, the ceilings rise in a series of smooth convex-upward arcs that contrast with the abrupt stair-step pattern of vadose passages (Figures 8.70–8.71). Confinement by resistant beds has forced some rising passages to follow up-dip courses. Further details on the geologic influence on Guadalupe caves are given in Chapter 9.

Parker Cave, Kentucky, was not formed by sulfuric acid, but it illustrates the effect of this acid on fresh groundwater from sinking streams. It is a branchwork cave in the Mississippian St. Louis Limestone, with five independent stream passages connected by a floodwater overflow passage (Quinlan and Rowe, 1978). One passage has a small saline tributary containing up to 50 mg/L H_2S, which is apparently fed by upward leakage through an abandoned unsealed oil well. The sulfide-rich water enters through a narrow canyon at the ceiling level of the larger passage into which it drains. The inlet becomes impassably narrow after a few meters.

Figure 8.71: Descending Boulder Falls in Lechuguilla Cave (See Figure 8.70).

The H_2S-rich stream actively deposits crystalline sulfur (Olson and Thompson, 1988). Where the water cascades into the larger passage, white filamentous bacterial mats have accumulated, the largest of which (the Phantom) is about 3 m tall. Several species of sulfur-fixing bacteria have been identified (Thompson and Olson, 1988).

This H_2S-rich water has not formed any major passages by itself, but it provides information on how H_2S and sulfuric acid can affect the chemistry of a freshwater cave stream. The effect over about 100 m of the stream is shown in the following table (calculated from chemical measurements by Roy, 1988):

	pH	SI calcite	SI dolomite	P_{CO_2} (atm)
Upstream:	7.98	+0.67	+0.43	0.0021
H_2S tributary:	7.20	+1.51	+1.28	0.097
Downstream:	6.40	−0.21	−0.53	0.071

At the time of measurement, the main stream and tributary were supersaturated with calcite and dolomite. As a result of H_2S oxidation and the mixing between fresh water and brine, the combined water is acidic and undersaturated with calcite and dolomite. The entrenchment rate of the main passage has increased, but there is no effect on the passage pattern.

In comparison to the examples described in this chapter, few sulfuric acid caves elsewhere have such clear genetic evidence. This is especially so in humid regions, where most of the clues to a former hypogenic origin have been removed by later water flow from the surface. For example, many of the small isolated maze caves in the Appalachian Mountains have puzzling origins because the processes that formed them are no longer active. One of many is Straley's Cave, Virginia, which consists of a small rectilinear maze at a single level, with a deep canyon-like shaft (Douglas, 1964). The shaft has a sloping, irregular profile that extends diagonally downward for about 70 m and terminates in wet mud fill. This pattern resembles that of many caves known to have a sulfuric acid origin. Interpreting the speleogenesis of such caves is a promising topic for the future.

Oxidation of iron minerals

Sulfuric acid can also be produced by oxidation of pyrite (or other sulfides) as shown in Reaction 5.22. Ordinarily the acid produces only local pockets around the original pyrite crystals, often leaving a kernel of iron oxide as a byproduct (Figure 5.7). If this process takes place in the vadose zone, the acid may attack limestone or dolomite vigorously enough to grow gypsum crystals (Figure 12.21). Many gypsum flowers in dry caves are produced in this way.

If pyrite oxidation is rapid, sulfuric acid carried by vadose water can produce local shafts and rills in the rock below. Yellow-red staining from iron oxides and hydroxides is common. Speleogenesis by pyrite oxidation was first described in detail by Morehouse (1968) in small caves in Iowa. A more dramatic example is Queen of the Guadalupes, New Mexico, a fluted shaft system that formed below a concentrated zone of weathered pyrite (Jagnow 1979). In the marble karst of Norway, oxidation of sulfides has taken place along many of the contacts with the insoluble adjacent strata. This process may have promoted cave development in the marble (Lauritzen, 2001).

Brazil's largest cave, Toca da Boa Vista, may have been formed by oxidation of iron sulfides in the local dolomite bedrock (Figure 2.60; Auler and Smart, 2003). The cave has many hypogenic characteristics, including solution pockets and cupolas, a network pattern, a lack of vadose features or scallops, large variations in cross section, and no apparent relationship to surface topography. Bedrock corrosion has produced thin deposits of dolomitic sand. There is apparently no underlying source of hydrogen sulfide, and the cave contains no massive gypsum deposits. The cave is also limited to a single level, which is not typical of a hypogenic maze formed by oxidation of hydrogen sulfide. Elsewhere in the region the dolomite contains stratified sulfide deposits, and although they are absent in the cave walls it is possible that they have been entirely removed by oxidation at and near the water table. Residual iron oxides and hydroxides from this reaction may have been obscured by later condensation corrosion and accumulation of sediment.

Iron carbonate (FeCO$_3$, the mineral *siderite*) is stable only in low-oxygen environments. When oxygen-rich water reacts with it, iron oxide and carbonic acid are produced (Reaction 5.23). Dissolution by the carbonic acid can form caves around the former siderite beds. These caves are mostly small and irregular, with many solution pockets and iron-oxide-rich sediment. They rarely have natural entrances. The best-known caves of this type have been encountered in the Harz Mountains of Germany by iron miners (Kempe, 1982).

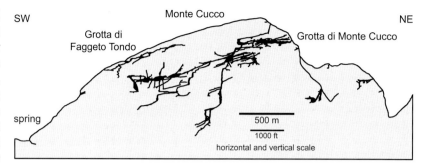

Figure 8.72: Monte Cucco Cave System, Umbria, Italy. Map by Centro Nazionale Speleologia di Costacciaro, and others; after (Menichetti, 1992).

Effects of other deep-seated acids

Igneous and metamorphic processes can release acids at great depth. Alteration of hydrocarbons to petroleum can produce a variety of organic acids (Han, 1993). Oxidation of hydrocarbons in the presence of iron oxides can also yield organic acids (Surdam and others, 1993). Porosity of carbonate rocks in and around oil reservoirs is enhanced by some of these processes, as shown by solution porosity in deep drill cores. Most of these pores are less than a millimeter in diameter.

Although these and similar acids can be important in forming small-scale solution porosity, their role in cave origin is uncertain. One might expect to find traces of these openings in the walls of presently accessible caves, but they seem to have had very little, if any, influence on the patterns of accessible caves. Evidence may have been destroyed by later shallow cave development, but it is also likely that these openings are so deep and localized that they are rarely intersected by later caves.

Polygenetic caves

Some caves are polygenetic — they have experienced more than one type of origin. Most have been modified at different times by several stages of dissolution and deposition, and in some it is difficult even to determine the primary mechanism of cave origin.

Many presently inactive caves in the Apennine Mountains of Italy show evidence for an origin that combines dissolution by meteoric groundwater in combination with sulfuric acid. An example is the Monte Cucco System, which includes one of the longest and deepest caves in Italy (Figure 8.72). Gypsum beds underlie the region and provide the hydrogen sulfide source to actively growing caves farther east at Frasassi (Figure 8.65). Gypsum wall deposits and replacement of limestone are common in the Monte Cucco System, but only in those parts of the cave that are capped by relatively impermeable beds (Figure 8.73). Several of its shafts are more than 100 m deep, but they have corkscrew patterns that show no evidence for an origin by descending vadose water. They were evidently formed by rising water instead.* The cave is located at a high elevation in a humid

climate. Descending vadose water has formed narrow canyon passages and has modified some of the older passages that were formed by sulfuric acid.

Certain caves in the Black Hills and Northern Rocky Mountains have developed over hundreds of millions of years. They have experienced several different modes of origin that include both epigenic and hypogenic processes, in chemical environments that range from simple dissolution to carbonate-sulfate interactions and mixing-zone speleogenesis. Well-known examples include Jewel and Wind Caves in the Black Hills and the Bighorn-Horsethief System in Montana-Wyoming. The complex history of the Black Hills caves is described on pages 354–358.

Influence of climate on caves

Climate has a strong influence on surface landscapes, but its effect on caves is subtle. Climatic karst studies peaked in the mid-1900s (e.g., Lehmann, 1954; Corbel, 1957), but since then many of the effects once thought to be determined by climate have been reinterpreted as mainly the result of local geology and hydrology. For a review of climatic effects on surface karst, see Ford and Williams (1989).

With regard to karst development, the chief climatic variables are precipitation and temperature. Overall dissolution rates depend partly on the amount of precipitation, minus the amount that is lost to evaporation and transpiration

Figure 8.73: A thick rind of gypsum has replaced limestone in this cupola in the Faggeto Tondo Cave, Mt. Cucco, Italy, shows evidence for an origin by sulfuric acid. Ceiling height is about 7 m.

<hr>

* Communication from Marco Menichetti, Gubbio, Italy, 2005.

(Atkinson and Smith, 1976). Climate also affects how fast caves enlarge, but its influence on cave patterns is indirect, as it is limited mainly to controlling the nature of groundwater recharge.

In terms of rock volume that can be dissolved, limestone, dolomite, marble, and anhydrite become less soluble as temperature increases, while gypsum and rock salt become more soluble. All rocks dissolve more rapidly at higher temperatures. Although carbon dioxide becomes less soluble as the temperature rises, more CO_2 is generated in the soil under those conditions, especially in wet climates. The higher levels of CO_2 and organic acids in warm, wet climates offset the negative effect of temperature, so the overall solubility of carbonate rocks is higher than in cold climates. When Reactions 5.3–5.8 all reach equilibrium, the amount of dissolved calcite is proportional to the cube root of the P_{CO_2}. If the P_{CO_2} increases 8 times, it doubles the calcite solubility. Rates of downward lowering of karst surfaces are influenced by P_{CO_2} in the same way (White, 1984).

The description of cave origin in Chapter 7 applies mainly to humid, temperate climates. Caves in climatic extremes are discussed here.

Caves in the humid tropics

There is little significant difference in pattern between caves in the humid tropics and those in temperate climates. Large river caves are more common in the tropics, but mainly because of the great amount of runoff and the presence of thick limestones in favorable positions to absorb it. Tower karst is more common in the tropics than elsewhere, as are small, intricate caves in their bases and relics of older caves in their flanks. Young, porous, seacoast limestones are concentrated in the tropics because limestone is preferentially deposited in warm oceans. As a result, coastal mixing-zone caves are most abundant in tropical climates. The main control over cave patterns in all of these examples is not climate, but the nature of the bedrock and the distribution of recharge and discharge points.

The breakthrough time required for cave inception in the tropics is not significantly different from that in cooler climates. High CO_2 levels decrease breakthrough times, but higher temperatures increase it (Figure 7.22). These divergent effects, both of which are characteristic of the humid tropics, nearly cancel each other. Once a cave enlarges beyond its inception phase, however, it enlarges more rapidly at high temperatures. Intense biological activity in tropical soil also produces a variety of organic acids that contribute to cave origin, but their overall influence is poorly understood (Figure 8.74; Trudgill, 1985).

In cave streams in Belize, Miller (1996) has measured a great increase in P_{CO_2} in the downstream direction, to values as high as 0.05 atm. This gain is due to the addition of water that has seeped through the overlying soil, as well as oxidation of organic material.

But if a cave has considerable air circulation through entrances, infiltrating water loses most of its CO_2 after it

Figure 8.74: The entrances of tropical caves are habitats for a wide variety of plants and animals. The many skylight entrances of Caverna Cuarteles (Tamaulipas, Mexico) are festooned with the roots and vines of strangler figs. Killer bees, scorpions, and snakes add to the tropical ambiance.

enters the cave. In warm, wet climates, where the initial CO_2 levels are high, this water will deposit more calcium carbonate than it would in cooler climates. As a result, many tropical caves are abundantly decorated with speleothems. Spring water is often supersaturated with calcite during low flow because of this CO_2 loss.

Sweeting (1995) and Williams (1997) provide further information on tropical karst.

Caves in cold climates

Cold climates can have considerable influence on cave distribution and patterns, but, as in other climates, the effects are mainly indirect. Soil cover tends to be thin and to have low CO_2 production, and for that reason the underlying caves have few speleothems. Internal runoff from alpine karst tends to be rapid, with relatively little dissolution at the surface or beneath soil, so it is able to form significant caves (Figures 8.75–8.76). In aerated caves there is little tendency for the water to lose CO_2 by degassing.

Cold water can hold more carbon dioxide, as well as more dissolved carbonate rock, than warm water (Chapter 5). Because of this relationship, Corbel (1957) argued that caves can form more readily in cold climates than in warm climates. But he overlooked the positive effects that warm climate and thick soil have in producing carbon dioxide, and today there is little support for his viewpoint. According to Jakucs (1977), the intensity of karst corrosion is twelve times higher in tropical climates than in alpine karst. He also presented data to show that atmospheric CO_2 accounts for roughly 45% of alpine karst corrosion but only 7% in temperate zones.

Runoff from acidic peat bogs in cold climates is very aggressive. It is responsible for surface rates of bedrock retreat up to 0.17 cm/yr in the islands of southeastern Alaska (Allred, 2004). Only a few higher rates have been measured,

Figure 8.75: The Kanin Plateau, along the Slovenia-Italy border, contains some of the world's deepest vertical shafts.

mainly in the humid tropics and in cold, wet climates (Spate and others, 1985). Caves fed directly by this water apparently enlarge at comparable rates.

Caves are rare in very cold climates where the soil is permanently frozen or there is a cover of glacial ice (Ford, 1983, 1987). As snow recrystallizes with time to form ice granules, its carbon dioxide content decreases greatly. Therefore, runoff from snowmelt is poorly aggressive toward limestone and dolomite. This is also true of meltwater from glaciers, particularly at their bases where the water has little contact with the outside atmosphere. The P_{CO_2} in basal meltwater can be as low as 10^{-6} atm, with calcite solubility down to 13 mg/L (Smart, 1981; Lauritzen, 1986). Freezing of glacial meltwater can precipitate thin sheets of calcite and other minerals on bedrock surfaces. Frost wedging in cold climates can clog surface depressions and shallow caves with shattered rock.

According to Lauritzen (1986), the CO_2-depleted water beneath glaciers is unlikely to form new caves, but it can enlarge existing conduits into significant caves if there is a high rate of basal melting . Faulkner (2005) notes that the oldest (highest) cave levels in Scandinavia have a phreatic character, and he suggests that most cave development was initiated by sub-glacial meltwater as glaciers retreated. He considers that the limitation of low P_{CO_2} in the water is off-set by low saturation ratios (C/C_s). He also notes that cave development is proportional to the thickness (and therefore weight) of former ice sheets.

Glacial meltwater can form caves in adjacent soluble rock (Lauritzen, 1986). A fine example is Castleguard Cave, which extends directly beneath the Columbia Ice Field, the largest surviving glacier in Canada (Ford and others, 1983). One of its passages terminates abruptly in an ice plug at the base of the glacier (Figure 2.56). Meltwaters surge through the cave during warm periods and prevent exploration during all but the coldest weather. It is less common for meltwater from continental glaciers to enlarge caves, although Rubin (1991) shows evidence for some examples in the northeastern U.S.

Climates that are only moderately cold offer some advantages to cave development. During the winter, thick snow banks accumulate on the prevailing downwind sides of ridges, which act like snow fences. When the snow melts during warmer seasons, a great deal of water is funneled into underlying and nearby openings. Caves are concentrated where the snow is thickest (Figure 8.76), rather than in windswept areas where it is thin or absent. Runoff from the bare bedrock surfaces of alpine karst delivers rapid groundwater recharge, as there is very little moisture retention by soil. Alpine caves that drain large surface areas are highly flood-prone, and as a result their patterns tend to be complicated by floodwater mazes and injection features. The world's largest alpine cave, Hölloch (Switzerland), contains more than 190 km of mainly anastomotic passages arranged on several crude levels. Short-term rises in water level often exceed 100 m (Bögli, 1970).

The CO_2 content of air decreases with altitude and is as low as 0.0002 atm in some high alpine regions, compared to about 0.00038 atm at sea level. This is not as detrimental to alpine cave development as it might seem, because breakthrough times are shorter at low temperatures. As shown in Figure 7.22, the positive effect of low temperature on the speed of cave inception is greater than the negative effect of low CO_2.

The deepest known caves in the world are located in alpine ranges. Because of the great relief of alpine karst, coupled with high permeability caused by intense fracturing, the water table in many areas lies more than 1000 m or even 2000 m below the land surface. A typical alpine cave consists of a steeply descending series of shafts and canyons with many small vadose inlets fed by bare surfaces of seasonally snow-covered bedrock. Most are branchwork caves, but because exploration and mapping are frequently interrupted by sumps or collapse material, their branching pattern is commonly masked.

The patterns of most alpine caves are controlled by geologic structure rather than climate. Many mountain chains have caves of similar character, regardless of climate. For example, caves in the limestone ranges of eastern Mexico have patterns very much like those in much colder alpine regions. A major difference is that the thicker soil in warm climates focuses groundwater recharge into fewer but larger inputs than those in alpine regions.

Erosion by alpine glaciers can be much more rapid than stream erosion in similar locations. In the Canadian Rockies, Shuster and others (2005) estimate the difference to be 6 times. Alpine glacial erosion can truncate the headwaters of pre-glacial caves and turn the caves into isolated fragments that seem to have little relation to present drainage patterns. For example, the complex Dent de Crolles System in France is an example that is perched high in a towering plateau (Lismonde, 1997). Many of its largest passages terminate headward at steep limestone cliffs, because their original catchment areas have been eroded away (Figures 3.46 and

Figure 8.76: Snowmelt enlarges sinkholes and underlying caves in alpine karst, Bob Marshall Wilderness, Montana.

13.27). The original passages, of late Tertiary age, were later modified by Pleistocene glacial meltwater.

Of all aspects of cold climate, continental glaciation has the greatest effect on solution caves. This influence is worldwide and extends well beyond the limits of glacial cover. As glaciers expand and retreat, sea level drops and rises in response to changes in the amount of water that is temporarily stored as ice. Glacially induced sea-level changes have considerable effect on river erosion and deposition. Many deep stages of cave development have been followed by later flooding or sediment fill as the result of glacially influenced sea-level fluctuations, depression and rebound of continents, and erosional-depositional episodes (Chapter 2). Carbonate island karst is affected most of all, as described on pages 209–212.

Caves rarely occupy more than a small percentage of the total rock volume and so are fairly resistant to crushing by the weight of glacial ice. Glacial deposits tend to choke preglacial cave entrances and surface fissures, as well as some lower levels of caves, but most caves survive fairly intact. This is true even where ice caps once reached 1–2 km thick, as in Ontario, New York, and northern Britain (Mylroie and Mylroie, 2004).

Where there is a cover of thick glacial sediment, surface runoff tends to be channeled into fewer but larger inputs. The effect is similar to that of thick soil in non-glaciated karst areas. Glacial sediment can block cave entrances, but where it is partially removed by underground channels it can enhance the size of surface depressions. Most glacial deposits are clay-rich and have low permeability. By perching surface water, these deposits can produce deranged drainage consisting of swampy land and wandering streams. Such drainage can overlie preglacial caves with little evidence for a hydrologic connection (Figure 9.45). In parts of the north-central U.S., pre-glacial karst and caves have been buried beneath tens or even hundreds of meters of glacial sediment, to produce flat, nearly featureless plains. Whether the underlying caves have survived intact is unknown.

Caves in arid climates

Karst processes are greatly subdued in arid climates (Jennings, 1983). On the other hand, highly soluble rocks such as gypsum and rock salt tend to be exposed over large areas because of the generally dry conditions (Figures 3.20–3.22). Caves can be formed in these rocks by the intermittent and flashy runoff typical of these regions. The best examples in North America are the broad gypsum plains that cover parts of Texas, New Mexico, and Oklahoma.

Carbonate rocks resist weathering in arid climates, where they tend to form ridges and cliffs more readily than in humid climates. Soil is thin and rocky and is often cemented with calcium carbonate (*calcrete*) that precipitates as water evaporates from the surface. The epikarst is poorly developed and sinkholes are rare, but karst features surviving from earlier humid climates can be preserved for a long time. Deep regional-scale groundwater flow is common in arid karst (Ford and Williams, 1989).

By subduing near-surface cave development, a dry climate allows deep-seated processes to operate with little interference. Carbon dioxide and organic acids are in short supply in the soil, and the effects of deep-seated acids tend to dominate. Most caves in the arid ranges of the southwestern U.S. were produced in this way (Figure 8.77). Deep-seated processes are also present in humid climates, but they are commonly overwhelmed by the effects of shallow groundwater rich in carbonic acid. The oxygen content of groundwater in dry climates is generally greater than in humid climates (Winograd and Robertson, 1982). As a result, oxidation of sulfides at depth tends to be favored by dry climates.

Many caves in dry climates contain abundant dripstone and flowstone, despite the dry conditions at the surface. Although these speleothems are often attributed to former wetter climates, many are still active today. Most of those in Carlsbad Cavern are dry, partly because the cave is well aerated. In nearby Lechuguilla Cave, which has only a single small entrance, nearly all speleothems are actively growing today. Water dripping into these caves has

Figure 8.77: Cave entrance in a semi-arid climate (Carlsbad Cavern, New Mexico).

CO_2 partial pressures as high as 0.01 atm. Although the soil is thin, dry, and patchy, it apparently supports considerable biological CO_2 production. Because the P_{CO_2} in the cave air is only about 0.001 atm, dripwaters lose a large amount of CO_2 and deposit profuse speleothems.

In very arid climates the relative humidity in caves can be below 50%. Crystals of halite (NaCl) can grow in these conditions, and in places they shatter bedrock and speleothems. Inactive caves can fill with windblown sand derived both from the surface and from local bedrock disintegration. Caves of the Nullarbor karst of southern Australia contain many of these features (Figure 2.88; Lowry and Jennings, 1974). These caves apparently formed at or near sea level but are now inactive relics that contain only brackish water.

Caves are large and abundant in salt beds in the Atacama Desert of Chile, which is one of the world's driest places (Fryer, 2005; Walck, 2005). The caves still carry occasional floods and contain logs and branches lodged high in their passages.

Interpretation of cave origin

If a cave is no longer actively forming, its origin may be obscure. This is especially true for caves in paleokarst, or those encountered at great depth below the surface in mines or drillholes. A well-founded cave interpretation helps to reveal past groundwater conditions and geologic events.

The following outline offers clues to cave origin, but they are not foolproof. Any interpretation should also be evaluated by how well it agrees with the local geologic history and with hydrologic and chemical principles. The most likely pattern of recharge and discharge points should be reconstructed. A useful guideline is that nearly all solution caves form along the paths of greatest discharge through the soluble strata. See also the summary of cave patterns in Figure 9.72 (page 270).

Sinkhole recharge

Branchwork caves are diagnostic. Passages emanate directly from a present or past land surface overlying or adjacent to the caves. Scallops are oriented in the direction of passage convergence. Stream-deposited sediment is derived from the overlying surface, and its grain size is compatible with the local passage gradient and scallop size. Vadose passages (canyons and shafts) are usually common, especially as tributary inlets. Most passage junctions are concordant, with floors (but not necessarily ceilings) that merge at the same level. The cross-sectional areas of passages tend to increase systematically in the direction of flow where tributaries enter, with few abrupt changes. Passages may occupy several levels connected by canyons or shafts. No passages have blind terminations (i.e., ending in bedrock) unless superposed by flooding. Dripstone is usually present, except beneath an insoluble cap-rock.

Floodwater

There should be evidence for recharge from sinking streams, backflooding from adjacent rivers, or rapid runoff from a bare rock surface. Most floodwater features are superposed on earlier branchworks. Anastomotic or crude network patterns are common. Sediment can vary from large boulders to fine mud. Some floors may consist of bare bedrock with narrow drains. Scallops are common locally but are usually absent in other areas where floodwaters have ponded. Common features include fracture-oriented ceiling and wall pockets and anastomoses along bedding planes, perhaps with rills below them. Passage gradients are irregular. Many junctions are discordant, with floors and ceilings that do not match in elevation. Abrupt changes in cross-section are common, especially at intersections, as are blind fissure terminations. In some floodwater caves, many fissures intersect in acute angles because of secondary fractures produced by local collapse. Passage levels are indistinct and speleothems are scant. Vegetal debris may be lodged high in passages.

Diffuse seepage from above

There is usually evidence for a present or former insoluble but permeable cap-rock. Caves are concentrated in a single level at the top of the underlying soluble rock. Well-developed fissure networks with perpendicular passage intersections are characteristic. Blind terminations are common. Fine-grained sediment covers most floors, although coarse sediment may have been carried in by backflooding from adjacent rivers. Floors and ceilings are irregular, and many intersections are discordant, although sediment may raise floors to a common level. Scallops are absent and speleothems are rare.

Diffuse seepage into porous limestone rarely forms caves but accounts for much epikarst porosity. Infiltration into numerous fissures produces karren at the surface and, in rare cases, network caves where the infiltrating water becomes perched on insoluble strata.

Diffuse seepage from below

Caves formed in this way are located in present or former groundwater discharge areas, such as beneath former river valleys, and they overlie less-soluble permeable rock. It must be demonstrated that rising water could retain its aggressiveness despite having followed deep flow paths. Caves are concentrated at the base of the soluble rock, but they may extend entirely through to the overlying rock or to the present (or former) land surface. Blind passage terminations are common. Where water has passed upward through the entire thickness of soluble rock into overlying less-soluble strata, extensive network caves are common. Scallops (if any) are only local, and sediment is fine-grained. Narrow floor and ceiling slots may indicate points of input and outflow, with indications of lateral flow between (Figure 8.37). Most such caves are in evaporite rocks.

Seacoast mixing

Caves formed by freshwater-seawater mixing show evidence for an origin in relatively young carbonate rocks along a present or former seacoast. They cluster in horizontal zones that were originally at sea level. Several cavernous zones may be present at different altitudes. Spongework patterns of intersecting rooms with arched ceilings are typical. Floors are irregular in local detail but fairly horizontal overall. Sediments are mainly carbonate sand, although there may be contamination with later sediment. Dripstone and flowstone are (or once were) common. Caves terminate abruptly along the former seacoast. Away from the coast they may finger into dead-end feeder tubes to form crude branchworks. Many cave rooms are tightly clustered, with narrow connections, like beads on a string. They rarely extend to the top or bottom of the soluble rock. Scallops and coarse sediment are absent. Long sinuous passages and anastomotic patterns are common in some seacoast caves, but only where there was aggressive recharge from continental sources, for example in the Yucatán Peninsula and Florida.

Rising thermal water

Caves may extend over a large vertical range but reach maximum size in their uppermost levels. Irregular network patterns are most common, and local spongework may be present. Some caves consist of single enlarged fissures. Sediment is generally fine grained and may include oxidized minerals (iron oxide, etc.) and rare trace elements such as thallium, arsenic, and barium. Speleothems tend to be rare, although there are exceptions in humid regions. Scallops are rare or absent. Passages have highly irregular profiles, cross sections and intersections. Blind passage terminations are common. Dome-shaped rooms and cupolas are typical. Most of these caves are formed by mixing between rising high-CO_2 water and shallow low-CO_2 water. A favorable setting for this kind of flow should be demonstrated. Thermal springs may still be present nearby. Fault zones are ideal for this kind of cave development.

Deep-seated mixing processes

Caves are mainly small isolated pockets with obscure sources of recharge. Many are highly mineralized and most are discovered by mining. Sediment is similar to that of thermal caves or sulfuric acid caves. Scallops are absent. Foul, sulfide-rich water may be detected when they are encountered in mines or by drilling.

Sulfuric acid

Caves have ramiform, network, or spongework patterns. Some large caves contain two or all three patterns. Many have blind fissures (former inputs for H_2S-rich water) that extend downward from the main levels, with bottoms choked by carbonate sediment or carbonate pool deposits. Ceilings have irregular profiles. Blind terminations are common. At a local scale the floors are irregular and may contain spongework, but some floors may be nearly flat over large areas. In large caves, passages tend to ramify outward from large central rooms at one or more distinct levels and diminish in size toward present or former surface outlets. Most entrances are former springs in stream valleys. Sediment is fine grained and consists mainly of weathered carbonate from local bedrock. Gypsum is (or was once) abundant and contains negative ^{34}S isotopic ratios (see page 129). There is abundant evidence for redox reactions and microbial processes. Clay alteration minerals such as alunite, which indicate low pH, are diagnostic. Deep rills may occur in carbonate-rock floors below present or former gypsum crusts. Pool fingers and subaqueous helictites are rare but are also fairly diagnostic.

Where sulfuric acid was produced by weathering of iron sulfide (e.g., pyrite) or iron carbonate, the caves are generally small, irregular, and stained by iron oxide.

9

Influence of geology on cave patterns

CAVE PATTERNS are described in the preceding chapter in terms of groundwater recharge. The main topics of this chapter are the effects of local geology and landscape evolution on solution caves.

Distribution of soluble rocks

The distribution of soluble rocks has the ultimate control over where solution caves are located. The soluble rock must lie in a position that allows groundwater to pass through it easily. This can be achieved in several ways (Figure 9.1).

The most favorable setting for caves is where soluble rock is exposed at the surface, whether or not it is mantled with soil (Figure 9.1a, b). There must also be enough topographic relief to provide the hydraulic gradients necessary for abundant groundwater flow. This is usually achieved through entrenchment of stream valleys. A soil cover enhances cave development by channeling runoff from the surface into a few prominent openings. Where the soil is thick, these points of recharge are larger but fewer. Soil or glacial deposits more than a few tens of meters thick tend to diminish the amount of recharge available for cave development.

Where soluble rocks are exposed over large areas, karst and caves are concentrated along entrenched river valleys. With time, the karst expands away from the valleys, and its headward limits are typically expressed as points where sinking streams disappear underground (Figure 9.1a). In broad karst plateaus, such as those of the east-central U.S., karst may extend over large areas between valleys, with groundwater divides separating individual subsurface drainage basins (Figure 9.1b). But it is common for vadose passages and abandoned phreatic passages to cross present divides and to connect caves that appear from well data to be to be located in entirely independent basins. This phenomenon is important to the understanding of karst hydrology and contaminant transport (Chapter 15).

Some broad areas of exposed soluble rock have few caves. For example, wide lowlands of thick carbonate rock in Virginia lie only slightly above the surrounding river valleys. Because of low hydraulic gradients and limited groundwater recharge, caves are scattered, and small, and are mainly inactive relics. Arid landscapes also tend to contain few caves, except where there is a deep source of acid or where highly soluble rocks such as gypsum are exposed to intermittent runoff.

Neighboring insoluble rock can have either a positive or negative impact on cave development, depending on its relationship to areas of recharge and discharge. Cave development is enhanced where rain and snowmelt collect on large areas of adjacent insoluble rock and form streams that sink where they cross onto soluble rocks. Caves can extend beneath caps of insoluble rock where there is sufficient

through-flow of groundwater, although passage density tends to be smaller beneath the cap-rock than in the adjacent feeder areas where infiltration is abundant (Figure 9.1c). Many of the karst plateaus of Kentucky, Tennessee, and neighboring states possess caves of this type. A good example is the Mammoth Cave System in Kentucky (Figure 1.3). In some regions the karst recharge is limited to small windows in the

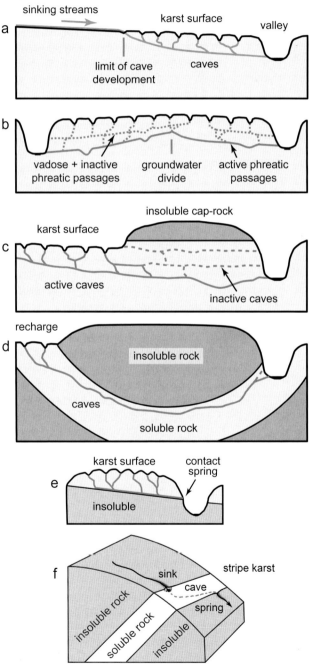

Figure 9.1: Common relationships between caves and the local distribution of soluble rocks. See text for details.

overlying cap-rock, as at Friar's Hole Cave, West Virginia (Figure 8.7). The insoluble cap helps to protect underlying caves from erosional destruction.

The thicker the insoluble cap, and the deeper it extends below base level, the less hospitable the underlying soluble rock is to cave origin. Over short distances it is possible to have deep confined cave development if recharge and discharge points are clearly defined (Figure 9.1d).Where the highly cavernous Mississippian limestones of the eastern U.S. extend beneath the Great Plains, they are covered by sandstones and shales to depths as much as several kilometers. Cave development is no longer active in these buried rocks because there is little or no solutionally aggressive water flow. Nevertheless, in places these rocks contain ancient pre-burial caves, now mostly filled with sediment, and there may also be some scattered hypogenic dissolution.

Where thick insoluble rocks *underlie* cavernous rocks, development of surface karst is not hindered, but caves are limited in depth (Figures 9.1e and 8.26). If the top of the insoluble rock is located above base level, perching of groundwater takes place along that contact. Drainage takes place mainly down the dip to contact springs above valley floors.

In folded strata, soluble rocks may be exposed at the surface only as thin bands. Even where soluble rock is sandwiched between insoluble rocks high on a steep hillside, there may be enough groundwater flow through the soluble rock to form caves (Figure 9.1f). If so, the caves commonly follow the approximate strike of the beds. Springs may be located far above the level of the nearest major entrenched valley. The term **stripe karst** is applied to these thin bands of cavernous rock (Horn, 1947; Lauritzen, 2001).

Where insoluble rocks block the outflow of groundwater, solution caves may be prevented from forming within a geologically feasible time. The presence of a low-permeability barrier may simply promote cave development elsewhere. If soluble rock is bordered by semi-permeable materials, water may seep downward or upward into it, or through the entire sequence. Extensive network mazes can form in this way (Figures 8.27–8.31; 8.35–8.37).

Although karst and caves form most easily in thick uninterrupted sequences of soluble rock, strata as thin at 5 meters are known to contain moderately extensive caves. Examples include those in the thin Pennsylvanian limestones of southwestern Colorado (Medville, 2001). In soluble rocks thinner than 1–2 meters, caves are usually trivial, if present at all (White and White, 2001).

Influence of rock type

The character of the host rock has a dramatic effect on a cave's appearance. The massive light-gray reef limestone of the Guadalupe Mountains contains vaulted rooms with an ethereal cathedral-like aspect. Pleistocene dune limestones of Bermuda and the Bahamas produce nearly white, highly porous cave walls that crumble easily to form unstable breakdown. The Mississippian carbonate rocks of the

east-central U.S. weather in caves to a cheery light gray or golden brown. Impure, dusky-colored Ordovician rocks in Virginia give many caves a somber aspect, and the organic-rich Devonian Manlius Limestone of New York produces nearly black cave walls that swallow light and make these cold caves seem even colder. Rock type also affects the dissolution rate (Chapters 5 and 7).

Limestone caves are the largest and most common types of solution caves and serve as a universal standard. They include the majority of caves described in this book. The effects of other rock types on cave patterns are outlined below.

Caves in dolomite

Most limestone formations contain some dolomite (Figure 9.2). If the dolomite is thick, massive, and pure, karst tends to be subdued and caves sparse, but in some regions there are very large caves in dolomite. Dolomite and limestone have roughly similar solubilities, but dolomite dissolves more slowly, especially as it nears saturation in the solvent water (Chapter 5).

Water from sinking streams is usually highly aggressive and can dissolve dolomite almost as rapidly as limestone. Some large caves in the Rocky Mountains are fed by streams that sink into early Paleozoic dolomites. Caves can also form where sinkholes deliver water directly into dolomite, as in Crevice Cave, Missouri (Figure 8.5). Sulfuric acid can easily form caves in dolomite. There are examples in the Permian back-reef beds in the Guadalupe Mountains of New Mexico, including a few of the passages in Lechuguilla Cave (Figure 8.67). Toca da Boa Vista, South America's longest cave, has also formed in dolomite, apparently by sulfuric acid generated by pyrite oxidation (Auler and Smart, 2003).

But most caves are formed by water that has lost much of its aggressiveness by previous contact with carbonate rock. At high saturation ratios, water does not have much

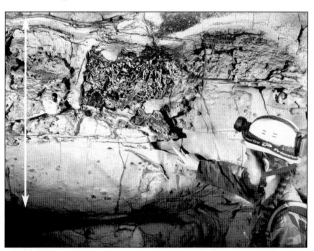

Figure 9.2: A dolomite bed in Mammoth Cave, Kentucky (arrow shows thickness). Like many dolomites, this has a smooth, silty texture and projects outward from the limestone above and below it. The person is pointing to nodules and veins of quartz, which replaced earlier gypsum or anhydrite (an indication that this bed was deposited in an evaporative environment).

Figure 9.3: Geologic cross section through the Kanin Plateau along the Slovenia-Italy border, showing the relation between caves and the contact between Triassic limestone and dolomite. The massive dolomite serves as a stratigraphic barrier to downward cave development. Faults are shown by steep diagonal lines. Along faults bounded by both limestone and dolomite, most cave development is in the limestone. (Synthesis from Audra, 2000; Antonini, 1990; Casagrande and others, 1999; and Komac, 2001.)

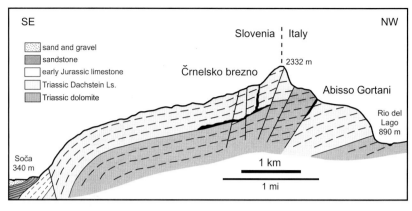

capacity to form caves in dolomite. In limestone caves, beds of dolomite may project slightly from solutional walls (Figure 9.2).

In the eastern Alps, massive, fairly pure dolomite underlies cavernous limestone. By the time groundwater reaches the dolomite, it is able to dissolve this rock only very slowly, far less rapidly than limestone. As a result, few caves extend downward into the massive dolomite, and those that do are narrow and commonly impassable (Figure 9.3).

In mixed limestone-dolomite strata the presence of dolomite may aid cave development. Some dolomite beds are highly fractured, and they provide favorable routes for the initial water flow that eventually forms caves in adjacent limestone strata (Powell, 1970). Also, as shown in Chapter 7, a slow dissolution rate can actually speed the early development of caves by spreading the dissolution throughout long flow paths. These processes may allow caves to form in dolomite where cave origin in other rocks is subdued. Once a cave begins to form, adjacent limestone strata will dissolve more rapidly, and the evidence for cave inception in the dolomite may be obscured.

Caves in evaporite rocks

Evaporite rocks (gypsum, anhydrite, and rock salt) dissolve much more rapidly than other rock types (Navas, 1990). Their high solubility does not necessarily favor cave development, however, because they are exposed mainly in dry climates. They are also soft and deform easily, so fractures and partings are sparse at great depths below the surface. Deep flow of groundwater is inhibited, and most caves in these rocks are shallow. This is not universally true, because isolated voids in gypsum have been encountered in mines hundreds of meters below the surface.

Gypsum is the most cavernous of these rocks (Figure 9.4). Karst in gypsum is described in detail by Klimchouk and others (1996), Calaforra (1998), and Klimchouk and Aksem (2005). Gypsum karst of the U.S. is described by Johnson and Neal (2003) and the gypsum plain of New Mexico by Belski (1992).

Turbulence greatly increases the dissolution rates of evaporite rocks. This effect is much feebler in carbonate rocks. Gypsum is about 100 times more soluble than limestone in distilled water, and in typical groundwater it is still about 10 times more soluble. As water passes through gypsum, the dissolution rate slows abruptly at about 95% saturation

(Dewers and Raines, 1997; Jeschke and others, 2001). This behavior resembles that of carbonate rocks, which show the same effect at lower saturation ratios (Chapter 7). In either rock type, this drop in dissolution rate causes the remaining dissolution to be drawn out over long distances, which greatly favors cave development. Whether other evaporite rocks besides gypsum behave in this way is not yet known.

Anhydrite is even more soluble than gypsum at typical cave temperatures, but karst is rare in anhydrite because it is so sparse at the surface. Russia contains some of the few known caves and karst features in anhydrite. At shallow depths, anhydrite tends to convert to gypsum by hydration. If there is little pressure from overlying rocks, hydration may cause the rock to expand and beds to warp. The same

Figure 9.4: Parks Ranch Cave, New Mexico, is an intermittently active cave located in Permian gypsum. Sudden downpours occasionally flood many of its passages.

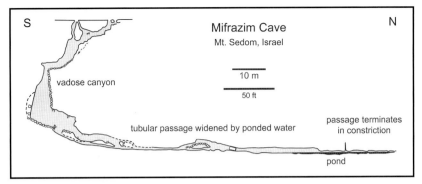

Figure 9.5: Profile of a typical salt cave, Mt. Sedom, Israel, showing an upstream canyon, a downstream tube, and a terminal constriction. Many parts of the lower section have flat roofs and solution bevels formed by standing water, as described on pages 153–154. From Frumkin (1994).

result can be produced by intermittent dissolution and re-precipitation of gypsum at the surface (Calaforra and Les, 2003). Bedding-plane partings and other openings can enlarge in this way, which allows water to pass through more readily.

Because evaporite rocks are structurally weak, most caves in them are small compared to those in carbonate rocks. The huge maze caves in gypsum in the Ukraine have a competent cap-rock of carbonate strata (Figures 8.35–8.37). Dissolution of evaporite rocks is so rapid that many stream caves in these rocks pinch to inaccessibly small openings within a kilometer, usually while still above the water table. The water continues to the spring outlets as diffuse seepage through narrow fissures and pores.

Caves in rock salt are less common than those in gypsum, even though rock salt is several tens of times more soluble. Surface exposures of such rocks as halite (NaCl) are rare, except in very dry climates (Figures 3.21–3.22). Caves in salt form rapidly, and unless the overall climate is very dry, the rock quickly dissolves away entirely.

Among the best-documented salt caves are those in Mt. Sedom, Israel, in the basin of the Dead Sea (Frumkin, 1994), where a salt dome has been forced upward by the pressure of surrounding rocks (a structure known as a *diapir*). Near the surface, fractures and partings are wide enough to allow sinking streams to form caves around the perimeter of the dome. The caves are mainly canyon-like, with a few short shafts. Most of the caves taper to impenetrable constrictions (Figure 9.5). Solution bevels and flat roofs are typical where pools have stood for long times. Stream entrenchment of cave floors has been measured at almost a centimeter per year, with a maximum of 2 cm during a single flood. Dissolved salt concentrations of several hundred grams/liter are common in the cave water. The oldest vegetal matter lodged in the Mt. Sedom caves has been dated at only 7000 years.

At 6.6 km, Iran's 3N Cave is the longest known cave in salt (Bruthans and others, 2006). It is also perhaps the most spectacular known salt cave. It contains many long halite speleothems similar to the gypsum chandeliers in limestone caves (see Figure 10.59). Like the caves of Mt. Sedom, the cave is in a salt dome (diapir). The ceilings and walls contain intensely deformed, multi-colored salt beds that look like the grain in polished wood.

The Atacama Desert of Chile contains hundreds of salt caves formed by sinking streams that are now inactive except during infrequent floods (Fryer, 2005; Walck, 2005). Much of the water sinks, runs through meandering cave passages and exits in the bottoms of surface canyons.

Effects of poorly soluble rock

Thick beds of insoluble rock, such as shale, sandstone, or chert, are normally barriers to cave development. The same is true for relatively soluble rock that has a large insoluble percentage. If thick insoluble beds are sandwiched between soluble rocks, cave-forming water can pass through them only by downward stream erosion or by following major fractures. A high insoluble content of quartz sand offers less resistance to cave development than clay (White and White, 2001).

The highly cavernous Mississippian limestones of West Virginia are interrupted by two major shale beds: the Greenville Shale, 15–20 m thick, and the Taggard Shale, 7 m thick. No caves are known to pass through the Greenville, but the Taggard is breached in many places by caves that follow fractures. At the base of this limestone sequence, more than a hundred kilometers of cave passages are concentrated at the top of the thick underlying Maccrady Shale, which contains only a small percentage of carbonate. Stream erosion has deepened many of these passages as much as 5 meters into the shale, while the limestone roof in many places been dissolved upward only a few centimeters (Figure 9.6).

The main passage of Bohemia Cave, New Zealand, is located in marble at the contact with underlying phyllite, a nearly insoluble metamorphic rock (Tásler and others, 2001). The passage is more than 100 m wide in places, and this

Figure 9.6: Many kilometers of cave passages in West Virginia have formed at the contact between the Hillsdale Limestone and the underlying Maccrady Shale, by vadose streams perched on the shale. In this passage in Ludington Cave, only the ceiling is composed of limestone, and almost all enlargement has been by stream erosion into the shale.

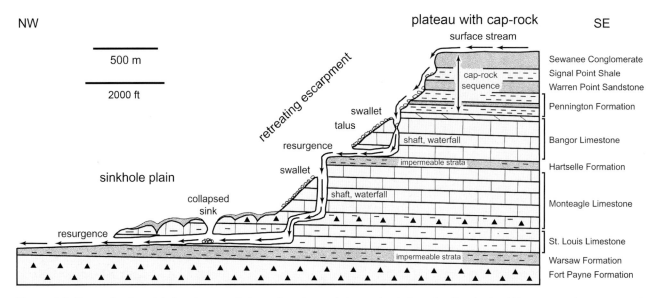

Figure 9.7: Generalized model of underground stream invasion and slope retreat along the Cumberland Escarpment in east-central Tennessee (from Crawford, in Crawford and Vineyard, 1981). Note effect of insoluble strata on cave development.

exceptional cave size is apparently due at least partly to long-term perching of the cave stream on the insoluble rock.

The effect of relatively insoluble beds is well illustrated by cave patterns in Mississippian Limestones along the eroding edge of the Cumberland Plateau in Tennessee (Figure 9.7). Water drains off a thick cap-rock of late Mississippian and Pennsylvanian sandstones and shales, down the face of the escarpment, and into caves in the Bangor Limestone. Where the caves reach the poorly permeable Hartselle Formation, the water resurges along the escarpment face, only to sink again near the top of the underlying Monteagle Limestone. The water passes into the underlying St. Louis Limestone and flows along the top of the shaly Warsaw Formation to springs. There are many local variants on this pattern.

Many caves contain vadose passages in which the original flow was perched on insoluble beds (see examples in Figures 4.4 and 6.13). Even thin crumbly shale beds can have this effect, because the slow seepage that initiates cave origin has virtually no erosive power. These shale beds commonly appear just below the ceiling levels of canyons (Figure 9.8). Shale, if fairly pure, is structurally so weak that it is easily eroded by cave streams. Exposed edges of shale beds tend to crumble into the caves to produce recessed niches (Figures 3.25 and 9.8). Many shafts were formed where vadose water was perched on shaly beds and broke through along joints. The recessed shale beds offer convenient footholds for climbing across the shafts to passages beyond.

Differential solution in cave walls is most conspicuous where nearly pure limestone alternates with beds having more than about 10% insoluble material. The most resistant impure beds project outward as resistant ledges (Figure 6.43).

Chert is abundant in some carbonate strata, and as the rocks weather at the surface, the residual fragments remain as a major ingredient in the soil. Some limestones in Missouri contain so much chert that the weathered fragments clog

sinkholes and other karst features (Figure 9.9). In the underlying caves, fluctuations in groundwater flow are subdued as a result.

Caves can form in soluble rock with a remarkably high percentage of chert — up to roughly 30% — because chert beds are easily broken by fractures that allow water to pass

Figure 9.8: X Pit, in Crystal Cave, Mammoth Cave National Park, is actually not a true shaft but an intersection between two canyons. The initial paths of the water that formed them were perched on shale beds less than a centimeter thick. The arrow points to the shale bed (recessed by weathering) that guided the flow for the canyon in the background.

Figure 9.9: Residual chert fragments in the soil walls of a collapse sinkhole in southwestern Missouri.

from one soluble bed to another. Figure 3.24 shows an example of cave passages that cross thick chert beds.

Deep cave inception in mixed rock types

Karst springs that are fed by deep regional groundwater flow typically have high concentrations of dissolved sulfate (Worthington, 1991). One possible interpretation is that caves are beginning to form deep beneath the surface by oxidation of pyrite along inception horizons (Lowe, 1992). This is a valid concept, although in deep groundwater the oxygen necessary to perform this task is limited. Dissolution of gypsum or anhydrite is a likely alternative, because it does not require dissolved gases from the surface. These sulfate rocks are commonly interbedded with limestone and dolomite, and deep flow systems have been detected in this combination of strata. Krothe and Libra (1983) and

Ash (1984) describe deep groundwater flow in gypsum-rich beds of the St. Louis Limestone of Indiana (Figure 9.10). Hydrogen sulfide also emerges from the springs fed by this water, which indicates that sulfate reduction is taking place somewhere in the system.

Gypsum and anhydrite dissolve so rapidly that groundwater that passes through them usually loses much of its aggressiveness over short distances. This is not always the case. In a mixture of carbonate and sulfate rocks, the various rock types interact with one another as they dissolve. As dolomite and sulfates dissolve, calcite is forced to precipitate, which allows much more gypsum and dolomite to dissolve than if each rock type were isolated from the others. Details of this process are described in Chapter 5 (see also Figures 5.12–5.13). The slow dissolution of dolomite causes the entire process to be drawn out over very long flow paths. The precipitated calcite occupies only about half the volume of the dissolved rocks, so considerable porosity can be produced. This may be a significant mode of cave origin, although the net effect has not yet been determined.

If deep caves form in this way, one would expect to find accessible caves near the surface that have retained some evidence for these early conduits, such as zones of scattered porosity, as well as passages that follow trends that are poorly adjusted to present groundwater patterns. But geologic mapping rarely shows any evidence for early porosity or its influence on the layout of caves. In Kentucky and Indiana, where deep flow paths along gypsum zones in carbonate rock are well documented (as in Figure 9.10), shallow caves in the same strata farther updip are well adjusted to the groundwater flow patterns of the present erosion cycle and show little or no indication of earlier deep dissolution (Palmer, 1981a). A few minor cave passages do seem out of adjustment with shallow groundwater processes, but they are uncommon and easily explained by flooding or by pyrite oxidation.

Influence of geologic structure

The pattern of individual cave passages is strongly adjusted to the structure of the host rocks (see Chapter 3). Caves are far more sensitive to geologic structure than are surface streams and their valleys, because groundwater can follow subtle bedding irregularities and fractures, some of which can be detected only by careful surveying. Only large structures can influence the trend of a surface valley.

Effects of bedding planes and fractures

Patterns of cave passages depend strongly on whether they are influenced mainly by bedding-plane partings or by fractures (joints and faults) that cut discordantly across the strata. Bedding-plane partings and joints are of roughly equal importance in the development of cave passages, and together they guide the great majority of initial cave development.

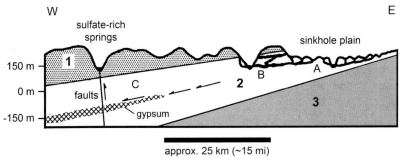

approx. 25 km (~15 mi)

Figure 9.10: Cross section through the Indiana karst, showing deep flow paths in the St. Louis Limestone along a gypsum zone (compare to Figure 5.12). 1 = mainly sandstone and shale; 2 = limestone; 3 = siltstone (all of Mississippian age). A = shallow caves beneath sinkhole plain; B = caves in sandstone-capped ridges; C = deep flow along gypsum zones in limestone. See Krothe and Libra (1983) for details.

Figure 9.11: Contrast between caves formed along bedding-plane partings (**a**) and caves that follow intersecting fractures (**b**). Passages are shown in map view, with typical cross sections.

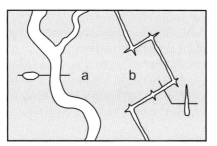

Fewer than 5% of all caves follow faults, and about the same percentage consist of enlarged intergranular pores.

Bedding-plane partings are most common in thin-bedded strata, but even massive rocks may include a few partings. Caves that follow partings tend to be sinuous and strongly concordant with the bedding (Figure 9.11a). Tubular passages have elliptical or lenticular cross sections elongated along the partings (Figure 9.12). In well-bedded rocks, most vadose canyons have ceilings that follow single partings for long distances and have been dissolved downward through underlying beds (Figure 9.13). Vertical shafts in these rocks usually contain a succession of drains that develop at progressively lower elevations as the descending water dissolves downward through the beds. Most joints in well-bedded rocks are narrow, cut across only single beds, and have little influence on passage shape.

Each parting tends to vary in prominence from place to place. When traced along the length of a passage, a given parting may be seen to disappear entirely, while another, or more than one, grows in prominence. The initial path of water migrates from one parting to another, according to which offers the most unobstructed path.

In some rock sequences, only a few bedding planes are favorable to cave development (Lowe, 1992). In certain thin-bedded rocks, such as the Ste. Genevieve and Monteagle Limestones of the east-central U.S., nearly every bedding plane has developed a parting favorable to speleogenesis. The strong dominance of bedding-plane partings in these formations is aided by thin dustings of clay along many of the bedding planes as the rocks were being deposited. When the rock is exposed to stress during tectonic activity or unloading by erosion of overlying rock, the individual beds are able to

Figure 9.12: A prominent parting in the Ste. Genevieve Limestone has guided the development of many phreatic passages such as this one in Mammoth Cave.

Figure 9.13: The Pass of El Ghor in Mammoth Cave is a typical canyon formed in prominently bedded rock, with bedding-plane partings as the guiding structures. Canyons in the cave are sinuous, as in Figure 9.11a, and nearly all extend directly down the local dip of the strata.

separate easily, especially if they slip past each other. Even tiny movements of this sort can help to open the partings to water flow, because the irregularities along each contact no longer match perfectly.

Large joints are most common in thick-bedded or massive rocks. In such rocks, joints tend to be spaced more widely and extend greater distances than in thin-bedded strata. Most cave passages in these rocks have highly angular patterns composed of relatively high, narrow, and straight segments that intersect at various angles, most commonly at nearly right angles (Figures 9.11b and 9.14). Figure 3.48 shows how cave passages in the massive, well-jointed Salem Limestone of Indiana contrast with those in the thin-bedded Monteagle and St. Louis Limestones of Tennessee, where bedding-plane partings control most cave patterns.

Note the lengthy fissure passages shown on the cave map in Figure 8.17. The joint-controlled passage (labeled **X** on the map) is more than 600 m long with only two insignificant offsets of about a meter each. The cavernous strata are only 34 m thick and form a thin brittle sheet bounded above and below by incompetent shaly beds.

Vertical shafts along prominent fractures can descend long distances without interruption, and the vertical intervals between shaft drains are much greater than in well-bedded rocks. Many fracture-guided shafts descend their entire depth in a single long step (Figure 9.14).

Figure 9.14: A fissure along a major joint in the Coeymans Limestone in McFail's Cave, New York. This is one of the shaft entrances to the cave, with a drop of 25 m. This and other nearby caves are fed by sinkhole recharge and are all branchworks, despite the prominent jointing (See Figure 9.45.)

Figure 9.15: The Ste. Genevieve Limestone of Kentucky contains many joints, especially in its thicker beds, but bedding-plane partings still dominate in guiding cave development. Note the ceiling joints that cut across the passage ceiling with no effect on the passage trend. This is Black Snake Avenue on the Historic Route of Mammoth Cave, Kentucky.

Network caves are restricted to prominently fractured rocks, although the mode of recharge, rather than the fracturing itself, is responsible for the origin of their maze pattern (Chapter 8).

Most joints are essentially perpendicular to the strata, so in gently dipping rocks the joints tend to be nearly vertical. In map view, the largest joints are usually oriented parallel to the dip of the beds, with the next-largest joints nearly at right angles to the dip. Steeply dipping or folded rocks have relatively complex fracture patterns, which include many joints arranged in two sets, each with an orientation about 30° from the direction of compression. For example, if a rock is compressed by forces that are directed east-west (E-W), much of the fracturing takes place along lines oriented WNW-ESE and ENE-WSW. In addition, joints in folded rocks are common along the strike of the beds, especially in folded rocks where there has been tension along the fold axes. Joints along the axes of folds tend to provide longer uninterrupted flow paths than do joints with other orientations.

Discordant fractures can also be important in thin-bedded rocks where many successive beds have no partings between them. In this case the entire sequence behaves like a single coherent unit, and the fracture provides the only significant path for water. The Devonian-age Coeymans Limestone of New York has an average bedding thickness of only a few tens of centimeters, but its beds are so tightly bound together that most of its cave passages follow major joints that cut through most or all of the beds (Figure 9.14).

Nearly all sedimentary rocks contain both bedding-plane partings and joints, and their effect on caves ranges over a continuous spectrum from strongly parting controlled to strongly joint or fault controlled. Figure 9.15 shows a passage in which both partings and joints are abundant, but the partings clearly dominate in determining the passage pattern. Wide, sinuous tubes are common, and where joints cross the passage they simply form minor fissures that

extend into the ceilings and walls without affecting the passage trends.

Figure 9.16 shows a passage in which both a joint and a parting have contributed equally to the passage pattern. The elevation and gradient are controlled by the parting, while the linear trend is controlled by the fracture. The stair-step profiles of many vadose passages, such as the one shown in Figure 6.6, also demonstrate the combined influence of fractures and partings. Some caves, such as the networks in Figures 8.29–8.32, show very little bedding influence.

Faults can cut across any kind of rock, but they are most likely to influence cave development in massive rocks. Many reverse faults and lateral faults are sealed with recrystallized rock, so normal faults (formed by tension) are inherently more favorable routes for cave development. As overlying rocks are eroded away, however, release of confining pressure usually allows all faults to open slightly

Figure 9.16: The Subway in Castleguard Cave, Alberta, follows an arrow-straight 500-m course along the intersection between a joint and a bedding-plane parting (Figure 2.56). Their traces have been obscured by dissolution. Photo by Derek Ford.

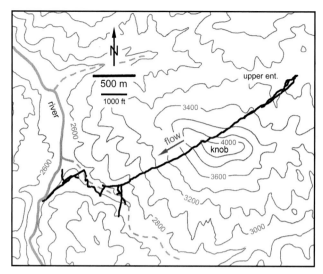

Figure 9.17: The linear trend of Simmons-Mingo Cave, West Virginia, follows a prominent fracture zone directly beneath a high knob. The cave is in the Greenbrier Group (Mississippian). Elevations are in feet; contour interval = 200 ft (60 m). Modified from Medville and Storage (1986).

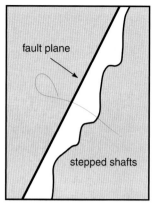

Figure 9.18: Cross section of a stair-step pattern of shafts beneath a fault-guided ceiling, a common passage pattern in alpine caves. (See Audra, 1994; Fernández-Gibert and others, 2000; Audra and others, 2002).

Caves in the Black Hills of South Dakota contain many faults that were either formed or reactivated after the caves developed, as shown by offsets in bedrock walls and fragmenting of the calcite coating that lines much of the caves (Chapter 13). By terminating and blocking passages, these fault zones pose major barriers to exploration in Wind Cave and Jewel Cave. Many of their passages end at these zones, and the effect can be seen as linear boundaries beyond which the caves have not yet been explored. These include the northeastern boundary of Wind Cave (Figure 13.9). Some fault zones have only one or two known routes through them, but the caves continue at full size beyond the barriers.

Veins of calcite, dolomite, and quartz are common along joints and faults. They may force cave walls to follow linear trends for short distances but rarely have much effect on over-

so that they become more suited to cave origin. A few caves are formed almost entirely along single prominent faults or fault zones. Werner (1972) and Kastning (1977) describe examples of the positive and negative influence of faults on cave development in the eastern U.S.

Major fractures can determine the direction of caves in such a way that the cave patterns seem out of adjustment with the surrounding landscape. Simmons-Mingo Cave, West Virginia, is an example that follows a prominent fracture zone beneath a major drainage divide and almost under the apex of a steep-sided mountain (Figure 9.17; Medville and Storage, 1986). No fault displacement has been noted, but the behavior resembles that of a fault. Much of Ellison's Cave, Georgia, is aligned along a major lateral fault that cuts right through Pigeon Mountain (Figure 6.5). The main passage of Mexico's Sistema Cheve, the deepest cave in the Western Hemisphere, follows a major fault zone for much of its length (Figure 3.36; Hose, 2000). In many alpine caves, vadose passages descend along steeply dipping faults, with their ceilings defined by the fault and their floors entrenched by streams into a series of high steps (Figure 9.18).

By causing passages to terminate in breakdown, some fault zones present barriers to cave exploration. Most faults pre-date caves, but they can be reactivated at any time (Chapter 3). But even if a fault remains inactive, the shattered rock around it is susceptible to collapse. Figure 9.19 shows an example of how old faults can influence both the pattern of a later cave and the breakdown of its ceiling.

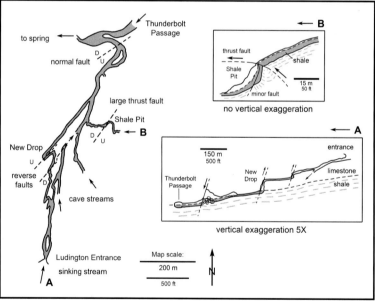

Figure 9.19: Influence of faulting on Ludington Cave, West Virginia. The map shows only a small part of the cave (see Figure 9.31). Much of the cave is located along the contact between the Hillsdale Limestone (Greenbrier Group) and the underlying Maccrady Shale, both of Mississippian age. Note the offsets in the horizontal and vertical passage patterns, where groundwater was deflected along preexisting faults. The faults are of late Paleozoic age, at least 200 million years older than the cave. A large thrust fault, a normal fault, and several reverse faults are shown. Note the breakdown along the normal fault (near the Thunderbolt Passage). The photo in Figure 9.6 is located about 100 m northeast of the New Drop. U, D = upward or downward movement along faults. Map by West Virginia Association for Cave Studies. Geology and profiles from Palmer (1974).

Figure 9.20: Mixing-zone porosity in a cave in young Pleistocene limestone less than 180,000 years old (Paget Formation, Bermuda). The cave walls are soft and crumbly. Rock hammer shows scale. The pile of rubble on the floor fell naturally and was not knocked down.

Figure 9.21: Diving in water-filled Ginnie Spring Cave, Florida. Note solution pockets and spongework texture in the walls. The white box is an early-style dive light. Photo by Sheck Exley.

all cave patterns. Certain caves in mining districts intersect large isolated fault-guided fissures that are lined with minerals. Examples are common in the caves of Derbyshire, England. These *vein cavities* serve as routes for later cave-forming water to flow discordantly across the bedding (T. Ford, 2000). The deepest shaft in the British Isles, the 160-meter Titan, in Peak Cavern, is an enlarged, formerly phreatic, vein cavity.

Florea and Vacher (2004) suggest that fracture density (i.e., spatial frequency) should be added to the model of Palmer (1991), which relates cave patterns to only two variables — recharge and pore type. Although fracture density has no effect on the overall type of cave pattern, it can affect the spacing of fissures in networks. Passage patterns are also less angular and more sinuous where fractures are small and closely spaced, even where bedding-plane partings have no apparent influence.

Effects of intergranular porosity

As described in Chapter 3, soft chemical sediments gradually recrystallize into hard rock as they age. Their porosity decreases greatly during this process. The effect of intergranular pores (matrix pores) on cave development is greatest in young porous limestones, particularly in coastal mixing zones (Figure 9.20). As the rock matures, the influence of intergranular porosity decreases. Most of this porosity is lost during the first few million years, especially if the rocks are exposed to pressure from burial by younger strata or from tectonic activity. Otherwise the porous nature of the rock can persist for tens or even hundreds of millions of years.

The Eocene limestones of northern Florida and adjacent states still retain much of their initial porosity. Caves that form in them typically have many irregular solution

pockets and spongework textures, despite the fact that the main passages are typically conduits (Figure 9.21; Wilson, 2002). In Figure 9.22, note the irregularities in the conduit walls detected by a digital mapping device, which contrast with the smoother wall contours in most older limestones (e.g., Figure 9.19). Nevertheless, fractures and partings have a strong influence on many Florida caves, as shown by the many networks with fissure-like passage cross sections (Figure 9.23). Exploration in the region is often halted by diminishing passage size, where groundwater flow has dispersed along many alternate routes that connect caves at sink points with those in discharge areas (Florea, 2006).

In the Yucatán Peninsula, limestones with a variety of ages from Pleistocene to Mesozoic have characteristics similar to those in Florida (Smart and others, 2002, 2006). The same is true for the Cretaceous Edwards Formation of Texas. In all of these examples there has been little burial of the rocks beneath younger strata, and no significant tectonic compression. Karst development in porous rocks of this type is discussed in a symposium volume edited by Martin and others (2002).

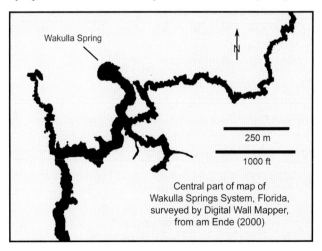

Figure 9.22: Part of the underwater Wakulla Spring Cave System, surveyed with the Digital Wall Mapper System developed by Bill Stone and others. Note the irregular passage walls. From am Ende (2000).

Figure 9.23: Fracture control of passages in the Ocala Limestone of Eocene age, Warren Cave, Florida. This view, looking steeply upward, shows intersecting fissure passages that dominate the passage pattern.

Figure 9.25: A spongework maze in Carlsbad Cavern, New Mexico. Although the rock is of Permian age (about 250 million years old), much of the original porosity of the local reef limestone remains and was enlarged by sulfuric acid (Chapter 8).

The Río Encantado System of Puerto Rico contains one of the longest continuously mapped underground rivers, which comprises most of the 17-km length of the cave. Located in the mid-Tertiary Lares Limestone, the cave is fed by sinking streams that drain from the central igneous core of the island, combined with seepage through intergranular pores in the limestone. This combined recharge accounts for the branchwork pattern with very sparse tributaries (Figure 9.24; see also Figure 6.32). Water that infiltrates from the karst surface becomes quickly saturated because of its large contact area with the bedrock, and passages from this source are few and rudimentary. The cave water is supersaturated with calcite during all but high flow.

The initial porosity can be preserved in certain rocks for a great length of time. For example, the massive Capitan reef limestone of the Guadalupe Mountains contains no bedding but is intersected by large joints and faults that direct most of its cave passages and rooms. Most of Carlsbad Cavern is located in this rock unit (Figures 6.19, 8.53, and 8.58). But the rock also contains many primary pores that have enlarged to produce spongework textures in places (Figure 9.25).

Carbonate breccia can retain irregular pores and fissures between the broken fragments long after most other rocks of its age have lost nearly all of its primary porosity (Figures 3.27 and 6.29). Local spongework mazes can be formed in these rocks by diffuse flow or by flooding (Figure 8.19). Most breccias contain very few partings and fractures capable of enlarging into caves.

Influence of dip and strike on passage trends

The passage trends in most caves, branchworks in particular, are strongly influenced by the dip and strike of the beds (Chapter 3). This relationship is clearest in well-bedded rocks, but even in highly fractured rock there is usually moderate control of this type. In a thin steeply dipping aquifer, the dip and strike of the entire formation influence the overall cave patterns, even if the fracturing is intense enough to control the direction of individual passage segments.

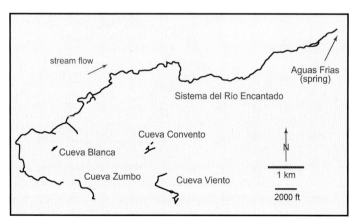

Figure 9.24: Map of Sistema del Río Encantado, Puerto Rico (National Speleological Society; see Kambesis, 2004).

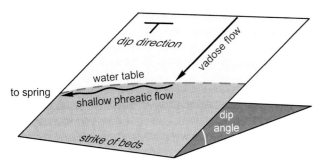

Figure 9.26: Idealized influence of dip on vadose passages, and of the strike on shallow phreatic passages. This pattern is most apparent in prominently bedded rocks. Most caves deviate from this pattern to various degrees, especially in massive, highly fractured rocks. Minor seepage is affected less by dip and strike than are the flows that form caves (see Figure 15.7).

Consider a bedded, gently dipping rock with prominent partings but only minor fractures (Figure 9.26). Vadose flow is drawn downward by gravity, so it follows the steepest available routes. Aside from minor seepage along joints, the majority of flow follows the inclined partings directly down the dip. The resulting cave passages stray from the dip direction only where water is diverted along a less-steep route by local narrowing of the parting, or by intersecting fractures (Figure 9.19).

On its journey to the water table, a vadose stream can follow the dip for hundreds of meters, or even kilometers. The popular idea that infiltrating water descends vertically to the water table is not valid in bedded rocks. Gently dipping beds typically contain long sinuous canyons with low-gradient profiles. The smaller the dip angle, the longer these passages tend to be. In contrast, vadose passages in steeply dipping beds are short and steep.

When vadose water reaches the water table it no longer has any inherent tendency to continue down the dip. Instead, it follows the most efficient paths to nearby outlets, which are usually located in nearby valleys. These paths can be in the dip direction, but only if that happens to be most favorable. On the contrary, most phreatic tubes

Figure 9.27: The main passage of New Trout Cave, West Virginia, follows the strike of the beds along the flank of an anticline in Devonian limestone. Note the effect on the passage cross section, even after modification by breakdown.

in well-bedded rocks are oriented roughly parallel to the local strike of the beds (Figure 9.27).

The incoming vadose water already occupies a favorable parting or bed, so there is little reason for the water to abandon it. The phreatic flow usually continues along the same parting or bed. Nearly all partings and fractures become narrower with depth, so in general the most favorable phreatic paths tend to be along the water table. Because the water table has little slope in the vicinity of a developing cave, the intersection between a dipping bedding-plane parting and the more gently inclined water table is a line nearly parallel to the strike of the beds.

The shallowest routes are not always the most efficient, though, and it is common for phreatic cave passages to loop below the water table here and there to follow the widest routes along the partings. This is especially true where the rocks have been deformed by faults or folds (see page 255).

In a cave passage, the change from down-dip trend to strike trend — or at least to a trend that is not directly down the dip — is strong evidence for a change from vadose to phreatic conditions. This evidence is most helpful in diagnosing the origin of passages that are now dry, or in which the position of the water table has shifted since the original cave development.

Where vadose water changes from a dip to a strike trend, it must turn either left or right. The water table already slopes in the direction of the most efficient outlet, where the parting is exposed in a valley at a lower elevation, so the water turns in that direction and flows down the existing hydraulic gradient to a spring.

This idealized model fits the pattern of many caves, and it also makes sense in hydraulic terms. In bedded strata with prominent partings, down-dip canyons are so common that it is often possible to interpret the local dip directions from cave maps alone. Examples include those in Figures 2.64, 6.9, and 9.13. Strike-oriented tubes are almost as common (Figures 6.12, 9.12, 9.27, and 9.34).

Even in regions of very low dip these relationships have been verified by extensive geologic mapping (e.g., Palmer, 1989a). They apply mainly to epigenic caves with discrete stream passages, and not to hypogenic caves. They also do not apply well to many caves fed by large sinking streams, because the influence of the water table is overwhelmed by frequent flooding. The model is also a poor fit to caves in massive, prominently fractured rock, because these caves can extend in any direction, even against the dip. An example is Mystery Cave, Minnesota (Figures 8.20 and 14.23).

It is tempting to assume that the regional dip shown on geologic maps is valid even at the local scale of individual caves. But nearly all geologic maps are prepared from surface data alone, and, unfortunately, surface rock exposures tend to be discontinuous and difficult to correlate. Furthermore, the geologic structure mapped on one particular geologic contact is not representative of the structure on other beds above and below it.

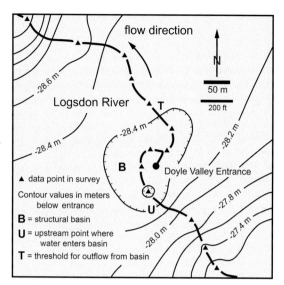

Figure 9.28: Influence of bedding structure on the trend of part of Logsdon River, Mammoth Cave, Kentucky. This section is located to the southwest of the name "Morrison" in Figure 1.3. Contour lines show the elevation of a prominent chert bed in the St. Louis Limestone. Zero elevation is the top of the drillhole casing at the entrance. The contour lines were plotted with *Surfer* (Golden Software, Golden, Colorado). Only the survey line is shown, which parallels the passage walls. In this area the passage follows the local dip and therefore appears to be vadose, except where the water was initially ponded in a structural basin (**B**) and flowed out at the basin's lowest threshold (**T**). From auto-level survey by A. and M. Palmer and R. Zopf.

Cave passages are adjusted to the local structure around them — not to the average structure of the region. Geologic mapping in caves shows that the local dip and strike differ from bed to bed according to variations in bed thickness (Palmer, 1989a). In places the local dip is even reversed from, or at right angles to, the regional dip determined from surface mapping.

Most caves have a more complex relationship to the geology than is shown in the ideal example of Figure 9.26. For example, Figure 9.28 shows the trend of part of the main river passage in Mammoth Cave, Kentucky, in relation to the local geologic structure. The survey was made with a tripod-mounted automatic level (see Chapter 14). Contours were drawn on a prominent chert bed. Note the variations in dip (both the angle and direction) in the nearly horizontal strata. Despite the limited data, the structural influence on the passage is clear. The passage has a rectangular cross section, which is not indicative of either vadose or phreatic conditions; but most of it has a down-dip orientation, which suggests a vadose origin.

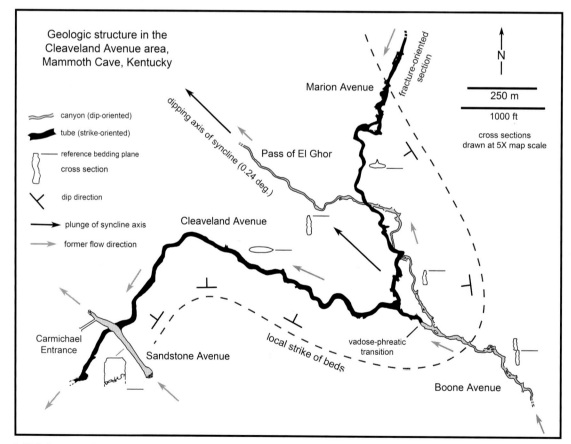

Figure 9.29 Influence of bedding structure on passage trends in part of Mammoth Cave, from Palmer (1981). Cleaveland Avenue is a large tube that formed at the former water table. It follows the local strike of the beds (dashed line). Boone Avenue, a canyon, was a vadose tributary of Cleaveland. Boone extends down the local dip, along the axis of a plunging syncline. The Pass of El Ghor was formed by vadose water when the water table dropped and Cleaveland was abandoned. Boone continued to deepen by vadose entrenchment, and El Ghor is its downstream extension. See text for details. (The spelling of *Cleaveland* is correct.)

There is one notable deviation from the down-dip pattern. In the center of the map (at **B**), the passage makes a distinctive wiggle that coincides with a shallow structural basin in the beds. Apparently the original water, when it was no more than a trickle, was perched above the water table. It flowed down the dip of the beds and into this basin, where it ponded and poured out over the lowest threshold (**T**). The jog in the passage extends across the basin from the upstream inflow point (**U**) to the outflow point. From there it continued on its down-dip path. Later, as the stream grew in volume, it cut downward to form the present passage, which has preserved the pattern of the earliest flow.

Survey points in Figure 9.28 are restricted to the passage in which they were measured, which may cast doubt on the validity of the contouring. On the other hand, commercial software provided non-subjective contouring, and the only interruption of the northwesterly dip coincides with the jog in the passage, which supports the integrity of the method.

The following example illustrates the relation between dip-oriented canyons and strike-oriented tubes in well-bedded rock (Figure 9.29). Cleaveland Avenue, in Mammoth Cave, is a wide tube that follows the strike of the beds almost exactly (Figure 6.12). Its overall gradient is less than 20 centimeters per kilometer. Its almost perfectly horizontal profile is interrupted only by a few short areas of breakdown. The conspicuous bends in the passage follow the trend of a prominent syncline in the northeast and an adjacent anticline in the southwest. Cleaveland Avenue was not necessarily water-filled during all of its development, but its strike orientation indicates development at the water table. The upstream end of Cleaveland Avenue (called Marion Avenue) cuts across the structural contours only where it follows local fractures instead of partings.

Boone Avenue, a canyon, was originally a vadose tributary of Cleaveland Avenue. Boone extends down the plunging axis of the syncline, which forms a subtle **U** in the beds. (The *plunge* is the angle that the syncline is tilted — i.e., the dip of its axis.) The water that formed Boone Avenue naturally flowed down the synclinal trough in the beds, just as it would in a sloping gutter. This water changed from down-dip flow to strike-oriented flow at the point labeled *vadose-phreatic transition*. The elevation of this point correlates with several others elsewhere in the cave, and it and represents a major level of passage development.

As the nearby Green River deepened its valley, the water table dropped. Cleaveland Avenue was abandoned by its flow, and its original water inputs continued down the dip to form canyons. The vadose stream in Boone Avenue continued to deepen its channel and bypassed Cleaveland Avenue to form the Pass of El Ghor (Figure 9.13).

Sandstone Avenue is a wide upper-level passage intersected by Cleaveland Avenue (Figure 9.29). Despite its great size, Sandstone Avenue is dip-oriented, which suggests a vadose origin. It is nearly filled with sediment, but at the junction with Cleaveland Avenue, where most of the sedi-

ment was carried off by the Cleaveland stream, Sandstone Avenue is clearly revealed as a tall canyon.

Elsewhere in the Mammoth Cave System are examples where two phreatic tubes at different elevations cross each other at nearly right angles, and others where two or more canyons do the same. These give the impression that the dip-strike model of tubes and canyons has failed. But these are merely examples of dip variation from one bed to another because of irregular thickness of the strata. Each tube follows the local strike of its beds, and each canyon is oriented down the local dip.

And yet the dip-strike model does not apply to all passages in Mammoth Cave. For example, the Pass of El Ghor (Figure 9.29) eventually becomes a tube (Echo River) that wanders in an erratic manner, along neither the strike nor the dip. It merely followed the most efficient phreatic route to the nearby Green River (Figure 1.3). None of these structures are visible to the eye. Passage profiles in this area are discussed later in this chapter (see Figure 9.49).

With increasingly prominent fracturing, more vadose passages cut diagonally across and against the dip, and phreatic passages may follow a zig-zag pattern of fractures, regardless of dip and strike orientations. Many caves in these rocks contain phreatic passages with loops that extend deep below the water table. Both active and abandoned examples of phreatic loops have been documented (Ford and Ewers, 1978).

Figure 9.30: Grand Caverns, a Virginia show cave, contains several kilometers of irregular passages in steeply dipping Cambrian carbonate rocks. The dip here is about 70°. Most of the passages extend along the strike. Others follow fractures at right angles to the strike. (See Kastning and others, 1995).

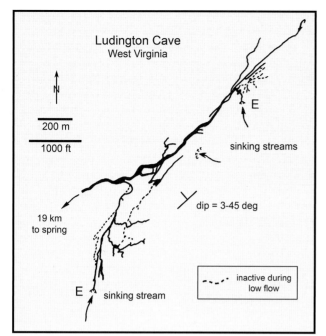

Figure 9.31: Map of Ludington Cave, West Virginia, showing a branchwork pattern distorted by faulting and locally steep dips. The cave is greatly extended along the strike of the beds and of faults. (Map by West Virginia Association for Cave Studies).

steep dips and faulting on an otherwise simple branchwork pattern. Note the great elongation along the strike, and the short, irregular vadose infeeders that join the main passage from the southeast.

Butler Cave, Virginia, illustrates the effect of steep dips and intense fracturing on cave patterns (Figure 2.44; see also Clemmer, 2005). The beds dip toward the southeast at an average of 10–15 degrees. Dip-oriented fissures and canyons form a complex tangle of passages that feed into a strike-oriented tube, which in many places takes on a fissure cross section. Although this is a branchwork cave, some parts superficially resemble a network maze because many closed loops have formed by diversion of water along fractures to successively lower levels.

The Siebenhengste-Hohgant System of western Switzerland is one of the world's longest and deepest caves (Figure 9.32). It is located in steeply dipping strata that are cut by extensive normal (tensional) faults. Its inputs are mainly converging down-dip canyons and vertical shafts (Figures 1.10 and 2.64), which lead to a complex strike-oriented system. Faulting in the strike section allows the groundwater flow to extend to considerable depth below the water table, and there is no presently accessible route through to the caves at the downstream end of the system.

Ford (1965b) describes some fine examples in the Mendip Hills of England. In that region, down-dip passages continue below the water table, where dip-oriented fractures provide the most favorable routes, and the available spring outlets are also in that direction.

Where the dip is steep (Figures 2.43, 9.30, and 9.31), the strike orientation of phreatic passages is usually much clearer than in the subtle examples in low-dip strata, and vadose passages tend to be short and steep.

For example, Ludington Cave, West Virginia, is located along a fault zone in the eastern part of the Appalachian Plateaus. Some typical effects of faulting on its passages are shown in Figure 9.19. The map of all major passages, shown in Figure 9.31, illustrates the effect of

Figure 9.32: Map of the Siebenhengste-Hohgant Cave System and related caves (Bern, Switzerland). It is located in a high alpine plateau of Cretaceous limestone, which dips 15–30° to the east-southeast and is cut by several major normal faults. Fault movements are labeled U (up) and D (down). Water enters dozens of entrances in the Siebenhengste and Hohgant areas and exits at the springs along the shore of Lake Thun. Note the down-dip character of the Siebenhengste section, which is mainly vadose. The strong strike orientation of the phreatic section, which leads to the springs, is accentuated by the faulting. Map by the Höhlenforschergemeinshaft Region Hohgant (from Häuselmann, 2002; Jeannin and others, 2000).

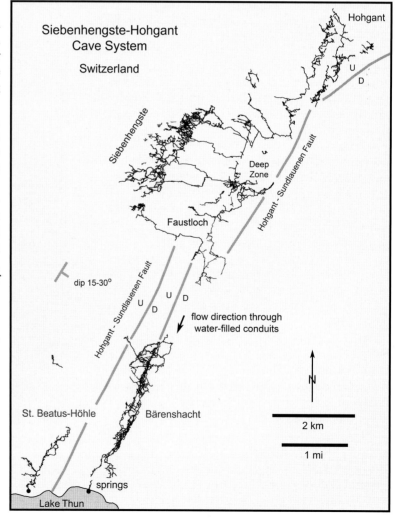

The pattern is roughly similar to those of Butler Cave (Figure 2.44) and, to a lesser extent, Sistema Huautla in Mexico (Figure 8.9).

In steeply dipping beds, network caves also tend to be elongate along the strike. Many have a pattern of large strike-oriented rooms connected by narrower dip-oriented passages (Osborne, 2001). Most of the broad strike passages have blind terminations. This pattern is typical of many caves in folded Appalachian Mountains and in southeastern Australia (Figure 9.33). A few appear to be inactive relics of hypogenic development. Some, such as the example in Figure 9.30, have been enlarged, and perhaps entirely formed, by flooding from nearby rivers.

Some distinctive cave patterns have developed along the axes of folds (Figures 9.34–9.35). The caves of Trout Rock, West Virginia, include an extensive network maze (Hamilton Cave) located at the crest of a plunging anticline of Devonian limestone. A short distance down the southeastern flank of the anticline is Trout Cave, which contains a few network sections but is dominated by a long strike-oriented passage. Farther down the flank is New Trout Cave, which consists almost entirely of strike-oriented tubes with cross sections that are elongated along the steep dip (Figure 9.27).

The origin of the networks in this system is ambiguous. The anticlinal ridge is capped by quartz sandstone, but it is fairly thick and most of the underlying cave passages, though close to the top of the limestone, do not extend up to the base of the sandstone. It is unlikely that the networks formed by diffuse seepage. Thick sediments suggest enlargement by backflooding from the adjacent South Branch of the Potomac River. Water wells along fold axes in carbonate rocks of the Appalachians tend to have relatively large yields because of widening of fractures during folding (LaMoreaux and Powell, 1963). It is likely that this widening, in combination with backflooding, accounts for the network caves at Trout Rock.

Ancient caves may be adjusted to structural trends that are no longer present. There is some evidence in the Rocky Mountains of Montana that the stratal dip has changed since

Figure 9.34: Entrance of Island Ford Cave, Virginia. The cave extends along the flank of the conspicuous anticline shown here — i.e., along the local strike of the limestone beds.

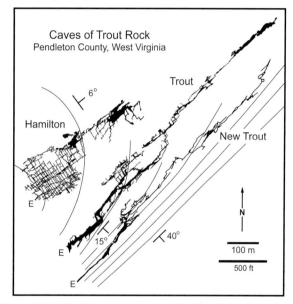

Figure 9.35: The Trout Rock caves, West Virginia, show development of tubular passages along the flank of an anticline, with maze caves along the crest where joints have been widened by tension. Structural contour lines have a contour interval of 10 m. E = entrance. Cave maps by David West. Geology by A. and M. Palmer. See Figure 9.27.

certain caves formed (Campbell, 1977). Mississippian-age caves in Wyoming and South Dakota originated in nearly flat-lying strata that have since been folded, so the present structure has nothing to do with the passage patterns (Palmer and Palmer, 1995a). This possibility should be considered wherever caves seem out of adjustment with the rock structure. This guideline applies especially to studies of nearly flat-lying rocks, where even a small amount of deformation can alter the dip direction.

Quantifying the structural influence on caves

With some simplifying, it is possible to quantify the effect of dip and strike on cave patterns. The following example is based on geologic mapping in about 50 caves in a variety of geologic settings (Palmer, 1999). The sample includes only caves with discrete stream passages, both active and inactive. The following measurements were made of the mean

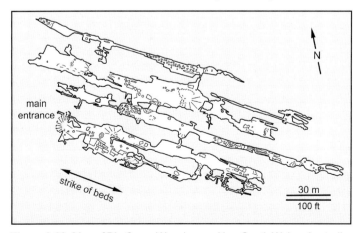

Figure 9.33: Map of Dip Cave, Wee Jasper, New South Wales, Australia, illustrating a network pattern of "halls and narrows" in nearly vertical strata (see Osborne, 2001). Map from Jennings (1963).

passage trends relative to mean dip and strike (see Figure 9.36):

- Deviation of vadose passages from the local dip direction. These include canyons and canyon-shaft series with no upward enlargement above the guiding parting. A passage extending exactly down the dip has a deviation of zero degrees. No distinction is made between deviations to the left or right of the dip; all are treated as absolute numbers.
- Discordance of vadose passages to the local strata. Nearly all vadose passages cut downward across the strata, so their gradients are steeper than the dip. The local dip angle is subtracted from the passage gradient (both in degrees). Passages that cut downward across the strata are assigned positive deviations.
- Deviation of phreatic passages (irregular gradients, upward dissolution of ceiling) from the strike of the beds. The overall passage trend is compared to the local strike in degrees. Deviations of passages in the down-dip direction from the strike are considered positive.

The geologic settings for sampled caves appear to fall into three groups: (**1**) prominently bedded, unfaulted, low-dip strata (dip <5°), e.g., Figures 9.8, and 9.13; (**2**) bedded and folded or faulted strata, e.g., Figures 9.27, 9.30, and 9.34; (**3**) massive, prominently fractured rock (e.g., Figures 8.22 and 9.37), including fractured, bedded rocks that do not split along partings (Figure 9.14). The boundaries between categories are vague, but the grouping can be made fairly consistently.

Probability plots for the data are summarized in Table 9.1. For example, in bedded, unfaulted, low-dip strata, 50% of the phreatic passages in the sample have less than 10° deviation from the local strike, and 90% have less than 60° deviation from the strike. To summarize:

Figure 9.37: Nearly impenetrable karren topography in massive, highly fractured rocks on Dall Island, Alaska. Photo by Jim Baichtal.

- Deviations of vadose passages from the dip direction are least in bedded, low-dip rocks, and greatest in massive, fractured rocks.
- Discordance of vadose passage gradients to the dip angle

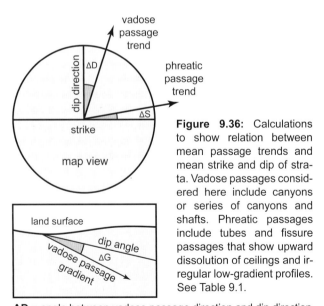

Figure 9.36: Calculations to show relation between mean passage trends and mean strike and dip of strata. Vadose passages considered here include canyons or series of canyons and shafts. Phreatic passages include tubes and fissure passages that show upward dissolution of ceilings and irregular low-gradient profiles. See Table 9.1.

ΔD = angle between vadose passage direction and dip direction
ΔG = angle between vadose passage gradient and dip angle
ΔS = angle between phreatic passage direction and strike

Maximum deviations between passage trends and geologic structure, at the 50th and 90th percentiles:

Bedded, unfaulted, low dip:

	50%	90% of sample
ΔD	5°	10°
ΔG	2°	15°
ΔS	10°	60°

Bedded, folded, faulted:

	50%	90% of sample
ΔD	10°	50°
ΔG	5°	30°
ΔS	5°	30°

Massive, fractured:

	50%	90% of sample
ΔD	50°	70°
ΔG	10°	80°
ΔS	50°	90°

Table 9.1: Summary of measurements from Figure 9.36, generalized from the data of Palmer (1999). Other data sets will probably differ.

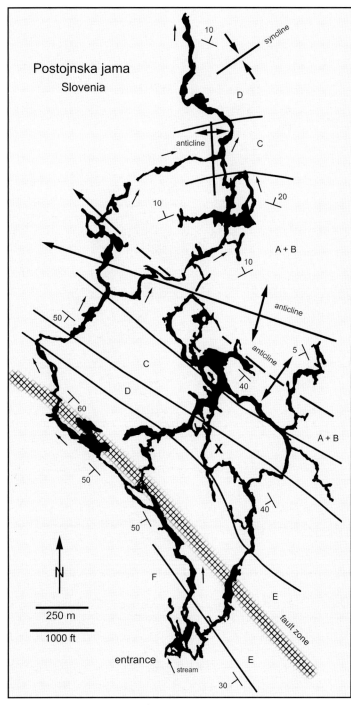

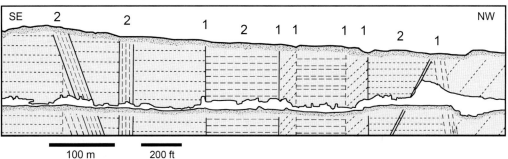

Figure 9.38: Map of Postojnska jama, Slovenia, showing the geologic setting and flow patterns (simplified from Šebela, 1998). Local strike and dip are indicated (as described on page 83). Paths of active flow are shown with arrows. The cave is located in Mesozoic limestone. A = thin-bedded, cherty limestone; B = thick-bedded limestone; C, E = massive limestones; D, F = thick-bedded limestones. Details of the major fault zone are from Šušteršič (2006).

is smallest in bedded, low-dip rocks, and greatest in massive, fractured rocks.

• Deviations of phreatic passages from the strike direction are least in bedded, folded or faulted rocks and greatest in massive, fractured rocks.

This is a limited sample, biased toward those areas visited personally, but it provides some broad guidelines for predicting and explaining cave patterns. In the future it may be possible to extend these relationships to karst groundwater flow in general, rather than just to caves, but there is not yet enough information to develop simple guidelines for groundwater management (see Chapter 15).

Complex structural settings

Some geologic settings are too complex to be categorized in the manner of the preceding section. This is typical in many mountainous regions, especially where compressive forces have deformed and metamorphosed the rocks (Figures 9.37–9.40). Caves follow major fracture swarms or intersections, so their passages may cut across fold patterns in a seemingly haphazard way, with what appear to be erratic trends, profiles, and cross sections. Caves jog so readily between different bedding planes, faults, and joints that the relation to strike and dip of the beds is highly localized and may not be apparent in the overall cave patterns.

For example, the classic karst region of western Slovenia is part of the extensive Tertiary-age Alpine mountain system and is composed of highly deformed Mesozoic carbonate rocks. Figures 9.38–9.39 show the geologic setting of Postojnska jama, Slovenia (Šebela, 1998). This low-gradient stream cave cuts across a variety of limestone types, faults, folds, and breccia zones. The pattern of the cave defies any attempt to simplify its relation to the strike and dip.

Figure 9.39: Profile through the passage shown at X on the map above. **1** = major fault, **2** = fractured and brecciated zone. From Šebela (1998).

Instead its passages look like the tracks of a football player weaving through a crowd of defenders. These routes were simply the most favorable ones for the groundwater to follow through the karst plateau. It is easy to recognize how the mapped passages are influenced by local geologic structures, but it would be difficult to predict their patterns beyond the explored parts. In addition, the geologic details shown on the map and profile are known only because they could be mapped in the cave. On the surface many of them are obscure. The cave has a low-gradient profile that reflects its mainly phreatic origin. Most passages loop up and down over their length. Their ceilings are highly irregular but most floors have been smoothed by the accumulation of sediment.

The large fault zone shown in cross-hatching on the cave map is an example of a ***deflector fault***, which presents a barrier to groundwater flow (Šušteršič, 2006). The brecciated fault zone apparently has a lower permeability than that of the surrounding rocks, so that groundwater is deflected for a long distance to a favorable route through the zone. The resulting cave follows the same path. The fault zone is disruptive even to the enlargement of the caves, because collapse along it has blocked many of the conduits and diverted groundwater along alternate routes. Collapse sinkholes are common in the surface overlying the fault.

The extensive Idria Fault passes through the same region. According to Šušteršič (2000), caves of similar character are clustered on both sides of the fault, but are offset about 12 km from each other. This offset coincides with the total displacement along the fault, which took place in small steps over a long time. Either the caves formed first and were later truncated by the fault, or zones favorable to cave development were first offset and later enlarged into caves. The offset of cave segments is uniform enough to suggest that the caves are older than the fault.

In the karst of southeastern Australia, Osborne (2005b) describes the partitioning of karst into **compartments** by structural features called **partitions**. The partitions include igneous intrusions and other vertical structures that act as barriers to groundwater flow. Each compartment acts as a small independent zone of cave development until the partition becomes breached by collapse, erosion, or dissolution, to connect caves that were originally isolated.

In the Sierra Nevada, California, most caves are located in narrow bands of marble surrounded by insoluble metamorphic and igneous rock. During the Mesozoic Era, the region was a zone of compression between two crustal plates at the western edge of the North American continent (Figure 2.2). As the continental edge was crumpled by pressure, additional rocks were carried in by the oceanic crustal plate and plastered against the growing mountains. Later igneous intrusions rose from below to form the main mass of the Sierra Nevada. Metamorphism by compression and by heat from the underlying igneous rock converted limestone into marble. Today eroded remnants of metamorphic rock are exposed in the tops of the igneous bodies.

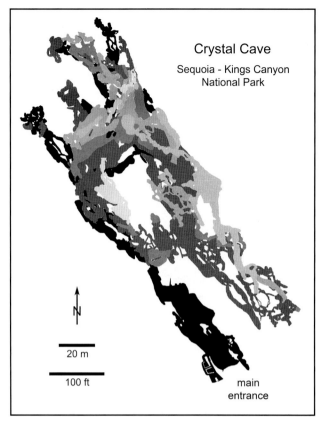

Figure 9.40: Map of Crystal Cave, Sequoia - Kings Canyon National Park, California. The lowest levels are dark and the higher levels are progressively lighter. The cave spans a vertical range of 66.5 m (218 ft). Simplified from map by Joel Despain.

The marble bands are typically no more than a few hundred meters wide, so the caves are constrained by the insoluble rocks on either side. They include Lilburn Cave, California's largest (Figure 3.19). Where the caves impinge on the adjacent insoluble rock the walls are dark gray in contrast to the marble, which is light gray or banded black-gray-white.

Figure 9.40 shows a map of Crystal Cave in Sequoia - Kings Canyon National Park, California, which is located in a band of marble about 70 m wide (Despain, 2003; Despain and Stock, 2005). The cave is bounded by insoluble metamorphic rock on the northeast and southwest, and to the northwest and southeast it is truncated by erosion and breakdown. The cave consists of a multi-level tangle of passages formed by streams that were confined between the adjacent insoluble rocks, so that diversions, overflows, and subsequent levels were all superposed on each other in a limited space. The map resembles a Jackson Pollock painting.

In marble, most of the fissures that guide cave development are partings between the marble and relatively insoluble beds within or bordering the marble, as observed in Norway and Sweden by Faulkner (2005, 2006). This is also true in parts of the Sierra Nevada, which partly accounts for the two parallel trends on the map in Figure 9.40.

Arkenstone Cave, in southern Arizona, is an example of a rare type of cave that formed along large, low-angle faults

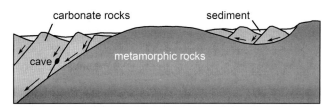

Figure 9.41: Simplified geologic setting of Arkenstone Cave, Arizona (from Peachey, 1993). The large fault above the metamorphic mass was once continuous but has been segmented by later erosion. The area shown is several tens of kilometers wide.

(Figure 9.41; Peachey, 1993). In the mid-Tertiary Period, Paleozoic carbonate rocks about 8–10 km below the surface were moved over metamorphic rock by a regional normal fault for a distance of about 20–40 km. The cave is thought to have been formed at that time by hydrothermal fluids. It was exposed by uplift about 9–12 million years ago but shows no relation to the surrounding hydrology and contains no surface-derived sediment. It has a ramiform pattern with irregular passage cross sections and profiles. Fluid inclusions in calcite crystals in nearby Colossal Cave indicate temperatures of more than 100°C, and 20% of their weight consists of dissolved salt.

Karst flow patterns revealed by groundwater tracing are nearly always more complicated than those of accessible cave streams. In regions with simple geologic structure, traces tend to show convergent flow from many inlets toward a few major outlets. Examples include extensive traces in the gently dipping limestones of the Mammoth Cave region, Kentucky (Quinlan and Ray, 1981; Meiman and Ryan, 1999). But even in structurally simple regions such as this, the basic tributary pattern is complicated by divergent flow, loops, and overflow routes.

In regions of complex geology, groundwater flow patterns are proportionally more complex. For example, the highly folded and faulted limestones of Slovenia, Croatia, and Bosnia contain poljes that are connected by underground flow through the intervening uplands. The poljes lie at a variety of elevations and have irregular bedrock floors mantled by as much as 800 m of sediment. Dye tracing shows extremely intricate groundwater patterns (Baučić, 1968; Gams, 1974; Gospodarič and Habič, 1976). In some areas, dye injected at any given point emerges at an average of 5 or 6 outlets (Figure 9.42). Large sinking streams tend to disperse to a greater numbers of springs than do the smaller inputs. At the same time, each spring tends to receive water from more than one inlet. Some flow paths cross others with no apparent connection. Groundwater in these regions tends to cut across large structural trends, with little regard for the dip and strike of the beds, as do the caves.

Dye tracing in the Austrian Alps by Zötl (1961) shows similar divergence and crossing of underground flow routes. In the Austrian karst, and apparently also the area shown in Figure 9.42, parts of many flow routes are perched in the vadose zone, where leakage along many alternate routes is common (see Figure 15.7). Nevertheless, much of the divergence in these areas appears take place in the phreatic zone.

Some dye traces extend under surface rivers and emerge on the side opposite from most of the catchment area. This is usually caused by partial filling of the valley with river or glacial sediments, which block the original springs and force groundwater to exit at alternative sites. In some cases the river has migrated laterally across the spring, so that the groundwater emerges along the shore opposite from where it originally discharged. These relationships can occur even in regions of simple geology.

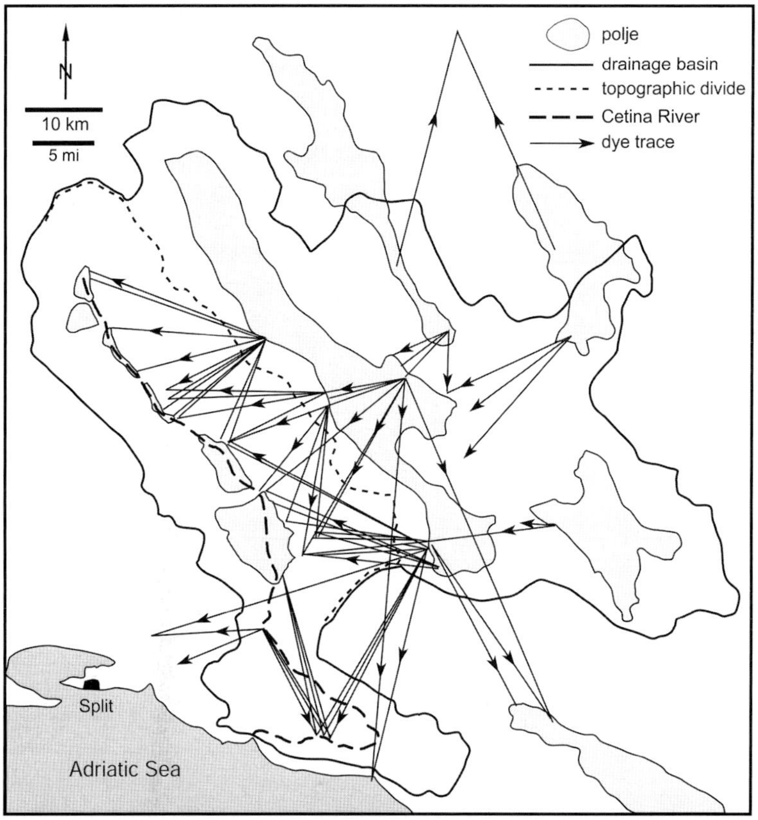

Passage sinuosity

Nearly all cave passages show some form of sinuosity, either as abrupt jogs along intersecting fractures, or as smooth, curving bends (Figure 9.11). The overall passage sinuosity (total length divided by its straight-line distance) is typically about 1.2 to 1.8.

In bedded, gently dipping rocks, the passages have patterns that resemble the meanders in surface rivers. Deike and White (1969) show that the bend spacing in these

Figure 9.42: Pattern of dye traces in highly deformed Mesozoic limestones of the Cetina River basin, Croatia-Bosnia (from Baučić, 1968). Note the divergence and subterranean crossings typical of traces in a complex geologic setting.

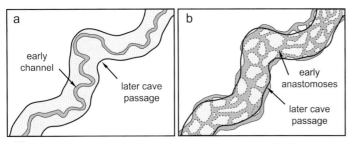

Figure 9.43: Evolution of cave-passage sinuosity in bedded rocks. The pattern of early channels is guided by minor irregularities along bedding-plane partings. As large passages develop from the early ones, they are guided by progressively larger structures and develop broader sinuosity that engulfs the tighter early pattern. (**a**) Many passages enlarge from single narrow channels. (**b**) Some passages may grow by enlargement of a band of anastomotic channels. Figure 6.28 shows a possible example.

caves increases with greater passage width, just as meander length increases with channel width in surface streams. In a freely flowing surface stream, meanders are caused by erosion and deposition of sediment in its channel, but the bends in a cave passage are encased by solid rock, so their origin must be different.

Geologic leveling surveys of caves in prominently bedded rocks (e.g., Figures 9.28–9.29) show that this kind of cave sinuosity, is controlled by subtle variations in dip imposed by irregularities in the strata. In Figure 9.29, note that the bends in the narrow canyons (Boone Avenue, El Ghor) are shorter and tighter than those in the wide tube (Cleaveland Avenue). The largest bends in Cleaveland Avenue are controlled by comparably large structures, such as broad anticlines and synclines. The smaller bends are caused by local irregularities in the beds. In very narrow canyons elsewhere in the cave the sinuosity is usually much greater than in any of the passages shown in Figure 9.29.

The smallest bedding irregularities are mounds, troughs, and ripples dating from the time the rock was originally deposited as sediment. These range from several centimeters up to a few meters in diameter or length. Larger structures are caused by tectonic deformation and variations in bed thickness. In highly fractured rocks, the angular sinuosity of a cave passage is controlled by the orientation and spacing of the initial fractures.

As a passage enlarges with time, its path is influenced by progressively larger structures. Any structure smaller than the passage width no longer affects the passage trend. In a narrow passage the small bends are commonly superposed on larger bends. As the passage widens it engulfs the small bends, so only the large ones remain (Figure 9.43a). As vadose water cuts downward from its original path, lateral erosion may cause the passage to deviate from its original pattern, but the sinuosity remains about the same.

Some passages do not grow in width, but seem to attain their full width right from the start. They may contain remnants of a wide band of early anastomotic channels (Figure 9.43b). As the passages enlarge and engulf the original anastomoses, the overall width may not increase. As the passages enlarge, remnants of anastomoses may be left in their walls.

Figure 6.28 shows a band of anastomoses in the ceiling of a passage where a thin slab of rock has dropped away. One can imagine that the entire passage might have originated as stacked swarms of anastomoses. But this is unlikely, because anastomoses are miniature maze caves that cannot easily form deep inside an aquifer where the water is near saturation with dissolved carbonate minerals (Chapter 8). Instead, nearly all anastomoses form late in the developmental history of a passage, when flooding injects water into exposed partings in the adjacent walls. The exception is the origin of anastomoses near the upstream end of a groundwater flow system, where the water still retains much of its aggressiveness. The anastomoses in Figure 6.28 could have formed either way. Although they resemble the initial channels of Figure 9.43b, they could also have been produced by floodwater injection into the parting above a thin wedge of bedrock in the ceiling. Elsewhere in the same passage, rills extending downward from anastomoses suggest a floodwater origin (Figure 6.27).

In many phreatic passages the sinuosity is caused not only by irregularities in dip, but also by variations in path efficiency between neighboring fractures and partings. Most phreatic passages jog from one parting or fracture to another, following the most favorable route, and this accounts for some of their sinuosity. In both vadose and phreatic passages, the horizontal sinuosity tends to decrease as the dip angle increases.

Effects of erosional unloading

As rocks are eroded away at the surface, the pressure on the underlying rocks decreases. This unloading causes fractures and partings in the remaining rock to become wider and more numerous. Stresses caused by glacial loading and unloading have a similar effect, as do internal stresses caused by tectonic processes and the tidal effect of the Moon and Sun.

In the centers of large plateaus or mountain chains, caves may be forced to remain shallow even where a great deal of soluble rock lies above base level, because most fissures at depth remain tight. The influence of joint patterns on cave passages tends to increase toward the perimeters of karst uplands, where stress release by unloading has been most active (Renault, 1970).

For the same reason, caves may cluster around deeply entrenched valleys. There are particularly clear examples in the Obey River Gorge, Tennessee, where limestone is exposed only where a thick cover of insoluble rock has been removed by deep entrenchment of valleys (Sasowsky and White, 1994). Several large caves are located in narrow bands near the valley bottoms. In a similar setting in eastern Kentucky, Ewers (1985) gives an example of a steep, youthful stream valley that has lost its water to the subsurface in several headward steps. The resulting cave follows the original course of the valley, with some passages that lie directly beneath it and others that closely parallel it.

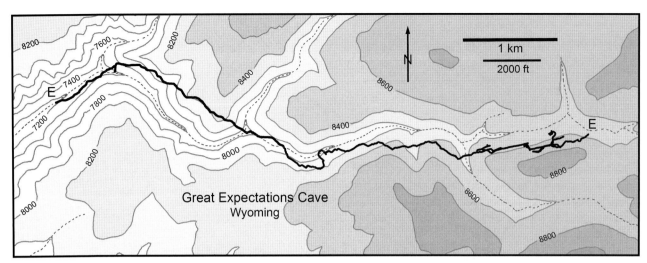

Figure 9.44: Great Expectations ("Great X") Cave, Wyoming, shows a close association with the overlying valley. The cave descends from right to left and its gradient is similar to that of the valley. Dark shading represents higher elevations. E = entrances. Used with permission of the National Speleological Society (*www.caves.org*); compiled by Peter Shifflett.

One of Wyoming's largest caves, Great Expectations ("Great X") Cave, is located beneath a deep mountainside canyon. The stream that carved the gorge is now the sinking stream that formed the cave. Because of stress release, the cave follows the original surface valley very closely (Figure 9.44).

A subtle example of stress release is shown by Barrack Zourie Cave in New York State (Figure 9.45). The cave is located in a plateau of gently dipping Silurian-Devonian limestone that was dissected by a deep valley prior to late Pleistocene glaciation. The valley is now filled with about 80 m of glacial sediment, as shown by well logs and gravity surveys (M. Palmer, 1976), so its true depth is not clear from the topographic map. The valley separates Barrack Zourie Cave from McFail's Cave, the largest cave in the Northeast. From the geologic structure and the pattern of water inputs, Barrack Zourie Cave might be expected to contain canyons extending down the dip to the south-southwest, leading to strike-oriented tubes draining east-southeast. McFail's and most other caves in the area follow that general pattern.

Instead, Barrack Zourie Cave parallels the flank of the preglacial valley as a series of joint-controlled passages that zig-zag along an overall course midway between the dip and strike. For the vadose passages to follow a down-dip path, it would have been necessary for them to extend beneath a thick insoluble cap-rock, where well data show that fractures are narrower and fewer. Instead, a more efficient route was provided by erosional unloading along the flanks of the valley. The cave is located at about the level of the deepest stage of preglacial valley erosion. The bedrock floor of the valley has a steep gradient and lay above the local base level during the deep stage of erosion. Therefore, Barrack Zourie Cave probably had a mainly vadose origin.

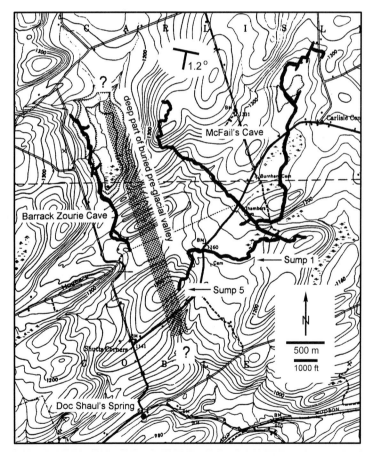

Figure 9.45: Effect of erosional unloading and preglacial drainage on cave patterns in eastern New York State. McFail's Cave and Barrack Zourie Cave are separated by a pre-glacial valley up to 80 m deep, which is now filled almost completely by glacial deposits. The beds dip SSW at 1.2°. McFail's Cave consists of a down-dip vadose canyon tributary to a strike-oriented tube. Most of Barrack Zourie Cave has a vadose origin, but instead of following the dip, it parallels the flank of the buried valley, which afforded more open fractures because of stress release. Compiled from M. Palmer (1976), Dumont (1995), and A. Palmer (1999). See also Figure 3.48 for a rose diagram of passage orientations in Barrack Zourie Cave.

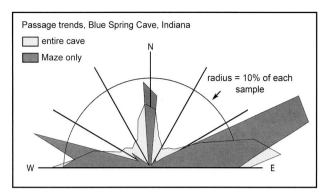

Figure 9.46: Rose diagram of passage trends in Blue Spring Cave, Indiana, comparing those in the Maze (dark gray) to those in the entire cave (light gray). The discrepancy is caused by enlargement of fractures that developed around a collapse zone in the main passage. See map in Figure 8.16. Compare the style of the rose diagram to that in Figure 3.48.

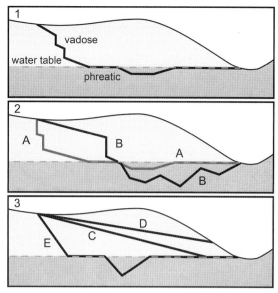

Figure 9.47: Generalized cave gradients in a variety of structural settings. **1** = typical vadose-phreatic profile. **2** = effect of stratigraphic sequence: **A** = massive, fractured rock above and bedded poorly fractured rock below (fracturing near the surface is also enhanced by erosional unloading, regardless of rock structure). **B** = bedded strata overlying massive, fractured rock. Note the deep phreatic loops in the massive rock. **3** = effect of dip angle in well-bedded rock: In **C**, the vadose passage is longer than in **1** or **2** because there is less discordance to the beds. In **D**, the dip is so low that the cave emerges at a perched spring in the valley wall. In **E**, where the dip is steep, the vadose section is short and steep, and phreatic loops are more common and deeper than in **C**. Depths of phreatic loops can be determined from diving, remotely operated vehicles, and drilling, but are mainly inferred from presently inactive examples that now lie above the water table.

Stress release around a karst depression can produce similar results. Blue Spring Cave, Indiana, preferentially follows two major joint sets in the Mississippian Salem Limestone (Figures 3.48 and 8.16a). More than half the passages follow joints that are roughly parallel to the average dip (west-southwest), and a smaller percentage follow strike-oriented joints. These trends can be shown by a rose diagram of individual passage segments obtained from the survey data and weighted by length (Figure 9.46).

But if only the passages in the Maze are considered, a different pattern emerges. Although much of the passage length in the Maze follows the same trends as those in the rest of the cave, an even greater length is oriented at angles about 15–25 degrees to either side of the dip-oriented trend. As a result, many passages in the Maze intersect at conspicuously acute and obtuse angles (Figure 8.16b). The additional passage orientations are almost unique to the Maze, which suggests that local joints were formed by stress patterns around the collapse zone. Preexisting fractures nearby were undoubtedly enlarged as well.

Entrenched meanders in river valleys are ideal sites for cave origin because of steep hydraulic gradients and optimum conditions for erosional stress release (Figures 2.3 and 2.24). For example, the drainage through Mystery Cave, Minnesota, follows a 2.3 km course that bypasses 8 km of meanders along the South Branch of the Root River (Figure 8.20).

A cave formed by a sinking stream may not follow the course of its predecessor valley if the hydraulic gradient is in a contrary direction. Culverson Creek Cave, West Virginia, deviates abruptly from the south-southwestern trend of the original surface valley and drains northeast for 7 km to a deeply entrenched stream (Jones, 1997). In doing so, it crosses beneath several minor ridges and surface divides. This type of mismatch between original surface drainage and cave patterns is also common where prominent fractures cut across drainage divides (Figure 9.17; see also White and White, 2001).

Passage profiles

The profile of a cave passage is governed by its hydrology, geomorphic setting, and geologic structure (Figure 9.47). Caves fed by surface recharge are considered here. Their upstream ends are generally vadose and feed into phreatic passages at their downstream ends. In this case their profiles tend to be concave-upward, because the vadose passages are steeper.

Widening of fissures by erosional stress release tends to make vadose passages steeper in their upstream ends, because shafts are concentrated there. Many caves in the plateaus of the east-central U.S. have this character. But this tendency can be disrupted if massive, highly fractured rocks underlie thin-bedded, poorly fractured strata. In this case, the upper levels are mostly low-gradient canyons and vadose tubes that feed into shafts at lower levels. Many caves in the eastern Alps and in northern England have this pattern.

In well-bedded strata, a gentle dip can allow vadose passages to be extensive. Most passages in the low plateaus of Kentucky and Tennessee are affected in this way. Many caves never reach the water table and simply discharge their water at perched springs in valley walls. Where the dip is steep, vadose passages are short and steep, and phreatic passages tend to have downward loops that are more frequent and deeper than in rocks with gentler dip.

Nearly all passages that form in the phreatic zone have sinuosity that is vertical as well as horizontal. Those parts of a passage that extend below the original water table are called *phreatic loops*, and the rising portion of a loop is called a *phreatic lift* or *lift tube* (Figure 9.48). These terms can be used even in passages that are now dry. Sediment may partly fill the lower parts of a phreatic loop to form a constriction in the passage cross section (Lauritzen and others, 2000). After a loop is abandoned by its original flow, sediment carried by periodic floodwaters may fill it completely. This can account for the rare situation where a passage appears to terminate abruptly where the ceiling slopes down to a floor of sediment.

The depth that phreatic loops can extend below the water table is a matter of debate. Some water-filled passages have been dived through their springs to depths of several hundred meters, at the limit of present-day techniques, and yet they still continue downward out of sight (Exley, 1994a). Most are located along major faults. Lift tubes up to 100 m in relief have been mapped in caves in Sarawak, Malaysia (Farrant and others, 1995). They are now abandoned and resemble vertical shafts. Phreatic loops of comparable depth have been

Figure 9.48: Upward view through a nearly vertical lift tube in Pološka jama, in the Julian Alps of Slovenia. This may once have been the downstream end of a phreatic loop, but now it serves as a floodwater overflow route. Scallops in the walls are oriented upward, and their lengths indicate a flow velocity of about half a meter per second. The height of the lift is about 8 m.

detected in caves of the Sierra de El Abra, Mexico (Fish, 1977).

Ford (1971) suggests that fissure frequency is the dominant control over the depth of phreatic loops (Figure 7.13). Where only a few initial fractures or partings are available, loops are few and they penetrate to great depth below the water table. Where fissures are numerous, phreatic loops are abundant and shallow. As caves form, stress release in the surrounding bedrock can help to open more fractures and partings. With time, these openings become abundant enough that passages tend to follow the water table.

The depth of phreatic loops is also limited by the narrowing that is typical of fractures and partings with increasing depth below the surface (Palmer, 1969). The initial laminar discharge through fissures depends on roughly the cube of the fissure width (as shown by combining Eqs. 4.6a and 4.1), and therefore phreatic passages tend to cluster at and just below the water table. Loops are deepest in areas of structural deformation, where the normal relation between depth and initial fissure width is disrupted. During the 1930s, much drilling was done in the Tennessee River valley in search of potential dam sites (Moneymaker, 1941). The records show that deep solution cavities are abundant in two areas — the folded and faulted Appalachian Mountains, and the fault zones of eastern Kentucky and Tennessee. Elsewhere, where the rocks are relatively undisturbed, cavities are relatively shallow. The two viewpoints (emphasis on fissure frequency vs. fissure width) are complementary, rather than contradictory.

The depths of phreatic loops do not invariably diminish with time. In Mammoth Cave, Kentucky, the deepest known phreatic loop (21 m) is in the lowest and most recent of the major passages (Figure 9.49). This is caused by thick-bedded, prominently jointed strata at that elevation. Another possible complication is that many floodwater diversion passages, which form above the low-flow water table under hydraulic pressure, also have irregular profiles with high-amplitude loops (Palmer, 1975; Audra, 1994; Häuselmann, 2005). In such caves, high-level passages with large vertical loops are not necessarily the oldest.

Field recognition of now-dry phreatic loops and lift tubes is required for proper interpretation of a cave's origin and hydraulic function. The distinction between a true phreatic loop and a floodwater loop (formed above the normal water table) is not always easy to make, because phreatic tubes can be exposed to flooding after they have been abandoned by their normal flow. Characteristic floodwater features include coarse-grained sediment, rills below anastomoses and solution pockets, and narrow drains in the floors of downward loops (pages 198–199), but these can easily be superposed on earlier phreatic passages. To verify that vertical loops were originally phreatic, they must be related to a former spring at or above their highest points, or to vadose-phreatic transition points, as shown in Figure 9.49.

Miller (2006) describes cave development in massive brecciated Cretaceous limestone in Belize, in which passages

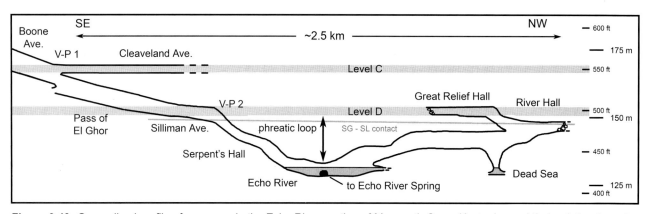

Figure 9.49: Generalized profile of passages in the Echo River section of Mammoth Cave, Kentucky, and their relation to major levels C and D (see Figure 9.54). V-P 1 and V-P 2 are vadose-phreatic transitions, which indicate former base levels. The original depth of the phreatic loop in Echo River is indicated by the double-ended arrow. The lowest passages have been flooded by a 15 m Pleistocene rise in base level, and by a 3 m water-level rise caused by a dam on the Green River. SG-SL = Ste. Genevieve - St. Louis contact.

of various origin gradually linked together by underground stream piracy. He notes that passages with the deepest phreatic loops were formed by streams with the smallest detrital sediment load.

In central Scandinavia, Faulkner (2005, 2006) shows that caves that follow paths opened by glacial unloading have a maximum depth below the overlying surface that is roughly 1/8 of the overall topographic relief of the hillside in which the caves are located. Few caves in the area exceed this ratio.

Worthington (2004) evaluated the profiles of more than 40 major caves throughout the world to determine the variables that influence the depth of conduit development below the water table. He found that conduit depth was strongly correlated with the overall flow length of the system, dip of the bedding, and relief between the highest recharge point and the lowest spring. He showed statistically that most of the variability in conduit depth can be accounted for by this relationship:

$$D = 0.18 \, (L \, sin \, \Theta)^{0.81} \qquad (9.1)$$

where D = mean conduit depth (meters) below the water table, L = flow path length in meters, and Θ = dip angle (degrees).

For example, the clearest and deepest measured phreatic loop in Mammoth Cave, Kentucky, is the 21-meter loop shown in Figure 9.49. The mean dip is about 0.3° and the total flow length is about 6 km. Eq. 9.1 predicts a maximum phreatic loop about 3 m deep. Although this particular estimate does not come close to the actual value, the equation gives a very good estimate for the average of all surveyed phreatic loops in the cave. The 21-meter loop was included in Worthington's data and simply represents part of the scatter.

Worthington's equation is not only based on field data, but it also makes sense in physical terms. Deep fissures are more common in folded strata than in gently dipping ones, so there is a direct relation between dip angle and depth. Along lengthy flow paths, water can follow downward loops without adding much to the overall flow distance. It is also likely that some deep paths will also be more efficient than their shallow counterparts. In short systems, a deep path would increase the relative flow length considerably and is less likely to be the favored route.

The World's deepest caves fall into two groups – those that penetrate deep beneath the surface, and those that achieve great vertical range by following relatively shallow routes not far below the surface. Caves that penetrate deep beneath the surface include Krubera in Georgia, Huautla in Mexico, and Siebenhengste in Switzerland. Caves with a large vertical range but with comparatively little depth below the overlying land surface include Jean Bernard in France. In the U.S., the entire depth of Lechuguilla Cave is achieved within a small area (Figure 8.67), whereas Wyoming's two deepest, Great X Cave (Figure 9.44) and Columbine Crawl, have gentle slopes parallel to the land surface. The difference between these two groups is related mainly to the thickness of the soluble formation and the intensity of faulting, both of which are greater in the caves that penetrate deep below the surface.

Topographic relief is often used as an approximation of groundwater gradient. When a sinking stream develops, initial cave development may sometimes involve hydraulic gradients that utilize the entire topographic relief. But more frequently, water follows vadose routes to the water table, and the gradients of neither the vadose nor the phreatic passages are affected by the relief of the land surface. The vadose passages have gradients simply equal to their slopes, because they do not build up pressure. Hydraulic gradients of phreatic passages are adjusted to the amount of flow and the size of the conduits, and they have no relation to the thickness of the vadose zone. Topographic relief is essential to most cave development, but once the caves have formed, the amount of relief has little bearing on hydraulic gradient or further enlargement rates in the caves.

Relation of caves to landscape evolution

The vertical arrangement of passages in most solution caves is influenced by the developmental history of the surrounding landscape. As valleys form and deepen, they become the

Figure 9.50: Floodplain of the South Branch of the Potomac River, viewed from the entrance of Trout Cave, West Virginia. The floodplain is the local base level. Its great width suggests that the river has been stable at or just below this elevation for a long time. Conditions are favorable for the development of caves at that same level.

outlets for groundwater that is supplied by infiltration into the surrounding uplands (Chapter 4). Although some valleys are produced by faulting, the great majority are carved by streams. As a stream erodes its valley deeper, karst springs that emerge in the valley tend to shift to progressively lower elevations. The cave passages that feed the springs also shift downward, following the drop in the water table. Therefore, in most caves the highest passages are oldest and the lowest are more recent. The following discussion applies mainly to epigenic caves fed by recharge from an overlying or adjacent karst surface. These caves show the closest association with the surrounding landscape.

Cave levels

Most caves contain passages at a variety of elevations. Each passage, or group of passages, that is confined to a narrow vertical range is commonly called a *cave level*. Most geologists apply the term only to passages that relate to present or former base levels in nearby valleys. To avoid the impression that the passages are perfectly horizontal, the term *tier* or *story* is often used instead (Chapter 6). These last two terms have no genetic connotations and are useful for general purposes. But the term *cave level* is well established in the literature and can be used to distinguish those passages that show a clear relation to base level.

Origin of cave passages at base level

If a valley deepens rapidly by river erosion, cave streams tend to shift to lower routes so frequently that their passages do not remain active long enough to grow large. When there is a pause or slowing of entrenchment, the valley bottom broadens into a floodplain (Figures 2.3 and 9.50), and cave passages at that level have time to grow large. These passages constitute a true cave level. Periods of valley filling have more complex effects on caves, because some passages may remain active, while others may fill with sediment as older, higher passages are reactivated (see pages 262–264).

The erratic pace of downward erosion, and the occasional periods of valley filling that interrupt it, are the result of several complex processes. They include changes in sea level, climate, and rates of uplift of the land. Glacial advances and retreats have a large effect. Changes in the course of rivers can cause sudden base-level changes, as described in Chapter 13. With all of these processes acting at different rates, sometimes in complementary ways and at other times in opposition, it is no wonder that the erosional history of river valleys is so complex. The same is true for the origin of caves that are tributaries of the rivers.

Cave passages are eventually abandoned as the outlet valley deepens by erosion or the land rises (Figures 9.50–9.51). Both uplift and erosion usually operate simultaneously. Some cave levels correlate with river terraces, which are the remnants of former floodplains. The correlation between terraces and cave levels has been used by many authors to support the idea that caves form at or just below the water table (Chapter 7). This concept was accepted by the majority of cave geologists during the last half of the 20th century. In recent decades a growing number of researchers find that the relationship of cave tiers to the water table is not at all certain. Alternative views are described on the next few pages. First, the idealized model, in which major cave passages are related to base levels in nearby river valleys, is described in detail (see Figure 9.52).

A river terrace can form in several ways. If a floodplain is produced by a lengthy pause in erosional downcutting, renewed downcutting will leave remnants of the floodplain in the valley walls (Figure 2.3). Bedrock-floored terraces are sometimes called *straths*. This kind of terrace is most likely

Figure 9.51: The main passage of Eisriesenwelt, in the Austrian Alps, is a large tube that developed at a former base level during the late Tertiary Period. It has since been uplifted far above the present river valley by a rise in the plateau and simultaneous erosional entrenchment of the valley. The water that formed this passage has diverted to lower routes.

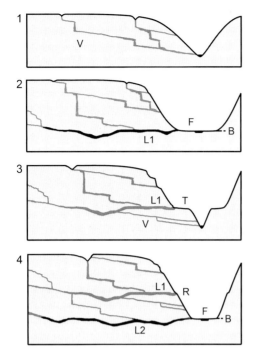

Figure 9.52: Traditional view of the passage sequence formed in response to a dropping base level. (**1**) Rapid river entrenchment (youthful stage of erosion); V = small, mainly vadose passages. (**2**) River reaches its erosional base level (B) and forms a floodplain (F); L1 = major cave level adjusted to that same elevation. (**3**) Uplift of the land and/or drop in base level causes renewed river entrenchment; major level L1 is abandoned. T = river terraces. (**4**) The river reaches a base level again, and major level L2 forms. R = remnants of former terraces. During all of these steps, the valley widens and the land surface erodes downward.

Figure 9.53: A perched cave spring in the Kakouetta Gorge, western Pyrenees, France. Rapid stream entrenchment, in response to glacial deepening of the valley into which the gorge drains, has outpaced the downward rate of cave development.

to correlate with cave passages. A floodplain can also form by partial filling of the valley by river sediment. Terraces form when the sediment is later entrenched by the river. This variety of terrace may not represent a long enough time for cave passages to have enlarged at that level.

Terraces can also be produced by resistant rocks. These are usually called ***structural benches*** to distinguish them from former base levels. Anyone who has visited the Grand Canyon has seen many structural benches. Although these features may or may not represent a pause in river entrenchment, caves can still be perched at those same elevations. Some terraces involve more than one process, and any interpretation of nearby caves should take these processes into account.

Terraces are easily eroded away, because as a valley deepens it also widens. Most recognizable terraces are only scattered remnants of former floodplains. Old ones have usually been removed almost entirely. For that reason, caves provide more information about the erosional-depositional history of nearby valleys than terraces provide about either the caves or the valleys.

In low-relief regions, where uplift is slow, cave development can generally keep pace with the rate of valley entrenchment (Figure 9.52). Cave levels are most distinct in these

areas. Sudden spurts of valley deepening, for example by glacial scouring, can outpace the rate at which cave entrenchment or diversion takes place, so perched karst springs can form (Figure 9.53).

The presence of a vadose passage shows that, while it was forming, the floor of its outlet valley must have been at a lower elevation than the passage. Vadose passages cannot qualify as true cave levels because they form along the descending paths of gravitational water, which are independent of one another. A poorly soluble bed may cause perching of vadose passages at a common elevation, but this is a structural phenomenon that does not relate to the position of base level.

Only phreatic passages can form true cave levels. The most clearly defined levels are adjusted to the low-flow conditions of the cave streams that formed them. The hydraulic gradient in a water-filled cave passage is so low, except during major floods, that the vadose-phreatic transition zone is essentially at the same elevation as the local spring. Caves enlarge fastest during floods, but floodwater dissolution extends over a wide vertical range, with no single dominant elevation. As the water table drops, floodwater enlargement can continue to modify passages or even form new ones. These effects must be distinguished for proper evaluation of cave development.

With careful surveys, the vadose-phreatic transition zone can be determined fairly precisely, even in passages that are now dry (Chapter 14). There is usually a decrease

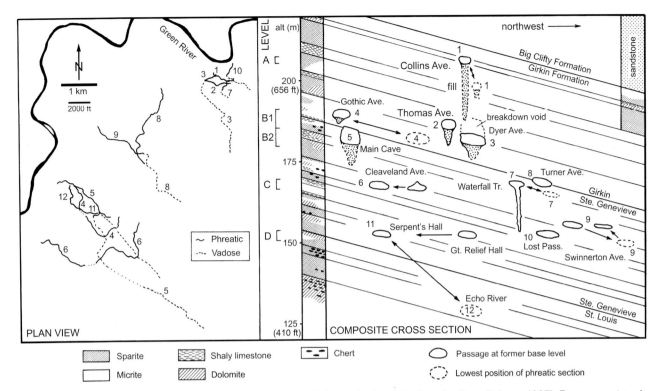

Figure 9.54: Major levels in Mammoth Cave, Kentucky, in relation to the local stratigraphy (from Palmer, 1987). Passages at each elevation occupy a variety of beds, which indicates that these are true levels developed at former positions of base level, rather than along favorable beds or structures.

in gradient, a change from canyon to tube shape, and, in prominently bedded rocks, a loss of down-dip orientation. Vadose passages may have no upward dissolution of their ceilings, whereas this is common in phreatic passages. Pin-point accuracy in locating this transition is not possible. For consistency, it is best to measure the solutional ceiling level at the point farthest downstream in the vadose section. Identification of a cave level is more convincing if vadose-phreatic transition zones can be recognized in several independent passages at similar elevations.

This interpretation of cave levels has been tested in many caves, most thoroughly at Mammoth Cave, Kentucky, which contains many independent passages that span a broad range of elevations (Figure 9.54). Geologic mapping in the cave shows clear vadose-phreatic transition points in many passages. Four or five distinct levels have been recognized, with up to five independent passages located at each level. Among the passages at any level, the elevations of the vadose-phreatic transitions coincide to within about one meter.

These elevations are not influenced by favorable strata, because the passages at any given level occupy different beds. Likewise they are not controlled by geologic structure, because the beds exposed in each passage have a broad variety of dip angles and directions. A river terrace is present at level D, but only fragmentary evidence remains for a terrace at level C. Level B correlates with parts of an extensive sinkhole plain (Pennyroyal Plateau) south and east of the cave. Level A pre-dates all of these features.

Clearly the passages at a given level must have formed more or less simultaneously. Dating of cave sediments also

supports this idea (Chapter 13; Granger and others, 2001). There is some scatter in the dates because the deposits represent only the last active phase of passage development. Some passages retained active streams longer than others, even long after the local base level had dropped.

Figures 9.29 and 9.49 show examples of how the vadose-phreatic transition can be recognized. The strike orientation of tubular Cleaveland Avenue (Figure 9.29) is an ideal indicator of development along the water table. This is identified as Level C on Figure 9.54. Later, when the base level dropped, water abandoned the Cleaveland Avenue tube in favor of continuing down-dip as a vadose canyon (Pass of El Ghor).

Figure 9.49 shows these same passages in profile. The El Ghor canyon, and its continuation as Silliman Avenue, extend to the next level (D), which lies 15 m (50 ft) lower than level C. In such a stable landscape, a base-level drop of this magnitude is significant. The drop was sudden, as shown by the almost total lack of entrenchment of the tube floor at level C. Also, there is no interruption of the vadose canyon between C and D. Such an abrupt and well-defined change could only have been caused by headward erosion of the Green River valley by rapids and waterfalls working their way upstream in response to a drop in base level farther downstream. Granger and others (2001) attribute this event to rearrangement of the Ohio River drainage pattern (pages 358–359). In contrast, downward erosion of the Green River along its full length would have been slow and irregular.

Cleaveland Avenue coincides perfectly with Level C, which was first identified in Waterfall Trail almost 5 km to the northeast. The vadose-phreatic transition at Level D is quite different from that at Level C. Beyond the point V-P 2, the level D tube swoops down in a series of steps all the way to the present base level of the Green River. The low point in the ceiling of Echo River is more than 20 m below the normal elevation for Level D. Palmer (1981a) originally misidentified Echo River as a lower, more recent passage level, rather than as a phreatic loop descending from level D.

In the downstream direction, the Echo River passage loops back upward into River Hall, where it is joined by Great Relief Hall, a tube at the true elevation of Level D (152 m), which drops downstream into River Hall. What happens farther downstream from this junction is uncertain, because the passage is blocked by breakdown about 20 m beyond. Echo River eventually developed a low-level drain to Echo River Spring, which now lies just below the present level of the Green River (Figure 9.49).

Identifying Echo River as a loop below Level D helps to liberate the concept of cave levels from the idea that phreatic passages must cluster at exactly the same elevation as the controlling base level. None of Echo River correlates in elevation with any of its contemporaries, except at its vadose-phreatic transition. Echo River remains active even today, and as a result it has grown larger than any of the passages around it.

The fidelity with which these passages follow the base-level model is difficult to explain. It is unlikely that the river level could remain stable over the entire history of passage development. Sediment dating by Granger and others (2001) indicates that levels C and D in Mammoth Cave each required about 500,000 years to form. This is long enough to span several glacial and interglacial episodes. One could argue that only enough time is required to produce a rudimentary cave, and that it will later continue to enlarge even after the base level has shifted. But if this were so, then there would be a scattering of many passages at different elevations.

Instead, the evidence supports a degree of base-level stability that is no longer present. Cave sediments at Level D are at least a million years old (Granger and others, 2001), so those passages pre-date the major Pleistocene glacial advances into the Ohio River valley north of Mammoth Cave. Later, as the regional drainage adjusted its pattern to the periodic incursions of glacial ice, base level changed frequently and at an irregular rate. Passages below Level D are scattered in elevation and show no distinct levels. The largest of these passages tend to be perched on resistant beds (Figure 9.28) or are the result of long-term enlargement of phreatic loops (Figure 9.49). The interpretation of the glacial history and its effect on river patterns is discussed in Chapter 13.

With the Mammoth Cave data in mind from Figures 9.49 and 9.54, there are several other topics to consider: Even when a surface river is at its erosional base level, the river still has a distinct gradient. Any related cave levels should lie at progressively higher elevations in the river's upstream direction. White and White (1974) demonstrate this pattern for major cave passages in the Potomac River basin of the

eastern U.S. Data points are sparse and scattered, but their overall distribution agrees with the concept of base-level control. This approach is also being applied in the Mammoth Cave region, but the low relief and thin limestones limit the vertical range of the data and make precise leveling surveys necessary.

To complicate the picture, as base level drops, the transition from one cave level to another is usually gradual. Entrenchment and diversion of passages in a cave system progress slowly upstream away from the valleys. Passages closest to the entrenching river are most likely to provide the clearest record of base-level changes. Johnson and Gomez (1994) describe examples in the Mitchell Plain of southern Indiana.

Woodward (1961) proposed an alternative view of the role of base level on cave development, but his idea has not received serious attention from other researchers. He considered that most caves form during periods of rapid valley entrenchment. His main field examples were the large natural bridges of Virginia (Chapter 2), which fit his model well. He considered that caves are most likely to form when the water table is steep, rather than adjusted to a static base level. Intervals between cave levels may match those of river terraces but their elevations will not match well. In fact, a great deal of cave enlargement does take place during periods of rapid river entrenchment, but the large low-gradient tubes normally associated with cave levels are not formed at those times.

Sequences of phreatic tiers
The tidy scenario of base-level control of cave passages has been questioned in recent decades. For example, Worthington (1991, 2004, 2005) offers a fresh view of cave levels, or more appropriately *tiers*, by relating them to geologic structure and the downward increase in groundwater temperature with depth. From a global examination of cave maps, he shows that the deepest phreatic loops range in magnitude from 0.3% to 3.0% of the overall lengths of their drainage basins (see also Eq. 9.1).

To explain this uniformity he notes that the viscosity of water decreases with depth, owing to the geothermal gradient (an average increase of 20 to 30°C per kilometer of depth in the Earth's crust). The variation of viscosity with temperature is shown in Table 4.1 (page 97). Lower viscosities allow water to move more easily through narrow openings. Thus the flow rate along certain deep routes may be greater than at shallow depth, and the deep paths may enlarge more rapidly than shallower ones. Cave tiers could develop at roughly fixed intervals as the region is dissected by erosion (Figure 9.55).

Deep paths are also favored where vertical permeability exceeds horizontal permeability. This requires large fractures discordant to the bedding, and these are most abundant in regions of deformed rocks, as in mountainous regions. Worthington suggests that a basin length of more than 3 km is required for paths to develop to depths of more than about 100 m.

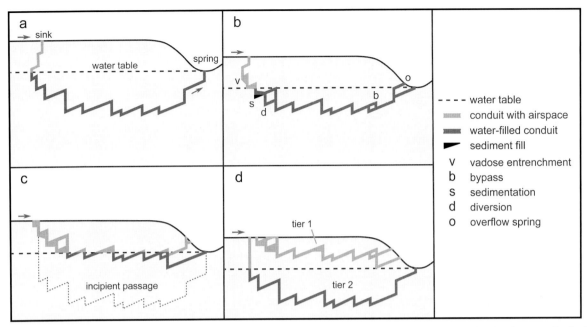

Figure 9.55: The relation of cave tiers to base-level lowering, according to Worthington (2005). (**a**) Origin of a cave both above and below the water table, with deep loops favored by geologic structure and increasing temperature. (**b**) Adjustments in passage patterns with time. (**c**, **d**) Abandonment of earlier phreatic passages and development of new ones. Successive stages of phreatic passage development are only loosely correlated with base level and between caves.

But, as shown in Chapters 5 and 7, temperature has a complex effect on dissolution chemistry. High temperatures decrease the amount of carbonate rock that can be dissolved, but they speed the dissolution rate. Contrary to intuition, faster dissolution causes the breakthrough time to *increase* (so a longer time is required for the initial phases of cave development). This is because rapid dissolution is concentrated in the upstream parts of groundwater flow paths, while the downstream parts stagnate with water near saturation.

Figure 7.22 shows the effect of temperature on breakthrough time. This figure takes into account water viscosity and density, as well as rock solubility and dissolution rate. For example, if the temperature rises from 10°C to 20°C, the breakthrough time approximately doubles. This is a potential obstacle to the Worthington model. But once a route enlarges enough that water can pass through while still retaining measurable aggressiveness, the dissolution rate increases with higher temperatures (Figure 7.19).

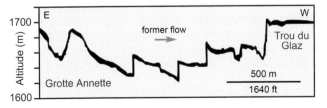

Figure 9.56: Projected profile through a now-dry phreatic passage in the Réseau de la Dent de Crolles, France: Grotte Annette to Trou du Glaz (Worthington, 2004, 2005, from Lismonde, 1997). This profile illustrates the jagged pattern of deep flow paths suggested in Figure 9.55. See Figure 3.46 for the regional geology and Figure 6.11 for a view of Trou du Glaz.

The flow patterns described by Worthington are based on many field examples (such as Figure 9.56). They are also compatible with the inception-horizon concept of Lowe (1992), in which deep cave origin takes place along geologic contacts that provide favorable chemical environments (Chapter 7). The model of Ford (1971), shown in Figure 7.13, is also pertinent.

The sequence in Figure 9.55 is eventually limited by the presence of insoluble rock beneath the cavernous strata (for example, in Figures 9.3 and 9.19). The depth of even the first tier may be limited in this way.

The phreatic loops in Mammoth Cave are merely subdued versions of those in Figure 9.55. But the loop amplitudes in Mammoth are generally much less than the intervals between passage levels, and as a result the base-level concept applies well to that cave. Where phreatic loops are deep, shifts in base level have relatively little influence on their growth, and the effect of base level is obscure. It is clear that the interpretation of cave tiers is not always a simple matter of equating sub-horizontal passages with pauses in river entrenchment.

Levels in hypogenic caves

Some hypogenic caves may also have well-defined levels. This is most conspicuous where hydrogen sulfide has oxidized to sulfuric acid at the water table (Chapter 8). In places this kind of water-table control is even more distinct than in epigenic caves. Carlsbad Cavern in New Mexico contains two or three good examples (Figure 8.53). For example, most of the Big Room has a nearly horizontal floor that cuts across several different rock units. In Figure 6.19 the bedrock floor is obscured by dripstone and sediment.

Structural guidance of cave tiers

The vertical arrangement of certain caves in Yorkshire, England, was once considered evidence for base-level control. Later field work by Waltham (1970) shows that the "levels" are controlled instead by perching of water on shaly beds. Ogden (2003) applies this idea to the origin of cave levels in all gently dipping rocks, particularly to those in the east-central U.S. He considers that river entrenchment is simply retarded by resistant beds, and that caves form atop the same beds for the same reason. Surveys of levels such as those in Figures 9.49 and 9.54 suggest otherwise, and yet the influence of rock structure on groundwater flow paths should not be underestimated (Chapter 15).

Although the major levels in Mammoth Cave show no stratigraphic influence, many individual passages are concordant to the bedding over much of their length. This structural effect is merely superposed on the overall base-level control. Still, the close relationship to the strike and dip of the strata in Figures 9.28–9.29 shows considerable structural control on a local scale that in places disrupts the orderly arrangement of levels.

Waterfall Trail, at Level C in Mammoth Cave (Figures 6.13 and 9.54), is still active over most of its length because it is perched on relatively insoluble cherty and shaly dolomite. Cosmogenic dating of cave sediments at this level gives ages up to 1.5 million years (Chapter 13; Granger and others, 2001). In the presently abandoned sections of Waterfall Trail the sediments are younger (a little more than a million years), because they were deposited by the perched stream long after the passage had formed and its contemporaries had long been abandoned. Perching of cave streams for such long periods had not been imagined before reliable dating methods were developed.

When rapid uplift first exposes soluble rocks to erosion, fractures may be sparse enough in the central parts of mountain masses to sustain a water table high above surface rivers (page 252). Deep cave development is retarded in these areas, which Audra (1994) terms *juvenile karst*. He cites the karst of Papua New Guinea as an example. Cave passages form far above base level and do not correlate with river terraces. Cave development is essentially perched, even where there are no underlying insoluble beds.

Effect of sea-level changes

During each major advance of continental glaciers, sea level drops as much as 200 m to account for the volume of water tied up as ice. Sea level then rebounds as the ice retreats. Compared to the lifespan of a typical cave, glacial episodes are fairly short (roughly 50,000–100,000 years). Coastal caves are strongly influenced by sea-level changes (Chapter 8), but in continental interiors the change in sea level has far less effect.

The relation between caves and sea level is most complex in large coastal aquifers fed by runoff from continental interiors. For example, most caves in Florida and the Yucatán Peninsula are water-filled, partly because of sea-level rise. But many of these caves originally formed beneath the water table, so the impact of sea-level rise is unclear. Some caves extend directly beneath large surface streams (Figure 2.41). Water normally flows from cave springs into the rivers, but during surface floods the flow often reverses. Cave development in these regions is poorly understood, but recent studies, such as those by Smart and others (2002, 2006), Beddows (2003), and Florea (2006), are beginning to shed light on the topic.

Perhaps the most dramatic example of sea-level change is the nearly complete drying of the Mediterranean Sea between 5.3 and 6 million years ago, when the water level dropped as much as 2 km. This was apparently caused by shifts in the pattern of plate movements in the Earth's crust, which blocked the connection with the Atlantic. This time span was long enough to allow major caves to form, so the regional effect must have been greater than that of the shorter glacially induced sea-level changes.

Karst around the Mediterranean adjusted first to the gradual drop in base level, and again to the rise when the sea reconnected to the Atlantic at the Strait of Gibraltar. Many caves, such as those in southern France, contain flooded passages deep beneath present sea level that apparently formed during the low stand of the Mediterranean (Bini, 1994; Audra and others, 2004; Mocochain and others, 2006). Some caves contain diversion passages that rise from these deep passages to feed springs, apparently because the deeper outlets are now blocked by sediment or collapse. For example, the Vaucluse Spring in southeastern France has been explored by a remotely operated vehicle (ROV) down a sloping conduit to a depth of more than 300 m, which is 224 m below present sea level. Rills in the walls suggest that it may have served as a vadose inlet when base level was lower. In a cautionary note, Worthington (2005) points out that similarly deep conduits in France have formed far from the Mediterranean, where its water-level fluctuations presumably had no influence, so not all deep passages in the region are necessarily related to the low stage of the Mediterranean Sea.

Caves that formed in the mixing zone between fresh and marine water are strong indicators of previous sea-level stands (Carew and Mylroie, 1987). In small stable carbonate islands a former high sea-level stand is represented by caves about 6 m above present sea level. Discrete levels of inactive caves have been observed in the steep submarine flanks of islands in the Bahamas at depths down to 125 m below present sea level (Mylroie and Carew, 1990). Divers report abundant caves at a depth of 18 m (Exley, 1994b). The record of sea-level change is complicated in tectonically active regions that are rapidly subsiding or rising. The caves of Isla de Mona, Puerto Rico, which paleomagnetic dating suggests are at least 2 million years old, are now exposed in sheer cliffs at various elevations up to 60 m above the seacoast (Figures 8.42–8.44; Frank and others, 1998).

Effect of rising base level

Rises in base level may disrupt the tendency for passages in a cave to become progressively younger with depth. Some

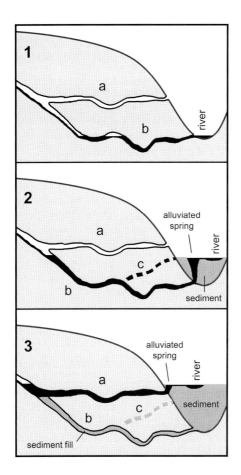

Figure 9.57: Potential effects of base-level rises on a previously formed cave:

1: Cave passages **a** and **b** form at different levels as the river valley deepens. Passage **a** is inactive.

2: A small rise in base level takes place. As sediment accumulates in the valley, the spring from passage **b** maintains an open path to the surface, to form an **alluviated spring**. This may rise directly into the river channel, or it may emerge on the floodplain and enter the river through a short surface channel. Passage **a** remains inactive, except perhaps during floods.

Periodic slumping of the sediment walls of the spring may cause water to back up in passage **b** and overflow into **a**. If so, **a** may become the main outlet. In that case, **b** may fill partly with sediment and retain only a small part of its original flow, or it may become entirely inactive. It is also likely for the increased head in the cave stream to force the spring open again. The sequence of blockage and re-opening of the spring may repeat many times. A new passage (**c**) may form, but this is unlikely, given the two alternative outlets and the short length of time available during a typical base-level rise.

3: A large base-level rise causes passage **a** to flood. It becomes the most efficient outlet. The outlet channel from passage **b** is likely to become choked with sediment carried in from the cave stream. Alternate routes such as **c** will probably also fill with sediment.

possible causes include rising sea level, decreasing stream flow, and glacial depression of the crust. Most of these effects are relatively short-lived, on the order of thousands or tens of thousands of years, but some have endured for millions of years. Even brief episodes can have long-lasting effects.

A base-level rise is usually accompanied by sediment filling in valleys to that new level (Figure 2.3). In most cases the sediment is deposited by the river itself (*alluviation*), although glacial or marine deposits may also be responsible. Cave passages below this level become flooded. They may eventually become sediment-filled, especially if their flow is feeble or is diverted into formerly abandoned passages at a higher level. Various results of a rising base level are shown in Figure 9.57.

In Indiana, seismic surveys and well logs show that as much as 25 meters of post-glacial sediment has accumulated in river valleys and caused low-level cave passages to flood. Many of these passages are still active and feed artesian springs along the river banks. At

the same time, about 15 m of alluviation occurred in central Kentucky. Dye released at a single upstream point in a cave or sinking stream often emerges at several outlets at slightly different times because of complex interconnections between flooded passages (Quinlan and Ray, 1981).

Upper-level cave passages throughout the karst of Indiana, Kentucky, and Tennessee contain thick sediment fill that resulted from a major alluviation phase that extended throughout the entire east-central United States during the late Tertiary Period (M. Palmer and A. Palmer, 1975; Granger and others, 2001; Anthony and Granger, 2004). These sediments are stratified sands and gravels that indicate a gradual infilling by high-velocity cave streams. Meanwhile, thick sediment accumulated at the surface and buried many of the earlier karst features. These deposits represent a widespread event probably triggered by a significant climatic change, such as a period of relatively arid conditions, but the details are uncertain.

Along the Cumberland Escarpment in northern Alabama, several phases of stream deposits have accumulated in the

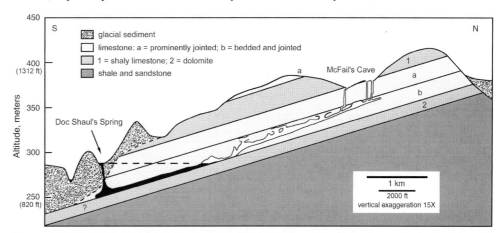

Figure 9.58: Profile through McFail's Cave, New York. The former spring outlet was buried by about 30 m of glacial and river deposits during the past 120,000 years, so that water is forced to rise through the sediment to an artesian spring. See Figure 9.45 for map view. (Modified from M. Palmer, 1976).

bottoms and along the flanks of broad valleys between karst uplands (Smart and Campbell, 2005). These sediments have blocked lower-level cave passages and redirected much of the subsurface drainage. Deep weathering of insoluble pebbles in the sediment suggests ages of more than a million years, according to soil scientists.* Although most of the lowlands in the region are floored by limestone, accessible caves are limited mainly to the high ridges that rise above the lowlands. Major karst springs are located mainly at the bases of the ridges at or near the contacts with the stream deposits.

In valleys of eastern New York, glacial sediments up to 30 m thick have blocked some karst springs entirely, so that the flow now escapes through alternate routes. Some of these routes are reactivated older passages, and some are new passages that formed during the 14,000 years since the glaciers disappeared from the region. A few springs maintained their original paths by rising through funnel-shaped openings in the glacial deposits (Figure 9.58).

In mountainous karst, Glazek and others (1977) describe small caves at various elevations that were formed by glacial meltwaters. Many of these caves have little or no relation to normal erosional base levels. Such caves can be younger than others in the vicinity that lie at lower elevations.

Damming of rivers, either artificially or by natural barriers such as lava flows, is usually too short-lived to have a significant effect on caves. Sloan's Valley Cave in eastern Kentucky contains some large previously mapped passages that are now inaccessible because of flooding by a reservoir on the Cumberland River. Occasional lowering of the reservoir reveals a slippery clay coating on all surfaces, but if the dam were removed the cave would quickly revert to essentially its former condition.

Evidence of a former rise in base level can include sedimentary valley terraces and widespread sediment fill in caves. Even where cave sediment has been removed by erosion or by subsidence into lower passages, drainage grooves in the cave walls can indicate its former presence (page 153). It may be difficult to distinguish between a former base-level rise and paragenesis (see below).

There are many ways to misinterpret cave sediments. Bretz (1942) assumed that the widespread mud in Missouri caves represents a distinct phase of deep-phreatic cave filling (page 168). Most such sediment is actually deposited during floods. Mud banks along cave streams rarely indicate a separate fill stage followed by a discrete erosion stage, but instead the continual alternation between fill and erosion due to short-term changes in stream flow. Some cave sediments are very local and do not represent widespread events. They may accumulate where passage gradients decrease or where cave streams are ponded by breakdown.

Paragenesis

Paragenesis is the upward dissolution of the ceiling in a water-filled cave passage because of sediment accumulation

* Communication from Warren Campbell, Western Kentucky University, 2005.

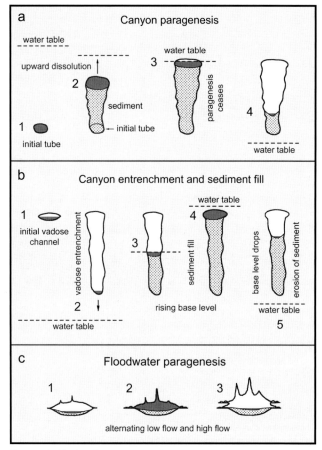

Figure 9.59: (**a**) The concept of paragenesis as applied to sediment-filled canyons. In contrast (**b**), most sediment-filled canyons are produced by rising and falling base level. Paragenesis is also noticeable in many floodwater caves, where upward dissolution takes place during high flow (**c**).

on the underlying floor (Renault, 1970). The sediment shields the floor from aggressive water, leaving only the upper surfaces of the passage exposed to dissolution. As the ceiling dissolves upward, more sediment accumulates on the floor to maintain the equilibrium among erosion, deposition, and water velocity (Figure 9.59a). Upward migration stops when the tube reaches the water table. Later, as the water table drops, the passage is either abandoned or its sediment is excavated by the cave stream. A recent review of the subject is given by Farrant (2004). The term *paragenesis* has other geologic meanings (Neuendorf and others, 2005), so it should be used only when the context is clear.

Many canyon passages contain sediment fill that nearly reaches the passage ceilings. The traditional explanation is that the sediment accumulated in formerly vadose canyons during a base-level rise (Figure 9.59b). But many such canyons are now attributed to paragenesis (Ewers, 1985).

Paragenetic ceiling retreat has been documented to reach heights as much as 50 m. It is common in descending phreatic loops, where sediment is likely to accumulate at the low points (Ford, 1971). In sediment-floored passages, paragenesis is the likely cause of relatively flat ceilings that cut across geologic structures. Because the sediment on the

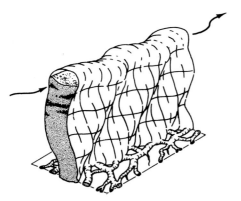

Figure 9.60: A paragenetic canyon (Ewers, 1985, based on examples in eastern Kentucky). The anastomoses at the bottom represent the initial solutional openings, which coalesced into a tube. Sediment on the tube floor caused the ceiling to retreat upward by paragenesis to form a canyon. The tube is still present at the top. Note that the meander grooves preserved in the walls slope downward in the upstream direction (toward the left).

passage floor does not cover the upper walls, paragenetic canyons are likely to widen upward.

A sediment cover does not entirely prevent dissolution of the underlying rock, because water in the sediment pores often remains aggressive (Vaughan, 1998). Nevertheless, thick sediments can greatly diminish the average dissolution rate, as shown by corrosion notches and ramps above former sediment surfaces (page 153).

The pattern of meanders preserved in the passage walls can help to distinguish between the two types of canyon development shown in Figure 9.59a and b. In a typical canyon passage the meanders tend to migrate downstream with time, just as they do in a surface stream. When one stands on the canyon floor at the apex of a meander, the past position of that meander can usually be traced upward toward the ceiling. When traced from ceiling to floor, the meander grooves should slope downward in the direction of flow. Ewers (1982, 1985) points out that in a paragenetic canyon the downward slope of the meander grooves should be in the *upstream* direction, because the meandering streams *rose* with time (Figure 9.60). In Norway, Lauritzen and Lauritsen (1995) used these clues to interpret the origin of a paragenetic canyon 10 m high and 5 m wide. They also noted wall scallops oriented in the upslope direction of passage profiles, which would be expected in phreatic loops but not in entrenched canyons.

The concept of canyon paragenesis is appealing because it is simple, but it should be applied with caution. Many sediment-filled canyons that might seem paragenetic at first glance actually represent a widespread rise in base level, which caused sediment to accumulate in older vadose canyons (Figure 9.59b; see examples in Figure 9.54).

During the fill stage in Figure 9.59b, some characteristics of paragenesis can be superposed on the original passage. Many canyons that were previously filled with sediment have large wall scallops a meter or more in length. The scallop edges have been smoothed by dissolution, perhaps

beneath the sediment. If the sediment is later removed by stream erosion, small, sharply defined scallops are sometimes imprinted on the larger ones by the stream (Palmer, 1981a) The old scallops are out of adjustment with this flow, and their contours may be smoothed by the later flow or removed entirely.

Paragenesis is often caused by floodwaters, which are highly aggressive, sediment-laden, and abrasive (Figures 9.59c and 8.22). Several passages in Skull Cave, New York, have been forced by intense flooding to migrate upward into poorly soluble strata in which caves are otherwise very rare (Figure 8.17).

Passage diversions

In any interpretation of a solution passage, it is helpful to ask two questions: What caused it to form where it did, in preference to the many other possible routes? And, if it is no longer actively forming, why and how did it become abandoned by its flow? The first question has been answered in this and previous chapters. The second is addressed here. It can add one more line of evidence for interpreting the erosional and hydrologic history of the region.

Migration of vadose flow

Ford (1988) describes two types of vadose passages. The earliest are formed when the water table is high, and as each one grows and transmits flow more readily, the water table is drawn down around it like a linear version of the cone of depression around a pumping well. These are ***drawdown vadose passages***. After the water table has declined, later ***invasion vadose passages*** can be formed above the water table by descending water. The drawdown type is perhaps not technically vadose, as it is not formed by purely gravitational water. The invasion type is the one discussed here.

The ideal vadose flow path is straight downward along vertical fissures. But if the available vertical openings are too narrow to transmit all incoming water, the excess will overflow along the next-steepest path, which is

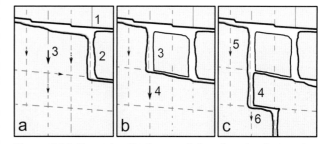

Figure 9.61: Example of leakage and diversion of vadose water. (**a**) The initial vadose route in this view was guided by a bedding-plane parting (1) but the water was later diverted along a fracture to form the shaft and shaft drain (2). Leakage continues to take place along fractures in the passage floor. Route 3 is widest and pirates the most water. (**b**) A shaft forms along route 3. Its drain by chance follows a parting to the earlier shaft. Leakage continues along route 4. (**c**) Route 4 eventually pirates the shaft water and abandons the former drain. Leakage along routes 5 and 6 may produce future diversions.

Figure 9.62: Development of a vertical shaft in the floor of a canyon (Mammoth Cave, Kentucky). The original canyon continues in the former downstream direction as an abandoned relic.

usually down the dip of a bedding-plane parting or inclined fracture. Vadose passages that follow these inclined routes have an inherent tendency to leak along all pores and fissures exposed in their floors. Few of these floor openings are sufficiently large or continuous to divert much water, but those that do are able to grow rapidly because of their steep gradients and ready supply of aggressive water. As these diversion paths widen, they capture progressively more water until the original passage is abandoned — at first only during low flow, but eventually year-round (Figure 9.61).

Diversionary flow may instead follow an inclined parting exposed in the passage floor. In steeply dipping beds this route will probably parallel the original passage. In gently dipping beds, the leakage is more likely to diverge from the original passage in the direction of the unique local dip of the parting. The new route must grow rapidly enough to capture most or all of the stream flow before the main passage has time to deepen its floor beyond the level of the parting. Otherwise the incipient diversion passage will be abandoned before it can enlarge significantly.

For this reason, most bedding-plane diversions are short enough to grow rapidly. The most favorable routes are those that lead back to the original passage after only a few tens or hundreds of meters (see example in Figure

Figure 9.64: A waterfall in Mammoth Cave enters a formerly phreatic passage that was intersected by an overlying vadose canyon. The water drops through the passage and its breakdown floor, then exits in the opposite direction through a newly forming canyon.

6.10). As this process is repeated, it produces a multi-story canyon with segments that split and rejoin in a braided pattern. Less common are passages that diverge for long distances in entirely new directions, because they require a proportionally longer time to reach their maximum enlargement rate (see Eqs. 7.5a and 7.5b).

If the diversion follows a steep fracture exposed in the stream floor, the time constraint is relaxed considerably. Even if the original passage continues to deepen, the flow to the exposed fracture will not be cut off. It grows into a steep fissure passage or canyon, or more commonly a vertical shaft (Figure 9.62). Because each new vadose passage is hydrologically independent of the olders, the only reason it might intersect another vadose passage, or even the original one farther downstream, is that the fractures and partings that guide it just happen to lead in that direction.

Shaft drains are the outlets for water at the bottoms of vertical shafts (Figure 9.61). As the shafts deepen, new drains develop at successively lower elevations. A shaft that forms along a major fracture tends to produce few drains, and perhaps only one. In bedded rock, shafts tend to deepen gradually, a few beds at a time, or in steps of just a

Figure 9.63: The only drain for the shaft in Figure 9.14 is a tributary of the main stream passage of McFail's Cave, New York. The drain is 33 m long and its ceiling is 25–30 cm high over most of its length. It is normally almost dry except during floods.

single bed. Shaft drains are normally much smaller in cross section than the shafts that feed them. The contact between water and bedrock is smaller in drains, and their floors may be shielded by insoluble sediment (Figure 9.63). Also, as the shafts deepen, many drains are abandoned before they have a chance to grow large.

The system of vadose passages remains active as long as their recharge continues from the overlying surface. They form many, or most, of the tributaries of phreatic passages. Canyons, shafts, and shaft drains can also intersect older passages that are otherwise dry. Although formerly phreatic passages are now located in the vadose zone, vadose water that enters them is out of adjustment with their geometry. Incoming vadose water tends to wander a short distance to a low place in the passage floor and exit through a newly formed canyon or shaft. Alternatively, the vadose water may simply cascade through the passage with hardly any influence from the original passage (Figure 9.64). Shafts and canyons can descend past the levels of older abandoned tubes and become tributaries to younger ones closer to the present base level.

Upward diversion of vadose water is very rare, except where a passage is blocked by breakdown or sediment and the only available bypass is along a higher fissure or an older passage. Such diversions tend to be short-lived.

Vadose divergence is a boon to explorers, because a single passage can split into several different ones that reach the water table in different places (Wells and Borden, 2005). Vadose passages can cross groundwater divides and serve as connecting routes between caves that are otherwise entirely independent (Figure 9.1b). Alpine cave exploration, in particular, is often halted at constrictions or blockages in the main passage, but by following alternative higher routes it is often possible to bypass the choke and reach greater depths. Several examples are shown on the profile of Krubera Cave (Figure 2.74).

Growth and abandonment of phreatic passages

Close inspection of phreatic passages can reveal much about the character of karst groundwater flow. Imagine a passage that is forming at the water table. Because the local water table drops as the passage enlarges, it is possible for the original conduit to be abandoned in favor of slightly lower ones, with the most recent one the lowest of all. The ceiling of the final passage should contain remnants of one or more of the early tubes, or perhaps only a ceiling channel (Figure 6.35). But many tubular passages that form at the water table have nearly horizontal profiles and show little or no evidence for older, higher-level tubes (Figure 9.65). Either these older fragments have been obliterated by periodic flooding, or the water table dropped to a stable position before major passage growth took place.

As nearby rivers entrench their valleys and allow the water table to drop further, phreatic passages may be abandoned by their flow. There are various ways in which the diversion can take place. As the water table drops, the stream

Figure 9.65: Turner Avenue, in Mammoth Cave, is a low-gradient tube that formed at the water table at Level C (Figure 9.54). Typical of many tubes, its ceiling shows no remnants of earlier tubes that may have formed before the water table stabilized at this level.

may simply cut a canyon in the floor to form a keyhole cross section (Figure 9.66). The canyon typically exits the tube after a short distance, to follow the down-dip paths favored by vadose water.

In a phreatic tube that meanders vertically along its length, the uppermost parts of the loops are the first to become vadose. They develop canyons in their floors, while the lower parts of the loops continue to enlarge as tubes. The resulting passage may alternate between high canyons and low, wide tubes (Figure 9.67; for an example, see White and Deike, 1989).

Figure 9.66: A canyon was cut in the floor of this tube as the flow changed from phreatic to vadose (Wells Cave, Kentucky).

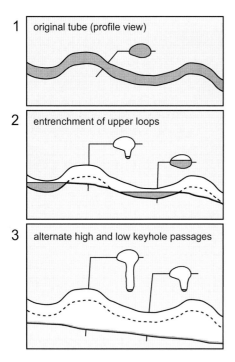

Figure 9.67: Development of alternating tubes and canyons, and keyhole passages of varied height.

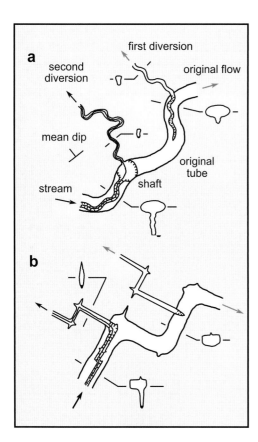

Figure 9.68: Typical vadose drains emanating from original phreatic passages. Two stages of drains are shown. The second diversion cuts off the water supply to the first. Map (**a**) shows the typical pattern in prominently bedded rock; Map (**b**) shows the same in prominently fractured rock. Labels in (**a**) also apply to (**b**). The drains in (**b**) are not necessarily in the dip direction.

Most often when a tube evolves from phreatic to vadose, the vadose water forms an entirely independent lower route (Figure 7.30). The distinction is usually clear, because phreatic passages have low overall gradients, usually some vertical sinuosity, and no relation to the dip of the strata, whereas many vadose drains are dip-oriented canyons (Figure 9.68a). Drains in prominently fractured rock are not guided so faithfully by the dip, although their trends are commonly in that approximate direction because of the influence of sparse partings and poorly soluble beds (Figures 9.68b and 9.69). Because of their steep gradients, vadose drains are usually much narrower than the original phreatic passage.

Drains emanating from a phreatic passage may form in several steps in the headward direction. Each diversion leaves the remaining downstream part of the passage dry, except by flood overflow, or unless a tributary continues to supply that passage segment with water. A headward sequence of

Figure 9.69: A joint-guided diversion passage for vadose water draining from a former, and much larger, phreatic tube in Blue Spring Cave, Indiana. This and others near it were used as the model for Figure 9.68b.

Figure 9.70: Early stages of diversion of a stream from its original strike-oriented tube to a parallel tube farther down the dip, Clarksville Cave, New York. A glove is shown for scale.

drains may indicate that the effect of the base-level drop has migrated upstream from the vicinity of the spring. But it appears that most diversions simply occur wherever there are low places in the original passages, or where favorable fractures or partings are present.

The ideal location for diversion from the phreatic passage is at the points where vadose infeeders join the original phreatic passage. This is the earliest opportunity for the

Figure 9.71: Irregular cross section and ceiling gradient of a phreatic passage in prominently fractured limestone, Butler Cave, Virginia.

incoming water to break free of the constraints of phreatic conditions. A fine example is shown at the Boone Avenue - Cleaveland Avenue junction in Mammoth Cave (Figures 9.29 and 9.49), where Cleaveland Avenue abruptly lost its water source as the Boone Avenue canyon deepened.

Some strike-oriented phreatic tubes are abandoned when their water slips out along the beds to routes farther down-dip, yet parallel to the original passages. Figure 9.70 shows this process in its early phase. An example of the resulting passage configuration is shown in Figure 9.15. This process is favored by a slowly dropping base level. Alternatively, it may represent a mutual adjustment between the passage and the water table, as described on page 267.

An active phreatic conduit is usually the collector for water from a variety of vadose infeeders. As the conduit is gradually abandoned, its water tends to become divided among several drains, each fed by water from one or more of the original infeeders. As the base level drops, cave streams tend to become dispersed along a greater number of routes than when the main phreatic passages were active.

In prominently fractured rock, the relationships described here may be obscure. Figure 9.71 shows an example from Butler Cave, Virginia. Even on the small-scale cave map (Figure 2.44) the effect of the 10–15° dip can be discerned in the strike orientation of the main passage and the many down-dip vadose tributaries. But note the irregular cross section and ceiling profile in the photograph. Detailed mapping of gradients and bedding at a local scale, though helpful, cannot reveal the level of detail shown in Figures 9.29 and 9.49, where the influence of bedding is strong.

Cave patterns: A summary

The relationship between geologic setting and cave patterns is summarized on the next page (Figure 9.72). Nearly all caves fit easily into one of the illustrated categories, despite the complications of multiple stages of development, rudimentary and single-passage caves, and isolated cave fragments in which most of the critical information is missing.

A two-variable classification accounts for most cave patterns: (1) recharge type (how water gets into the soluble rock, and the nature of its aggressiveness), and (2) the nature of the guiding structures (partings, discordant fractures, intergranular pores). In general, more than 60% of all known caves are branchworks, and there is an almost even balance between parting and fracture control. About 15–20% are networks, 5–10% ramiform, 5–10% anastomotic, and about 5% spongework. Weighted by cave length, the percentages are roughly the same, except for spongework, which includes a great many small caves which, by length, represent only about one percent. These percentages vary a great deal with the local geologic and hydrologic setting. It is common for almost all of the caves in a given area to belong to a single cave type.

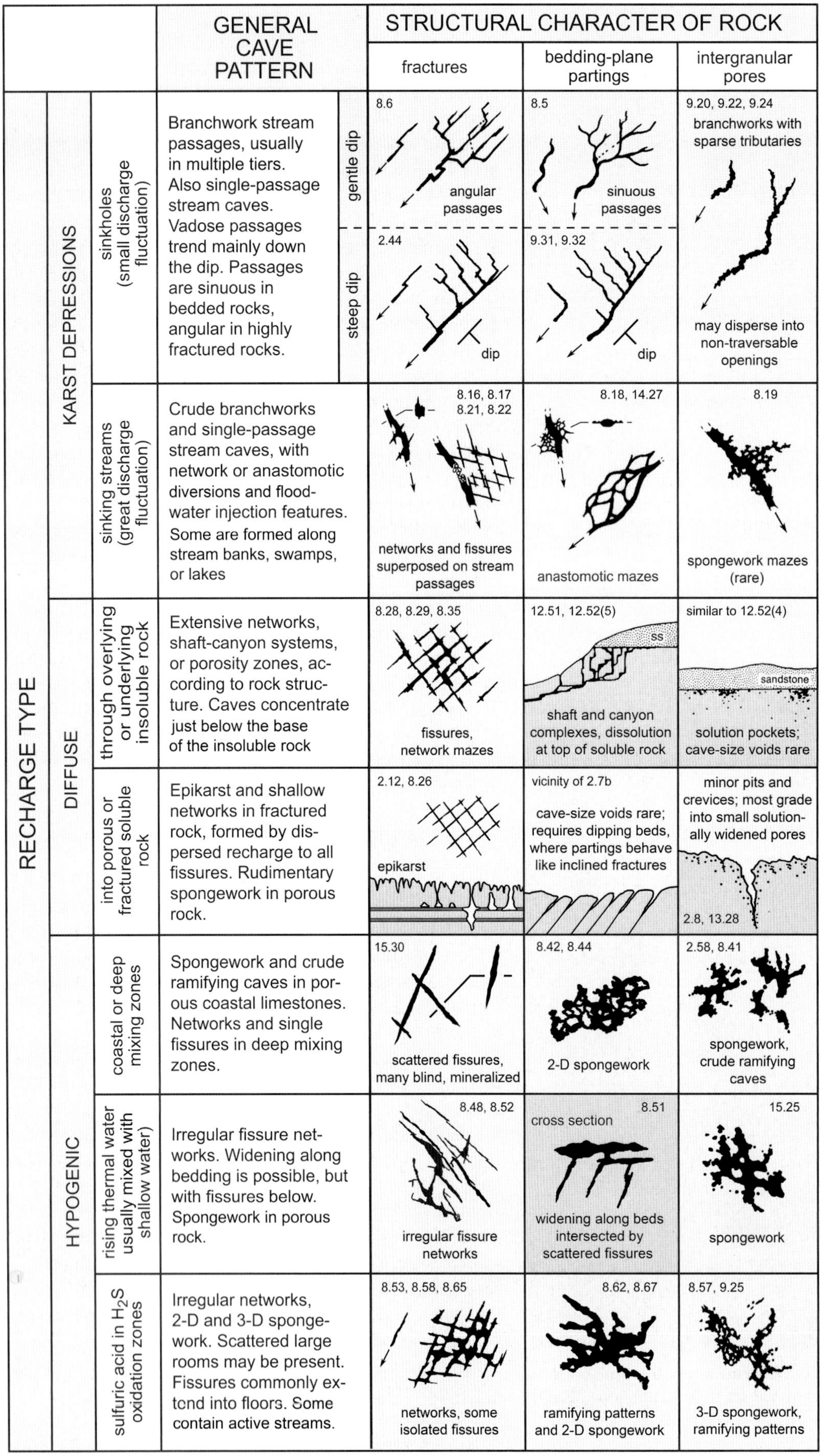

		GENERAL CAVE PATTERN	STRUCTURAL CHARACTER OF ROCK		
			fractures	bedding-plane partings	intergranular pores
RECHARGE TYPE	KARST DEPRESSIONS — sinkholes (small discharge fluctuation)	Branchwork stream passages, usually in multiple tiers. Also single-passage stream caves. Vadose passages trend mainly down the dip. Passages are sinuous in bedded rocks, angular in highly fractured rocks.	gentle dip: 8.6 — angular passages; steep dip: 2.44 — dip	gentle dip: 8.5 — sinuous passages; steep dip: 9.31, 9.32 — dip	9.20, 9.22, 9.24 — branchworks with sparse tributaries; may disperse into non-traversable openings
	sinking streams (great discharge fluctuation)	Crude branchworks and single-passage stream caves, with network or anastomotic diversions and flood-water injection features. Some are formed along stream banks, swamps, or lakes	8.16, 8.17, 8.21, 8.22 — networks and fissures superposed on stream passages	8.18, 14.27 — anastomotic mazes	8.19 — spongework mazes (rare)
	DIFFUSE — through overlying or underlying insoluble rock	Extensive networks, shaft-canyon systems, or porosity zones, according to rock structure. Caves concentrate just below the base of the insoluble rock	8.28, 8.29, 8.35 — fissures, network mazes	12.51, 12.52(5) — shaft and canyon complexes, dissolution at top of soluble rock	similar to 12.52(4) — solution pockets; cave-size voids rare
	into porous or fractured soluble rock	Epikarst and shallow networks in fractured rock, formed by dispersed recharge to all fissures. Rudimentary spongework in porous rock.	2.12, 8.26 — epikarst	vicinity of 2.7b — cave-size voids rare; requires dipping beds, where partings behave like inclined fractures	minor pits and crevices; most grade into small solutionally widened pores; 2.8, 13.28
	HYPOGENIC — coastal or deep mixing zones	Spongework and crude ramifying caves in porous coastal limestones. Networks and single fissures in deep mixing zones.	15.30 — scattered fissures, many blind, mineralized	8.42, 8.44 — 2-D spongework	2.58, 8.41 — spongework, crude ramifying caves
	rising thermal water usually mixed with shallow water	Irregular fissure networks. Widening along bedding is possible, but with fissures below. Spongework in porous rock.	8.48, 8.52 — irregular fissure networks	8.51 cross section — widening along beds intersected by scattered fissures	15.25 — spongework
	sulfuric acid in H$_2$S oxidation zones	Irregular networks, 2-D and 3-D spongework. Scattered large rooms may be present. Fissures commonly extend into floors. Some contain active streams.	8.53, 8.58, 8.65 — networks, some isolated fissures	8.62, 8.67 — ramifying patterns and 2-D spongework	8.57, 9.25 — 3-D spongework, ramifying patterns

Figure 9.72: Summary of cave patterns in relation to the type of groundwater recharge and structural character of the rock. Cave patterns are shown in map view, except where labeled otherwise. Those shaded in dark gray are cross sections.

Numbers in the boxes refer to other figures that illustrate field examples.

10

Cave minerals

ONCE A CAVE HAS FORMED, it becomes the host for a variety of mineral deposits. These are the *speleothems* (popularly known as "cave formations") that give caves much of their allure and variety (Moore, 1952). Most of them appear only after the cave becomes air-filled. The book *Cave Minerals of the World*, by Hill and Forti (1997), is by far the most comprehensive reference to the subject.

Geologists traditionally group minerals by chemical composition and internal structure. Speleothems require a more elaborate classification scheme, because a single kind of mineral can produce many different speleothem shapes that vary according to local cave conditions. In this chapter, speleothems are grouped according to the environments in which they form. Each speleothem type is then identified by its basic shape, with mineral composition or origin included in the name where appropriate. Some names are fanciful, having been devised by the high-spirited explorers who first discovered them. Speleothem terminology could no doubt use a rigorous overhaul to make it more technically precise, but at the risk of losing much of its charm.

Origin and growth of cave minerals

In caves in carbonate rocks (limestone, dolomite, and marble), the most common speleothems are composed of calcium carbonate ($CaCO_3$). As water passes through soil, it absorbs high levels of carbon dioxide (CO_2), and as a result it is able to dissolve a large amount of the underlying rock (see Chapter

5). Cave air has less CO_2 because it mixes with air from the surface that passes through entrances and smaller openings. When water seeps into an air-filled cave, most of the dissolved CO_2 escapes into the cave atmosphere. As a result, the water is able to hold less calcium carbonate, and some of the dissolved load is deposited as speleothems (Figure 10.1). This process is exactly the opposite of what happens when limestone dissolves. Heating of water can also cause carbonate minerals to precipitate, but this process is more common in hot-water pipes than in caves.

The calcium and carbonate ions that produce the mineral can come from a variety of sources (Chapter 5). But when the combination of dissolved components that exceed a critical level of supersaturation, the mineral begins to precipitate. In these conditions it is appropriate to say that the water is *supersaturated with respect to* that particular mineral. It is common to say simply that the water is "supersaturated with" the mineral, but this wording gives the impression that the dissolved materials were supplied only by that particular mineral. For example, much of the calcium in a $CaCO_3$ mineral may come from dissolution of other calcium-bearing minerals, such as gypsum ($CaSO_4 \cdot 2H_2O$). There is often no way to tell the exact mineral that supplied the original ions. The most reliable way to determine if a water sample is supersaturated or undersaturated with a particular mineral is

Figure 10.1: Calcite crystals forming at the tip of a stalactite by loss of carbon dioxide from dripwater. The CO_2 loss is not visible and must be measured (Chapter 5). Width of drop is about 0.5 cm.

Origin of common cave minerals

CO_2 loss — calcite dripstone, flowstone, helictites, rimstone, cave-pool crusts, some aragonite frostwork.

Evaporation — gypsum and similar minerals, calcite coralloids, aragonite, dolomite, Mg minerals, opal, quartz — some overlap with CO_2 loss and other processes.

Alteration of existing minerals — production of alunite, opal, and quartz from clay, for example by sulfuric acid.

Mineral replacement — change from less stable to more stable form — for example, calcite to aragonite, anhydrite to gypsum, Mg carbonates to dolomite.

Oxidation — iron and manganese oxides.

Reduction — iron sulfides in organic-rich oxygen-poor pools.

pH change — opal, quartz (closed to open CO_2 system).

Cooling — opal, quartz, ice.

Heating — carbonate minerals (veins at depth, but examples are rare from caves).

Common-ion effect — subaqueous $CaCO_3$ deposits, dedolomitization in the presence of dissolved sulfates.

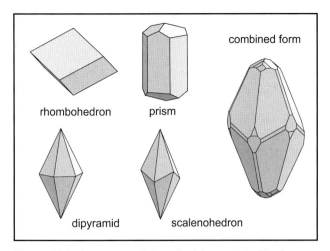

Figure 10.2: Common varieties of calcite crystals. The form on the right is a combination of several rhombohedra, scalenohedra, and prisms.

to measure the water chemistry and calculate the saturation index (see Chapter 5).

Calcium carbonate forms two common mineral types: *calcite* and *aragonite* (Chapter 3). Calcite takes on many shapes, such as stubby blocks, elongate sharp-ended crystals, and complex many-sided prisms. About 2700 different calcite crystal shapes have been recognized, and several forms may be incorporated in a single crystal (Huizing and others, 2003). Figure 10.2 shows some of the more common forms.

Freshwater deposits of calcium carbonate (either calcite or aragonite) are known to geologists as *travertine*. This term is usually applied to deposits at springs or in spring-fed surface streams. *Cave travertine* is sometimes used as a generic term for any kind of calcium carbonate speleothem.

Aragonite crystals are typically thin and needle-like, and less commonly tabular or bladed. The needle-shaped form is shown in Figure 1.23. Aragonite is more soluble than calcite at the temperatures of most caves, so any water that is supersaturated with aragonite is automatically supersaturated with calcite as well. In this environment, the needle-shaped aragonite crystals form more readily than the blockier crystals of calcite, and so aragonite will be the first to form. For water to become supersaturated with aragonite, there must either be very rapid CO_2 loss or evaporation, or the water must have a high magnesium/calcium ratio, which inhibits calcite growth (Bischoff and Fyfe, 1968; Folk, 1974). Experiments show that aragonite crystallizes in preference to calcite when magnesium/calcium ratios are greater than about 5:1 at 6°C, but as the temperature rises the critical ratio drops rapidly to about 0.25:1 at 25°C (Morse and others, 1997). All of the required conditions are fairly common in certain caves, and so is aragonite.

Deposition of highly soluble minerals almost always requires evaporation of water. These minerals are abundant in many dry caves, especially where there is substantial air movement. In wet caves they are uncommon or entirely absent. *Gypsum* ($CaSO_4 \cdot 2H_2O$) is the most common

evaporative cave mineral. Usually the calcium is provided by dissolution of carbonate rocks and the sulfate by oxidation of local iron sulfides such as pyrite (FeS_2). Some gypsum is simply dissolved from older deposits and re-precipitated as speleothems.

Highly soluble cave minerals, such as *epsomite* ($MgSO_4 \cdot 7H_2O$) are stable only at low humidity and can grow and disappear seasonally. The magnesium is supplied mainly by dolomite bedrock, but it can also come from weathering of certain igneous or metamorphic rocks. Other evaporative minerals are introduced later in this chapter. Some very soluble minerals contain sodium from a variety of sources, but they are rare except in very dry caves. Evaporite minerals tend to form white crusts or wispy flower-like growths.

Evaporation can also force calcite and aragonite to precipitate, although most calcite is deposited by loss of CO_2 from water. As evaporation causes calcite to precipitate, the concentration of remaining dissolved calcium remains fairly steady. Other ions tend to become more concentrated, because the minerals they form are more soluble than calcite and they remain in solution. Magnesium is one of the ions that increases as evaporation takes place, and high magnesium/calcium ratios favor the deposition of aragonite rather than calcite. For that reason, aragonite is more abundant than calcite in evaporative areas. It is common to find aragonite growing on earlier calcite. Precipitation of calcite or aragonite by CO_2 loss alone does not increase the concentrations of remaining ions. The distinction between CO_2 loss and evaporation as a trigger for precipitating cave minerals is discussed by Holland and others (1964) and Thrailkill (1971).

Some minerals are stable only at low temperatures. The most common is *ice*, which is an intermittent or semi-permanent deposit in some caves where the temperature drops below 0°C (Chapter 12). Freezing of water can also precipitate minerals from solution, but only as fine powders or thin coatings.

Clay is a common ingredient in many sediments and sedimentary rocks (Chapter 3). It includes a variety of minerals composed of silicon, oxygen, and aluminum in combination with other elements. When they are altered (for example by reacting with sulfuric acid), byproducts include *alunite* ($KAl_3(SO_4)_2(OH)_6$) and *hydrated halloysite* ($Al_2Si_2O_5(OH)_4 \cdot 2H_2O$), which accumulate as layers or pocket fillings (page 119).

Quartz (crystalline SiO_2) and *opal* (non-crystalline SiO_2 bonded with water) rarely form extensive cave deposits, even though they are common in other geologic settings. Quartz and opal precipitate in several ways, including evaporation, temperature drop, and decrease from high pH to a moderate or low pH (Chapter 5). They are also produced by alteration of clay and other complex silicon-bearing minerals, especially when in contact with strong acids such as sulfuric acid. These reactions release silicic acid, H_4SiO_4, often in quantities sufficient to cause supersaturation and rapid precipitation of opal or quartz. Quartz precipitates rapidly at high temperatures but slowly at normal cave temperatures. Opal is more soluble than quartz, but opal is the more likely one to precipitate in water that is supersaturated with both minerals. This is because it takes less energy to form the non-crystalline opal than the tightly structured crystals of quartz. Regardless of their origin, quartz and opal usually form irregular layers or coatings that barely qualify as speleothems. Large quartz crystals are rare in caves. Some minerals, particularly *iron and manganese hydroxides and oxides*, are produced by oxidation of other minerals or of iron and manganese dissolved in water. White (1997) describes the physical and chemical conditions at which many cave minerals tend to form.

Crystal growth

When minerals form, the shapes that they acquire are called *crystals* (Chapter 3; see Figure 10.2). Crystal growth begins when a small clump of molecules precipitate as tiny specks, usually at the contact between water and a solid surface. They may grow on small particles, such as dust on a water surface. Once the initial crystals begin to form, additional molecule-thick layers accumulate on their surfaces. Their individual faces and corners are usually preserved as the crystals grow, although they often contain imperfections caused by incomplete layers, impurities, or interference with other crystals.

Speleothem growth varies with time, according to environmental conditions and the supply of dissolved material. Layering is a common result, as in tree rings. The layers are produced mainly by accumulation of insoluble sediment, pauses in deposition, or even temporary dissolution and are accentuated by variations in crystal size or in color from impurities (Figure 10.3).

Individual crystals in a speleothem can vary in size from microscopic to several centimeters long, and in rare cases up to several meters. Crystal size depends mainly on growth rate. Large crystals tend to form slowly, for example in water that is only slightly supersaturated with that specific mineral, and where the drive toward supersaturation (such as CO_2 loss) is very slow. Caves intersected by the Naica lead-zinc mine in Mexico contain gypsum crystals up to 11 m long, which grew at about 54°C in very stable solutions while anhydrite simultaneously dissolved to supply the calcium sulfate (García-Ruiz and others, 2007). Small crystals are usually produced by rapid deposition at high levels of supersaturation. Overgrowths of small crystals on the surfaces of speleothems can produce a velvety sheen (Figure 10.4).

Recrystallization of minerals

Each mineral is deposited in conditions that are especially favorable for it to crystallize. If the environmental conditions change, that mineral may *recrystallize* to a different mineral that is stable under the new conditions. For example, aragonite is unstable in most fresh water, including water that is slightly supersaturated with calcite. Much limestone is originally deposited in seawater as aragonite, but as it is exposed above sea level and fresh water begins to filter

Figure 10.3: Crusts of calcite formed in ponded water, Lechuguilla Cave, New Mexico. This is a naturally broken fragment of a wall projection with a bedrock core.

through it, the aragonite eventually recrystallizes to calcite. It may take many thousands of years for all of the aragonite to be converted. Aragonite is common in many caves, but it converts to calcite if it is exposed to fresh water with a low Mg/Ca ratio. Calcite can be converted to dolomite in magnesium-rich fluids. Dolomite can convert to calcite (*dedolomitization*) if calcite is forced to deposit as dolomite dissolves, as is common in a mixture of carbonate and sulfate rocks (pages 121–122).

At low humidity and temperatures below roughly 40°C, anhydrite ($CaSO_4$) may revert to gypsum. In wet environments the conversion takes place below roughly 60°C. Gypsum may be converted to anhydrite at high temperature or under the pressure of overlying rocks.

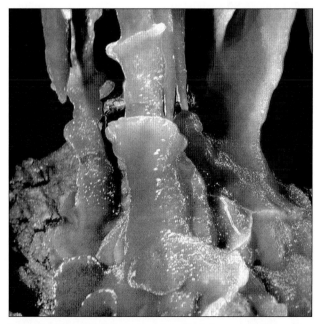

Figure 10.4: "Velvet" texture caused by late growth of very fine calcite crystals (reflective, white) on more massive speleothems, Fort Stanton Cave, New Mexico. Width of photo is 25 cm.

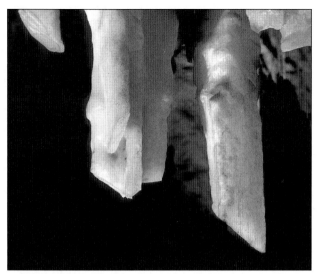

Figure 10.5: Growth and recrystallization of stalactite tips into single calcite crystals, Crystal Cave, Bermuda. Recrystallization took place in brackish water when sea level was higher. Today sea level lies about 1.5 m below them. Photo width is ~25 cm.

Another common example of mineral replacement is the conversion of gypsum to calcite. As carbonate-rich groundwater moves through gypsum, the water tends to become supersaturated with calcite, and calcite often replaces the gypsum (pages 121–122).

If the reaction is slow and fairly uniform, the replacement mineral may inherit the crystal shape of the original mineral. These are called *pseudomorphs*. Weathering of pyrite to iron oxide often produces cubic pseudomorphs of iron oxide that mimic the original cubic crystal shape of the pyrite.

With time, it is possible for speleothems to recrystallize to a larger crystal size, especially if they are immersed in water that is at or near saturation (Figure 10.5). Although recrystallization may involve a change to a more stable mineral, often only the crystal size enlarges while the mineral remains the same. Either process usually engulfs the growth bands, and although the layering may be obscured, it is often preserved by colored banding from the impurities.

Speleothem colors and luminescence

Most limestone bedrock is composed of calcite that is gray from impurities such as silt, clay, and organic material. In speleothems the crystals are larger, purer, and oriented in more uniform patterns than in bedrock. The most common cave minerals — calcite, aragonite, and gypsum — are typically translucent and colorless in large crystals, but in speleothems they often appear white because of scattering of light by the many crystal boundaries, especially where the crystal size is small, or by tiny inclusions of water. Also, even small amounts of foreign material can produce a wide range of colors, most often brown, cream, yellow, orange, and red. Organic acids are the main sources of delicate translucent colors in carbonate speleothems (White, 1981). Iron and manganese oxides can produce similar but darker colors. Earth-colored, opaque speleothems generally

contain insoluble sediment such as clay or organic carbon. Copper and nickel from nearby ore bodies produce rare and exotic colors such as blue and green (Cabrol, 1978).

Some speleothems luminesce in the presence of certain energy sources, particularly ultraviolet light (Shopov, 1997, 2006). Impurities such as organic acids and trace elements are chiefly responsible. *Fluorescence* is the emission of light from a mineral while the mineral is exposed to the energy source. Shining an ultraviolet light ("black light") on minerals and rocks can reveal discrete zones of luminescence that represent different minerals and stages of mineral deposition. *Phosphorescence* is the emission of light from a mineral after the energy source is removed. Many speleothems phosphoresce for several seconds after being exposed to a photo flash unit. This effect is best seen when one's eyes are closed during the flash and then opened immediately afterward. White, yellow, pink, red, green, and blue are the most common luminescent colors. The exact color and intensity depends on the mineral type, defects in crystal structure, and presence of trace elements, as well as the wavelength of the light source.

Speleothem types

The most common and significant speleothem types are described here. They are arranged in groups according to the nature of the water that deposits them, from wettest to driest environments. Speleothems in the same group are most likely to be found together, and a few representative examples can serve as clues to the past history of a cave. Changes in climate or moisture conditions can be documented by the growth of one type of speleothem on another. Grouping of minerals according to the environments in which they form was pioneered in Russia (for reviews, see Kantor, 2003; Self and Hill, 2003).

The following list of speleothems omits many minor types and variants. Full details and literature citations are given by Hill and Forti (1997).

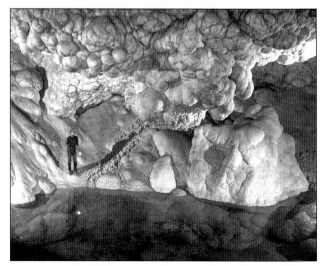

Figure 10.6: Mammillary crust at Lake of the Clouds, Carlsbad Cavern, New Mexico.

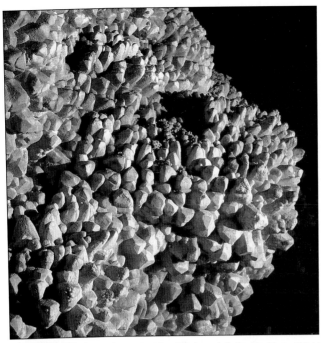

Figure 10.7: Knobby growths of calcite crystals formed in ponded water, Jewel Cave, South Dakota. Width of photo is 40 cm.

Pool deposits

Calcium carbonate normally crystallizes in pools as calcite. Loss of CO_2 to the cave air is most active at pool surfaces, so the rate and thickness of mineral accumulation are also greatest there. At greater depth in pools the water remains only mildly supersaturated, which allows large crystals to grow in fairly uniform layers, but more slowly than those near the surface.

In most pool deposits the crystals form a crust, which grows most rapidly on bedrock projections to form rounded knobs. Crusts are common in hypogenic caves, which are more likely to have standing water than flowing streams. In a ***mammillary crust*** the crystal layer is thick enough that the knobs coalesce into a cloud-like surfaces (Figure 10.6).

Where the crystals in a pool lining are large, their tips protrude in a pattern that looks like the surface of a pineapple (Figure 10.7). Jewel Cave and Sitting Bull Caverns, in South Dakota, are well known for their thick wall crusts of calcite. Many pool crusts are colored by impurities that fall from weathered surfaces of overlying bedrock. Various shades of brown, red, yellow, orange, and gray are common.

Crystals grow fastest in the direction of their longest dimension. In a calcite pool deposit, for example, many crystals are competing for space, and those with their long dimensions perpendicular to the bedrock surface grow fastest. They crowd out the slower-growing crystals to form long palisade-like columns (Figures 10.8–10.9). This pattern is most obvious in thick crusts where the crystal organization has had time to mature.

Two forms of calcite are common in pool deposits. Crystals with sharply pointed ends are called ***dogtooth spar***, and those with blunt terminations are called ***nailhead spar*** (Figure 10.10). Dogtooth spar consists mainly of

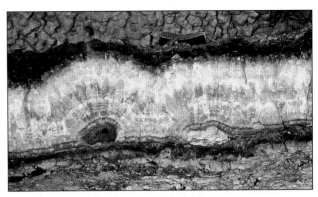

Figure 10.8: Columnar structure of calcite crystals on a shattered wall in Jewel Cave, South Dakota. Note the banding, some of which represents periodic staining by impurities such as clay during crystal growth. Thickness of crust is 15 cm. Such thick, uniform crusts are typical of thermal cave deposits (Chapter 8).

scalenohedral crystals, and nailhead spar includes mainly rhombohedral and combined forms (Figure 10.2). The conditions that determine the two different types are poorly understood, although dogtooth spar is more common in high-temperature deposits.

Where water drips into a pool from which CO_2 is slowly lost, branching crystal structures often form on the pool floor that resemble shrubs or flower petals (Figure 10.11). These are variants of coralloids, a name that also applies to certain

Figure 10.9: A fragment of columnar calcite wall crust from Lechuguilla Cave, New Mexico, shown in a photomicrograph of a thin section. Growth was mainly upward in the photo. The large columnar crystals were deposited in ponded water. The thin, fine-grained bands on top were deposited mainly during intermittent evaporation above water. Photo by Margaret Palmer.

Figure 10.11: Branching shrub-like calcite crystals line a former pool in Grotte de l'Aguzou, eastern Pyrenees, France. Width of photo is about 30 cm.

Figure 10.10: Examples of calcite and aragonite pool linings: (**a**) dogtooth spar, (**b**) nailhead spar, (**c**) aragonite. Photo **a** is about 10 cm wide, **b** is about 15 cm wide, and **c** is about 20 cm wide. The aragonite in this photo is immersed in a pool that is supersaturated with aragonite, as well as calcite and dolomite, but of the three, aragonite crystallizes most rapidly.

aragonite crystals tend to split and warp as they grow, to form needles and shingled plates (Figure 10.12).

Quartz coatings are also rare in caves. More commonly they line small pre-cave voids in the bedrock. Quartz crystals are usually as clear as ice and reflect light brilliantly. In places, quartz has crystallized around organic filaments to produce thin fingers that hang vertically from void ceilings (Figure 10.13). These and similar features are sometimes called *scintillites* (Deal, 1968). Quartz crystallizes very slowly at normal groundwater temperatures, so large quartz crystals usually indicate a hot-water origin.

Quartz is abundant in the vicinity of faults, which serve as pathways for warm water to rise from great depth. Deposits of quartz or opal are also common in the vicinity of oxidation-reduction boundaries, for example where

evaporative speleothems (see page 288). Each shrub consists of a bulbous crystalline base from which multiple crystals grow upward and slightly outward without merging with their neighbors. They typically range in width and height from a few millimeters to several centimeters. The longer crystals tend to grow most rapidly and inhibit the growth of their shorter neighbors.

Pool linings of aragonite are rare, but in the few known examples it forms needles that protrude from solid surfaces like cactus spines. Aragonite-lined pools in Carlsbad Cavern, New Mexico, contain remnants of hydromagnesite blobs that have fallen from evaporative zones above (Figure 10.10c). Hydromagnesite is hydrated magnesium carbonate, and the boost in Mg in the pool water inhibited calcite growth and allowed aragonite to crystallize instead. Aragonite also grows in the high-Mg/Ca seawater pools of coastal caves.

Where the loss of carbon dioxide is rapid, or concentrations of dissolved magnesium or sulfate are high, calcite and

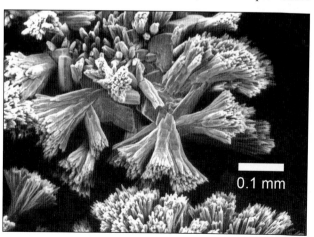

Figure 10.12: As calcite and aragonite crystals grow, they may split into fine needles if there is rapid CO_2 loss, or high concentrations of magnesium or sulfate in the water. These crystals were grown under controlled conditions in the laboratory at high rates of CO_2 loss. Scanning electron microscope image.

sulfides are oxidized to sulfate (Chapter 5). Bacteria thrive in these environments, and their fossil filaments can be clearly preserved by quartz, chert, or opal (Figure 5.19). They are all composed of SiO_2 (*silica*) which is least soluble at moderate to low pH and can be deposited if the quartz is transported into caves from zones of higher pH (Figure 5.17). Interaction with organic compounds may also contribute to silica precipitation.

Gypsum pool linings and underwater crystals are very rare in caves. Most cave gypsum forms in contact with air. One of the few documented examples of gypsum crystals growing in a simple dripwater pool is in Lechuguilla Cave, New

Figure 10.13: Quartz speleothems in Wind Cave, South Dakota. These formed in a pre-cave solution pocket that was intersected by later cave development. Height of photo is 15 cm.

Mexico, where long, slender gypsum blades are growing in a shallow pool nestled in a large gypsum block. Huge gypsum crystals up to 11 m long have been discovered in deep water-filled pockets intersected by mines in Mexico (Lazcano Sahagun, 2001; Badino and Forti, 2007; García-Ruiz and others, 2007; see page 273).

Some cave walls contain cavities that may be lined with crystals. These cavities, whether crystal-lined or not, are called *vugs* (Figure 10.10a). They pre-date the cave and are relics of earlier events. Some are remnants of paleokarst or are residual voids between breccia fragments that were not completely filled by a mineral cement. *Geodes* are similar, but they are rounder and usually lined with opal or other forms of silica, which provide a base for additional crystals that project into the voids but do not fill them. The additional crystals are commonly quartz, but they can include a great variety of minerals. Geodes tend to weather out of the bedrock as resistant hollow balls. Many geodes result from partial replacement of evaporite bodies by other minerals. Most vugs in soluble rocks are the product of karst-related processes and they are often intersected by later caves. Most geodes are not directly related to karst, and they are rarely encountered in caves.

Folia are wall growths that are densely stacked in subhorizontal arrays, almost always on overhanging walls (Figure 10.14). They resemble miniature bracket fungi. Nearly all are composed of calcite. Folia are concentrated at and near

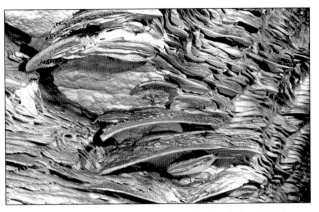

Figure 10.14: Folia in a Nevada cave. Width of photo is 25 cm.

pool surfaces, usually where calcite rafts are also forming. Individual folia typically project from the walls about 1–5 cm, with vertical thicknesses of about 0.5–1 centimeter. Their vertical spacing is typically 1–5 cm. Thin and closely spaced folia do not protrude so far. The vertical stacking of folia may result from fluctuating water levels, but it is more likely that they form simultaneously at various depths below a single pool surface. Some show channels that communicate from one rank of folia to those immediately above, which may indicate the flow of gas bubbles escaping toward the overlying water surface (Green, 1991). Kolesar and Riggs (2004) consider that small tidal fluctuations may contribute to the origin of folia in Devil's Hole, Nevada.

Many folia are located in hypogenic caves, which gives the impression that they form only in water of deep-seated origin. But they are also found in distinctly cold-water caves such as Hurricane Crawl in the Sierra Nevada and Mystery Cave, Minnesota. All seem to have formed in high-CO_2 water supersaturated with calcite that enters a pool from below, so that CO_2 escapes rapidly from the pool surface. A very rare occurrence of *sulfur* folia occurs in Cueva de Villa Luz, Mexico, where degassing of hydrogen sulfide may be the driving process (Figure 8.64). Partial regrowth of damaged sulfur folia in that cave suggests that they may form *above* water levels.*

Rimstone is a deposit of calcite that forms around the edges of cave pools fed by running or dripping water (Figure 10.15). The pools are sometimes referred to by their French name, *gours*. Crystallization is most rapid where the water flows over the rimstone lips because the CO_2 loss is greatest there. The pools deepen as the rimstone grows upward. Rimstone dams on steep slopes tend to be taller and less sinuous than those on gentle slopes. Dam tops are horizontal and range in height from less than a centimeter to several meters. Their spillover surfaces usually consist of rough-textured calcite that slopes away from the pool in the downstream direction, although rimstone formed by small trickles can have vertical or even slightly overhanging outer walls. The inner sides of a dam beneath the pool

* Communication from Louise Hose, Carlsbad, NM, 2005.

Figure 10.15: Rimstone pools in Mammoth Cave, Kentucky.

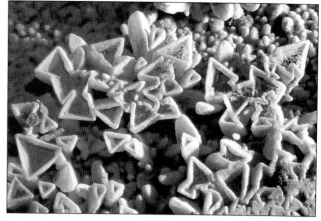

Figure 10.17: Calcite sometimes forms hollow triangular crystals, especially where it grows just below the surface of a pool. This example is in a Virginia Cave. Width of photo is 25 cm.

surface are usually lined with coralloid or shrub-like calcite growths. Rimstone can also form in stream beds or on the slopes of large dripstone or flowstone mounds. When a cave becomes air filled, its streams begin to lose much of their CO_2 by air exchange through open entrances, so that calcite may precipitate rather than dissolve.

Shelfstone consists of flat ledges of calcite that grow inward along the water surface from the shores of fairly static pools. The pools are fed only by drips or small trickles of water. Shelfstone is usually a few centimeters thick but can extend laterally for several meters. It can also form rims around earlier dripstone that has been immersed by a rise in water level (Figure 10.16). If there is a change in pool level, the former pool surface can be recognized by old shelfstone levels.

Calcite crystals that form in shallow standing water have flat tops where they extend to the water surface. Some have intricate hopper-shaped structures with triangular or nested patterns (Figure 10.17). Very rare hexagonal patterns have also been observed.

Cave rafts are thin sheet-like mineral deposits that crystallize on pool surfaces. They look like ice or thin lily pads (Figure 10.18). Nearly all are composed of calcite or, less commonly, aragonite. Most are paper-thin and white, yellowish, or brown. They can either grow outward from the shores or remain isolated from one another on the pool surface. Under very stable conditions, an entire pool surface may become covered by a thin sheet. *Cave bubbles* are rare variants that form where minerals crystallize around a bubble on a standing water surface.

Rafts are denser than water, and they float only because of surface tension, the same force that allows a water bug to stride across the surface of a puddle. In comparison, shelfstone is thicker and cannot rely on surface tension to keep it in place. As rafts thicken, crystal growth extends downward from them to produce rough undersides, while the upper surfaces remain nearly flat. Rafts sink to the bottom if they grow thick enough to overcome surface tension or are hit by falling water drops. Fallen rafts may be stacked chaotically like autumn leaves, but if a raft-covered water

Figure 10.16: Shelfstone in Cottonwood Cave, New Mexico, has formed around older stalactites and stalagmites. A carbide lamp 12 cm tall gives scale.

Figure 10.18: Calcite rafts on the floor of a former pool in Fort Stanton Cave, New Mexico. Width of photo is 10 cm.

Figure 10.19: Calcite rafts growing on the surface of a pool in Wind Cave, South Dakota. Where the water level has dropped, a litter of rafts is left above the shore (lower left). Width of photo is 40 cm.

Figure 10.21: Raft cones in Mystery Cave, Minnesota, cemented by later calcite pool deposits. The tallest is about 2 m high. The internal rafts are visible in naturally broken specimens nearby.

surface drops gradually, the rafts are draped over the floor in parallel sheets (Figure 10.19). Rafts grow only on quiet water surfaces. In the rare examples where a raft-covered pool is fed by a rapidly flowing stream, rafts are absent where the water surface is agitated by waves or ripples.

Where rafts accumulate underwater beneath drip points, they pile up as flaky mounds called ***raft cones*** (Figure 10.20). Often the mounds become cemented together by calcite pool deposits so their flaky internal structure is obscured (Figure 10.21). If the pool later drains and exposes the cones to air, they may become coated or tipped by evaporative deposits such as popcorn or frostwork (pages 288–289). Raft cones can superficially resemble stalagmites, except that they are usually not matched by overhead stalactites. Some have indentations in their tops where drips continued to fall after they were exposed above water. Polyak and Provencio

(2005) describe elongate raft cones with tapered tails (***comet cones***), which formed in slow-moving water.

Subaqueous helictites are eccentric finger-like growths in pools (Figure 10.22). These are rare underwater examples of a kind of speleothem that normally forms in air (see *helictites* on page 285). The subaqueous variety usually emanate from

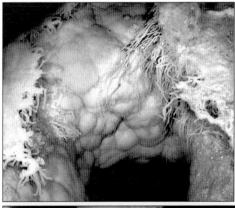
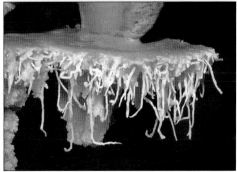

Figure 10.22: Subaqueous helictites in Lechuguilla Cave, New Mexico: (top) actively growing in a pool — the first recognized example; and (bottom) left high and dry by a drop in pool level. Widths of photos: top ~75 cm, bottom ~40 cm.

Figure 10.20: Raft cones in Pál-völgy Cave, Budapest, Hungary.

shelfstone. Where calcite-saturated water enters a pool that is rich in dissolved gypsum, the incoming water abruptly becomes supersaturated because of the common-ion effect (Chapter 5). Most of the calcite precipitates as pool linings and shelfstone, and helictites form only where the water enters the pools in tiny tendrils of flow. As the helictites grow, the water moves through narrow central canals and calcite crystals grow perpendicular to the canals. These speleothems are known mainly from Lechuguilla Cave, New Mexico, which contains unusual amounts of massive gypsum as the result of sulfuric acid cave origin (Davis and others, 1990). Even in pools that are now dry, subaqueous helictites can be recognized by the fact that they extend only downward and outward from old shelfstone levels (Figure 10.22, bottom). Helictites that form in air may be inundated later by a rise in water level, but they can usually be identified by characteristics such as their lack of relationship to a distinct shoreline.

Speleothems formed by flowing and dripping water

Where water drips into a cave or flows freely down its walls, it deposits speleothems with gravitationally influenced shapes that either coat the steepest available slopes, hang downward from the ceiling, or build upward from the floor. Speleothems of this type tend to merge together into composite forms. They are composed of calcite and rarely such minerals as aragonite, epsomite, gypsum, or quartz. They grow in distinct layers, like those of an onion. Each layer is composed of tightly packed, rod-shaped or needle-shaped crystals that are usually arranged perpendicular to the growth surface.

Cave pearls are calcite or aragonite balls that generally form in shallow pools beneath water drips. The minerals coat tiny grains such as quartz sand with successive layers of calcium carbonate (Figure 10.23). They typically range from a few millimeters up to about 5 cm in diameter. Cave pearls become more rounded as they grow, even though they are rarely immersed completely in pool water. Most are nearly spherical, but some are irregular, rod-shaped, or flattened,

Figure 10.24: Cascade of flowstone and dripstone in Carlsbad Cavern, New Mexico. Height of photo is about 7 m. Photo by A. Palmer, J. Michael Queen, and Jack Soman.

depending on the shape of the host particle and the nature of water agitation. Rare cubic and hexagonal varieties have also been discovered.

It is generally thought that pearls must be agitated by drips, or by some other source of vibration, to prevent them from adhering to each other or to adjacent surfaces. Many eventually do coalesce or become cemented to the floor. Microbial activity may be involved in the growth of some cave pearls, although there is no conclusive evidence. The most unusual known occurrence of cave pearls is in Gruta de las Canicas, Mexico, where literally millions cover large areas of the passage floors (Porter Nuñez, 2002). These have no obvious sources of dripping water, which leaves their origin open to question.

Flowstone consists of sheets, mounds, and curtains, composed mainly of calcite, which are deposited where water runs in thin films down cave walls or sloping floors (Figure 10.24). It has smooth, rippled surfaces that at first mimic the irregularities of the underlying surface. Later, as the flowstone thickens, the irregularities become more pronounced because of enhanced CO_2 loss from convex surfaces. For the same reason, ripples in the water film tend to produce similar ripples in the flowstone surface at fairly regular intervals. Gently sloping flowstone surfaces may eventually develop rimstone pools. If flowstone accumulates on sediment that is later eroded away, the

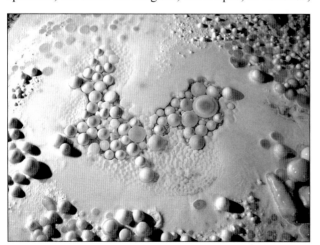

Figure 10.23: Cave pearls in Lechuguilla Cave, New Mexico. Width of photo is about 35 cm.

Figure 10.25: Stalactites and stalagmites in Blood Cave, Montana.

flowstone may remain as a shelf or canopy that projects from the surface to which it is attached.

Dripstone is a general term for any deposits that crystallize from water that drips freely from cave ceilings or ledges. Speleologists sometimes group dripstone and flowstone informally as *"stal,"* in reference to their most common forms, stalactites and stalagmites. Flowstone and dripstone often combine into a single complex mass resembling frozen waterfalls. Dripstone includes the following types:

Stalactites hang from ceilings or overhanging ledges like icicles (Figure 10.25). Each stalactite contains a hollow central tube a few millimeters in diameter. Water typically seeps through the tube, emerges, and then clings

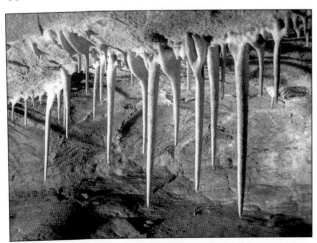

Figure 10.26: Alignment of stalactites along a fracture, Dry Cave, New Mexico. Width of photo is about 1.3 m.

briefly while it loses CO_2 and precipitates calcite around its contact with the stalactite tip. In this way the stalactite grows longer. Meanwhile, it may also grow in diameter if calcite is deposited by water running down the outer walls. Its girth may also be enlarged by water that slowly seeps out of the central tube through the stalactite walls along crystal boundaries. The upper parts of a stalactite are older and have had more time to grow. The tip is the narrowest part, with the diameter of a water drop. The tapered shape of stalactites may also be influenced by variations in the rate of calcite deposition (Short and others, 2005).

Groups of stalactites are often aligned along ceiling fractures, which are the most common paths for inflowing water (Figure 10.26). But the central canals of stalactites rarely line up exactly with fractures, and in fact feeder cracks are not necessary at all. Seepage water naturally accumulates at low points in the ceiling and forms drips that can initiate stalactite growth. Stalactites can form by seepage along their outer surfaces, with no water descending through their central canals. If so, the hollow central tubes are merely the result of crystallization around the perimeter of the terminal drip. In the same way, stalactites can grow from overhanging ledges of bedrock or from other speleothems.

Soda straws (or ***straw stalactites***) are stalactites that consist of thin-walled tubes with nearly uniform diameters (Figures 10.27–10.28). Over their entire length they maintain a diameter of only a few millimeters — essentially the diameter of a water drop — with walls about 0.2–0.5 mm thick. The growing tip of a normal stalactite has the same characteristics. For a straw stalactite to form, the internal tube must remain wide enough for water to descend freely without seeping out through the walls or running down the outside. Straw stalactites often form closely spaced clusters and can reach lengths of nearly 10 m, although the great majority are less than half a meter long. Because surface tension decreases with temperature, soda straws are likely to be thinner in warm climates (Curl, 1972, 1973).

Where substantial trickles of calcite-saturated water enter a cave, irregular, flared calcite growths may form around the outlets during low flow. Such speleothems are known as ***showerheads***. Small ones are known informally as ***dribblers***.

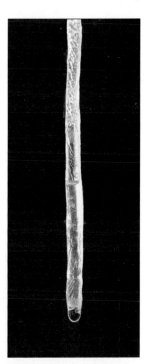

Figure 10.27: Straw stalactite in a Virginia cave. Note the water level part-way up the internal tube and the crystal structure of the walls. Water drop shows scale.

Figure 10.28: Straw stalactites in Grotte de Choranche, France.

During high flow the water retains some of its solutional capacity, so that the interiors of these rudimentary stalactites are slightly enlarged. Their tips are broad and irregular, and water drips from a number of places during low flow

Figure 10.29: Flowstone draperies in Helictite Cave, Virginia. Height of photo is about 40 cm.

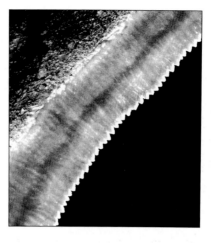

Figure 10.30: A drapery with a serrated edge, formed by drops of ponded water and etched by later corrosion, Cueva de los Pájaros, Isla de Mona, Puerto Rico. Width of photo is about 20 cm.

but forms steady streams during wet periods. Outflow may be intermittent where water in the aperture collects by capillarity for a short time and then suddenly dribbles out.

When a trickle of water runs down an overhanging surface and clings to the wall by surface tension, a narrow trail of calcite is deposited that grows into a ribbon-like *drapery* that is only a little thicker than a water drop (Figure 10.29). Many draperies terminate downward in stalactites. Water may be trapped by irregularities along the drapery edges, to form the equivalent of tiny inverted rimstone pools, in which the rims grow faster than the interiors. The internal crystal structure of the drapery tends to impose a fairly uniform spacing between droplets, so that the edge of the drapery becomes toothed like a saw blade (Figure 10.30).

Stalagmites are mounds that form where drops of falling water hit the cave floor (Figures 10.25 and 10.31). The descending water splashes and runs down the sides in a thin film. With time, most stalagmites grow in both height and diameter. Usually the faster the drip rate, the larger the stalagmite relative to that of the overlying stalactite. It is common for the water that splashes and runs off stalagmites to produce aprons of flowstone that extend across the floor below. If outward splashing at the point of impact prevents most of the drip water from running down the

Figure 10.31: A "totem-pole" stalagmite in Peştera Urşilor, Romania. Height of stalagmite is about 4.5 m.

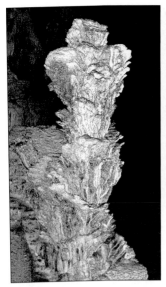

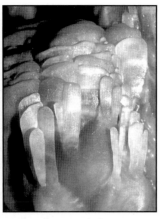

Figure 10.33: Blades projecting from a stalagmite in Carlsbad Cavern, New Mexico. The continuity of the banding in the blades suggests that these were not formed by chaotic splashes but by alternate crystal growth and dissolution, which has exposed the internal structure of the stalagmite. Width of photo is about 30 cm.

Figure 10.32: Fingers and blades that project outward and upward in a stalagmite are typical where the water falls a great distance (in this case, more than 30 m) and splashes. Yuang Jang Cave, Fengshan, China. Height of photo is about 3 m.

Figure 10.35: Thirty-meter-high dripstone columns in Ogle Cave, New Mexico.

sides, a stalagmite can remain remarkably narrow as it grows, so that it resembles a totem pole (Figure 10.31). Some grow upward in tiers with projecting shoulders at the top of each tier, as in the base of the column in Figure 10.34.

Where water falls from a great height, it may deposit calcite in the splash zone that looks like nested leaves or mittens that project at upward at steep angles (Figure 10.32). Outward-projecting blades on the sides of a stalagmite may also be formed in that way, or by alternating precipitation and dissolution (Figure 10.33). Water dripping off the irregular walls of a stalagmite can produce a complex array of stalactites, draperies, and pillars, so that each speleothem has a unique shape.

A stalactite and stalagmite may grow together to form a ***column*** that reaches from floor to ceiling (Figure 10.34). Some stalagmites and columns are more than 30 meters high (Figure 10.35).

Figure 10.34: A column formed by the merging of a stalactite and stalagmite, Lechuguilla Cave, New Mexico. Height of photo is about 2 m.

If dripstone and flowstone deposits become partly submerged by a rise in nearby pool levels, the earlier deposits acquire collars of shelfstone (Figures 10.16 and 10.36). The combination of gravitational forms and horizontal pool deposits can produce some very striking speleothems.

Bell canopies are flared flowstone sheets in the shape of bells or hoods that terminate downward in thin, rounded or serrated edges. Many of them form caps over older stalagmites, although some hang free from ceilings, walls, or other speleothems (Figure 10.37). They are typically asymmetrical and flare outward only in a few directions. Some canopies are formed by weathering of old speleothems, or of the overlying bedrock, so that a wet pasty material flows downward over the speleothem and later hardens (Chapter 12). Canopies can also be deposited by water that evaporates before it is able to drip off the lower edges (Hill, 1978). If the canopy covers loose sediment, the sediment may later be eroded away,

Figure 10.36: Periodic changes in climate have caused pool levels in Lechuguilla Cave to fluctuate and to deposit jackets of calcite around older dripstone and flowstone. Weathered bedrock material has colored the pool deposits deep red. Special soft-rubber footwear is worn when crossing such delicate areas.

Figure 10.37: A bell canopy in Peştera Urşilor, Romania. Height of photo is about 2 m.

Figure 10.38: A grim-looking stalagmite hooded by the growth of a bell canopy, Slaughter Canyon Cave, New Mexico. Height of photo is about 5 m.

so that only the hollow canopy remains. Some canopied stalagmites have amusing shapes that resemble cartoon characters, while others look like scenes from a bad dream (Figure 10.38).

Conulites are cone-shaped deposits that line the walls of drip holes in sediment (Thayer, 1967; Figure 10.39). Most are composed of calcite. Partial removal of the sediment at a later time (e.g., by stream erosion) can cause the conulites to stand in relief like empty ice-cream cones. Projecting conulites filled with water may resemble bird-baths.

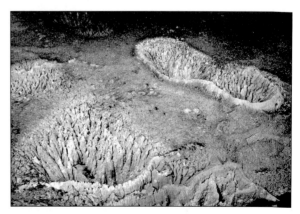

Figure 10.39: Conulites in a sediment-covered cave floor, Peştera Humpleu, Romania. Width of photo is about 80 cm.

Speleothems formed by capillary water

Where water forms thin films or emerges from tiny fissures or pores, capillarity can overcome the effect of gravity.* If evaporation is present, the water film is drawn toward drier areas. Speleothems formed by this capillary water have no preferred vertical orientation. They tend to grow most rapidly where the water film has the sharpest curvature, because rates of CO_2 loss and evaporation are greatest there. Knobby and erratic growths are the typical result. If the water supply varies with time, the dominant control on speleothem growth may alternate between gravity and capillarity to produce composite forms.

Helictites are erratic finger-like growths of calcite or aragonite that twist and branch like gnarled roots (Figure 10.40). They are formed by water that seeps in tiny amounts from fissures and pores in bedrock or from preexisting speleothems. They have tiny internal canals about 0.01–0.5 mm in diameter that supply water to the growing tips. Laboratory experiments suggest that helictites grow most readily where hydrostatic pressure builds up inside them because of the tiny size of the aperture through which the water must escape (Huff, 1940). Whether a pressure build-up is a requirement for helictite growth is uncertain. In any case, the tiny canal does not deliver discrete droplets, such as those that form stalactites, but instead supplies a thin capillary film to the helictite surface. A helictite thickens by mineral deposition from this water film.

In dry environments, water in the central canals is drawn by evaporative wicking to the outer surfaces through the interfaces between crystals. The walls are composed of fibrous curved crystals that grow outward to fatten the helictite. In wet environments, the helictites grow mainly from the tips by deposition of clear crystals around the central tube. This is the type shown in Figure 10.40.

Some helictites are graceful and delicate, and others resemble thick rocky fingers. The largest are several meters long, but most grow to only a few centimeters. Their erratic shapes are controlled mainly by internal crystal structure, and also by the fact that their growth is fastest at the canal

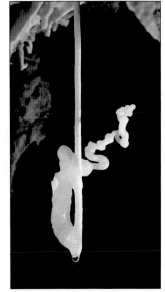

Figure 10.40: A helictite growing from the tip of a straw stalactite, Lechuguilla Cave, New Mexico. The scale is indicated by the water droplet.

outlets and on other convex surfaces. Periodic changes in growth rate can produce *beaded helictites*, which look like beads on a string. The various types of helictites and related features are described by Davis (2005).

When a helictite approaches another surface, such as a cave wall or another speleothem, it may tend to be deflected because the crowding diminishes the rate of CO_2 loss. This is most common in areas of little air flow. Also, the crystal structure of the helictite does not usually match those of the surface it approaches, which makes it difficult for the helictite to bond to it. Some helictites (especially those that are thin and straight) reverse their directions abruptly where they approach another surface and can even bend back sharply at acute angles that are controlled by the local crystal structure. These sharp reversals give the impression that the helictites are ricocheting off the interfering surfaces. A few in Figure 10.41 show this pattern.

If there is a decrease in water supply to dripstone, helictites may grow off the original speleothem (Figure 10.40). If the moisture supply to a helictite increases, straw stalactites may grow from it. Alternatively, the change from a straw to a helictite, or vice versa, may be controlled by changes in tip size of the internal canal.

Helictites that grow upward from a ledge or floor are sometimes called "heligmites." This term is probably not appropriate, because helictites show no regard for gravity, and those that grow upward usually have the same origin as those that do not. On the other hand, many upward-growing helictites grow from banks of carbonate sediment that has weathered from the ceiling. They are likely to form, at least in

Figure 10.41: Helictites growing on stalactites, Caverns of Sonora, Texas. Some of the helictites consist of straight segments that bend in sharp angles where they approach obstructions. Width of photo is about 30 cm. Photo by Kevin Downey.

---

* The term *capillarity* is usually applied to the attraction between fluids and solid surfaces in narrow tubes or fissures. Here it is also applied to thin fluid films on solid surfaces. The adhesive and cohesive forces involved are identical.

Figure 10.42: This helictite bush grew upward from a ledge covered by weathered limestone powder in Wind Cave, South Dakota. Later ponding coated the helictites and carbonate sediment with a multi-layer crust of calcite. Width of photo is about 30 cm.

part, by upward wicking of water that saturated the sediment during periods of water-level rise. Many of the helictites are later fattened by pool deposits (Figure 10.42). Some upward-growing helictites have been attributed to rising thermal water (Davis, 1989; LaRock and Cunningham, 1995).

Until recently it was thought that helictites could form only in air. But in rare circumstances they can form underwater as a result of the common-ion effect (see ***subaqueous helictites***, pages 279–280). Perhaps the normal kind should be called *subaerial helictites* (i.e., formed in air), but this term is hardly necessary because the underwater type is so rare.

Figure 10.43: Anthodites in Hicks Cave, New Mexico. Width of photo is about 20 cm.

Figure 10.44: Shields in Crystal Cave, Sequoia - King's Canyon National Park, California.

Anthodites are similar to helictites but are composed of long quill-like fingers that are straight or only gently curved (Figure 10.43). They are composed mainly of aragonite, or calcite that has replaced aragonite. The needle-like aragonite crystals appear to limit the curvature of the fingers. Anthodites are rare in general but are profuse in certain caves, such as Skyline Caverns, Virginia, which have the essential combination of abundant moisture with a high Mg/Ca ratio, combined with evaporation (White, 1994).

Shields consist of two parallel plates of calcite separated by a thin crack. They are roughly circular or oval and grow outward along the lips of the crack (Figure 10.44). Their attachment points, which are also their water sources, consist of either bedrock or other speleothems. Dripstone columns seem to be the most favorable speleothems for hosting shields. Some shields appear to grow off older shields, like the ears of a prickly pear cactus, perhaps when all but a single narrow outlet have been blocked by calcite deposits.

Although shields are uncommon, they are abundant in some caves. Most are located in deformed rocks, perhaps because of differential movement between rock masses caused by internal stress (Moore, 1958). This process is likely to initiate shield growth, but repeated movement may not be necessary to maintain it. Around the shield perimeter

Figure 10.45: The internal gap between plates is visible in this weathered shield in Crystal Cave, California. Flashlight 15 cm long gives scale.

the internal crack is usually narrow enough to support only capillary seepage, which propagates the radial growth. After intense rain, water under pressure squirts out of the cracks around the perimeters of some shields. From the few shields that are visible in cross section, it is clear that the growth is concentric around the recharge point. It also appears that the internal gap widens toward the shield interior (Figure 10.45).

The water inside may be slightly undersaturated, which would enlarge the interior parts of the gap while calcite is deposited around the perimeter where CO_2 is able to escape. Increasing flow can overwhelm the capillarity and cause gravitational water to deposit stalactites and draperies around the shield edges. Some shields appear to be isolated from any likely source of water, but later dissolution or breakdown may have removed their original support. Shields are among the major attractions of Grand Caverns (Virginia), Lehman Cave (Great Basin National Park, Nevada), and Crystal Cave (California). The origin of shields is still something of a puzzle.

Welts are outward growths from fractures in speleothems (Figure 10.46). Welts resemble rudimentary shields, except that the origin of welts is fairly clear. Water seeps out along a natural or artificial crack and precipitates calcite or aragonite (rarely other minerals) where it emerges. Welts usually

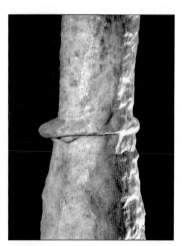

Figure 10.46: Welt along a fracture in a column in Hidden Cave, New Mexico. Height of photo is 25 cm.

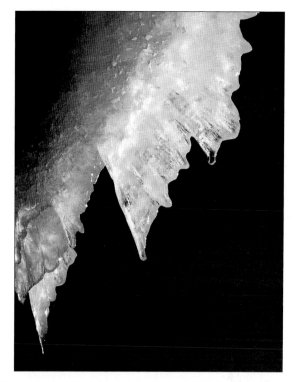

Figure 10.47: Fin-shaped draperies in a southern Georgia cave. Slow recrystallization of the calcite produces a translucent glassy-looking structure. This process is typical in caves with limited air circulation in which the humidity hovers near 100%. Width of photo is about 30 cm.

form collars around dripstone columns or ridges along cracks in flowstone.

Caves with limited air circulation and abundant water tend to have humid, high-CO_2 atmospheres. Loss of CO_2 is very slow, so that the water remains only slightly supersaturated with calcite or aragonite. Irregular fins, blades, and helictites are able to grow, and their crystals are glassy and clear. These include some of the most profuse and delicate helictite displays, such as those in Caverns of Sonora (Figure 10.41). Recrystallization to larger crystal size is common. Note the unusual growth patterns and lack of layering in the drapery in Figure 10.47, compared to the one in Figure 10.30.

Evaporative speleothems

Most caves have a relative humidity greater than 90%. Evaporation can form or modify speleothems even in these humid conditions, although it is most effective in dryer caves. Air currents can speed evaporation. In their effect on speleothems, there is a broad overlap between evaporation and CO_2 loss.

As evaporation proceeds, water is wicked out of moist rock and speleothems by capillary attraction, in the same way that moisture seeps from the wet to dry parts of a sponge. Evaporation concentrates the dissolved load and causes minerals to precipitate in a distinct order, from least soluble to most soluble. Calcite normally forms first, mostly by the loss of carbon dioxide, although evaporation can augment

Figure 10.48: Cave popcorn with a fringe of aragonite frostwork, Wind Cave, South Dakota. Width of photo is 15 cm.

the process. As calcium is removed from the water, the magnesium/calcium ratio increases and calcite growth is inhibited. This allows the more-soluble mineral aragonite to crystallize instead.

With further evaporation, other minerals follow in order, depending on the nature of the dissolved materials. A typical sequence is *calcite*, *aragonite* (both $CaCO_3$), *huntite* ($CaMg_3(CO_3)_4$), *hydromagnesite* (either $Mg_5(CO_3)_4(OH)_2 \cdot 4H_2O$ or $Mg_4(CO_3)_3OH)_2 \cdot 3H_2O$), *magnesite* ($MgSO_4$) and finally *dolomite* ($CaMg(CO_3)_2$). *Gypsum* ($CaSO_4 \cdot 2H_2O$) can then precipitate if sulfate is present. Certain other sulfate minerals are even more soluble, including *epsomite* ($MgSO_4 \cdot 7H_2O$), *mirabilite* ($NaSO_4 \cdot 10H_2O$), and *halite* ($NaCl$). Some evaporative minerals that are common in many dry caves are rare at the land surface.

A few magnesium and sodium minerals are so soluble that they crystallize only at low humidity. They may form rapidly when conditions are favorable, for example when cold winter air descends into a cave and loses some of its relative humidity as it warms. When the humidity rises again the minerals re-dissolve (page 293).

All of these minerals are either white or clear. They form a variety of shapes including crusts, fronds, knobs, blobs, and flower-like or finger-like projections. Some form crusts on cave walls or on older speleothems. Where water drips into a cave and evaporates, these minerals can occasionally form dripstone and flowstone.

Typical speleothems produced by evaporative minerals are described below:

Coralloids are nodular growths of various types. The most common is *cave popcorn*, which consists of small balls of calcite, aragonite, or (rarely) gypsum that project outward from bedrock surfaces or other speleothems (Figure 10.48). Popcorn makes cave surfaces rough and abrasive. In places it grows preferentially into windy areas or along the edges of bedrock projections like the teeth of a dull saw. Some is precipitated by CO_2 loss, especially in splash zones, and has the texture of flowstone. Evaporative popcorn is chalky white and round, so it resembles the edible variety of popcorn, with

Figure 10.49: Popcorn "trays" in Lechuguilla Cave, New Mexico.

knobs typically 5–20 mm in diameter. Some knobs terminate in aragonite needles (Figure 10.48).

In caves with poor air exchange with the surface, evaporation is limited to crudely stratified zones, so that popcorn growth terminates abruptly in the upward and sometimes downward direction. Evaporative popcorn growths that are limited to the lower parts of walls and speleothems are sometimes erroneously interpreted as former pool deposits.

Dense growths of popcorn that terminate downward in distinctly horizontal surfaces are sometimes called *trays* (Figure 10.49; Martini, 1986). The nodules in trays often contain hanging water droplets that indicate a wetter condition than is typical for the growth of most popcorn. Trays seem to be controlled by humidity stratification in the cave atmosphere, because many are located in the vicinity of standing water or other humid air sources. Tray levels commonly occur at several closely spaced intervals in the same deposit, so a more subtle process may be responsible. Martini (1986) proposes evaporative enrichment of magnesium in moisture that seeps through the popcorn, so that aragonite needles are favored instead. Other mechanisms must be important, because a few trays are also composed of gypsum.

Cave coral is a variety of coralloid that protrudes from rock or sediment surfaces as irregular fingers, usually composed of calcite (Figure 10.50). It is most common in wet, windy passages, where moisture is drawn from bedrock

Figure 10.50: Cave coral in Mammoth Cave, Kentucky, composed of calcite with interspersed grains of quartz silt. Ball-point pen for scale.

Figure 10.52: Hollow drip cone of calcite and aragonite in Jewel Cave, South Dakota. The cone formed when popcorn and frostwork grew by evaporation around drips of condensation moisture from the ceiling. There is no corresponding stalactite above. Weathering of the ceiling caused the drip to shift, and the solutionally aggressive water drilled a groove in the side of the cone.

or sediment during the dry periods between floods. Most cave coral grows upward and into the wind. It usually contains floodwater sediment, which colors it a gloomy dark brown or gray. In Sistema Purificación, Mexico, the coral fingers are so large and jagged that they pose a hazard to explorers, who refer to them wryly as "death coral."

Frostwork consists of delicate, white, needle-shaped aragonite crystals about 0.1–2 mm wide and up to several centimeters long, which radiate or branch in delicate clusters

Figure 10.51: A little tree of aragonite in Wind Cave, South Dakota. It formed by evaporation of Mg-rich, aragonite-saturated ceiling drips. Height of tree is about 25 cm.

(Figures 10.48 and 10.51). It grows by evaporation of moisture from bedrock or other speleothems, particularly popcorn. Unlike helictites, frostwork needles have no central canals. As in popcorn, it is common for aragonite needles to end upward or downward in subhorizontal surfaces, and the various explanations for *trays* may also apply. Beneath water drips, evaporation can cause frostwork to build shapes that resemble bushes or fir trees, or hollow stalagmite-like cones resembling that in Figure 10.52. Some frostwork is made of calcite that has recrystallized from aragonite while retaining the original needle-like structure.

Drip cones are composed of popcorn, frostwork, or gypsum that grow upward in water drips. Although they resemble stalagmites, they are not true dripstone. They have no matching stalactites overhead and usually contain drip holes in their centers. If the dripping water is not supersaturated with the mineral in the cone, nothing is deposited where the drip hits. Instead, evaporation causes crystals to grow around the drip points to form a rim that builds upward as a hollow shell (Figure 10.52). Migration of the drip may dissolve away part of the cone wall. Drip cones of popcorn and frostwork are usually formed where condensation water falls from low points in the ceiling above. Meanwhile the ceiling is corroded by the condensation moisture. As chemical conditions change, drip cones may evolve into true stalagmites or vice versa.

Gypsum forms a large percentage of evaporative speleothems. The source of the dissolved calcium and sulfate is most often the reaction of sulfuric acid with carbonate bedrock. Oxidation of hydrogen sulfide or iron sulfide is the typical source of the sulfuric acid (Chapters 5 and 12). Iron hydroxides and oxides derived from iron sulfide contribute to the golden brown color of many gypsum speleothems. Less common sources of gypsum include seawater, guano, and primary gypsum in nearby bedrock.

Gypsum crusts on cave walls range in thickness from paper-thin to about half a meter. Gypsum also grows in cracks in bedrock and wedges apart the intervening blocks. It may also replace the outer parts of the carbonate bedrock

Figure 10.53: Gypsum crust on the walls of Grotta di Faggeto Tondo, Italy. Infiltrating water has partly dissolved and re-precipitated the gypsum as larger crystals. Thickness of crust is about 15 cm. Width of photo is about 40 cm.

(Chapter 12). The resulting crust has a blistery cloud-like texture that can resemble packed snow (Figure 10.53). If there is an increase in seepage of water from the bedrock, the base of the gypsum crust dissolves. The crust then breaks free from the wall and may shatter into fragments.

Gypsum stalagmites, drip cones, and towers can form where dripping water either falls onto preexisting gypsum deposits or already has a high concentration of dissolved calcium sulfate. Dripwater is nearly always undersaturated with gypsum, so it usually cores a hole in any previous

Figure 10.55: Cotton-like strands of fibrous gypsum in Mammoth Cave, Kentucky. Width of photo is 20 cm.

gypsum directly beneath it, while evaporation around the drip site causes gypsum to build up either as a hollow drip cone or a narrow tower (Figure 10.54).

The most delicate gypsum speleothems have a remarkable range of shapes and textures, which include individual fibers, bundles of fibers, or well-formed crystals. Differences are caused mainly by variations in the sulfate source, pore structure of the bedrock or sediment, and growth rate. Most of these deposits are white or translucent. Clear, translucent gypsum is also known as *selenite*. Single needles of selenite up to 7 m long but only about 0.1 mm thick have been observed hanging from cave ceilings. More commonly the

Figure 10.54: Towers of gypsum (the Three Amigos) in Lechuguilla Cave are the remnants of rudimentary drip cones, which formed in evaporative zones around the points where water dripped onto massive gypsum. The tallest tower is about 3 m high.

Figure 10.56: This rope of delicate gypsum strands in Wind Cave, South Dakota, has fallen to the floor by its own weight. Width of photo is 15 cm.

Figure 10.57: Gypsum flower in Mammoth Cave, Kentucky, formed on a pyrite-rich area of dolomite bedrock. Width of photo is 25 cm.

strands grow in clusters that resemble beards, fiberglass, rope, and cotton (Figures 10.55–10.56).

Needles and blades of gypsum often grow upward from sediment surfaces, and individual gypsum crystals can form inside the sediment, pushing aside the sediment grains as the crystals grow. Gypsum crystals can also form flat, radiating clusters on bedrock or carbonate speleothems.

Figure 10.58: Gypsum "spiders" in Jewel Cave, South Dakota, formed when growing selenite needles pushed flakes of weathered bedrock from the wall. The photo has been rotated 90° to the left to emphasize that crystal growth, rather than gravity, has moved the bedrock flakes. Width of photo is 15 cm.

Gypsum flowers form where sources of calcium sulfate are concentrated, especially where pyrite crystals oxidize in the bedrock near the cave (Figure 10.57). They grow outward in curving fronds that resemble lilies. Most are a few centimeters or tens of centimeters long, but some extend more than a meter. A gypsum flower grows from its base, often in the outermost pores of the exposed bedrock. Newly crystallized gypsum pushes the older deposits outward like toothpaste from a tube. Thus the tip of the flower is usually the oldest part. The curvature of a gypsum flower seems to be controlled by differences in growth rate. Although some gypsum flowers are pure white, most are tinged brown in places by iron oxide. In the centers of some small gypsum flowers are tiny nuggets of iron oxide that are the weathered remnants of pyrite (see Figure 12.21). Gypsum blades may grow just below the bedrock surface and push thin flakes of weathered bedrock ahead of them to form spider-like speleothems (Figure 10.58).

The most impressive of all gypsum speleothems are crystalline displays known informally as *chandeliers* (Figure 10.59). They grow downward from cave ceilings or overhanging walls as branching arrays. Although chandeliers tend to grow downward, their twisting, sinuous forms show little regard for gravity. They usually form long, robust, arm-like structures that reach from the cave ceiling, thinning downward and terminating in a cluster of sharp selenite

Figure 10.59: Gypsum chandeliers in Lechuguilla Cave. This photo was taken soon after their discovery. The trail occupied by the cavers has since been rerouted to a more protective position.

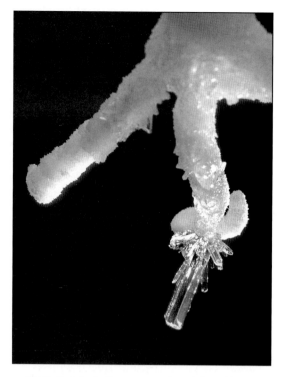

Figure 10.60: Detail of a tiny gypsum chandelier, with unidentified crystals growing from the tip, Kap-Kutan Cave, Turkmenistan. Width of photo is about 10–15 cm. Photo by Peter and Ann Bosted.

Figure 10.61: Mineral growths from evaporative pools show a distinct sequence from calcite to aragonite, and often further to the Mg-rich minerals huntite, hydromagnesite, magnesite, and finally dolomite. Dolomite is supersaturated while many of the other minerals are precipitating, but it forms slowly and usually by replacement of an earlier mineral such as huntite. This mound, which projects about 15 cm from a pool in Lechuguilla Cave, consists of all the minerals listed above. The dark base is mainly calcite, and the whitish caps are composed mainly of the other minerals.

crystals. Some look menacing, like claws. They grow at their tips, and it is common to see drops of water clinging to them. This water is supersaturated with gypsum as the result of evaporation. In a typical gypsum chandelier, the older coarsely crystalline center becomes coated by a jacket of white, finely crystalline gypsum, which thickens with time. Most chandeliers occur in caves formed by sulfuric acid, where deposits of massive gypsum in upper levels are dissolved and reprecipitated in lower levels. In other types of caves they can emanate from beds that contain oxidized pyrite. The best-known examples of gypsum chandeliers are in Lechuguilla Cave, New Mexico, and Kap-Kutan Cave in Turkmenistan (Figures 10.59–10.60).

Gypsum wall crusts and floor deposits can also form during sulfuric acid speleogenesis (Chapter 8). This type of gypsum tends to be more massive than evaporative gypsum, and it can have textures derived from the carbonate rock that it has replaced.

Huntite and ***magnesite*** form fine-grained white crusts, blobs, and powder (Figure 10.61). ***Hydromagnesite*** usually forms pasty white masses with the appearance and texture of cottage cheese (Figure 10.61). ***Hydromagnesite balloons*** are hollow shells of white hydromagnesite with thin, delicate walls, which appear to have been inflated by a gas (Figure 10.62). They range up to about 3 cm in diameter, with walls only about 0.05 mm thick that consist of thin overlapping plates of hydromagnesite. Balloons grow mainly on bedrock and less commonly on other speleothems. Hydromagnesite is the only verified balloon-forming mineral, but some may have recrystallized to other minerals. Balloons are known from only about a dozen caves in the world, mostly in the semi-arid western U.S., although a few caves in the Austrian Alps also contain balloons.

All known hydromagnesite balloons seem to be inactive, but this is difficult to verify. Most are now convoluted and deflated. How they inflate is not yet known. This mineral is highly plastic when moist. Blobs of pasty hydromagnesite may be inflated by carbon dioxide gas released by microorganisms, or the hydromagnesite may be deposited on an organic film. Although small quantities of carbon have been detected in a hydromagnesite balloon, there is, so far, no concrete evidence for mi-

Figure 10.62: Hydromagnesite balloon in Jewel Cave. Balloon is 4 cm long.

Figure 10.63: Wispy epsomite crystals up to 3 cm high grew across this trail in Great Onyx Cave, Kentucky, in a single cold, dry season. They disappeared entirely within a few months.

crobial influence on balloon growth.* Hydromagnesite is unstable at high CO_2 levels, which raises the question of whether this gas can inflate balloons without converting the hydromagnesite to another mineral. Perhaps the inflation is rapid enough that the hydromagnesite has no time to alter. Hydromagnesite balloons are most common on cave walls near windy constrictions, which suggests that balloons may be inflated by air that seeps from narrow wall cracks during high-velocity winds. But this process cannot account for the few balloons that hang from bedrock corners or from speleothems. There may be more than one way for them to inflate.

Epsomite is soft, white or clear, and bitter-tasting, and can form needles, fibers, or dripstone masses (Figures 10.63–10.64). *Mirabilite* is soft and usually has ice-like clarity and a slightly bitter or salty taste. *Halite* is white or

---

* Communication from Rick Olson, Mammoth Cave, Ky. (1991), and Paula Provencio, Albuquerque, N.M. (2004).

Figure 10.64: Epsomite stalactites in a Georgia cave.

clear and forms crusts, strands, dripstone, or blocky crystals. It dissolves so readily that it forms speleothems only in very arid climates. The other evaporative minerals described here are less soluble than halite and can grow in the dry parts of caves even in humid climates, for example beneath an impermeable cap-rock.

Cave blisters (sometimes called *crinkle blisters*) are brittle crusts that form thin, rounded, hollow balls on cave walls or other speleothems. They are rarely more than a few centimeters in diameter, with walls that range from half a millimeter to almost a centimeter thick. Most blisters consist of calcite or gypsum, but they also include many less-common minerals. Those with thin walls may form by crystallization around bubbles where water is expelled from bedrock. Weathering of rock in moist cave air can produce powder or paste that drops into cave pools. When the water evaporates, the weathered material can recrystallize into white, pasty minerals that form blobs like shaving cream. Hydromagnesite can be formed in this way. When they dry, these pasty minerals tend to form cave blisters or curling flakes (Figure 10.65).

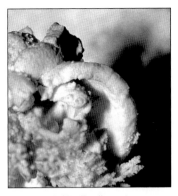

Figure 10.65: Rudimentary cave blister of dolomite, Carlsbad Cavern, New Mexico. Width of photo = 5 cm.

In caves, *dolomite* is normally the last mineral to precipitate by evaporation. It usually forms white plaster-like crusts (Figure 10.65). Although dolomite is supersaturated in many cave waters, it requires a long time to crystallize. Meanwhile other more soluble minerals, such as huntite, form instead, simply because they crystallize more rapidly. Over time these minerals can eventually recrystallize to dolomite.

Many evaporative growths are preferentially oriented either on the upwind or downwind sides of bedrock projections or speleothems. If the air is humid, they form on the downwind side and are often accompanied by dissolution on the upwind sides by condensation moisture. Evaporation in dry air causes speleothems to grow on the upwind side. Wind-oriented features are described further in Chapter 12 (pages 331–333).

Evaporation can also wick moisture out of sediment, and dissolved constituents can precipitate as evaporative minerals. In areas of high air flow, nearby bodies of water can speed the process by keeping the sediment moist internally while it dries on the surface.

An alternative explanation for some of these speleothems is that they are deposited by *aerosols* (Gádoros and Cser, 1986; Klimchouk and others, 1995). Aerosols consist of microscopic droplets formed by splashing or by condensation on dust particles. Release of ions by radioactive decay may also produce aerosols. Any dissolved solids contained in the droplets are precipitated where the aerosols condense or settle on solid surfaces. This mechanism can produce certain calcite and aragonite deposits, but it cannot account for the sequential deposition of minerals in order of increasing solubility. Some evaporative speleothems contain small inclusions of uncommon cave minerals such as fluorite (calcium fluoride, CaF_2), which may be deposited from aerosols (see pages 339–340). Special care must be taken when monitoring aerosols, because simply visiting the site can alter the environmental conditions. There is some debate about the significance of aerosols and the role of radioactivity in releasing them (Maltsev, 1997; Cigna and Hill, 1997; Pashenko and Dublyansky, 1997), but their potential role in speleothem deposition should not be overlooked.

Minerals formed by chemical alteration

Some minerals are formed by alteration of preexisting minerals by changes in pH, temperature, oxygen level, or nature of the dissolved components in water. Most are described elsewhere (Chapters 5, 8, and 12), and only a few easily recognized examples are mentioned here.

Iron and manganese oxides are common cave deposits, although their volumes are usually small. Iron oxides are easily recognized by their red, yellow, or brown colors. Manganese oxides are nearly always black, but so are some iron oxides. Although these minerals usually form only coatings, layers, or scattered specks, they can also produce a variety of speleothem shapes.

Iron and manganese are soluble in oxygen-poor water, and where oxygen becomes abundant they precipitate as oxides, or as hydroxides that eventually recrystallize to oxides. Of the oxides, the most common are FeOOH (***goethite****, or the non-crystalline form ***limonite***) and MnO_2 (***pyrolusite*** or ***birnessite***, depending on the crystal structure). Although manganese oxides can be cave minerals, they rarely produce speleothems. They most commonly form a thin coating on insoluble surfaces such as chert or quartz sandstone. Dissolved manganese does not oxidize readily, but microbial intervention can speed the process (Ehrlich, 1996).

Oxidation of pyrite (FeS_2) can also produce iron oxide, with gypsum as a byproduct (Chapter 12). Another source of iron and manganese oxides is sulfuric acid attack of other minerals such as clay (Chapters 5 and 12). Bacterial activity can speed these oxidation processes, and bacterial filaments are often found in the deposits (see ***rusticles*** on page 297).

Iron and manganese oxides are also soluble in acidic water with a pH less than about 3, and it is possible for this water to transport these dissolved materials and deposit them where the pH is higher, usually as very fine-grained crystals with an earthy texture. Local production of sulfuric acid is the usual cause of such a low pH. Some calcite speleothems in the vicinity of pyrite oxidation have iron oxide cores (Figure 10.66).

Another common source of both iron and manganese

---

* Named for the famous German author and amateur geologist Goethe, and thus pronounced, approximately, "***ger-tite***." With time it tends to recrystallize to the more stable hematite (Fe_2O_3).

Figure 10.66: Calcite speleothems with iron oxide cores derived from oxidation of nearby pyrite, Mystery Cave, Minnesota. This drapery has broken as the result of frost action during the latest glaciation, and its resemblance to a shield is misleading. Goethite forms the soft dark interior.

oxides is water rising from depth along faults. Manganese can also be carried into caves in solution from stagnant surface waters. Manganese oxides trap heavy metals, such as copper and zinc, which can total as much as 1.5% of the total mass (White, 2004b).

Manganese oxides cover the floors of many passages in Jewel Cave, South Dakota (Conn and Conn, 1977; Figure 10.67). Some of these deposits are more than a meter thick. It is likely that some came from rising water. Manganese oxides are also common in Pennsylvanian-age sediments exposed in the cave, which have been distributed throughout lower passages during periodic high-water events.

Weathering of clay, igneous rocks, and metamorphic rocks releases dissolved SiO_2 in the form of silicic acid (H_4SiO_4), which can precipitate as quartz or opal (Chapter 5). These form minor speleothems in some caves, especially

Figure 10.67: Beds of manganese oxides in Jewel Cave, South Dakota, have cracked into polygonal blocks by drying and are partly coated with evaporite minerals.

caves in lava (Chapter 11), but most often they simply fill pores or form thin linings on solid surfaces.

In and around caves formed by sulfuric acid, where oxidation-reduction reactions are common, metals such as uranium can become concentrated. Uranium (U) is more soluble in its oxidized state than in reduced form, especially in carbonate-rich water, and uranium minerals tend to concentrate along redox boundaries where groundwater becomes depleted of its oxygen. Uranium also precipitates in the presence of even small traces of dissolved vanadium (V). The rare uranium-vanadium minerals *tyuyamunite* ($Ca(UO_2)_2V_2O_8 \cdot 5-8H_2O$) and *metatyuyamunite* (produced by partial loss of water from tyuyamunite) have been observed in caves of sulfuric acid origin, such as those in the Guadalupe Mountains (Polyak and Mosch, 1995; Polyak and Provencio, 2001). These are bright yellow minerals that resemble sulfur but are slightly radioactive. They usually form thin coatings on clay deposits and crusts of opal, dolomite and gypsum, and have individual crystals rarely more than about a millimeter in length. They apparently originate in air-filled caves by evaporation.

Alteration of clays by sulfuric acid can produce a variety of minerals such as *alunite* ($KAl_3(SO_4)_2(OH)_6$). The significance of these minerals to environmental interpretation and to dating of speleogenesis is discussed on pages 338–339 and 348.

Minerals from organic sources

Bat or bird guano can produce a variety of acids, either directly or by weathering, especially in warm climates. These include phosphoric, nitric, and sulfuric acid, as well as organic acids, which can corrode the local bedrock and also produce speleothems (Forti, 2001). *Phosphate* speleothems are usually derived from this source. They usually form crusts or corraloids on bedrock surfaces or layers on or in guano and other sediments. They can also form small flowstone or dripstone speleothems. The most common phosphate minerals are *brushite* ($CaHPO_4 \cdot 2H_2O$) and *hydroxylapatite* ($Ca_5(PO_4)_3OH$). Both are present in Figure 6.59. Brushite is usually a light-yellow powder or pasty material derived directly from acidic guano. Hydroxylapatite usually forms white, brown, or almost black crusts produced by the reaction between guano and carbonate rock. Gypsum can also form in caves where sulfuric acid derived from guano reacts with carbonate rock. Many Caribbean caves have gypsum crusts of this type, as well as a variety of phosphate minerals related to guano decomposition (Onac and others, 2001).

Nitrates in caves are mostly derived from guano, although some can be carried in by seepage that has passed through decaying organic litter. Nitrifying bacteria are important in their production. They are so soluble that they crystallize only in extremely dry conditions. In wet caves they are held in solution by capillary water in sediment or bedrock pores (Hill, 1981b). In the U.S. during the Revolutionary War, War of 1812, and Civil War, cave nitrates (saltpeter) provided an essential ingredient in gunpowder, which is a

Figure 10.68: Leaching of nitrates from cave sediment to make saltpeter is demonstrated at Mammoth Cave, Kentucky, by this temporary reconstruction of a 19th century procedure.

mixture of potassium nitrate (KNO_3), carbon, and sulfur. But the most abundant nitrate in caves is calcium nitrate, and potassium nitrate is rare. To produce KNO_3, saltpeter miners followed a multi-step process. They first dug up cave sediment and placed it in wooden hoppers or barrels. They then poured water through it to remove the nitrates in solution (Figure 10.68), and mixed the liquid with wood ashes or lye to convert the calcium nitrate to potassium nitrate. Finally they boiled down the solution to concentrate the nitrate and to precipitate unwanted less-soluble minerals. During the War of 1812, the largest saltpeter operation was at Mammoth Cave, and for the manufacture of gunpowder most of the unprocessed nitrate was sent to a small, young eastern company, which is still named DuPont.

Speleothems influenced by microbial activity

Microorganisms (microbes) can help to form certain features that do not easily fit the traditional classification of speleothems. In general, cave deposits whose shape or origin is determined biologically are called *biothems* (Queen and Melim, 2006). Some are produced when minerals coat microbial filaments. The filaments themselves are thin, generally about 0.1 μm (0.0001 mm) in diameter.

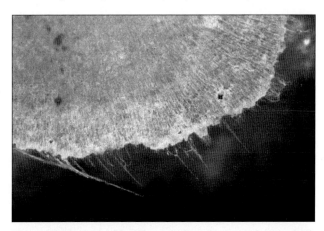

Figure 10.69: Unidentified filaments form the matrix for thin shelf-stone in Mystery Cave, Minnesota. Photo width is about 4 cm.

They are visible by eye only where they form bundles, as in Figure 10.69. Mineral coatings such as iron oxide or calcite can fatten them considerably.

Microbial activity can also affect the way in which minerals precipitate. Such speleothems grow most readily in moist areas where there is active oxidation or reduction. Microbes can derive energy from many of these reactions and can also speed the reactions (pages 126–127).

When magnified greatly with an electron microscope, many samples of limestone and speleothems reveal tiny blobs as small as 0.03 μm, which are attributed to **nannobacteria** (Folk, 1993). There is debate as to whether such a small structure could contain all the necessary parts of a bacterium, and whether they are even organic in origin. Their influence on calcite deposition is still uncertain.

Some speleothems are clearly influenced by microbes. **Pool fingers** are finger-like projections that form in cave pools (Davis and others, 1990). They consist of bundles of mineral-coated microbial filaments and have been observed both in existing pools and in former pools that are now dry (Figure 10.70). Some are accompanied by more recent uncoated filaments. The internal filament bundles in pool fingers are generally less than half a millimeter in diameter. Many pool fingers hang vertically and resemble soda straws, but have irregular knobby surfaces. Some form bridges between neighboring fingers, often in U-shaped loops. Others form delicate lattices of interconnecting web-like strands. A few have roughly parallel but non-vertical orientations, as though they had been deflected by currents. They can also grow upward (Figure 10.71). Pool fingers and subaqueous helictites with triangular cross sections have been observed in Mullamullang Cave in the arid Nullarbor Plain of Australia (Rowling, 2003). Adolphe and others (1991) isolated bac-

Figure 10.71: Pool fingers that grew in a now-dry rimstone pool in Hidden Cave, New Mexico. Although their internal structure has not yet been analyzed, they are suspected of having a microbial influence, as do many other speleothems in the cave. Width of photo is about 30 cm.

teria from a pool finger in France. By using radioactive calcium as a tracer, they found that the bacteria also play a role in precipitating the calcite coating.

The origin of certain pool fingers has been clarified by recent discoveries of bacterial strands in caves where hydrogen sulfide is oxidizing to sulfuric acid. Fine examples are seen in Cueva de Villa Luz, Mexico (Hose and others, 2000). The strands can also form in mines where the acid is produced by oxidation of pyrite. The strands are elastic bundles of bacterial filaments that hang from ceilings and walls (Figure 10.72). Many have U-shaped connections. Some are reinforced by loose aggregates of thin gypsum crystals. Droplets on their tips consist of sulfuric acid with pH values as low as zero. In limestone caves they generally form on a gypsum crust that isolates them from the neutralizing effect of the carbonate bedrock. It is likely that the strands are the precursors of certain pool

Figure 10.70: Pool fingers and U-loops in Lechuguilla Cave. These are composed of calcite-coated filaments (probably bacterial). Width of photo is 25 cm.

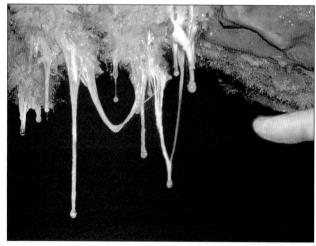

Figure 10.72: "Snottite" biothems in Cueva de Villa Luz, Mexico, composed mainly of filaments of sulfur-oxidizing bacteria. The water droplets have been converted to sulfuric acid by the oxidation of absorbed hydrogen sulfide and oxygen from the cave atmosphere. Their pH averages 1.4, with a minimum of about zero. Note the similarity to the pool fingers in Figure 10.70.

Figure 10.73: Rusticles in Lechuguilla Cave. Height of photo is about 2 m.

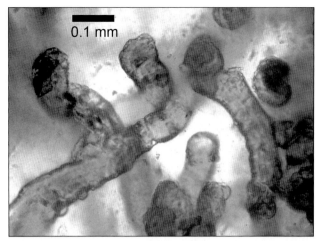

Figure 10.74: Filaments of iron-oxidizing bacteria in a rusticle fragment from Lechuguilla Cave. They have been coated with red translucent iron hydroxide or oxide, which is many times thicker than the original filaments. The clear material is calcite.

fingers. In shape they resemble the original examples of pool fingers in Lechuguilla Cave, and they also occur in the same environment that presumably once existed in that cave (compare Figures 10.70 and 10.72).

Because of their consistency and appearance, the bacterial strands in active sulfuric acid caves have earned the name **snottites**. There are efforts to devise a less expressive name, and the terms **biofilms** or **mucolites** are gaining favor in the technical literature. According to their patterns, such organic deposits may also be called **microbial mats**, **microbial veils**, and similar terms. Very rare biofilm bubbles up to one centimeter in diameter have been observed in Grotta Nuova del Rio Garrafo, Italy (Hose, 2005). Whether they might serve as the foundation for later hydromagnesite balloons is unlikely.

Rusticles are iron oxide speleothems. In most, the iron oxide has deposited in and around a tangle of fossilized bacterial filaments (Figures 10.73–10.74). Calcite forms a coating on some rusticles. Examples in Lechuguilla Cave, New Mexico, include rough-textured soda straws and columns composed of iron oxide with dark gray calcite coatings. Davis and others (1990) consider them to have formed underwater, like those found on the sunken ocean liner *Titanic*. Some iron oxide speleothems can also form in air (Figure 10.66).

Most rusticles are produced by oxidation of pyrite, which releases sulfuric acid and dissolved iron. The acid is quickly neutralized when it encounters limestone or dolomite, or water that contains these rocks in solution. As a result, iron oxides and hydroxides are forced to precipitate. Once the pyrite has been fully oxidized, calcite tends to coat the iron-rich speleothem. In Lechuguilla Cave, iron and manganese oxides have also been released by the alteration of certain clays and other minerals by sulfuric acid derived from H_2S (Chapters 5 and 12).

Chenille spar consists of vertical drapery-like fingers of calcite. It usually forms just below water surfaces and is rarely more than a meter long (Figure 10.75). It has essentially the same origin as pool fingers, with closely spaced bundles of microbial filaments serving as the host for calcite growth. Their vertical orientation is apparently controlled by an array of downward-hanging filaments at the edges of standing pools of water. Various speleothems with vertical orientations but slightly different forms seem also to be influenced by microbial filaments. The quartz deposits

Figure 10.75 Chenille spar in Lechuguilla Cave. The shelfstone indicates the former pool surface. Width of photo is 80 cm.

Figure 10.76: Scene in the "Japanese Garden" in Jewel Cave, South Dakota. These fingers of aragonite (now mostly converted to calcite) fell from the ceiling but were apparently vertical in their original growth position. Although there is no visual evidence for microbial influence, it is likely that the fingers formed around thin organic filaments, as in Figure 10.13. Width of photo is 15 cm.

in Figure 10.13 are in this class, and the aragonite-calcite fingers in Figure 10.76 may also qualify.

Moonmilk is a white deposit of microscopic crystals, usually calcite (Bernasconi, 1961). Other types consist of evaporative minerals such as hydromagnesite or huntite (Figure 10.61). All varieties of moonmilk are composed of finely crystalline needles, plates, or strands, and their loose crystal packing and high porosity allow them to hold a large amount of moisture. They are pasty when wet (their typical

Figure 10.77: Certain pool deposits in the Guadalupe Mountains, New Mexico, consist of moonmilk with a pasty, lard-like texture. They contain bacterial and fungal filaments, and light carbon and oxygen isotopic signatures that can be attributed to microbial activity, but the role of microbes in their origin is uncertain (Boston and others, 2001; Perrone, 2005). These examples are in Hidden Cave.

state) and powdery when dry.

The conditions necessary to form calcite moonmilk are unclear. Microbial activity is widely considered a requirement, but this is not a necessary condition. Calcite moonmilk can form by direct precipitation from solution, by replacement of earlier minerals, or by limestone weathering, all with or without microbial influence (Hill and Forti, 1997; Onac and Ghergari, 1993). Some moonmilk

Figure 10.78: Moonmilk speleothems in Peştera Humpleu, Romania. These draperies look like normal flowstone but are as soft and flexible as cheese. Photo is 1.5 m high.

has the form of pool deposits, dripstone, or flowstone and may result from replacement or alteration of earlier calcite speleothems (Figures 10.77–10.78). Bacterial filaments, or threads of extra-cellular material, appear to serve as nuclei for the strand-like textures in some calcite moonmilk.

In contrast, hydromagnesite moonmilk is deposited directly by evaporation from magnesium-rich moisture. It forms mainly in contact with air, but related types, such as huntite moonmilk, can line evaporative pools (Figure 10.61). These topics are discussed further, in reference to weathering, in Chapter 12.

Speleothem growth rates

How old are those things? This is one of the most frequently asked questions by visitors to show caves, as they point to speleothems. This is like asking how old the trees are in a forest: there is no single age or growth rate. Speleothem growth depends on how fast the dissolved materials are carried in, and how supersaturated the minerals are in the water. These in turn depend on a wide range of factors that vary with time and location.

Growth rates for calcite dripstone and flowstone can be as much as a centimeter of thickness per year in rare conditions, but they are usually much slower. For example, Franke and Geyh (1970) measured the increase in height of 30 active stalagmites at between 0.01 and 0.5 mm/yr. Further references to speleothem growth rates are given by Hill and Forti (1997, pages 285–287).

The overall reaction for calcite deposition is

$$Ca^{++} + 2HCO_3^- \longrightarrow CaCO_3 + CO_2 + H_2O \quad (10.1)$$

In general, this reaction in speleothems is governed by loss of CO_2 from the solution, which draws the reaction toward the right. This is essentially the reverse of the dissolution

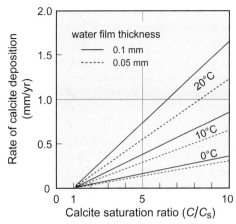

Figure 10.79: Approximate rates of calcite deposition by laminar water films in relation to saturation ratio, temperature and film thickness. A saturation ratio of 1.0 represents 100% saturation, and greater values represent supersaturation. The graph is valid for P_{CO_2} = 0.0003–0.005 atm. A vadose film rapidly acquires the P_{CO_2} of the cave air. Many caves and vadose seeps have higher P_{CO_2} (Chapter 5), but the graph shows the general trends. (Based on Dreybrodt, 2005).

process described by Reactions 5.3–5.7. A small amount of supersaturation is required for precipitation to take place, typically a saturation ratio (C/C_s) of at least 1.1 (Chapter 5).

Dreybrodt (2005) gives a concise summary of the chemical kinetics. Where the water volume is small relative to the solid surface area exposed to calcite deposition, the main limit to speleothem growth is the fairly slow production of CO_2 and its release from the solution. The speed that ions travel through the water, to and away from the solid surface, has a secondary effect on growth rate. The calcite deposition rate is proportional to the degree of calcite supersaturation, but also to the thickness of the water film (Figure 10.79). At any given level of supersaturation, calcite is deposited more rapidly in thick water films than in thin films. In a given body of flowing water, however, the rate is usually faster where the film is *thinnest*, because CO_2 is lost more rapidly there, and calcite supersaturation is greater. The rate also increases with temperature — by about 8 times from 0 to 25°C.

The supply of water to a speleothem must be fairly uniform for the graph in Figure 10.79 to be valid. Laminar flow is assumed (see Eq. 4.2 and pages 96–97). On a typical dripstone speleothem the water film is only about 0.1 mm thick. In Eq. 4.2 the film thickness replaces the term A/p, and the flow almost certainly falls in the laminar range. If the discharge increases, the rate of calcite deposition also rises, because the film thickness increases.

Consider a speleothem surface with a film thickness of 0.1 mm at 10°C, P_{CO_2} of 0.005 atm, and a dissolved calcite concentration of 300 mg/L. According to Figure 5.3, the saturation concentration of dissolved calcite is 0.061 cm^3/liter. Calcite has a density of 2.71 g/cm^3, so this is equivalent to 165 mg/L. So the saturation ratio (C/C_s) is 300/165 = 1.8. From Figure 10.79, the growth rate is about 0.1 mm/yr. If these conditions persist, it will take 100 years for one centimeter of flowstone to be deposited. Many vadose films have P_{CO_2} values above the range for which Figure 10.79 is valid, but the graph shows the overall relationships.

If the flow is turbulent, as in streams that cascade over rimstone, turbulent eddies help to transport the dissolved materials between the water and the solid surface. Deposition rates are much greater than in laminar flow under similar conditions, and they increase with flow velocity. At any degree of supersaturation, calcite deposition rates increase with water depth but become nearly constant beyond a depth of 10 cm. At water depths less than about a millimeter, deposition rates in turbulent and laminar flow are roughly the same. Details are given by Liu and Dreybrodt (1997).

Growth of speleothems is also governed by the mass balance, which was introduced in Chapter 7 to clarify cave origin (Eq. 7.2). For either process, the equation is

$$\Delta V = Q \, t \, \Delta C / \rho \qquad (10.2)$$

In this equation, however, ΔV = volume of mineral *deposited* during time t, ΔC = *decrease* in concentration of the dissolved mineral in that same time, Q = discharge of water, and ρ = mineral density (e.g., 2.71 g/cm^3 for calcite; see page 177). The units must be compatible — preferably with ΔV in cm^3, Q in cm^3/sec, t in sec, and ΔC and ρ in g/cm^3. The water must be *supersaturated* with the mineral. For cave enlargement the water must be *undersaturated* with the minerals in the exposed bedrock, ΔV = volume *removed,* and ΔC = *increase* in concentration of the dissolved minerals.

Figure 10.79 shows the deposition rate at any saturation ratio. With Eq. 10.2 it is possible to estimate how much dissolved calcite remains at each point in the flow system. A full model of speleothem growth requires dividing the length of flow into many tiny increments. In each increment the deposition rate is determined. Then the remaining dissolved load is calculated by solving Eq. 10.2 for ΔC. The procedure is repeated in each of the remaining increments.

In this way, the shapes of dripstone and flowstone deposits can be explained in terms of deposition rates at different places and times. The concepts of chemical supersaturation (Chapter 5) and flow depths in relation to slope and discharge (Chapter 4) are also appropriate. These approaches, or similar ones, have been used to explain speleothem shapes by Curl (1972, 1973), Dreybrodt (1999, 2005), and Short and others (2005).

A simplified example can be given. Consider a water film running down the side of a totem-pole stalagmite, as in Figure 10.31. Much of the deposition takes place on the tip of the stalagmite, where the initial impact causes a great deal of CO_2 to be lost, and a large percentage of the water sprays outward over the surrounding cave floor. As the remaining water travels down the sides of the stalagmite it loses much of its dissolved calcite, and the rate of deposition decreases with distance. As a result, the rate of growth decreases downward, propagating the thin pole-like shape. If the flow rate or the concentrations of CO_2 and dissolved calcite change with time, the shape of the growing stalagmite changes accordingly.

In the field it is better to measure growth rates directly. For example, calcite growth in the static calcite-saturated waters of Devil's Hole, Nevada, was measured by the U.S. Geological Survey in the 1980s by suspending clear calcite crystals in the water for several years.* The saturation ratio (C/C_s) was about 1.17 (see Chapter 5). Growth gradually ended in the near-entrance areas, while those far from the entrance continued to grow. Slowing and termination of growth was attributed to accumulation of a thin organic layer in the vicinity of entrance light.

Speleothem ages and long-term growth rates can be determined by measuring the ages of the deposits directly, usually with radiometric dating (Chapter 13). These techniques show that most dripstone and flowstone deposits have required at least tens of thousands of years to accumulate. Many are hundreds of thousands of years old. They have all varied in growth rate with time. There can be periods when nothing at all is deposited. At intervals, some speleothems may even be partly dissolved by periodic flooding.

Growth layers in flowstone and dripstone usually result from differences in deposition rate caused by variable water chemistry or flow rate. Some very thin and faint ones may be annual rings, like those of a tree, which reflect seasonal changes, but the most conspicuous ones indicate longer-term climatic variations or accumulation of impurities.

There are many examples of fairly rapid speleothem growth under ideal conditions. Some modern human artifacts

in caves, such as ladders, pipes, and bottles, are liberally coated with calcite (Figure 10.80). Calcite rafts have been observed forming on pool surfaces within a few days.** Soda straws are frequently observed hanging from the roofs of tunnels or monuments, but most of these are nurtured by the weathering of concrete. Calcium hydroxide released by this process combines with carbon dioxide to deposit calcium carbonate more rapidly than in natural caves.

Growth rates of evaporative speleothems are difficult to predict because the supply of ingredients cannot be measured easily. Under ideal conditions they can grow very rapidly but are susceptible to dissolution when the humidity or moisture supply increases. Some bedrock surfaces that were marred by soot from early explorers have been pushed outward by gypsum flowers at rates of about half a centimeter per century.

Speleothem decay

As cave environments change, some speleothems may become unstable while others are encouraged to grow. Passages that were once dry enough to contain evaporite minerals may acquire enough water seepage to deposit dripstone and flowstone. As moisture levels rise, evaporative speleothems fall and eventually dissolve. Even minor changes in humidity or air movement can affect the nature of speleothem growth, for example from one type of evaporative mineral to another, or from dripstone to capillary-water deposits. Examples are given in Chapter 12.

Speleothems can preserve evidence for long-term fluctuations in water chemistry caused by changes in climate, flow patterns, or geologic setting. Dripstone and flowstone are favored by diffuse infiltration, warm climate, and thick soil directly overlying limestone. Some dripstone speleothems acquire drip holes where solutionally aggressive water dissolves minerals that it formerly deposited (Figure 10.81). Some canyons are no longer deepening by dissolution, but instead are developing rimstone pools, which indicates a change from undersaturated to supersaturated streams. Further

---

* Communication from L. Neil Plummer, USGS, Reston, Va., 2004.

** Communication from Warren Netherton, Forestville State Park, Minnesota, 1992.

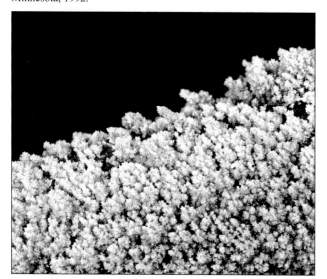

Figure 10.80: Growth of calcite coralloids on an iron pipe in the spray of a waterfall, Old Mystery Cave, Minnesota. The pipe was installed about 1935, 60 years before this photo was taken. SI of drip water = +0.59 (so C/C_s = 1.6), P_{CO_2} = 0.0055 atm, T = 7.6°C. Maximum thickness of coralloid crust is about one centimeter. The growth rate is slightly higher than that predicted in Figure 10.79 because much of the flow is not in laminar films, and the crust is highly porous.

Figure 10.81: A change in drip-water chemistry has corroded holes in the top of this stalagmite in Great Onyx Cave, Kentucky. A flash bulb 5 cm long gives scale.

Figure 10.82: Corroded rimstone in Mammoth Cave, Kentucky, partly removed aggressive water. Alternation from dissolution to precipitation back to dissolution may have been the result of climate change or changes in catchment area for the stream water. The stream now flows beneath the rimstone.

environmental shifts can cause the rimstone to be partly removed, producing remnant bridges (Figure 10.82). In the same way, shafts that originally formed by aggressive water may develop dripstone and flowstone, which may later be partly dissolved because of a shift back to aggressive

Figure 10.83: Periodic floodwaters have partly dissolved this flowstone drapery in a river passage in Mammoth Cave. Width of photo is about 40 cm.

Figure 10.84: Grotesque stalactites in the twilight zone of Cueva de los Pájaros, Isla de Mona, Puerto Rico. Biological activity, especially that of algae, has corroded the speleothems and altered their growth patterns.

conditions. Today many travertine deposits on the land surface are being eroded, or smothered by sediment, apparently because of increased sediment load and flooding influenced by land-use changes (Hubbard and Herman, 1991). Some cave deposits are affected as well.

Calcite speleothems are sometimes attacked by aggressive floodwaters or condensation moisture, which preferentially dissolve the deposits along crystal boundaries to reveal their internal structure in a skeletal pattern. The internal crystal

Figure 10.85: Shattering of a dripstone column in a Nevada cave caused by sagging of the bedrock ceiling and drying of the cave atmosphere. Width of photo is about 30 cm.

structure is especially clear in thin draperies that have been partly dissolved (Figure 10.83).

Speleothems can also be corroded into bizarre forms by exposure to phosphoric, sulfuric, and nitric acids generated by thick guano deposits (Chapter 12). An influx of gases from deep sources, such as CO_2 or H_2S, can cause temporary corrosion of cave walls and speleothems. The opening or enlargement of nearby entrances can expose speleothems to corrosion by microbial activity, especially on the sides exposed to light. If the speleothems are able to continue growing throughout this process, they usually acquire grotesque twisted shapes with porous textures (Taboroši and Hirakawa, 2003; Taboroši and others, 2005; Figure 10.84).

Pre-glacial speleothems in some shallow alpine or high-latitude caves have been shattered by freeze-thaw cycles during later glaciation. In Minnesota caves, calcite speleothems dated to more than about 15,000 years old are highly fractured, while younger ones remain intact (Milske and others, 1983). Other examples are common in caves throughout the mountains of western North America.

A cave that is presently dry, with no streams or active drips, is often referred to as a "dead cave." Dripstone and flowstone can lose their glistening sheen and acquire dull surfaces. This is the case for parts of Carlsbad Cavern, which accumulated a great amount of dripstone in the past (Figures 2.52 and 6.19) but is comparatively dry today. The drying is probably the combined result of climate change and increased circulation of desert air from entrances. In very dry caves, calcite speleothems may begin to flake apart along growth layers (Figure 10.85).

But no cave is truly "dead," and certainly not Carlsbad. Active drips may have ceased, but capillary moisture still enters and can produce a great range of more delicate speleothems such as aragonite needles and gypsum. The variety and complexity of the deposits in such caves can be far greater than those in caves fed only by active drips.

Figure 10.86: Some speleothem displays are so delicate and unusual that stringent measures are taken to protect them. This is the "Secret Straw Forest," located in a French cave with severely limited access. Photo by Kevin Downey.

11

Caves in volcanic rocks

CAVES IN VOLCANIC ROCKS, often called *lava caves*, have an origin entirely different from those in soluble rock. The term *lava* refers not only to molten material that erupts from the Earth's interior, but also to the solidified rock that it forms on the surface when it cools. Volcanic activity is concentrated mainly along the boundaries between moving plates of the Earth's crust, where mountain chains and tensional rift zones are actively forming (Figure 11.1). Most lava caves are byproducts of the volcanic processes themselves, and so the caves are essentially the same age as the rock.

Interest in the topic has grown rapidly in recent years, and so has its literature. *Vulcanospeleology* is now a major branch of cave science. Although the basics of lava-cave origin are fairly well understood, there are still many unanswered questions. It is obviously difficult to study a lava cave while it is still forming, but the chance to view volcanic eruptions first hand, and to examine the resulting caves soon afterward, gives an immediacy that few other geologic studies can offer. At Hawai'i Volcanoes National Park, located on Mt. Kilauea, even casual visitors can see volcanic activity at close range (Figure 11.2). Another intriguing aspect of vulcanospeleology is its possible extension to other planets and moons, particularly our Moon and Mars, both of which have experienced volcanic activity. So have Venus and Jupiter's moon Io (Greeley, 1992).

The rising interest in vulcanospeleology has been fueled mainly by recent discoveries on the island of Hawai'i,* which include some of the world's largest and most varied lava caves (Halliday, 1995). The caves are concentrated mainly on the flanks of the active or recently active volcanoes Kilauea, Mauna Loa, Hualalai, and Mauna Kea (Figure 11.3). Although the other Hawaiian islands are also volcanic, their lava flows are older and more deeply eroded, and caves are much less abundant.

Figure 11.2: A stream of liquid lava pours into the ocean along the flanks of Kilauea, Hawai'i. It is no longer possible to approach this closely, because the shoreline recently collapsed. Photo by Dave Bunnell.

For example, the volcanic crater Na One, on the flank of Hualalai, was explored for the first time in 1994, and some consider it the deepest known natural free-fall pit in the U.S. It is a sheer-walled, nearly circular crater about 185 m wide and 125 m deep with a narrow lower shaft at the bottom that brings the total depth to 263 m.

In the same decade, on the eastern slope of Kilauea, a series of connections were discovered between Kazumura Cave and nearby lava caves, which extended the system to 1102 meters in vertical extent and 65.5 km in length (Allred, 2005). This is by far the world's longest known lava cave, and the one with the greatest

---

* In Hawaiian words the symbol ' (called an *'okina*) indicates a stop or break between syllables. Words such as *a'a* are puzzling without it. It is omitted from *Hawaii* in reference to the state. It is often included in the name of the largest island (Hawai'i), as is done here for consistency.

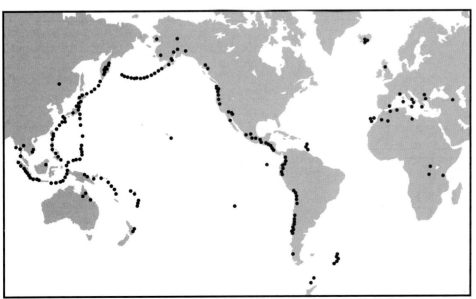

Figure 11.1: World distribution of volcanic activity in historic times (excluding that below sea level). Activity is concentrated along the margins of crustal plates. (See Chapters 2 and 3).

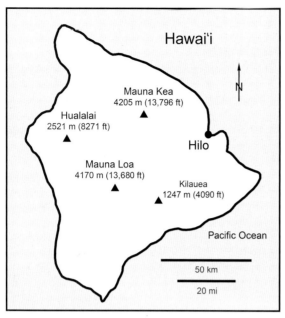

Figure 11.3: Map of the "big island" of Hawai'i, showing the locations and elevations of the major volcanic peaks.

Figure 11.4: A sudden night-time outburst of lava along the lower flanks of Kilauea. The flow is moving toward the right. The main part of the flow, at the top, is about 8–10 m wide.

Volcanic processes and landscapes

Lava is a mixture of minerals composed of silicon and oxygen combined with various amounts of iron, magnesium, calcium, sodium, aluminum, and other less abundant elements. In liquid form, lava is technically known as *magma*. Most magma comes from the Earth's upper mantle, a region of dense rock about 50–700 km below the surface, where temperatures hover near the melting point. Driven by differences in rock density, plumes of hot mantle material rise by plastic flow, like putty (Figure 2.2). As the pressure decreases toward the surface, some of the rising material melts to form magma. Additional melting can take place along the boundaries of converging plates of the Earth's crust, where slabs of rock are forced to descend into the underlying mantle. As their temperatures rise, these slabs metamorphose and release carbon dioxide. This dissolved gas lowers the melting point of the surrounding mantle and causes more melting. Further heat is added by friction and radioactivity in the crust.

Only about 2–3% of the Earth's upper mantle is actually molten. This magma rises and engulfs neighboring rocks along the way. In places the molten material reaches the surface, either oozing through lengthy rifts or rising in local

vertical range. Its straight-line extent from one end to the other exceeds that of any other known cave of any kind (32.2 km). This cave was originally even more extensive, but its upper end was inadvertently cut off by road construction.

Other states with large areas of cave-bearing lava include California, Oregon, Washington, Idaho, and New Mexico. Utah and Alaska also have a few lava caves. Other volcanic regions with many lava caves are located in Iceland, Australia, Italy, South Korea, eastern and southern Africa, Argentina, Canada, New Zealand, and many oceanic islands such as the Azores, Canary Islands, and Mauritius.

A well-illustrated glossary of features found in and around lava caves has been compiled by Larson (1993). A Web search will reveal much additional information. As in any emerging subject, the study of lava caves has acquired a fair number of contradictory terms and hypotheses. These conflicts are now being resolved through careful field observations and reassessment of earlier literature.

There is debate as to whether lava-cave statistics should be considered independently from those of solution caves. The depth of a cave is usually considered the vertical range between its highest and lowest points, regardless of its depth beneath the overlying land surface. Most lava caves lie only a few meters below the surface, and vertical pitches are few and small, so even those with great vertical extent can hardly be called deep. Despite its vertical extent of more than a kilometer, Kazumura Cave is roofed by no more than 20 m of rock, and there are more than 60 entrances.

Explorers who search for volcanic caves should examine the most recent lava flows, particularly those that follow long paths that descend gently. Openings caused by ceiling collapse are the most common entrance types. Aerial photographs are helpful in distinguishing individual lava flows, tracking their patterns, and identifying cave entrances.

Figure 11.5: This small stream of lava escaping from the slopes of Kilauea solidified after only about a dozen meters of flow. Over that distance the lava cooled from bright yellow-red to dark gray. By that time the lava had acquired a firm rocky crust but was still molten inside. Width of foreground is roughly 20 m.

Figure 11.6: Vulcanospeleologist Fred Stone probes the lava in a window to an actively forming lava cave on Kilauea. Such a close encounter should be made only by those familiar with volcanic processes. A thermally reflective suit is usually preferred.

Figure 11.8: The smooth, wrinkled surface of a recent pahoehoe lava flow, Kilauea, Hawai'i. Width of photo is about one meter. Photo by Bern Szukalski.

plumes to erupt as volcanoes. Most of the fissures along which the magma rises have been used many times before. They are forced open by the pressure of the rising liquid, and their walls may remelt in the intense heat.

Types of lava

Solid lava has many varieties that differ in composition, crystal size, and the temperature at which they solidify. For details, refer to any introductory geology book. Most lava caves are located in the dark, finely crystalline variety called **basalt** (Chapter 3). When it emerges at the surface, basaltic lava is especially fluid and also very hot, even by volcanic standards, with temperatures of 1100–1200°C. At those temperatures the lava glows bright yellow-red (note the glow in Figures 11.4–11.6). As it cools, the liquid lava changes color to bright red (~850°C), then dark red (~650°C), and finally solidifies as dark gray rock.

Basalt has the highest melting point and the lowest silicon and oxygen content of any type of lava (about 50% **silica**, as the combination of silicon and oxygen is called). It is mainly the high temperature that gives basalt its fluid character (low viscosity). Lava types with higher silica content, such as **andesite** (~60% silica) and **rhyolite** (~70%) have proportionally lower melting points and higher viscosity. Their high silica content is supplied by the large proportion of continental crust (mainly granite) through which their magma rises. These rocks vary from medium to light gray, and some rhyolite is slightly pink. Andesite is the major component in steep volcanic cones, and rhyolite is most common in broad volcanic plateaus. Their lava does not flow easily and the rocks contain few caves.

Lava varies in texture, with conspicuous effects on the land surface and on the character of lava caves. Many of the common volcanic terms have been borrowed from the native Hawaiian language. **Pahoehoe** lava (pronounced *pa-hoy-hoy*) has smooth surfaces with ropy wrinkles, like the folds of skin on an elephant, where the solidifying material bunched up as it cooled (Figures 11.7–11.8). It is most commonly formed by thin sheets of very fluid lava. In places the surface of fresh pahoehoe lava can have a thin glassy surface of faintly silver, gold, or greenish color that peels into razor-sharp flakes (Figure 11.9). The glassy surface rapidly weathers to a crumbly dark gray or black material.

In contrast, **a'a** lava (pronounced **ah-ah**) is rough and blocky, with many gas-bubble holes (**vesicles**). Figures 11.10–11.11 show examples. It is usually formed by lava that is more viscous and with a smaller quantity of dissolved gases than the pahoehoe type. A'a lava alone rarely forms significant caves, but in places it appears on the surface overlying caves or on the floors of some passages. Traversing it is difficult and uncomfortable, especially in low cave passages. Solidifying lava can evolve from pahoehoe toward the a'a type as its temperature drops, gases bubble off, and viscosity rises. A'a lava may entirely bury earlier lava caves.

Figure 11.7: Pahoehoe lava, New Mexico.

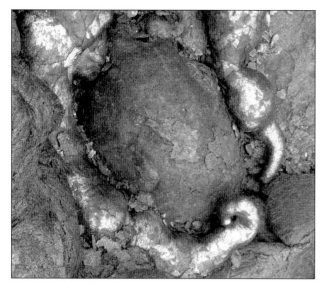

Figure 11.9: The glassy surfaces of recent pahoehoe lavas have colors that depend on the composition of the lava. Some on the lower flanks of Mt. Kilauea have a distinctive brassy color. The thin glassy skin quickly weathers away. Width of photo is about 50 cm.

When a high-silica magma cools at the surface, its high viscosity slows the rearrangement of molecules so that the glassy material *obsidian* may form (Figure 11.12). This rock is usually green, black, or brown, slightly translucent, and breaks along smooth irregular surfaces. It is a more massive version of the thin glassy skin that forms on some pahoehoe lava as the result of rapid cooling (Figure 11.9).

Rapid loss of gases during an eruption can shoot glowing curtains of lava several hundred meters high. Clots of molten material that are hurled upward can solidify in mid-air, some even while they are still rising through the volcanic vent. These fragments rain down as loose *pyroclastic* material (Figure 11.13), which includes *ash* and *cinders* with the texture of sand and fine gravel, block-like *volcanic bombs*, and *pumice*, which is frothy, like a fine-textured sponge. Fragments of older rock may be torn off the walls of the vent

Figure 11.11: The rough texture of a'a lava, Arizona.

and emerge as *xenoliths*, which contrast in rock type with the surrounding volcanic material. Once it falls, pyroclastic material may become welded together by its own heat or cemented by later minerals to form hard, irregular layers called *tuff*.

Recently formed lava landscapes are porous and highly fractured, and they support very few surface streams and only sparse vegetation. As the photos show, these barren rocky terrains can resemble moonscapes.

Volcanic landforms

The shape of the volcanic mass at the surface depends mainly on the style of eruption and the shape of the vent. The following classification of volcano types has seen long service, but it is over-simplified and is going out of fashion. Yet at this introductory level it provides an easy way to compare the different types (Figure 11.14).

The *Hawaiian type* of eruption is fairly quiet and produces large volumes of basaltic lava. "Quiet" is a relative term, because expanding gas can propel the lava high in the air, while floods of lava burst from the volcanic crater and from radiating fissures along the volcano flanks. Over the years, these eruptions form large, broad mountains called

Figure 11.10: The blocky surface of an a'a lava flow, Hawai'i.

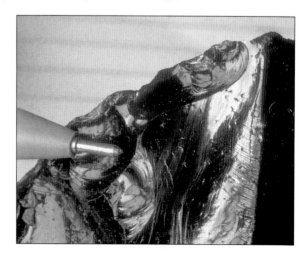

Figure 11.12: Obsidian is volcanic glass that forms when highly viscous, silica-rich lava cools rapidly at the surface. Tip of ball-point pen for scale.

Figure 11.13: Pyroclastic deposits (cinders and bombs) on the flank of the cinder cone Sunset Crater, Arizona.

shield volcanoes. The Hawaiian Islands are the world's foremost examples. They not only reach up to 4000 m above sea level, but have also been built upward from the sea floor 6000 m below, making them taller than Mt. Everest's height above sea level. Because of their low viscosity, some individual Hawaiian flows are relatively thin, as little as a few centimeters in places.

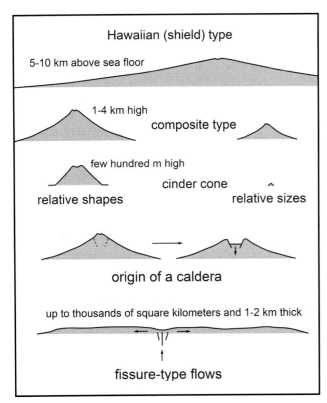

Figure 11.14: Types of volcanic cones and landscape features, their relative shapes, and relative sizes. The scale of the fissure flow is greatly reduced relative to the others.

The Hawaiian Islands were formed by a local plume of lava that rose (and still rises) many kilometers from the Earth's upper mantle and penetrates through the thin oceanic crust, which is only about 5 km thick. The plate of crust that contains the islands has been moving northwestward for millions of years, but meanwhile the location of the rising lava plume has not moved. As a result the active volcanoes keep forming at the southeastern end of the island chain, while the inactive ones are carried off toward the northwest. The big island of Hawai'i, at the southeastern end of the chain, contains the most active volcanoes, the highest peaks, and the greatest number of lava caves of any Hawaiian island. On nearby older islands the volcanic mountains have been eroded into steep and craggy terrain, but they contain few caves. Further to the northwest the landscapes are older and progressively less rugged, and caves are rarer. The most remote islands, such as Midway, lie several thousand kilometers to the northwest of Hawai'i and are several tens of millions of years old.

Among the Hawaiian volcanoes, only Kilauea is presently active. Mauna Loa erupted as recently as 1984 and is expected to renew its activity soon. Hualalai last erupted in 1801, and Mauna Kea has been dormant for the past 4000 years. On Maui, the nearest island to the northwest, the volcano Haleakala erupted in 1790. Details on the Hawaiian volcanoes are provided by a lengthy collection of papers edited by Decker and others (1987).

Fissure eruptions emerge from lengthy fractures or rifts in which there is no central vent. The lava consists mainly of low-viscosity basalt, and as a result it spreads widely over the surface. Most fissure eruptions take place along oceanic rifts, and their lava spreads out on the sea floor. Iceland originated in this way, where the lava is thick enough to form an island. Similar flows take place in areas of tension in the continental crust (Figure 2.2). The Columbia River Plateau of Washington and Oregon is built of this kind of lava, which covers 500,000 km^2 with individual flows 10–30 m thick. A similar example from the San Juan Mountains of Colorado is shown in Figure 3.1f. Smaller lava flows of this type once emerged along faults between mountain blocks in Nevada and neighboring states.

The extensive volcanic plateaus of Yellowstone National Park and the neighboring Snake River Plateau, mainly in Wyoming and Idaho, were produced by a continental version of a rising lava plume over a crustal plate that was moving southwest. The rocks vary in composition from basalt to rhyolite. Caves are most abundant in the basalt.

The *vulcanian type* of eruption produces silica-rich lava that is more viscous than that of the preceding types, and it releases more of its gas as it cools. These eruptions are common where converging crustal plates are forming mountain chains such as the Cascades and island arcs such as the Aleutian Islands. Eruptions are less frequent but more violent than in other volcano types because the vent is easily plugged with old lava, which allows gases to build pressure. Eruptions begin with an explosive discharge of rock fragments and pyroclastic material, followed by

Figure 11.15: Steam rising from the Kilauea caldera, Hawai'i.

Figure 11.16: A typical lava-tube cave (Jawdropper Cave, Idaho).

leakage of liquid lava through fissures in the sides of the cone. These events are punctuated by violent explosions that may blow the volcano to pieces. The catastrophic destruction of the Indonesian island of Krakatoa in 1883 is an example. The widely publicized 1980 eruption of Mt. St. Helens in Washington was comparatively mild.

Two types of mountains are produced by vulcanian eruptions. ***Cinder cones*** are small mounds composed almost entirely of pyroclastic material. Sunset Crater in Arizona is a well-known example. ***Composite cones*** are steep sided, with slopes as great as 30 degrees near their summits, and which are built of pyroclastic material interspersed with lava flows. Composite cones include most of the famous volcanic peaks of the world, such as Mt. Rainier, Fujiyama, and Mt. Etna.

Most volcanoes build up gradually, layer on layer, with lengthy intervening quiet periods, so it is difficult to tell whether a volcano is truly inactive or merely dormant. A single explosive volcanic eruption may last only a few hours, but the more fluid types may continue for many days, months, or even years. As the eruption proceeds, the accumulation of lava affects the pattern of later flows. Often the pattern of flow will shift from one route to another, as earlier routes become clogged with lava. The vent locations often change from one eruption to the next. In fluid eruptions, rivers of lava may diverge and converge in anastomotic patterns. The flow rate of lava usually pulsates, and during the main bursts it may escape from its channel and spread outward in thin sheets that quickly solidify. The volcanic vent may subside and broaden with time to form a large depression called a ***caldera*** (Figures 11.14–11.15). Crater Lake, in Oregon, is an example of a large inactive caldera that is now nearly filled with water. Less commonly, calderas can be formed by large explosive eruptions.

Because basaltic lava is rich in iron-bearing minerals, compass readings in lava caves or on the surface of lava flows may have errors of several degrees, and occasionally more than 10°. The magnetism induced in a large sheet of lava by the Earth's magnetic field tends to cancel out, but discontinuities such as caves can distort the field and

produce compass errors.* Local concentrations of iron-rich minerals such as magnetite (Fe_3O_4) can cause significant local variations in the magnetic field. Transit surveys are preferred where this problem is severe (Chapter 14).

At the land surface, the chemical weathering of lava produces a clay-rich soil. If a new lava flow covers the surface, the clay can serve as a barrier to infiltrating water. To augment local water supplies, tunnels are sometimes dug along the upper surfaces of clay beds to intercept underground water and deliver it to where it is needed. Some lava caves are floored by these old soil zones, and, like the tunnels, they may carry streams during wet periods.

Figure 11.17: Puka entrance to a Hawaiian lava-tube cave. Note the shield volcano, Mauna Kea, in the background. Photo by Bern Szukalski.

* Validated in the field by Dale Green, Salt Lake City, Utah.

Figure 11.18: A volcanic tumulus in Hawai'i. Photo by Dave Bunnell.

Figure 11.20: A pit crater in Hawai'i Volcanoes National Park.

Types of lava caves

Lava caves can occur in any kind of volcanic material, but the largest and most common are in pahoehoe basalt flows. Halliday (2004d) summarizes the various types.

Lava tubes are formed by the outflow of liquid lava from beneath a hardened crust (Figure 11.16). Most are too small to enter, or have collapsed, so the term *lava-tube cave* is used to distinguish the explorable variety. Sometimes only the flow lobes along the advancing edge of a lava flow will drain, to produce small caves roofed by thin crusts. Collapse of the roof of a lava-tube cave produces abrupt, round or oval entrances called *pukas* (Figure 11.17). Natural bridges between closely spaced pukas are common.

Near volcanic vents, very thin-walled caves can form called *shelly pahoehoe tubes*. Their fragile walls break easily into fragments, exposing the tubes to the surface.

A *tumulus* is a small hill formed by upwelling lava that acquires a hard crust and then recedes (Figure 11.18). Many are hollow. Where liquid lava is confined to a basin by steep banks of older rock, a thin solidified crust often forms on the lava. If the liquid lava then recedes from beneath the crust,

Figure 11.19: A lava ring formed by injection of lava beneath a hardened crust, with later deflation as the lava drained out (Ocean View, Hawai'i). Larger examples may contain boundary-ridge caves and lava-rise caves around the inside perimeters.

wide and shallow *boundary ridge caves* may form along the edges where slabs of crust slope away from the older rock. Most are only a few meters wide and long. Similar caves are produced when solidifying lava is puffed up by gas from within or beneath the flow.

A *lava rise* is the roughly flat-topped portion of a solidified pahoehoe lava flow, which has been lifted by later injection of liquid lava beneath a surface crust. The lava may drain out before it solidifies, forming *lava-rise caves*. Sagging of the roofs while the lava is still hot and plastic can produce ring-shaped ridges (Figure 11.19), which may contain boundary-ridge caves or multiple parallel passages. Some lava-rise caves are mere fragments around the perimeters of collapsed domes. In long, narrow lava rises the caves are low tubes. Lava rises may serve as the initial stage in the development of lava-tube caves.

Pit craters are vertical shafts produced by subsidence or collapse above columns of magma that never quite reached the surface and receded slightly to form voids (Figure 11.20). *Volcanic fissure caves* are simple cracks caused by stress in lava during and after solidification. They can be more than 50 m deep. *Open vertical volcanic conduits* (OVVCs) are verti-

310   Chapter 11: Caves in volcanic rocks

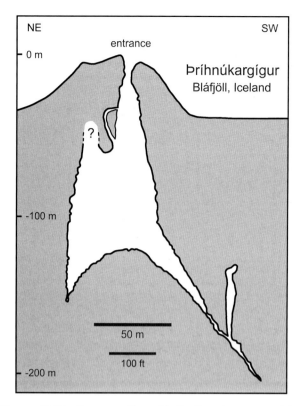

Figure 11.21: Cross section of Þríhnúkargigur, one of the deepest known open vertical volcanic conduits. (After Á.B. Stefánsson, 1992.)

Figure 11.23: Wall details of the tree-mold cave shown in Figure 11.22. Finger for scale. Photo by Peter and Ann Bosted.

Lava-mold caves are formed when organic material is engulfed by lava and either decomposes or is driven off as gas (mainly carbon dioxide). Engulfed logs can produce caves up to 2 m in diameter and 20 m long (Figures 11.22–11.23). Some caves follow the outlines of several stacked logs that intersect in a complex array, and trees still in growth position can even resemble vertical shafts. Perhaps the strangest cave of this type was formed about 15 million years ago in central Washington, when lava covered the body of an apparently pre-deceased rhinoceros. The resulting Blue Lake Rhino Cave almost perfectly preserves the creature's former shape, including its two horns (Figure

cal shafts complicated by the presence of horizontal passages or chambers (Skinner, 1983). Many are bottle-shaped with narrow necks. Some were once vents for the escape of highly fluid lava, and they may later have served as drains for lava running back underground. Iceland's Þríhnúkargigur is the deepest known OVVC, at 204 m (Stefánsson, 1992; Figure 11.21). The pit crater Na One on Hawai'i is even deeper (263 m) if its broad upper crater is included, but its entire depth can be descended in a free-fall only from a traverse line stretched across the mouth of the crater.

Figure 11.22: Lava-mold cave formed by a former tree trunk, Fujiyama, Japan. Photo by Peter and Ann Bosted.

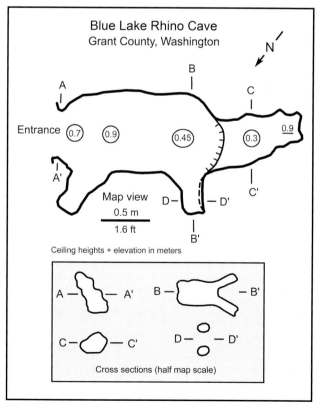

Figure 11.24: Blue Lake Rhino Cave, a lava-mold cave of an extinct rhinoceros. Map by Cato Holler.

Figure 11.25: Arched ceiling and rough floor of a typical lava-tube cave (Classic Cave, New Mexico).

11.24). Lava molds of elephants are reported from central Africa (Halliday, 2004d).

Some caves in lava are formed, or greatly enlarged, by non-volcanic processes. Lava can contain shelter caves, sea caves, and other cave types. Clay-rich zones produced by weathering of lava at the surface, and then buried by later lava, can form low-permeability barriers that perch groundwater and focus the erosional effects of subsurface streams. This process can initiate or enhance erosional cave development in the lava. Kempe and Werner (2003) describe a Hawaiian cave in lava that was formed in this way. The cave cuts across successive lava flows and contains sharp bends. These are characteristics not found in true lava tubes. A stream still runs through the cave.

Origin and character of lava-tube caves

Lava-tube caves deserve special attention because they are the largest and most common caves in volcanic rock (Figure 11.25). Their shapes and patterns depend on the nature of the lava flows that form them. See Manga and Ventura (2005) for a discussion of lava-flow dynamics.

In Hawaiian lava tubes the direction relative to the present or former flow direction is often indicated by the following terms in the native language: ***makai*** means "toward the ocean" (almost always the direction the lava once flowed), and ***mauka*** means "toward the mountains" (in the upflow direction).

Processes of tube development

During the early stages of a fluid volcanic eruption, lava wells out of the main vents, spreads over the cold surface, and rapidly congeals. It may eventually flood the crater at the top of the volcanic peak and periodically overflow down the side of the mountain. Often lava also escapes through openings in the side of the volcano. As the lava drains out of the crater, the newly solidified floor collapses. The process may repeat itself several times before the volcano quiets down again.

The liquid lava flows downhill in streams typically about 10–50 m wide that follow existing valleys. It moves at varying rates up to several meters per second, depending on its composition and thickness and the slope of the land surface. Kauahikaua and others (1998) measured velocities up to 5.6 m/sec in an active Hawaiian lava tube. Like a true river, a lava flow can meander, undercut its banks, deepen its channel by erosion, and pirate neighboring flows. During surges, lava may rise a meter or more above the normal level of the lava stream, and levees can build up along the banks by spattering and overflow. The longest documented lava flow, located in eastern Australia, extends for 160 km, although it contains only 6 km of explored lava tubes (Atkinson, 1992).

Lava moves most rapidly in the thicker central parts of the flow, while its edges and upper surface quickly chill to form a dark rocky crust over the red-hot liquid interior. Basaltic lava ceases to flow when about 50–55% of the liquid has crystallized (Wright and Okamura, 1977). It begins to solidify at temperatures as high as 1000°C (Wood, 1974, 1976; Kauahikaua and others, 1998). In lava caves the air temperature above the lava may be as hot as 1200°C due to combustion of flammable gases (Peterson and Swanson, 1974).

Early in an eruption, unroofed flows may extend for long distances down the sides of the volcano, but later, as solid crusts begin to form, the channels tend to be roofed everywhere except around the vent. Crusts may consist of isolated slabs of pahoehoe lava or blocks of a'a lava that float on the surface and jam together (Wentworth and MacDonald, 1953). Roofs can also form by the inward growth of solid crust from the banks of the flow, or by the solidifying of a stationary crust across the entire width of the stream. The crust then grows in the upstream direction as additional blocks lodge against it.

At its downflow end the lava hardens into irregular lobes. The width of each lobe is spanned by crescent-shaped pressure ridges that are convex in the downflow direction and up to about a meter high. As the internal liquid continues to move, the crust at first breaks into blocks that tumble over the advancing lava front and are overridden by the flow. Later the crust becomes thick enough to remain in place, so that lava tubes are formed as the liquid drains from beneath it. The front of the flow advances spasmodically as liquid lava bursts through the hardened crusts of old lobes, quickly chills, and then repeats the sequence (Figures 11.4–11.5). Lava can also be injected along the planes of weakness in previous flows or through the fractures that overlie the conduits. Roofs of lava tubes are typically only about 1–10 m thick, which is thin in comparison with those of solution caves. Many caves in lava contain a tangle of roots from overlying vegetation (Figure 6.58). The floors of most lava-tube caves are rough with small fragments of shattered lava (**clinker**) or cauliflower-shaped knobs (Figure 11.25).

Lava-tube caves are formed most effectively by low-viscosity lava that has a uniform, low-to-moderate discharge (Peterson and others, 1994). The few lava-tube caves that form in high-viscosity lava tend to be short and irregular. To form a lava-tube cave, the flow of lava must be prolonged and steady enough that a solid crust can grow across it without being disrupted. The remaining liquid can evacuate the tube only if it is able to drain to a lower elevation. A steep drop below the outlet of the tube facilitates the draining.

The ability of a fresh lava flow to enlarge preexisting tubes depends mostly on remelting, rather than abrasion. Enlargement of caves by remelting is most rapid when they are invaded by fast-moving, high-discharge flows that retain their heat over long distances. Melting is enhanced where turbulent eddies distribute heat from the interior of the lava toward the walls. Streams of molten lava that enter older lava-tube caves are rarely more than a couple of meters deep and fill the entire tubes only in a few places, particularly upstream from constrictions. In a sloping or horizontal tunnel, a freely draining fluid reaches its maximum discharge when it does not quite fill the entire cross section. In a filled tube the resistance caused by the greater liquid-solid contact area offsets the small gain in cross-sectional area of flow. This can be demonstrated with Eq. 4.7.

By probing through a gap in the solidified crust over an active Hawaiian lava tube, Kauahikaua and others (1998) observed that the solid floor beneath the liquid lava melted downward at an average of 10 cm/day for two months. The floors of older tubes may inflate or deflate as liquid lava wells up or drains out beneath a partly solidified crust, in the same way that the overlying land surface can be inflated

Figure 11.26: Lava-tube caves and their entrances are commonly located in low ridges formed by lava flows.

when liquid lava ponds under pressure beneath an older solid crust.

Liquid lava is strongly cohesive and tends to form discrete flows that maintain their identity rather than merge with earlier lava. This is especially so in lava that is on the verge of solidifying, as shown in Figures 11.5 and 11.9. A lava flow drains downward along the steepest available slope, and it tends to form low, sinuous mounds that contain the lava-tube caves. As a result, many caves and their puka entrances are located in gentle topographic highs (Figure 11.26).

Passage patterns

Figures 11.27–11.29 illustrate some of the characteristic patterns of lava-tube caves. The caves are oriented more or less parallel to the main direction of the lava flow, which in turn is controlled mainly by preexisting topography. Steep gradients or gullied terrain tend to produce fairly straight single conduits. Where the slope is only a few degrees or less, broad flow lobes with sinuous tubes are typical.

A representative lava-tube cave contains the following components (Wood, 1981): (1) a long, sinuous, partly braided feeder tube along the main axis of the lava flow, (2) complexes of smaller tubes, sub-parallel to the main tube, which carry molten lava only during major surges, (3) higher tubes that are vacated when the flow is captured by underlying tubes, and (4) a radiating pattern of small distributary tubes at the flow front. Characteristic 1 is present in every cave, 4 is found in most, and 2 and 3 are less common.

The largest tubes tend to form in the upper ends of the flows, where lava is concentrated in a single narrow channel. The size of the main tube is controlled by the volume and flow rate of lava and by the amount of erosion or filling by later flows. Rounded, arched cross sections up to 10 m wide are typical in the main passages. Some distributary tubes serve as the main outlets for later flows and may be enlarged, modified, or choked as a result.

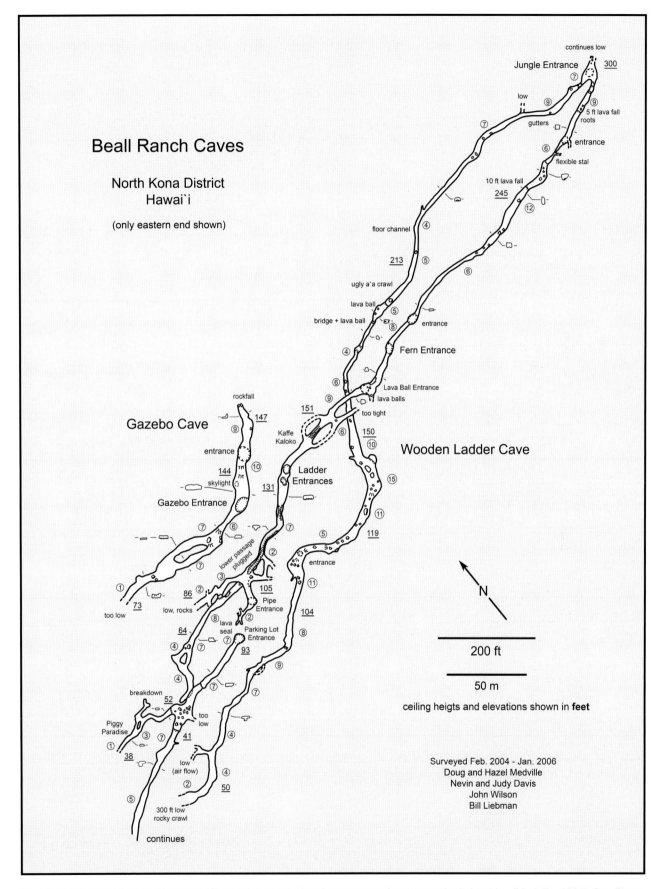

Beall Ranch Caves

North Kona District
Hawai`i

(only eastern end shown)

Figure 11.27: Map of a typical system of lava-tube caves, showing passage character and relationships (Medville, 2006). See Figure 1.18 for map symbols. The western quarter of the map is omitted to allow a larger scale for the part shown. Dimensions are in feet.

Figure 11.28: Map of Kazumura Cave, at the western tip of the island of Hawai'i (simplified from Allred and Allred, 1997). The cave appears as a thin black line. It formed in the Ai-laau lava flows that erupted about 350–500 years ago from Kilauea Iki, a subsidiary vent on the flanks of Kilauea. Other lava flows are shaded. Flows to the north of Kazumura Cave are partly from Mauna Loa, located about 35 km to the west-northwest of Kilauea.

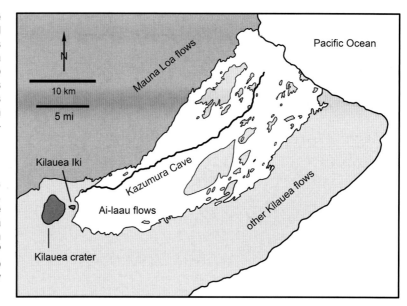

Figure 11.29: Profile of Kazumura Cave, Hawai'i, divided into three segments. The upper end (**A**), 1128 m above sea level, is blocked by collapse from road construction. The lower end (**D**) is a lava plug only 29 m above sea level. The mean slope is 1.9° and decreases gradually from 2.5° to 1.3° in the downflow direction, conforming to the topography that pre-dated the lava. Profile by Kevin and Carlene Allred and Bob Richards.

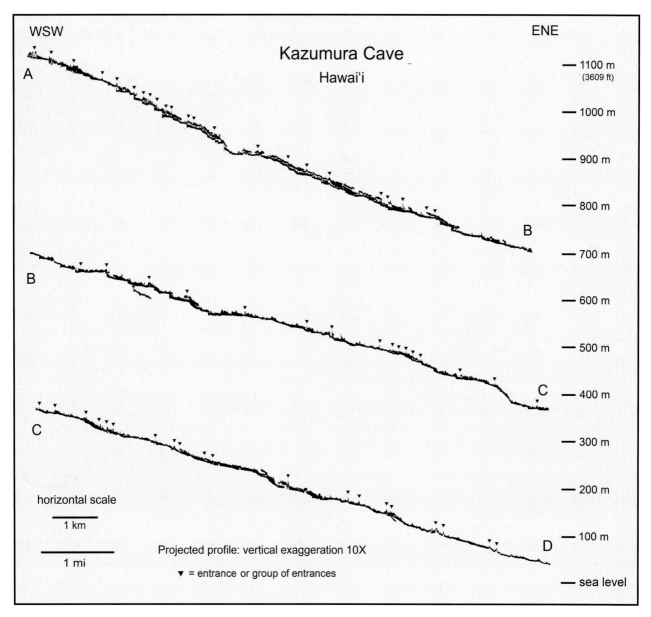

Figure 11.30: Braided tubes in the Kanohina Cave System, on the southwestern flank of Mauna Loa, Hawai'i. Photo by Dave Bunnell.

Eventually the lava tends to entrench into the older underlying rock below the initial level of tubes. The number of flow routes becomes fewer as entrenchment proceeds, so the lower levels consist mainly of simple canyons and tubes. Entrenchment may take place in several stages with intermediate partitions separating the levels. Coons (2004) shows that anastomotic patterns in lava-tube caves are favored by large-volume flows but seem to have no relation to slope or age of the flow (Figure 11.30). Upper-level mazes are partly filled by spillover from the later flows that carve the canyons.

As the flow front moves forward, some older tubes stagnate, while others serve as feeders for younger tubes that develop farther downslope. Flow of lava in the main conduits continues to increase until it is all carried by a few favorable channels, or perhaps just one (Allred and Allred, 1997).

The sinuosity of lava tubes is gentle and open, with total passage length typically about 1.1–1.2 times greater than the straight-line distance from one end to the other. This is somewhat less than in comparable solution caves, which typically have sinuosity ratios of about 1.2–1.8. In lava-tube caves the sinuosity is apparently caused by two factors: irregularities in the land surface over which the lava flows, and meandering flow patterns inside the liquid lava. Many tubes have a tendency to wander from one side of the lava flow to the other.

Long uninterrupted tubes seem to be favored in many places by steep slopes. Yet the average slope of the extremely long Kazumura Cave is only a few degrees (Figure 11.29), so the relation between slope and length is inconsistent. *Uniformity* of slope is probably more important than *degree* of slope in the development of long lava-tube caves. Lava-tube caves tend to vary in cross section and terminate abruptly. In addition, changes in the discharge of lava and in the rate of crust formation can cause irregularities in tube shape. As a result, each cave has a unique pattern.

A ***lava fall*** is a steep pitch in the cave floor where headward erosion has stalled at one spot for a long time, for example because of a threshold of resistant rock (Figure 11.31). Lava falls account for many of the abrupt changes in passage height and floor elevation that are common in lava-tube caves. Turbulent eddies at their bases may form high, wide chambers floored by ***plunge pools*** up to 20 m in diameter and several meters deep. When the lava pool solidifies it forms a smooth, roughly circular surface that

Figure 11.31: Lava fall in the Kanohina Cave System.

Figure 11.32: Solidified plunge pool in a Hawaiian lava-tube cave. Photo by Dave Bunnell.

Figure 11.34: Window between passages in Octapuka Cave, Hawai'i, in an area of successive lava flows. Photo by Bern Szukalski.

looks like a skating rink (Figure 11.32). Crusts on large lava pools may collapse if the underlying lava drains out. Many entrances are located just downstream from lava falls or at major bends because of the widening of the passages at those points. The floor gradient commonly steepens downstream from the falls.

While a lava tube is forming, or when it is re-invaded by later lava, the lava may drain downward into older tubes from higher levels or from the surface. Alternatively, tubes may be overwhelmed by the flow so that excess lava wells up through openings into higher passages or onto the surface. Liquid lava can spurt upward through holes in the roofs of lava tubes or break through the thin crust, to build small lava

hills called ***hornitos*** (Figure 11.33). A new upper-level tube can join an older one where lava pours through a skylight in the roof of the older tube, or where the weakened roof of the older tube collapses beneath the weight of the new flow. Successive tiers of tubes may collapse to form complex passage relationships. Some lava tubes in Washington contain as many as five distinct tiers (Halliday, 1963).

Where a later lava flow only partly fills an earlier cave, a thin ceiling can form over the top of the flow and produce small secondary tubes in the lower part of the older cave. These are especially common below steep drops in the passage floor where later lava does not completely fill the older tube. Many lava-tube floors have drains in the secondary crust through which the most recent lava has flowed (Figure 11.34). Thin crusts often collapse and leave a jumble of angular breakdown slabs on the cave floor.

Figure 11.33: A hornito formed by lava welling up from an underlying lava tube, Kilauea, Hawai'i.

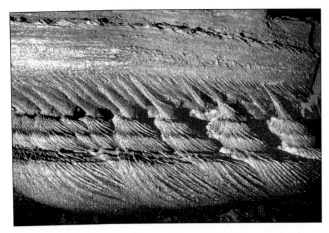

Figure 11.35: Stretch marks in the walls of a lava-tube cave. Width of photo is about 50 cm. Photo by Dave Bunnell.

Figure 11.36: "Shark's teeth" of lava formed where a ceiling block dropped away while the lava above it was still partly molten (Kanohina Cave System). Width of photo is about 50 cm.

Where liquid lava flows through older tubes, the insulating properties of the overlying rock allow it to move much farther downslope than would be possible in unroofed flows. In caves, liquid lava can flow tens of kilometers without solidifying (Halliday, 2004d). In this way, land is sometimes engulfed that would otherwise lie well beyond danger. To protect populated areas of Hawai'i during eruptions, lava tubes have occasionally been bombed to close them off and force liquid lava to the surface, where it can solidify more rapidly.

A typical lava-tube cave contains multiple puka entrances and skylights. Some pukas form while lava tubes are still active, as is evident where their breakdown blocks have been swept away or engulfed by solidified lava. Because of roof collapse, it is hardly ever possible to follow a lava-tube cave over its entire distance from lava source to outlet. The segmenting of lava-tube caves has caused confusion in the naming of cave systems and estimating their total lengths.

Internal details of lava-tube caves

The walls of many lava-tube caves cut across a variety of older lava beds, which indicates that liquid lava has eroded and melted its way down through preexisting flows (Wood, 1981). Layers from previous flows may buckle, leaving open spaces between these layers where they are exposed in the cave walls. Stretched lava fingers may span the gaps, like bubble gum stuck to the sole of a shoe. Stretch marks are often preserved in the solidified lava (Figure 11.35). Soft, hot wall and ceiling material may peel away from the solid rock and sag into the cave. ***Shark's tooth projections*** are pointed spikes that protrude where liquid lava has adhered to the cave roof while an underlying block has dropped away (Figure 11.36). They may grow by acquiring new layers if they are briefly inundated by later flows. They have the same composition as nearby wall linings. ***Lava blades*** are regularly spaced parallel ridges that fan out in the downflow direction where lava flow was locally rapid. They are typically about 10–15 cm long.

Rock surfaces are dark gray in most lava caves, but some are colored bright red from iron oxides. The red is produced by oxidation before the lava cools, when hot air is drawn through the tubes by convection from lower to higher entrances. In some lava-tube caves, successive lava flows have different colors. Red, orange, brown, greenish, and jet black lava flows can succeed each other, not necessarily in that order, with each color dependent on the composition of the lava and the environmental conditions in which it solidifies (Figures 11.37–11.38). Many lava tubes have smooth glazed veneers on their walls that apparently result from remelting of the rock by hot gases, followed by rapid solidification (Figure 11.39). Glazed surfaces may also consist of the chilled borders of lava flows that adhere to preexisting walls. Cracks may develop in the lava lining as it cools and shrinks.

Figure 11.37: Taffy-colored late-stage lava flow in Emesine Cave, Hawai'i. Photo by Bern Szukalski.

Figure 11.38: Various late-stage lava flows in Manu Nui Cave, Hawai'i have spattered the original walls with chocolate-brown, red, and orange lava. Width of photo is about 30 cm.

Figure 11.41: A curb in the Kanohina System, a remnant of a late-stage lava flow.

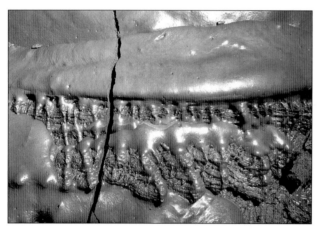

Figure 11.39: Glazed surface of lava walls in Emesine Cave, Hawai'i. Width of photo is about 40 cm. Photo by Dave Bunnell.

Accretion of cooled lava on the roof, walls, and floor of a tube forms a variety of linings, shelves, false floors, and benches (Figures 11.40–11.43). *Curbs* are remnants of late-stage lava flows that form linings on cave walls. In places they are arranged in several tiers left by successive levels of lava. *Levees* are raised banks caused by crusting along the shores of late-stage lava streams that did not cover the entire cave floor. Curbs and levees are most common around entrances, where air circulation causes rapid cooling. Where flowing lava deepens the floor of a tube, erosion on the outside of a meander may leave an apron-shaped slope called a *slip-bank* along the base of the opposite wall.

As tubes develop, slabs of solid lava peel off their walls or ceilings and are carried along by the flow. Blocks are also supplied by roof collapse and undercutting of cave walls by late-stage lava streams. Unlike the sediment carried by a stream of water, which has an average density about 2.5 times that of water, solid blocks of lava have nearly the same density as the liquid lava (about 3.0 grams/cm^3) and may even float because of their high porosity. They frequently lodge in narrow places and may block the cave entirely.

Figure 11.40: Lining of finely crystalline lava peeling away from the wall of Classic Cave, New Mexico.

Figure 11.42: Levees produced by a late-stage lava flow in Kazumura Cave, Hawai'i. Photo by Dave Bunnell.

Figure 11.43: A rock pillar in the Kanohina System, with a rudimentary slip-bank lined with curbs, gives a startling effect.

Most breakdown blocks either melt or are flushed through the cave as rafts. Some are welded together by their own heat or engulfed by later flows. Breakdown can impede the flow and cause lava to overflow into higher passages or onto the surface. As a result, the lower passages may terminate in lava plugs.

Lava balls are partly remelted blocks of solid lava caught up by the flow and later frozen to the floor or jammed between the cave walls in narrow spots (Figure 11.44). As they tumble along in the flow, they may grow by accretion of lava. In general, because of their soft outer layers, the blocks are not very abrasive, but angular corners may scratch grooves in the cave walls.

Roof collapse of long segments of lava-tube caves can produce trenches with a variety of possible shapes (Rogers and Rice, 1992). Sharp-edged trenches typically have overhanging wall segments that preserve parts of the

Figure 11.44: A lava ball solidified into the floor in the Kanohina System, Hawai'i.

original tube. Sag depressions are produced by subsidence of hot lava into the cave by plastic deformation of the roof, without chaotic collapse. Either type can become floored by soil that typically supports vegetation.

Lava-tube caves can be partly filled by water after they form, for example by sea-level rise. The water-filled end of the Atlantida Tunnel, in the cave Jameos del Aqua, Canary Islands, has been followed seaward by scuba divers to a distance of 1.4 km and a depth of 50 m below sea level, with no end in sight (Exley, 1994a).

Speleogens and Speleothems in lava caves

Secondary deposits in lava caves form in several ways, including the solidification of flowing or dripping lava, deposition of minerals by hot gases, weathering and redeposition of material from the surrounding rock, and accumulation of material carried into the cave from outside sources.

Those features formed by lava before it has completely solidified are *speleogens*. They are related to the cave origin. In contrast, *speleothems* are deposits that accumulate after the cave has formed. In lava caves the distinction between the two can be vague, and some features have a composite origin. Alternatively these two types of features can be classed as *primary* and *secondary* deposits, or they can be grouped together as *speleofacts*. Hill and Forti (1997) provide details.

Lava speleogens

As liquid lava drains from a cave, molten material drips from the ceiling to form what may resemble the dripstone and flowstone in solution caves. Objects of this kind usually have smooth, glazed surfaces that indicate rapid solidification, but their interiors are riddled with gas-bubble holes. Molten lava dribbling down a cave wall forms flowstone or draperies. The more viscous the lava, the more massive the deposit. Many lava speleogens have been inundated several times by liquid lava, which builds up in layers.

As a lava flow solidifies, local zones of molten material can remain briefly within the solid lava (Wright and Okamura, 1977). They are usually rich in dissolved gases, especially dissolved water vapor, which gives the lava a low viscosity. This residual liquid may squirt into the cave through its roof, walls, or floors after the main flow of fluid lava has drained from the cave. These injections can produce lava stalactites, helictites, and stalagmites.

Tubular stalactites are produced in this way. An injection of lava through the ceiling tends to solidify on the outside, while the inside remains molten and drains out. In origin they resemble miniature lava tubes. They can reach 2 to 3 m in length. Horizontal grooves around the tube walls show the original open ends at various stages of stalactite growth. Underlying stalagmites may have up to 100 times the volume of the stalactites, which demonstrates the great amount of liquid lava that can be been expelled by this process.

Figure 11.45: Lava pendants in the ceiling of Jawdropper Cave, Idaho.

Not all lava stalactites have central canals. Some are formed where liquid lava splashes onto the walls and ceilings and drips off. Most stalactites of this type range from about 0.4 to 1 cm in diameter. Similar features are shaped like bulbous, blob-like pendants (Figure 11.45). Water may drip from lava stalactites, but it has nothing to do with the stalactite origin or shape.

Lava helictites (Figure 11.46) appear to have the same origin as tubular stalactites, but they have a small enough flow that cohesion in the liquid lava partly disrupts the effect of gravity.

Lava that drips onto the floor congeals in irregular globs that build upward as *lava stalagmites*. Stalagmites range from small spatters to tall, knobby mounds up to 2 m tall (Figure 11.47). They can be straight, twisted, curved, or bulbous. Some form rows beneath drip lines. Lava that has formed many upward-thinning stalagmites may have become more viscous as the lava cooled, so it spread less with time.

Driblet spires are lava stalagmites that taper upward to sharp points. The presence of stalagmites and other floor deposits shows that the main

Figure 11.46: Lava helictite in Emesine Cave, Hawai'i. Width of photo is about 15 cm. Photo by Bern Szukalski.

Figure 11.47: Lava stalagmite with runner in an Idaho lava-tube cave.

lava flow in the tube had already ceased in their vicinity when they formed.

Runners are hollow tubes with thin walls, which extend downward on the surfaces of bedrock or lava speleogens (Larson, 1993; Figures 11.47–11.48). They are typically a few centimeters in diameter, with circular or oval cross sections. Some are more than a meter long. Their origin appears to be similar to that of tubular stalactites.

Squeeze-ups form where lava squirts out like toothpaste through narrow openings in a solidified surface, for example between an older wall and the solidifying crust of an internal lava flow. Sagging of the partly solidified floor often supplies the necessary pressure. Squeeze-ups are usually either bulbous or linear, and some have sides that are grooved by the rough walls of the opening through which they were extruded. Some squeeze-ups are shaped like flower petals, fins, or hands.

Because they are composed of lava that has segregated from material that has already solidified, cave deposits from these late-stage injections differ in composition from the main body of lava. The outer glaze on speleogens is very finely crystalline and often rich in *magnetite* (Fe_3O_4). Magnetite is a magnetic black or dark brown iron oxide that forms

Figure 11.48: Close-up view of runners at the top of the lava stalagmite shown in Figure 11.47.

at very low oxygen concentrations. Pieces can be picked up with a magnet. With lengthy exposure in caves it tends to oxidize to *hematite* (Fe_2O_3), which has a reddish color. The compositions of some typical lava speleogens are listed by Allred and Allred (1998).

Speleothems in volcanic caves

Speleothems are sparse in most volcanic caves, but they include a wide variety of minerals derived from the lava and from other nearby rocks and soil. Summaries of the topic are provided by Hill and Forti (1997) and Forti (2005).

Many of the mineral deposits vary with the stage of cooling of the host lava. As soon as a lava tube is at least partly drained of its liquid lava, hot volcanic gases can deposit minerals on the interior surfaces. The most common is sulfur, which is deposited in oxygen-poor environments where the atmosphere is rich in gaseous sulfur compounds including hydrogen sulfide. It usually forms thin yellow coatings. A variety of oxides and hydroxides can also form

Figure 11.50: Pahoehoe flow ridges in the floor of a New Mexico lava-tube cave. White evaporative minerals have grown on their crests since the cave formed.

by oxidation of volcanic minerals as the oxygen content in the cave air increases.

As the temperature drops, various salts can also precipitate. Most of these materials are highly unstable and soon removed by infiltrating water. Their main source is fresh lava, which weathers easily at the surface, especially in humid climates. Weathering is favored by the small crystal sizes in the rock and by the large exposed surface areas provided by fractures and gas-bubble holes. The high temperature of newly formed lava also speeds the reactions. Iron oxides and clay minerals are also common weathering products at this stage.

As water infiltrates from the surface, dissolved components from weathering, such as magnesium, calcium, sodium, aluminum, and potassium, can precipitate as salts to form white crusts, dripstone, tendril-like growths, and pasty blobs (Figures 11.49–11.52). Most are also rich in sulfates and chlorides. Evaporation is the main process that allows them to precipitate. Early in the lava's cooling history, some of the larger speleothems can acquire thin helictitic filaments of various salts that extend in the downwind direction of moving air and volcanic gases (Forti, 2005). Many of the evaporite minerals are difficult to identify without laboratory analysis.

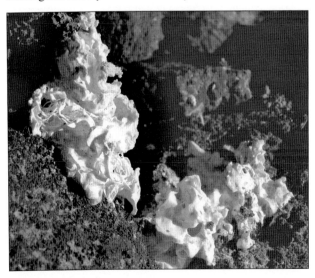

Figure 11.49: Unidentified pasty evaporative mineral in Bobcat Trail Habitation Cave, Hawai'i. Width of photo = 25 cm.

Figure 11.51: Gypsum balls formed by evaporation around lava stalactites, Kanohina Cave System, Hawai'i. Photo width = 20 cm.

Figure 11.52: Calcite coralloids formed by evaporation in the Kanohina Cave System, Hawai'i. Width of photo = 15 cm.

Sodium is produced directly by the weathering of many igneous rocks, and as a result, sodium minerals such as *mirabilite* ($Na_2SO_4 \cdot 10H_2O$), *thenardite* (Na_2SO_4), and *bloedite* ($Na_2Mg(SO_4)_2 \cdot 4H_2O$) are more common in lava caves than in solution caves. Pockets of *anhydrite* ($CaSO_4$) and *gypsum* ($CaSO_4 \cdot 2H_2O$) can occur in recently solidified lava, and they are easily dissolved and reprecipitated as speleothems by evaporation (Figure 11.51). *Bassanite* ($2CaSO_4 \cdot H_2O$), which is usually a high-temperature and low-humidity alteration product of gypsum, is also present in some lava caves.

Calcite and *aragonite* ($CaCO_3$) can form small blobs or delicate fingers (Figure 11.52), and less commonly dripstone, but carbonate sources are much less abundant in volcanic rock than in sedimentary rock. In forming carbonate minerals in lava caves, evaporation is more significant, and loss of CO_2 is less significant, than in typical solution caves. Soil on young lava tends to be thin and porous, so its CO_2 content is commonly lower than in karst. Although calcium and magnesium are common weathering products of lava, they are released only slowly by weathering. Carbonate is a byproduct when CO_2 is absorbed from the atmosphere and soil, but the combined concentrations of Ca^{2+} and CO_3^{2-} are rarely high enough to bring calcite and other carbonate minerals to saturation by CO_2 degassing, as in most limestone caves. That is why most carbonate speleothems in lava caves are evaporative. Some carbonate and gypsum deposits in lava caves are derived from air-borne dust blown into the area from other regions and then carried into the caves in solution by infiltrating water.

Most of the earliest speleothems that form in a volcanic cave disappear later as they are dissolved by infiltrating groundwater. A wide variety of minerals were observed in Cutrona Lava Tube, on the flanks of Mt. Etna, Italy, 8–10 months after the eruption of the host lava (Forti and others, 1994). They included many massive, multi-colored speleothems. Nearly all of the early deposits have since been

removed by dripping and flowing fresh water. Alteration minerals from weathering of the lava persist much longer and can continue to form during the lifetime of the cave.

Silicic acid (H_4SiO_4) released by weathering of the lava can precipitate as *opal* as the result of cooling and evaporation. In lava caves, opal deposits often form stalactites and draperies, and they can also replace other minerals and mimic their original shapes.

Unusual minerals can be produced by the interaction of volcanic fluids with their surroundings. Alum Cave, on Vulcano Island, Sicily, formed where intermittent volcanic vapors rose from below and reacted with the local volcanic rock (Forti and others, 1996). Weathering products from this reaction have mixed with marine sea spray to produce 21 different sulfate minerals, many of them very rare. They typically form wall crusts up to 3 cm thick composed of needle-like crystals.

A few volcanic caves are located in a rare type of carbonate-rich igneous rock called *carbonatite*. Karbonatito-vaya Cave in the East Sayan Upland of Russia is perhaps the world's only example of a typical solution cave in carbonatite (Filippov, 2004). McFarlane and others (2004) describe a cave in Tanzania that formed in a sodium-calcium carbonatite lava as the result of escaping volcanic gases. Infiltrating water has partly dissolved the overlying rock and deposited dripstone in the cave composed of a variety of salts such as *trona* ($Na_3(CO_3)(HCO_3) \cdot 2H_2O$).

As in other types of caves, biological activity in lava caves can produce minerals rich in phosphate, nitrate, sulfate, and chloride (Chapter 10). In Skipton Lava Cave, Australia, 8 different phosphate minerals have formed by the reaction of local weathering products with bat guano and are distributed according to variations in pH (Webb, 1997). They are typically brown, yellowish, or white, and form thin plates rarely more than 2 cm long. Forti and others (2004) describe rare mineral assemblages of this kind in the Saudi Arabian lava cave Ghar Al Hibashi, where a litter rich in bones and guano has been altered by fires. Also, like other types of caves, many old lava caves are dead-end cold traps in which ice can persist year-round.

Although limited in size, speleothems in lava caves rival those of solution caves in variety and novelty. Studies of these phenomena have barely begun, and they are certain to provide further insight into the origin of lava caves and the weathering of lava.

Time scale of lava caves

In comparison with solution caves, lava caves are fairly transient. Most caves in lava are less than a few thousand years old. Kazumura Cave occupies lava flows that are only 350–500 years old in a volcano that is still intermittently active. Extensive caves are known in even younger flows nearby. Most lava is very porous and easily absorbs rainfall, so surface erosion is greatly retarded. But unless the lava is buried beneath later flows, it will soon be weathered and eroded, and its caves will be destroyed.

How soon can a lava cave be explored after it has formed? If cooling is very rapid, and the cavers have a high heat tolerance, lava caves can be explored, at least for short distances, less than a year after the volcanic eruption (Camara, 2000). The cooling rate depends mainly on the thickness of the cave roof, the amount of air circulation, the outside temperature, and the amount of rainfall. Ordinarily it takes several years for lava to cool enough to allow exploration far beyond the entrances, and even then the remote sections may be uncomfortably hot. Porter (2000) gives a vivid account of exploration in a Hawaiian lava tube less than two years old.

Although water vapor is the dominant volcanic gas, some eruptions also give off less benign emissions such as hydrochloric and hydrofluoric acid, and early explorers may encounter highly acidic pools, drips, or sediments. The acid is soon diluted and carried away by air or infiltrating water.

The same methods that are used for dating of rocks are well suited to dating lava caves, because the caves are the same age as the rock. In this way lava caves contrast with solution caves, which are generally much younger than the host rock. Chapter 13 introduces many of the methods that are used to determine rock ages. The C-14 method, which is of little use in dating solution caves, is appropriate for determining the ages of lava caves. Remnants of trees and other vegetation trapped in lava flows, especially around their perimeters, can be dated in this way. The vegetation is the same age as the lava, and so are the caves. Some caves are in such recent lava flows that they can be dated from historical records. The age of the flow in Figure 11.53 can be pinpointed to the exact day.

Most lava caves are shallow and readily subject to weathering, erosion, and collapse. They can also be modified or destroyed by further volcanic activity. Segmenting by collapse is common where thin roofs fail. The life of a lava cave is also limited by the unstable nature of its parent volcano. For example, Ape Cave, on the southern flank of Mount St. Helens in Washington, survived the 1980 eruptive blast that tore out the opposite face of the mountain, but the cave was later partly filled with mud and ash because of mudflows and flash floods triggered by the destruction of vegetation and the accumulation of ash on the surface (Halliday, 1982). Nearby Hopeless Cave, only 100 m upslope from Ape Cave, was completely filled by mudflows.

Old cavernous lava flows may be covered and protected by later flows, so it is possible for lava caves to be preserved for fairly long times and later exhumed by stream erosion. A few lava caves in Bulgaria are as old as the Oligocene Epoch, about 24–36 million years ago (Kolev and Shopov, 1992; see Figure 2.1). The Hawaiian island of Maui contains some caves that are several million years old (Halliday, 2004d). Certain lava caves in Saudi Arabia are more than a million years old (Pint and Pint, 2005) and have probably been preserved because of the low rate of surface weathering and erosion in that arid climate.

Although the probability is low, there is no reason why volcanic caves cannot persist for even longer times. In general, however, the lifespan of a volcanic cave is short but dynamic.

Figure 11.53: A recent lava flow has partly covered this road in Hawai'i Volcanoes National Park.

12

Cave meteorology and internal weathering

WHEN EXPOSED TO AIR, the bedrock and mineral surfaces of a cave undergo slow changes by chemical weathering. Cave meteorology plays a leading role in this process. Details of cave meteorology are discussed by several authors, including Wigley and Brown (1976), Cigna and Forti (1986), and Cigna (2004), but internal weathering in caves has received relatively little prior attention.

Composition of cave air

The air in most caves has a composition somewhat similar to that of the outside atmosphere as the result of air exchange through entrances and smaller openings. The most important difference is that the average cave air contains roughly 10 times *more* carbon dioxide than surface air, and about 10 times *less* carbon dioxide than soil air. When water infiltrates through soil and then descends into caves, the water tends to lose CO_2 to the cave air. Cave water emerging at springs may also lose CO_2 to the outside atmosphere. In either case, calcium carbonate is often forced to precipitate (Chapters 5 and 10).

Nearly all cave air provides a healthy environment for visitors. It rarely contains enough CO_2 to be dangerous, and the likelihood of high concentrations is usually predictable (James and others, 1975; James, 1977). Where a large amount of organic material is carried into deep dead-end caves, oxidation of the organics partly depletes the oxygen in the air and causes CO_2 to build up. Active thermal caves are often enriched in CO_2 carried by ascending water. Anyone who experiences shortness of breath, nausea, or dizziness should leave the cave immediately. CO_2 levels greater than about 2% can cause these symptoms. Concentrations greater than about 7% can be lethal.

In rare situations, caves near industrial sites, storage tanks, or highways have been exposed to leaks of volatile compounds such as gasoline. Explorers should turn back at the first hint of odd chemical smells and report the situation to local authorities. The state Department of Health is an appropriate contact.

Cave divers occasionally swim through water-filled passages and emerge into short air-filled sections that have little or no direct contact with the outside atmosphere. This air is usually close to equilibrium with the gases dissolved in the water, which in turn are near equilibrium with those of the air in the more open parts of the cave. As a result, the air pocket may contain no more carbon dioxide and no less oxygen than the more aerated parts of the cave. Still, divers know enough to breathe from air bells only with caution and to be alert to possible accumulations of toxic gases, as well as low oxygen levels caused by decomposition of organic material and by the divers' own respiration.

Hydrogen sulfide (H_2S) is seldom encountered, even though it plays a major role in forming certain caves. Most

caves that formed in this way (e.g., Carlsbad Cavern) are now inactive. This is fortunate, because in even moderate concentrations H_2S can be poisonous. Where H_2S is present it is quite noticeable by its nauseating rotten-egg smell. Even if the smell is barely detectable, it is important not to explore further without testing the gas concentration. Levels of several hundred parts per million can be deadly. Such high concentrations are rare in caves. Cueva de Villa Luz, Tabasco, Mexico, is an example of an actively forming cave with dangerously high H_2S concentrations in the areas remote from entrances (Hose and others, 2000). Up to 210 ppm of H_2S and 0.035 atm of CO_2 have been measured. Sulfur dioxide and carbon monoxide are also present. Respirators with "acid gas" filters are appropriate for caves that have a hydrogen sulfide smell (Figure 12.1). Such air is corrosive to metals, and delicate equipment should be kept in protective housings. Silver and gold jewelry quickly turns black.

Radon, a radioactive gas, is more concentrated in cave air than in the surface atmosphere or in most homes, and there was once some concern that it could pose a health hazard. But risk assessments at such low levels are difficult to quantify, and there is no medical evidence that exposure to cave radon is detrimental to health (Gunn, 2004b; Cigna, 2005b; Craven and Smit, 2006). Very few people spend enough time in caves to warrant concern about their exposure to radon. Cave radon levels are relatively high in certain mining areas (Gunn and others, 1991) and may be slightly elevated in caves that contain much shale, chert, and flowing water. Radon concentrations rise sharply during decreases in atmospheric pressure, when air seeps into caves from the surrounding bedrock (Lively and Krafthefer, 1994).

In very dry caves, dust stirred up by visitors from sediments may pose a health hazard, especially as it may contain pathogens from guano and

Figure 12.1: A gas mask used in caves rich in hydrogen sulfide. An automatic detector of toxic gases is also shown. It beeps when the gas concentration exceeds safe limits. At this point, in the jungle shadows *outside* Cueva de Villa Luz, about 10 m from the entrance, the meter was already beeping from H_2S escaping from the entrance.

Figure 12.2: An early venture in speleotherapy: huts for tuberculosis patients in Mammoth Cave, Kentucky, which date from the 1840s.

other organic sources (Halliday, 2004e). Dust masks are appropriate in such caves.

In general, however, cave air is relatively pure. It can even alleviate respiratory problems because of its high humidity and low level of airborne particles (Debevec, 2004). Certain health spas, most notably in continental Europe, offer *speleotherapy* to visitors who wish to lounge in the moist comfort of caves. People who suffer from allergies, stress, and problems with immune systems can find temporary relief, although the long-term benefits are uncertain.

The only significant American attempt at speleotherapy took place in the 1840s, when a former owner of Mammoth Cave, who was also a doctor, had the misguided inspiration to house tuberculosis patients in the cave (Sides and Meloy, 1971). But even the purest cave air cannot cure infectious diseases, and the experiment was soon terminated. Some of the stone huts occupied by the patients still stand forlornly along one of the tour trails (Figure 12.2).

Cave temperatures

The air and water temperatures of most caves are close to the mean-annual temperature of the overlying surface. Cave temperatures depend on altitude, latitude, heat flux from the surface and from the Earth's interior, and local chemical reactions. A map that shows the distribution of cave temperatures cannot be drawn simply from climatic data.

Cave temperatures in the northern U.S. are about 7−9°C, while those in the southern states are about 15−20°C. Most alpine caves, such as those in the Montana Rockies, have temperatures of 1−5°C, and some are below freezing year-round. Caves fed by hot springs have much higher temperatures than the regional average. Exchange of air and water with the surface can heat or cool parts of a cave, depending on the season. Cave temperatures fluctuate in complex ways, even far from entrances, and are delayed in relation to changes at the surface (Cropley, 1965). At any given time, the air temperature in a cave can often be a few degrees higher or lower than the water temperature. A

dead-end cave can trap cold air if the cave slopes downward from the entrance, or warm air if the cave ascends from the entrance.

In deep caves with little through-flow of air and water, the temperature increases with depth because of the Earth's thermal gradient. An example is Wind Cave, South Dakota, which has only a few small entrances at its upper end. Its air temperature increases from about 11°C near the surface to 14°C at its lowest point 170 meters below, for a vertical temperature gradient of roughly 18°C per km of depth. This figure is compatible with the average thermal gradient of 20−30°C per kilometer in the Earth's crust (Turcotte and Schubert, 1982). In stream caves the gradient tends to be much lower because of heat transfer between the flowing water and the surrounding bedrock. For example, in Krubera Cave, Republic of Georgia, the world's deepest known cave, measurements in 2005 show a rise from 2.1°C at a depth of 90 m to 7.7°C at 2080 m.* This gives an overall gradient of only 2.8°C per km. Underground heat flow in karst is discussed further by Badino (2005).

Air circulation smoothes out the temperature gradient in some deep caves by warming their upper sections and cooling their lower regions. Release or absorption of heat by condensation or evaporation can also help to heat or cool caves. Many chemical reactions do the same. For example, oxidation reactions release heat.

The effect of winter cold is lost at fairly shallow depths below the surface. At only 15 m below the surface, winter cooling is less than 1°C and is delayed by about 6 months. In some wells, minor residual effects of glaciation can still be measured at depths of hundreds of meters.

Cave ice

In regions with sub-freezing winter temperatures, temporary ice forms in the entrance sections of nearly all caves. In some caves, ice persists year round (Balch, 1900; Merriam, 1950; Silvestru, 1999; Yonge, 2004). Caves with perennial ice are sometimes called by their French name, *glacières*, meaning ice-containing voids, *not* glaciers. Halliday (1954) describes the major ice caves of the United States. Perennial ice is most common in caves at high latitudes or altitudes where the mean-annual temperature is below freezing, but occasional thawing at the surface is also necessary to supply dripping or flowing water that can freeze in the caves and replenish the ice that is lost by sublimation (evaporation from solid ice).

Some caves in temperate climates contain perennial ice even where mean-annual temperatures are well above freezing. Such ice can persist only in caves that are dead-end pockets (Figure 12.3). Cold air is denser than warm air, so it sinks into caves with openings at their high ends and is trapped. Seasonal temperature fluctuations are

---

* Communication from Alexander Klimchouk, Kiev, 2005.

Figure 12.3: Perennial ice deposits in Şcărişoara Ice Cave, Romania.

usually negligible deep inside these caves, but as climates undergo long-term changes, cave ice grows, wanes, and may periodically disappear altogether. Most multi-entrance caves in temperate climates have too much air circulation to sustain permanent ice.

Cave ice that is formed by dripping or flowing water consists mainly of massive sheets, mounds, cascades, icicles, and ice stalagmites. Icicles hanging from cave roofs are not common, because they tend to melt in the warmer air that hovers near the ceiling. The surfaces of cave pools can freeze and remain frozen for many decades or centuries. Condensation of moisture from air can produce delicate crystals with a variety of shapes.

Many ice stalagmites contain bulbous knobs of clear ice separated by thinner necks of white, cloudy ice, arranged vertically as in a spooled bedpost. Viehmann and Racoviță (1982, cited in Onac, 2000) show that the narrow, white sections form by rapid freezing at relatively cold temperatures, while the clear sections form by slow freezing just below 0°C.

The best-known examples of caves that contain perennial ice are Eisriesenwelt and the Dachstein Ice Caves in the Austrian Alps. In nearby Eismembranhöhle, the surface of a cave lake became frozen, and later the lake drained, leaving a 7-cm-thick ice sheet that completely sealed off the lower half of the cave (Klappacher and Knapczyk, 1976).

The discoverers had to chop a hole through the ice to gain access to the underlying passages. It is common for ice to fill passages completely (Figure 12.4). In Coulthard Cave, Alberta, it is possible to gaze through crystal-clear ice plugs into large but inaccessible passages (Thompson, 1976).

Ice caves are highly sensitive to their surrounding environment, and they serve as archives for changes in climate and air quality. It was once commonly thought that extensive cave ice is a relic of glaciation. But dating of wood fragments trapped in ice in European caves, such as the Dachstein Ice Caves, Austria, and Şcărişoara Ice Cave, Romania (Figure 12.3), give maximum ages of only about 800–1000 years (Audra and Pavuza, 2004). Such young ages suggest that the existing ice in these and most other caves is not glacial.

From a study of the Monlési Ice Cave, in the Jura Mountains of Switzerland, Luetscher (2005) calculates that about 79% of the cold temperature is the result of winter air circulation, and that nearly all of the remainder is caused by snow drifting into the entrance. Ice in the cave averages only about 120 years old, although some other caves in the region contain ice more than 1000 years old.

Air movement

Cave air is rarely static. Movement of air in and out of caves, as well as inside them, plays a large role in modifying its composition, temperature, and humidity. The main causes of air movement are differences in air pressure and temperature, and the drag force caused by moving water (Figure 12.5). Unlike water, air can undergo great compression and expansion, and this property makes air flow quite difficult to predict, especially in the irregular confines of a cave. When air moves into a dead-end section of cave, the air compresses as the pressure builds up. Once its inward momentum drops to zero, the air begins to expand and move back out. Complex harmonic motions can be produced in some caves, or parts of caves, and cause a breathing phenomenon (Faust, 1947). Slow sub-sonic oscillations can also be caused by outside air moving across

Figure 12.4: Termination of a cave passage by perennial layered ice, Big Brush Creek Cave, Utah. Note the tree branch emerging from the melting face.

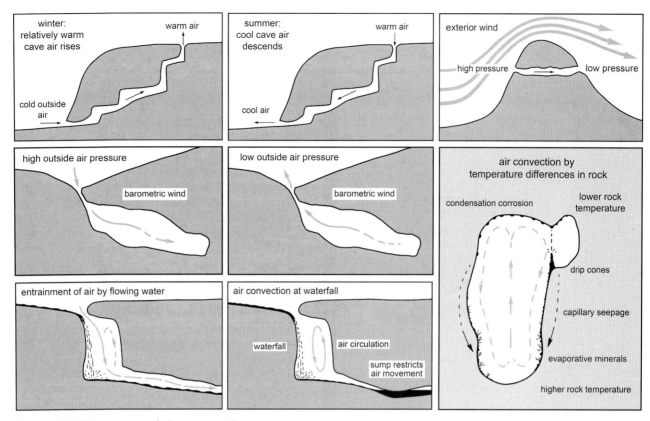

Figure 12.5: Major causes of air movement in caves.

a cave entrance, so that it behaves like a large instrument in a jug band.

Differences in air pressure account for most air movement. Air moves from areas of high pressure to areas of low pressure, so if the pressure at one end of a cave passage is greater than at the other end, air will move through the passage in the direction of the pressure gradient. Rates of air movement range from undetectable all the way to gale-force winds (Figure 12.6).

Over the length of any cave passage, air velocity increases with the pressure difference and with the mean passage diameter. Local velocities in the passage adjust to variations in cross section by increasing in the narrow parts and decreasing where the cross section is large. Air velocity is inhibited where the passage length, sinuosity, and roughness are high. Air flow is proportional to the square root of the pressure difference, so a doubling of air flow requires a four-fold increase in pressure gradient. These relationships are fairly similar to those in turbulent water flow (Eq. 4.7), but because of the high compressibility of air, fluctuations in air velocity tend to be gradual.

Pressure differences are produced in several ways, as described below and in Figure 12.5:

Temperature differences: Cool air is denser than warm air, so a given amount of air tends to exert a greater pressure if it is cool. During winter months, when the cave is warmer than the outside air, the less-dense cave air generally moves upward and blows out of high-level entrances, as in a chimney, while cold air is drawn into

lower entrances. The opposite process is common during summer months. In caves with entrances only at their upper ends, and which contain no streams to affect their internal temperatures, warm moist air from lower levels is able to rise into cooler upper levels, while cool air completes the cycle by sinking into the lower levels. A temperature

Figure 12.6: Intense wind in Hölloch, Switzerland, caused when high-pressure air, trapped beyond a sump, was released as the water level fell. Note the flapping hair and helmet chin strap. The wall and door serve as an air lock to minimize winds in the entrance area of the cave, which is open to tours.

variation of 5°C changes the air density by about 2%, which is enough to support perceptible air currents.

Some caves with temperature-driven air movement have no obvious high entrances that can serve as inlets or outlets for air. A considerable amount of air can move through pores and narrow fissures in bedrock where there are no traversable entrances. This can be especially significant in caves overlain by a thin insoluble but fractured cap-rock.

Differences in humidity: The presence of water vapor *reduces* the density of air. Density differences of this sort have the same effect as those caused by differences in temperature, but the humidity variation in a typical cave affects the density by less than 0.1%. The effects of temperature and humidity usually complement each other and rarely operate alone. Warm moist air often travels along the ceiling while cold dense air returns along the floor. This can cause sharp, nearly horizontal breaks between dissolution and precipitation, as described later in this chapter.

External wind velocity: When there is wind at the surface, cave openings on the upwind side of a hill are exposed to a positive pressure, while those on the downwind side experience a negative pressure. This pressure difference causes air movement through the cave. The regional pressure gradients that drive the outside winds are usually too broad to contribute directly to the air movement in caves.

Barometric pressure changes at the surface: This effect can be remarkable in large caves, especially those with only a few closely spaced entrances. When the outside pressure drops, as when a storm approaches, air moves out of the caves. When the outside pressure rises, as often happens during the approach of a cold front, air moves into the caves. Barometric winds can be recognized not only by their synchronized response to atmospheric pressure changes, but also by the fact that all entrances inhale simultaneously when air pressures rise and exhale when the pressure falls. In complex caves that have only a few openings to the surface, air movement may be rapid in the entrance passages but faint farther in where it is dispersed among many interconnected passages.

Dramatic examples of barometric winds can be observed in the large maze caves of the western U.S., such as Jewel, Wind, and Lechuguilla Caves (Figure 12.7). Winds of more than 110 km/hr (70 mph) have been clocked roaring into the walk-in entrance of Wind Cave.* The meter shot instantly to its maximum reading, so the actual velocity must have been far greater. Crude estimates of cave volume can be made by calculating the amount of air entering or exiting such caves. These estimates are often extraordinarily high. According to airflow measurements in Wind and Jewel Caves (Conn, 1966), less than 10% of either cave has been discovered, despite the fact that their explored lengths are already huge (page 40). These estimates show the presence of great volumes of open space, but much of it is likely to consist of inaccessibly small pores and fissures.

* Communication from James Pisarowicz, Custer, SD, 1988.

Figure 12.7: Barometric wind is almost always present at the entrances of Wind Cave, South Dakota. All cave entrances in the region inhale or exhale in unison, depending on whether the outside air pressure is increasing or decreasing.

Entrainment of air by moving water is an entirely different mode of air movement from the others previously described. Local cave winds are produced by the shear stress between the flowing water and the adjacent air. This is most apparent around waterfalls. Cave streams can cause similar air movement. If the streams connect with both upper and lower entrances, a net movement of air through the cave is possible. But if the cave is blocked at the upstream or downstream end (e.g., by a sump), the downstream movement of air near the stream is balanced by a return circulation of air close to the ceiling.

Evaporation and condensation

The ***relative humidity*** (RH) of air is the ratio of the amount of water vapor in the air compared to the maximum amount the air can hold, if all other variables are constant. The maximum moisture content varies with temperature (Figure 12.8). Most caves have an abundant supply of water vapor because they are surrounded by bedrock that contains a great deal of moisture. Active streams and drips are also common. Thus the RH in caves is usually near 100%. Even passages with no streams or active drips usually have RH values of more than 90%. Humidity in the vicinity of cave entrances is strongly affected by air exchange with the surface. Exchange of heat and moisture in caves is discussed by de Freitas and Littlejohn (1987).

When the relative humidity of cave air is less than 100%, evaporation takes place from water bodies. Meanwhile,

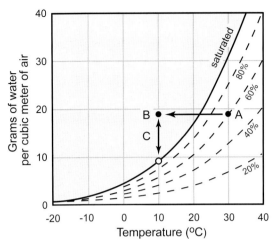

Figure 12.8: Moisture capacity of air at different temperatures. Example: If outside air (A) at 30°C and 60% relative humidity flows into a 10° cave (B), the air becomes supersaturated with moisture. Each cubic meter of air in the cave has the potential to produce roughly 9 g (= 9 cm³) of condensation water (C). Numbers on the graph are accurate only if the air pressure remains fairly constant. Standard atmospheric pressure is assumed here. Modified from Strahler (1971).

moisture is drawn out of the bedrock pores, and as this moisture evaporates it precipitates certain speleothems such as popcorn, frostwork, and gypsum flowers (Chapter 10).

The ***dew point*** is the temperature to which undersaturated air must drop to reach 100% RH. Below that temperature, condensation takes place. In the outside atmosphere, most condensation takes place on tiny air-borne particles, and if the process continues long enough it begins to rain or snow.

Cold winter air warms when it enters caves, reducing the relative humidity. Warm moist air that enters caves during the summer loses part of its capacity to hold moisture as it cools, and moisture may condense as droplets on solid surfaces, and less commonly as mist in the cave air that wets any surface it encounters. Moist air rising from warm lower levels can produce the same effect. Condensation moisture readily absorbs aerosols from the cave air, and so the chemical content of long-standing condensation droplets can be high. They are also good habitats for actinomycete bacteria, which are responsible for the striking silver, pink, or gold reflectance of certain droplets.

Where a large quantity of moist air flows into a cool cave, it may be possible for condensation to boost the rate of underground water flow perceptibly (Dublyansky and Dublyansky, 2000). Some authors suggest instead that the effect is minor (e.g., Maire, 1990).

Figure 12.9: Condensation moisture on a cave ceiling, produced by warm summer air entering a cold cave (South Cave, Kentucky).

Condensation operates most effectively at high temperatures, such as those in thermal caves. A 1°C temperature drop at RH = 100% can cause 0.63 grams of water to condense from a cubic meter of air at 10°C, in comparison to 2.5 grams at 40°C.

Condensation moisture is most noticeable on non-porous surfaces such as fine-textured bedrock. Artificial materials such as flagging tape can become coated with droplets in less than a day under favorable conditions. Where the bedrock surface is porous and weathered, condensation moisture is absorbed by the rock and is not easily recognized.

Hygroscopic water forms a thin film on solid surfaces by adhesion. Additional water can be attracted to it by cohesion between water molecules. Both can be provided by condensation. On non-absorbent surfaces, condensation moisture often forms clusters of discrete, isolated droplets with edges that meet the wall at steep angles (Figure 12.9). Further condensation takes place preferentially on them. In contrast, water that seeps out of fractures already has intimate contact with the bedrock and tends to spread as a thin film, which forms discrete drops only on downward projections.

Droplets of moisture that absorb dissolved minerals and gases may build up such a high concentration of ions that the activity of water (its "effective concentration") is diminished in the droplets. As a result, additional moisture from the cave air can be absorbed by the droplets and cause them to grow and fall to the floor. This process is especially potent in cave air that is rich in hydrogen sulfide (Chapters 5 and 8).

Weathering in the cave atmosphere

Most caves are formed by simple dissolution, which usually leaves fresh bedrock surfaces. With time, these surfaces tend to become weathered in the cave atmosphere. Physical weathering by freezing and thawing is normally limited to entrance zones, except during glacial periods. In the moist interior of a cave, bedrock and inactive speleothems are exposed to long-term chemical weathering, which alters the composition of their surfaces and enhances subtle differences in texture. As described below, the internal weathering of caves can be as complex as the processes that formed the caves in the first place. See Zupan-Hajna (2003) for a further discussion of weathering in the cave environment.

Condensation corrosion

Condensation moisture starts with little or no dissolved load but quickly absorbs gases from the air, such as CO_2 or H_2S, which make the water solutionally aggressive. As a result, the moisture can dissolve small amounts of any carbonate surface on which it condenses. Given enough time, these surfaces are dissolved into smooth faces that can cut across a variety of bedrock types and crystalline wall coatings. This is the process of ***condensation corrosion***.

In some caves the air is perceptibly warmer in lower levels than in higher levels because of the Earth's natural temperature gradient. Warm, moist air rises from the lower

Figure 12.10: Condensation moisture on calcite crystals, Jewel Cave, South Dakota. Note how the solutionally aggressive moisture etches the crystals, rounds them, and reveals the internal crystal structure.

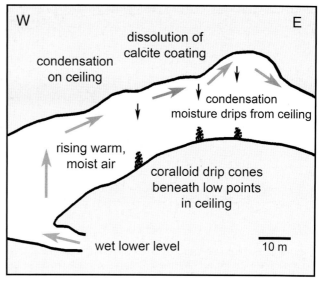

Figure 12.12: Diagram of condensation corrosion in Jewel Cave, South Dakota (part of Scenic Tour). Warm moist air rises from a wet lower level and moves along the upward slope of the overlying ceiling, which is coated with an old 15-cm-thick calcite crust. Moisture condenses from the air and corrodes the crust, as shown by a bright yellow path in the crust along the line of steepest ascent. Elsewhere the crust has a thin gray veneer of insoluble materials. Drips of water fall from low points in the ceiling where the moisture accumulates. Hollow, porous coralloid drip cones grow beneath the drip points.* The process ceases where the ceiling (and some air flow) slope downward to the east.

regions, and some of its moisture condenses on the colder surfaces above. Speleothems become etched by corrosion so that their internal crystal structure is revealed (Figure 12.10). Corroded surfaces may also become smooth and chalky. Dissolution along grain boundaries in bedrock can produce a disintegrated sandy or fluffy residue. Piles of calcite and dolomite powder accumulate on the floors below. In caves with rising moist air, condensation corrosion can form irregular tubes, domes, and cupolas that extend upward from the original passages (Figure 12.11).

Much of the water that condenses in the upper parts of a cave seeps downward through bedrock pores, or on the surface as thin films of water, and carries with it the materials it has dissolved. Lower down, this water tends to re-evaporate back into the cave air and deposit speleothems such as popcorn and frostwork. In many places the condensation moisture drips from low points in the ceiling and builds aragonite bushes and popcorn stalagmites on the floor below (Figures 12.5 and 12.12). Most drip cones and hollow stalagmites are formed in this way (Figures 10.20, 10.21, and 10.52). If the lower levels of the cave become dryer, these processes are less active and may cease altogether.

This evaporation-condensation pattern is most common in caves where circulation of air between entrances is limited and where there is little running water. It is typical of hypogenic caves in dry climates, including both active and inactive caves (Dublyansky and Dublyansky, 2000). For example, Caverns of Sonora, in Texas, contains striking crystal displays in its lower levels, while condensation corrosion in the upper levels has weathered the bedrock to smooth, sculpted forms with very few speleothems. The contrast between corrosion above and evaporative mineral growth below is common in stalactites and columns (Figure 12.13).

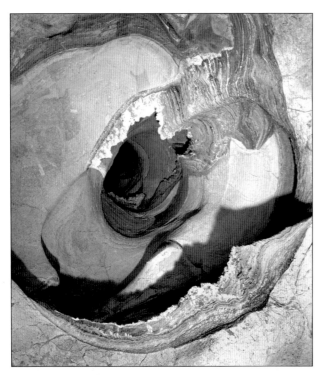

Figure 12.11: Ceiling dome in Jewel Cave, enlarged by condensation corrosion in currents of rising moist air. Note layers of corroded residue, which themselves have been shaved by corrosion. Height of dome is about 10 m. View is straight up from the passage floor into the dome. Width of photo is about 2.5 m.

---

* These processes were noted by some of the first explorers of Jewel Cave as early as the 1950s (Conn and Conn, 1977).

The upward change from evaporation to condensation may be present even in caves with little vertical relief. Evaporation-pan measurements in Mystery Cave, Minnesota, by Alexander and Jameson (1994), show evaporation in the lower few meters of certain passages, accompanied by condensation in the upper few meters, even where the passage height is only 6–7 m. The evaporative zones correlate with a thin growth of aragonite needles on the lower walls.

Heat is released by condensation — about 584 calories per gram of water at 25°C. The amount is slightly less at lower temperatures. This heat warms the local bedrock, moisture, and cave air slightly. (Evaporation cools the environment by the same amount.)

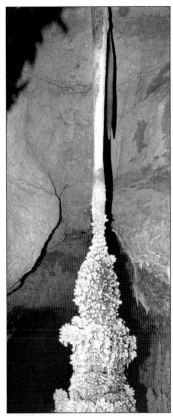

Figure 12.13: Corrosion of the upper half of a dripstone column in Caverns of Sonora, Texas, by condensation corrosion. Meanwhile, coralloids have formed on the lower half. Height of photo = 4 m.

This heat is slow to dissipate because bedrock transmits it very slowly, and this suppresses the tendency for further condensation (Dreybrodt, 2003). Over the long term, condensation corrosion must rely on periods of inactivity, which give the rock surfaces a chance to cool down toward the normal background temperature. Intake of cold winter air from the surface is particularly effective in reactivating the condensation process.

Further calculations by Dreybrodt and others (2005) show that daily and seasonal temperature fluctuations are enough to sustain condensation corrosion at a low level. The process is more rapid in shallow caves, where the accumulated heat is lost more readily to the surface. In a typical model, with a temperature change of 10°C per season (a high amount for a cave), the long-term calcite dissolution rate was calculated to be about 0.35 mm/1000 years. Daily fluctuations of the same amount would apparently raise that rate about 8.6 times. Evaporative cooling during the dry phase of the daily cycle would roughly triple the net dissolution rate.

In Snedegar's Cave, West Virginia, Jameson (1995) measured condensation rates of 30–90 grams/m²/day as the result of warm summer air entering the cave. To illustrate the potential impact on the cave, consider a typical P_{CO_2} of roughly 0.001 atm for mixtures of cave air and surface air,

and a temperature of 15°C. The saturation concentration for dissolved calcite would be about 0.09 g/liter (Figure 5.3). The dissolution rate caused by the condensation water would be roughly equivalent to 0.3–1.0 mm/1000 years. Because Jameson's measured condensation rates probably operate less than half the year, the annual dissolution rates estimated from them are probably overestimated.

Sarbu and Lascu (1997) describe condensation corrosion in the upper level of Movile Cave, Romania, where the mean temperature is 19.5°C and P_{CO_2} = 0.015 atm. Vapor rising from a lower level (T = 21°C) condenses on the walls and ceiling of the upper level at measured rates of 10–15 ml/100 cm²/month. H_2S can be detected in the lower level but not in the upper level. The saturation concentration of calcite is about 0.21 g/L in those conditions (Figure 5.3), and the corrosion rate would be about 1.0–1.4 mm/1000 years. The conditions in Movile do not vary seasonally, so the dissolution rate is likely to remain fairly constant. A thin sand of weathered bedrock grains on the floor indicates a greater rate of wall retreat than estimated but does not affect the net removal of limestone. It is possible that the dissolution rate is increased periodically by temporary influxes of H_2S from below.

According to Sarbu and Lascu (1997), CO_2 in the Movile Cave air has $\delta^{18}O$ = +4.9 to +5.7‰ PDB and $\delta^{13}C$ = −22 to −24‰ PDB, much more negative than the −7.8‰ of the surface air. (See pages 127–131 for a discussion of isotopes.) The authors attribute the low $\delta^{13}C$ to oxidation of methane (CH_4). Evaporation has caused aragonite deposits to be very light in both C and O isotopes ($\delta^{13}C$ = −16.6 to −21.4‰; $\delta^{18}O$ = −10.9 to −11.17‰), which suggests that its carbonate comes from a combination of cave air, condensed water vapor, and nearby corroded limestone bedrock ($\delta^{13}C$ = −4 to −12‰; $\delta^{18}O$ = −2 to −7‰).

Despite the contrasts in chemistry and mechanism, all three estimates of condensation corrosion — those of Sarbu and Lascu (1997), calculations from measurements of Jameson (1995), and the model of Dreybrodt and others (2005) — all fall into the same general range of values. Condensation corrosion has thus been validated, but its rate is low in comparison to cave enlargement by aggressive streams (Chapter 7). For example, the calculated amount of condensation corrosion in Snedegar's Cave would be overwhelmed by the dissolution produced by occasional floods. But the strong visual evidence for condensation corrosion in certain caves (as in Figures 12.10–12.13) suggests either long times or high concentrations of CO_2 or H_2S in the cave atmosphere. Both conditions are common in hypogenic caves, and it is in those caves that condensation corrosion is most prominent. High CO_2 and H_2S levels are absent in many of these caves today, as are steep thermal gradients, so it is likely that many corroded surfaces are relics from earlier periods.

Wind-oriented cave features

When moisture-laden air moves through a narrow opening between passages or rooms, the aperture may be enlarged and smoothed into a throat-like feature called a *vent* (Figure

Figure 12.14: Vents and rims in a wall coating of gypsum, Lechuguilla Cave, New Mexico. The vents are the holes between the main passage and a hidden void beyond. The rims are the white flared deposits whose inner surfaces have been shaved off by condensation corrosion. Width of photo is about 50 cm.

Figure 12.15: A rim at the top of a long descent to Lake of the Clouds, Carlsbad Cavern, New Mexico, showing condensation corrosion on the upwind side (on the right, toward the lake), and calcite deposition on the downwind side, which is exposed only to evaporation. The rim is the flared wing-shaped feature in the center of the photo.

Figure 12.16: Rim in an eastern Tennessee cave, formed by precipitation of evaporative minerals (white calcite, aragonite, gypsum) by cold descending air. It and the adjacent bedrock have been shaved into a continuous smooth surface by condensation corrosion from warm moist air moving upward. Width of photo is about 1 m.

12.14). Meanwhile, calcite, aragonite, or gypsum often grow on the downwind side. Continued corrosion shaves off the upwind side of the mineral growth, to form a continuous smooth surface that cuts across both the bedrock and the minerals. The projecting mineral growth with its shaved-off side is called a *rim* (Figures 12.14–12.16).

These and similar cave features cannot be classified strictly as either speleogens or speleothems, because they involve a combination of dissolution, weathering, and deposition. They are more appropriately called *atmospheric speleofacts* (Davis, 1995). Wind-oriented cave features of any kind are also known by the seldom-used term *anemolites.*

The origin of the down-wind crystal deposits is debated. Evaporation takes place on the side facing the cave entrance, and it is possible that the condensation moisture on the corroded inner side simply seeps through the vent to the depositional side. But it is unlikely that evaporation can take place in the same stream of air that causes the corrosion. Instead, it may require dry wind moving in the opposite direction, and at different times, as the result of changes in barometric pressure at the surface.

Green (1991, 1997) offers the alternative hypothesis that certain vents and rims are phreatic features formed by rising thermal water, as shown by correlations with folia. But some rims are composed of evaporative gypsum, which indicates aerated conditions (Figure 12.14). Another alternative is that aerosols may provide a mechanism for forming rims (Klimchouk and others, 1995; see pages 293–294). Although these are minority viewpoints, they are both based on careful field work and deserve consideration.

In some caves, vents and rims are found in close association with thick accumulations of calcite rafts and deep rills in the bedrock floor. Rafts are formed where CO_2 is lost rapidly from cave pools. As the CO_2 is released it is absorbed by condensation moisture above the pools. If there is enough condensation water to drip from the ceiling, it can be aggressive enough to form solution rills in the floor (Davis, 1995).

Rims and related features are almost entirely absent in the humid eastern U.S. A major exception, in an eastern Tennessee cave, may shed some light on the origin of these features. A stream passage is overlain by a dry upper-level tube, and the two passages have several connections. A narrow

Figure 12.17: Preferential growth of popcorn on a stalactite in Carlsbad Cavern, New Mexico. Dry air moving toward the right causes evaporative wicking on one side of the stalactite. At other times, moist air moving toward the left corrodes the right side. Width of photo is about 50 cm.

Figure 12.18: Corrosion by seepage water entering a cave through overlying quartz sandstone. Incoming water is saturated with respect to calcite but at a very low P_{CO_2} as the result of closed-system dissolution. The water rapidly absorbs CO_2 from the cave atmosphere and becomes aggressive. The feeder crack that delivers seepage is not visibly enlarged by dissolution. See text for details. This example is in Crystal Cave, Kentucky. Ball-point pen for scale.

canyon branches from the upper walls of the dry tube and leads upward to a large karst depression at the surface. Although the connection to the surface is blocked by breakdown, large quantities of air can pass through. The walls of the canyon are lined by evaporative growths of calcite, aragonite, and gypsum. These deposits have been sculpted into rims around the mouth of the canyon where it drops into the tube. Below the canyon, the tube's floor and lower walls are also coated by evaporative minerals. Evidently, during cold periods, dry air descends from the surface depression into the cave, and as it warms up, its relative humidity drops. This causes evaporative mineral growth in the canyon and dry tube. When the cave stream is warmer than the cave air, moist air rises from the stream passage and corrodes the cool upper walls of the dry tube by condensation. This process also shaves off the mineral deposits around the mouth of the canyon, so the bedrock and mineral rim form a continuous smooth surface (Figure 12.16). The rising warm air continues up the canyon to the surface, except during those times when the winter air trapped in the depression is cold enough to force air to flow downward instead.

In many caves, regardless of the local climate, popcorn and frostwork usually show preferential growth in areas of strong or persistent air movement (Queen, 1994b; Hill, 1987). These features often grow on one side of a preexisting dripstone speleothem, while the other side may be corroded, in the same manner as a rim (Figure 12.17).

Dissolution by vadose seepage

Vadose seepage into a cave is usually saturated with dissolved calcite at a high P_{CO_2}, and it tends to precipitate speleothems as it loses CO_2 to the cave air (Chapter 5). But in some caves the seepage water becomes more aggressive by absorbing gases from the cave air. This process is most common in active hypogenic caves in which H_2S or high concentrations of CO_2 seep into the cave from below. Hydrogen sulfide is readily absorbed by infiltrating moisture, which is likely to contain no H_2S at all before it enters the caves. But for cave CO_2 to renew the aggressiveness of infiltrating water, it normally means that the P_{CO_2} of the cave

air must exceed that of the soil through which the water has infiltrated (about 0.01–0.05 atm). Rising water in some active hypogenic caves does contain CO_2 levels higher than those of the soil. It loses CO_2 to the cave atmosphere, and although the rising water may precipitate calcite, the escaping gas can be absorbed by incoming vadose water to cause corrosion higher in the caves. Much of the extensive bedrock corrosion in hypogenic caves may be due to this mechanism.

But even in caves with moderate or low CO_2 levels, cave surfaces may be dissolved where water seeps in through a permeable but insoluble cap-rock, such as quartz sandstone (Chapter 5). By passing through the soil directly into underlying sandstone, the water soon becomes isolated from the soil CO_2. If the water then encounters limestone or dolomite, most of the CO_2 is used up as the rock dissolves, because the gas cannot be replenished. As a result, the water approaches saturation at very low concentrations of dissolved rock. The pH rises to above 8 or 9. If it later seeps into a cave, this water quickly absorbs CO_2 from the cave air and dissolves the rock surfaces instead of precipitating calcium carbonate (Palmer and Palmer, 1995b). The process is most easily recognized where water seeps into caves through narrow fissures, where it corrodes patches of zig-zag channels in the wall below (Figure 12.18). These represent a special form of the ***etched surfaces*** described in Chapter 6 (page 154). The inlet fissures show little or no solutional widening, but in places the channels below them are more than a centimeter deep. Their patterns are irregular and sinuous because the influence of capillarity on the thin water films is almost as great as gravity. The channels become shallower downward and are inconspicuous a meter or two below the inlets.

Corrosion by biogenic acids

Acids derived from bat or bird guano are most abundant in warm climates (Martini and Moen, 1998; Onac, 2000). These include phosphoric, nitric, and sulfuric acid, as well as organic acids, which can corrode the local bedrock and speleothems but also produce other speleothems (Forti, 2001;

Figure 12.19: Speleothems corroded by biogenic acids from guano in Cueva Lirio, Isla de Mona, Puerto Rico. The cave was once partly filled with bird and bat guano, which was mined almost completely away in the late 19th century. Some corrosion may also have been caused by condensation (Tarhule-Lips and Ford, 1998), and also by plant growth near entrances (Figure 12.49).

see also pages 301–302). Caves that are exposed to large amounts of guano have deeply corroded surfaces. Dripstone in particular can take on intricate and bizarre forms as a result (Figure 12.19). They may be coated by secondary minerals derived from the interaction between the acids and the local bedrock or speleothems. For example, thin crusts of phosphate minerals and gypsum are common in these caves.

Oxidation of sulfides

Many carbonate rocks contain scattered grains of iron sulfide, particularly pyrite (FeS_2), which forms in oxygen-poor environments (Figure 12.20). When they are exposed to oxygen-rich water, typical of most caves, the sulfides oxidize readily to produce sulfuric acid and iron hydroxides. With time, the hydroxides tend to recrystallize to iron oxides. For simplicity they are all referred to below merely as *iron oxides*.

The sulfuric acid reacts with the surrounding bedrock and may form white haloes of gypsum surrounding brown oxide grains (Figure 12.21). In wet areas the gypsum is carried away in solution, leaving round hollows in the cave walls. In dry areas the gypsum becomes concentrated at the cave

Figure 12.20: A handful of organic muck from the stream bed of Cueva de Villa Luz, Mexico, contains iron sulfides (FeS, FeS_2) produced by reduction of dissolved iron. In later oxidizing conditions the sulfides will be converted to sulfuric acid and colorful iron oxides.

walls by evaporation and may form crusts or flowers.

Iron oxides are also soluble in highly acidic water (especially at pH < 2). If iron sulfides continue to oxidize after a gypsum rind has isolated them from the surrounding carbonate rock, the local acidity may build up enough for some or all of the oxides to be carried away in solution. When the acid encounters carbonate rocks or minerals, the carbonates are rapidly dissolved, causing the pH to rise and the oxides to precipitate as brownish stains. The oxides can also be deposited by evaporation. The outer edges of many gypsum crusts are colored golden brown by these deposits.

It is possible to tell whether a gypsum deposit was produced by oxidation of sulfide or by migration from bodies of primary evaporative gypsum inside the nearby bedrock. Sulfur isotopic ratios tend to be negative in gypsum that is derived from oxidation of sulfides but are positive in primary gypsum (page 129).

It is usually possible to determine whether pyrite or H_2S was the sulfate source. Pyrite oxidation is fairly local, and the resulting gypsum commonly concentrates along certain beds or bedding-plane partings. The light brown color of many gypsum deposits is usually caused by iron oxide staining from pyrite oxidation. For example, note the dark tips of the gypsum flower in Figure 10.57. Iron oxides are not produced by H_2S oxidation, but the resulting sulfuric acid may attack impurities in the soluble rock, such as clay, and produce masses of iron oxides such as those in Figure 12.31 (page 338). By either oxidation process, the sulfuric acid often forces gypsum to replace a thin zone of limestone at the cave walls — not simply coating the walls but converting the calcite to gypsum (Chapter 5, Reaction 5.20). Smooth, dimpled bedrock surfaces are exposed where the gypsum has peeled away (Figure 12.22). Scallops, flutes, and rills are modified or obliterated by this process.

Palmer and Palmer (1995b) suggest that

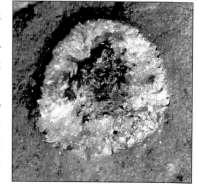

Figure 12.21: Halo of gypsum around an oxidizing grain of pyrite in the walls of Mammoth Cave, Kentucky. Width of photo is about 5 cm.

Figure 12.22: Pocketed limestone surface left by the dropping away of a gypsum crust (white), Mammoth Cave, Kentucky. Ballpoint pen for scale. Photo by A. Palmer and John Andersland.

gypsum can replace calcite in cave walls even without sulfuric acid, as long as the water approaching the wall is saturated with both calcite and gypsum, and also has high pH and low CO_2 from the closed-system dissolution described on page 333. Saturation with gypsum can be caused either by oxidation of pyrite or by dissolution of gypsum in the bedrock. Deep inside the bedrock, the seepage water does not have a high enough sulfate/carbonate ratio ($SO_4^=/CO_3^=$) to allow gypsum to replace calcite. But when the water comes close enough to the cave to absorb CO_2 from the cave air, the pH drops and much of the carbonate is converted to bicarbonate. The $SO_4^=/CO_3^=$ ratio rises enough to allow gypsum to replace calcite. At the same time, the CO_2 uptake causes the water to become aggressive toward calcite. As calcite dissolves, it boosts the calcium concentration in the water and enhances the gypsum supersaturation.*

Water that infiltrates through organic-rich soil loses most of its dissolved oxygen because of microbial respiration and reactions with organic compounds. Oxygen continues to be consumed wherever sulfide oxidation takes place. Thus one would expect the oxidation of sulfides to be concentrated at shallow depth where the sulfides are first encountered. The oxidation zone is likely to move downward with time as the sulfides are used up. Pohl and White (1965) and White and White (2003) suggest that most of the gypsum in the Mammoth Cave region, Kentucky, is derived from pyrite that is concentrated in the insoluble cap-rock above the cavernous limestone. At the opposite extreme, Palmer and Palmer (1995b) identify sulfides in and around the cave walls as the main source of gypsum. Certain beds exposed in Mammoth Cave once contained enough pyrite that an oxidation zone around the passage only one meter thick could

have produced even the thickest of existing gypsum crusts in the cave. Oxygen apparently diffuses into the bedrock around the cave and reacts with the sulfides.

Both processes are valid, but it is so difficult to measure what is happening deep inside the bedrock that the relative importance of each cannot be determined easily. The Pohl-White model probably accounts for widespread gypsum that coats cave walls over broad areas. The other model accounts for gypsum that is concentrated along certain sulfide-rich beds exposed in the cave.

How much pyrite is needed to produce a given amount of gypsum? Under ideal conditions the resulting gypsum has a volume 6.2 times greater than that of the pyrite source.** This ratio is smaller if not all of the sulfur is converted to gypsum. But gypsum speleothems and crusts are highly porous, which makes their overall densities less than the density of individual crystals. So the real increase in volume can be even greater than calculated. If the gypsum is later dissolved away by vadose seepage, there can be a substantial increase in passage size with no need for reflooding.

Weathering rinds

Many bedrock surfaces that are exposed to cave air acquire a light-colored weathering rind of altered rock (Figures 12.23–12.24). This rind can be formed by disintegration of the exposed bedrock to a smaller crystal size. This process alone can make the bedrock look white.

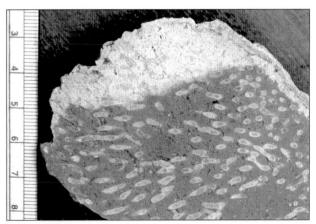

Figure 12.23: White weathering rind on dark gray coralline limestone (shown on a sawed slab of Ste. Genevieve Limestone, Mammoth Cave). The fossil colonial coral in the unaltered rock is composed of coarsely crystalline calcite surrounded by finer-grained fossil fragments and calcite crystals. Long exposure to the moist cave air has etched the calcite crystal boundaries to produce a fine-grained opaque rind. Much of the rind is composed of quartz precipitated during the weathering. The numbered scale is in centimeters. Figure 12.24 gives a closer view.

---

* Some researchers have cast doubt on this mechanism by suggesting that the sulfate/carbonate ratio will be about 10 times too small. But their estimates are based on calculating the carbonate concentration with Reactions 5.3–5.10, and the sulfate concentration independently with Reaction 5.1. This procedure violates the charge balance (page 136). If all reactions are considered simultaneously, the sulfate/carbonate ratio is sufficiently large.

** The density of pyrite (FeS_2) is 5.0 g/cm^3, so one cm^3 weighs 5 g. One mole of pyrite = 120 g (sum of atomic weights, one Fe + 2 S), so one cm^3 of pyrite = 0.0417 mole. Pyrite contains twice as much sulfur as does gypsum, so 0.0417 mole of pyrite produces 0.0833 mole of gypsum. Gypsum has a molar mass of 172 g/mole and a density of 2.32 g/cm^3, so 0.0833 moles of gypsum = 6.2 cm^3, so the complete conversion of pyrite to gypsum involves a volume increase of about 6.2 times (neglecting porosity).

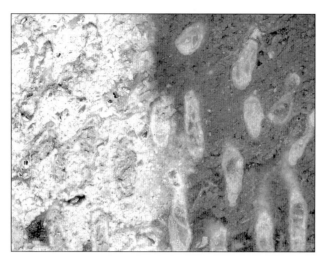

Figure 12.24: Enlarged view of the white weathering rind in the previous figure. The coarsely crystalline fossils in the weathered zone disintegrate into loose fragments that tend to fall out at the cave wall and leave pockets. Width of photo is 2 cm.

In many places the rind also includes other minerals that are deposited in the local bedrock pores. Its thickness depends on the rock type, amount of moisture present, and the length of time the rock has been exposed to air. Inactive speleothems can also be corroded by the same mechanism, which often turns them ghostly white (Figure 12.25). Meanwhile they may peel apart along their original layers (Figure 12.26).

Figure 12.25: Deeply weathered dripstone speleothems in Spider Cave, New Mexico, have soft, chalky white weathering rinds several centimeters thick.

These processes are driven mainly by seepage of water into the cave. If the cave air contains more carbon dioxide than the seepage water, the water absorbs CO_2 from the air and becomes slightly corrosive. This process is even more effective if the cave air is rich in hydrogen sulfide, as described in the next section.

Some white weathering rinds are also visible on bedrock that was once covered by moist sediment. Periodic wetting of the sediment exposes the underlying bedrock to mild corrosion, but without the rapid dissolution or erosion caused by streams in direct contact with the bedrock.

The weathering rind may also contain minerals that precipitate in the outer few centimeters of exposed bedrock. Where water seeps through a sandstone cap-rock and dissolves carbonate rock under closed conditions so that its pH rises (page 333), quartz, and related forms such as chert and opal, are more soluble than at moderate pH (Figure 5.17). Clay also tends to break down slightly at high pH and liberates H_4SiO_4. When the water approaches a cave and absorbs CO_2 or H_2S, the pH drops rapidly, even before the seepage water reaches the cave wall. As a result, quartz or opal can precipitate in the weathering rind (Figures 12.23–12.24). Oxidation of organic material in the rock may contribute to the pallor of the rind.

This kind of weathering rind tends to be soft and white, although many are coated with a thin brown veneer of iron oxide, mainly from oxidation of iron sulfides. Where graffiti have been scratched into them, the contrast in color between the golden brown bedrock surface and the underlying white makes the scratches stand out boldly. This practice is prohibited today, but many old signatures are still highly legible in caves because of the nature of the bedrock weathering (Figure 12.27).

Soft material from weathered bedrock or speleothems can be shaped into slender fingers by dripping or splashing water (Figure 12.28). These are known as ***splash fingers***. Most

Figure 12.26: A weathered stalagmite in the Left Hand Tunnel of Carlsbad Cavern is peeling apart along its growth layers. Width of photo is about 1.5 m.

Figure 12.27: A signature scratched into weathered limestone in Crystal Cave, Kentucky. The negative impact on the cave is overshadowed by the historical value of this record left by the legendary explorer Floyd Collins.

hang downward like miniature draperies, and some point radially outward from the points of splash impact. They are usually moist and soft, but if the cave becomes drier they harden and become brittle.

Corrosion residue

The weathering rinds described in the preceding two pages are typical of epigenic caves. In contrast, weathering in some hypogenic caves produces fluffy, multi-colored zones up to several tens of centimeters thick in which the original texture of the rock is disrupted and often unrecognizable (Figure 12.29). This *corrosion residue* is most conspicuous on impure

Figure 12.29: Corrosion residue in Spider Cave, New Mexico. White = calcite wall crust; light gray = dolomite bedrock; dark gray = clay-rich dolomite, with iron and manganese oxides prominent in the residue. The "dark gray" is actually a vivid brownish red. All surfaces are deeply weathered. Width of photo is 15 cm.

bedrock that contains clay and other non-carbonate minerals. Weathered zones of this kind are sometimes known informally as "punk rock" (Hill, 1987). Most corrosion residue is just sandy material that remains from disintegration of the bedrock (Figure 12.30). Some is also seen on ledges in the walls of the dome in Figure 12.11. In pores, this material is known to sedimentologists as *internal sediment*, and it seems to apply as well to caves. In many caves the corrosion residue is enhanced by chemical reactions that produce a variety of new minerals, textures, and colors.

In the production of corrosion residue, the most soluble materials in the surfaces of bedrock and speleothems are removed in solution by condensation moisture and by aggressive pore moisture that is absorbing H_2S or CO_2 from

Figure 12.28: Curtains and splash fingers of white weathered material, which has been shaped by aggressive drip-water, Carlsbad Cavern. Width of photo is about 30 cm.

Figure 12.30: Internal carbonate sediment produced by weathering of bedrock surfaces in Carlsbad Cavern, New Mexico. The outer part of the sediment has recrystallized into a crust, while some of the soft sediment has compacted beneath it to produce a thin void. The crust has been broken by trail-building. Width of photo is about 1.5 m.

Figure 12.31: Remnant of a solution pothole with bleached floor and Fe-Mn oxide fill, formed by sulfuric acid corrosion, Lechuguilla Cave, New Mexico.

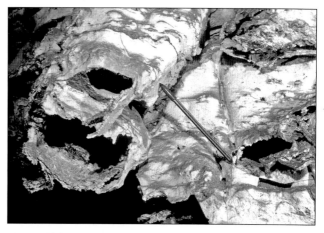

Figure 12.32: A quartz rind in Wind Cave, South Dakota. A shell of quartz coated the oldest cave surfaces in a sulfate-rich environment during the Mississippian Period. Later dissolution, during the main Cenozoic phase of cave origin, removed much of the coated limestone and left the quartz rinds standing in relief.

the cave air. The less soluble materials are left behind. For example, dolomite tends to vary in purity, and in places its Ca:Mg ratios are higher than the ideal 1:1 ratio. The calcium-rich portions dissolve preferentially and leave behind a granular residue of almost pure dolomite sand.

Subtle tones of yellow and red are common in most kinds of weathered rock, but in the punky walls of certain hypogenic caves these colors run wild. Oxidation of pyrite in the bedrock is one of the major causes. From the sulfuric acid that is released, the surrounding bedrock may be bleached white by oxidation of carbon compounds (Figure 12.31). Iron oxides contribute a wide variety of reds, yellows, and black, while manganese oxides add dark hues, often black. Oxidation reactions in the weathering zone serve as energy sources for microorganisms, such as iron-oxidizing bacteria. The microbes also speed the reactions greatly, and they make some reactions possible that otherwise would require either high temperatures or long times.

Many caves in the Guadalupe Mountains of New Mexico contain superb examples of corrosion residue (Cunningham and others, 1995; Northup and others, 2000, 2003). Similar residues up to 20 cm thick occur in the thermally altered limestone walls of Kap-Kutan Cave, Turkmenistan (Maltsev and others, 1997). The Kap-Kutan researchers point out that the combination of weathered rock and organic material qualifies the residue as a kind of soil. There is a growing trend to call these zones *speleosols* (note spelling: from the Latin *solum* = soil).

Condensation corrosion is limited on deeply corroded surfaces. The outer portions of the weathered zone do not easily maintain cold temperatures, because they absorb most of the heat liberated by condensation. Also, as moisture is drawn into the weathered fluff by capillarity, it dissolves the outer parts most vigorously and loses most of its solutional capacity by the time it reaches the unaltered bedrock.

How, then, does the weathered zone become so thick? It is most likely that growth of thick corrosion residue is aided by the kind of seepage water that absorbs CO_2 or H_2S from the cave air as it enters the cave. This moisture becomes aggressive when it encounters the cave atmosphere, at the contact between the residue and the unaltered bedrock, and can therefore propagate the corrosion zone inward from its base. As the water disperses through the weathering rind, it dissolves grain boundaries and enhances the porous, crumbly texture. CO_2 or H_2S can be released into hypogenic caves even after the main phase of speleogenesis has ended. Some speleothems show evidence for alternating phases of growth and corrosion as a result.

Abundant quartz or opal in a weathering rind usually indicates decomposition of clay by strong acids, typically sulfuric acid. When silicic acid (H_4SiO_4) is released by breakdown of clay, opal tends to precipitate rapidly, as does quartz over longer time (Figure 12.32). Clays are most stable at a pH of about 6, so weathering of clays to quartz and opal is enhanced not only by acids but also by the high pH produced by evaporation or closed-system carbonate dissolution (Chapter 5).

Alunite ($KAl_3(SO_4)_2(OH)_6$; Figure 12.33) is a weathering product of clays such as potassium montmorillonite ($KAl_7Si_{11}O_{30}(OH)_6$):

$$KAl_7Si_{11}O_{30}(OH)_6 + 16H^+ + 2SO_4^{2-} + 14H_2O$$
$$\rightleftharpoons KAl_3(SO_4)_2(OH)_6 + 11H_4SiO_4 + 4Al^{3+} \quad (12.1)$$

Alunite is a faithful indicator of strong sulfuric acid and can be used for dating cave enlargement by this acid (page 348). The stability fields for alunite and potassium montmorillonite are shown in Figure 12.34 for a solution saturated with gypsum. The amount of H_4SiO_4 released by Reaction 12.1 is likely to be more than enough to precipitate quartz and opal. Crystalline quartz is slow to precipitate at low temperatures, so opal tends to precipitate instead, at least at first. Both quartz and opal are common in the weathered zones of Guadalupe caves (Polyak and Provencio, 2001).

The typical range for Al^{3+} in karst water is shown in Figure 12.34 (lower values in epigenic caves, higher ones

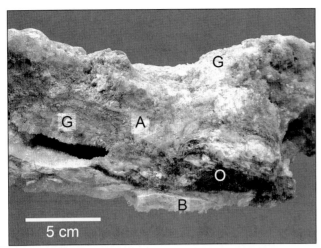

Figure 12.33: Weathering products from sulfuric acid corrosion of clay-rich carbonate rock, Lechuguilla Cave: **O** = iron and manganese oxides; **G** = gypsum; **A** = alunite; **B** = original bedrock (dolomitic limestone).

in hypogenic caves and thermal springs). Where clay decomposes in sulfuric acid, the concentration of dissolved aluminum is likely to be higher than either of these. The alunite field is squeezed into the light-gray triangle on the graph at pH values less than about 4. Because high acidity and a source of sulfate are both required to produce alunite, the reaction is almost certainly driven by sulfuric acid.

But if sulfuric acid is produced under water in a limestone cave, the resulting solution is only mildly acidic because it is rapidly neutralized by contact with the carbonate rocks. Sulfuric acid is most likely to reach the low pH needed to produce alunite only in vadose moisture droplets on non-carbonate surfaces such as clay. Most of the alunite in caves is therefore produced above the water

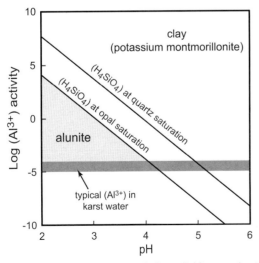

Figure 12.34: Alunite (pronounced *al-yu-nite*) forms only at low pH values produced by sulfuric acid. This plot shows the stability field for alunite at 25°C. The lines separating alunite from its parent clay material are drawn for the sulfate values for gypsum saturation. In these waters, opal is usually saturated and aluminum values are higher than in typical karst water. So alunite must form at pH values less than about 4. (Data on graph calculated from free-energy values in Faure, 1998).

table, although phreatic alunite is also known from mines. Later, when the sulfuric acid activity ceases and the pH rises, alunite may become unstable. Nevertheless, in dry environments it can persist for long times without altering to other minerals.

In Kap-Kutan Cave, Turkmenistan, hydrofluoric acid (HF) is produced by the weathering of hydrothermal veins of fluorite (calcium fluoride, CaF_2), which are exposed in the cave walls (Maltsev and Korshunov, 1998; see Figure 12.35). Although hydrofluoric acid has not yet been confirmed in the cave by direct measurements, its presence is inferred from the fact that crystals of fluorite are currently being deposited on gypsum speleothems by the reaction between HF and calcium-bearing minerals. Weathering of the fluorite is speeded by sulfuric acid derived from hydrogen sulfide that enters the cave from depth. In this cave's bizarre environment, a 30-meter cable ladder of steel and aluminum corroded away in only three years. HF can corrode quartz, as well, not because of its acidity, but because it forms complexes of silicon and fluoride. Sulfuric and hydrofluoric acids both corrode carbonate minerals as well.

Corrosion of aluminum takes place even in Carlsbad Cavern, New Mexico, which has not enlarged significantly by sulfuric acid for the past 4 million years (Chapter 13). Aluminum climbing hardware left in a passage at the highest point in the Big Room (Figure 6.19) became so badly corroded after only a few years that it lost virtually all its strength. Aluminum is highly soluble in strong acids. The corrosion may have been caused by tiny concentrations of H_2S absorbed by water droplets. Carlsbad Cavern and certain other Guadalupe caves also contain tiny fluorite crystals in evaporative popcorn (Figure 12.36). The fluorite may have formed by airborne hydrofluoric acid, as in Kap-Kutan Cave, although it is uncertain whether the acid is still present in the caves. Evaporative wicking of moisture from the cave walls may have deposited the fluroite.

It is usually possible to distinguish whether CO_2 or H_2S has been the dominant cause of bedrock and speleothem

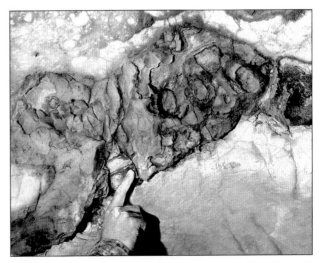

Figure 12.35: A fluorite vein exposed in the walls of Grotta di Faggeto Tondo, Italy.

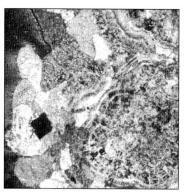

Figure 12.36: Thin section of a fluorite crystal embedded in calcite popcorn, Lechuguilla Cave. Under polarized light, fluorite appears black. The crystal is unweathered, so it is probably not fallen weathering residue. Width of photo = 1.5 mm.

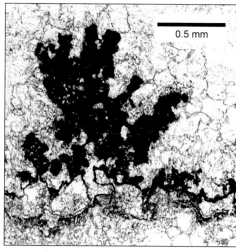

Figure 12.38: Shrubs of iron-manganese oxides (black), which grew on the corroded surface of a calcite pool crust in Lechuguilla Cave. Their growth and pattern are likely to have been influenced by bacteria. The shrubs were later encased in additional calcite (crystal boundaries are visible as thin lines). Thin-section photomicrograph by M. V. Palmer.

corrosion. Evidence for H_2S includes iron and manganese oxides and various sulfur minerals, which are the product of oxidation-reduction reactions. There is usually evidence for microbial activity. CO_2 is responsible for most white weathering rinds. Microbial associations are much less common and often have an ambiguous relationship to weathering. In general, H_2S is accompanied by elevated values of CO_2 as well, so may be difficult to isolate their individual effects.

Microbial influence on weathering

The microbial influence on many corrosion residues is well substantiated (Cunningham and others, 1995; Boston, 1999; Northup and others, 2000, 2003). For example, Figures 5.18–5.19, 10.74, and 12.37–12.38 show evidence for microbes, both living and fossil, that have taken part in chemical reactions in caves or karst springs. But certain minerals, especially alteration products such as clay, can also have filamentous structures (Figure 12.39). Some of them can be difficult to distinguish from the microbial kind. Mineral filaments are most common where weathering has taken place at low pH, as in sulfuric acid caves. These filaments are usually tapered and wispy. Some branch into structures resembling horse tails. They are usually rich in silicon and aluminum, two of the most diagnostic elements in clay. Opal can form similar structures.

If microbial structures are suspected, it is important to verify that they are truly organic, so their geochemical role can be

interpreted properly. Proof of an organic origin requires tests such as cultures, DNA extraction, biological indicators or staining with organic-specific dyes (Boston and others, 2001), but these procedures apply mainly to living specimens. Biological signatures such as shape, isotopic ratios, and presence of certain elements can be used even in some fossilized examples. Recognition of individual cells under microscopic inspection is a strong clue (Figure 5.19), as is the association of filaments with environments known to favor microbial growth. For example, evidence for iron- and manganese-oxidizing bacteria are abundant in corrosion residue.

Proper sampling procedure is critical in field microbiology. Microbes can grow rapidly on samples that have been

Figure 12.37: Fossil filaments of iron-oxidizing bacteria embedded in a calcite breccia matrix, Jewel Cave, South Dakota. Thin section photomicrograph by M. V. Palmer. Width of photo is about 0.3 mm.

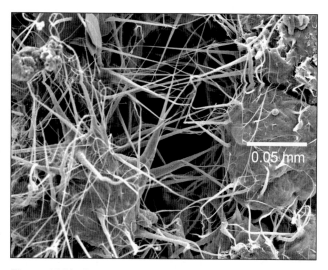

Figure 12.39: Strands of a clay mineral in the ***smectite*** group, from Carlsbad Cavern, viewed with a scanning electron microscope. These particular filaments are not biological. Note their varied diameters, uniform texture, and continuity with the crystals. X-ray analysis shows the presence of elements characteristic of clay, such as Si, Al, and Mg.

Figure 12.40: Calcite rods (needle-fibers, or lublinite) from the surface of a weathered stalagmite, Goshute Cave, Nevada (scanning electron microscope image). One micrometer (μm) = 0.001 mm.

removed from caves without sterilization. As soon as possible, samples should be fixed with a preservative such as glutaraldehyde to prevent further microbial growth. Microbial traces can also accumulate on cave surfaces that have been contaminated by passing humans or animals. In all of the above situations they tend merely to coat the sample surfaces. Penetration of bedrock or crystals by organic filaments is a clue that microbes have probably played a role in the local cave processes.

Finely crystalline, white, pasty materials in caves are often referred to by the general term *moonmilk* (page 298). This term is applied not only to a variety of primary mineral deposits such as calcite and hydromagnesite, but also to soft white byproducts of weathering. A common type, composed of thin calcite rods, is called *needle-fiber calcite* or *lublinite* (Figure 12.40). Some moonmilk takes the form of noodle-like strands (Figure 12.41).

Verrecchia and Verrecchia (1994) find material similar to cave moonmilk in the soil of arid regions. They determined that it is often associated with rapid precipitation and evaporation, with short wet periods alternating with long dry periods. The framework of this material is an organic slime that isolates microbes from the external environment. Many of the needles

are composed of calcium oxalate (CaC_2O_4 + various amounts of water), which can later be replaced by calcite. Living microbes are common in cave moonmilk, but recrystallization of the calcite often destroys the microbial structures (Gradzinski and others, 1997). According to Northup and Lavoie (2001), many types of microbes occur in calcite moonmilk and can be cultured from it, but no one has yet proved that microbes contribute to the origin of moonmilk.

Recrystallization of corrosion residue

Residue from chemical weathering can recrystallize into a hard, lumpy crust. In places it forms sheets up to several centimeters thick. These deposits are most common in hypogenic caves such as those of the semi-arid Southwest, where condensation corrosion plays a major role in altering bedrock and speleothem surfaces. In dry passages the weathered material collects as piles of soft powder, but with intermittent wetting, or evaporation of capillary moisture from the surface, the surface hardens into a crust that conceals the powdery mass inside (Figure 12.30). The crust may be only a few millimeters or centimeters thick, but in places the entire weathered mass is recrystallized into a hard substance that may be mistaken for flowstone, coralloid speleothems, or even bedrock. Before it recrystallizes, wet weathering material can form a soft paste.

In places the powdery or pasty weathered material is removed from beneath the crust by erosion or subsidence, and the crust is left behind as a hood-like canopy whose origin may seem puzzling. Similarly, a hardened crust of weathered material may cover crystals of soluble minerals, and if the crystals are later dissolved away, the residual hoods remain with the negative forms of the crystals embedded in them (Figure 12.42). Typically the hoods are composed of poorly soluble iron oxide, quartz, opal, or clay.

Recrystallization of corrosion residue can produce a variety of secondary minerals. The effects are greatest where evaporation takes place from residue that is in contact with

Figure 12.41: Strands of calcite in weathered limestone from Goshute Cave, Nevada, possibly guided by microbial activity (scanning electron microscope image).

Figure 12. 42: Residual hoods of yellow limonite (iron oxide), in upper right, which once coated calcite crystals in an early solution pocket in Wind Cave, South Dakota. Quartz crystals (on left) line much of the pocket. Tip of ball-point pen for scale.

Figure 12.43: Evaporative deposits in magnesium-rich cave pools form in this general order: calcite, aragonite, huntite, hydromagnesite, magnesite, and dolomite. The dark bases are composed mainly of calcite, and the white caps are composed of the later minerals. This pool is in Lechuguilla Cave, New Mexico. Width of photo is about 1.5 m. See also page 292.

standing water. Evaporation draws water from wet to dry areas, and various minerals are forced to precipitate as the concentration of dissolved solids in the water increases. Meanwhile the chemistry of the remaining water changes, as does its ability to precipitate minerals. This is the process of *fractionation*. The details of fractionation depend mainly on the chemical nature of the solution. Changes in temperature and gas concentrations can also have an effect, as do any other solid materials that fall into the water.

Calcite ($CaCO_3$) is usually the first mineral to crystallize from cave water, and it removes much of the calcium from solution. The Mg/Ca ratio increases, and further calcite growth is inhibited (see page 272). Instead, aragonite (a more soluble form of $CaCO_3$) begins to precipitate. As calcium becomes even more depleted, a series of magnesium-rich minerals begins to form. These often include huntite ($CaMg_3(CO_3)_4$), hydromagnesite ($Mg_5(CO_3)_4(OH)_2 \cdot 4H_2O$),

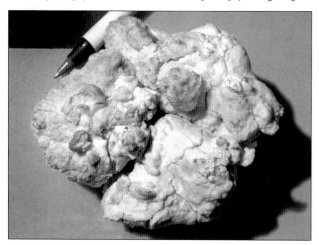

Figure 12.44: Nodule of moderately well-ordered dolomite, formed by evaporation around a wet area in Carlsbad Cavern. Ball-point pen for scale.

and magnesite ($MgSO_4$). These evaporative minerals protrude as nodules or mounds. In shallow pools they sometimes form little islands (Figure 12.43).

While other magnesium-rich minerals are precipitating, dolomite ($CaMg(CO_3)_2$) is nearly always the most stable of them all. But dolomite is very slow to crystallize at typical cave temperatures, so the less-stable Mg minerals form first. With time, these minerals may recrystallize to dolomite by drawing calcium from the remaining moisture in pools and nearby minerals. When weathering paste is the source, dolomite tends to form white biscuit-like blobs (Figure 12.44). In some caves, many of the older speleothems around pool deposits have converted to dolomite. For example, calcite popcorn and aragonite frostwork or anthodites may be converted to dolomite while retaining their original shapes. They are known as *pseudomorphs* because they have the crystal shape of an earlier mineral but the composition of a later mineral (page 274).

Some dolomite deposits have a perfect 1:1 ratio of calcium to magnesium, as the chemical formula suggests. This is *well-ordered* dolomite. Other dolomite bodies have more Ca than Mg, or, rarely, more Mg than Ca. In general, the ordering becomes less perfect toward the water sources that provide the dissolved material, and alteration minerals such as smectite (Figure 12.39) become more common. Slow, lengthy evaporation appears to enhance the dolomite ordering.

As evaporation continues, the pH usually rises in the remaining water. This is caused by the increase in concentration of the dissolved minerals, which reduces the H^+ activity (see Chapter 5). If the precipitation of carbonate minerals cannot keep pace with evaporation, the build-up of HCO_3^- and CO_3^{2-} contributes to the rise in pH.

If weathered material drops into a cave pool, unusual minerals and crystal shapes may form because of the sudden change in water chemistry. For example, calcite is the most common pool crust, but aragonite is rare. Carlsbad Cavern contains isolated pools lined with aragonite needles that project into the water (Figure 10.10c), while surrounding pools are lined only with calcite. Aragonite was able to form when blobs of magnesium-rich minerals (probably hydromagnesite) dropped into the pools from the cave ceiling. The boost in magnesium temporarily halted calcite growth and allowed aragonite to form instead. Since then, the water chemistry in many of the aragonite pools has reverted back to its original state and now resembles that of the surrounding calcite-lined pools. White pasty deposits around the aragonite pools show where the magnesium-rich minerals fell. Many of them have since recrystallized to other minerals.

Crystal wedging of bedrock

When gypsum and other evaporative minerals are deposited in caves, much of the material crystallizes in fractures in the surrounding bedrock. As they crystallize, the minerals exert a force on the fissure walls that wedges apart blocks and slivers of bedrock (Figure 12.45). Gypsum is the

Figure 12.45: Fragmenting of limestone by growth of gypsum in fractures, Lechuguilla Cave. Flashlight 15 cm long for scale.

Figure 12.46: Peeling and warping of bedrock slabs in Mammoth Cave, Kentucky, by internal growth of gypsum crystals in dry conditions.

main mineral involved in this process, but other evaporite minerals can also participate where conditions are favorable. The sand piles in Mullamullang Cave, Australia (Figure 2.88), are produced mainly by disintegration of limestone by the growth of halite crystals (NaCl). Mineral wedging can eventually cause breakdown, although the minerals also tend to cement the pieces together, which temporarily keeps the blocks from falling. Gypsum may also replace some of the carbonate bedrock (pages 334–335). Thin slabs of carbonate rock that are partly replaced by gypsum can bend by their own weight, or by the stress of gypsum crystallization

(Figure 12.46; White and White, 2003). Much breakdown in these zones takes place when the gypsum is dissolved away by increasing amounts of moisture.

Origin of boxwork

Boxwork consists of intersecting mineral veins that project into caves as resistant fins when the intervening bedrock is weathered or dissolved away (Figure 12.47). The intersecting fins form box-shaped voids. Most boxwork veins are calcite, but other minerals such as quartz or gypsum can produce the same result. Any resistant veins in bedrock tend to project into caves, but in well-developed boxwork the veins are so abundant and project so boldly from the cave walls that simple differential solution cannot be solely responsible. This is especially true for the world-class boxwork in caves of the Black Hills, South Dakota. Wind Cave alone may contain more boxwork than all other known caves combined. Similar but less well-developed examples are seen in some mining areas, including the Mississippian limestones of Colorado and Missouri.

Examination of breakdown blocks and artificially widened sections of tour routes in the Black Hills caves shows that the boxwork veins extend only a few tens of centimeters into the surrounding bedrock and then die out almost completely. This might suggest that the veins are related to the cave origin. But a closer look shows that the boxwork is located in beds that originally contained a great deal of gypsum and anhydrite, which have since disappeared by dissolution and conversion to other minerals

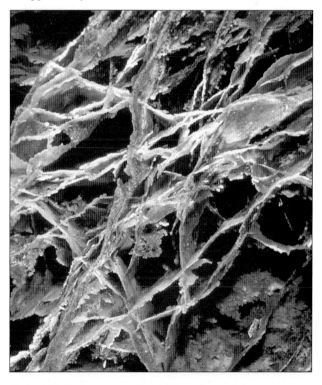

Figure 12.47: Boxwork in Wind Cave, South Dakota, consists of intersecting calcite veins that protrude as resistant fins from the surrounding crumbly, weathered bedrock. Height of photo is about 70 cm.

(Palmer and Palmer, 1989). The caves are located in the Mississippian-age Madison Formation. Deep below the surface, in the plains surrounding the Black Hills, these same rocks still include the sulfate rocks gypsum and anhydrite (Sando, 1988). During the Mississippian Period, soon after the limestones were deposited, dissolution and recrystallization of the sulfates produced a network of small fractures in the surrounding harder dolomite. Gypsum was the first mineral to fill these cracks. But this was only the beginning.

Meanwhile, reduction of sulfate rocks beneath the surface produced local zones of pyrite (FeS_2). Later, when mild uplift of the region allowed fresh groundwater to pass through, pyrite was oxidized to sulfuric acid and iron oxides. The sulfuric acid corroded the nearby carbonate rocks and converted them to a loose sandy material cemented loosely by quartz. Quartz is a major byproduct when clay is altered by sulfuric acid. But the gypsum veins were preserved intact, because gypsum is nearly immune to dissolution by sulfuric acid.

The next stage of boxwork evolution followed soon afterward. Near the end of the Mississippian Period, as further uplift increased the inflow of fresh groundwater, the gypsum was dissolved away and replaced by calcite. This is a common type of replacement, because karst groundwater becomes supersaturated with calcite as gypsum dissolves (page 121).

Much later, as the Black Hills were rising, about 50–70 million years ago, cave enlargement removed most of the remaining porous bedrock, so that the calcite veins were left projecting into the caves. That is what is visible today. The boxwork veins are generally paper-thin, but many have recrystallized to a more robust form and have acquired a strengthening fringe of popcorn or aragonite frostwork. The calcite veins are brown with iron oxide particles and with fossil filaments of iron-fixing bacteria. The boxwork is concentrated

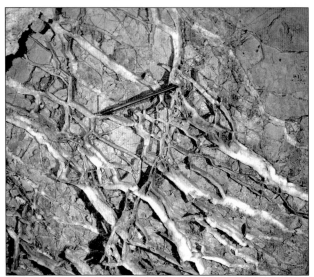

Figure 12.48: Boxwork formed by gypsum veins in dolomite bedrock, Crockett's Cave, New Mexico. This is apparently an early step in the process that formed the more extensive boxwork in the South Dakota caves. These gypsum veins grade laterally into thinner calcite veins like those in Figure 12.47.

Figure 12.49: Corrosion of stalagmites exposed to daylight in Cueva Lirio, Isla de Mona, Puerto Rico, caused at least partly by the growth of algae. See also Figure 10.84.

in certain beds and in pods of highly altered bedrock. In places the surrounding bedrock is bleached white, a typical product of weathering by sulfuric acid (see example in Figure 12.31).

The various stages in this sequence can be observed in other caves where carbonate and sulfate rocks occur together. A few caves in central New Mexico contain boxwork veins of gypsum that grade along their length into thin calcite veins. Both types of veins project from the bedrock in the same manner as the calcite boxwork of the Black Hills caves (Figure 12.48).

The complexity of this particular form of boxwork shows why it is so uncommon. The necessary sequence of events is provided very well by the geologic history of the Black Hills but is matched by few other cave areas.

Corrosion by lamp-flora

Naturally occurring cave flora are most common in the twilight zones of entrances and are able to corrode bedrock and speleothem surfaces (Figure 12.49). Some rudimentary organic growths, mainly microbial, may occur deep inside caves, but rarely in visible concentrations. The major exception is in the vicinity of long-term artificial lighting.

The artificial lights in show caves encourage the growth of algae, cyanobacteria, moss, and similar vegetation. These are called *lamp-flora* (or the German equivalent, *Lampenflora*). Such growths are unwelcome not only because they are unnatural, but also because they tend to corrode speleothems and rock surfaces. Lamp-flora are especially damaging to rock art, such as prehistoric paintings. Corrosion by organic acids and penetration of surfaces by rootlets and filaments make it difficult to restore the surfaces to their natural state.

Lamp-flora grow most vigorously on moist surfaces around high-intensity, hot lamps with a wide light spectrum. The problem is greatest in tropical climates. For example, in Grutas de Coconá, Tabasco, Mexico, leafy plants grow so exuberantly around floodlights that they must be chopped back periodically with machetes (Figure 12.50).

Figure 12.50: Dense vegetation grows around lights in the show cave Grutas de Coconá, Mexico. Width of photo is about 2 m.

There are several remedies for lamp-flora (Aley, 2004). A decrease in the intensity and duration of artificial lighting is the most effective. Intermittent lighting is less conducive to growth, even if the total duration of lighting is not reduced. Narrowing the wavelength spectrum can help. Spraying with bleach subdues their growth. Lamp-flora can be removed by application of bleach or hydrogen peroxide in combination with gentle wiping of surfaces with a soft fabric or brush.

A similar but more insidious problem is the degradation of the irreplaceable Paleolithic cave paintings at Lascaux, France, by a fungal growth apparently caused or accelerated by an ill-conceived air-conditioning scheme (Graff, 2006). Removing the fungus without damaging the paintings has required painstaking chemical and physical methods, but the outbreak seems at least temporarily to be under control. To avoid further contamination, the main parts of the cave and its rock art have been meticulously reproduced nearby. This "Lascaux II" is the one now shown to visitors.

Chemical zones in air-filled caves

After a cave passage has been abandoned by the water that formed it, the character of the passage gradually adjusts to spatial variations in the type of infiltrating water. The resulting zonation makes it possible to interpret the nature of local water sources, as well as changes that have taken place with time (Figures 12.51–12.52). The basic concepts are introduced in Chapter 5 and earlier in this chapter, so only a brief outline is given here. Other types of chemi-cal zonation might be envisioned, but this is the most common.

Passages overlain by insoluble, low-permeability beds are likely to receive only sparse capillary seepage. Speleothems are limited

to evaporative minerals, and gypsum crusts are the most abundant deposits. Toward the eroded edge of the insoluble cap, the chemistry of infiltrating water is zoned as follows.

Zone 1: Evaporative minerals are tightly bonded to the bedrock surfaces on which they grow. Water enters the cave at such a low rate that there is no observable water film. Evaporation consumes nearly all the moisture. Gypsum and other evaporite minerals precipitate. Gypsum can replace carbonate rock in the crust. Replacement is enhanced by the rapid decrease in CO_3^{2-} in the cave wall if the water is able to absorb CO_2 from the cave atmosphere (page 335). Gypsum growth along fractures disrupts the bedrock surface by wedging of rock fragments and cementing the dislodged fragments in place (Figures 12.45–12.46).

Zone 2: Capillary seepage makes the walls moist enough that gypsum and other evaporative mineral deposits cannot form. As this zone encroaches on zone 1, the evaporative minerals drop off the ceiling and walls.

Zone 3: Capillary water fed by infiltration through the sandstone cap-rock reaches calcite saturation in a closed system, which nearly depletes the CO_2 content. Where the water enters the cave it absorbs CO_2 from the cave atmosphere and becomes aggressive once more. It forms only a microscopic film of moisture on the walls and is only able to etch and recrystallize the bedrock surfaces (Figure 12.23). The crystal size becomes smaller and a white weathering rind forms. Quartz and opal precipitate in places because of the sudden drop in pH. Oxidation of organic materials in the rock helps to account for the light color of the weathering rind. Conditions are too moist for gypsum and other evaporative minerals to form.

Zone 4: Water similar to that of zone 3 enters the cave as diffuse seepage but has enough flow to form etched surfaces and rills in the cave walls below the input points (Figure 12.18).

Zone 5: Water infiltrates through the sandstone cap-rock and concentrates as active drips and flows that stay

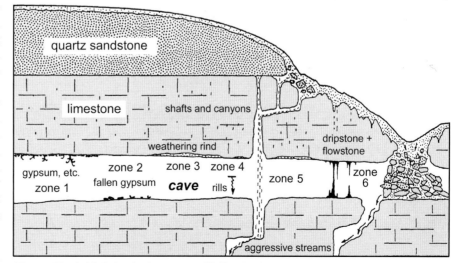

Figure 12.51: Variation in the nature of infiltration into a sandstone-capped cave, such as those in the karst plateaus of east-central U.S., and the resulting effects on the cave. See text for zone descriptions. (From Palmer and Palmer, 1995b.)

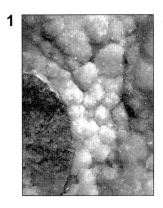
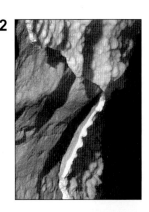
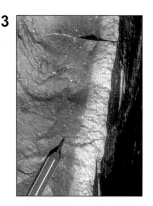
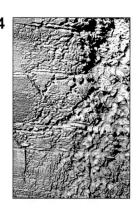

Figure 12.52: Variations in passage character caused by the nature of seepage water, as shown in Figure 12.51.

Zone 1: growth of highly soluble evaporative minerals. Width = 15 cm.

Zone 2: increasing moisture causes evaporative minerals to fall. Width = 50 cm.

Zone 3: weathering rinds develop.

Zone 4: water absorbs CO_2 from the cave air and produces rills on walls. Width = 15 cm.

Zone 5: aggressive water entering through a thin insoluble cap forms solution passages.

Zone 6: seepage through soil-covered carbonate rock deposits dripstone and flowstone (width = 3 m). Larger flows produce solution passages.

aggressive over their entire paths through the cave. The sandy soil has a P_{CO_2} about half as great as in zone 6, where the sandstone cap has been removed by erosion, but in zone 5 the water reaches the cave with little or no dissolved carbonate. No solutional capacity is lost at the soil-bedrock contact, and so dissolution is expended mainly on cave development. Shafts and canyons are typical in the upstream portions.

Zone 6: Water infiltrates through soil-covered limestone and reaches equilibrium with dissolved calcite at the same high CO_2 values as those of the soil. Water loses much CO_2 when it enters the cave, and calcite is forced to precipitate as speleothems. This is typical of small flows and drips. Larger flows fed by sinkholes generally remain aggressive and produce solution passages.

Boundaries between zones migrate with time as the edge of the cap-rock retreats by erosion. In general, formerly dry passages become wetter with time. As moisture levels increase, evaporative minerals begin to lose their grip

on the bedrock and peel away. Bare walls and a litter of gypsum fragments on the floor indicate that the passage has become wetter with time, even if moisture is not readily visible. Dripstone and flowstone that line the walls of shafts are typical where the former edge of a sandstone cap has been eroded so that it no longer lies overhead. On the other hand, passages may get drier because of changes in topography, climate, or vegetal growth at the surface. Many of these changes are recorded as alternating episodes of deposition and corrosion. See White (1988) for additional comments.

Explorers intuitively recognize this zonation and what it means, even if they have no geological background. As they pass from one zone to another, they learn to anticipate the changes that lie ahead. Gradual drying of a passage may signal the beginning of a long uninterrupted section protected by a thick insoluble cap. A slight increase in moisture may indicate a nearby junction with canyons and shafts, or perhaps terminal breakdown.

13

Caves and time

CAVE DEVELOPMENT is slow compared to a human lifespan but fast by geologic standards. Once a cave has formed, it can persist for a long time and provide useful clues to the regional geologic and climatic history. To decipher these clues it is necessary to see where caves fit into the geologic time scale (Figure 2.1).

Because caves are voids, it is often difficult to determine their precise ages. The problem is "to date what isn't there" (Sasowsky, 1998). Moreover, a cave evolves with time and is not the product of a single event. One approach is to relate the cave origin to other geologic events whose ages are already known. Another is to date the deposits in caves, although this technique gives only a minimum age for the cave passages themselves.

Relative and numerical ages

Relative ages reveal a sequence of events without reference to actual dates. They are usually determined by the physical relationships among geologic features. For example, the sediment in a cave must be younger (more recent) than the cave itself. A combination of simple observations of this kind can unravel some very complex relationships.

Numerical ages are estimates of actual dates, which are acquired from laboratory analysis of rocks, minerals, or sediments. Determination of numerical ages is commonly called "absolute" age dating, but this term is less appropriate because the dates cannot be measured with pinpoint accuracy. Dating techniques are constantly being refined to obtain more accurate estimates. This slight uncertainty leads some people to dismiss the entire procedure. But any kind of measurement involves some uncertainty, however minor. It does not mean that the measurement is wrong.

First it is essential to establish a framework of relative ages, so the absolute dates can be inserted into the overall picture. Two principles are used as guidelines: superposition and cross-cutting relationships.

Superposition means that in a sequence of deposits the age decreases upward. The oldest is on the bottom and the youngest is on top. This seemingly trivial rule is more complex and useful that it might appear. As an example, the origin of a given cave must predate the sediment in it. The sediment lies on the passage floor. Speleothems may be deposited over the sediment in places, but some later sediment may be incorporated as layers within the speleothems and other layers may overlie the speleothems.

Cross-cutting is equally simple: if one feature cuts across another, the one that does the cutting is more recent. Some examples in caves include the intersection of one passage by another, erosional entrenchment of sediment, and fracturing of speleothems by ice wedging.

Relative and numerical dating should be combined for maximum effect. An example comes from the Italian Alps near Verona, where limestone caves at two different elevations were filled with basaltic lava (Rossi and Zorzin, 1986). The lava is clearly younger than the caves. The lava metamorphosed the limestone around the caves, adding further proof of their relative ages. Much of the lava was later removed by erosion when stream passages intersected the original caves. Walls of the intersecting passages are not metamorphosed. With the aid of radioactive elements in the rock, the lava in the upper cave was dated at 38 million years old, and in the lower cave it was dated at 33 million years. In each cave the original passages are clearly older than the absolute age of the lava inside them, while the passages that intersect the lava are younger. But from this information it is not certain whether the two original caves are the same age. Perhaps the lower cave was not there when the upper cave was filled with lava, or it too would have been filled with the older lava. Is this a valid assumption? What kind of field evidence would prove or disprove the point?

Determining cave ages

The most popular quantitative techniques for dating caves are briefly described here. For further details, refer to White (1988), Ford and Williams (1989), Ford (1997), and Onac (2000).

The most reliable method for dating geologic materials is to examine the decay of unstable elements (radionuclides) within them. Their rate of decay can be measured in the laboratory, and the age of the material can be calculated by measuring the activity ratio of the original element to the daughter element produced by the decay (while eliminating those that were there originally).

Carbon-14 dating

Carbon is a major ingredient in organic material and carbonate minerals. Carbon-12 (^{12}C) is the most common carbon isotope. Isotopes are varieties of an element that differ in atomic mass (pages 127–131). ^{12}C has an atomic mass of 12. ^{14}C is an unstable isotope formed by cosmic radiation. It decays to ^{14}N (nitrogen-14) and requires about 5730 years for half of any given mass of ^{14}C to do so. Thus the *half-life* for ^{14}C is 5730 years. After two half-lives only 1/4 of the original quantity is left, and so forth (Figure 13.1). This method is well suited to dating organic materials such as bones and wood. It is a potent tool for archeologists and paleontologists, but it is of little use in dating most solution caves because its applicable time range is too small (generally no more than about 50,000 years), and because the original ^{14}C concentration in speleothems and sediments is difficult to determine. The ^{14}C method is

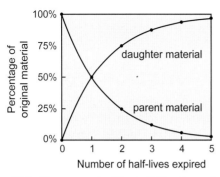

Figure 13.1: The concept of the half-life of a radioactive substance, and how it is used to determine the age of the host material. The graph applies to all radioactive materials, but the length of the half-life depends on the type of material involved.

well suited to dating most lava caves, because remnants of vegetation encased by the lava can be dated. Most lava caves are the same age as the lava around them.

Uranium-thorium dating

Uranium is a radioactive element with various isotopes that decay in several steps and at different rates. For cave dating the most important reaction is the decay of ^{234}U to ^{230}Th (thorium), with a half-life of 248,000 years. Uranium is present in small quantities in most shallow groundwater. It therefore occurs in trace amounts in most calcite speleothems. Thorium forms nearly insoluble compounds, so it is not carried or deposited by infiltrating water. Speleothems, particularly non-porous dripstone, can be dated as long as they contain sufficient amounts of original uranium (at least 0.1 ppm) and have no original thorium-bearing impurities. The $^{230}Th/^{234}U$ ratio indicates the age of the speleothem (Harmon and others, 1975; Thompson and others, 1976). Recrystallization of the speleothem destroys the relationship. Because the concentrations are so small, the technique is limited to ages up to about 350,000–600,000 years, depending on the analytical method. There is extensive literature on U/Th dating of speleothems, and pertinent references are given by Ford (1997) and Baker and others (1998).

Uranium-lead dating

The decay of ^{238}U to ^{206}Pb (lead) can be used for dating older calcite deposits if the original Pb concentration can be ascertained. ^{238}U has a half-life of 4.47 billion years, so under ideal conditions this method is suitable for very old samples. Unfortunately, old cave minerals rarely provide data of high enough quality to give reliable dates. Because lead is a contaminant in many speleothems, it is necessary to analyze several samples having widely differing uranium content to determine the background lead value (Ludwig, 1977; Richards and others, 1996). Lundberg and others (2000) used this technique to date Mesozoic calcite deposits in a cave in the Guadalupe Mountains, New Mexico, to 91.3 million years (±7.8 million years).

Argon dating

The mineral alunite $(KAl_3(SO_4)_2(OH)_6)$ is a byproduct of the weathering of clay by sulfuric acid. Many caves formed by this acid contain small quantities of alunite in solution pockets (Figure 12.33). Therefore, dating of this mineral can provide the actual date of cave origin, or at least of its latest phase of enlargement by sulfuric acid. Most alunite in caves is produced just above the water table, where low pH can be maintained while sulfuric acid is generated by oxidation of hydrogen sulfide in moisture that is shielded from the local limestone (page 339). Radioactive decay of ^{40}K (potassium) in alunite produces ^{40}Ar (argon), which remains trapped in the mineral, and the $^{40}K/^{40}Ar$ activity ratio can be used to determine the age of the sample. The half-life of ^{40}K is about 1.3 billion years, so the method can be applied to caves with a broad range of ages. This method, and the related $^{40}Ar/^{39}Ar$ method, were first applied to cave origin by Polyak and others (1998) for caves in the Guadalupe Mountains, New Mexico (see page 360).

Cosmogenic radionuclides

Cosmogenic radionuclides are radioactive elements produced by solar radiation. They allow quartz-rich sediments in caves to be dated up to about 5 million years (Granger and Fabel, 2005; Anthony and Granger, 2006). This is an important age range, because it spans the developmental history of most caves. The method also relies on a very common type of cave sediment, so the sampling has little impact on the cave.

Quartz sand and gravel, when exposed to cosmic rays at the Earth's surface, acquire trace amounts of the radioactive isotopes ^{26}Al and ^{10}Be (aluminum and beryllium) in a ratio of 6 to 1. If these grains are later shielded from cosmic rays by being transported into caves, the two isotopes are no longer generated and they decay from their original values, each at a different rate, toward smaller $^{26}Al/^{10}Be$ ratios. From this ratio it is possible to determine the time since the grains were last exposed at the surface (Figures 13.2–13.3). The technique also applies to surface sediment that has been

Figure 13.2: Particle accelerator at Purdue University, Indiana, used to determine isotopic compositions of samples.

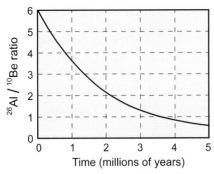

Figure 13.3: Relative decay rates of ^{26}Al and ^{10}Be in quartz-rich sediment samples. From the ratio of the two isotopes, the time since the sediment was carried underground can be determined. (In detail the procedure is more complex.) See Granger and others (2001); Anthony and Granger (2004, 2006). Recent re-calibration of the ^{10}Be decay rate suggests that the ages shown here should be multiplied by about 1.14. At present there is no consensus on this point.

buried to a depth of at least 10 m. The uncertainty is about 5–20%, depending on the nature of the field data.

Granger and others (1997) used ^{26}Al/^{10}Be ratios in cave sediments to date the erosion of the New River Gorge in the Appalachian Mountains. This technique has also been used to date sediments in the plateaus of Kentucky and Tennessee (Granger and others, 2001; Anthony and Granger, 2004), which allows erosional and depositional events to be correlated across large parts of the eastern U.S.

Stock and others (2006) have applied ^{26}Al/^{10}Be dating to volcanic ash deposits carried into caves of the Bighorn Basin, Wyoming, during volcanic eruptions. The dating of volcanic ash is known as **_tephrochronology_**. Deposits from a given volcanic eruption are all of the same age, and they serve as a uniform time reference.

Interpretation of sediment burial ages requires a clear under-standing of cave origin and development. The usual interpretation is that the sediment represents the last active stream flow through the passage in which it is located. But sediments may accumulate as thick deposits at the surface before they are carried into a cave, so their shielding from cosmic rays may pre-date their subterranean journey. Sediments can also be carried from upper levels into lower levels, which may cause the age of the lower passages to be overestimated. Young sediment can be washed into older passages, so the sediment date may underestimate the age of the passages. For example, a rise in base level can cause ancient passages to be filled with deposits of young sediment. Some passages at the same level may have widely different dates because the passages were abandoned by their flow at different times. This is common where certain cave streams are perched on resistant beds and remain active long after their contemporaries have lost their flow.

In the early 2000s the decay rate of ^{10}Be was recalibrated from laboratory measurements. The results suggest that the dates shown in Figure 13.3 should be multiplied by about 1.14 (see Anthony and Granger, 2004). If publications include no mention of this point, their data may need to be adjusted.

Electron-spin resonance

As calcite is bombarded with natural radiation from various sources, a few electrons are knocked from their original locations in the crystal structure and lodge elsewhere within the calcite. The rate at which this takes place depends on the average background radiation at the site. Eventually a steady state is reached where the sites of electron trapping degenerate as fast as they are formed. Until that time, the age of the calcite can be estimated by comparing the total concentration of displaced electrons to the average strength of the radioactivity (Ikeya, 1975). This can be done in calcite by electron-spin resonance (ESR), which relies on the ability of displaced electrons to absorb microwave radiation. Background radiation is determined by measuring the concentrations of nearby radioactive materials and adjusting for cosmic radiation. The technique can be used to determine ages up to about a million years, but the accuracy is low, especially in old samples.

Paleomagnetism

When a rock crystallizes, or sediment is deposited, any iron minerals in it tend to align statistically with the orientation of the Earth's magnetic field. Over long periods of time, the Earth's field shifts and periodically reverses (Figure 13.4). Although this changes the orientation of the magnetism induced in the iron-rich material by the present Earth's field, some of the original magnetism is retained with its original orientation. This residual amount is called **_paleomagnetism_**, or, more technically, **_remanent magnetism_** (note spelling). Remanent magnetism in sediments may increase soon after deposition by microbial concentration of iron compounds.

In caves, undisturbed and carefully oriented samples of detrital sediment are obtained by sliding them into small plastic containers while the surrounding material is sliced away (Figure 13.5). In the laboratory the samples are rotated and their magnetism is measured. The induced field in each spinning sample remains oriented along the Earth's field, but the remanent magnetism rotates with the sample. This indicates the orientation of the Earth's field at the time the sediment was deposited.

The most recent polarity reversal took place about 783,000 years ago. Therefore, if a cave contains sediments with reversed magnetic polarity, the cave must be

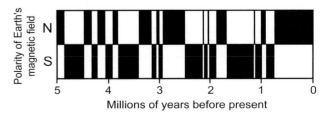

Figure 13.4: Changes in polarity of the Earth's magnetic field over the past 5 million years. Today's polarity is arbitrarily considered to be northward. The field has reversed periodically in the past. The most recent polarity shift was about 783,000 years ago, from south to north. Based on data from Cande and Kent (1992); see also Sasowsky (2005).

Figure 13.5: A geologist from the Minnesota Geological Survey obtains samples of laminated silt and clay from Mystery Cave, Minnesota, for paleomagnetic analysis.

older than that. Many older magnetic reversals have also been documented (Figure 13.4), but extension of the paleomagnetic technique to these events requires continuous and undisturbed sediments, which are rare in caves. It is easy to miss a polarity reversal where sediments are poorly exposed or have been removed by erosion. Paleomagnetic analysis of a sample provides a range of possible ages, rather than a single absolute age.

The first large-scale paleomagnetic cave study was by Schmidt (1982), who examined sediments from various levels in Mammoth Cave, Kentucky. He found several reversals over the vertical range of the cave, giving the first quantitative evidence that the uppermost passages are older than a million years. Pease and others (1994) correlated the Mammoth Cave data with measurements in caves in southern Indiana. Sasowsky and others (1995) used paleomagnetic data from cave sediments to estimate the rate of entrenchment of the Obey River Gorge in Tennessee. In the Cheat River Gorge of northern West Virginia, Springer and others (1997) combined paleomagnetic measurements with sedimentary and geomorphic data to estimate the range of error when using cave sediments as indicators of former base levels. Paleomagnetism can also be measured in many calcite speleothems (Latham and others, 1979), and if they can also be dated radiometrically, the history of magnetic variations can be calibrated. A summary of paleomagnetic techniques and their application to caves is given by Sasowsky (2005).

Use of fossils for dating

Fossil identification can be used to obtain approximate ages for sedimentary deposits. Each species originated at a certain time in Earth's history, and most have also become extinct at certain times. Those with the narrowest time ranges are the most useful for dating purposes. The numerical age of a fossil is usually determined by dating the rocks that contain it, or less commonly, by dating the

fossil itself. Then when the same species of fossil is found elsewhere, it is fairly certain that it, and its host strata, fall within the same time range. Fossils are common in the bedrock that is exposed in caves, but they tell little about the ages of the caves themselves. Some caves contain fossil bones, tracks, shells, etc. (Chapter 6), but they are rarely old enough to provide information about the caves' developmental history. Instead, they give a faithful record of environmental conditions after the caves formed.

Interpreting cave ages from rates of geologic processes

The processes that form solution caves operate at rates that are controlled by local chemistry and hydrology. Measurements of present conditions, accompanied by assumptions about those in the past, can provide rough estimates of how long it has taken to form certain caves or cave deposits (Gunn, 2004c). This approach works well in karst, because the processes are easily quantified. The major limitation is that geologic processes do not follow a fixed timetable. One must obtain chemical field data for many years to obtain valid estimates of dissolution and deposition rates, and the results have to be expressed as statistical probabilities rather than fixed values. Rates of geologic processes are affected by long-term changes in climate, hydrology, and geologic setting. When current rates are projected into the past, the resulting age estimates must be corroborated by other lines of evidence.

Direct measurements of cave enlargement can be made with micro-erosion meters, which are dial micrometers mounted on bolts placed in surface bedrock or in active cave streams (Figure 7.7). The bolts are left in place and the micrometers are screwed into them periodically, usually once a year, to measure the amount of bedrock retreat. Measured rates of limestone dissolution are as much as 0.05–0.1 cm/yr in the beds of cave streams fed by direct surface runoff (High, 1970; Coward, 1975). See Ford and Williams (1989) for a selection of measured rates in karst.

The ***mass balance*** can also be used to estimate rates of dissolution or deposition. This approach uses measurements of average discharge and changes in dissolved load from place to place to solve Eqs. 7.1–7.3 (page 177). One of the earliest of these studies was made in Polnagollum Cave, Ireland, which is fed by highly aggressive sinking streams (Smith and others, 1969). In the main stream passage they estimated the rate of bedrock retreat to be about 0.18 cm/yr.

Kinetic equations can also be used to estimate rates of bedrock dissolution. This approach is described in Chapter 7. For example, Groves and Meiman (1996, 2005) and Anthony (1998) determined saturation indices and rates of mass removal in the main river passage of Mammoth Cave, Kentucky. The water is most aggressive during major floods and is supersaturated during low flow (Anthony and Groves, 1997). Passage growth rate is uncertain because of thick sediment at the main monitoring site. In New York State, measurements of chemical equilibria in the main stream canyon of McFail's Cave have been applied to experimental

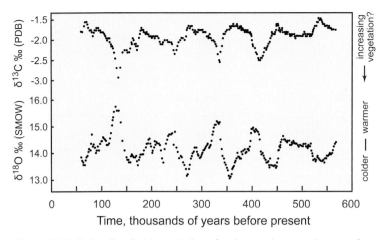

Figure 13.6: Paleoclimatic interpretation of carbon and oxygen isotopes from a calcite wall crust in Devil's Hole, Nevada (from Coplen and others, 1994).

rate equations such as Eq. 7.4 (Palmer, 1996, 2007). The mean entrenchment rate is estimated to be only 0.001–0.003 cm/yr. During low flow (most of the year) the stream is so supersaturated that it occasionally precipitates calcite because of loss of CO_2 from nearby entrances (Figure 7.26). During most years these accumulations are entirely removed by aggressive flow during spring runoff.

Studies of past climates

Climate change is a volatile topic in the news today because of the prospect of global warming. Prediction of future trends is aided by knowing past climatic history, and caves are among the richest sources of this information. Their patterns indicate former conditions of water flow and the erosional-depositional history of the surrounding region, all of which are in turn affected by climatic factors. But the best sources of paleoclimatic data are cave deposits (White 2004a; Onac and others, 2006).

Oxygen isotopes from cores of sea-floor sediment are the most commonly used standards for determining past variation in global temperature. Calcite speleothems can also provide considerable detail about past climates, especially during the past half million years, and they can also be dated to provide a fairly exact climatic history. Furthermore, the information is specific to the actual measurement sites and is more useful for determining geographic trends than the global averages from marine data.

The most successful method for estimating past temperatures from speleothems is to measure their oxygen-isotope ratios, $\delta^{18}O$ (Chapter 5). These values decrease as the temperature rises, so the mean-annual temperature at the time of deposition can be approximated (Hendy and Wilson, 1968). Further information is given by Harmon and others (1977), Gascoyne and others (1981), Ford and Williams (1989), Winograd and others (1992), Gascoyne (1992), Lauritzen (1996), and Shopov (2004). It is often not possible to determine exact temperatures, but only warming or cooling trends (Schwarcz, 1986), although isotopic measurements of fluid inclusions and of present-day dripwaters can provide

a rough calibration. Dripstone, flowstone, and pool linings are best for paleoclimate studies because they consist of successive layers that can provide a nearly continuous range of radiomentric dates. Stalagmites are most useful because their growth is easily related to drip rates and water chemistry.

Variations in carbon isotopes help to determine the types of vegetation at different times. Values of $\delta^{13}C$ in deposits derived from the CO_2 in forest soils are about 7‰ lighter than those from grasslands (Dorale and others, 1992, 1998). Caran and others (1995) describe methods for distinguishing between carbon from organic sources and those from carbonate sediments.

A 120,000-year paleoclimate record has been determined from isotopic analysis of a calcite wall crust in Devil's Hole, Nevada, by the U.S. Geological Survey (Winograd and Szabo, 1988; Winograd and others, 1992; Coplen and others, 1994; Szabo and others, 1994). The oxygen-isotope record shows cyclic warming and cooling, with corresponding variations in carbon isotopes that suggest changes in vegetal cover (Figure 13.6). The cave itself is thought to be a tectonic fissure, owing to its highly parallel walls, orientation parallel to major fault trends, and lack of differential solution (Riggs and others, 1994).

Van Beynen and others (2004) used analysis of oxygen isotopes of a stalagmite, combined with U/Th dating, to show that 7000–7600 years ago the climate in New York State was wetter and roughly 5°C warmer than today, and that except for a brief warm interlude 2500 years ago the climate has been cooling steadily ever since. Forest cover peaked around 7000 years ago, as shown by a sharp dip in $\delta^{13}C$, and has been thinning ever since. This level of detail is difficult to obtain by other paleoclimatic methods. Still, this represents long-term averages and does not relate to current short-term predictions.

Fluid inclusions in speleothems can indicate the nature and sometimes the temperature of the original water that deposited them (Hendy, 1971; Schwarcz and others, 1976; Harmon and others, 1979; Yonge, 1981). Openings that contain water are usually small, often only about 0.1–1 mm long. A sample is crushed to obtain the trapped water, which is then analyzed. This provides information on the chemistry of the original infiltrating water. Its isotopic composition can be used to interpret cave temperatures at the time of deposition, which are usually assumed to be the mean-annual surface temperature (Dennis and others, 2001). In speleothems younger than about a million years, fluid inclusions usually retain their original isotopic character. With greater age, fluid inclusions are unreliable because of leakage into or out of the voids.

Some calcite speleothems contain organic matter that luminesces with an intensity that varies between annual layers (Shopov and others, 1994; Genty and Quinif, 1996; Shopov, 2006). The intensity of luminescence also seems to correlate with sunspot variations, probably because of the influence of solar activity on plant growth.

Changes in the nature of speleothems can indicate variations in the availability of moisture. As described in Chapter 10, some speleothems form only where there is an abundant water supply, others where water movement is controlled by capillarity, and still others where mineral deposition is controlled by evaporation. Alternation between dissolution and precipitation can also indicate wet-dry cycles (Figures 10.81–10.82). Measurements by Lauritzen and Onac (1995) suggest that the greatest rates of calcite speleothem growth have occurred during either warm interglacial periods or when the climate was cool and wet, but not while the region was undergoing active glaciation.

A change from calcite to aragonite deposition can be triggered by variations in the Mg/Ca ratio in dripwater (Chapter 10). Aragonite forms in preference to calcite when the Mg/Ca ratio is high (see page 272). The threshold Mg/Ca, above which aragonite is the stable mineral, increases from about 0.25 at 25°C to about 5 at 6°C (Morse and others, 1997). A high Mg/Ca ratio is generally produced by evaporation. Much of this enrichment takes place in soil that overlies dolomite or Mg-rich limestones. During rainy periods, water infiltrates into the soil and dissolves these rocks. During dry periods, the remaining moisture is drawn back to the surface and evaporates, so that calcite and aragonite are forced to precipitate. This depletes the Ca in any remaining moisture but leaves the Mg in solution. When infiltrating water eventually reaches underlying caves, the Mg/Ca ratios can be well above the threshold needed to deposit aragonite. Thus a variation between calcite and aragonite in speleothems may help to distinguish between relatively wet and dry episodes in the past, and possibly also warm and cold periods.

Cave sediments also provide evidence for past environmental and climatic conditions (Springer and others, 1997; Onac, 2000; Sasowsky and Mylroie, 2004). Their full potential has not yet been reached because it is difficult to obtain long-term continuous sequences of sedimentary strata in caves and to correlate them between caves.

Caves through the ages

Caves offer a wealth of information about geologic events that have occurred around them. They are like the "black box" flight recorders on an airplane, filled with clues about the past, some explicit and some very cryptic.

The dry upper-level passages of a cave tend to hide their great antiquity, because they may not look at all old. In such caves, delicate features can remain essentially unchanged for millions of years. It is a haunting experience to view the paintings made by ancient humans tens of thousands of years ago in European caves. They look so full of life that one almost expects the artists to step out of the shadows at any moment. Some caves have intersected paleokarst features hundreds of millions of years old.

Figure 13.7: Paleo-sinkhole of late Mississippian age, later filled by Pennsylvanian sands and clays (Black Hills, South Dakota).

The oldest caves and their relation to paleokarst

Paleokarst consists of karst that has been buried and preserved by younger overlying sediments, sedimentary rocks, or lava (Chapter 2). The karst zones themselves have had a variety of origins. Most were formed by simple dissolution of carbonate rocks by shallow meteoric water. Some were produced by the dissolution of interbedded sulfate rocks, or by the chemical interaction between carbonate and sulfate rocks. A few are the result of deep-seated processes.

Paleokarst generally includes the remains of both caves and surface karst features (Figure 13.7). Burial of a karst surface by continental deposits such as wind-blown sand, river-deposited deltaic sediments, or lava tend to preserve karst surfaces more or less intact. Burial by marine sediments is usually preceded by wave erosion along the encroaching coast, so what remains of the original karst may be limited to isolated fragments. It is common for paleokarst surfaces to grade laterally from place to place into simple erosional unconformities that show no evidence for karst, even though the rock type is favorable. Where it is absent, either the karst was obliterated by erosion or the environmental conditions were so unfavorable that it did not form at all.

If solution features are well preserved, the process that formed them should be fairly clear. Filled fissures, sinkholes, and most shallow caves are characteristic of dissolution by meteoric water. Epikarst features diminish in size and number with depth below the erosion surface. Former surface features may contain remnants of soil, and the caves may contain stream-borne detrital sediment that contrasts with the younger deposits that buried the karst surface. If cave patterns can be distinguished, it may be possible to interpret the original topography and hydrology. For example, simple stream conduits and branching patterns are typical of caves formed by recharge from a karst surface, and irregular interconnected rooms are typical of caves formed by the mixing of waters of contrasting chemistry, or by hypogenic processes (see Chapters 8 and 9 for details).

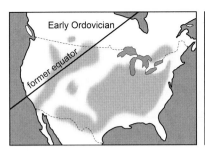 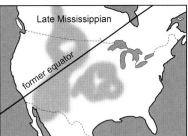

Figure 13.8: Extent of the two major paleokarst zones in North America. Left = early Ordovician paleokarst; right = late Mississippian paleokarst. Boundaries are very approximate, because in many places the paleokarst has been eroded away or deeply buried. (From M. Palmer and A. Palmer, 1989; Ford, 1989b; and Bosák, 1989).

Interpretations of paleokarst should take into account the fact that the latitude and climate may have been quite different from today (as in Figure 13.8). Ancient karst may have formed when surface vegetation and carbon dioxide levels were much less than today. Karst could form under those conditions, but perhaps at a reduced rate. Most paleokarst surfaces contain remnants of the original soil, known as ***paleosol*** (note spelling). Paleosols are typically brown, granular, and irregular (Figure 3.10). They provide helpful information concerning former climates.

If sinkholes and surface fissures are buried by later sediments, the sedimentary beds tend to subside in U-shaped patterns as they are compacted by overlying strata. Although former surface depressions in paleokarst are almost invariably filled completely with the overlying sediment or rock, some caves may be only partly filled or escape filling entirely. Brown detrital sediments are typical of active caves, but with deep burial in the presence of reducing agents such as organic carbon, some may be converted to black, green, or gray.

When breakdown takes place in an open cave passage, the fragments move almost exclusively downward by gravity. In size and shape they are adjusted to the thickness and competence of the bedding. Thin beds tend to break into slab-shaped fragments, whereas massive beds break into large, more equidimensional blocks. In addition, either type of bed can split into tiny chips by weathering or by the wedging action of evaporative mineral growth. Fragmentation during deep burial can also produce small chips.

These breakdown patterns are quite different from the fragmentation caused by the dissolution, movement, and recrystallization of interbedded evaporite rocks such as gypsum. These processes tend to leave broad irregular surfaces or stratigraphic zones overlain with breccia. Breccia bodies produced by recrystallization of sulfate beds (gypsum or anhydrite) typically form a chaotic jumble of angular fragments of varied size and shape, which includes blocks that have been wedged upward against gravity (Figure 3.27). The fragments rarely move far, so their original fit can usually be deciphered, as in a puzzle. Fragments range from partly rounded to angular, depending on whether the bedrock was

soft and poorly consolidated prior to collapse, or had hardened to a dense, compact material (compare Figures 2.36 and 13.12). The role of sulfates in the development of certain paleokarst and breccia zones can easily be overlooked where the sulfates are no longer present. The highly soluble gypsum and anhydrite are easily removed by dissolution, so their impact on surrounding carbonate rocks can be obscured.

Breccias can also be produced by stress from tectonic activity. These tend to be elongate in map view, tens of kilometers or more in length, and parallel to fault zones. They typically show concurrent or later alteration by thermal fluids (Mazzullo and Harris, 1991; Furman, 1993). Many of them cross paleokarst unconformities into the overlying strata and are clearly not the result of paleokarst alone.

To recognize paleokarst and related caves, it is helpful to demonstrate that they are out of adjustment with the present geology and hydrology. One problem is that many paleokarst features have been reactivated and may be difficult to distinguish from modern karst. Filling of karst voids by minerals or compact sediment is a helpful indication of former paleokarst. A suspected paleokarst must be compatible with the regional geologic history in which it originally formed. For example, paleokarst that formed at the surface usually correlates with unconformities on insoluble rock. Identification of ancient karst is most difficult where it originated at great depth by hypogenic processes. Its relation to the surface is obscure, and it is difficult to fix the dates at which subsurface processes begin and end. The best way to identify paleokarst is to date the deposits within it.

It can be difficult in some areas to reconstruct the nature of the original karst. Features in shallow caves are rarely preserved intact. Speleothems may survive only as corroded or fragmented remnants. When deeply buried, karst features are exposed to shattering, alteration, and mineral deposition under high pressures and temperatures. The result may bear little resemblance to the original karst.

The world's oldest known paleokarst is in the Transvaal of South Africa. It dates from the Precambrian Era, about 2.3 billion years ago (Martini, 1981; see geologic time scale, Figure 2.1). It contains caves and sinkholes in dolomite, but they are completely filled with sediment, so it is impossible to examine them from the inside.

In general, Precambrian caves have either collapsed or been filled. A few contain metal sulfide ores rich enough to be mined (Olson, 1984; Ford, 1986). Some open caves have been found in Precambrian paleokarst, but most were apparently once filled by sediment and later exhumed by erosion. The majority of caves in Precambrian rock were formed long after the rock itself and are not necessarily very old themselves. An example is shown in Figure 2.42.

From K-Ar dating and other methods, Osborne and others (2006) determined that clays and other minerals in the Jenolan Caves of Australia are up to 394 million years old. These minerals appear to have formed in the caves and were not transported in. If so, these are some of the world's oldest humanly traversable caves.

Fossils in paleokarst sediment can be used to date the deposits (Horáček and Kordos, 1989). The most spectacular fossil discovery in paleokarst was in 1878 in Bernissart, Belgium, when dozens of *Iguanodon* dinosaur skeletons were encountered by coal miners in a sediment-filled solution shaft (Quinif, 1989). The shaft is more than 80 m in diameter and of unknown depth. The host rock is Carboniferous, but the pit is a paleokarst feature of early Cretaceous age, more than 100 million years old but 200 million years younger than the bedrock. Drilling showed that the pit reached a depth of more than 1000 m and was probably the result of gradual collapse into underlying voids. The pit had been filled with breccia and detrital sediment cemented with calcite. The bones were located in shaly interbeds. When using fossils to date karst, it is important to verify that they have not been carried into caves from erosion of deposits elsewhere. In the Belgian example the bones were clearly contemporary with the sediment.

For further information on paleokarst and its interpretation, see James and Choquette (1988), Bosák and others (1989), and Osborne (2005a).

Paleokarst of North America

There are two widespread paleokarst zones in North America, one of early Ordovician age and another of late Mississippian age (see geologic time scale, Figure 2.1). Their approximate distributions are shown in Figure 13.8. Boundaries on the map are purposely vague because the exact distribution of the paleokarst is uncertain. In many places it has been removed by erosion or is deeply buried. Also, there is some controversy as to whether certain features, such as breccias, are entirely of karst origin. Paleomagnetic measurements show that North America was located along the equator during both the Ordovician and Mississippian, and the continent was rotated clockwise about 45 degrees relative to the present equator.

The older paleokarst (early Ordovician) formed about 490 million years ago and extends into limestones and dolomites of late Cambrian and early Ordovician age. It was buried by middle Ordovician strata, which are also mostly carbonate rocks. This paleokarst is economically important because it is the host for extensive ore deposits and petroleum reservoirs. Mineral-lined voids are commonly encountered in mines and drill holes in the southeastern and central U.S. This paleokarst contains few large caves, and they are mainly sediment-filled. In some oilfields of the southwest this paleokarst consists of brecciated carbonate rocks with intervening crystal-lined voids. Some breccias appear to have formed by the collapse of caves, where the walls have fractured under intense burial pressure thousands of meters below the surface (Loucks,

1999). Certain breccias may instead have been produced by deep faulting (Mazzullo and Harris, 1991; Katz and others, 2006).

The younger paleokarst (late Mississippian) dates from about 320 million years ago. This surface was buried by late Mississippian and early Pennsylvanian rocks consisting mainly of sandstone and shale. It is nearly as extensive as the Ordovician paleokarst and is more widely exposed at the surface, especially in the Rocky Mountains. Mississippian plant cover was more extensive than that of the Ordovician, so soil thickness and carbon dioxide levels were probably also greater. This may help to account for the fact that Mississippian caves and surface karst are better developed than those of the earlier paleokarst.

Many Mississippian caves survived more or less intact, and although most are filled with sediment, some have survived with little or no filling. Throughout much of the western U.S., cliffs of Mississippian limestone are pocked by caves that survived the weight of burial beneath as much as 1000–2000 m of younger rocks. Caves are fairly resistant to such pressures because the stress is distributed throughout the surrounding rock. Most of these caves have vaulted cross sections up to 10 m in diameter. Most of them can be explored only a few tens of meters before they terminate in sediment fill or bedrock walls. Some that have been intersected by later caves can be followed for several hundred meters.

Less extensive paleokarst is present between various stratigraphic units throughout North America. For example, a local but significant paleokarst in the Permian rocks of New Mexico consists of fracture-oriented voids, breccia dikes, and minor caves, all lined by prominent calcite spar. This paleokarst, and later solution features guided by it, have been used to help decipher the tectonic and sedimentary history of the Guadalupe Mountains (Koša and Hunt, 2006). Much of the later cave development in the Guadalupe Mountains follows these early paleokarst trends perpendicular and parallel to the reef front that defines the southeastern boundary of the mountains (see Figure 8.66).

Caves of the Black Hills: A complex story

Among the oldest caves in North America are those in the Black Hills of South Dakota and nearby mountain ranges of the Northern Rockies. They include Wind Cave and Jewel Cave, which are some of the world's longest and most complex caves (Figures 13.9 and 2.51). Over the past century they have been interpreted in several different ways. Suggestions for the source of dissolution include artesian flow, rising thermal water, mixing of contrasting water sources, diffuse infiltration through the overlying sandstone, sulfuric acid, and enlargement of paleokarst. Each hypothesis is supported by at least some evidence, but because the caves are no longer forming, this evidence is circumstantial.

The geologic setting is shown in Figure 13.10. The caves are located in the Madison Formation of Mississippian age (limestone and dolomite), which dips away from the center

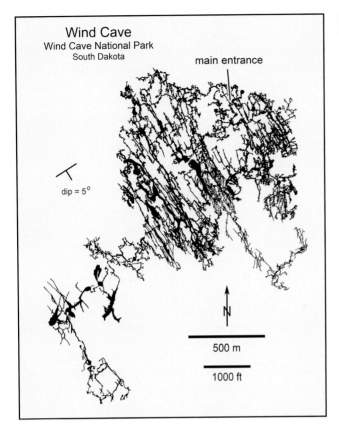

Figure 13.9: Map of Wind Cave, South Dakota. The cave is located on the southeastern flank of the Black Hills (see Figure 13.10). Map courtesy of the National Park Service.

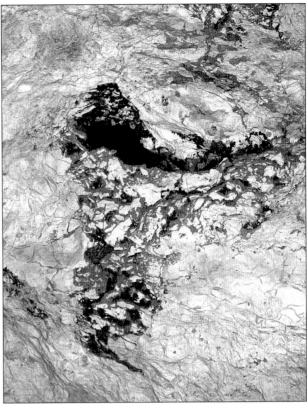

Figure 13.11: Mississippian-age solution pockets and breccia exposed in a breakdown wall in Jewel Cave, South Dakota. The breccia is cemented by dark brown calcite that shows evidence for having replaced earlier gypsum and anhydrite. Width of photo is about 1.5 m.

of the uplift at various angles, 3–10° in most areas, and is capped by the Pennsylvanian Minnelusa Formation (mainly sandstone). The prominent Mississippian paleokarst surface separates the two formations. The overall geologic history is fairly clear, and so are a few of the peripheral cave-forming processes; but the main cause of solutional enlargement is not.

Passages are arranged in several tiers that are inclined along the dip of the strata. They are not controlled by erosional base levels. Maximum cave development follows a former zone of gypsum and anhydrite that was once interbedded in the carbonate rock. In the cave area these sulfate rocks were long ago removed by dissolution and by calcite replacement, but they are still present deep below the surface to the west and north of the Black Hills. In the caves these zones are recognized by intense fracturing and brecciation of the limestone, and by a reddish brown calcite cement (Figures 2.36 and 3.27). In places the breccia contains isolated pockets and small caves that are lined by the brown calcite (Figure 13.11). Boxwork in the present caves dates from this time (Figure 12.47). It consists of the same brown calcite that fills fissures and gaps between breccia blocks. Intact examples of the early solution pockets are limited to areas where they were not destroyed by later cave development, and for that reason they are exposed in major caves only where there has been extensive collapse.

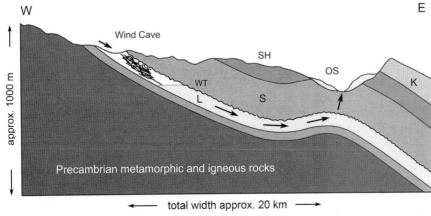

Figure 13.10: Geologic cross section through Wind Cave, South Dakota, showing the location of the cave relative to the present topography and patterns of groundwater flow (arrows). L = Mississippian Madison Formation (mainly limestone and dolomite), S = Pennsylvanian Minnelusa Formation (mainly quartz sandstone), SH = mostly shales and siltstones of Permian to Cretaceous age, K = resistant Cretaceous sandstone, and OS = remnants of Oligocene siltstone. WT = present water table. From A. Palmer and M. Palmer, 1989).

Figure 13.12: Beds of weathered carbonate rock ("internal sediment") fill the voids between early breccia fragments in Wind Cave. Note the rounded surfaces of the blocks. Width of photo is about 60 cm.

As fresh groundwater passed through, calcite tended to replace the sulfates as a result of the common-ion effect (Chapter 5). Calcite breccia matrix and veins are typically brown from iron oxides released by oxidation of iron sulfides, which themselves are byproducts of sulfate reduction (Chapter 12). Bacterial filaments show the importance of redox reactions in these processes (Figures 5.19 and 12.37). Dissolution of sulfates also produced solution vugs, most of which are lined with later calcite (Figure 10.10a). In places, sandy beds of carbonate and quartz grains (***internal sediment***) fill solution pockets and voids between breccia fragments (Figure 13.12). The sand is produced in any (or a combination) of the following ways: disintegration of bedrock in dry environments, sulfuric acid decomposition of the rock, or wedging of grains by gypsum crystallization. Some sandy beds contain interspersed rounded fragments of weathered carbonate rock, or bodies of white calcite that have replaced original sulfates.

Figure 13.13: Pennsylvanian-age sand and clay fill (~310 million years old) occupies paleo-caves near the top of the Madison Limestone (~330 m.y. old) in Jewel Cave, South Dakota. Pockets that were not filled by the sediment were lined by white calcite during deep burial beneath the surface, apparently during the Mesozoic Era (~250 to 65 m.y. ago). Width of photo = 30 cm.

The breccias and solution pockets formed about 330 million years ago (late in the Mississippian Period), soon after the limestone was deposited. Their age is shown by the fact that they are intersected by the paleokarst, which dates to about 320 million years ago. These early rock textures and caves are not related to the main cave events that followed, but they helped to guide later dissolution.

The late Mississippian paleokarst includes sediment-filled fissures, sinkholes, and caves (Figures 13.7 and 13.13). This represents a second phase of cave development. The sediment is of late Mississippian and early Pennsylvanian age (about 300–320 million years old). Some of the paleo-caves were not completely filled with sediment. These and all earlier features are exposed in the present caves.

From the Pennsylvanian through the Cretaceous Periods (about 300 to 65 million years ago) the region was deeply buried by sedimentary rocks to a thickness as much as 2 km. During this time the first two cave phases remained intact, and any open pockets and caves were lined by a thin layer of white or clear calcite (Figures 10.10a and 13.13). This calcite has strongly negative oxygen isotope ratios ($\delta^{18}O \sim -17$ to -19‰; see Figure 5.20), which indicates deposition at warm temperatures. Toward the end of the burial episode, clear quartz crystals formed on most exposed surfaces, including those already lined by calcite (Figures 10.13 and 12.42).

The Black Hills uplift began near the end of the Cretaceous Period, about 65 million years ago. The quartz crystals probably date from the beginning phases of uplift, when deep thermal fluids were moving through the rock. The overlying sedimentary rocks were partly eroded away, so that the old Precambrian igneous and metamorphic rocks were exposed in the high peaks (Figure 3.1c). Thermal water probably rose and escaped to the surface around the perimeter of the hills. As more of the sedimentary cover was removed, artesian groundwater flow was established, where water draining off the central mountains entered the limestone, moved deep below the surface, and rose back to the surface along fractures at the crests of anticlines (Figure 13.10). Most of the cave development took place during these episodes, but its pattern was guided largely by the caves, pockets, and breccia zones from much earlier times. The prominent joints that control most of the cave patterns were already present during the late Mississippian paleokarst, because the region experienced mild uplift soon after the limestone was deposited.

Most of the present land surface in the vicinity of the Black Hills caves was carved by stream erosion during the Paleocene and Eocene Epochs about 65–40 million years ago. The climate was much wetter than it is today, and little additional erosion has taken place since. The age of the landscape is clear, because it is partly buried by fossil-rich Oligocene sediments about 30–40 million years old, which were eroded from the higher hills. They extended as a sheet far to the east, where they are the main attraction of Badlands National Park. Most have been eroded away from the cave areas, but remnants still persist (labeled **OS** in Figure 13.10). They once covered the areas where the present springs emerge from the Madison aquifer. They must have greatly impeded the flow from the springs, and probably plugged them entirely.

A thick layer of calcite crystals lined the walls of many Black Hills caves after the main dissolutional event (Figures 1.22 and 10.7–10.8). A likely time for most of the calcite deposits was when the water flow was impeded by the Oligocene sediment cover, when slow-moving, warm water must have filled the caves. Calcite is still being deposited in the lowest levels of Wind Cave today (Ford and others, 1993), so its relation to the Oligocene sediment is not clearly defined.

To interpret the origin of these caves, certain points must be clarified. The caves extend to the top of the limestone in very few places, and these are where minor domes reach the contact more or less by accident (Figure 12.11). The caves do not reach the bottom of the limestone, either. Jewel Cave, for example, occupies only the upper third of the limestone. The caves do not extend indefinitely down the dip, but instead they peter out in that direction. The known parts of Jewel Cave do not even reach the present water table. The caves also do not persist into the outcrop areas of the limestone, except in a few places. Instead, the caves cluster beneath the sandstone-capped hills where the sandstone is thin. They do not extend beneath thick sandstone or low-permeability shale. Where the sandstone has been breached by narrow valleys, very few cave passages extend beneath them. There is no evidence that many passages once crossed these zones and have since been destroyed by the valleys. Cave development extends along the strike of the beds and maintains a narrow vertical range of about 170 m. The broad curving outline of Jewel Cave, shown in Figure 2.51, follows variations in the local strike.

The main cave-forming event of the Paleocene and Eocene Epochs must have involved mixing of two or more contrasting water types along the former gypsum-anhydrite zone. This was the zone of highest permeability. Thermal water may have been one of the early sources, but it could not have dominated, because the passages would have targeted spring outlets along the outcrops. Still, the passage pattern and character are similar to those of thermal caves. There is also some evidence for sulfuric acid dissolution, such as bleaching of bedrock around solution pockets, similar to that in Figure 12.31, but this is of very limited extent.

Normal groundwater flow from the outcrop area has clearly been important, as that is the pattern of flow today, but it too cannot have dominated the cave origin because the caves do not cluster around the recharge areas or extend into the artesian part of the aquifer. Some recharge through the overlying sandstone takes place today and must have been more intense during the humid Paleocene and Eocene Epochs, but the cave does not extend up to the contact, where the greatest dissolution would be expected.

If mixing is the best way to explain this cave pattern, which sources were most important? Water sinking along the limestone outcrop was most abundant, and still is. Thermal water has the potential to form maze caves and was probably available during the uplift of the Black Hills. Unlikely as it seems, diffuse recharge through the sandstone cap would

account for the clustering of passages beneath it. Limestone and dolomite beds interspersed within the sandstone would have brought the infiltrating water to saturation before it reached the Madison Limestone, and in that closed system the P_{CO_2} would have dropped to very low values (Chapter 12). The P_{CO_2} in both the other water sources would have been much higher. Mixing of either of them with the low-P_{CO_2} water could have produced caves in the zone of greatest mixing, which was along the high-permeability zones of former sulfates, about 2/3 of the way up from the bottom of the limestone. The sparse cave development in exposed areas may also lend minor support to a sulfuric acid origin (see pages 218–219).

This is merely a brief summary of the origin of the Black Hills caves. Other views are offered in papers by Tullis and Gries (1938), Howard (1964b), Deal (1968), Palmer (1981c), Bakalowicz and others (1987), Ford (1989b), and finally A. and M. Palmer (1989), who suggested the model described above. So far there is no consensus. The interpretation is clouded by the fact that much (perhaps most) of the cave patterns appear to have been outlined during the complex cave and karst events of the Mississippian Period and still affect the appearance of the caves today (Figures 13.14–13.15). Superposition of so many diverse events has produced caves of unusual complexity, in which details from a large span of geologic history are preserved.

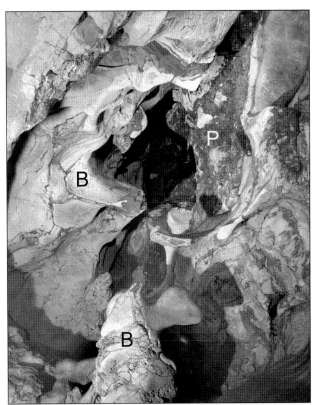

Figure 13.14: The sequence of events exposed in a typical Black Hills cave includes breccia (B) of middle Mississippian age, and paleokarst pockets and fill (P) of Mississippian-Pennsylvanian age, both intersected by solution pockets of probable Eocene age. (Photo from Wind Cave; width is about 2 meters.)

Figure 13.15: Boxwork exposed in Wind Cave. Because all the past events of its long geologic history are recorded in its passages, it is difficult to determine the exact age of this cave and many others in the Black Hills.

Late Cenozoic caves

The great majority of the world's accessible caves were formed within the past ten million years, and many of them within the past million years. They are fairly well adjusted to the surrounding landscapes, and most are still being enlarged by underground water. The late Cenozoic Era (comprising the late Tertiary Period and the Quaternary Period) has been a time of extreme climate change. This topic concerns us greatly, because climatic shifts can have serious effects on living conditions throughout the world.

Interpretation of landscape development

On the continents, caves that date from this time interval provide much information about the evolution of present-day landscapes and drainage patterns. One of the best sources of information is Mammoth Cave, Kentucky, which contains a variety of passages whose developmental history and relation to surface rivers have been worked out in detail. These studies are aided by extensive cave sediments that can be dated with paleomagnetism and cosmogenic radionuclides.

The uppermost passages in Mammoth Cave are wide canyons and tubes. Dating of sediments in these passages

by Granger and others (2001) shows several phases of deep sediment fill up to nearly 4 million years old. About 2.2 million years ago there was a widespread episode of sediment fill that reached the highest passages in the system (Figures 6.51 and 9.54). The passage character and sediments indicate very slow erosion of east-central North America during the late Tertiary Period, with alternating sedimentary episodes in valleys and caves (Miotke and Palmer, 1972). Fill stages may represent cooler and drier climates in the region during early continental glaciations farther to the north.

At the time of the major fill event, most of the streams from the Appalachian Mountains of eastern North America appear to have drained northward into what is now the St. Lawrence River (see question mark on Figure 13.16). This interpretation is speculative because so much of this early drainage history has been obscured by later erosion and glacial sediment.

As continental glaciers advanced into what is now the northern U.S., surface drainage was diverted westward into the Mississippi River. The main drainage line extended though northern Indiana and Illinois as what geologists refer to as the *Teays River* (Figure 13.16). With this increased flow, the older rivers in the region, such as the Mississippi, began to deepen their channels rapidly. The same was true for tributaries of the Mississippi, such as the Ohio, which at that time had only about 10% of its present drainage area. The Ohio's major tributary, the Green River, also deepened its valley.

Caves in the Green River basin, such as Mammoth Cave, adjusted accordingly. Their sediment-choked upper levels were abandoned by their flow and new, smaller passages formed at lower levels. Groundwater flow eventually stabilized to form a major cave level (labeled **C** in Figures 9.49 and 9.54). This passage level was abruptly abandoned, and another major level was formed 15 m lower (**D** in Figures 9.49 and 9.54). Further entrenchment was triggered by diversion of the Teays drainage into the Ohio River when the Teays valley was obliterated by renewed advance of continental glaciers farther south than they had previously reached (Figure 13.17). Suddenly the Ohio River became the largest river in the eastern U.S., and the boost in its erosional power caused further valley deepening. Headward erosion up the Green River from the Ohio may have caused the sharp change from level C to D. There are many scattered passages below level D, which indicate further entrenchment of the Green River with no major period of stable base level.

Glacial advances and retreats at these times were complex, and the exact history is still being worked out. It is possible that the entrenchment from level C to D was caused by earlier adjustments in the Teays River drainage, rather than by its diversion into the Ohio. If so, the sudden growth and deepening of the Ohio would account for the origin of the rapid entrenchment below level D.

The present drainage pattern in the east-central U.S. is shown in Figure 13.18. The close relationship between the cave and surface drainage is supported by the fact that

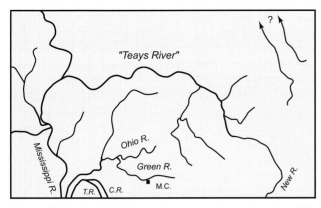

Figure 13.16: Early Pleistocene drainage in the northeastern U.S. Most water in the present Ohio valley passed through what is now Ohio, Indiana, and Illinois. Note the position of the Ohio River, which was then much shorter. Modified from Thornbury (1965).

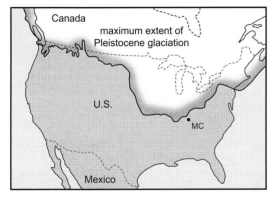

Figure 13.17: Maximum extent of Pleistocene glaciation in North America. The southern boundary coincided approximately with the present location of the Ohio River, just north of Mammoth Cave (MC). The maximum advance did not take place everywhere at the same time. The maximum ice thickness was roughly two kilometers. Based on information from Wright (1989).

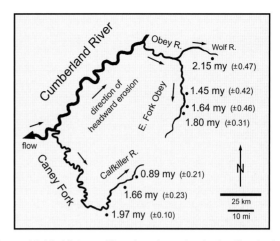

Figure 13.19: History of headward erosion in the Cumberland River and its tributaries in Tennessee, as interpreted from cosmogenic dating of sediments in caves at approximately uniform elevations above modern river levels (Anthony and Granger, 2004). Ages are indicated in millions of years. Note the overall decrease in age of cave sediments in the upstream direction. The small inconsistency of ages in the East Fork of Obey River is probably due to local variations in the sedimentary history of the caves.

thick sediments at the surface can be dated with cosmogenic radionuclides to about the same age as the upper-level cave sediments (Granger and others, 2001).

Anthony and Granger (2004) used similar dating methods in caves of the Cumberland River valley in northeastern Tennessee. They show that the caves had a history of development similar to that of Mammoth Cave. Also, along short tributaries, the uppermost cave passages at about the same elevation above local modern river levels decrease in age in the headward direction away from the Cumberland River (Figure 13.19). A thick sandstone cap had to be breached by headward erosion before caves could form in the underlying limestone. So the interpretation of cave levels must take into account local variations along the length of a river, as well as changes in valley depth with time. Compatible results are given by White and White (1974) for the Potomac River basin of the eastern U.S. They found that major cave levels tend to decrease in elevation in the downstream direction, while maintaining roughly similar elevations above present rivers. These interpretations come as no surprise, but until the recent application of cosmogenic dating to caves it was difficult to verify these relationships.

The history and rates of tectonic events, such as mountain uplift, can also be interpreted

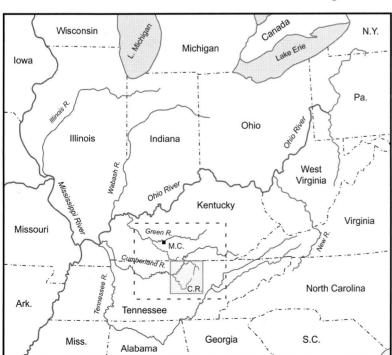

Figure 13.18: Present drainage pattern in the Ohio River basin as the result of continental glaciation. Compare with Figure 13.16.

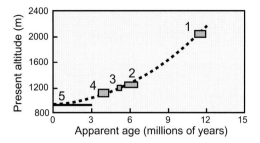

Figure 13.20: Relation of cave age to elevation in the Guada-
lupe Mountains, New Mexico (from Polyak and others, 1998).
1= Cottonwood Cave and Virgin Cave; 2 = Endless Cave and
Glacier Bay (Lechuguilla Cave); 3 = Lake Lebarge (Lechuguilla
Cave); 4 = New Mexico Room, Big Room, and Green Clay Room
(Carlsbad Cavern); 5 = present water table.

from cave dating. For example, cosmogenic radionuclide dates
for cave sediments in the Sierra Nevada, California, show that
the maximum rate of river entrenchment took place between
2 and 5 million years ago (Stock, 2003). This probably
represents the time of fastest uplift of the Sierra Nevada.

Another example is that of the Guadalupe Mountains,
New Mexico, where Polyak and others (1998) applied argon
dating of the mineral alunite to determine the ages of major
cave levels (Figure 13.20). Alunite is a byproduct of sulfuric
acid attack of clays (Chapter 12), so it appears to represent
phases of cave development at or slightly above former
positions of the water table. Figure 13.20 shows a smooth
but non-uniform increase in age with elevation.

This information not only dates the caves, but it also
clarifies the history of the Guadalupe Mountains and
surrounding region. One interpretation is as follows:
Throughout the history of Guadalupe cave development, the
water table probably remained at about the same elevation
as local rivers. If so, Figure 13.20 represents the history of
uplift of the Guadalupe Mountain block — rapid at first and
slowing with time.

An alternate interpretation is given by DuChene and
Cunningham (2006), who suggest that the
cave levels represent periodic lowering of the
water table as the result of tectonic activity.
During active cave development, a large upland

Figure 13.21: The drop in water table in the Guadalupe Mountains, N.M., and the ceasing of sulfuric
acid cave development, may be related to loss of
recharge (interpretation by DuChene and Cunningham, 2006, based partly on data by Matchus and
Jones, 1984, and Lindsay, 1998). (a) During the late
Tertiary Period, the Permian carbonate rocks that
contain the Guadalupe caves received groundwater
from extensive uplands farther west. Oxygen-rich
water could mix with H2S-rich water in petroleum
reservoirs in the area. (b) In the interval of roughly
14–4 million years ago, the region to the west
dropped downward because of tension and faulting.
The water table dropped during this interval. Now the
mountains stand high above the surrounding region,
and most of their recharge has been cut off.

catchment area extended far to the west of the present
Guadalupes (Figure 13.21a). Fresh groundwater from this
source mixed with hydrogen sulfide from deeper beds in the
same strata to form the caves. By 4 million years ago, down-
faulting to the west had removed most of this recharge area,
and sulfuric acid speleogenesis has not been active in the
Guadalupes since then (Figure 13.21b). This interpretation
provides a large fresh-water input to balance the amount of
hydrogen sulfide needed to produce sulfuric acid while the
caves were forming. Many of the Guadalupe caves show
evidence for early development along deep flow paths, and
this hypothesis may help to account for that pattern.

In a more geologically stable setting, the study of
cosmogenic radionuclides in surface exposures of quartz-
rich sediment in the Mammoth Cave region by Granger and
others (2001) shows that the rate of surface degradation is
one of the lowest yet measured in North America, at about 1.7
meters/million years. Dating of the Mammoth Cave passages
suggests that this rate has remained somewhat stable over
the past 2 million years, despite the deep entrenchment of
valleys that cut through the plateau.

Attempts are being made to apply various dating techniques
toward deciphering the erosional history of the Grand Canyon
(Hill and others, 2004). One of the major questions about the
Grand Canyon is how the Colorado River evolved with time.
The many diverse hypotheses on this topic tend to center on
piracy of formerly independent rivers into the Colorado, and
that the increase in erosive power helped to carve the Grand
Canyon (Ranney, 2005). The difficulty is to explain how the
once-independent rivers could join the Colorado, because, to
do so, they would have had to cut through a highland produced
by structural upwarping. A promising hypotheses being
pursued by Hill and her team is that diversion of rivers into the
Colorado initially took place by cave development through the
150-meter-thick Redwall Limestone (Figure 13.22), and that
later collapse and erosion have obscured much of the evidence.
The results of their study are still in preparation.

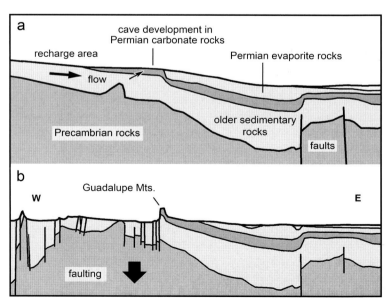

Figure 13.22: Dating of mineral and sediment deposits in caves is helping to define the history of the Grand Canyon in Arizona.

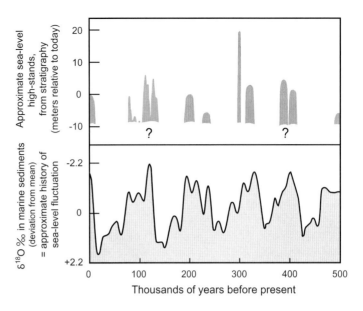

Figure 13.23: Approximate history of sea-level changes during the past 500,000 years, based on stratigraphic data in the Bahamas (Kindler and Hearty, 1997) and oxygen isotope measurements in marine sediments (Imbrie and others, 1984). In the upper graph, the details below the peaks are uncertain.

Brown and others (1992) used cosmogenic dating to show that one of the high plateaus of Venezuela, which contains large caves in quartzite, has a denudation rate of only about one meter per million years. This very slow rate illustrates how much time has been available for cave development in this normally non-cavernous rock.

In caves on the Mediterranean island of Mallorca, speleothems contain phreatic overgrowths that formed at and below a former sea level (Ginés, 1995). U/Th dating shows that they range in age from 60,000 to 150,000 years. Today they rise in elevation northward, and it is possible to estimate the rate and amount of land tilting since the most recent overgrowths (Fornós and others, 2002).

Cave studies are helping to clarify the history of uplift and erosion in the Alps. In Switzerland's extensive Siebenhengste-Hohgant Cave System, displacement of bedrock walls and speleothems by faulting shows that the cave pre-dates the latest tectonic disturbances (Jeannin, 1990). Häuselmann (2002) used cave patterns and sediments to suggest that the oldest conduits date from the Miocene-Pliocene (at least 5 million years ago), before entrenchment of the nearby river valleys. He noted evidence for six glaciations, with cave levels formed mostly between them. The cave sediments have recently been dated to as much as several million years with cosmogenic radionuclides, which confirms the Miocene-Pliocene dates (Häuselmann and Granger, 2005).

Interpretation of glacial history

Over the past two or three million years there have been at least 17 major glacial episodes that caused sea level to fluctuate from roughly −130 m during maximum glaciations to at least +6 m during interglacial stages, relative to present sea level (Figure 13.23). Early glaciations, up to about 900,000 years ago, were moderate in extent and recurred about every 41,000 years; but since then glacial advances have been more extensive and have a cyclicity of about 100,000 years (Maslin and others, 1998). The recent glacial cycles appear to be controlled mainly by variations in the ellipticity of the Earth's orbit around the sun. During those cycles, about 90% of the time has been cold, and only 10% has been warm (i.e., like today). At the beginning of each cold period there are many temperature fluctuations, but there is a fairly rapid rise in temperature at the end. Warm periods last about 10,000 years. If that pattern holds true today, we are nearing the end of the present warm period.

For nearly half the time during the past quarter million years, sea level has hovered between −20 and −50 m below its present level (Ford and Williams, 1989). Sea-level changes are only partly caused by melting of ice. Much is caused by expansion and contraction from temperature-related changes in sea-water density. Today sea level is rising at an average rate of 1–2 mm/yr (Church and others, 2004).

Data from ice cores in Greenland and Antarctic glaciers show that the CO_2 concentration in the air prior to industrialization, about 200 years ago, was less than about 0.00025 atm (Etheridge and others, 1996). Today the level is about 0.00038 atm and climbing. The lower values were probably present while most cave development was taking place, but soil CO_2 may not have been any less than it is today.

Changes in sea level are clearly recorded by seacoast caves that formed at different times and are now dispersed over a variety of elevations (Carew and Mylroie, 1987). Flank margin caves that lie above and below present sea level are good indicators of past sea-level stands and

Figure 13.24: Evidence for rising sea level is shown by the inundation of vadose speleothems by sea water in Admiral's Cave, Bermuda. This is a stable island with no significant vertical movement in the Earth's crust. Width of photo = 1.7 m.

contain a record of the major global climate variations of the Quaternary Period (Mylroie and Vacher, 1999). Cave levels in carbonate islands in the Caribbean are common at +6m and −18 m relative to present sea level. Fluctuations in Pleistocene sea level are also shown by vadose speleothems that are now drowned to depths of more than 30 m in places (Figure 13.24; Vesica and others, 2000).

Some caves felt the full brunt of Pleistocene continental glaciers, having been covered by ice sheets at least 1000 m thick. Caves of Yorkshire, England, show a strong relationship to

Figure 13.25: Boulders and clay deposited by glacial ice and meltwater clog many caves in the northeastern U.S. Deposits such as this, in the ceiling of a fissure in Caboose Cave, New York, hold clues to the interaction between karst and glacial history. Carbide lamp 12 cm high for scale.

glaciation that once covered that region (Waltham, 1974b). Castleguard Cave, in western Alberta, drains meltwater from the Columbia Icefield, which still covers its upstream end with 200–300 m of ice (Ford and others, 1983).

New England and New York caves were covered by thick ice during at least one major continental glaciation (Mylroie and Mylroie, 2004). Some shallow caves were crushed, but most survived remarkably intact, with only local sediment fill. Coarse gravels were carried in by meltwaters and partly filled passages, while glacial ice plowed a tight mixture of clay and boulders into sinkholes, surface fissures, and cave entrances (Figure 13.25). Laminated clays were deposited in static, ponded water where caves were drowned by lakes up to 100 m deep, which formed when glacial ice dammed surface rivers (M. Palmer, 1976; Mylroie, 1977; Dumont, 1995; Figure 13.26). A few caves show evidence for a post-glacial origin (i.e., within the past 14,000 years), but most are limited to narrow bypasses around glacially deposited sediments that blocked the original spring outlets.

Details of Pleistocene glacial history are also evident in caves that were not covered by glacial ice but were close to the paths of glaciers. Caves in southeastern Minnesota, including Mystery Cave, are located in an area that was almost completely spared direct continental glaciation, but it contains a great deal of wind-blown sediment carried in from nearby glaciated areas and transported into the cave by sinking streams. Fracturing of old dripstone speleothems indicates a severe cold period when glaciers advanced into the neighborhood, beginning about 145,000 years ago (Milske and others, 1983). Much alpine karst has experienced similar events. For example, Burger (2004) describes depositional sequences in Colorado caves that

Figure 13.26: Thinly laminated clay in Caboose Cave, New York. These beds were deposited when late Pleistocene glaciers blocked the local surface river, which ponded it to a depth of 100 m and inundated caves in the vicinity. Coarser-grained deposits above and below were deposited by rapid stream flow. Carbide lamp 12 cm high for scale.

Figure 13.27: The eastern escarpment of the Dent de Crolles, in the Chartreuse region of France. Large caves terminate at this cliff in their original upstream directions. Recent evidence shows that the caves pre-date the deepening of the valley.

Figure 13.28: Eogenetic karst processes in Pleistocene dune limestone (eolianite) exposed in the walls of an artificial cut, Bermuda.

help to distinguish between caves that were overridden by glacial ice and those that were periglacial — i.e., merely in the vicinity of the ice.

Glacial control of karst development can sometimes be misinterpreted. Many of the high karst plateaus of east-central France, along the western edge of the Alps, stand more than 1000 m above the local valleys. In the Chartreuse region the plateaus consist of Cretaceous limestone underlain by relatively insoluble rocks (Figure 3.46). Their contact is perched high above the present rivers (Figure 13.27). Some of the most extensive caves in the limestone have large passages that terminate headward in steep cliffs at the edges of the plateaus. Evidently the water that fed these passages came from a source that is no longer there. Formerly it was thought that the source was meltwater from glaciers that filled the adjacent valleys. More recent evidence suggests instead that the caves pre-date the erosional entrenchment of the valleys (Audra, 1994). This view is supported by the composition of sediments in the caves (Delannoy and Caillault, 1998).

Caves in recently deposited limestone

Geologists who specialize in carbonate rocks have always taken karst studies seriously. The "soft beach sand" advertised in travel brochures for Bermuda and the Bahamas is simply limestone in the making — small particles of calcium carbonate, such as wave-pounded shell fragments, which will eventually become cemented together into rock. Farther inland, this rock-forming process can be seen in action where fresh water seeps downward through dunes or former beaches of this sandy material.

Most of the marine sand is aragonite because the more stable calcite rarely precipitates in the high-magnesium seawater. But fresh water is relatively free of magnesium, so as this water dissolves the aragonite it quickly redeposits the dissolved material as calcite. Firm but porous limestone is produced in this way. Meanwhile, caves can form in the limestone where infiltrating water mixes with phreatic water, and also where the fresh water comes in contact with underlying salt water. Where organic material is present, some of the sulfate in the seawater is reduced to hydrogen sulfide, which forms a corrosive, acidic solution, especially if it has the opportunity to oxidize to sulfuric acid.

All of these processes help to form ***eogenetic karst***, which is barely younger than the surrounding limestone (Chapter 8; Mylroie and Vacher, 1999). Many eogenetic caves, and the limestones they occupy, are only a few thousand or tens of thousands of years old. Cave walls are porous from the small-scale intergranular porosity of the young rock, and they are pocketed with spongework produced by selective enlargement of that porosity by dissolution (Figure 13.28). In very young limestone, cave walls may be so crumbly and porous that they hardly qualify as rock. As caves form, their roofs of more thoroughly cemented limestone crack into blocks, which subside and form sinkholes. In these ways, eogenetic caves are linked to the processes by which limy sediment is converted into rock.

14

Geologic studies of caves

BUDDING CAVE SCIENTISTS often wonder where to begin their studies. What are the major problems to be solved? Where do you find the information necessary to answer them? This chapter gives only a brief glimpse of the subject. It is more rewarding to discover your own way than to follow a set of rules.

Field mapping

A promising first step is to identify the goals of the project, but often they are not clear until the study is already in progress. Goals also have a way of expanding and changing with time. Some geologic studies begin as soon as exploration and mapping of a cave are underway, and they grow from there.

The techniques described here have seen long use, and they work well in caves. Many will soon be replaced by newer technology, but the basic kinds of measurements described here are unlikely to change significantly.

Cave exploration and mapping

Exploration and mapping are best done as a team effort. It is not difficult to enlist help. The ultimate goal is a map that accurately shows the three-dimensional layout of the cave (see Chapter 1 for the basic technique). The map can serve this purpose even if it contains little geologic information. These details can be added later. Explorers themselves may wish to examine the geology to help them understand the cave and to target promising areas for further discoveries, and often this step leads to more advanced studies.

Relation of caves to topography

The cave map is then superposed on a topographic map to show its relation to the surrounding landscape. Take care to orient the cave map to true north and to adjust its scale to that of the topographic map. Aerial photos can also be used. They show more surface details than topographic maps but have slight distortion and do not show elevations. Digital elevation models (DEMs) provide an attractive option, where the landscape is portrayed as a three-dimensional image that can be viewed on the computer from any perspective.

There are several on-line sources of topographic maps, aerial photos, and digital elevation models. Try an individual search for each of these terms. A DEM requires software to download and display the maps, so search also for "*DEM reader.*"

A three-dimensional view of the cave can be obtained with cave survey software (Chapter 1). When superposed on a DEM, the combined image can be enhanced with color, re-sized, and rotated so that it can be viewed from any angle. A simple map with profiles and cross sections has less visual impact, but it is easier to use in quantitative studies.

Note the relation of the cave to the surrounding landscape. Chapters 8 and 9 give some approaches on how to interpret cave patterns on this basis. The cave's position relative to other caves and to surface features is also important. Potential entrances, promising leads, and causes of terminal breakdown can be identified.

Relation to regional drainage

Cave streams are just part of the regional drainage pattern. To determine where the cave fits into the overall picture, identify upland recharge areas and valley discharge areas on the topographic map. Field work may be needed to sort out the details. Does the known cave extend as far as it can? Look for karst areas that lie beyond the cave map, and note any passages that extend in those directions.

Passages with the greatest stream discharge have the largest recharge areas. This is a very close relationship, so a passage with twice the discharge of another will have a drainage basin about twice as extensive. Techniques for measuring discharge are described in Chapter 4.

Dye tracing can be used to show the source of the cave water. To avoid unpleasant surprises for local residents, it should be done only with low dye levels and guided by someone with experience. Traces are traditionally done to define the drainage basins for springs, but for the purpose of understanding a cave it is more useful to trace the sources of each of its tributaries. Dye tracing helps to define the extent of passages beyond their explored limits. It can also identify potential new entrances. Travel times and shapes of dye breakthrough curves can indicate the size and nature of these passages. See pages 104−108 for details.

Relation to local geology

It is not difficult to obtain information about the local geology. Geologic maps and related information are available from state geological surveys and at university libraries. Use maps and guidebooks to find rock exposures on the surface and to interpret which rocks are exposed in the cave. Locate them in the cave, describe the various rock types, even if in non-technical terms, and measure their thicknesses in various places. Rock exposures in the cave may be more extensive than on the surface. With little effort, one can discover details that are overlooked on the surface, even by professionals. Note the distribution of geologic contacts in the cave and the effect that each bed or rock type has on the character of its walls. The cave begins to make more sense.

Remapping of passage details

The entire cave, or at least its major passages, may require remapping to add precision and detail missed during the original survey. It is often beneficial to remap a cave twice — once to improve the detail of the original map, and again to add the geology. Mapping in this way is more focused and systematic, so it is less likely that important details will be overlooked. Small dedicated teams are appropriate.

The exploration, mapping, and remapping of a cave require much time, and they are not wise investments for anyone who is trying to finish a scientific project or complete an academic thesis. For those who pursue science alone, it is more efficient to study the geology of caves that have already been well explored and mapped.

This book is aimed toward those who are interested mainly in the cave, not in its ability to advance a career, so the entire sequence of steps is recommended here. Besides, remapping to add passage detail is the best way to appreciate the cave's individual character.

Geologic mapping

Once the strata have been identified, it is possible to survey their distribution and the contacts between them. This may seem like a logical step, but it is rarely done, perhaps because the benefits are not widely recognized. Passage locations, patterns, and profiles are all governed mainly by the local strata and geologic structure, and mapping them can shed light on the cave origin and pattern. Solution caves are given most attention here, although most of the techniques apply as well to other cave types.

What to measure

In geology, elevations are more important than horizontal locations. Passage gradients, passage levels, water surfaces, and stratigraphic contacts all depend on precise vertical measurements, while their horizontal layout can have a fair amount of error without jeopardizing the geologic interpretation. Careful leveling surveys are recommended, especially in caves with low gradients or low stratal dips.

At each survey station in a geologic survey, ties are made to geologic contacts and major bedding planes, especially those that have undergone solutional widening. Measurements are also made to ceilings, floors, erosional benches, sediment levels, and to present and past water levels. The location and orientation of structural features such as faults and joints are noted. It is best to draw a complete profile of the passage.

In each passage it is important to identify the earliest path of the solvent water as accurately as possible. In a canyon this may be an enlarged bedding plane at or near the ceiling. In a tubular passage it may be the widest part. Anastomoses help to identify the most transmissive bedding planes. In some passages the initial paths are obscured by breakdown. Solutional widening above sediment surfaces may complicate the interpretation.

Figure 14.1 shows some of the important features to be included in a geologic survey. From each survey station, the distance upward or downward to each of these features is recorded as a positive (upward) or negative (downward)

number. If the station is on the floor, all measurements are positive. The survey methods described here are also required for hydrologic studies where differences in water level must be measured accurately (see Chapter 4).

Survey techniques

The techniques described below may seem low-tech in this electronic age, but, until more advanced equipment is widely available, they are still the most accurate and reliable. They are also well suited to cave conditions and the average speleologist's budget. Survey techniques will become more automated in the future, but this may be a mixed blessing. The very act of measuring by hand forces one to think about spatial relationships and to evaluate the goals of the measurements while still in the cave.

For any measurement to be accurate, whether in the field or laboratory, the instrument must be properly calibrated (see *Calibration of survey instruments* on pages 370–371). This is especially important in precise surveying.

The basic compass-and-tape method described in Chapter 1 is adequate for normal cave surveys, and it is sufficient for some geologic studies as well. But for detailed geologic or hydrologic relationships it is often necessary to obtain more precise measurements, as described below.

With a *tripod-mounted compass* a non-magnetic tripod is used to steady the instrument. It is combined with a durable tape measure to run a compass-and-tape survey. The target is a small light that may also be mounted on a separate tripod. The most appropriate compass for this purpose is the Brunton "pocket transit," which provides both horizontal bearings and vertical angles. Steep-angle shots are easily made with it. Steadied by the tripod, the Brunton compass can be read to the nearest 0.1–0.2 degree with a non-magnetic hand lens. Without a tripod it loses most of its precision.

Commercially available tripod mounts for the Brunton compass do not provide a smooth enough motion for precision surveys. With little effort they can be reconstructed with hand-made parts to allow the compass to rotate smoothly in both the horizontal and vertical planes (Figure 14.2).

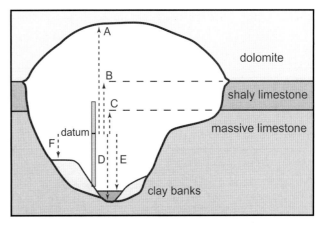

Figure 14.1: At each station in a geologic survey of a cave, the distances up or down to significant features are measured. A few are shown here.

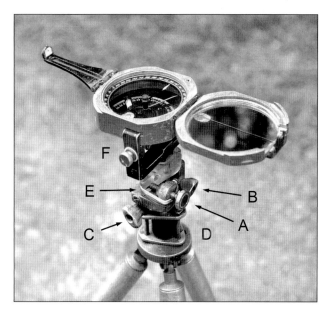

Figure 14.2: Tripod-mounted Brunton compass. This one is held by a home-made non-magnetic mount that allows it to be aimed precisely, both horizontally and vertically, by turning knob **A**. The lock **B** holds the vertical or horizontal orientation. **C** = lock to maintain the rotational position. **D** = ball-and-socket to level the compass, with clamp to adjust friction. Rubber bands (**E**) maintain tension against knob **A**. **F** = commercial yoke to hold compass. Older compasses, such as this, take longer to stabilize than recent models but can be read more accurately.

A *laser rangefinder* (Figure 14.3) can be substituted for the survey tape. Although the rangefinder has greater precision than a tape, it is difficult to hold it steady enough to sight on a small target. It is very effective in obtaining distances to cave features and geologic contacts.

With a tripod-mounted compass it is inconvenient, though still feasible, to check each reading with a backsight between the same two stations. This is easier if both the compass and target light are on tripods with interchangeable mounts. It is simpler and faster to alternate between foresights and backsights in the following way (Figure 14.4): A point is selected to represent the first station in the survey. Point 2 is established by setting up the tripod-mounted compass at a convenient spot farther into the cave, and a backshot is made to Point 1. The compass itself is the second station. Point 3 is then established farther into the cave, and readings are made from Point 2 to Point 3. Thus, from one station to the next, the compass (and inclinometer) readings alternate between foresights and backsights. Semi-permanent markers can be left at the non-tripod stations, which can be placed wherever desired. At tripod stations such markers can be placed at measured distances directly below (or above) the compass.

Figure 14.3: A laser rangefinder. This model has a range of about 100 m. Smaller models are available but have shorter ranges.

If backsights are not used to check the accuracy of foresights, the compass and inclinometer readings should be re-read at least once to verify their accuracy. On a tripod, the compass is unlikely to be affected by magnetic objects. Even along tour routes in show caves there is rarely a problem with magnetic deflection of the compass. To prevent a sticky needle, clean and sharpen its pivot.

This survey method is well suited to caves with much vertical relief. With its telescoping legs, the tripod can be positioned securely even in awkward places. A solid stance is required, so deep mud or water are best avoided. When done with care, this method can give a combined horizontal and vertical error of less than 50 cm over a 1 km survey.

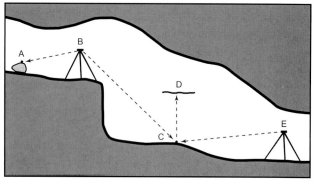

Figure 14.4: A geologic survey with a tripod-mounted compass and tape. A backsight is made from **B** to the base station at **A**. A foresight is then made from **B** to **C**, followed by a backsight from **E** to **C**. At each station the ceiling, floor, and geologic features are measured above or below it (e.g., from **C** to the bedding plane at **D**). If the target is also mounted on a tripod, the compass and target can be interchanged to check for errors by making backsights. Otherwise each reading should be double-checked.

The following techniques are most useful in areas of low dip, or in caves with low gradients. In many areas both the dips and gradients are so small that they cannot be detected by eye. With these methods it is possible to map subtle structures and their effects on passage patterns that would otherwise go undetected.

A *hand level* is a hollow tube that contains a bubble level and peephole sight, which is used to project a horizontal line between stations (Figures 14.5–14.6). For stability it is simply held against a vertical rod. The target is usually a small hand-held light held against a similar rod. Thin wooden rods about 2 m long work well. A couple of shorter ones may be brought along for use in low passages. The rods need no markings. A sliding collar or cradle can be attached to each rod to maintain the station positions (Figure 14.5).

The hand-level technique is best suited to caves that have already been mapped with compass and tape. It is ideal for improving the vertical accuracy of the map and for adding geologic details. Leveling stations are rarely labeled in the cave, but instead the level survey is tied to the previous compass-and-tape stations or to easily identified features.

As shown in Figure 14.7, the first shot is made backward to the base station (typically the first survey marker from the

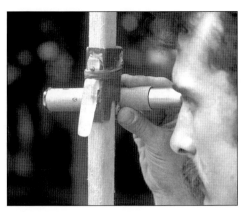

Figure 14.5: A hand level provides rapid and fairly accurate horizontal readings. Shots are made between two rods, each provided with a locking slider. The target is a small light mounted on the other rod.

original survey). The hand level is moved vertically along the rod until its line of sight coincides with the base station. Then the level is swiveled around to sight on the target light at the second station, which is on the second rod. The *light* is moved vertically until the hand-level operator signals that it lines up exactly with the hand level. Then the hand-level operator moves ahead and shoots back to the target light. In this leapfrog manner a horizontal line is projected through the cave, and at each station the distance is measured up or down from the line to important features. This is known as the ***datum-line method***.

This procedure is repeated all the way through the cave. The location of each point can be marked on the map, although it is important to tie to many of the preexisting stations to provide exact locations and to correct the vertical component of the original survey.

A horizontal line cannot be projected very far before changes in floor and ceiling elevation make it necessary to change the reference elevation (datum). Where this is necessary, the datum is changed an even number of feet or meters (Figure 14.7). If a long deep pool is encountered, it is convenient to measure down to the water surface and to use that as the temporary datum. Except for datum changes, and for distances to features of interest, no measurements are needed to run the survey. The method is fast and there is little opportunity for blunders. It is easy to tally the datum changes to determine the elevation at any time during the survey. If the survey loops back to the original station, the total survey error can be calculated right in the cave. This method was first

applied to geologic mapping of caves in the mid-1960s by Richard Powell of the Indiana Geological Survey.

Although hand-leveling can be used for the primary survey of a cave by adding distance measurements and compass bearings, it is preferable not to combine techniques. During an independent level survey, attention can be focused on the geology, rather than on mapping the passage.

The hand level must be carefully calibrated (page 371). Any residual calibration error tends to be canceled by the alternating foreshots and backshots, as long as the total length of all foreshots is roughly equal to those of the backshots. With practice, the error can be consistently held within 10–20 cm over a 1 km survey. People who wear glasses or are unsteady on their feet may have trouble reading the level.

The datum-line method can also be used with a ***water tube***. Take a clear vinyl tube about 10–20 m long, with an internal diameter of about 1 cm, and fill it almost completely with water. When the ends of the tube are held upward to form a broad U, the two water levels are at equal height. The bottom of the curved meniscus in the water surface is used as the measuring point. The water level in one end is held at a station while the water in the other end is used to identify the same elevation farther down the passage (Figure 14.8). The two ends must be raised or lowered simultaneously until the water level is properly positioned. To avoid loss of water from the tube, care must be taken not to raise one end higher than the other, although the person at the upper end may find this amusing. Valves or stopcocks can be used to close the ends until the tube is ready for action. A little food coloring can be added to the water to aid visibility. Two unmarked rods are normally used, as in a hand-level survey.

Small errors are introduced if the reader's eye is not lined up horizontally with the water level. A bubble trapped in the tube is a more serious problem. Occasionally the ends of the tube should be held together to verify that the two water levels match. The water levels may also differ slightly if the tube interior is dusty,

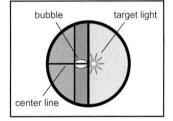

Figure 14.6: View through a hand level.

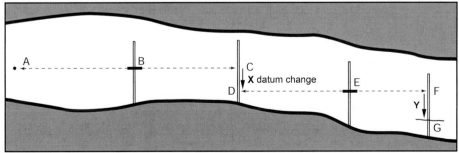

Figure 14.7: Details of a hand-level survey. The light is placed at the base station (A). In a backshot, the hand level at B is adjusted to the same height as A. Then, in a foreshot from B to C, the target light at C is adjusted to the height of the hand level at B. A change of datum is necessary at C. It is dropped a uniform number of feet or meters (or perhaps decimeters) to D. A backshot is made from E to D, then a foreshot from E to F. At each station the distance up or down to important features is measured (as from F to G). **Example:** If **X** = −1.000 m and **Y** = −0.892 m, the elevation of G relative to A = −1.00 + −0.892 = −1.892 m.

Figure 14.8: The water tube in use. One end of the flexible tube is shown here, with the lower point of the water surface at the same level as the notch in the slider. The water surface at the other end is at exactly the same elevation. Parallax in aligning the water level with the notch by eye is the only significant source of error. Loop closures of less than 10 cm/km are common.

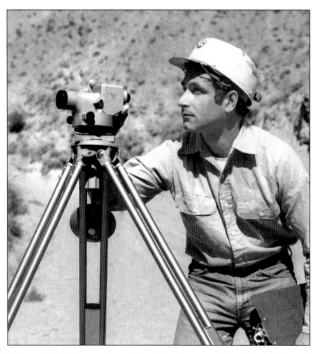

greasy, or abraded. The water tube is well suited to large, low-gradient passages. It is difficult to use in crawlways and over break-down.

An ***automatic level***, also known as an engineer's level, or "auto-level" for short, provides precise horizontal lines of sight (Figure 14.9). For stability it is mounted on a tripod. It is not quite as automatic as its name implies. It is first leveled roughly by hand with the aid of a bull's eye level, and from there the instrument levels itself very precisely with an internal balance. The view through the eyepiece is magnified to allow long-distance readings. A single rod is used that is marked with vertical distances measured upward from the ground. It can be hand-made by attaching aluminum meter sticks to segmented wooden rods.

With some auto-levels it is possible to calculate shot distances. The view through the eyepiece shows a long horizontal line that is used for the actual level sighting (Fig-

Figure 14.9: Surveying with a tripod-mounted automatic level. Photo by Margaret Palmer.

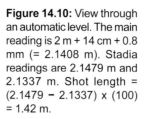
Figure 14.10: View through an automatic level. The main reading is 2 m + 14 cm + 0.8 mm (= 2.1408 m). Stadia readings are 2.1479 m and 2.1337 m. Shot length = (2.1479 − 2.1337) x (100) = 1.42 m.

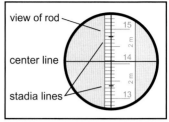

ure 14.10). Two shorter lines above and below it allow two additional readings to be made (***stadia*** readings). The shot distance is the difference between the two stadia readings x 100. This works regardless of whether the readings are in feet or meters. Distances calculated in this way are not as accurate as taped distances.

The survey technique is similar to that with a hand level, except that elevation readings are read on the rod. If stations are less than about 30 m apart, readings can be made to the nearest millimeter or less. The tripod legs can be shortened for use in small passages. About 50 km of Mammoth Cave, Kentucky, has been mapped with an auto-level in large passages and a hand level in small ones, to determine the passage elevations and geology as shown in Figures 9.28–9.29. The technique for running an auto-level survey through a cave is shown in Figure 14.11.

The rod is positioned at the base station, and the elevation of the station is noted from the scale on the rod. With the auto-level set up farther down the passage, a backsight is then made to the rod. The rod is then moved farther into the cave. The level is rotated and a foresight is made to the rod. This procedure is repeated throughout the survey. At each rod station the vertical positions of geologic features are noted. A hand level is convenient for measuring the elevation of wall features from the rod. A carpenter's string level can also be used if the distance to the wall is short (Figure 14.12).

The elevation of any point along the survey, relative to the base station, is obtained by subtracting the first measurement (elevation of the base station on the rod), adding the backsights, subtracting the foresights, and adding the elevation of the desired point as measured on the rod. Draw a diagram the first few times, to ensure that the calculation is being made correctly. With care, the error can be kept within 5 mm over a 1 km survey.

A ***laser level*** is a device that projects a horizontal laser beam that is visible on cave walls or other surfaces. Elevations to various features, such as geologic contacts, can be measured relative to the point of light. The level can be rotated in any direction so that variations in elevation can be mapped. This technique works well over small distances but is less suited to lengthy surveys.

The following methods are appropriate only for large dry caves, regardless of their gradient and geologic structure, or for surface surveys.

A ***transit*** has a telescopic sight with which horizontal and vertical angles can be measured precisely. A ***theodolite*** is similar but has an internal optical system that allows more precise measurements (Figure 14.13). Either one must be

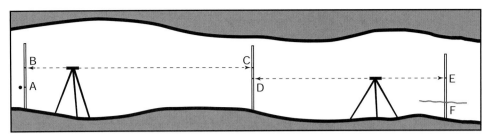

Figure 14.11: An automatic level survey. The rod is placed at the base station (A) and the elevation of A is measured on the rod. A backshot is made to the rod with the auto-level (reading = B). The rod is moved to the next position, and a foreshot is made to C. Then a backshot is made to D and a foreshot to E. Geologic features are measured at each rod station (e.g., the bedding plane at F).
Example: Elevation of F relative to A = −reading A + reading B − reading C + reading D − reading E + reading F. (Subtract first reading and all foresights, and add all other readings.)

mounted on a rigid tripod. Most transits can be read to the nearest 10 minutes of arc. Many theodolites can be read to the nearest 2 seconds. (One degree = 60 min and one min = 60 sec, so two seconds = 0.00056 degree). The telescope can be rotated horizontally and then inverted, so that the same line of sight can be repeated 180 degrees from the original reading. When the two readings are averaged, calibration errors tend to cancel. Theodolites are ideal for long shots. With an attached or internal electronic distance meter (EDM), distances up to about 2 km can be measured to roughly the nearest centimeter. A reflective prism is used as a target. Two-way radios are helpful for communicating in the field.

A survey is begun by setting up the instrument over the first station and shooting on a distant point to which the direction is exactly known, for example the North Star (corrected for time), then rotating the instrument and shooting to the next station. Horizontal and vertical readings are made between the two stations. The instrument is then placed over the second station. Shots are made back to the first station and forward to the third. To plot the progress of the survey, the vertical angles and differences between horizontal angles are calculated. Because there is no compass reading there is no problem with nearby magnetic materials such as steel or lava, or with varia-

tions in the Earth's magnetic field with time. Total error is usually within a centimeter over a 1 km distance.

Most transits are equipped with compass needles, but most theodolites are not. A transit can be used like a glorified compass and inclinometer for extremely accurate compass-and-tape surveys. Used transits are readily available at fairly low cost.

The most popular and convenient method of locating oneself in the field is with **GPS** (global positioning system). Although handy for general-purpose mapping on the surface, most GPS units are not precise enough for highly detailed surveys, especially in the vertical dimension. The accuracy of the signals can also vary without warning. Some expensive systems, when carefully calibrated, are accurate to within a few centimeters. Satellite signals do not penetrate underground, so GPS cannot be used in caves. The method also does not work reliably where there is thick forest cover.

Among the many functions of a GPS unit, one of the most useful for geologic studies is to obtain coordinates of known points so they can be plotted on a map. For example, the contact between two rock formations can be mapped quickly and easily in this way, as long as there is no need for great accuracy. Elevations can be obtained in either meters or feet, and horizontal coordinates can be obtained in either latitude and longitude (degrees, minutes, and seconds) or in UTM (= Universal Transverse Mercator) coordinates. UTM coordinates give east-west and north-south positions in meters and can be easily plotted on maps. Conversion routines between latitude-longitude and UTM are available on the Web (search for *UTM conversion*). To prepare a stand-alone map that is not linked to a topographic map, it is only necessary to plot the UTM coordinates of all points by calculating the differences in east-west and north-south readings between them and the first point.

Some surveys make use of several different instruments to accommodate a variety of field conditions. As part of a

Figure 14.12: Tying a bedding-plane parting into an auto-level survey with the aid of a string level. The string is attached to a thin nail, which is inserted into the parting. A hand level also works well for this purpose.

Figure 14.13: Surveying with a theodolite and electronic distance meter (EDM). On this model the EDM is mounted on top. For stability, the entire apparatus is supported by a tripod.

Calibrating survey instruments

Almost every instrument needs to be calibrated to ensure that its readings are accurate. The simple methods described here have changed little over the past century and may soon be replaced by more automated equipment. But the new instruments too will need calibration in much the same ways that are described here.

Calibration of a compass to true north

The direction of true north must be shown on every map, because it is an unvarying standard. Magnetic north varies with time.

The easiest way to calibrate a compass to true north is to stand at a point that is identifiable on a topographic map and has a long view. Find another point that is visible in the distance and can also be located precisely on the map. Make a series of careful compass readings between the points to the nearest 0.1 degree and average them. With a protractor, as shown in Figure 14.14, measure the angle on the map between the line of sight and true north (the closest side border on the map). At high latitudes the two borders are not exactly parallel, and true north must be interpolated between them.

The difference between the compass reading and the actual direction on the map is the correction factor that must be added to every compass reading. For this, as in any calibration, **the correction factor is what the reading *should* be, minus what the instrument actually reads**. If the compass reads 37.5 degrees and the true direction is 29.2 degrees, the correction factor is 29.2 − 37.5 = −8.3 degrees. So (−8.3) is added to each compass reading. It combines both the magnetic declination of the Earth's field (deviation from true north) and any internal error in the compass itself. It can vary as much as 0.1 degree between adjacent topographic

quadrangles, so it is best to do the calibration as close as possible to where the survey will take place.

For cave surveys it is convenient to set up two points at the entrance with a known angle between them, so a calibration can be made before and/or after each survey trip. To do this, sight on the North Star (Polaris) with a transit or theodolite. (This is difficult to do with a compass.) Polaris is visible only in the northern hemisphere. To find it, first locate the two end stars of the Big Dipper, those that form the end of the dipper farthest from the handle. These are called the *pointer stars*. Project a line through the pointer stars in the direction of the open end of the dipper, extending the line about 4 times the distance between the two stars. This brings you close to Polaris, a fairly bright star that stands alone.

Polaris deviates from true north by as much as a couple of degrees. It is oriented exactly toward true north only when the two pointer stars are oriented 39° to the right of a line extending straight down from Polaris (Figure 14.15), or 39° to the left of a line extending straight up from Polaris. Hold up a protractor or an inclinometer to measure the angle. When the angle is correct, that is when to make the sighting. If the angle is not 39°, the direction can still be calculated with the aid of navigation tables. If Polaris is not visible in your region, other stars can be used, but they all require the aid of navigation tables.

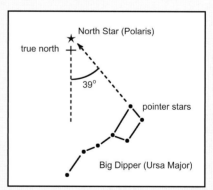

Figure 14.15: The position of Polaris when it is aligned with true north. Polaris is also at true north if the position of the Big Dipper is 180° from that shown here.

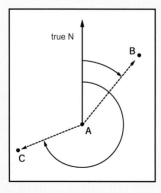

Figure 14.14: The true direction of a line of sight is the clockwise angle from a northward line on the map to the line of sight. For example, the direction from A to B is 40°. The direction from A to C is 250°.

The magnetic field drifts with time and varies with location. Compass calibrations should be checked during each day of a survey. This is especially important for long-term projects where many different compasses are used. Do not rely on the declinations shown on topographic maps, which are probably out of date. The Web site, *www.ngdc.noaa.gov/seg/geomag/jsp/struts/*

calcDeclination provides approximate declinations for any date and location in the U.S. They are based on generalized models and are less accurate than those obtained by the methods described here.

Inclinometer calibration

To calibrate an inclinometer, make foreshots and backshots between the same two points and note the discrepancy. The correction factor is the positive or negative angle that must be added to each to make the two readings equal. Try it several times, and at different angles. Even if the inclinometer can be adjusted manually, there will probably still be a residual correction factor that must be added to each reading.

Hand-level calibration

One advantage of a level survey is that if perfectly horizontal lines are projected, the distance does not matter. For this to be valid, the leveling instrument must be adjusted so there is no detectable error.

To calibrate the hand level, shoot between two rods or other stable structures (corners of neighboring buildings are ideal) at least 10 m apart. First shoot from one to the other (A to B in Figure 14.16). Mark both A and B on the rods. Then move to point B and shoot back to the first rod (to point C). If the level is perfectly calibrated, A and C will coincide. If not, divide the vertical distance between A and C in half and call the mid-point D. Points B and D will define a horizontal line. With the level still at B, aim at D. Turn the adjustment screw in the hand level until the bubble is perfectly level when sighting between B and D. If there is no calibration screw, the level is not suitable for surveys unless it happens to be in perfect adjustment.

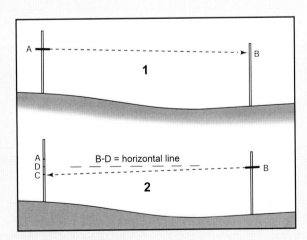

Figure 14.16: Calibration of the hand level.

Calibration of the automatic level

Set up two vertical rods with metric scales that can be read to the nearest millimeter or less (two aluminum meter sticks will do). Place the auto-level near one and shoot to it (reading A in Figure 14.17). Then shoot to the other rod (reading B). Then move the level close to the second rod and re-shoot to the two rods (readings C and D). Measure the length of each shot with a tape. Sum the lengths of the two foreshots (B + D) and subtract the lengths of the backshots (A + C). This gives the net forward length (FL). Then calculate the vertical error in the loop: (A − B + C − D) = VE. The correction factor is VE/FL. This factor is added to each auto-level reading.

For example, if A = 1.4613 m, B = 2.0425 m, C = 1.8589 m, D = 1.3106 m, then VE = 1.4613 − 2.0425 + 1.8589 − 1.3106 = −0.0329 m. If FL = 27.41 m, the correction factor is −0.0329/27.41 = −0.00120 m per meter of shot length. So, for example, a reading of 2.7835 m over a distance of 35.8 m would be corrected like this: 2.7835 + (−0.00120 x 35.8) = 2.7405 m.

Try to adjust the centering of the eyepiece to eliminate as much of this error as possible, and then repeat the calibration procedure. A small correction factor is almost always needed.

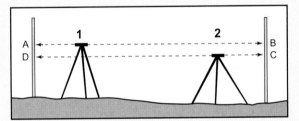

Figure 14.17: Calibration of the automatic level.

Combining backshots and foreshots

During a survey, if both a foreshot and a backshot are made between each pair of stations, the average of the two will be the correct value. Compass readers often try to make the two readings exactly compatible, so that the compass readings are 180° apart and the vertical angles are exactly the same but of opposite sign. Unless the instrument is perfectly calibrated the readings will not agree. Averaging the foreshot and backshot ideally gives the correct value. This is automatically done with a transit or theodolite by re-reading with the telescope inverted and reversed. In some surveys it is not convenient to combine backshots and foreshots between the same pair of stations, and with an automatic level it is almost never done. In this case, each reading must be adjusted with the appropriate correction factor.

geologic study of Mystery Cave, in Forestville State Park, Minnesota, a 4 km leveling survey was made through the cave between two entrances and reconnected to the starting point with a surface survey.* Large passages were surveyed with an auto-level, small ones with a hand level, and the surface with a theodolite. At one point in the plotted survey a geologic contact in the cave showed an unexpected one-foot elevation drop. A return visit showed that by carelessness a datum change in the hand-level survey had not been recorded at that point. With this correction made, the vertical discrepancy for the entire loop was only 4.6 cm.

Automated survey techniques

Today many theodolites for professional use have built-in electronic distance meters and data recorders that automate the collection of survey data. These so-called **total stations** are ideal for surface surveys but are suitable only for large, dry caves.

Laser-based instruments are becoming popular for cave surveys. Some combine a laser rangefinder, digital compass, and inclinometer, all of which feed directly to a hand-held computer (try a Web search for *laser technology*). It is likely that such systems will dominate cave surveying in the future. Still, the most important and time-consuming part of a geologic survey is to track and interpret geologic contacts and other relevant features. These steps cannot be automated.

Survey accuracy

In long surveys such as that at Mystery Cave, the percentage errors in loop closure (error ÷ survey length) are usually small because the minor errors in the shots tend to cancel one another. For example, the number of hand-level readings that are slightly too high should be about the same as those that are slightly too low. In this way, the closure error, as a percentage of total survey length, is usually much smaller for a long loop than for a single shot. Many small shots are preferable to a few long ones in terms of overall accuracy.

Blunders and systematic errors disrupt this pattern. Avoid blunders by reading twice, and have the note-taker repeat the reading verbally. An example of a systematic error is the deflection of a hand-held compass by magnetic materials in a helmet or light, or even by the metal screws in eyeglasses.

A survey instrument should be read as closely as possible, but there is no merit in squeezing out more precision than is justified. Rounding to 0.2 deg instead of forcing a reading to 0.1 deg will make little difference.

Obtaining ties to bench marks

If exact elevations are critical, the cave survey should be tied to the nearest standard bench mark. These are marked in the field by brass caps about 5 cm in diameter, which are cemented into concrete posts or other structures. American topographic maps identify bench marks with a "+" and "BM"

---

* A. and M. Palmer, for the Minnesota Department of Natural Resources, 1993.

and show the elevation to the nearest foot. Precise elevations, locations, and site descriptions are given on the Web site *http://www.ngs.noaa.gov/cgi-bin/ds_mm.prl*. Access must be gained as follows: (1) go to *www.ngs.noaa.gov*; (2) select "data sheets (find/update a point)"; (3) select "datasheet (retrieval link)"; (4) select "rectangular search." To obtain information on bench marks in a certain area, identify the maximum and minimum latitudes and longitudes of the area from the topographic map. For example, W0743000, W0742230, N424500 and N423730, define the area from [74 deg, 22 min, 30 sec] to [74 deg, 30 min, 00 sec] west longitude, and from [42 deg, 37 min, 30 sec] to [42 deg, 45 min, 00 sec] north latitude. These are the coordinates for the Cobleskill, NY, Quadrangle, which includes the bench marks to which McFail's Cave and its neighbors have been tied (Figure 9.45). Select the bench mark of interest and choose "get data sheets."

Bench-mark altitudes are given to the nearest 0.001 foot, although 0.01 to 0.1 foot is the practical limit of accuracy. Many bench marks are missing or obscured, or have shifted. Those on solid structures, such as bridge abutments or bedrock, are most stable. Contour lines on topographic maps are not located precisely enough to be used in place of bench marks during a leveling survey.

From the nearest bench mark, an auto-level survey is best for obtaining the exact elevations of surrounding features, but a transit or theodolite is better if exact horizontal coordinates are also needed. With care, a water-tube survey can be almost as accurate in determining elevations.

Geophysical surveys

Epikarst features and shallow caves can be detected with geophysical surveys (Kirk and Werner, 1981; Lange, 1999; Stierman, 2004; Gibson and others, 2004). For a general description of geophysical field techniques see Dobrin and Savit (1988). Gravity, electrical resistivity, and natural potential are some of the most common geophysical approaches in karst studies. Only large and shallow caves can be detected by these methods. They are best applied to small areas where the presence of caves is already suspected.

Gravity surveys

Gravity surveys detect local differences in the Earth's gravitational field. A highly sensitive meter is required (Figure 14.18), and corrections must be made for elevation, latitude, topography, and variations with time (i.e., from drift in the instrument, changes in the position of the Sun and Moon, etc.). Caves have lower densities than their surroundings and therefore produce zones of relatively low gravitational field (**negative anomalies**). Figure 14.19 shows the anomaly over an ideal tunnel with a circular cross section.

In typical limestone, an air-filled cave passage can be detected reliably by gravity if $Z < d^2$, where Z = depth of the passage midline below the surface, and d = passage diameter (both in meters). For example, a cave 5 m in diameter can be detected if its center is no deeper than about 25 m. Interference from geologic irregularities can

Figure 14.18: A gravity survey.

reduce the detection depth to less than that suggested by the equation. For water-filled caves the maximum detection depth is about 60% of that for an air-filled cave.

Electrical resistivity

Electrical resistivity is the inverse of conductivity and is a property of the material through which the current passes. A resistivity survey involves passing a low-frequency alternating current through the ground between two electrodes. The electrodes consist of metal stakes driven into the soil. In the most popular method, the voltage difference is measured between two additional electrodes placed along the line between the current electrodes, so that all four electrodes are spaced a uniform distance (*a*) from each other (Figure 14.20).

At any given spot, successive readings can be made at increasing values of *a*, so that the electrical field penetrates to progressively greater depths. Electrode spacing is crudely proportional to depth of penetration, so the change in resistivity with depth can be estimated. The results do not give the true resistivity of any single rock unit because all the layers, including the soil, contribute to the readings. The electrode array can also be moved to nearby sites to show the variation of resistivity from place to place. Air-filled caves produce high-resistivity anomalies, and clay-filled or water-filled caves produce low-resistivity anomalies.

Some modern resistivity meters provide automated measurements from a long array of many electrodes. They give a cross-sectional view of the area beneath the array showing the horizontal and vertical resistivity patterns (Figure 14.21). Precise calculation of the data from resistivity profiles requires complex software. Try an Internet search for free demonstration packages (e.g., *Res2dinv* by M.H. Loke).

For example, a resistivity survey was made by McLean and Luke (2006) across Fort Stanton Cave, New Mexico. Many of their profiles showed evidence for known underlying passages. Traverses in areas with no known caves

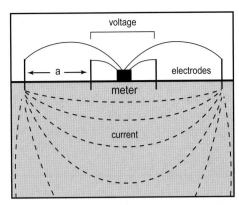

Figure 14.20: A simple 4-electrode resistivity survey. The spacing between adjacent electrodes (a) is usually kept uniform. Current is passed through the outer electrodes and voltage is measured between the inner ones. The effective depth of penetration increases with the electrode spacing.

showed similar anomalies that may indicate undiscovered caves. Their approach used a long array of electrodes and a software calculation routine, but the field readings were made by hand.

Natural potential

A survey of natural potential (also called **spontaneous potential**) involves the measurement of natural electrical fields. The simplest method is to measure the natural voltage between a pair of electrodes placed in the soil. Measurements are made in a systematic grid throughout the field area, while the spacing between the electrodes is kept uniform. A map of the voltage readings may show positive or negative anomalies that represent either zones of water flow or interfaces between different materials. More advanced techniques are also available. Natural potential is especially effective in detecting stream passages, but the relationships between anomaly patterns and cave locations are not as clear as those for most other geophysical techniques.

Magnetic surveys

Magnetic surveys detect differences in magnetism that is induced in iron-rich materials by the Earth's field. Most volcanic rocks have a high magnetic susceptibility, and negative magnetic anomalies over a lava flow may indicate the location of underlying caves (Green, 2003). Because of

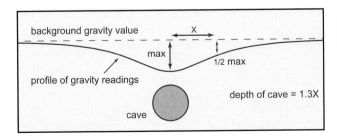

Figure 14.19: A gravity survey can detect the presence of shallow caves where the geology and topography are fairly uniform. The depth from the land surface to the center of the cave can be estimated from the shape of the gravity profile.

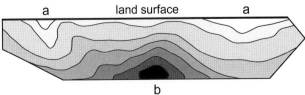

Figure 14.21: Example of an electrical resistivity profile over a solution cave. The light areas labeled **a** (low resistivity) probably indicate varied depths of clay-rich soil over an irregular bedrock surface. The dark area labeled **b** (high resistivity) probably represents a cave. The width of the profile is typically several hundred meters and the depth of penetration a few tens of meters.

distortion of the magnetic field around caves, the low values over the center of a cave may be bordered by slightly elevated readings toward the edges.

On rare occasions, magnetic surveys can be useful for detecting caves in soluble rock. At Magnetometer Pot, in Yorkshire, England, a previous owner was known to have buried the entrance with soil supported by iron rails, and a quick magnetic survey revealed the location.

Ground-penetrating radar

Ground-penetrating radar (GPR) involves generating electromagnetic waves that are directed downward, while an antenna detects reflections caused by differences in electrical or magnetic properties. The instrument is usually towed across the surface while a continuous profile is produced that shows subsurface structures. It is well suited to mapping the soil-bedrock interface, but caves must be fairly shallow to be detected. Under ideal conditions it is possible to detect large objects as deep as 30–50 m, but the effective depth of penetration is diminished by the clay-rich soil typical of most karst areas. Applications of GPR to caves and their sediments are described by Murphy and others (2005) and Chamberlain and others (2000).

Seismic surveys

Seismology is useful for detecting and interpreting earthquakes, and by generating artificial shocks the method can be applied to mapping subsurface structures. This is the most popular method for petroleum prospecting. A shock is produced with an explosive or by impact, and the shock waves are detected with an array of small seismometers called *geophones*. **Reflection seismology** relies on reflections from subsurface boundaries between materials that differ in seismic wave velocity. Reflections received by the geophones are ideal for mapping deep structures. **Refraction seismology** uses similar techniques but is optimized for detecting waves that are refracted through various layers. This method is better for detecting shallow structures. Stratigraphic boundaries, stratal dip, faults, variations in rock type, depth to bedrock, and position of the water table in unconsolidated sediment are some of the typical features that can be mapped with seismic data. But neither seismic method is well suited to detecting caves. Three-dimensional mapping with shallow reflection seismology shows promise, but only if aided by formidable computer processing (Stierman, 2004). Perhaps the best application of seismology to caves is in detecting the geologic structures that determine their location and patterns.

Geologic interpretations

Most geologic cave studies are aimed at revealing the cave's origin, explaining its pattern, and interpreting its relationship to the surrounding landscape. Additional topics are described in other chapters. Some of the most basic approaches are discussed here.

Portraying geologic data

A stratigraphic column (Chapter 3) serves as a good anchor for the geologic interpretation. This can be assembled from local descriptions and measurements of beds in various parts of the cave, or from a leveling survey that extends through all or most of the cave passages. Identifying the position of a passage in the stratigraphic column is like establishing its geologic coordinates.

Geologic contacts can be added to the cave profile and to cross sections on the plan-view map. Be aware that the strata may vary in thicknesses and character from place to place. On the cross sections it is a nice touch to add the weathering character of each bed and of the bedding planes between them, as shown on the stratigraphic column in Figure 3.6. The individuality of each passage becomes clear, and the cave no longer seems like just a dark hole.

Identify the bedding plane, fracture, or other structure that guided the original water flow. Where that information is obscure, a range of possibilities can still be recognized for interpretive purposes. In areas of breakdown, the positions of the original passage ceilings and floors should be indicated, perhaps as dashed lines on the profile. Reconstruction of the cave's geologic history depends on this kind of information. Using this approach, combined with water-tube leveling, Jameson (1985, 2006) shows that where the geology is complex, every passage segment in a cave deserves a unique interpretation of its structural control and evolution.

Passage profiles are normally drawn with an exaggerated vertical scale to reveal more clearly the changes in elevation and gradient. This is usually done also with topographic and geologic cross sections. As a result, passage gradients and bedding dips will also be exaggerated. Too great an exaggeration makes the profile or cross section look bizarre and difficult to comprehend. A vertical exaggeration of 2–10 times is typical, but the choice depends on how well it portrays the data.

Interpreting passage profiles

Profiles from the geologic survey of a cave can be interpreted as in Chapter 9: Passages of vadose origin are likely to extend down the dip, and nearly all of the initial flow paths either follow the strata or cut only downward across the strata. Those with a phreatic origin tend to have no systematic relation to the dip, and many are roughly parallel to the strike. This approach is more rigorous than using only the passage shape (e.g., canyon or tube) to distinguish between the two passage types.

The influence of resistant or poorly soluble beds on cave profiles is helpful in defining the passage origin (Chapter 6). If the initial flow in a passage was perched on a bed of this kind, the passage was probably of vadose origin and fed by water from the overlying surface. A passage lying just below a resistant or insoluble bed may indicate confinement of water that has risen from below.

A helpful example from Mammoth Cave is shown in Figure 14.22. In that region of very low dip and passage gradient, the unusually large 50X vertical exaggeration aids in sorting out the geologic relationships. The passage is at level C in Figures 9.49 and 9.54. The vadose upstream section is perched on a bed of shaly limestone, the Aux Vases Member of the Ste. Genevieve Limestone (Figures 3.6 and 6.13). The phreatic downstream section rises into the overlying Levias Member. Most of the vadose section still contains an active stream. The phreatic section has long been abandoned by its flow, which escaped through shafts and canyons in the passage floor as the base level dropped. Dating of sediment in the phreatic section by Granger and others (2001) shows an age of more than a million years (Chapter 13). This ancient date in a perched and still-active tube shows how variable the rates of cave development can be.

Note the point where the ceiling profile of Waterfall Trail changes from continuously downward to undulatory. This is clearly the position of the former water table. This topic has been explored in Chapter 9. The following section illustrates the benefit of including stratigraphy and structure in leveling surveys.

Recognizing cave levels

Large, low-gradient passages usually represent the major stages of cave development. Did the passages form over a long time at or near base level? Do they follow particularly favorable beds? Are they large simply because they carried a lot of water?

Figure 14.22 shows one way to approach these questions. Floored by shaly limestone, the active stream in Waterfall Trail follows the dip faithfully. Where the dip abruptly changes angle or direction, so does the passage. Sinuosity in the passage trend between A and X on the map is caused by these irregularities. Clearly this is not a true "level." But farther downstream, in the presently dry section, the wide tube migrates away from the top of the shaly limestone and instead follows a parting in the overlying Levias, a much purer limestone (see photo in Figure 14.22). As it does so, the passage bends to a path roughly along the strike and meanders along the parting. The gently undulating ceiling profile between points X and B is caused by the passage wandering along the parting, while looping to various depths below the water table. The vadose-phreatic transition point correlates in elevation with similar passages located in different strata (Figure 9.54), so the phreatic section is not simply the result of ponding in a local structural basin, as in Figure 9.28.

These relationships were determined from a hand-level survey. With average inclinations of less than half a degree, neither the dip nor the gradient is distinguishable by eye, nor are the undulations in the profile. There are many variations in dip in this area, and as a result the effect of geologic structure on the passage trend is obscure on the map. In this example the distinction between the perched tube and the base-level tube is subtle and could be recognized only from the geologic leveling survey.

The tube between points X and B is not very large, but it is one of the largest in the vicinity. It has grown more than its neighbors because of a fairly static

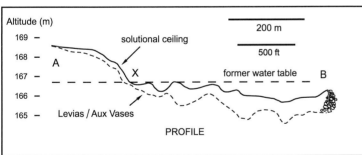

PROFILE

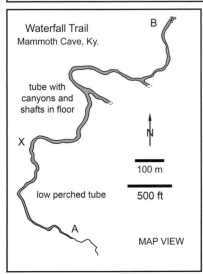

MAP VIEW

Figure 14.22: Map and profile of Waterfall Trail, Mammoth Cave, Kentucky, showing a perched vadose tube grading into a phreatic tube (Palmer, 1977). A, B, and X show the corresponding points on the map and profile. X = former vadose-phreatic transition zone Vertical exaggeration on the profile is **50 times**.

The photo at right shows the Levias / Aux Vases contact (**a**) in the formerly phreatic section of Waterfall Trail. The tubular part of the passage follows a parting (**b**) above the contact. The tube floor has been entrenched as a canyon interspersed with shafts.

base level, as shown by the correlation with other large passages. Waterfall Trail also carried a large flow delivered by the main stream and three tributaries. The combination of large discharge and lengthy time accounts for the passage size. Stratigraphy and structure affected its pattern but were not significant in determining its size.

The former phreatic section has been deeply entrenched by vadose water. To a casual observer this might confuse the relationship between the perched vadose tube and the phreatic tube. The average shaft cross section (viewed vertically) is more than twice the cross-sectional area of the tubular passage above it (viewed horizontally). The shafts are larger because of the great amount of flow spraying outward in waterfalls. Some are still active today (Figure 9.62). The shaly Aux Vases unit that floors the perched tube does not dissolve readily, but it erodes quickly in waterfalls. But all of this vadose enlargement is secondary to the development of the main tube at the ceiling level, both in time and in genetic importance.

Structural evaluation of cave patterns
Structural contouring

If the elevations of a geologic contact or bedding plane can be mapped at many points throughout a cave, contour maps can be drawn on that contact. Each point has three-dimensional coordinates in the east, north, and vertical directions (E, N, and V), and all coordinates are measured relative to the base station of the survey, where the coordinates are 0,0,0. The base station can be anywhere, but it is usually at the cave entrance. Negative E values indicate a point west of the base station, and negative N values indicate a point south of the base station. Points that lie below the entrance have negative V values.

The E, N, V coordinates for each point can be imported into contouring software to produce the contour map. Information on this kind of computer application can obtained from a Web search for *contouring software*. The results are most useful when the information comes from several passages that occupy the same stratigraphic interval. Contouring may be of questionable value if it is based on data from a single passage, although if the passage is highly sinuous it can still reveal many structural details (see Figure 9.28). To obtain more data points on a contact, its elevation of the contact can be calculated by mapping other beds in higher or lower passages and adding or subtracting the thickness of the intervening beds. Small errors caused by variation in bed thickness can be expected.

Figure 14.23 shows the contour map of a prominent geologic contact in Mystery Cave, Minnesota, based on data from auto-level and hand-level surveys through the main passages (see page 372). The contour lines represent the local strike of the beds along the contact. The dip direction is toward the west-northwest, perpendicular to the contour lines. The dip angle can be calculated from the amount of drop over a given horizontal distance. The closer the spacing between contour lines, the steeper the dip angle.

Note the steepening of the dip from area B to area A. Part of the main passage that connects the southwestern and northeastern sections of the cave appears to follow the line between A and B, as though this zone of flexing afforded the most favorable path for cave development. This idea could use further investigation.

The contour map in Figure 14.23 is based on a very uneven distribution of data points. Although the maze pattern made it possible to obtain data over a wide area, the conditions outside the limits of the cave remain unknown. A quarry north of the map boundary provided several data points, but they have little effect on the contouring around the cave. The patterns of lines near the borders of the map (zones marked D) are not valid, as they merely represent the software's attempt to extend the cave data outward into the unknown. The steepening of dip from B to A is valid because of the high density and broad coverage of data points in the vicinity. Note how the clustering of data points can warp the contours (e.g., around point C), where the contouring is adjusted to local structural irregularities. Areas with little data tend to have misleadingly smooth contour lines.

Determining mean dip

It is sometimes useful to calculate the best-fitting plane through a set of geologic data points. From it, the mean dip direction and angle of dip can be determined. The technique also applies to any kind of slope, such as the tops of sediment banks or old pool deposits. Discrepancies between the ideal plane and actual data points can help to reveal local structures, survey errors, or fault displacements. The mean dip direction, dip angle, and strike direction can be determined by performing a planar regression on the data points. The technique is described in most statistics books and is available in advanced statistics software. The result is an equation:

$$V = a + bE + cN \qquad (14.1)$$

where a, b, and c are constants (see footnote on next page*). Given any location on the map, with known east and north (E and N) coordinates, the elevation of the best-fitting plane can be calculated at that point. The average direction and angle of dip can be calculated as follows:

Mean *dip angle* = arctan[sqrt(b^2+c^2)]. Sqrt = square root. Arctan (arctangent) is labeled **tan**$^{-1}$ on most calculators. Be sure the calculator is set to read angles in degrees, rather than radians or grads. To calculate the mean *dip direction* (relative to north), follow this procedure:

Let X = arctan |b/c|, where | | means ignore any minus signs.
If b and c are both positive, dip direction = X + 180 degrees.
If b = positive and c = negative, then dip direction = 360 − X.
If b = negative and c = positive, then dip direction = 180 − X.
If b and c are both negative, then dip direction = X.

Figure 14.23: Structural contour map of Mystery Cave, Minnesota. Contours are on the contact between the dolomitic Stewartville Formation and the overlying shaly limestone of the Dubuque Formation (both of Ordovician age). Elevations on the contact were obtained with auto-level and hand-level surveys. Elevations and distances are in feet, to be compatible with the local topographic map. The outline of the cave is shown in gray. Black dots indicate survey points on the contact. Contouring by *Surfer* (Golden Software, Golden, Colorado). See page 376 for interpretation.

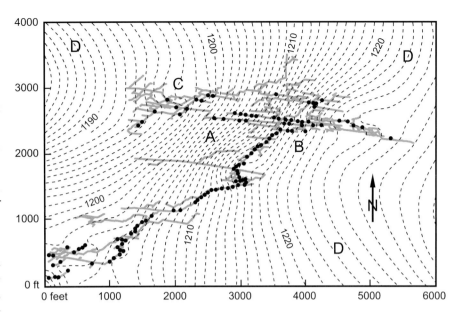

Consider a geologic contact with only 4 data points. The E,N,V coordinates of the four points are (0,0,1), (10,0,2), (0,20,5), and (10,20,7) meters. The best-fitting plane through the points is V = 0.75 + 0.15E + 0.225N. The mean dip angle is 15.1 degrees, and the mean dip direction is 213.7 degrees relative to true north. The strike is perpendicular to the dip direction, at 303.7 or 123.7 degrees (it is a horizontal line that extends in both directions, northwest-southeast).

Once the best-fitting plane is known, the actual data from the cave can be compared to it. Any point that plots above the plane has a measured V value that is higher than that of the best-fitting plane. The opposite is true for a point that falls below the plane. In the problem above, the actual geologic contact at points 2 and 3 lies above the ideal plane, and at points 1 and 4 the contact lies below it.

Deviations from the ideal plane can be plotted, and structural highs and lows can easily be identified. Likewise, local

dips observed in the cave can be compared to the average dip, and local areas of relatively steep or gentle gradient can be determined. Although not so intuitive, this approach is more sensitive than a simple contour map in revealing variations in geologic structure.

Disruptions of the dip

In an ancient cave, the local dip may have changed or even reversed since the cave formed. This may be caused by tectonic movements, or, in nearly horizontal beds, simply by relaxation of the strata through release of stress as overlying rocks are removed by erosion. Disruption of the geologic structure can make it difficult to interpret the cave's origin.

An example is seen in Jewel Cave, in the Black Hills, where the upper level follows an unconformity along a former sulfate zone (Palmer and Palmer, 1989; see Chapter 12). It consists of paleo-caves that pre-date the uplift of the Black Hills. The dip of the unconformity was northwestward when this level formed, but uplift of the mountains about 60 million years ago disrupted the initial structure, and now the overall dip is toward the southwest. Much cave enlargement took place after the tilting, but the original structural control of the upper level can still be inferred from geologic mapping of the passages.

In the 300-meter-deep Obey River Gorge of eastern Tennessee, caves near the bottom of the gorge contain a few canyons that presently extend up a very gentle dip, as shown by leveling surveys. The dip is less than half a degree. It is possible that the canyons originally extended down the dip, as most canyons do, and that later stress release along the ridge flanks has allowed the cavernous beds to flex upward. The caves are up to 1.8 million years old (Anthony and Granger, 2004). Stress release in this area has been cited as a factor in localizing cave development (Sasowsky and White, 1994). Mild dip reversals would fit this scenario,

---

* For those who wish to calculate the best-fitting plane on their own, the procedure is:

Add all the E values (result = ΣE). For simplicity, call the result **A**.
Add all the N values (= ΣN). Call the result **B**.
Add all the V values (= ΣV). Call the result **C**.
Square each E, add them all (= ΣE^2). Call the result **D**.
Square each N, add them all (= ΣN^2). Call the result **F**.
At each point, multiply E times N; add them all (= ΣEN). Result = **G**.
At each point, multiply E times V; add them all (= ΣEV). Result = **H**.
At each point, multiply N times V, add them all (= ΣNV). Result = **J**.
Let **K** = the number of data points. *There must be at least 3!*
Let **L** = D − (G^2/F).
Let **M** = A − (BG/F).
Let **P** = L(C − BJ/F) + M(GJ/F − H).
Let **Q** = M(GB/F − A) − L(B^2/F − K).

Then find a, b, and c in Eq. 14.1:
a = P/Q.
b = [H − aA + G(aB/F − J/F)]/L.
c = (J − aB − bG)/F.

Test this on a tilted plane with only 3 known points. The routine above is correct as printed, but to avoid errors it should be *carefully* programmed into a computer, spreadsheet software, or scientific calculator.

although the evidence for them is not conclusive and needs to be supported by more widespread field data.

In contrast, leveling surveys in Mammoth Cave, Kentucky, show no discrepancy between passage pattern and present dips, despite the fact that the cave is several million years old and occupies beds with dips that average only about a third of a degree (Palmer, 1989a; Granger and others, 2001). Topographic relief in the Mammoth Cave region is only about 100 m, and the rate of river entrenchment is relatively slow. Both the relief and erosion rate are much lower than at the Obey River Gorge, and stress release along valleys at Mammoth Cave is more uniform and not so intense.

Correlation of cave deposits

In the geologic survey of a cave, it is important to include the elevations and character of cave deposits. This information can be useful in determining episodes of sediment accumulation and whether they represent widespread events or only local conditions. For example, sediments in the upper levels of caves in central Kentucky and Tennessee correlate with those throughout the entire region, both underground and on the surface, and they can be dated (Granger and others, 2001; Anthony and Granger, 2004). Mapping of their distribution over large areas can help to clarify the regional sedimentary and climatic history.

Most speleothems reflect only local conditions, but some have widespread significance. Lechuguilla Cave, New Mexico, contains many calcite wall crusts that formed under water after the cave formed. They have a variety of colors contributed by weathering residue from the local bedrock (Chapter 12), so they considerably post-date the cave origin. Deposits of this sort often form in perched pools that have no relation to each other, but geologic mapping shows that the tops of the major deposits and water lines in Lechuguilla lie at essentially the same elevation throughout the cave, within the limits of accuracy of the tripod-mounted Brunton and tape survey (Figure 14.24). They indicate a widespread rise in the water table after the cave had previously drained, and suggest that there has been no measurable tilting of the mountain block since then. The correlation is not as simple as it might appear, because the walls below the uppermost pool deposits are commonly bare or are covered only by rafts, folia, or thin veneers of calcite, and many pool deposits are removed entirely by later weathering.

Interpreting cave origin

One of the major goals of a geologic cave study is to determine the cave's origin. This topic is best approached after the basic geologic mapping and interpretation are well underway. Details are given in earlier chapters, so only a few suggestions are offered here.

Several questions arise: What was the water source? What was the source of the solutional aggressiveness? How did the water move through the cave, and where did it discharge? The answers will help to characterize the cave as one of the types described in Chapters 8, and 9.

Figure 14.24: Water line from a late-stage rise of water in the Near East of Lechuguilla Cave, New Mexico. The person is pointing to the upper of two visible lines. The highest distinct water lines and tops of pool deposits lie at the same elevation throughout the various branches of the cave (see map of cave in Figure 8.67). Photo by Mark Tracy.

As suggested in previous chapters, any interpretation of cave origin must fit the local geologic history and obey hydrologic and chemical principles. Nearly all solution caves form along the paths of greatest discharge through the soluble strata.

Even in old fragments of caves it is usually possible to identify the former drainage patterns. This distinction is often clear from cave maps and profiles. Sediments usually indicate a variety of flow rates, and they can indicate source areas and former patterns of water flow (Chapter 6).

The nature of the recharge can change with time. For example, floodwater often imposes its own characteristics on caves that originated by some other mechanism. Hypogenic caves are frequently invaded by surface water and their original character may be masked.

Guidelines for interpreting cave origin are summarized on pages 230–231 and 270.

Relation to regional geologic history

The final step in acquiring a basic understanding of a cave is to relate it to the geologic history of the region. This puts the cave into perspective and paves the way toward a dialog with geologists in other fields. An extensive literature search is helpful, so the cave interpretation can be built on a solid foundation of previous work. Even the oldest literature contains useful details, even if some of its ideas have been superseded.

The history begins with deposition of the rocks. Many cave characteristics are determined by the nature of the rocks and the structure they acquired during and after deposition. Again, some important questions arise: Were the rocks buried by younger ones before caves began to develop? Did anything happen to the rocks while they were covered? What caused the rocks to be exposed at the surface? How long ago was that? How does the cave relate to the evolution of the present landscape? These topics are discussed in Chapters 7–9.

The survey techniques discussed in this chapter can be extended to the surface around the cave. Few of the pertinent karst features are shown on topographic maps or digital elevation models, so some exploration on the surface is appropriate. Surveying the distribution and elevations of these features will help to relate them to the cave. It may be useful to include them on the cave map.

Identification of major phases of cave development, together with dating of cave deposits, can provide information about the cave's relation to the surrounding region. In this way, the cave may tell more about the landscape evolution than most surface investigations.

Comparison with other caves

To understand the geology and development of a cave, it is helpful to visit other caves in the region, as well as caves with entirely different settings and origins. The contrast with other caves gives an important perspective. Personal experience in all of the cave types described in Chapter 8 can enhance one's understanding of any single kind of cave. There is also merit in long-term studies, where a cave is revisited many times over the years and its interpretation is modified repeatedly on the strength of insight gained from other regions.

Testing interpretations for validity

In scientific research an idea is tested by making a large number of observations or measurements and determining how well they support the idea. Anyone who wishes to apply for a grant, submit plans for an academic thesis, or publish the results, should outline the procedures exactly, determine what ideas will be tested, and devise a way to test each one for validity. The goals may change with time, but each change should be accompanied by adjustments in the research design. This rigorous approach is not necessary in casual projects that are done for pleasure, but even so it can help to guide the project.

Hypothesis testing

It is impossible to *prove* a hypothesis, but it is important to estimate how likely it is to be true. Statistical tests for validity are used routinely in fields such as medicine, biology, and psychology, in which current phenomena can be observed, and where the outcome is not easy to predict from natural laws. Lehmann (1997) provides a good background for general hypothesis testing.

In geology this approach is more difficult, especially where samples are sparse and non-uniform, or where processes have ceased to operate long ago. But geological processes are governed by natural laws of physics and chemistry, and an idea can be tested by how well it fits those laws. The governing principles may include conservation of mass and energy, chemical equilibria, and flow equations. Examples are given in previous chapters.

Interpretations should be tempered by the possibility that past conditions may have been different from those of today. This is most often true for the chemistry and flow of water. Over geologic time it is also true for the character of the local rocks, minerals, landscapes and caves.

An interpretation is best supported by quantitative measurements, rather than speculation on the basis of appearance alone. The problem is to show not just that an idea is feasible, but that it is the *only* reasonable explanation. Multiple hypotheses are appropriate, so that the research does not reach a dead end if a single interpretation fails. More seriously, a single-minded researcher can easily come to the wrong conclusions.

Statistical tests

Some geologic research can be evaluated by traditional statistical tests, many of which are available on common spreadsheet software. The use of statistics in geology is covered thoroughly by Davis (2002). Only a brief glimpse is given here.

Suppose, for example, that several dozen scallops are measured in each of two passages. Is there a statistically valid difference between the two samples? Each sample must be selected at random. Each measurement must be independent of the others, and the entire group should be homogeneous in general character. For example, the study is not valid if the researcher chooses the scallops by how large or accessible they are. It is also not appropriate to measure scallops that happen to be adjacent to each other, for convenience. A sample should not consist of several different types of scallops, for example a combination of those produced by low flow and those produced by flooding from a nearby river. Ideally each sample should have the same variability and a normal (bell-shaped) size distribution.

The two samples are then compared to each other statistically. For example, a *t-test* determines whether there is a significant difference between the mean values of the two samples. The degree of confidence that there is a significant difference between the samples increases with sample size and decreases with the amount of scatter in the samples.

One of the most popular statistical approaches in geology is *regression analysis*, where the best-fitting line is calculated for the data (for example, in a comparison of scallop length vs. sediment grain size). Examples are shown in Figures 5.22 and 7.20. A straight line or various types of curves can be applied to the data according to how the variables relate to each other. For three-dimensional data, in the form X-Y-Z, the best-fitting plane or curved surface can be calculated. An example is shown in the footnote on page 377.

There are two indicators of how well the line or surface fits the data. The *standard error* indicates, essentially, the average deviation of the points from the best-fitting line. The *correlation coefficient* is a measure of how closely the shape of the line fits the trend of the data (see Figure 7.20). For a perfect fit, the correlation coefficient is +1.0 for a positive slope and −1.0 for a negative slope. The value of −0.8 in Figure 7.20 is considered a fairly good indication that the two variables relate to each other. But showing a correlation does not prove a direct cause-effect relationship. They may both depend on other factors that are not considered.

Conceptual models

Interpretations of caves and karst, such as those in Chapter 7, are often described as *hypotheses* or *theories*, but these terms are rarely appropriate for such a multifaceted topic. The most robust interpretations are based on a combination of field observation and application of physical principles, and are best described as **conceptual models**. Such models may gain or lose favor as new evidence is found, but even if a model is shown to apply in only a few cases (or even in none), it still remains available for use when needed. For example, the concept of deep-phreatic cave development, favored by some early researchers, fell into disfavor in the mid-1900s but has since been validated in many field areas. Only if a conceptual model contains a demonstrable flaw in reasoning is it appropriate to dismiss it entirely.

Common pitfalls in cave research

There are several potential stumbling blocks in geologic research, and most of them apply to any kind of research. Fortunately they are easily avoided if one is aware of them.

Flawed research design

The greatest challenge when starting a project is to ask the right questions. Some otherwise competent work has simply followed the wrong path. An example is the early emphasis on water-table control on cave development, which was later shown to have little relevance to the actual process of cave origin (Chapter 7).

Even when the goal is valid, it is easy to stumble over details. Suppose that one's goal is to show whether the presence of dolomite-limestone contacts is critical to cave development in a particular field area. Sure enough, such contacts are discovered in every cave passage of walking size. But after publication, someone points out that the entire carbonate sequence consists of interbedded dolomite and limestone with intervals of less than two meters, and that every large passage would necessarily intersect at least one of them. This example is not exaggerated.

Another common mistake is to assume that flaws in one argument automatically support a contrasting idea. An interpretation must be based on positive evidence and cannot be proved simply by casting doubt on others.

A common saying in geology is "The present is the key to the past." This is generally true for processes, but keep in mind that topography, climate, and geologic settings have varied with time. Some changes can take place even over short time spans. In studies of cave enlargement, for example,

it is easy to miss the major floods during which most of the enlargement takes place.

It is also tempting to assume that a visual similarity implies a functional one. This is a common mistake. For example, the wiggly trickles of water on a sloping glass plate have been compared by several researchers to meanders in rivers. Their publications suggested that the behavior of the trickles could even help to *explain* the origin of river meanders. Even though such measurements may show a valid statistical fit, there is no proof of a functional relationship. Old-time field geologists used to say, "If two things look the same, they've got to be different."

Problems of sampling

Most geologic studies require sampling. Measurement of water flow and chemistry pose little problem, but the number of good examples of geologic features is clearly finite. It is a sad fact that most sampling leads nowhere. Samples should be taken only if they are likely to produce tangible results, and only after their general geologic setting is known. Check with earlier researchers to make sure your study is not redundant. Unique features should never be sampled, regardless of how important they might seem to one's research.

Observations of subsurface features are limited to only a few sites. For example, much published subsurface information comes from drill holes, but they give only local glimpses of underground conditions. Caves provide more continuous data and first-hand views, but even their exposures are of limited extent. Mines can offer good three-dimensional views but are usually restricted to narrow zones of economic deposits.

After a project is completed, it is helpful if remaining samples are made available to other researchers. Samples obtained from federal or state lands should be returned to the appropriate agency, as long as it offers a secure repository with proper documentation.

Misapplication of principles

The difficulty in applying physical principles to a geologic problem is that they must be fully understood by the researcher. Often a person will grasp at a relationship that is only partly applicable, or which does not apply to the subject at all. Few people are immune to this problem, because the state of knowledge in all scientific fields is so vast.

For example, some early researchers noted that calcite dissolution increases greatly with the rate of flow of hydrochloric acid (Chapter 7). This assumption was used in several early interpretations that led to confusion about cave origin. It was later shown that calcite dissolution rates, at the moderate to high pH of typical karst water, are affected only a little by velocity.

Worse is the use of personal impressions instead of valid principles. Some real examples include the impression that a feature "looks old," or that it must be of thermal origin because it differs from what one sees in a typical stream cave. People often continue to support their original ideas long after new information contradicts them.

Failure of dynamic similarity

When an experiment is made with a scale model, it is critical to scale down (or, rarely, up) not just the size of the model but also the ratio of forces involved. This provides ***dynamic similarity*** between the model and the real thing. For example, it is possible to build a very stable model of an overhanging cliff with foam rubber, but it tells nothing about the stability of a real outcrop, because the model differs so much from the real thing in its ratio of stress to resistance.

In hydrology, a model that involves open-channel flow or floating bodies must have roughly the same Froude Number (Eq. 4.3) as in the real case. In studies of closed-conduit flow, bodies immersed in fluid, or flow in which fluid viscosity has a significant effect, the Reynolds Number (Eq. 4.2) must be approximately the same for both the model and the original. An important criterion that is widely overlooked is that the hydraulic gradient in the model must be identical to that in the field, unless special adjustments are made to compensate for the difference.

Past studies that compared the meandering of tiny dribbles of water to that of rivers (described on the previous page) failed to take into account dynamic similarity. Not only were the Froude Number and Reynolds Number wildly different between the models and the real thing, but so was the ratio of surface tension to gravitational force. There was also a great difference in hydraulic gradient.

In any model the physical or chemical processes must be the same as in the field. For example, it is not appropriate to use dissolution of salt to model karst development in limestone because the dissolution kinetics and processes are different. Nevertheless, salt models have been used successfully to demonstrate how solution conduits link with one another (Chapter 7), because the contrast in dissolution rates does not disrupt the linking process.

Pigeonholing

It is tempting to group geologic events into discrete episodes, in which each one is considered to end before the next begins. This is rarely true in geology, where processes continually increase and decrease in intensity, overlap with each other, and recur periodically. Cave development is often viewed as a sequence of discrete steps: phreatic dissolution, followed by vadose dissolution, sedimentation, abandonment by streams, and finally speleothem growth. In reality, these events usually overlap a great deal.

Narrowness of scope

Many researchers draw the boundaries too tightly around their topics, while the correct answers lie outside. An example is the doomed attempt in the early 20th century to explain Carlsbad Cavern as the product of carbonic acid in meteoric water. The idea that there could be any other kind of cave origin was not considered at that time. Evidence for a sulfuric acid origin was plainly visible, but expanded horizons were needed before the clues could be interpreted (Chapter 7).

A typical cave study

Onesquethaw Cave, in Albany County, New York, has been described as a classic example of a floodwater cave, in which not only its origin but its entire pattern depends on the interaction between a sinking stream and the local geology (Palmer, 1972). It is located in limestones of the Devonian-age Onondaga Formation. The cave is small, wet, and by some standards unpleasant, but few caves show so much geologic variety over such a short distance. The cave map and geologic setting are shown in Figures 14.25–14.28. The following paragraphs illustrate how the cave can be interpreted at a very fundamental level.

Cave description

The limestone bench in which the cave is located is in a perfect position to receive recharge from sinking streams. Streams pour into the limestone from nearby hills of insoluble rock, and an entrenched valley along the edge of the bench serves as a convenient outlet (Figure 14.25).

Onesquethaw Cave is just one of several caves that formed in this area. The cave was surveyed with a compass and tape, and later its profile and geology were mapped with a water tube in the main passages and with a hand level elsewhere. The map is shown in Figure 14.27. The sinking stream that feeds the cave has a low flow of about 10 liters/sec and a typical yearly peak flow of at least 3 m^3/sec. During low flow the water sinks several hundred meters upstream from the entrance and emerges through a fissure along a lateral

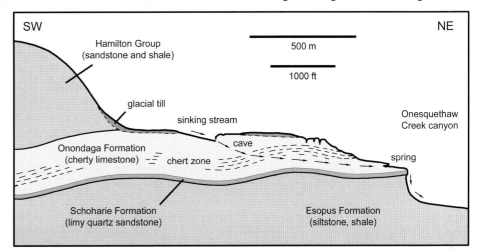

Figure 14.25: Geologic setting of Onesquethaw Cave, NY. Vertical exaggeration is 8X.

fault midway through the cave (location **L** on Figure 14.27). During higher discharge most of the water overflows into the entrance (location **A**). The entire cave fills with water every few years during the highest floods. Logs jammed into the entrance passage at ceiling level are shifted and replaced by periodic flooding.

The entrance passage (**B** on Figure 14.27) is a narrow canyon that extends directly down the local 2.5° dip. This passage is paralleled by another canyon (**C**) whose ceiling follows the same bedding-plane parting as the entrance passage. Canyon **C** contains only a small stream that is fed by a shallow soil-choked sinkhole. This canyon has entrenched less than half the depth of the entrance passage. It deviates from the dip in a few places where it is guided by fractures.

Both canyons have been pirated by a lateral fault that extends through much of the cave. A fissure (**E**) along the fault lies nearly along the strike of the beds. Where it intersects the fault, canyon **C** drops into the main passage through a small shaft (**D**). The fault and other deformation features in the limestone were formed during the late phases of Appalachian uplift about 200–300 million years ago. There has been no major compression of the area since that time, and earlier phases of deformation pre-date the limestone.

The fault-controlled fissure, which carries the main stream, cuts through several closely spaced chert beds up to 20 cm thick that are offset slightly by the fault. The stream continues through a low, down-dip crawlway sandwiched between chert beds, then intersects a second fissure (**G**). At one time, as recently as 1968, this fissure extended downward more than 4 m into lower passages (shown on the profile). It has since been filled to the level of the incoming crawlway by gravel derived from erosion of the hills of sandstone and shale that overlook the cave. Most of this filling took place during a single flood in 1969. While low-level passages fill partly with sediment, their ceilings continue to enlarge upward by paragenesis (pages 264–265).

For several hundred meters the passage jogs irregularly across about a dozen chert beds (**H**). It descends steeply across the beds along a low-angle thrust fault and then bends 90° to follow the strike of the beds along the northwestern flank of a small but abrupt anticline. (See also Figure 14.26.) From here on, the main passage has a low gradient and lies only slightly above the level of the present spring. White gash veins of calcite indicate severe deformation of the bedrock. They contrast vividly with the dark gray limestone.

At one point (**J**) the passage appears to terminate in a blank wall, but a fissure in the floor leads to a continuation between chert beds that bends 180° directly beneath the incoming passage. Two other passages bypass this point to form a crude anastomotic pattern.

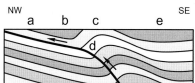

Figure 14.26: Simplified structural cross section through Onesquethaw Cave: (**a**) = gently dipping beds exposed in canyons; (**b**) = syncline; (**c**) = anticline paralleled by tubular passages; (**d**) = thrust fault, which forms local bedding-plane thrusts exposed in canyons; (**e**) = broad syncline exposed in Jordan Cave.

The main passage sweeps upward, following the 25° dip of the anticlinal flank, and again encounters the lateral fault. Here the fault cuts obliquely across the axis of the anticline and provides a path for the main stream (**K**), which forms a deep water-table pool. Water from the sinking stream enters through a deep fissure in the floor (**L**). A bedding-controlled crawlway complex (**M**) skirts along the western flank of the anticline and bypasses the fault passage. The crawls feed a narrow canyon that jogs along fissures where it crosses the axis of the anticline.

The last third of the cave is a parallel array of anastomotic tubes (**N**) that follows the strike of the beds along the eastern flank of the anticline. The local dip is about 15° in this area. The anticlinal axis plunges about a degree toward the southwest, in the opposite direction from the trend of the main passage. As a result, the stream migrates away from the fold axis into a gentle adjacent syncline. A divable sump (**P**) about 120 m long leads to the deep waters of Jordan Cave. This cave follows the contours of the syncline in a broad arc toward the southwest. The stream emerges at a spring (**Q**) perched on the sandstone of the underlying Schoharie Formation. The stream cascades into the entrenched valley of Onesquethaw Creek through a slot-like side canyon, which is guided by the same fault that appears in the cave.

Interpretation

This project was done long ago out of personal interest, and there was no discrete research design. Instead, various ideas were formulated as the field work progressed, and their validity was tested later by applying hydraulic theory. This backward approach is common but inefficient. In many geologic studies it is first necessary to determine what is there before planning what to do with it. Perhaps this approach is not so aimless as it seems.

The overall pattern of Onesquethaw Cave consists of down-dip vadose canyons tributary to a strike-oriented tube of phreatic origin. The cave was generated exclusively by the sinking stream, because all passages emanate from past and present sink points. The earliest routes evidently followed the same pattern, but with their vadose-phreatic transitions at a higher elevation. This early pattern is visible today as the ceiling levels of the canyons (**B** and **C**) as well as the high-level tubes that were once their continuations on the southeastern side of the fault. The two tubes merge into a single passage that bends along the strike and shortly becomes impassably low (**F**). The change from dip to strike orientation in these passages is located about 13 m above the present spring and higher than any passages farther in the cave. This level appears to represent the original water table when the cave first began to form. It correlates roughly with an erosional bench that lies above the present spring (Figure 14.27). So

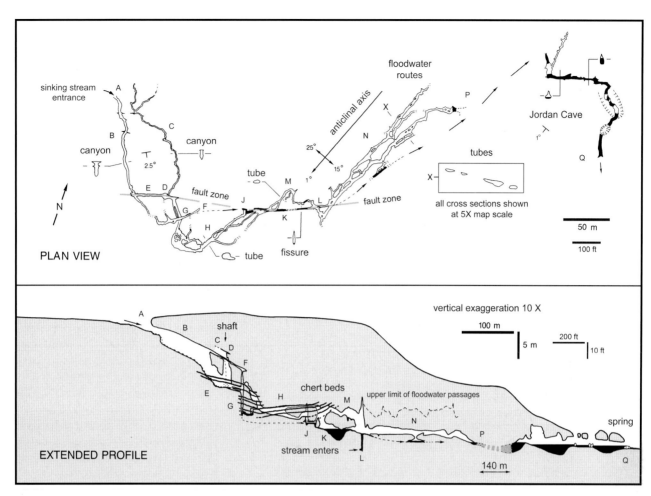

Figure 14.27: Map and profile of Onesquethaw Cave, Albany County, New York.

Figure 14.28: A geologic tour of Ones-quethaw Cave (the large parts). Locations are identified by letters on the map, Figure 14.27. *Top, left to right:* entrance canyon (**B** on map); fault-guided fissure with offset chert beds (**E**); fissure (**F**) floored by 3 m of gravel and sand deposited in a single flood; fault-guided fissure in floor, through which sinking stream enters (**L**); gash veins along fault at **L**. *Bottom, left to right:* anastomotic maze of floodwater tubes along the eastern flank of the anticline (**N**); Jordan Cave spring (**Q**).

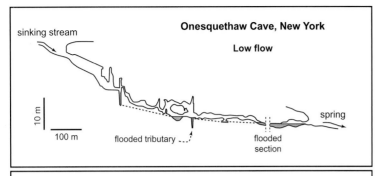

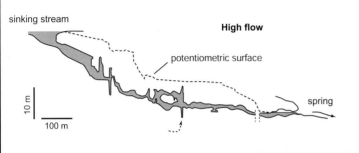

Figure 14.29: Onesquethaw Cave during low flow (**a**) and during severe floods (**b**), when the cave fills completely with water. During floods the calculated potentiometric surface lies far above the cave ceiling. This is the level to which water would rise in a well penetrating the cave. In places the potentiometric surface rises in the downstream direction because the high velocity creates a relatively low pressure. These results are based on head-loss equations similar to those used to construct Figure 8.14.

it is fairly certain that when the sinking stream first began to form the cave, the water table lay about 10 m below the stream bed.

The fault has a major influence on the passages. In several places, however, bedding-controlled passages bypass the fault, even where the fault provides a more direct route (as at **M** in Figure 14.27). The fault did not form later than these bedding passages, because the main passage follows it in places, as at **E**. The fault probably widened physically with time as the result of erosional unloading. The relatively recent stresses caused by glacial depression and rebound are likely to have had the greatest effect. Solutional widening of fissures must have became more intense with time. One result is diversion of the main stream along the fault to form a lower phreatic route (**L**). It is interesting to note that this relatively deep flow path is superseding a shallower one. See Chapters 7 and 9 for discussions on this topic.

The basic pattern of the cave has been complicated by periodic flooding and occasional diversions of the main stream to alternate routes. Flooding has also superposed complex loops and fissures on the original cave. Passages formed in this way can be recognized by irregular profiles that do not relate to each other or to a stable water table. Blind fissures have also formed by aggressive water injected into fractures during high flow. The hydraulics and chemistry of this process are described in Chapters 5 and 8. Because the cave floods to the ceiling every few years, enlargement is still taking place (Figure 4.8). In one passage, several cen-

timeters of bedrock were removed by dissolution and abrasion in about 10 years.

A minor incident during a mapping trip illustrates the nature of flooding in the cave. When we entered, there was a modest stream flowing in, but not enough to cause concern. As usual, it disappeared into a fissure at point G on Figure 14.27 and reappeared at point J. But we noticed that the inflow at point J was far less than the inflow at the entrance. If more flow enters a system than leaves it, there must be a gain in storage in the system and the water level is rising somewhere. We turned back to find that water was in fact rising through side passages and beginning to fill the only negotiable crawlway out of the cave (between H and J). Clogging of the fissure with sediment and vegetal debris was apparently responsible. Attention to Eq. 4.15 helped to avoid an uncomfortable waiting period in the cave.

In the spirit of designing alternative hypotheses, could we consider the many blind fissures in the cave to be deep phreatic predecessors of the main cave that were simply intersected by later dissolution from the sinking stream? This possibility is mentioned occasionally in the speleological literature, and, as shown in Chapter 8, it is distinctly feasible in many areas. But it is not an option at Onesquethaw Cave, because many of the fissures branch from passages that are diversion routes around earlier paths of water. They are all located where flooding is most intense today and are likely to be contemporaries of the sinking stream. Calcite fill, which is so abundant in the hypogenic gash veins exposed in the cave, does not occur along the fractures that guide the fissures. Finally, a computation of the head distribution in the cave when it is in flood shows that even the highest fissures are entirely filled with water at those times (Figure 14.29).

Sediment and scallop studies (M. Palmer, 1976) show that cobble diameters, which range up to 15 cm, correlate poorly with mean flow velocities determined from scallops. This is apparently a result of sediment redistribution during short-term floods. Passages are occasionally filled with sediment during floods, and at other times the sediment is excavated. All of these observations indicate a dynamic cave that is still very active today. No single piece of evidence is proof of a floodwater origin for many of the passages, but their cumulative weight comes fairly close.

The region was exposed to the latest (Wisconsinan) glaciation, which reached its maximum extent about 20,000 years ago and ended about 14,000 years ago. The limestone bench in which the cave is located is covered by patchy glacial sediment. At first glance the entire cave appears to be post-glacial, because in places the sinking stream crosses this sediment, and the cave is well adjusted to the location and flow of the present sinking stream. Dissolution rates given in Chapter 7 suggest that in ideal conditions the entire cave could have formed since the glaciation. U/Th analyses of speleothems by Lauritzen and Mylroie (1996, 2000) give ages of about 10,000 years or less, which might seem to support the post-glacial hypothesis.

But the speleothems post-date most of the cave enlargement, and it is unlikely that the cave could have reached nearly its present size within the preceding few thousand years. Instead it appears that the cave pre-dates the latest glaciation, and that the present sinking stream has simply recovered its earlier pre-glacial pattern despite disruption by the glacial deposits. Some speleothem dates elsewhere in the region extend beyond 350,000 years (Lauritzen and Mylroie, 1996), which shows that caves can persist undamaged beneath several kilometers of glacial ice.

This case study is offered here to show the kinds of interpretation that can be made with simple equipment and no research budget. U/Th dating is clearly not in this category, but it was also not part of the original study. Many lines of inquiry have been left hanging. A likely target for future research would be continuous monitoring of water levels (and pressures during high flow), combined with chemical data, which would provide information about the dynamics of floodwater in relation to cave enlargement.

Further goals

The projects described in this chapter have answered some of the basic questions about the geology, origin, and pattern of individual caves. These are just the first steps in understanding the karst of their regions. Paths for further study are described in other chapters. Many of these topics are accessible to anyone with the interest and energy to do the field work.

The most technical advances in science, however, require extensive equipment and support, which is available mainly at universities and research centers. Advanced research is best pursued with a strict timetable and goals. It is important to stay abreast of developments in the technical literature, attend conferences, and share ideas. Most large-scale science is collaborative now, because few individuals have all the necessary resources and background to pursue it alone. Chapter 13 contains several examples of this kind of project.

Most cave studies are done on a more intimate level and have different expectations. This leaves ample room for amateurs (in the finest sense of the word) to pursue science for the love of it. Some highly technical articles are produced by individuals who rely on low-budget approaches such as geologic mapping, computer modeling, and field chemistry.

15

Application of cave geology to other geosciences

KARST AND CAVES can have serious environmental and economic impacts, some positive and some negative. Cave origin and distribution play an important role in several diverse fields, such as water supply, engineering, petroleum geology, mining, and geologic interpretation.

Regrettably, most textbooks in hydrology and geology mention karst only in the most simplistic way. Several books by karst specialists have helped to fill the gap in recent years (e.g., Milanović, 1981, 2000, 2004; Bonacci, 1987; White, 1988; White and White, 1989; Ford and Williams, 1989, 2007; and Klimchouk and others, 2000). These are read mainly by karst specialists, and their message has not yet spread widely into other fields. But by a gradual diffusion of ideas, karst is becoming more widely appreciated. Some credit is also due to recent articles in professional journals and news magazines. The American Geological Institute has published an informative booklet, *Living with Karst*, written by cave specialists, which clearly illustrates the engineering and environmental problems encountered in karst regions (Veni and others, 2001). Recent national conventions of the Geological Society of America have included more sessions on karst than on most other fields of geology.

This exchange of ideas is a two-way street. Other geosciences benefit from speleology, but speleologists have just as much to gain from the fields described in this chapter. Even topics that seem remote from cave science, such as petroleum geology and mining, can shed a great deal of light on cave origin.

The problem of sampling bias

It is not always easy to apply a knowledge of caves to the geologic and hydrologic problems described in this chapter. A speleologist's view is limited mainly to caves that are large enough to explore. It is tempting to think that the porosity encountered in wells is simply a small version of traversable caves, but this is rarely true, and it is inappropriate simply to extrapolate cave observations to much smaller scales. It is also difficult to project known cave patterns beyond their limits of exploration. Any statistical treatment of data must be limited to what can be observed and measured. Adding to this data base is one of the greatest contributions of cave explorers and mappers.

A few basic statistical approaches have been successful in evaluating cave distribution and patterns (Curl, 1986). For example, the number of caves in an area can be plotted against the number of their known entrances. Those with one entrance are more common than those with more entrances. Extrapolating the graph to zero entrances offers a possible estimate of the number of caves yet to be discovered (Varnadoe, 1973).

Still, the general application of speleology to other fields, as described in this chapter, is greatly limited by sampling bias. This problem is not unique to speleology, because all subsurface information is similarly limited. Any science that relies on drill holes and geophysics for its data has an even greater problem with sampling bias. Well information is usually limited to scattered points that relate poorly to each other in their hydrology, geochemistry, and geologic structure. They are discontinuous and do not reflect the gradual evolution of groundwater flow and chemistry from inputs to outlets.

For these reasons, one of the most promising (and most pressing) topics for future research is to integrate speleological observations with data from wells, cores, and mines. The vast majority of drilling logs, cores, mining records, and geophysical data have been irretrievably lost. A great boost to karst science and to geology in general would be to establish repositories for this kind of information, to make it available to researchers in all fields.

Water supply

Roughly one quarter of the world's population obtains its water from karst aquifers (Onac, 2000). Surprisingly, though, the interactive relationship between groundwater supply and solution caves has been widely ignored by many traditional groundwater hydrologists (Ewers, 2006).

As described in Chapter 4, karst aquifers possess three kinds of porosity: intergranular pores, narrow fissures that have little or no solutional enlargement, and solution conduits (including caves). Virtually all intergranular pores and narrow fissures transmit laminar flow, while the flow in solution conduits is nearly always turbulent.

Most of the *water volume* in a karst aquifer consists of laminar flow through narrow openings that have been enlarged little, if at all, by dissolution. On the other hand, most of the *discharge* takes place through solution conduits in which water moves rapidly. Conduits form along favorable flow paths, and as they enlarge they capture progressively more water until they become the main drains for the aquifer. Groundwater

Figure 15.1: A well test to determine aquifer properties.

Figure 15.2: Trash-filled sinkholes are common sources of groundwater contamination.

Figure 15.3: Foam accumulates in this cave stream contaminated by barnyard runoff.

tends to move toward active conduits from surrounding narrow openings, just as it does toward surface river valleys. Many conduits are continuous from groundwater inputs all the way to springs. Even where conduits are punctuated by breakdown, the turbulent flow is rarely interrupted. Although the turbulent-flow conduits are also fed by laminar seepage through small pores or fissures, few conduits are known to disperse downstream into laminar flow routes.

In a typical non-karst aquifer, a few simple pumping tests are enough to reveal the aquifer's ability to deliver water (Figure 15.1). This is not true in cavernous regions. Most wells penetrate only non-solutional openings, and their yields are similar to those in other types of fractured bedrock. They reveal a permeability that is rarely more than that of sand. Wells that encounter cave streams, or even slightly enlarged solution conduits, may be able to deliver almost unlimited quantities of water while experiencing almost no drop in water level. Unfortunately the advantage of high well yield is usually offset by poor water quality.

Contrasting viewpoints

It seems odd that these simple ideas are not more widely recognized, because they are crucial to understanding the issues of water supply and water quality in karst. One of the main reasons for this gap is that the information obtained by traditional groundwater hydrologists is substantially different from that of karst specialists.

Most speleologists have an intuitive feel for karst hydrology because they have a first-hand view of cave processes. To them, caves are the key to understanding karst groundwater. And what they see is not encouraging: caves transmit water so rapidly, and with so little filtering, that the quality of most cave water is poor by drinking-water standards (Figures 15.2–15.3). But

many speleologists fail to appreciate the importance of the non-conduit parts of a karst aquifer.

Few groundwater hydrologists obtain field information from caves. Instead they nearly always rely on well tests. Usually what they see resembles the conditions found in most kinds of fractured bedrock. That is because the majority of well production is from narrow non-cavernous fissures. (This is less true in young, highly porous limestones such as those of Florida.) Even those wells that encounter caves rarely draw water from them. It is normal for well drillers to seal off the caves with casings to isolate the cave water from the well (Figure 15.4). Furthermore, well tests rarely show any evidence for conduits, so it is natural for hydrologists to assume that caves have little or no effect on water supply. Some have the opinion that *cavers* study caves and springs, but *professionals* study wells.

Even though most wells in karst are not affected significantly by conduits, it is wrong to ignore them. To do so is equivalent to ignoring the effect of surface stream valleys on groundwater flow.

A tragic case history

The difference in viewpoint between karst specialists and traditional hydrologists is more than philosophical. Worthington and others (2003) describe an example of what can go wrong when rapid flow in solution conduits is ignored:

In the spring of 2000, a small town in Ontario was struck by an outbreak of pathogenic bacteria, including *Escherichia coli* (the virulent strain O157:H7) and *Campylobacter jujuni*. Seven people died and more than 2000 people became ill, some chronically. The contamination was traced to the village water wells. Ordinarily the water would have received sufficient chlorination to meet the threat, but at that time the level of treatment was inadequate. The bacteria closely matched those from nearby fields on which manure had been spread a few weeks before.

The wells are located in an aquifer of limestone and dolomite, and there are nearby karst springs with flows as much as 20 liters/sec. No traversable caves are known in the area, but solution conduits are clearly present.

A costly study was made by a team of highly regarded consultants. After extensive pumping tests and groundwater modeling, the conclusion was that the aquifer behaved like a porous medium, and that its typical groundwater velocity was about 6.7 m per day. At that flow rate the contaminated fields could not have affected the wells within the small available time. Contamination of the wells by overland flow was suspected. The springs were described by the consultants as "seeps."

At the urging of two local karst hydrologists, dye traces were performed in the area. Different dyes were injected into two inactive wells and recovered in a pumping well. The traces showed velocities of 480 m/day and 320 m/day — about 50 to 70 times faster than predicted by the pumping tests and models. At these rates, the contaminated fields lay well within the catchment areas of the wells.

The failure to recognize conduit flow in the aquifer had led not only to relaxed standards of contaminant monitoring but also to a false assessment of the aquifer properties. Those who shun the study of caves and karst should reconsider their position.

Figure 15.4: A water-well casing in Blue Spring Cave, Indiana. The cave was encountered unexpectedly while the well was being drilled, and the open interval was sealed off with the casing to prevent contamination of the water supply by the cave stream.

Interaction between solution conduits and wells

Even a well that bypasses a nearby solution conduit can still be influenced by the conduit. Water in a karst aquifer generally converges on conduits, at least during low flow. When a well is pumped, any conduit within the resulting cone of depression has the potential to leak through the intervening parts of the aquifer into the well. A roughly similar result is achieved when floodwaters raise the pressure in the conduit and force water into the surrounding aquifer. Contaminants can be carried into nearby wells in either of these ways.

The connections between conduits and wells may consist merely of the non-solutional fissures and pores typical of most of the aquifer, or they may be small solutionally enlarged fissures and tubes around the main conduit. The importance of minor dissolution features, smaller than those of turbulent-flow conduits, is often overlooked in aquifer studies.

Substantial interaction between a well and a nearby conduit can be verified in several ways. The most direct way, although the least likely to succeed, is to add dye to the conduit water and monitor surrounding wells for its appearance. The hydraulic head in the conduit must be greater than that in the monitored wells, so it is usually necessary for the conduit to be in flood, or for one or more wells to be pumping. The amount of dye transmitted in this way is likely to be very small and possibly undetectable.

Another approach is to monitor the water levels in wells near a

conduit with continuous recorders (Smart, 1999). Wells with efficient connections to the conduit will show abrupt rises and falls of water level that correlate closely with those in the conduit. Wells with inefficient connections with the conduit will show delayed response and smaller variations in head (Johnson and Meiman, 1994; see page 94).

A third way to recognize connections between wells and conduits is to evaluate the data from pumping tests. When a well is pumped, it and other nearby wells experience a decline in water level. The amount of water-level drop is the **drawdown** (Chapter 4). Drawdown is monitored in non-pumping observation wells located at various distances from the pumping well. Analysis of drawdown data allows one to calculate the various aquifer properties, such as hydraulic conductivity.

The rate of drawdown in any well diminishes with time, unless the water table is rising for some reason, for example because of increased infiltration during a storm. Deviations in the rate of drawdown can be caused by hydrologic boundaries

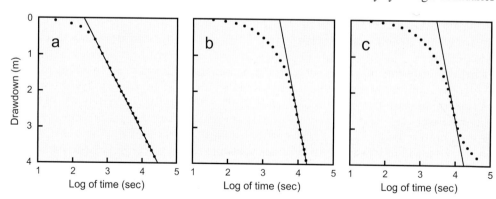

Figure 15.5: Plots of drawdown vs. log of time: (a) confined aquifer, (b) unconfined aquifer, (c) unconfined aquifer fed by leakage from adjacent beds, a stream, or a leaky conduit. In an unconfined aquifer the drawdown takes a long time to stabilize to a straight line. The final slope in **a** and **b** depends on the hydraulic conductivity (K) and saturated thickness. In **c**, if leakage keeps pace with pumping, the drawdown approaches a horizontal line. Less leakage causes a smaller deviation from the straight line.

and irregularities in the aquifer. Interpretations are simplest on a plot of drawdown vs. log of time. Traditional well-test techniques, but without reference to karst, are described in most groundwater texts (e.g., Fetter, 2001).

In an ideal confined aquifer the drawdown plot quickly stabilizes to a straight line. The slope of the line increases with discharge and decreases with permeability and aquifer thickness. In an unconfined aquifer the drawdown curve gradually steepens with time as the saturated thickness of the aquifer diminishes (Figure 15.5). Abrupt steepening of the drawdown curve can also indicate a nearby low-permeability zone. Some well tests in unconfined bedrock aquifers produce confined-type drawdown curves, because the movement of water through the aquifer is constrained by prominent bedding.

Many aquifers are imperfectly confined — their overlying or underlying strata are semi-permeable and allow water to leak into the aquifer. The rate of leakage increases as the head declines in the aquifer, so the slope of the drawdown curve decreases with time, as in Figure 15.5c. A decrease in slope can also mean that there is a nearby recharge zone, such as a river, lake, or active solution conduit.

In theory, it is not difficult to determine whether a decreasing rate of drawdown is caused by a conduit. At any given distance from the pumping well, observation wells near the conduit will show less drawdown than other wells. If leaky beds are responsible, the drawdown will be fairly uniform in all directions from the pumping well. Any nearby lake or river at the surface should be obvious.

If the drawdown curve near a conduit gradually flattens toward a zero slope, there is an efficient connection with the conduit, and the well yield is eventually supplied entirely by it (Figure 15.6). In this case the natural discharge in the conduit must equal or exceed the pumping rate of the well.

If a well penetrates a high-discharge conduit and the drill hole is not sealed, pumping the well may produce no drawdown at all. Many well tests in the Edwards Aquifer of Texas show no measurable drawdown even at large pumping rates. One well near San Antonio produced a jet of water 10 m high and 0.75 m in diameter, with a discharge of about 1.9 m³/sec. It was eventually tamed by specialists trained in capping oil-well blowouts.

Far more commonly, the effect of a conduit is subtle or entirely absent. If the slope of the drawdown curve decreases only slightly, the conduit may be supplying a small but constant leakage that is far less than the pumping rate from

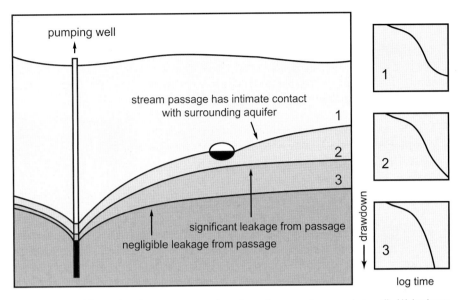

Figure 15.6: Effect of a stream cave on drawdown in a nearby pumping well: (1) leakage from the cave is so intense that no drawdown is possible in the vicinity; (2) substantial leakage, but not enough to prevent a drop in the nearby water table; (3) little or no leakage, with no measurable effect on drawdown. Typical drawdown curves are shown for each case. Drawdown is plotted downward, to portray the drop in water level more clearly.

the well (Figure 15.6). If there is no discernable effect, either the conduit is poorly integrated with the aquifer (for example, the conduit walls may be locally impermeable), or the conduit is too far away to show any effect. There may be no conduit at all.

Even though these techniques seem convincing and highly quantifiable, aquifers rarely behave as expected. This is true for many aquifers and especially so for those in karst. Pumping tests can provide much information about the nature of karst aquifers, but interpreting it is often difficult. So far there have not been many studies to document the relationship between well drawdown and solution conduits.

Contaminant tracking and remediation

One of the most perplexing problems in karst is how to predict, monitor, and clean up groundwater contaminants (Sasowsky and Wicks, 2000). Speleologists have a strong grasp of how water flows through soluble rock, but even when there is detailed information about caves and karst it is difficult to devise strategies for effective tracking and remediation of contaminated groundwater.

All hydrologists should be aware of three common but poorly recognized concepts that apply to most bedrock aquifers, but especially to karst:

- Drainage divides shift with time, as groundwater flow rates vary. This is true in any aquifer, but it is most significant in karst.
- Perched vadose water can follow favorable beds or partings down the dip for great lateral distances before reaching the water table. It is not only possible, but *common* for this water to cross drainage divides, even those that have been carefully mapped by water levels in wells. Well data can

rarely detect perched flow. Crossing of a drainage divide can be anticipated from the dip direction, dip angle, and prominence of bedding (Figure 15.7).

- Vadose water easily disperses along many divergent routes. In prominently bedded rock, much of the water follows inclined bedding-plane partings. Water also seeps downward along any steeper fissures it encounters. But if a fissure is too narrow to transmit all the flow, the overflow will continue along the original path. Because of this divergence, it is possible for a single water source to drain in several directions, and commonly to both sides of a divide (Figure 15.7). These processes are easily confirmed by examining the patterns of caves and of the water within them. They can help to explain divergent flow paths detected by dye tracing (e.g., in Missouri by Aley, 1988).

Microbial contaminants, such as viruses and bacteria, are easily carried by groundwater that encounters little or no filtering through fine-grained sediment. Solid wastes such as trash can also be carried by flowing water. Karst water is ideal for carrying these contaminants. For this reason, karst springs and caves are rarely suitable sources of drinking water.

Non-microbial groundwater contaminants consist mainly of agricultural, industrial, and domestic wastes (Hoke and Wicks, 1997; Loop, 2005; Vesper, 2005). Some are water-soluble and follow the same paths as underground water. These include nitrates, phosphates, road salts, and some organic compounds. Many industrial contaminants mix poorly with water. Some of these are less dense than water and float on water surfaces, including the water table. Most petroleum products behave in this way. Certain other poorly soluble materials are denser than water and sink to the bottoms of water bodies or aquifers. These include many solvents and cleaning agents. Metals tend to adsorb onto solid surfaces and may be carried through karst aquifers on sand grains.

Low-density contaminants may concentrate at sumps. Volatile materials can seep upward through overlying fissures to the surface and enter nearby buildings. This is especially common when floodwaters force the volatiles into narrow openings around the conduits, which spreads them widely (Figure 15.8). In rare examples, explosive levels of volatile gases have been measured in subsoil fissures and in basements (Crawford, 1984; Kuehn and others, 1994). Caves near service stations or industrial sites should be entered with caution. Use of electric lamps, rather than carbide lamps, is essential where there is danger of contamination by petroleum products.

Slow seepage of water through porous but low-permeability material tends to trap and delay contaminants, allowing them more time to break down chemically. This is especially common in the soil and epikarst. Residual pollutants tend to leak slowly into underlying fissures, with occasional pulses triggered by rainstorms and snowmelt.

Water in the narrowest openings of a karst aquifer is generally freer of contaminants than water in solution conduits. These narrow openings, though unlikely to contain

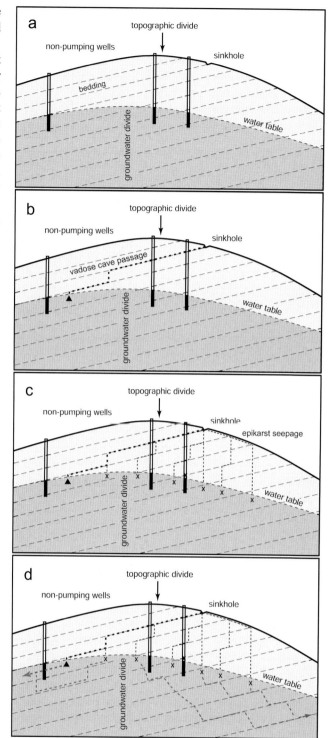

Figure 15.7: Flow dispersion in soluble rocks. (**a**) From well data the groundwater divide seems clearly defined. (**b**) Vadose flow and caves commonly follow the dip in bedded rocks. Flow can cross beneath the topographic divide and over the groundwater divide before it reaches the water table at ▲. (**c**) Some seepage follows narrow non-solutional paths. Contamination from a single source can disperse widely (to other points marked **X**). Dispersion through the epikarst can further complicate the flow pattern. (**d**) Below the water table, water flows down the local hydraulic gradient. It tends to converge on conduits, but elsewhere it can follow dispersed paths for large distances.

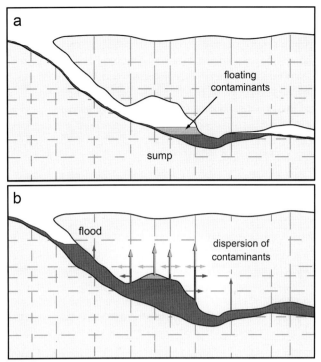

Figure 15.8: Dispersion of volatile gases in a karst aquifer caused by flooding of a contaminated solution conduit: (**a**) Low-density volatile contaminants float on water surfaces at sumps. (**b**) During floods, the contaminants are trapped in ceiling pockets and forced into fissures in the overlying rock. Volatile gases can spread among many fissures that extend to the surface.

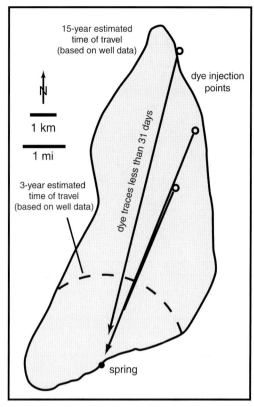

Figure 15.9: Why it is risky to ignore the presence of caves: Modeling this karst drainage basin in Utah, based on well data, suggested that groundwater would require up to 15 years to reach the spring. Later dye traces showed a travel time of less than 31 days. (After Spangler, 1999.)

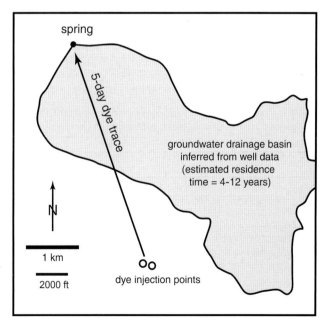

Figure 15.10: The catchment area for this Utah groundwater basin was delineated from well data. It consists of permeable carbonate rock. Tritium dating of the spring water indicated that groundwater requires an average of 4 to 12 years to reach the spring. Later dye traces showed that conduit flow can pass over the suspected groundwater divides, and with a travel time of only 5 days. (After Spangler, 1999.)

high concentrations of impurities, are more numerous and less easily accounted for than solution conduits. Also, during floods, water from nearby conduits can be forced into surrounding openings and carry pollutants with it. As the floods subside, the contaminated water gradually drains back into the conduits, so flooding rarely causes long-term contamination of wells. This temporary storage can greatly delay contaminant movement through the aquifer.

Dye tracing (Chapter 4) is the most versatile tool for predicting contaminant paths. If done carefully, it can delineate groundwater basins and divides, directions and velocities of flow, contaminant dispersion, and variations in groundwater conditions with time. No study of a karst aquifer is complete without extensive tracer tests. Dye-tracing techniques are described by Käss (1998), Aley (2002), Field (2002a), and Jones (2005). Use of dye for determining travel times often conflicts with other more standard methods for estimating groundwater velocities, such as the use of hydraulic conductivities determined from pumping tests (Figures 15.9–15.10).

Tracing with colored particles is especially suited to contaminant studies in karst. Spores of the club moss *Lycopodium* are sometimes used because, with an average diameter of 0.03 mm, they are larger than typical bacteria, yet small enough to travel through narrow fissures. They are filtered out by low-permeability materials that are unlikely to transmit bacteria. They can be dyed a variety of colors

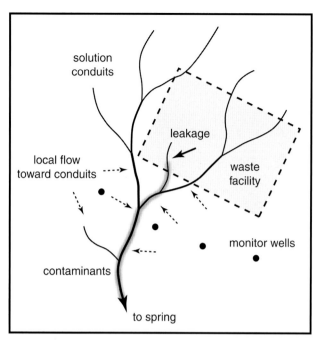

Figure 15.11: The difficulty of detecting contaminants in karst areas with monitor wells. The wells rarely intersect the solution conduits that carry most of the wastes, but instead are far more likely to encounter groundwater that is tributary to the conduits.

to allow several simultaneous traces. Small-mesh nets are placed in likely resurgences and are sampled periodically. Microscopic examination is necessary to identify the spores. Artificial fluorescent spheres that range down to sub-micrometer size can be used as an alternative. Because of its complexity, particle tracing is rarely used, except where an assessment of microbial filtering is desired.

It is difficult to monitor contaminant leakage from potential contaminant sources in karst (Figure 15.11). Where these sources are known, as in landfills and waste lagoons, federal and state regulations mandate the installation of an array of monitor wells in the down-gradient direction, with one or more in the up-gradient direction to monitor background water quality. Unfortunately, contaminant leakage into conduits can be detected by a monitor well only if the well intersects one of the affected conduits. But most wells drilled at random rarely intersect conduits and instead penetrate only the network of narrow fissures that feed water into the conduits. Contaminants cannot be monitored effectively in such wells. Wastes can run between or around the wells without being detected.

Groundwater in a monitor well is normally tested only a few times a year. Because of the high flow velocities along the main drainage lines in karst, it is likely that short-term leaks will be missed entirely by such widely spaced sampling. Wastes can travel hundreds of meters in a single day. Even if the monitoring schedule is stepped up considerably, the main contamination pulse will probably have passed long before remedial action can be taken. Even in a monitor well that encounters a conduit, it is likely that contaminant leaks will be missed entirely because of the high flow velocity (Quinlan and Alexander, 1987).

Another approach to karst groundwater monitoring is to sample springs that drain potential contaminant source areas. Monitoring of springs has not been widely accepted because the sources cannot be located accurately by this method. Contaminants detected at a spring can be derived from anywhere in its groundwater basin. This procedure works best in springs with small catchment areas. Another complexity is that during the progress of a flood, different parts of a drainage basin tend to contribute water to the spring at different times (Vesper and White, 2006).

In general, waste facilities and potential sources of hazardous materials should not be situated on karst. Nevertheless this practice continues. Most of these sites have undergone extensive study, and yet in even the most secure ones there are serious questions as to whether leakage paths have been properly identified. In the worst examples, rampant contamination has been taking place for decades.

Remediation of contaminants in karst can proceed as in other geologic settings, but attention should be paid to the presence and distribution of solution conduits. There is little benefit in treating conduit water because it is so transient. Sustained contamination of conduits and springs may indicate continuous leakage from a surface source in the basin, or gradual draining of pollutants from storage in the soil or epikarst where there has been a short-term spill. In the former situation, the obvious first step is to identify and eliminate the source. If the problem persists, efforts should focus on remediating the pollutants held in storage in the non-conduit parts of an aquifer. Common approaches include pumping out contaminated groundwater for treatment, extracting the vapors of volatile materials from soil, and bioremediation (where a microbial soup, in combination with oxygen, is introduced to break down organic compounds). Appropriate methods and strategies are described in many publications (e.g., Morrison and Murphy, 2005; Hardisty and Özdemiroğlu, 2004).

Salt-water intrusion into aquifers is severe in seacoast karst. As the permeability increases by dissolution, the freshwater lens decreases in thickness, often to a thin brackish zone. Nothing can be done to prevent this natural and long-term process or to remediate its effect, but at least it is possible to explain the resulting water-supply problems.

Information from caves can be helpful in estimating and explaining karst water patterns. For example, Ogden and Redman (1993) applied cave data, joint patterns, sinkhole trends and photo-lineaments to the prediction of groundwater flow patterns in the Tennessee karst. They found a strong strike orientation in strongly folded rocks and more scattered patterns in low-dip settings. Worthington (1999, 2001, 2004) has used published cave data to quantify the vertical distribution of conduits in karst aquifers (Chapter 9).

Palmer (1986, 1999) used surveys of cave geology in a variety of settings to show the relation of stream conduits to geologic structure. A summary is given in Chapter 9. Although the ideal model of dip-strike flow patterns holds true in the majority of cases, great deviations can be expected in at least 20% of field examples. Massive, fractured rocks are least

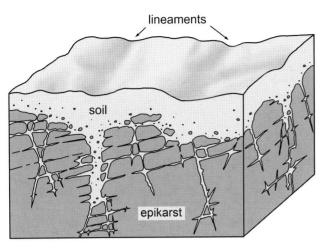

Figure 15.12: Lineaments are the surface expressions of underlying fracture zones. Where bedrock is overlain by soil, as shown here, most lineaments are merely subtle alignments of surface features, dark soil, or lush vegetation. (See Lattman and Parizek, 1964.)

faithful to the ideal model. Simplifying the data to allow easy management decisions does not work well (e.g., Ginsberg and Palmer, 2002), because practitioners want rules that will cover all contingencies without the bother of uncertainty.

Prediction of contaminant storage, flow paths, velocities, and destinations thus depends on understanding the nature of all types of karst water, not simply cave streams. Nevertheless, solution conduits control the flow pattern of the surrounding groundwater, just as surface streams do, and they also originate along the paths of greatest flow. For both reasons they can reveal a great deal about the overall aquifer characteristics.

Locating favorable well sites in karst

In the search for a favorable well site, both water quality and water yield must be considered. The threat of groundwater contamination may turn people away from water supplies in karst, but many of the problems can be avoided.

Contamination of a well requires an upgradient contaminant source. In the unlikely event that there is conclusive proof that no such source exists, there should be no problem. If the water level in a well

Figure 15.13: Range of hydraulic conductivities in the Mississippian limestones of Lawrence County, Indiana, calculated from 157 well-test logs supplied by the Indiana Department of Natural Resources. The prominently bedded Ste. Genevieve and St. Louis Formations contrast with the prominently fractured Salem and Harrodsburg Formations. Their structural characteristics are shown in the photographs (**top** = Ste. Genevieve Limestone in Sullivan Cave, photo by M. Palmer; **bottom** = dimension-stone quarry in the Salem Limestone). For comparison, hydraulic conductivities of 10^{-5} to 10^{-3} cm/sec are typical of fine sand.

lies at a higher elevation than the water table beneath any potential contaminant sources, traditional wisdom would declare it impossible for the contaminants to reach the well. But it should be clear by now that karst rarely obeys traditional wisdom.

Application of cave data to water supply must be approached with caution. Much of the water in carbonate aquifers is at or near saturation with dissolved calcite, and a great deal of water moves through narrow fissures with no tendency to form caves. This water can contribute to well yields, but also to contaminant transport.

In most highly fractured rocks, fracture traces (lineaments) are visible on maps and aerial photos. Lineaments can serve as a guide to high-yield well sites (Lattman and Parizek, 1964; Parizek, 1976). They are typically the surface expression of fracture swarms along which there is deep weathering (Figure 15.12). Soils tend to be thicker along them, and therefore vegetation may be more lush than in surrounding areas. The vegetation contrast is particularly clear during dry periods. Intersections of two or more lineaments are especially likely to supply high-capacity wells. On the other hand, fracture traces are rarely of help in locating conduits (White, 1988). With careful scrutiny, it is possible to interpret the effects of lineaments on accessible caves that underlie them, but in most areas the evidence is ambiguous (Ogden, 1974; George, 1984).

In carbonate rocks with prominent widely spaced joints, water wells tend to cluster in two groups, one with high yield and one with low yield (Figure 15.13). In prominently bedded rocks, or in those with many small, closely spaced fractures, wells tend to fall into a single broad group of moderate yield, with few wells of either high or very low yield. In Figure 5.13, about 8% of the wells in jointed rock and 3% in bedded rock were unable to supply enough water for homes. On the other hand, the benefit of high yield is offset by a greater potential for contamination. From this information it appears that wells in bedded rocks have a more predictable yield and a lower

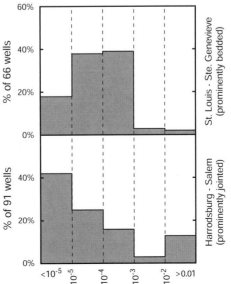

Figure 15.14: Generalized cross section through the Cretaceous Edwards Aquifer of Texas, showing the unconfined recharge zone, the confined artesian zone, and the boundary between fresh water and sulfide-rich water (the so-called "bad water line"). Faults are shown by nearly vertical lines, and arrows show relative movement. Width of diagram is several tens of kilometers. From data by the Edwards Aquifer Authority and the San Antonio Water System.

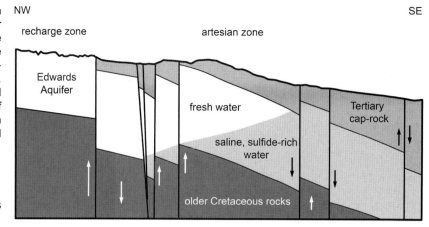

chance for poor quality than those in rocks with large but relatively few fractures.

Wells that encounter only narrow fissures may need to be drilled to considerable depth before they can supply the desired yield. But deep wells are susceptible to several natural water-quality problems. *Hydrogen sulfide* (the cause of "sulfur water") produces an unpleasant smell and taste hinting of rotten eggs. *Dissolved salt* degrades the taste and is corrosive to metals. *Iron* or *manganese* can cause staining and also clogging of fixtures with the filaments of bacteria that derive energy from metal oxidation. *Methane* is flammable and may pose a fire hazard. It is not wise to drill a bedrock well deeper than about 200 meters, unless local field evidence indicates sufficient permeability and water quality at greater depth. If this depth is reached without success, it is usually more cost-effective to abandon the well and drill at a new site.

The Edwards Aquifer of east-central Texas provides an example of diminishing water quality with depth. The aquifer is a thick Cretaceous limestone that has been faulted so that parts of the aquifer have dropped downward to considerable depth below the surface and are capped by relatively impermeable beds (Figure 15.14). In the main part of the aquifer, fresh water is available to depths as much as 1000 m. Water levels drop during dry periods because of sustained pumping, but the aquifer is replenished rapidly during heavy rains (Schindel and Johnson, 2005). Farther to the southeast, where the aquifer is confined, hydrogen sulfide is a serious contaminant that makes the water unusable. The so-called "bad water line" that separates it from the fresh water is actually a transition zone that shifts back and forth according to the relative rates of groundwater recharge and discharge from springs and wells. Farther southeast, beneath the Coastal Plain, the Edwards is a petroleum reservoir.

Many people consider the Edwards Aquifer to behave as a typical porous medium, like gravel or sand. Dye tracing contradicts this view, as do the extremely high permeabilities encountered in certain wells. Worthington and others (2002) show that the conduit permeability in the Edwards is equivalent to that of many well-known cavernous aquifers such as those of the Mammoth Cave region.

Several methods have been devised to assess groundwater quality and environmental problems in karst. Although they are complementary, each method has slightly different ap-

proaches and goals. Ray and O'Dell (1993) have developed a method for evaluating potential for groundwater contamination. Although it is based on field work in Kentucky, it can be used in most other karst areas as well. The method considers pore size of infiltration routes (based on type of material), groundwater velocity (from tracer tests), and angles of dispersion (from tracers and field observations). From these, aquifer recharge, flow velocity, and dispersion patterns can be graphed semi-quantitatively to give a visual portrayal of potential groundwater vulnerability. On the basis of field mapping and sampling at various flow stages, Quinlan and others (1995) and Schindel and others (1997) have developed guidelines for protecting the catchment areas of wells in karst, with particular emphasis on small drainage basins. In Europe, Doerfliger (1996) and Jeannin and others (1999) have devised a method for assessing environmental vulnerability in karst, called EPIK (for Epikarst, Protective cover, Infiltration type, and Karst conduit network). Vulnerability maps are produced by evaluating the relative capacities for each these four systems to transmit or store underground water. Veni (2004) describes methods for preparing environmental assessments in karst, with special concern for the fact that most readers will be unfamiliar with karst.

Computer modeling of karst groundwater

Most groundwater investigations are constrained by limited time and budget. Projects must be done rapidly and efficiently with the help of insight from past work. The most efficient way to meet these requirements is to rely on remote sensing and computer models, rather than on laborious field work. These shortcuts have many drawbacks.

Digital models can determine idealized flow directions, velocities, and contaminant dispersion to make it possible, at least theoretically, to explain and predict aquifer behavior on the basis of only a few measurements. These are powerful tools, but they are often misused. Their limitations are especially problematic in karst (Worthington and Smart, 2004; Wicks, 2005; Palmer, 2006).

In a digital model, an aquifer is divided into many small blocks, and each is assigned the local hydrologic variables. These variables include aquifer thickness, hydraulic conductivity, storage characteristics, leakage from adjacent strata, infiltration, and several other characteristics. Because this information is almost never available for every block, the data must be interpolated between known points. Most of the information comes from only a few well tests. A major problem is that conduits are usually overlooked completely, because wells rarely detect them. A computer model can do a fair job of predicting water-table elevations between wells, even in karst to some extent, but it is unable to predict the spread of contaminants with accuracy. In fact, the most widely used models assume only laminar flow and cannot deal with the turbulent flow that occurs in solution conduits.

To overcome this limitation, modelers who are familiar with karst have attempted to include the heterogeneous structure and flow conditions in bedrock aquifers (Kiraly, 1975, 2002; Teutsch and Sauter, 1991; Sauter, 1992). Modeling of flow through natural and artificial channels and conduits has helped to interpret the hydrographs of cave springs (Jeannin, 1996). Annable and Sudicky (1999) have designed a three-dimensional computer model that predicts contaminant transport through fissured aquifers, which represent pre-karst conditions. They found that the pattern of inflow and outflow tells little about the internal complexity of this kind of aquifer. They also show that the results cannot be duplicated with models that assume only intergranular (matrix) porosity. These and similar approaches are giving modelers insight into previously unrecognized aspects of karst aquifer behavior.

A karst aquifer can be treated as a "black box" in which the internal structure and mechanics are interpreted by comparing aquifer recharge with spring outflow (Dreiss, 1982). Although this approach seldom reveals the detailed mechanics within the aquifer, the results can be valid for certain water-management purposes.

Understanding a karst aquifer requires a great deal of field work and experience, and there is no quick fix. Computer models should be used mainly as a way to guide the field work. By noting the contrast between what a model predicts and what is actually observed in the field, one can gain insight into the behavior of similar aquifers.

For further information on groundwater models see Anderson and Woessner (2005) and the Web site *http://water. usgs.gov/software/ground_water.html*.

Engineering applications

Structural engineers can accomplish impressive feats, but the durability of their work depends on solid footing. In karst, the complex and uncertain conditions of the bedrock and soil pose a serious challenge. Ground instability leads to subsiding foundations, deteriorating roadbeds, and leaky dams. The scope and complexity of this problem are described by Beck and Herring (2001), Milanović (2000, 2004), Klimchouk and Lowe (2002), Beck (2003, 2005), and Waltham and others (2005). Biennial conferences on engineering in karst are hosted in the U.S. by a variety of

Figure 15.15: Sinkhole collapse in the front yard of an unenthusiastic suburban homeowner (on left), Kentucky.

karst research organizations. These events draw engineers and environmental consultants from around the world to present their research (see, for example, Beck, 1993).

Sinkhole collapse

Sinkhole collapse is the most publicized cave-related inconvenience. The news media contain frequent pictures of gaping holes that have opened up virtually overnight, swallowing homes, businesses, and highways (Figures 15.15–15.16). With a little digging these holes might serve as cave entrances, but landowners rarely welcome this opportunity.

The potential for sinkhole collapse is greatest where sinkholes are already abundant, but the rate at which new ones develop can vary with time. Most sinkhole collapse is triggered by rapid changes in groundwater conditions, such as flooding or lowering of water tables by pumping. Sinkhole prediction is best achieved by extrapolating past trends. Enough historical information is now available in some areas to determine the statistical probability of future sinkhole problems (Wilson, 1995).

Subsidence and collapse of sinkholes can be accelerated in two ways. They can be induced by the reduction in

Figure 15.16: Catastrophic collapse into the limestone beneath commercial sites in Winter Park, Florida, 1981. Photo courtesy of U.S. Geological Survey.

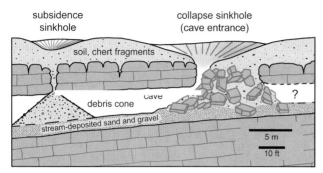

Figure 15.17: Profile through one of the small entrances of Blue Spring Cave, Indiana, showing a subsidence sinkhole and a collapse sinkhole with debris cones beneath each.

Figure 15.18: Debris cone beneath the sinkhole shown on the left in Figure 15.17.

buoyancy caused by a drop in the water table. This process is most active where soluble rock is overlain by soft and relatively insoluble strata. In contrast, sinkhole collapse can be stimulated by high groundwater flow during floods, when sinkhole fill is undermined by cave streams. A high moisture content contributes to the instability of the fill material. Collapse during high flow is most common where soluble rock is exposed directly beneath soil. Many sinkholes are influenced by a combination of several processes. The probability of sinkhole collapse is least in areas of thin soil or bare bedrock.

A dramatic example of sinkhole collapse stimulated by a water-table decline is described by Quinlan (1974). Dewatering of gold mines in the Transvaal of South Africa caused the catastrophic collapse of more than 200 sinkholes in the overlying dolomite, which is mantled by as much as 300 m of unconsolidated material. The water table was lowered by several hundred meters. Sinkholes reached sizes up to 125 m in diameter and 100 m deep. Dozens of lives were lost, and costly remedial efforts were required. Although loss of buoyancy was the main trigger, differential dewatering of the soil added to the instability through cracking and shrinkage.

Caves provide a way of examining sinkhole development from below, where the causes lie. Maps of caves show their relationship to sinkhole distribution, and subsidence is easily documented (Figures 15.17–5.19). Most ground instability is caused by reactivation of earlier collapse features, rather than by the development of entirely new sinkholes. Without the flow

of turbulent water through conduits, most collapse features would become choked with soil and sediment. Subsurface streams can carry these materials away and undermine the overlying loose material (Figure 2.13). Undermining is most common during floods, when cave streams are most erosive. The actual collapse may take place during the same flood, but it may instead be delayed until a later time, so that the collapse seems random. Soils that are moist from recent rainfall or snowmelt tend to be most unstable.

Once collapse occurs, the cave stream may be diverted to alternate routes around the collapse zone, either along the perimeter of the original passage or through other passages that bypass the collapse. If the blockage is severe or repetitive, entirely new passages may form around it (Chapter 8). The exposure of buried trash and surface vegetal debris in some newly enlarged sinkholes shows evidence for repeated collapse and filling.

Figure 15.19 shows the distribution of sinkholes over Blue Spring Cave, Indiana. The center of each sinkhole is represented by a black circle with the diameter proportional to sinkhole depth. The map includes only those sinkholes that appear on the 1:24,000 topographic quadrangle, and the depths represent the number of depression contour lines (contour interval of 10 ft ≈ 3 m). The actual number of sinkholes is several times greater than is shown on the topographic map. The main passages in the cave are about 8–12 m in diameter. Limestone is exposed at the surface, beneath 2–5 m of soil, over the entire cave. The surface rock unit is mainly the prominently bedded St. Louis Limestone. Most of the cave is located in the underlying massive Salem Limestone. The St. Louis is absent only along the very eastern edge of the map, where sinkholes are less abundant.

There are hundreds of sinkholes in the cave's drainage basin. Small sinkholes seem to have a random distribution in relation to the cave, but the deepest are located over the main stream passage. Even without the cave map, the position of the main stream could be predicted from the distribution of deep sinkholes. Dye tracing shows that the main stream continues upstream toward the southeast for several kilometers beyond the explored section. The pattern of deep sinkholes appears to follow that trend. Deep sinkholes also occur north of Blue Spring cave in the drainage basin of another large cave with active streams.

The long western passage that leads to the spring is one of the youngest in the cave (mid-late Pleistocene), and the lack of deep sinkholes above it may relate to the relative youth of the passage. Nor are there any deep sinkholes above the extensive northeastern and southern branches of the cave. These branches include many large passages, some of which are abandoned upper levels, but the streams in both areas have only small flows in comparison to the main passage of the cave. Many passages in the northeastern and southern branches terminate in breakdown, but sinkholes are small or entirely absent above these terminations as well. The large flood-prone main river (which extends from M to S on the map) is an important agent in removing sediment

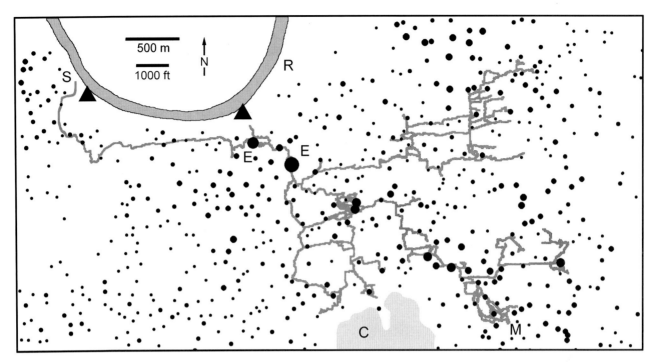

Figure 15.19: Sinkhole distribution over Blue Spring Cave, Indiana. Nearly all sinkholes are in the bedded St. Louis Limestone, which allows vadose water to drain laterally for large distances. The largest penetrate into the underlying prominently jointed Salem Limestone. Cave passages are shown in gray. E = main entrances, M = inflow of main cave stream, S = Blue Spring, R = East Fork of White River, C = sandstone cap-rock over limestone. ▲ = abandoned spring alcove. ● = sinkhole at least 25 m deep (8 contour lines, 10 ft each). • = sinkhole about 3 m deep (1 contour line). Intermediate sinkhole depths are shown in proportion to their dot size. Cave map from Palmer (1969).

and collapse debris from deep sinkholes. The volume of the deepest sinkhole is about 50 times greater than the estimated volume of fill material in the passages beneath it.

Most of the infiltration in the region enters small sinkholes that have no apparent relation to the mapped cave passages. Where all this water flows is uncertain. Presumably each sinkhole is drained by at least one solutionally enlarged conduit, but the explored passages have few inaccessibly small infeeders that can account for them all. Apparently most of the sinkhole drainage converges into relatively few streams before it joins the traversable parts of the cave. By using the same style of linkage as is seen in the known parts of the cave, Worthington (1999) provides a conceptual view of how the sinkhole inputs may link together before entering the cave.

Field information of this kind invites statistical analysis. Unfortunately, as shown at the beginning of this chapter, there is a problem of sampling bias. The conditions beyond the explored limits of the cave are not known. Statistics can be applied to sinkhole data alone, but if there is no information about the underlying conditions and processes, this approach is unlikely to add to our understanding of how sinkholes form.

Sinkhole flooding

Many sinkholes are subject to flooding during wet periods. This is especially true in low-relief sinkhole plains where most of the depressions are floored by thick residual soil. During wet periods, water may partly fill sinkholes that are poorly drained, to form ponds that are perched above the

water table. Some sinkhole flooding is caused by water rising from underlying water-filled caves. Sinkhole flooding in rural areas is sometimes appreciated as a convenient source of stock ponds. Packing of soil by grazing livestock can increase the tendency for ponding (note cows in the right-hand sinkhole pond in Figure 2.18).

Much land development takes place on surfaces that are barely recognizable as karst, where soil-choked sinkholes are broad and shallow and have no visible drains. Because of the inefficient drainage, water readily collects in these depressions and can spread over large areas (Kemmerly, 1981; Crawford, 1981, 2001; Ogden and others, 1998; Barner, 1999). To alleviate this problem, the low points of sinkholes are sometimes fitted with artificial drains. These are simply pipes that extend down to bedrock, preferably into open voids (Figure 15.20). The sinkhole fill and rock material beneath it are highly unstable, and Figure 15.20 also shows the typical subsidence and collapse that may follow. A pipe used as a sinkhole drain is also considered a form of injection well, so it may be necessary to monitor the amount and quality of water that enters it.

Leaky reservoirs and tunnels

Reservoir leakage is another typical problem in karst. Construction of a dam produces abnormally steep hydraulic gradients beneath and around it, which leads to ground instability, bedrock fracturing, subsurface erosion, and enhanced dissolution. In karst, many reservoirs leak at an

Figure 15.20: This artificial sinkhole drain was designed to alleviate sinkhole flooding, but it has been damaged by subsidence.

alarming rate, and some do not fill with water at all. The greatest recorded leakage rates of dams in karst are 26 m³/sec at the Keban Dam in Turkey and 25 m³/sec at the Vrtac Dam in Serbia (Milanović, 2004). During construction at the Keban site, about 30 caves were filled with bedrock blocks, sand, and clay, with little effect.

Jarvis (2003) describes the notorious Anchor Dam in northwestern Wyoming, which was built on a gypsum-limestone karst. As the reservoir began to fill, large sinkholes developed beneath and around it. A dike was built around the largest depression, reducing the reservoir capacity by 55%. Despite decades of costly remedial measures, continual leakage has prevented the reservoir from reaching more than a small fraction of even this reduced capacity.

In 1893, the McMillan Dam in southeastern New Mexico was built across the Pecos River on Permian gypsum. Almost immediately the reservoir began to leak through sinkholes that formed in the lake bed (Cox, 1967; Land and Love, 2006). Water flowed through solution conduits back into the river through springs about 5.6 km downstream. Karst development was negligible through less-soluble dolomite that was exposed along part of the reservoir shore. Dikes were built at various times to isolate major sinkhole areas, but the dikes occasionally failed, and whirlpools were reported above sinkholes at those times. The reservoir was abandoned in 1991 in favor of a new one built mainly on dolomite farther downstream.

In assessing this problem it is helpful to know the mechanism of cave origin in soluble rocks. The short flow paths, steep gradients, and large water sources in the vicinity of dams are ideal for rapid enlargement of openings by dissolution (Dreybrodt, 1996; Bauer and others, 1999). Very high dissolution rates are available right from the time when the reservoir begins to fill. Only small amounts of conduit enlargement will allow a great increase in flow rate, as is shown by high sensitivity of discharge to conduit size in Eqs. 4.6 and 4.7. The increase of leakage beneath and around dams in limestone may match that predicted for cave development under similar hydrologic and chemical conditions (Palmer, 1988; Dreybrodt, 1996). The build-up of pressure behind dams may also force sediment out of preexisting openings. This leads to sudden increases in leakage rate that are unlike the steady acceleration of leakage caused by dissolutional enlargement of conduits.

Patterns of known caves can serve as a guide to likely sites of reservoir leakage (Milanović, 2004. Leakage is generally less in youthful valleys where river erosion has outpaced the rate of cave development. Mature river valleys are poor choices for reservoirs, especially if there are prominent terraces present, because the slow rate of downward erosion has provided ample time for cave development. Intense leakage can also take place from perched stream valleys that lie above the water table, but these are seldom used as dam sites.

During the 1930s the Tennessee River Authority drilled a large number of borings at prospective dam sites in the Tennessee River basin of the southeastern U.S. Many of these sites were in carbonate rocks. To document the presence of sub-river solution conduits, Moneymaker (1941) examined the drilling logs and cores at 30 sites and explored some accessible caves penetrated by large-diameter boreholes. He noted thousands of cavities, some as deep as 68 m below river level and with vertical extents up to 20 m. All but four of the sites were in bedrock-floored valleys. Many of the cavities discharged substantial quantities of water. Detrital sediment filled some cavities either partly or entirely, with grain sizes ranging from clay to boulder size. There was no apparent relationship between sediment fill and cavity depth. Cavities became fewer with depth in nearly all boreholes.

The largest and most numerous openings at the TVA sites were above present river levels. Those with the greatest depths below river level were in regions of faulted or folded strata, which agrees with the conceptual models of cave development described in Chapter 7. Fracture and parting widths ordinarily decrease with depth, thus inhibiting deep cave development, but this tendency can be disrupted by structural deformation. In places the maximum depth of significant cavities was limited by a low-permeability shale bed.

Sealing of karst conduits at dam sites requires extensive grouting (pressurized injection of cement or other sealants through drill holes). Other techniques to combat leakage include blanketing of the reservoir bed with impermeable materials and plugging of visible openings in valley floors. It is virtually impossible to seal all openings, especially those that are sediment-filled. Any benefits offered by dams in karst are likely to be outweighed by the cost of leakage remediation.

There is a similar problem with tunnels. For example, between 1984 and 1993, 31 km of tunnels were constructed at depths of 80–100 m in the Silurian Niagara Dolomite beneath Milwaukee, Wisconsin, as part of a pollution-abatement program (Day, 2004). Karst-related problems caused a cost overrun of $50 million and completion of the project was delayed 9 months. Rock collapse, subsidence, and groundwater intrusion required grouting and lining of about 45% of the tunnel length. The problems persist.

Irregular bedrock surfaces

Where soluble bedrock is covered only by soil or unconsolidated sediment, the bedrock surface may be highly irregular. These are characteristics of the epikarst (Figure 2.12). Fissures, thin residual blades of rock, and loose rock fragments are typical. Competent rock, to which the foundations of buildings, bridges, and other load-bearing structures must be anchored, is often difficult to find. Extensive grouting or installation of pilings or concrete slabs may be required (Waltham and others, 2005). Road design is especially tricky in karst because of the great amounts of cut and fill required, and the inherent instability of the terrain (Fischer and others, 2003). In Slovenia, for example, more than 300 caves and solution cavities were encountered in 60 km of highway construction (Knez and Slabe, 2004).

Problems of waste isolation

In general, karst is a poor choice for waste disposal. On the other hand, evaporite rocks such as salt and gypsum may be suitable waste-isolation sites because far below the surface they behave as plastic solids in which all voids tend to remain sealed and impermeable.

An example of such a site is the Waste Isolation Pilot Plant in southeastern New Mexico, which was designed for the storage of nuclear wastes (Neill and others, 1983). The site is located in the Permian Salado Formation, which consists mainly of halite with thicknesses of 500–600 m. It is capped by the Rustler Formation, which includes up to 450 m of anhydrite. The waste repository is a system of artificial tunnels in the Salado 655 m below the surface.

Because rock salt flows under pressure, fractures are rare, especially at depth, and artificial openings quickly squeeze shut. But a few geologists suggest that karst development in and around the site has the potential to allow leakage. For example, Hill (2003) points to the presence of karst depressions, dissolution zones, breccia bodies, and related features as evidence for karst activity. Negative gravity anomalies suggest subsurface voids. Water leaks into at least one of the artificial shafts at the storage site, and pumping tests on wells often yield unpredictable drawdowns. From the dissolved mineral content of groundwater in the Rustler Formation, Bodine and Jones (1990) measured many local deviations from the ideal salt content of water in equilibrium with the formation, which indicates considerable variation in the rates and paths of groundwater flow in the formation. Hill points out that none of these observations is proof that karst processes can damage the site or allow significant leakage from it, but that there is still potential for trouble. If the site

is ever shown to be unstable, then what? On the other hand, it is difficult to find better sites for waste isolation. There are no simple answers, but an understanding of karst processes is essential in formulating them.

Even at non-karst sites, insight from cave studies can be helpful in assessing the suitability for waste isolation. At the repository for nuclear wastes at Yucca Mountain, Nevada, Dublyansky and Smirnov (2005) have used the character of vein mineralization to suggest that faults in the area have been reactivated several times in the past. This raises the question as to whether the site can provide adequate long-term isolation from its surroundings.

One is tempted to look for culprits when things go wrong in karst, but the majority of scientists and engineers have only recently come to recognize karst problems. Karst specialists need to make their voices heard more clearly. But they should also be aware that environmental decisions are based more on politics, economics, and law than on science, and that environmental goals are best achieved by enlisting advocates from these fields rather than by opposing them.

Land management

Effective land use in karst requires special attention to drainage problems and soil erosion (Gillieson, 1996; Veni and others, 2001). Further, some types of karst landscape are fragile and susceptible to irreversible damage (Figure 15.21).

Most soils on karst are thin and have low infiltration capacity. Soil erosion can be severe on the locally steep slopes that drain into fissures and sinkholes, even in otherwise low-relief landscapes. Much soil is transported as sediment through caves, emerges at springs, and is carried away by surface rivers. The magnitude of this problem is shown by the high turbidity of spring and cave water during floods. Soil conservation methods such as terracing, contour plowing, and vegetation management are especially important in karst.

Karst soils are poorly suited for septic tanks. To be effective, a septic tank must have an outlet that drains

Figure 15.21: Highway construction through the karst of northern Puerto Rico involves many expensive cut-and-fill procedures, and even after they are built the roads are susceptible to damage by subsidence. Aerial photograph by José A. Colón.

Figure 15.22: About 750 m of Silurian limestone is exposed in parts of Prince of Wales Island, Alaska. This and other areas of the Tongass National Forest are being considered for timber harvesting. Clear-cutting in this region would block many caves and make access difficult. Photo by Jim Baichtal.

through at least a meter of moderately permeable soil. This gives the effluent an ample opportunity to be aerated and filtered. The thin, low-permeability soils typical of karst are often not sufficient. The effluent may overflow into open fissures with almost no filtering. Cave streams beneath developed land can be contaminated by poorly filtered wastes. It is often necessary to build artificial leach fields consisting of trucked-in sand, into which the septic tank can drain.

Deforestation and overgrazing have decimated the vegetation in some karst areas, accelerating the removal of soil and producing bleak karren landscapes. This has been a vexing problem in the dry Mediterranean climate of southern Europe. In parts of New Guinea, soil erosion accelerated by slash-and-burn clearing has exposed bedrock pinnacles that have developed knife-like edges by dissolution. Soil erosion in mountainous karst of southern China has made it difficult to sustain agriculture. Even the tiniest patches of remaining soil in karst depressions are treasured for their ability to grow crops. Logging on the limestone islands off the coast of southern Alaska is endangering the integrity of the local karst by clogging caves and surface fissures with the remnants of felled trees (Figure 15.22).

And yet, under favorable conditions, soil and vegetation can regenerate quickly on bare karst. For example, a new growth of forests has spread over much of the classical karst of western Slovenia over the past several decades (Kranjc, 2004). As a result, the dramatic karst and karren features that once dominated the landscape are now, for better or worse, less visible than when they were originally studied a century ago.

A karst landscape itself is a non-renewable resource, at least on the human time scale. Solutionally sculptured bedrock, especially in karren fields, is prized as decorative ornaments by landscapers. Many areas of karren are being stripped for this purpose. As these features become scattered they are removed from their natural context and lose their geological significance. In some places entire

karst landscapes are sacrificed. In the hilly karst of northern Puerto Rico, mogotes are often planed off to provide flat areas for housing developments. Conservation efforts are being mounted to protect this natural heritage, but economic pressures often prevail.

Attitudes toward karst vary a great deal across the globe. In China many of the delicate karst features are protected and open to the public (Ford and others, 1996). In Hungary, land development over caves is severely restricted. Discovery of the beautifully decorated József-hegy Cave in Budapest halted the development of one of the most expensive tracts of real estate in the city (Adamkó and others, 1992; Leél-Őssy, 2003; Figure 15.23).

Interpretation of geologic processes

Sedimentologists and stratigraphers are keenly interested in how rocks dissolve and precipitate. Processes of cave development apply to the chemical evolution of recently deposited carbonate sediments. Any caves that happen to form as a result are merely part of the overall phenomenon of ***diagenesis*** — which includes all the chemical and physical changes that take place in sediments and sedimentary rocks, excluding surface weathering and metamorphism. Eogenetic karst (Chapter 7) is an aspect of the early diagenesis of limestone.

To a sedimentologist, the development of caves and karst, and their burial as paleokarst, provide evidence for past geological conditions (Chapter 13). Many carbonate sedimentologists have contributed ideas that benefit karst researchers. Topics of mutual interest are discussed in several books by sedimentary geologists. These topics include carbonate rocks and their diagenesis (Bathurst, 1971; Scholle and others, 1983; Tucker and Wright, 1990), the classification and distribution of porosity types in carbonate rocks (Choquette and Pray, 1970; Moore, 1989; Budd and others, 1995), and paleokarst (James and Choquette, 1988; Wright and others, 1991). Further examples of this overlap are described below and in other chapters.

Figure 15.23: József-hegy, a low hill overlooking Budapest, contains Hungary's most beautifully decorated cave. As an exclusive neighborhood encroached, the land was scheduled for development. But when the cave was discovered by excavation of a deep sediment-filled shaft, development was halted and the land is now protected. Width of cave photo is about 5 m.

The developmental history of caves can also reveal information about rates and timing of tectonic events. This topic is discussed in Chapter 13.

Petroleum geology

Most of the world's large oil and gas fields are located in limestone and dolomite reservoirs (Roehl and Choquette, 1985). Much of the porosity consists of fractures and small-scale pores (Fritz and others, 1993), but some of the most productive petroleum reservoirs are in solution zones and karst-related breccias (Figures 15.24–15.25). Petroleum geologists have directed much research toward examining paleokarst and hypogenic porosity, and they rely to an increasing degree on research by karst scientists. Statistical approaches are helpful in quantifying the nature and distribution of karst porosity (Howard, 1971; Curl, 1964, 1986; White and White, 1995), and it is probable that these methods can improve the chances of encountering petroleum reservoirs.

The production of organic acids (e.g., Reactions 5.24–5.27) is most active at temperatures that are also ideal for the evolution and migration of petroleum. Oilfield waters are commonly undersaturated with respect to carbonate minerals (Surdam and others, 1993), and it is sometimes said that a petroleum reservoir "creates its own carbonate porosity."

Figure 15.24: Pumping oil from a paleokarst reservoir in the Ordovician Ellenburger Formation, west Texas.

Examples of karst petroleum reservoirs include huge oilfields in western Texas that are located in deeply buried Ordovician paleokarst (Chapter 13). There is debate about the nature of the paleokarst and how the porosity relates to it. The rock is highly brecciated, and some of the voids between breccia fragments have been enlarged by dissolution (Figure 15.25). Partly collapsed solution voids extend in broad patterns hundreds of meters wide, more than 100 m thick, and several kilometers or even tens of kilometers long. Some researchers have interpreted them as collapsed caves. Those with experience in modern caves realize that their scale is far too large to represent individual caves, and that they were more likely produced by coalescing of many neighboring cave passages by collapse under the pressure of overlying rock (Loucks, 1999). In some areas the distribution of solution pores resembles that of caves in seacoast mixing zones (Craig, 1988). In a few other parts of the continent these same rocks contain scattered breccias and solution

Figure 15.25: The Ordovician Ellenburger Formation, west Texas, is the reservoir for one of America's largest oilfields (Kerans, 1988). The blocks are limestone and the white rinds are thermal dolomite that lined the pores when they were at considerable depth below the surface. Much of the petroleum comes from fractures in breccia, rather than large voids such as these (Loucks and Anderson, 1985). Tip of pen for scale.

Figure 15.26: Large calcite crystals line the walls of a hypogenic cave exposed in a Nevada mine. Photo by Kevin Downey.

Figure 15.27: Mineralized breccia in a zinc mine in eastern Tennessee. The ore is located in Ordovician dolomite. Although the breccia is located below a major paleokarst surface, much of the brecciation took place at considerable depth below the surface. See Figure 15.28 for details. Rock hammer for scale.

pores produced by dissolution of evaporite beds (Friedman and Radke, 1979; Beals and Hardy, 1980).

In the search for modern analogs to the origin of petroleum reservoirs, the examination of breakdown in accessible caves can be misleading, because breakdown mechanisms at shallow depths differ from those at great depth (Loucks, 2007). Under considerable pressure, rocks in the walls of voids can shatter and produce a chaotic jumble of angular fragments with little relation to the leisurely subsidence of breakdown slabs under their own weight, which is typical in shallow caves.

Paleokarst is also known to form important petroleum reservoirs in many other parts of the world. For example, in the Rospo Mare oilfield, off the eastern coast of Italy, the main voids are in Oligocene-Miocene paleokarst (DuBois and others, 1993). The cavernous origin of the voids is shown by speleothem fragments and red fill, and by an overlying paleokarst with closed depressions and valleys, which correlates with an exposed paleokarst surface on the nearby mainland. Similar oilfields are common throughout the Mediterranean region.

Alternatively, there is evidence that much of the porosity and brecciation in carbonate petroleum reservoirs is produced by faulting and accompanying hypogenic dissolution (Mazzullo and Harris, 1991). Some petroleum-bearing breccias are related to underlying lateral faults deep in the Earth's crust, which finger upward into a complex of smaller fractures (Smith and others, 2003; Katz and others, 2006).

Evidently more than one process is responsible for the carbonate porosity in petroleum reservoirs throughout the world. Clear criteria are needed to distinguish among the various origins, and the concepts of speleogenesis are playing an important role.

Mining

Karst can be a host for certain economically valuable mineral deposits, particularly lead, zinc, and iron ores, and bauxite (Bosák and others, 1989; Filippov, 2004). Economic geologists have written a great deal about the

relation between karst and ores. Some ore genesis involves microbial processes that are similar to those in hypogenic caves (Southam and Saunders (2005). The location and mineralogy of caves may help to clarify the origin and distribution of ores, although there has as yet been little attempt to do so.

Caves are often observed in deep mines from which the water has been pumped to gain access to ore bodies. Most of

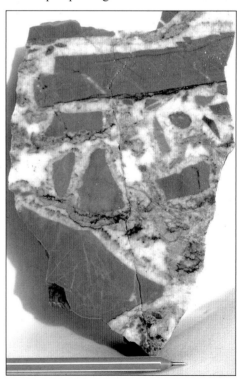

Figure 15.28: Paleokarst breccia in the Ordovician Mascot Dolomite of Tennessee is host to major deposits of zinc ore. The ore, a zinc sulfide (sphalerite), is honey yellow and appears here as light gray. The dark gray is the dolomite bedrock, and the white is secondary dolomite mineralization. This sample is from the Jefferson City Mine.

these caves are irregular dead-end pockets with mineralized walls and are clearly hypogenic (Figure 15.26). Nearly all of the caves are consumed by further mining, or filled to prevent bedrock instability, so there is limited opportunity to view them.

Lead-zinc ores are mined from karst breccias in many parts of the world (Sangster, 1996). The ores are mainly sulfides, which form only below the surface where the supply of oxygen is limited. Lead-colored *galena* (PbS) and yellow or brown *sphalerite* (ZnS) are the common lead and zinc ores (Figures 15.27–15.28). They are most often produced by the reaction of dissolved metals with hydrogen sulfide, which in turn is a byproduct of the reduction of gypsum, anhydrite, and other sulfur-rich compounds (Chapter 5). Production of hydrogen sulfide is also a step in the origin of certain caves (Chapter 8), so there is a genetic link between hypogenic karst and ore deposits, as well as with the hydrocarbons that help to generate the H_2S. Ores of various kinds can also accumulate in preexisting solution voids.

Mississippi Valley-type (MVT) sulfide deposits are fairly shallow, moderate-temperature ores that preferentially follow limestone and dolomite strata. They are especially abundant throughout much of the central Mississippi drainage basin. Lead-zinc ores are most common. These ores were deposited in several phases (as many as 10) throughout the Paleozoic Era (Kesler, 1996). Many ores are concentrated in and around the paleokarst and breccia zones described above, but the genetic relationship between the ores and the paleokarst is unclear. The largest deposits are located in extensive paleokarst aquifers, which easily transmit the mineralized fluids. The lead and zinc were probably transported as chloride complexes in salty low-H_2S brines, which were released from igneous sources in zones of compression in the Earth's crust (Hanor, 1996). They precipitated as sulfide ores by reacting with H_2S wherever sulfates were being reduced by hydrocarbons. Some MVT deposits also contain *barite* ($BaSO_4$), a brown, dense barium mineral, and *fluorite* (CaF_2), a soft mineral that is usually yellow or purple.

Mapping of MVT deposits in Poland suggests that thermal fluids dissolved the host carbonate rock at about the same time that they deposited the ores (Sass-Gustkiewicz and others, 1982). Evidence includes collapse breccias in which the ore has precipitated in the sandy residue left by dissolution of the bedrock (Figure 15.29). Sagging of overlying beds, tilting of beds toward solutional zones, widespread brecciation, and solutional thinning of mineralized areas are all thought to be typical characteristics of ore-related hydrothermal karst (Sass-Gustkiewicz, 1996). These rock structures can be used as a guide to ore prospecting.

In certain other areas of the world the sulfide ores are related to deep faults that

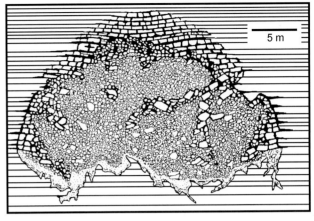

Figure 15.29: Early Tertiary MVT lead-zinc mineralization (heavy black) in collapse breccia exposed by mining in Triassic carbonate rocks, Silesia-Cracow region, Poland. Apparently the collapse took place into a solution void. The floor is covered by internally derived dolomite sand. (Simplified from Sass-Gustkiewicz and others, 1982).

carried rising hydrothermal fluids (Spirakis and Heyl, 1995; Vearncombe and others, 1996). Some ore minerals form speleothem-like deposits, such as coralloids and stalactites, which partly fill solution pockets (Bogacz and others, 1973; Motycka and Szuwarzynski, 1989).

Some mining geologists have noted that the patterns of certain ore deposits resemble those of hypogenic network caves such as Jewel Cave, South Dakota (Ohle, 1985). Their similarity in shape may be more apparent than real, because the gallery-and-pillar method of mining can exaggerate the resemblance to network caves (Figure 15.30). But Furman (1993) makes an explicit comparison between MVT ore bodies and hypogenic cave development in both pattern and genesis. He emphasizes that the controls of hypogenic karst by sulfate reduction and generation of sulfuric acid are related to those involved in sulfide ore deposition.

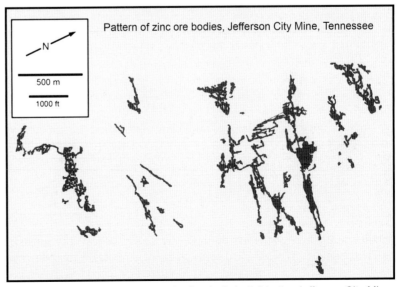

Figure 15.30: Pattern of zinc ore bodies (sphalerite) in the Jefferson City Mine, eastern Tennessee (after Ohle, 1985, from data supplied by R. Fulweiler).

Some caves that are intersected by mines are lined with iron sulfates, such as the minerals *melanterite* (FeSO$_4$·7H$_2$O) and *jarosite* (KFe$_3$(SO$_4$)$_2$(OH)$_6$). These minerals are stable only at low pH and moderate oxygen content. They become unstable when the caves are drained or exposed to fresh water, in which case they alter to sulfuric acid and iron oxides. The sulfuric acid is capable of further enlarging the caves.

In the Pine Point District, in the Northwest Territories of Canada, sulfide ore fills hydrothermal breccias, caves, and solution pockets that cut across an older paleokarst of Devonian age. The ore is concentrated along high areas in the host rock and forms wide tabular bodies interrupted in places by vertical breccia pipes (Rhodes and others, 1984). The ore filled available open space and also replaced dolomitic sediment and breccias. It is is surrounded by coarsely crystalline hydrothermal dolomite, which replaced the bedrock during and just before ore deposition. This characteristic is typical of hydrothermal dissolution. Kyle (1983), however, interprets such voids as the product of normal karst dissolution in coarsely crystalline dolomite. Ford and Williams (1989) suggest that the voids formed in a marine mixing zone. In places the ore is accompanied by residual hydrocarbons. Qing and Mountjoy (1994) suggest that the metal-bearing solutions migrated up-dip about 500 km from an oil-rich structural basin. The region is so cold and remote that the annual employee turnover was several hundred percent while the mine was in operation. The mine closed in 1987.

The Nanisivik Mine on Baffin Island, northeastern Canada, offers even less inviting conditions but more spectacular geology. It too has been abandoned. Lead-zinc ore once filled a single large strike-oriented cave in Precambrian dolomite. The cave is a sinuous conduit 100 m wide and 8 m high with fragile fins of corroded bedrock that extend horizontally as much as 20 m into the void. The walls also contain deep solution notches filled with pyrite. Deposition of sulfide ores during the Ordovician Period was periodically interrupted by erosion and collapse. Ford (1986) considers that rock dissolution and ore deposition took place simultaneously as the result of paragenesis (see pages 264–265). This process took place either close to the water table, or along a phase boundary between hydrothermal fluids. Sulfides were deposited on the floor as the ceiling was dissolved upward. The delicate fins of protruding rock could not have supported themselves if the cave had pre-dated the ore.

Uranium minerals are scattered throughout many karst areas, including several parts of the western U.S. They are not common in typical karst, because the oxidized forms of uranium are easily dissolved by fresh water. Dissolved uranium is most often deposited when it is transported into oxygen-poor zones (Drever, 1997). For this reason, uranium can accumulate where hydrogen sulfide is present, perhaps during hypogenic cave development. Later, in the oxidizing conditions of air-filled caves, these minerals can be dissolved and then redeposited by evaporation. This process may account for the presence of the bright yellow uranium-vanadium minerals *tyuyamunite* (Ca(UO$_2$)$_2$V$_2$O$_8$·5–8H$_2$O) and *metatyuyamunite* (Ca(UO$_2$)$_2$V$_2$O$_8$·3H$_2$O), which form in small amounts on evaporative surfaces such as gypsum crusts. They are too sparse to be considered ores, but their presence helps to clarify the origin and distribution of uranium in carbonate rocks. Scattered examples are encountered in caves of the Guadalupe Mountains, New Mexico, and the Bighorn Mountains of Wyoming-Montana. The minerals are usually associated with quartz and opal released by the alteration of clay by sulfuric acid (Polyak and Provencio, 2001).

Most ores in karst have had a complex history. They are often interspersed with deposits of carbonate minerals and interrupted by various phases of bedrock dissolution and brecciation. To explain this sequence in MVT deposits, Spirakis and Heyl (1988) suggest the following processes (see Reactions 5.24–5.27): As temperature rises past about 80°C, bedrock dissolution takes place because of the production of organic acids from hydrocarbons. At higher temperatures these acids decompose to carbon dioxide and methane, while buffering by organic compounds prevents a drop in pH. Calcite wall linings are deposited as a result. Eventually, the organic acids become less concentrated, while continued CO$_2$ production lowers the pH and causes a second phase of carbonate dissolution. During the early parts of the second dissolution phase, fluorite, quartz and sulfide ores are deposited as the carbonates dissolve. Later, as temperatures drop, scalenohedral calcite ("dogtooth spar") is deposited. This model involves some speculation, but it agrees with the known behavior of organic compounds and explains the sequence observed in many MVT deposits.

Bauxite is a clay-like material rich in aluminum hydroxide (Al(OH)$_3$ or Al$_2$O$_3$·H$_2$O), which is produced by intense weathering in warm, humid climates. About 10% of the world's bauxite production comes from sinkhole and paleokarst fills in karst (Bárdossy, 1989). Most bauxite is thought to originate as air-borne volcanic ash that is trapped in karst depressions and later altered by chemical weathering (Bárány-Kevei, 2004). Soluble rocks alone contain few of the essential ingredients for bauxite. Karst-related bauxite is mined in many parts of the world. Some of these deposits are ancient enough that they are now located in cold climates.

Phosphate deposits can be produced in the same way (Bourrouilh-Le Jan, 1989). Both phosphates and bauxites are mined on certain carbonate islands in the southwestern Pacific. The composition of the local volcanic rock determines which of the two is dominant. This origin for phosphate contrasts with the view that phosphates are derived from bird or bat guano (page 295).

Scientific frontiers

The enthusiasm for cave exploring that appears throughout this book may seem contrary to the scientific viewpoint. But many other scientists share this view. The current surge in space exploration is driven as much by the thrill of discovery as by the quest for scientific knowledge. Some of the leading researchers in extra-terrestrial geology are former speleologists. Even the pioneering astronomer Edwin Hubble was once a Missouri cave explorer.

Caves of various kinds, especially volcanic caves, are likely to be present elsewhere in the Solar System. Investigation of these caves should provide information about the local geologic history. Caves also have the potential to provide visiting humans and scientific equipment with shelter against cosmic radiation and extreme temperature fluctuations.

Attention is also drawn to possible similarities between microbial life in caves on Earth and that on other planets and moons (Boston, 2000; Boston and others, 2001, 2003, 2006). The robust character of microbes is shown by their presence in the boiling-hot water of geysers and steam vents in areas of igneous activity and in bedrock pores many kilometers below the surface. Although still unverified, there is some evidence for life on Mars, at least in the distant past. On such an inhospitable planet, any life is most likely to survive in subsurface environments.

As cave science matures, it will see an increasing emphasis on a systems approach, in which all aspects of the field are drawn together and interrelated. Speleologists have long ago moved from individual cave studies to a basin-wide perspective. A future goal will be to track the development of karst systems throughout geologic history, and to draw together the entire spectrum of geologic, chemical, climatic, and biological interactions. Distribution of aquatic invertebrates in caves, combined with rates at which individual species develop, can help to delineate long-term changes in karst drainage patterns (Holsinger, 2000; Sket, 2007). Caves are valuable repositories for clues to past events, and as this fact becomes more widely appreciated it will strengthen the case for cave preservation.

Cave science will be adopted increasingly by scientists in other fields, as suggested by the examples in this chapter. Information on caves is increasingly sought when practical problems arise in karst. On the other hand, speleologists will find themselves sharing ground with researchers who have no specific interest in caves, and for whom caves are mainly a source of information that is helpful in their own fields. It is appropriate for karst specialists to meet them halfway and even to join the ranks of leadership in these related disciplines. Hydrology and environmental engineering are among the many promising paths for cave scientists. To participate most effectively in these fields, one can benefit from a strong quantitative background.

Most people think of Earth's interior as an inert mass. Geologists know better, but even they have to admit that their knowledge of deep-seated processes is cloudy. Even topics of economic importance, such as the origin of certain petroleum reservoirs and ore deposits, have many uncertainties. It is difficult to study deep geological, geochemical, and hydrologic processes because most of the direct observations are limited to wells and mines. Much of the relevant evidence is lost by mine closures and the discarding of unwanted drilling logs and cores. Water wells reveal many aquifer characteristics, but their information is spatially discontinuous.

Caves help to fill some of these gaps. They provide access to rock exposures and geochemical environments that are not readily observed elsewhere. Their distribution and patterns demonstrate where specific subsurface processes are concentrated and how they change from place to place. Caves do not hold the answers to all questions about these topics, but what evidence they can offer is increasingly valued. Cave science should have a bright future.

The limits of discovery

THERE IS A CLOSE LINK between discovery and science. Much of the impetus for cave science comes from the discovery of new caves, especially those that reveal unusual characteristics or origins. What does the future hold?

Today, at the global scale, new exploration is taking place as rapidly as ever, even in caves that have long been known. The 2000-meter mark for cave depth has just been passed in Krubera Cave, in the Republic of Georgia. The record-holding length of Mammoth Cave, Kentucky, continues to march upward slowly, while mapping in Jewel Cave and Wind Cave in South Dakota, and in the vast underwater systems of the Yucatán Peninsula, is advancing at a rapid pace. Other caves throughout the world show promise for great discoveries, especially in China. With such expanding horizons, cave science is thriving.

But every discovery brings us closer to that unwelcome point of diminishing returns. One wonders if cave scientists will eventually run out of topics to investigate. No other science has ever encountered this barrier, and it is unlikely that cave science will be any different.

In 1970, one of the most skilled karst geologists of his or any other generation asked this rhetorical question: *What more is there to say about cave origin?* The implication was that the limit had been reached, and that just about all that could be done *had* been done. The answer to his question, at least for now, occupies most of Chapters 7–9.

Compared to most other human endeavors, speleology has a rare advantage that keeps it fresh. Caves, even well-traveled ones, reveal their secrets only to those who are willing to explore. Each generation has the opportunity to become acquainted with them as though for the first time. This requires a level of personal commitment that inevitably opens new horizons.

Not far from our home is a large cave, large at least by Northeastern standards. Cavers go there often, sometimes for science or exploration, but usually just to be there. A lively stream flows through its main passage, swirling around corners and plunging over waterfalls into dark pools. It keeps the cave pristine. With each visit there is joy in noticing unexpected details, as though discovering new personality traits in an old friend. No matter how many times we visit that stream passage, it has new things to say to us. The stream is running through the cave today, and it will continue to do so for as long as we care to imagine.

Arthur N. Palmer is former director of the Water Resources program at the State University of New York (SUNY) at Oneonta, where he is Professor Emeritus of Hydrology and Geochemistry. He and his wife Peggy have been involved with cave and karst studies for several decades and are both honorary members of the National Speleological Society. Art has received the Science Award from the National Speleological Society, the Lifetime Achievement Award from the Karst Waters Institute, SUNY Chancellor's Awards for teaching and research, and a Distinguished Teaching Professorship. He is a member of the Cave Research Foundation and British Cave Research Association, a fellow of the Geological Society of America and a GSA Kirk Bryan Award recipient. He also teaches a summer course on Karst Geology for Western Kentucky University at Mammoth Cave National Park.

Glossary

Important terms are defined here with emphasis on those that are used in several different places in this book. Some words are included mainly to clarify their meanings or application. Pronunciations are those used in English-speaking countries. Additional terms relevant to caves and karst are defined in glossaries by Lowe and Waltham (1995), Field (2002b), and Neuendorf and others (2005).

aerosol   A suspension of tiny particles of solid or liquid in air.

aggressive   Characteristic of water that is unsaturated with respect to the local bedrock and thus is able to dissolve it.

alkalinity   Ability of a solution to react with acid as the result of HCO_3^-, CO_3^{2-}, and OH^- content. Water becomes alkaline as it dissolves carbonate rocks.

allogenic recharge (*al-o-gen-ic*)   Inflow of water from an outside area. In speleology it applies to water that collects on a non-karst surface and then drains into caves when it encounters soluble rock. (Compare with *autogenic.*)

alluviation   Deposition of sediment by a flowing river. *Alluvium* is the material deposited by the process.

anastomoses   A braided network of interconnecting curvilinear tubes, usually 5–20 cm in diameter, rarely large enough to admit humans. (See *anastomotic cave pattern.*)

anastomotic cave pattern   A maze of interconnected curving tubes, similar to anastomoses but of traversable size. The difference is more than one of scale: anastomoses are minor features formed during the initial stages of cave development, or as floodwater injection features, whereas anastomotic cave passages serve as major conduits for groundwater movement in the direction of the spring outlet.

anhydrite   Calcium sulfate ($CaSO_4$). It is similar to gypsum but its mineral structure does not contain water.

anticline   An upward fold in a sequence of rock layers, formed by compression, usually in areas of mountain formation. In an anticline the layers are bent into an arch. (Compare with *syncline.*)

aquifer   A rock of high permeability capable of delivering abundant water to a well. (See *permeability.*)

aragonite (*ar-ag-on-ite*)   A form of calcium carbonate ($CaCO_3$) with a needle-shaped crystal structure. It is usually deposited instead of calcite only where there is abundant evaporation, high rate of CO_2 loss, or in water that has a high magnesium content. (Compare with *calcite.*)

artesian aquifer   An aquifer in which the potentiometric surface lies above the land surface and thus contains flowing wells. Artesian conditions are almost always produced by low-permeability strata that overlie the aquifer.

autogenic recharge (*au-to-gen-ic*)   Recharge to a cave from rainfall or snow melt that collects on the local karst area. Also called *authigenic*. (Compare with *allogenic.*)

basalt (*ba-salt*)   A dark gray or black igneous rock containing microscopic crystals. Basalt forms by rapid solidification of lava at or near the land surface. Most volcanic caves are in this rock type.

base level   The lowest level to which a river is able to erode its channel. A river is at its base level if it has ceased to deepen its channel and has developed a floodplain.

bathyphreatic   Conditions deep beneath the water table. Usually used in the context of deep-phreatic cave origin.

bed   A layer of stratified rock, generally of sedimentary rock. A sedimentary *formation* consists of a sequence of many individual beds. (See *strata.*)

bedding plane   The plane of contact between adjacent sedimentary beds, usually representing a change of composition or grain size. A *bedding-plane parting* is the narrow irregular gap that forms along bedding planes as the rock weathers.

bioerosion   Erosion or dissolution caused by (or enhanced by) biological processes. It includes physical erosion by boring organisms or dissolution by organic acids. Seacoast notches and *phytokarst* are typical results.

biothem   A speleothem produced by, or initiated by, biological activity.

branchwork cave   A cave formed by underground streams that converge in a dendritic or branching pattern, with tributaries joining downstream to form progressively fewer but (usually) larger passages.

breakdown   Blocks, slabs, or chips of bedrock that have fallen from the ceiling or walls of a cave. Also the *process* by which these materials fall and accumulate.

breccia (*bretch-ee-a*)   A sedimentary rock consisting of angular fragments of preexisting rock that have been broken apart and recemented more or less in place, with little movement. It is a variety of *conglomerate.*

calcite (*cal-site*)   A form of calcium carbonate ($CaCO_3$) with blocky or prism-shaped crystals. It is the most stable form of calcium carbonate and is the main ingredient of all but the most recent limestones. (Compare with *aragonite.*)

canyon passage (canyon)   A cave passage formed by a vadose stream in which the floor has been dissolved and/or eroded downward below the initial path of flow. Canyons are usually sinuous, narrow, and of greater height than width.

capillary water   Water that moves, or is held in place, by the combined effect of adhesion of water to solid surfaces and cohesion between water molecules. (Compare with *gravitational water.*)

carbon dioxide   A compound (CO_2) liberated by oxidation of carbon, most commonly by the decay of organic carbon compounds. It is normally a gas but dissolves in water to form *carbonic acid*, the most common source of aggressiveness in cave water.

carbonate rocks   Rocks composed mainly of minerals that contain carbonate (CO_3). The only common carbonate rocks are *limestone* (composed mainly of $CaCO_3$) and *dolomite* (composed mainly of $CaMg(CO_3)_2$), as well as *marble* derived from them by metamorphism.

carbonic acid   The most common source of aggressiveness in karst water, formed by the hydration of dissolved carbon dioxide.

catchment area   The area of the land surface that collects the rain and snowmelt that feeds a given surface stream, cave passage, or spring.

cenote (*sen-oh-tay*)   A steep-walled karst depression floored by water, formed by collapse into an active cave passage.

Cenozoic (***sen**-o-**zo**-ic*)   The most recent era of geologic time (see Figure 2.1), which includes approximately the past 66 million years. The limestones of the Florida karst and Caribbean islands are of Cenozoic age.

chert   A microcrystalline form of quartz (SiO_2) that commonly forms nodules and irregular beds in limestone. Broken surfaces are usually smooth and sharp-edged. Its common name is *flint*.

closed system   With regard to cave origin, conditions in which carbon dioxide is not available to replace that which is consumed by dissolution of limestone or dolomite. This is typical of the phreatic zone. (Compare with *open system*.)

common-ion effect   The decrease in solubility of dissolved minerals that contain one or more ions in common. For example, when calcite ($CaCO_3$) and gypsum ($CaSO_4 \cdot 2H_2O$) dissolve in the same water, they both produce a Ca^{2+} ion, which diminishes the solubility of each mineral.

cone karst   Karst topography dominated by steep conical hills separated by deep polygonal depressions, most common in tropical climates.

cone of depression   The cone-shaped depression in the water table or potentiometric surface of an aquifer caused by pumping a well. (See *drawdown*.)

confined aquifer   A permeable rock overlain by a less-permeable rock, in which the potentiometric surface lies above the top of the permeable rock. Wells that penetrate the confined aquifer contain water that stands at a level higher than the aquifer top.

contour interval   The vertical distance represented by adjacent contour lines on a topographic map. For example, if the contour interval is 5 m, each contour line represents a 5 m step above or below the ones adjacent to it.

corrosion residue   Soft, crumbly weathered surface on cave walls produced by intense weathering in air. It is typically brightly colored by a variety of minerals such as iron oxides.

detrital sediment (*de-try-tal*)   A sediment composed of weathered material from preexisting rocks, usually transported and deposited by flowing water or wind. A *detrital sedimentary rock* is formed by the compaction or cementing of detrital sediment.

diagenesis (*di-a-**gen**-e-sis*)   The chemical and physical changes that take place in a sedimentary rock with time (not including weathering or metamorphism). Compaction, cementation, and development of porosity are among the most significant diagenetic changes.

dip   The inclination of beds in a deformed sedimentary rock, or of any geologic structure (such as a fault). It refers both to the direction of tilt as well as the angle of tilt to the horizontal (for example, 25° to the west).

discharge   The flow rate of water measured in volume per time (for example, cubic meters per second).

dissolution   The process by with a rock or mineral dissolves (generally in water).

doline (***doh**-leen*)   European term for *sinkhole*, a karst depression formed by dissolution of bedrock, collapse of an underlying cave, or both. (See *sinkhole*.)

dolomite (***doh**-lo-mite*)   A fairly soluble mineral with the composition $CaMg(CO_3)_2$, or the rock composed mainly of that mineral. The rock is sometimes called *dolostone* to distinguish it from the mineral.

drainage basin   On the land surface, the area that collects rain and snowmelt and drains into a single stream. For example, the Mississippi drainage basin includes the entire area that feeds water into that river. The term also applies to groundwater systems, although the boundaries are more vague.

drainage divide   The boundary between adjacent drainage basins, either on the surface or underground. (See *drainage basin*.)

drawdown   The drop in the water table or potentiometric surface in and around a well as the result of pumping. The drawdown decreases away from the pumping well. (See *cone of depression*.)

dripstone   Speleothems (usually composed of calcite) deposited by dripping supersaturated water. Stalactites, stalagmites, draperies, and columns are the most common forms.

echinolith (*ee-**kine**-o-lith*)   A sharp-edged blade of rock produced by the intersection of solution pockets or flutes.

efficiency (applied to water flow)   Relative ease with which water moves through a system - i.e., amount of discharge that can be transmitted for a given amount of head ($Q/\Delta h$). Not equivalent to its use in other applications (as in engines or work).

eogenetic (*ee-o-gen-et-ic*)   Associated with the depositional environment of a rock. For example, eogenetic karst forms in young limestone that is still undergoing consolidation and early diagenesis. Also called *syngenetic karst* (***sin**-gen-et-ic*). Compare with *mesogenetic* and *telogenetic*.

epigenic (*ep-i-**gen**-ic*)   Refers to an origin near the Earth's surface. Epigenic caves are produced by acids generated by processes at or near the surface. Also *epigenetic*.

epikarst   The highly porous uppermost zone of dissolution in soluble bedrock at the surface or just below the soil. In the latter case, most of the openings are soil-filled. Nearly all initial openings have been enlarged at comparable rates by highly undersaturated water.

erosion   The removal of solid material from a rock, sediment, or soil surface, either as particles or in solution, usually by flowing water, glacial ice, or wind. *Mechanical erosion* removes the material as solid particles. *Chemical erosion (dissolution)* removes the material as a solution in water.

evaporite rocks (or **evaporites**)   Rocks formed primarily by evaporation of surface water in arid regions, most commonly in lagoons or closed basins. Evaporites include gypsum, anhydrite, and rock salt.

fault   A fracture in bedrock along which movement has taken place between the two adjacent blocks of rock.

fengcong karst (*fung-sung*)   Chinese term for a hilly karst landscape that develops well above the erosional base level and water table. Hills are typically cone-shaped, with intervening sinkholes. (See *cone karst*.)

fenglin karst (*fung-lin*)   Chinese term for a hilly karst landscape that develops at or just above the erosional base level. Hills are typically tower-shaped and rise from a flat erosion surface or alluviated plain. (See *tower karst*.)

fissure passage (fissure) A straight segment of cave passage guided by a joint or fault (or a series of parallel joints or faults) with a high, narrow cross section.

flank-margin cave A cave formed in young seacoast limestone in the freshwater-seawater mixing zone, along the flanks of a freshwater lens. (Compare with *halo-phreatic cave*.)

floodplain The nearly flat bottom of a valley that contains a mature or old-age stream. (See *base level*).

floodwater cave A cave formed by (or greatly modified by) one or more sinking streams that undergo severe periodic flooding.

flowstone Speleothems (usually composed of calcite) deposited by thin sheets of supersaturated water flowing down sloping cave walls or other surfaces.

flute A vertical groove with a U-shaped cross section, dissolved in the bedrock wall of a cave by flowing or dripping water. Flutes usually occur in parallel arrays like the flutes in the columns on classical architecture.

fractionation Changes in water chemistry and mineral stability caused by the precipitation of minerals from the water. In caves this process is most significant where evaporation takes place. (More often used in other contexts, such as in the evolution of crystallizing magma.)

frostwork A speleothem composed of bushes of aragonite (a needle-shaped form of calcium carbonate).

geode (*jee-ode*) A small rounded cavity in bedrock that is lined with a resistant mineral, usually amorphous silica, and with crystals projecting into the void. Geodes typically weather out of the bedrock as resistant hollow balls. (Compare with *vug*, which has no resistant lining.)

glacial outwash Sediments deposited by the meltwater from a glacier.

glacial till Sediments deposited directly by the movement of glacial ice. In comparison with glacial outwash, they include a combination of many grain sizes and show little or no stratification.

granite An igneous rock composed of mostly light-colored minerals with visible crystals, formed by solidification of molten material deep beneath the surface.

gravitational water Underground water that has enough volume to overcome capillary effects, so that it flows by gravity down the steepest available paths. It accounts for the main flow of water through the *vadose zone*.

groundwater Traditionally, water within the phreatic zone; but increasingly the term is applied to underground water of any kind.

guano Deposits composed of bat or bird droppings, or their alteration products.

gypsum (*jip-sum*) A mineral composed of hydrated calcium sulfate ($CaSO_4 \cdot 2H_2O$) that is deposited mainly in areas where water evaporates. The term also applies to the rock composed of the mineral gypsum.

gypsum flower A speleothem composed of radiating fronds of gypsum that resembles a flower.

halite (*hay-lite*) The mineral name for sodium chloride (NaCl), which is used as common table salt. It is highly soluble and precipitates only where there is intense evaporation.

halocline (*hay-lo-cline*) Interface between fresh water and underlying salt water (generally sea water), commonly the site of carbonate dissolution. (See *halo-phreatic cave*.)

halo-phreatic cave (*hay-lo free-at-ic*) A cave formed by mixing of fresh water and saline water at a halocline. (Compare with *flank margin cave*.)

helictite (*hel-ic-tite*, or *heel-ic-tite*) A speleothem that twists and branches in an erratic manner without regard for gravity. Helictites have narrow central canals that feed capillary water to the growing tips. Most are composed of calcite or aragonite.

hydraulic gradient The drop in hydraulic head divided by the distance of water flow. It is equivalent to the rate of energy loss within a hydrologic system. The slope of the water table or potentiometric surface is a rough approximation of the hydraulic gradient in an aquifer.

hydraulic head The energy possessed by water at any point. It involves a combination of elevation and pressure. (On a local scale it can also involve the kinetic energy possessed by rapidly flowing water, which allows jets of water to rise against gravity.) Differences in head are what make water flow, and the flow is from high head to low head.

hydrogen sulfide A gas that is generated by the reduction of sulfates or sulfur and smells like rotten eggs. It easily dissolves in water, and when it encounters oxygen it oxidizes to sulfuric acid, which is a potent cave-forming agent.

hydrograph A graph of discharge (volume of water flow) vs. time.

hypogenic (*hy-po-gen-ic*) Refers to an origin deep beneath the Earth's surface. *Hypogenic caves* are formed by acids generated partly or entirely at depth below the surface. Also *hypogenetic*.

igneous rock Rock formed by crystallization of molten material, either below or at the Earth's surface.

inception horizon A bedding plane, or contact between beds, which guides the initial paths of cave-forming water owing to favorable rock conditions or chemical reactivity. An example is a zone rich in pyrite that oxidizes to sulfuric acid when fresh water passes through it. Contrasting rock types, such as thin shale laminae between limestone beds, can also promote bedding-plane partings that are wider than their neighbors and thus are favorable to cave development.

infiltration The process by which surface water seeps or flows into the ground.

injection features Solutional enlargements or extensions of preexisting cave passages resulting from periodic floodwater activity. Examples include solution pockets, fissures, and anastomoses extending away from the original passage.

insurgence The sink point of a sinking stream (see *ponor*). Not widely accepted because, among other reasons, its Latin root is contradictory (*surgere* = "rise up").

intergranular porosity (matrix porosity) The openings between the grains or crystals of a rock.

joint A fracture in bedrock along which no visible shift has taken place. (Compare with *fault* and *bedding-plane parting*.)

karren (*carr-en*) Superficial solution features in bare bedrock (generally at the land surface). Examples include fissures, rills, flutes, and small canyons. *Karren topography* is a landscape of bare bedrock dominated by solution features of this kind.

karst A landscape in which the dominant features owe their origin mainly to dissolution of bedrock.

karst window A sinkhole with a flowing cave stream at the bottom.

keyhole passage A cave passage with a keyhole-shaped cross section, usually formed by entrenchment of a vadose canyon in the floor of an earlier tube.

kinetic trigger A threshold chemical or physical condition that, when present, allows a process to accelerate rapidly. In speleology it refers to the conditions that cause aggressive groundwater to begin rapid enlargement of caves.

laminar flow Water flow in which there are no eddies and little or no crossing or mixing of flow paths. It includes most groundwater, seepage through narrow fissures, and thin films of water. In contrast, water in streams and solution conduits is almost always *turbulent*.

lava tube A tubular cave passage formed during a volcanic eruption where liquid lava flows out from beneath a cooler, solidified lava roof.

level (cave level) A level at which cave passages tend to cluster as the result of a pause in the downward erosion of local river valleys. In comparison, *stories* or *tiers* refer to the vertical arrangement of cave passages regardless of their relation to erosional history.

lift tube The ascending part of a downward loop in a phreatic passage, through which water rises, or once rose. Also *phreatic lift*.

limestone A sedimentary rock composed mainly of calcium carbonate (calcite and/or aragonite). It is the most common cavernous rock type.

lineament (*lin-ee-a-ment*) A large-scale linear feature that appears on an aerial photo or map, caused by major fractures or swarms of fractures. Those that are discerned from aerial photos are sometimes called *photolineaments*.

magma Molten material from deep within the Earth's crust or mantle, which solidifies into igneous rocks. *Lava* is magma that emerges at the surface through volcanoes.

marble A metamorphic rock formed from limestone or dolomite by heat and pressure beneath the surface. It is composed mainly of the same minerals as the original rock, but with larger crystals and with impurities segregated into dark bands.

mass balance A version of the law of conservation of mass and energy. When applied to water flow, the volume of water entering a system over any period of time equals the volume leaving, plus any change in volume. The concept also applies to the concentration of chemicals in solution (see Chapter 4, Figure 4.32).

matrix porosity The openings between the grains or crystals of a rock (also called *intergranular porosity*).

mature stage The stage in the evolution of a river at which it ceases to deepen its valley and instead begins to widen it to form a floodplain. (Compare with *youthful* and *old-age* stages.)

Major cave levels may form at this time (see *level*).

maze cave A cave composed of a complex grid of intersecting passages, usually with many closed loops. (See *network*, *anastomotic*, *ramiform*, and *spongework*).

mesogenetic (*mez-o-gen-et-ic*) Processes or features associated with deep burial of a rock beneath younger rocks. In karst, mesogenetic processes may include pore filling, ore deposition, dissolution of pores by deep-seated fluids, etc. Compare with *eogenetic* and *telogenetic*.

Mesozoic (*mez-o-zo-ic*) The era of the dinosaurs, extending from about 245 to 66 million years ago. Many of the largest karst areas of Europe and Mexico are in Mesozoic rocks. (See Figure 2.1.)

metamorphic rock A rock formed from preexisting rock by heat and pressure within the Earth.

micrite (*mick-rite*) Fine-grained limestone in which the individual crystals are microscopic (except for fossils, which often remain intact). It is formed in quiet water that has no wave agitation. (Compare with *sparite*.)

mineral A naturally occurring compound with a distinct crystal structure. Minerals are the building blocks that compose the rocks of the Earth's crust.

mixing dissolution Dissolution of soluble rock by renewed aggressiveness resulting from the mixing of two or more solutions that are individually not aggressive.

mixing zone The zone of mixing between two or more solutions of different composition (for example, between seawater and fresh water). They are commonly zones of enhanced dissolution. (See *mixing dissolution*.)

mogote (*mo-go-tay*) A cone-shaped residual hill in a karst area surrounded by an erosional or alluvial plain. (See *tower karst*. Karst towers have steeper walls.)

network pattern The pattern of a maze cave formed by intersecting fissure passages. Network caves follow the trends of joints or faults, and most have patterns resembling the layout of city streets.

numerical age (absolute age) The age of a geologic feature or fossil, in years, estimated from radiometric or other laboratory measurements. Numerical age estimates are not exact ("absolute"), as they involve small uncertainties that depend on the laboratory method and the nature of the sample.

old-age stage The stage in the evolution of a river in which floodplains become very wide and the land surface has been weathered and eroded to low relief. (Compare with *youthful* and *mature* stages.)

opal A non-crystalline form of silicon dioxide (SiO_2). (Compare with *chert* and *quartz*.)

open system With regard to cave origin, conditions where carbon dioxide is available to replace that which is consumed by dissolution of limestone or dolomite. This is typical of the vadose zone. (Compare with *closed system*.)

oxidation The transfer of electrons away from a substance during a reaction. Oxygen is involved in most such reactions, for example in the oxidation of hydrogen sulfide or iron sulfide to sulfuric acid. (Compare with *reduction*.)

paleokarst Karst features that have been buried by younger sediments or rock.

paleomagnetism The residual orientation of magnetic grains in sediment or rock in the direction of the Earth's magnetic field at the time the material was formed. Comparison of directions with today's field can help to determine the age of the material.

Paleozoic (*pale-ee-o-zo-ic*) The era in which complex organisms first developed. It extends from about 570 to 245 million years ago. Most of the major karst areas of the United States are located in rocks of this age. (See Figure 2.1).

paragenesis (*pair-a-gen-e-sis*) Upward dissolution of a cave ceiling in a passage that is accumulating sediment. (The term is more commonly used by geologists to describe mineral sequences, particularly in ore deposits.)

parting (bedding-plane parting) The irregular gap produced by the splitting apart of two beds of sedimentary rock. More generally, partings result from the separation of any rock or mineral along planes of weakness. (Compare with *joint* and *fault*.)

P$_{CO_2}$ The partial pressure of carbon dioxide in air, or in water that is in equilibrium with the air. The P$_{CO_2}$ of the atmosphere near the Earth's surface is about 0.00035 atm. It is about 10 times greater in caves and about 100 times greater in soil. It is commonly but erroneously written pCO$_2$, which implies the negative logarithm of CO$_2$ concentration, (as in pH).

perched aquifer An isolated body of phreatic water within the vadose zone, above the normal level of the water table, hung up on material of relatively low permeability.

perched spring (contact spring) A spring located above the level of the local stream or river, usually held at that elevation by underlying low-permeability rock.

permeability (hydraulic conductivity) The ability of a material to transmit water. An *aquifer* is a rock of high permeability.

pH A measure of the acidity of a solution. It is the negative logarithm of the hydrogen-ion activity. Therefore a low value indicates a high acidity, and each pH unit represents a ten-fold change in H$^+$. A pH of 7 is considered neutral (neither basic nor acidic). Most karst water has a pH between 7 and 8.

piping Subsidence of loose soil or sediment into an underground water course to form voids.

phototrophic corrosion biogenic dissolution pits oriented in the direction of sunlight. Most common in the twilight zones inside cave entrances in warm, humid climates. (See *bioerosion, phytokarst*.)

phreatic zone (*free-at-ic*) The zone in the ground in which all the openings are filled with water. Its top surface is the *water table*. It is also called the *saturated zone*, but this term is inappropriate because of the confusion with chemical saturation. (Compare with *vadose zone*.)

phytokarst (*fite-o-karst*) Bare bedrock exposed along the seacoast and deeply pitted by biologically enhanced dissolution. The rock is commonly black or dark gray from the growth of boring algae and other organisms. (See *bioerosion*.)

polje (*pole-yeh*) A large karst depression with a flat floor that is commonly covered by river sediments. Springs in one or more walls feed surface streams that cross the polje and sink in another wall. The flat polje floor is generally at the local base level and is analogous to the floodplain of a mature river valley. Also

called a *gulf*. Small versions are called *karst windows*.

ponor (*pone-or*) A solutional hole into which a surface stream sinks underground, either completely or partially. Typically the sink point at the downstream end of a sinking stream. A term of Balkan origin used throughout most of the world. Also *swallow hole*.

popcorn (cave popcorn) A coralloid speleothem consisting of knobby growths of calcite, aragonite, or (rarely) evaporative minerals such as gypsum or dolomite. Most cave popcorn is formed by diffuse seepage from the cave walls in areas of evaporation, although some forms in splash zones.

porosity The percentage of open space in a material, including all intergranular pores, fractures, and solution pores.

potentiometric surface The surface that defines the level to which water rises in wells that penetrate a confined aquifer. It therefore represents the distribution of hydraulic head in the aquifer. In unconfined aquifers the potentiometric surface is equivalent to the *water table*.

Precambrian (*pre-cam-bri-an*) The earliest division of geologic time, before about 570 million years. It represents about 90% of all geologic time (see Figure 2.1). There are only a few scattered patches of Precambrian limestone and marble throughout the world, and thus very little karst occurs in rocks of that age.

pseudokarst A landscape that includes features that resemble those in karst (including caves) but which is the product of non-solutional processes, or which is the result of long-term dissolution of rocks that are normally too insoluble to form karst.

puka (*poo-ka*) A Hawaiian term for a hole in a lava surface formed by the collapse of an underlying cave. Many pukas serve as cave entrances.

pyroclastic (*py-ro-clas-tic*) Pertaining to volcanic material that is blown into the air by a volcanic eruption and solidifies before it reaches the ground. Pyroclastic material includes volcanic dust, ash, and irregular fragments.

quartz The crystalline form of silicon dioxide (SiO$_2$). (Compare with *opal* and *chert*, which are non-crystalline and micro-crystalline forms of SiO$_2$ respectively.)

radiometric dating Estimation of the age of a rock, fossil, or other natural object by measuring the amount of a radioactive element relative to its byproducts (for example, uranium vs. thorium).

raft (calcite raft) A thin sheet of calcite (rarely aragonite or another mineral) that forms on the surface of a standing pool of supersaturated cave water. Rafts usually break apart and settle to the pool bottom when they are hit by falling water drops or if they grow too heavy to float by surface tension.

ramifying (ramiform) pattern The pattern of a type of maze cave consisting of interconnected rooms and spongework, with passages extending outward as present or former outlet routes.

reduction The transfer of electrons to a substance during a reaction. Reduction takes place at the same time as *oxidation*. For example, during the reduction of sulfate to sulfide in the presence of organic material, reduction of sulfur takes place at the same rate that carbon is oxidized.

rejuvenation   Renewed downward river erosion in a formerly mature or old-age landscape as the result of uplift of the land or a drop in sea level (or a combination of both).

relative age   The age of a rock, fossil, or geologic structure in relation to other objects or structures. No actual age is implied, but only the sequence of events.

rhombohedral calcite (*rom-bo-heed-ral*)   One of the most typical forms of calcite, in which the crystal faces form parallelograms.

rill   A narrow groove dissolved or eroded in a sloping bedrock or sediment surface by a small stream of flowing water. Rills commonly occur in closely spaced parallel arrays. *Flutes* are vertical rills.

rimstone   A mineral deposit, usually calcite, that grows around the overflow edge of a pool that is supersaturated with the precipitating mineral. The resulting *rimstone dams* produce *rimstone pools* (also called *gours*).

rock   The material that makes up the hard outer layers of the Earth. Rocks are composed of aggregates of minerals.

saltpeter   The common name for potassium nitrate, which can be derived from nitrate-rich cave sediments. It is an essential ingredient of most gunpowder.

sandstone   A sedimentary rock composed of sand-size grains, usually quartz, derived from the weathering of other rocks and sorted into rather uniform sizes by streams or wave action. Calcium carbonate beach or dune sand can also form a variety of sandstone known as *calcarenite*.

saturation (undersaturation, supersaturation)   A comparison between the amount of dissolved mineral a water body actually contains and the maximum amount it can hold. If the two are equal, the water is saturated with respect to the mineral in question. An undersaturated solution contains less than the maximum and can dissolve more of the mineral. Depending on the mineral type, a supersaturated solution can be produced by one or more of the following: loss of carbon dioxide, evaporation, a change in temperature, and interaction with other minerals. A supersaturated solution tends to precipitate the mineral. Some supersaturation must be maintained for the mineral to precipitate.

saturation index (SI)   A measure of the degree of saturation of a solution with respect to a given mineral. It is calculated as log(IAP/K), where IAP = ion activity product (multiply the activities of the ions produced by the mineral) and K = equilibrium constant for the dissolution reaction. Negative SI values indicate undersaturation, zero indicates saturation, and positive values indicate supersaturation. (See *saturation*).

scallop   An asymmetrical hollow dissolved in a bedrock surface by turbulent water flow. Scallops intersect one another in extensive arrays that may cover the entire perimeter of a cave passage. The steep side of the hollow indicates the direction of water flow (as in a sand dune). The velocity of the flow that formed them is inversely proportional to the scallop length. Thus the direction and velocity of the most recent flow can be determined even in cave passages that are now dry.

sediment   An accumulation of loose grains of weathered bedrock (rarely other material) deposited by moving water, wind, or ice. Grain sizes include boulders, cobbles, gravel, sand, silt, and clay. Different grain sizes may be mixed together (as in glacial deposits), but more commonly they are sorted into narrow size ranges by moving water or wind.

sedimentary rock   A rock that consists of compacted or cemented sediment. Detrital sedimentary rocks contain weathered material deposited by flowing water or wind. Chemical sedimentary rocks consist mainly of cemented mineral deposits that have precipitated in bodies of water.

shaft (vertical shaft)   A well-like underground void formed by vertical movement of water. Nearly all are formed by descending vadose water, but some are formed by rising phreatic water.

shale   A sedimentary rock composed of compacted and solidified clay. It is soft and easily eroded but its low permeability and solubility allow even thin beds of shale to inhibit the downward flow of vadose water.

shelfstone   A thin shelf of mineral (usually calcite) that grows inward from the edges of supersaturated pools at and just below the water surface. Water flow is very low, and the water level is more stable than in pools dammed by rimstone.

shelter cave   A cave formed by the selective weathering of rock by mechanical processes. For example, a shelter cave may be formed in rock that is less resistant or thinner bedded than the rock above and below it.

sinkhole   A surface depression formed by dissolution of bedrock or by collapse of an underlying cave (and often a combination of both). *Doline* is the common international term for sinkhole.

sinkhole plain   A broad, low-relief surface on soluble rock that contains numerous sinkholes.

sinkhole pond   A perennial or seasonal body of water that occupies a sinkhole. Most sinkhole ponds are floored by low-permeability clay-rich soil that inhibits infiltration. Ponds of this type are perched above the water table. The surfaces of some sinkhole ponds, particularly in low-elevation karst such as that of Florida, represent intersections of the water table by sinkholes.

sinking stream   A surface stream that is perched above the water table and which loses its water to subsurface solution conduits.

siphon   A water-filled conduit in the shape of an inverted U. (Compare with *sump*.)

solution conduit   A solutionally enlarged path of groundwater flow. The term applies not only to traversable passages (caves), but also to those too small to explore.

solution pocket   A dead-end opening in the wall or ceiling of a solution cave.

sparite (*sparr-ite*)   Limestone in which the calcite crystals are visible to the unaided eye. It forms in water that is agitated by wave action, as along the seacoast, and consists of fossil fragments and other grains cemented together by crystalline calcite.

speleogenesis (*speel-ee-o-gen-e-sis*)   The origin of caves.

speleology (*speel-ee-ol-o-gy*)   The scientific study of caves. Sport caving is often included, especially in Europe.

speleothem (*speel-ee-o-them*)   A mineral deposit in a cave. Speleothems are popularly known as *cave formations*.

spongework   Interconnecting voids like those in a sponge, usually formed by the solutional enlargement of intergranular pores. A *spongework maze* contains openings large enough to explore.

spring The opening for a concentrated outflow of groundwater. *Cave springs* are fed by cave-sized openings. (See *perched spring*.)

stalactite An icicle-shaped mineral deposit (usually calcite) formed by dripping water. It grows downward from a cave ceiling or overhang.

stalagmite A mounded mineral accumulation (usually calcite) formed by water dripping onto a cave floor or ledge. It is usually fed by the same water that forms stalactites, and therefore a stalactite and stalagmite often form matching pairs that may eventually coalesce as a *column*.

story (cave story; British = **storey)** A level of cave development, with no genetic connotation. (See *level, tier*.)

strata The beds in a stratified rock, usually in reference to a sedimentary rock. (See *bed*.)

stratigraphy (*stra-tig-raff-ee*) The study of sedimentary rocks, particularly their sequence through time. A *stratigraphic column* is a diagram that shows the relative position, age, thickness, and rock type of sedimentary strata.

strike The direction perpendicular to the dip of a bed or geologic structure. For example, if a sedimentary rock contains beds that dip to the south, the strike is east-west. (The same is true for beds dipping to the north.)

stylolites Irregular surfaces along which the rocks on opposite sides interpenetrate, as the result of dissolution under pressure.

subaerial Surrounded by air (in reference to either processes or materials). Subaerial mineral origin takes place in air, even though the minerals are usually precipitated from a thin film of water. A stalactite is an example of a subaerial speleothem.

subaqueous Surrounded by water (in reference to either processes or materials). For example, the precipitation of a mineral in a pool or below the water table is a subaqueous process. Mammillary calcite crusts are generally subaqueous deposits.

sulfuric acid (British = **sulphuric**) An acid produced by the oxidation of sulfur or sulfides (e.g. hydrogen sulfide or iron sulfide). It is very potent in forming caves in areas where hydrogen sulfide rises into oxygen-rich zones. Its formula is H_2SO_4, but at pH greater than about 2 it fully dissociates into $2H^+ + SO_4^{2-}$, and at lower pH it is mainly $H^+ + HSO_4^-$.

surface tension Resistance to deformation of a fluid surface in contact with other fluid phases, for example the water surface in contact with air, or at a water-air-rock interface.

sump A water-filled section of cave passage. Sumps are often incorrectly called *siphons*, and the term *sump* is occasionally applied, also incorrectly, to sections of a cave that are not completely filled with water.

swallow hole A hole into which a surface stream sinks underground, either entirely or partially. Also *ponor, swallet*.

syncline A downward fold in a sequence of rock layers, formed by compression, usually in areas of mountain formation. In a syncline the layers are bent into a broad inverted U. (Compare with *anticline*.)

tectonic (*tec-ton-ic*) Refers to internal stresses in the Earth's crust, such as those that form mountains. *Tectonic caves* are formed by these forces.

telogenetic (***teel**-o-gen-et-ic*) Applied to processes or features associated with the erosion of rocks after they have experienced burial beneath younger rocks, which isolates them from the depositional and erosional environments at the surface. Most karst and caves are of telogenetic origin. Compare with *eogenetic* and *mesogenetic*.

tier (cave tier) A level of cave development. The term has no genetic connotation. (See *level, story*.)

tower karst A karst landscape dominated by isolated steep-walled peaks.

tubular passage (tube) A cave passage with a tubular shape. Most have elliptical or lens-shaped cross sections elongated along the local beds. These shapes indicate an origin either at or below the water table, or in the floodwater zone where flooding frequently reached the ceiling.

turbulent flow Fluid flow that contains eddies that allow mixing between adjacent flow paths. Nearly all streams, pipes, and caves contain turbulent flow. Dye introduced into turbulent flow quickly disperses throughout the stream or conduit. (Compare with *laminar flow*.)

unconfined aquifer A high-permeability rock that contains a water table. It is not confined by overlying low-permeability material.

unconformity The erosion surface that separates two rock formations where the underlying rock was exposed to surface weathering and erosion before the overlying rock was deposited.

vadose zone (*vad-ose*, or *vay-dose*) The zone above the water table in which water moves by gravity and capillarity. Water does not fill all the openings and does not build up pressures greater than atmospheric. (See *gravitational water* and *capillary water*. Compare with *phreatic zone*.)

vertical exaggeration On a cross section or profile (for example, of a cave passage), the ratio of the horizontal scale to the vertical scale. This is used to make the vertical relationships clearer than if a 1-to-1 ratio were used. Example: if the horizontal scale on a profile is 1 cm = 100 m and the vertical scale is 1 cm = 50 m, the vertical exaggeration is 100/50 = 2 times. The profile looks stretched by that amount in the vertical direction.

vug A small cavity in bedrock, usually lined with crystals that contrast with those of the bedrock. (Compare with *geode*.)

water table The upper surface of the phreatic zone. A *perched water table* is the top of a local phreatic zone perched on low-permeability material within the vadose zone. To be able to yield water, a well must penetrate below the water table.

weathering The decomposition of a rock or mineral while it is exposed at or near the land surface. Mechanical weathering involves the breakdown of material into smaller pieces (for example, by repeated freezing and thawing). Chemical weathering involves either chemical alteration or dissolution of material. Compare with *erosion*, which is the removal of weathered material, usually by flowing water, wind, or glacial ice.

youthful stage The earliest stage in the evolution of a river valley, in which the river lies above its base level and is still eroding downward. Valleys have V-shaped cross sections, usually with steep walls. (Compare with *mature* and *old-age* stages.)

References

Adamkó, P., G. Dénes, and S. Leél-Őssy, 1992, The caves of Buda: Budapest, Council of Hungarian Capitol, 47 p.

Adolphe, J.-P., J. Choppy, B. Choppy, J.-F.Loubière, J. Paradas, and F. Soleil-havoup, 1991, Biologie et concretionnement: Un exemple, les baguettes de gours [*Biology and speleothems: An example of rimstone pool fingers*]: Karstologia, v. 18, p. 49–55.

Alexander, E.C., and R.A. Jameson, 1994, A mass-based evaporation pan study in Mystery Cave, Minnesota [abstract]: National Speleological Society Bulletin, v. 56, no. 2, p. 111.

Aley, T., 1964, Echinoliths — an important solution feature in the stream caves of Jamaica: Cave Notes, v. 6, p. 3–5.

Aley, T., 1988, Complex radial flow of ground water in flat-lying, residuum-mantled limestone in the Arkansas Ozarks: Second Conference on Environmental Problems in Karst Terranes and their Solutions, Dublin, Ohio, Association of Groundwater Scientists and Engineers, p. 159–170.

Aley, T., 2002, Groundwater tracing handbook: Protem, Mo., Ozark Underground Laboratory, 35 p.

Aley, T., 2004, Tourist caves: Algae and lampenflora, in J. Gunn (ed.), Encyclopedia of caves and karst science: New York, Fitzroy Dearborn, p. 733–734.

Allred, K., 2004, Some carbonate erosion rates of southeast Alaska: Journal of Cave and Karst Studies, v. 66, no. 3, p. 89–97.

Allred, K., 2005, Kazumura Cave, Hawaii, in D.C. Culver and W.B. White (eds.), Encyclopedia of caves: San Diego, Elsevier / Academic Press, p. 330–335.

Allred, K., and D. Allred, 1997, Development and morphology of Kazumura Cave, Hawaii: Journal of Cave and Karst Studies, v. 59, no. 2, p. 67–80.

Allred, K., and Allred, C., 1998, Tubular lava stalactites and other related segregations: Journal of Cave and Karst Studies, v. 60, no. 3, p. 131–140.

am Ende, B., 2000, Wakulla 2 — building the first fully 3-D cave map: National Speleological Society, National Speleological Society News, v. 58, no. 9, p. 244–260, 270.

am Ende, B., 2005, Wakulla Spring underwater cave system, Florida, in D.C. Culver and W.B. White (eds.), Encyclopedia of caves: San Diego, Elsevier / Academic Press, p. 603–609.

Anderson, C.H., M.R. Vining, and C.M. Nichols, 1994, Evolution of the Paradise/Stephens Glacier ice caves: National Speleological Society Bulletin, v. 56, no. 2, p. 70–81.

Anderson, M.P., and W.W. Woessner, 2005, Applied groundwater modeling (2nd ed.): New York, Elsevier, 448 p.

Andre, B.J., and H. Rajaram, 2005, Dissolution of limestone fractures by cooling waters: Early development of hypogene karst systems: Water Resources Research, v. 41 (in press).

Annable, W.K., and E.A. Sudicky, 1999, On predicting contaminant transport in carbonate terrains: Behavior and prediction, in A.N. Palmer, M.V. Palmer, and I.D. Sasowsky (eds.), Karst modeling: Charles Town, W. Va., Karst Waters Institute, Special Publication 5, p. 133–145.

Anthony, D.M., 1998, Seasonal effects on the geochemical evolution of the Logsdon River, Mammoth Cave, Kentucky: M.S. thesis, Western Kentucky University, Bowling Green, Ky., 140 p.

Anthony, D.M., and D.E. Granger, 2004, A Late Tertiary origin for multilevel caves along the western escarpment of the Cumberland Plateau, Tennessee and Kentucky, established by cosmogenic [26]Al and [10]Be: Journal of Cave and Karst Studies, v. 66, no. 2, p. 46–55.

Anthony, D.M., and D.E. Granger, 2006, Five million years of Appalachian landscape evolution preserved in cave sediments, in R.S. Harmon and C.M. Wicks (eds.), Perspectives on karst geomorphology, hydrology, and geochemistry — A tribute volume to Derek C. Ford and William B. White: Geological Society of America, Special Paper 404, p. 39–50.

Anthony, D.M., and C.G. Groves, 1997, Preliminary investigations of seasonal changes in the geochemical evolution of the Logdson River, Mammoth Cave, Kentucky: Proceedings of 6th Mammoth Cave Science Conference, Mammoth Cave, Kentucky, p. 15–23.

Antonini, R., 1990, Veliko Sbrego: Geologia e carsismo della zona [*Geology and karst development in the Veliko Sbrego zone*]: Progressione, no. 22, p. 23–24.

Arnaud, H., 1978, Principales données structurales et lithologiques influant sur les circulations kartiques souterraines et les phénomènes karstiques du Vercors [*Structural and lithologic influence on karst groundwater flow and karst phenomena of the Vercors, France*]: Grottes et scialets du Vercors, Comité départemental de Spéléologie de l'Isère, Grenoble, France, v. 1, p. 13–28.

Ash, D.W., 1984, Evidence for deep-seated groundwater movement in Middle Mississippian carbonate lithologies of south-central Indiana [abstract]: Proceedings of National Speleological Society annual convention, Sheridan, Wyoming, p. 28.

Ashton, K., 1966, The analyses of flow data from karst drainage systems: Transactions of the Cave Research Group of Great Britain, v. 7, no. 2, p. 161–203.

Atkinson, A., 1992, The Undara lava tube system, North Queensland, Australia: Updated data and notes on the mode of formation and possible lunar analogue: National Speleological Society, Proceedings of 6th International Symposium of Vulcanospeleology, 1991, Hilo, Hawai'i, p. 95–120.

Atkinson, T.C., 1977a, Carbon dioxide in the atmosphere of the unsaturated zone: An important control of ground-water hardness in limestones: Journal of Hydrology, v. 35, p. 111–123.

Atkinson, T.C., 1977b, Diffuse flow and conduit flow in limestone terrain in the Mendip Hills, Somerset (Great Britain): Journal of Hydrology, v. 35, p. 93–110.

Atkinson, T.C., and D.I. Smith, 1976, The erosion of limestones, in T.D. Ford and C.H.D. Cullingford (eds.), The science of speleology: London, Academic Press, p. 151–177.

Audra, P., 1994, Karsts alpins, genèse de grands réseaux souterrains. Exemples: le Tennengebirge (Autriche), l'Ile de Crémieu, la Chartreuse et le Vercors (France) [*Genesis of large cave systems in alpine karst*]: Karstologia Mémoires no. 5, 280 p.

Audra, P., 2000, Le karst haut alpin du Kanin (Alpes juliennes, Slovénie-Italie [*High alpine karst of Kanin (Julian Alps, Slovenia-Italy)*]: Karstologia, v. 35, no. 1, p. 27–38.

Audra, P., P. de Coninck, and J.-P. Sounier (eds.), 2001, Nakanaï, 1978–1998, 20 years of exploration: Antibes, Association Hémisphère Sud, 224 p.

Audra, P., L. Mocochain, H. Camus, E. Gilli, G. Clauzon, and J.-Y. Bigot, 2004, The effect of the Messinian deep stage on karst development around the Mediterranean Sea. Examples from southern France: Geodinamica Acta, v. 17, no. 6, p. 27–38.

Audra, P., and R. Pavuza, 2004, Calcareous Alps, Austria, in J. Gunn (ed.), Encyclopedia of caves and karst science: New York, Fitzroy Dearborn, p. 173–175.

Audra, P., Y. Quinif, and P. Rochette, 2002, The genesis of the Tennengebirge karst and caves (Salzburg, Austria): Journal of Cave and Karst Studies, v. 64, no. 3, p. 153–164.

Auler, A., 1995, Lakes as a speleogenetic agent in the karst of Lagoa Santa, Brazil: Cave and Karst Science, v. 21, no. 3, p. 105–110.

Auler, A.S., and P.L. Smart, 2003, The influence of bedrock-derived acidity in the development of surface and underground karst: Evidence from the Precambrian carbonates of semi-arid northeastern Brazil: Earth Surface Processes and Landforms, v. 28, p. 157–168.

Back, W.B., B.B. Hanshaw, L.N. Plummer, P.H. Rahn, C.T. Rightmire, and M. Rubin, 1983, Process and rate of dedolomitization; mass transfer and ^{14}C dating in a regional carbonate aquifer: Geological Society of America

Bulletin, v. 94, no. 12, p. 1415–1429.

Back, W., B. Hanshaw, and J.N. Van Driel, 1984, Role of groundwater in shaping the eastern coastline of the Yucatán Peninsula, Mexico, *in* R. G. LaFleur (ed.), Groundwater as a geomorphic agent: Boston, Massachusetts, Allen and Unwin, Inc., p. 281–293.

Badino, G., 2001, Glacial karst phenomenology: Proceedings of 13th International Congress of Speleology, Brasilia, Brazil, paper 13, 5 p.

Badino, G., 2005, Underground drainage systems and geothermal flux: Acta Carsologica, v. 34, no. 2, p. 277–316.

Badino, G. and P. Forti, 2007, The exploration of the Caves of the Giant Crystals (Naica, Mexico): National Speleological Society, NSS News, v. 65, no. 2, p. 12–15, 18.

Bakalowicz, M.J., 1979, Contribution de la géochimie des eaux à la connaissance de l'aquifère karstique et de la karstification [*Contribution of water geochemistry to the understanding of karst aquifers and karstification*]: Ph.D. thesis, University of Pierre and Marie Curie, Paris, published by Laboratoire Souterrain du Centre National de la Récherche Scientifique, Moulis, France, 269 p.

Bakalowicz, M.J., 2005, Epikarst, *in* D.C. Culver and W.B. White (eds.), Encyclopedia of caves: San Diego, Elsevier / Academic Press, p. 220–223.

Bakalowicz, M.J., D.C. Ford, T.E. Miller, A.N. Palmer, and M.V. Palmer, 1987, Thermal genesis of dissolution caves in the Black Hills, South Dakota: Geological Society of America Bulletin, v. 99, p. 729–738.

Baker, A., D. Genty, W. Dreybrodt, W. Barnes, N. Mockler, and J. Grapes, 1998, Testing theoretically predicted stalagmite growth rate with recent annually laminated samples: Implications for past stalagmite deposition: Geochimica et Cosmochimica Acta, v. 62, p. 393–404.

Balch, E.S., 1900, Glacières or freezing caverns: Philadelphia, Allen, Lane, and Scott, 337 p. (Reprinted 1970 by Johnson Reprint Corp., New York.)

Banfield, J.F., and K.H. Nealson (eds.), 1997, Geomicrobiology: Interactions between microbes and minerals: Mineralogical Society of America, Reviews in Mineralogy, v. 35, 448 p.

Bannink, P., G. Bannink, K. Magraith, and B. Swain, 1995, Multi-level maze cave development in the Northern Territory, *in* G. Baddeley (ed.), Volcon Proceedings (20th Conference of Australian Speleological Federation), Victorian Speleological Association, Melbourne, p. 49–54.

Bárány-Kevei, I., 2004, Bauxite deposits in karst, *in* J. Gunn (ed.), Encyclopedia of caves and karst science: New York, Fitzroy Dearborn, p. 135–137.

Barbary, J.-P., and Zhang S., 2004, Historique et point sur les recherches spéléologiques en Chine [*History and status of speleological research in China*], *in* R. Maire, J.-P. Barbary, Zhang S., N. Vanara, and J. Bottazzi (eds.), Spéléo-karstologie et environnement en Chine (Guizhou, Yunnan, Liaoning) [*Studies of Caves, karst, and their environment in Guizhou, Yunnan, and Liaoning Provinces, China*]: Karstologia Mémoires no. 9, p.459–474.

Bárdossy, G., 1989, Bauxites, *in* P. Bosák, D. Ford, J. Glazek, and I. Horáček (eds.), Paleokarst: Prague and Amsterdam, Academia and Elsevier, p. 399–418.

Barner, W.L., 1999, Comparison of stormwater management in a karst terrain in Springfield, Missouri — case histories: Engineering Geology, v. 52, p. 105–112.

Bastian, L., 2003, Hydrology and speleogenesis update, the Yanchep cave area, Western Australia: Proceedings of 24th Biennial Speleological Conference, Northern Australia Speleological Federation, p. 36–44.

Barton, H.A., 2006, Introduction to cave microbiology: A review for the non-specialist: Journal of Cave and Karst Studies, v. 68, no. 2, p. 43–54.

Barton, H.A., and F. Luiszer, 2005, Microbial metabolic structure in a sulfidic cave hot spring: Potential mechanisms of biospeleogenesis: Journal of Cave and Karst Science, v. 67, no. 1, p. 28–38.

Bathurst, R.G.C., 1971, Carbonate sediments and their diagenesis: Amsterdam, Netherlands, Elsevier, Developments in Sedimentology 12, 620 p.

Baučić, I., 1968, Subterranean connections in the hydrological drainage basin of the Cetina River: Proceedings of 4th International Congress of

Speleology, Ljubljana, Slovenia, p. 271–277.

Bauer, S., S. Birk, R. Liedl, and M. Sauter, 1999, Solutionally enhanced leakage rates of dams in karst regions, *in* A.N. Palmer, M.V. Palmer, and I.D. Sasowsky (eds.), Karst Modeling: Charles Town, W.Va., Karst Waters Institute Special Publication 5, p. 158–162.

Beals, F.W., and J.L. Hardy, 1980, Criteria for the recognition of diverse dolomite types with an emphasis on studies on host rocks for Mississippi-Valley-type ore deposits, *in* D.H. Zenger, J.B. Dunham, and R.L. Ethington (eds.), Concepts and models of dolomitization: Society of Economic Paleontologists and Mineralogists, Special Publication 25, p. 197–213.

Bean, L.E., 1987, A geologic and hydrologic investigation of Fisher Ridge Cave System: M.S. thesis, Wayne State University, Detroit, Michigan, 112 p.

Beck, B.F., 1993, Applied karst geology: Proceedings of 4th conference on engineering and environmental impacts of karst, Lisse, Netherlands, A.A. Balkema, 304 p.

Beck, B.F. (ed.), 2003, Sinkholes and the Engineering and Environmental Impacts of Karst: American Society of Civil Engineers, Geotechnical Special Publication No. 122, 744 p.

Beck, B.F., 2005, Soil piping and sinkhole failures, *in* D.C. Culver and W.B. White (eds.), Encyclopedia of caves: San Diego, Elsevier / Academic Press, p. 521–526.

Beck, B.F., and J.G. Herring (eds.), 2001, Geotechnical and environmental applications of karst geology and hydrology: Proceedings of 8th Multidisciplinary Conference on Sinkholes and Karst, Lisse, Netherlands, A.A. Balkema, 437 p.

Beddows, P.A., 2003, Cave hydrology of the Caribbean Yucatán coast: Austin, Texas, Association for Mexican Cave Studies, AMCS Bulletin 11, 96 p.

Beede, J.W., 1911, The cycle of subterranean drainage as illustrated in the Bloomington, Indiana, Quadrangle: Indiana Academy of Science Proceedings, v. 26, p. 81–211.

Belski, D.S. (ed.), 1992, GYPKAP report on 1988–1991: National Speleological Society, Southwestern Region, 56 p.

Benn, D., and J. Gulley, 2006, Under thin air: The 2005 Ngozumpa Glacier Caves Research Project: National Speleological Society, NSS News, v. 64, no. 10., p. 13–17.

Bennett, P.C., 1991, Quartz dissolution in organic-rich aqueous systems: Geochimica et Cosmochimica Acta, v. 55, p. 1781–1797.

Bernasconi, R., 1961, L'évolution physico-chemique du mondmilch [*Physico-chemical evolution of moonmilk*]: Como, Italy, Rassegna speleologica Italiana, Memoria 5, tomo 2, p. 75–100. Reprinted in 1976 by National Speleological Society, Section on Cave Geology and Geography, Cave Geology, v. 1, no. 3, p. 63–68.

Berner, R.A., and J.W. Morse, 1974, Dissolution kinetics of calcium carbonate in sea water; IV: Theory of calcite dissolution: American Journal of Science, v. 274, p. 108–134.

Bini, A., 1994, Rapports entre la karstification périméditerranéenne et la crise de salinité du Messinien: l'Exemple du karst Lombard (Italie) [*Relationship between karst development around the Mediterranean and the Messinian Crisis: The example of the Lombardy Karst of Italy*]: Karstologia, v. 23, p. 33–53.

Birk, S., R. Liedl, M. Sauter, and G. Teutsch, 2005, Simulation of the development of gypsum maze caves: Environmental Geology, v. 48, no. 3, p. 296–306.

Bischoff, J.L., and Fyfe, W.S., 1968, Catalysis, inhibition, and the calcite-aragonite problem: American Journal of Science, v. 266, p. 65–79.

Bischoff, J.L., R. Julia, W.C. Shanks, and R.J. Rosenbauer, 1994, Karstification without carbonic acid; bedrock dissolution by gypsum-driven dedolomitization: Geology, v. 22, no. 11, p. 995–998.

Blumberg, P.G., and R.L. Curl, 1974, Experimental and theoretical studies of dissolution roughness: Journal of Fluid Mechanics, v. 65, p. 735–751.

Böcker. T., 1969, Karstic water research in Hungary: Bulletin of International Association of Scientific Hydrology, v. 14, no. 4, p. 7–20.

Bodine, M.W., and B.F. Jones, 1990, Normative analysis of groundwaters from the Rustler Formation associated with the Waste Isolation Pilot Plant (WIPP), southeastern New Mexico, *in* R.J. Spencer and I.-M. Chou (eds.), Fluid-mineral interactions: A tribute to H.P. Eugster: The Geochemical Society, Special Publication 2, p. 213–269.

Bogacz, K., S. Dzulynski, and C. Haranczyk, 1973, Caves filled with clastic dolomite and galena mineralization in disaggregated dolomites: Annals of the Geological Society of Poland, v. 43, p. 59–73.

Bögli, A., 1964, Mischungskorrosion, ein Beitrag zur Verkarstungs-problem [*Mixing corrosion, a contribution to the karst problem*]: Erdkunde, v. 18, p. 83–92.

Bögli, A., 1970, Le Hölloch et son karst [*Hölloch and its karst*]: Neuchâtel, Éditions de la Baconnièr, 109 p.

Bögli, A., 1980, Karst hydrology and physical speleology: Berlin, Springer-Verlag, 284 p.

Bonacci, O., 1987, Karst hydrology: Berlin, Springer-Verlag, 184 p.

Borden, J.D., and R.W. Brucker, 2000, Beyond Mammoth Cave: Carbondale and Edwardsville, Illinois, Southern Illinois University Press, 353 p.

Bosák, P., 1989, Problems of the origin and fossilization of karst forms, *in* P. Bosák, D. Ford, J. Glazek, and I. Horáček (eds.), Paleokarst: Prague and Amsterdam, Academia and Elsevier, p. 577–598.

Bosák, P., D. Ford, J. Glazek, and I. Horáček (eds.), 1989, Paleokarst: Prague and Amsterdam, Academia and Elsevier, 725 p.

Bosch, R.F., and W.B. White, 2004, Lithofacies and transport of clastic sediments in karstic aquifers, *in* I.D. Sasowsky and J.E. Mylroie (eds.), Studies of cave sediments: New York, Academic/Plenum Publishers, p. 1–22.

Boston, P., 1999, A bit of peace and quiet: The microbes of Lechuguilla: National Speleological Society, NSS News, v. 57, no. 8, p. 237–238.

Boston, P., 2000, Life below and life 'out there': Geotimes, v. 45, no. 8, p. 14–17.

Boston, P.J., R.D. Frederick, S.M. Welch, J. Werker, T.R. Meyer, B. Sprungman, V. Hildreth-Werker, S.L. Thompson, and D.L. Murphy, 2003, Human utilization of subsurface extraterrestrial environments: Gravitational and Space Biology Bulletin, v. 16, no. 2, p. 121–131.

Boston, P.J., L.D. Hose, D.E. Northup, and M.N. Spilde, 2006, The microbial communities of sulfur caves: A newly appreciated geologically driven system on Earth and potential model for Mars, *in* R.S. Harmon and C.M. Wicks (eds.), Perspectives on karst geomorphology, hydrology, and geochemistry — A tribute volume to Derek C. Ford and William B. White: Geological Society of America, Special Paper 404, p. 331–344.

Boston, P., M. Spilde, D. Northup, L. Melim, D. Soroka, L. Kleina, K. Lavoie, L. Hose, L. Mallory, C. Dahm, L. Crossey, and R. Scheible, 2001, Cave biosignature suites: Microbes, Minerals, Mars: Astrobiological Journal, v. 1, p. 25–55.

Bourrouilh-Le Jan, F.G., 1989, The oceanic karst: Modern bauxite and phosphate ore deposits on the high carbonate islands (so-called "uplifted atolls") of the Pacific Ocean, *in* P. Bosák, D. Ford, J. Glazek, and I. Horáček (eds.), Paleokarst: Prague and Amsterdam, Academia and Elsevier, p. 443–471.

Bray, L.G., 1972, Preliminary oxidation studies on some cave waters from south Wales: Cave Research Group of Great Britain, Transactions, v. 14, p. 59–66.

Bretz, J H., 1942, Vadose and phreatic features of limestone caverns: Journal of Geology, v. 50, p. 675–811.

Bretz, J H., 1956, Caves of Missouri: Missouri Geological Survey and Water Resources, v. 29, Series 2, 490 p.

Brod, L.G., 1964, Artesian origin of fissure caves in Missouri: National Speleological Society Bulletin, v. 26, no. 3, p. 83–112.

Brook, G.A., M.E. Folkoff, and E.O. Box, 1983, A world model of soil carbon dioxide: Earth Surface Processes and Landforms, v. 8, p. 79–88.

Brook, G.A., and D.C. Ford, 1978, The origin of labyrinth and tower karst and the climatic conditions necessary for their development: Nature, v. 275, p. 493–496.

Brown, E.T., R.F. Stallard, G.M. Raisbeck, and F. Yiou, 1992, Determination of the denudation rate of Mount Roraima, Venezuela using cosmogenic [10]Be and [26]Al: EOS (Transactions of the American Geophysical Union), v. 73, p.170.

Brown, M.C., 1972, Karst hydrogeology and infrared imagery, an example: Geological Society of America Bulletin, v. 83, no. 10, p. 3151–3154.

Brownlow, A.H., 1996, Geochemistry (2nd ed.): Upper Saddle River, N.J., Prentice-Hall, 580 p.

Brucker, R.W., and R.A. Watson, 1976, The longest cave: New York, Alfred A. Knopf, 316 p.

Bruthans, J., M. Filippi, M. Zare, N. Asadi, and Z. Vihelm, 2006, 3N Cave: The longest salt cave in the world: National Speleological Society, NSS News, v. 64, no. 9, p. 10–18.

Buck, M.J., D.C. Ford, and H. Schwarcz, 1994, Classification of cave gypsum deposits derived from oxidation of H_2S, *in* I.D. Sasowsky and M.V. Palmer (eds.), Breakthroughs in karst geomicrobiology: Charles Town, W.Va., Karst Waters Institute, Special Publication 1, p. 5–9.

Budd, D.A., A.H. Saller, and P.M. Harris (eds.), 1995, Unconformities and porosity in carbonate strata: Tulsa, Oklahoma, American Association of Petroleum Geologists, Memoir 63, 313 p.

Buhmann, D., and W. Dreybrodt, 1985a, The kinetics of calcite solution and precipitation in geologically relevant situations of karst areas. 1: Open system: Chemical Geology, v. 48, p.189–211.

Buhmann, D., and W. Dreybrodt, 1985b, The kinetics of calcite solution and precipitation in geologically relevant situations of karst areas. 2: Closed system: Chemical Geology, v. 53, p. 109–124.

Bull, P.A., 1981, Some fine-grained sedimentation phenomena in caves: Earth Surface Processes and Landforms, v. 6, p. 11–22.

Bunnell, D., 1995, Preliminary list of the long (>100 m) sea caves of the world: GEO^2, National Speleological Society, Section on Cave Geology and Geography, v. 22, no. 2, p. 38–39.

Bunnell, D., 2004, Riko Riko Cave, New Zealand — world's largest sea cave? National Speleological Society, NSS News, v. 62, no. 5, p. 145–147.

Burger, P.A., 2004, Glacially-influenced sediment cycles in the Lime Creek karst, Eagle County, Colorado *in* I.D. Sasowsky and J. Mylroie (eds.), Studies of Cave Sediments, physical and chemical records of paleoclimate: New York, Kluwer Academic/Plenum Publishers, p. 107–122.

Burger, P., 2006, Cave exploring: The definitive guide to caving technique, safety, gear, and trip leadership: Falcon Guide, Guilford, Conn., Globe Pequot Press, 120 p.

Butler, J.N., 1982, Carbon dioxide equilibria and their applications: Reading, Mass., Addison-Wesley, 259 p.

Cabrol, P., 1978, Contribution a l'étude du concretionnement carbonate des grottes du sud de la France: Morphologie, génèse, diagénèse [*Contribution to the study of carbonate speleothems in caves from the south of France: Morphology, origin, diagenesis*]: Université de Montpellier, France, Mémoires du Centre d'Études et de Recherches Géologiques et Hydrogéologiques, v. 12, 275 p.

Cacchio, P., R. Contento, C. Ercole, G. Cappuccio, M.P. Marinez, and A. Lepidi, 2004, Involvement of microorganisms in the formation of carbonate speleothems in Cervo Cave (L'Aquila-Italy): Geomicrobiology Journal, v. 21, p. 497–509.

Cai Z., Yang W., and R. Maire, 1993, Le géographe chinois Xu Xiake: Un précurseur de la karstologie et de la spéléologie [*The geographer Xu Xiake: A pioneer of karst science and speleology*]: Karstologia, v. 21, no. 1, p. 43–50.

Calaforra, J.M., 1998, Karstología de yesos [*Gypsum karst studies*]: Ciencia y Tecnología Monografía 3, Instituto de Estudios Amerienses, Univ. of Almería, Spain, 384 p.

Calaforra, J.M., and J. Les, 2003, The gypsum karst of Sorbas: A subterranean journey through the interior of the gypsum [in English and Spanish]: Estella, Spain, Publicaciones Calle Mayor, 87 p.

Camara, B., 2000, Down the tubes at Hawai'i Volcanoes National Park: National Speleological Society, NSS News, v. 58, no. 1, p. 13.

Campbell, C., M. Latif, and J. Foster, 1996, Application of thermography to karst hydrology: Journal of Cave and Karst Studies, v. 58, no. 3, p. 163–167.

Campbell, N. P., 1977, Possible exhumed fossil caverns in the Madison Group

(Mississippian) of the northern Rocky Mountains: A discussion: National Speleological Society Bulletin, v. 39, p. 43–54.

Cande, S.C., and D.V. Kent, 1992, A new geomagnetic polarity time scale for the Cretaceous and Cenozoic: Journal of Geophysical Research, v. 97, p. 13917–13951.

Caran, S.C., B.M. Winsborough, J.A. Neely, and S. Valastro, 1995, Radiocarbon age of carbonate sediments (travertine, pedoconcretions, and biogenic carbonates); a new method based on organic residues, employing stable-isotope control of carbon sources: Oregon State University, Current Research in the Pleistocene, v. 12, p. 75–77.

Carew, J.L., and J.E. Mylroie, 1987, Submerged evidence of Pleistocene low sea levels on San Salvador, Bahamas, in R.A. Cooper and A.N. Shepard (eds.): National Oceanographic and Atmospheric Administration Undersea Program Symposium Series for Undersea Research, v. 2, p. 167–175.

Carothers, W.W., and Y.K. Kharaka, 1978, Aliphalic acid anions in oil-field water — implications for origin of natural gas: American Association of Petroleum Geologists Bulletin, v. 62, p. 2441–2453.

Casagrande, G., F. Cucchi, P. Manca, and L. Zini, 1999, Deep hypogean karst phenomena of Mt. Canin (western Julian Alps): A synthesis of the state of present research: Acta Carsologica, v. 28, no. 1, p. 57–69.

Castillo, E., G.M. Karadi, and R.J. Krizek, 1972, Unconfined flow through jointed rock: Water Resources Bulletin, v. 8, p. 266–281.

Catlin, D. (ed.), 1973, The caves of Ethiopia: Cave Research Group of Great Britain, Transactions, v. 15, no. 3, p. 107–168.

Chabert, C., and P. Courbon, 1997, Atlas des cavités non calcaires du monde [*World atlas of caves in non-carbonate rocks*]: International Union of Speleology, 109 p.

Chafetz, H.S., and R.L. Folk, 1984, Travertines: Depositional morphology and the bacterially constructed constituents: Journal of Sedimentary Petrology, v. 54, no. 1, p. 289–316.

Chamberlain, A.T., W. Sellers, C. Proctor, and R. Coard, 2000, Cave detection in limestone using ground-penetrating radar: Journal of Archeological Science, v. 27, p. 957–964.

Chapelle, F.H., 2001, Ground-water microbiology and geochemistry (2nd ed.): New York, Wiley, 477 p.

Choppy, J., 2002, The origin of limestone caves: A new theory: Cave Geology, National Speleological Society, Section of Cave Geology and Geography, v. 2, no. 5, p. 222–240.

Choquette, P.W., and L.C. Pray, 1970, Geologic nomenclature and classification of porosity in sedimentary carbonates: American Association of Petroleum Geologists Bulletin, v. 54, p. 207–250.

Chow, V.T., 1959, Open-channel hydraulics: New York, McGraw-Hill, 680 p.

Christenson, K., 1999, Comments on the speleogenesis of Vanport caves: GEO², National Speleological Society, Section on Cave Geology and Geography, v. 26, no. 2–3, p. 17–20.

Church, J.A., N.J. White, R. Coleman, K. Lambeck, and J.X. Mitrovica, 2004, Estimates of the regional distribution of sea level rise over the 1950–2000 period: Journal of Climate, v. 17, no. 13, p. 2609–2625.

Cigna, A.A., 2004, Climate of caves, in J. Gunn (ed.), Encyclopedia of caves and karst science: New York, Fitzroy Dearborn, p. 228–230.

Cigna, A.A., 2005a, Show caves, in D.C. Culver and W.B. White (eds.), Encyclopedia of caves: San Diego, Elsevier / Academic Press, p. 495–500.

Cigna, A.A., 2005b, Radon in caves: International Journal of Speleology, v. 34, no. 1–2, p. 1–18.

Cigna, A.A., and P. Forti, 1986, The speleogenetic role of airflow caused by convection: International Journal of Speleology, v. 15, p. 41–52.

Cigna, A.A., and C.A. Hill, 1997, Aerosols: Are they a mechanism of speleothem growth? in C.A. Hill and P. Forti, Cave minerals of the world: Huntsville, Alabama, National Speleological Society, p. 255–258.

Clark, I.D., and P. Fritz (eds.), 1997, Environmental isotopes in hydrogeology: Boca Raton, Fla., CRC Press, 352 p.

Clausen, E.N., 1970, Badland caves of Wyoming: National Speleological Society Bulletin, v. 32, no. 3, p. 59–69.

Clemens, T., D. Hückinghaus, M. Sauter, R. Liedl, and G. Teutsch, 1996, A combined continuum and discrete network reactive transport model for the simulation of karst development, in K. Kovar and P. van der Heijde (eds.), Calibration and reliability in groundwater modeling: International Association of Scientific Hydrology, Publication 237, p. 309–318.

Clemmer, G.S., 2005, Burnsville Cove, Virginia, in D.C. Culver and W.B. White (eds.), Encyclopedia of caves: San Diego, Elsevier / Academic Press, p. 60–71.

Clescerl, L.S., A.E. Greenberg, and A.D. Eaton (eds.), 1999, Standard methods for the examination of water and wastewater (20th ed.): American Public Health Association, 1325 p.

Claypool, G., W. Holser, I. Kaplan, H. Sakai, and I. Zak, 1980, The age curves of sulfur and oxygen isotopes in marine sulfate and their mutual interpretations: Chemical Geology, v. 28, p. 199–260.

Conn, H.W., 1966, Barometric wind in Wind and Jewel Caves, South Dakota: National Speleological Society Bulletin, v. 28, no. 2, p. 55–79.

Conn, H., and J. Conn, 1977, The Jewel Cave adventure, fifty miles of discovery under South Dakota: Teaneck, NJ, Zephyrus Press, 238 p.

Coons, D., 2004, Maze development in Hawai‘i lava tubes: A statistical analysis [abstract]: National Speleological Society, Program of 2004 annual convention, Marquette, Mich., p. 42.

Coplen, T.B., I.J. Winograd, J.M. Landwehr, and A.C. Riggs, 1994, 500,000-year stable carbon isotopic record from Devils Hole, Nevada: Science, v. 263, p. 361–365.

Corbel, J., 1957, Les karsts du nord-ouest de l'Europe et de quelques régions de comparaison [*Karst of northwestern Europe and several regions of comparison*]: Institut des Études Rhodaniennes de l'Université de Lyon, Mémoires et Documents 12, 541 p. + 100 plates.

Courbon, P., C. Chabert, P. Bosted, and K. Lindsley, 1989, Atlas of the great caves of the world: St. Louis, Cave Books, 369 p.

Coward, J.M.H., 1975, Paleohydrology and streamflow simulation of three karst basins in southeastern West Virginia: Ph.D. thesis, McMaster University, Hamilton, Ontario, Canada, 394 p.

Cox, E.R., 1967, Geology and hydrology between Lake McMillan and Carlsbad Springs, Eddy County, New Mexico: Washington, D.C., U.S. Government Printing Office, 48 p.

Craig, D.H., 1988, Caves and other features of Permian karst in San Andres Dolomite, Yates Field reservoir, west Texas, in N.P. James and P.W. Choquette, (eds.), Paleokarst: New York, Springer-Verlag, p. 342–363.

Craven, S.A., and B.J. Smit, 2006, Radon in caves: Clinical aspects: International Journal of Speleology, v. 35, no. 2, p. 93–101.

Crawford, N.C., 1981, Karst flooding in urban areas: Proceedings of 8th International Congress of Speleology, Bowling Green, Ky., p. 763–765.

Crawford, N.C., 1984, Toxic and explosive fumes rising from carbonate aquifers: A hazard for residents of sinkhole plains, in B.F. Beck (ed.), Sinkholes: Their geology, engineering, and environmental impact: Rotterdam, A.A. Balkema, p. 297–304.

Crawford, N.C., 2001, Environmental problems associated with urban development upon karst, Bowling Green, Kentucky, in B.F. Beck and J.G. Herring (eds.), Geotechnical and environmental applications of karst geology and hydrology: Lisse, Netherlands, A.A. Balkema, p. 397–424.

Crawford, N.C., and J.D. Vineyard, 1981, Guidebook to the karst and caves of Tennessee: Emphasis on the Cumberland Escarpment region, *and* Guidebook to karst and caves of the Ozark region of Missouri and Arkansas: 8th International Congress of Speleology, Bowling Green, Ky., 176 p.

Cropley, J.B., 1965, Influence of surface conditions on temperatures in large cave systems: National Speleological Society Bulletin, v. 27, no. 1, p. 1–10.

Culver, D.C., 1982, Cave life: Evolution and ecology: Cambridge, Mass., Harvard University Press, 223 p.

Culver, D.C., and W.B. White (eds.), 2005, Encyclopedia of caves: San Diego, Elsevier / Academic Press, 696 p.

Cunningham, K.I., D.E. Northup, R.M. Pollastro, W.G. Wright, and E.J. LaRock, 1995, Bacteria, fungi and biokarst in Lechuguilla Cave, Carlsbad Caverns

National Park, New Mexico: Environmental Geology, v. 25, no. 1, p. 2–8.

Curl, R.L., 1964, On the definition of a cave: National Speleological Society Bulletin, v. 26, no. 1, p. 1–6.

Curl, R.L., 1966, Scallops and flutes: Transactions of Cave Research Group of Great Britain, v. 7, no. 2, p. 121–160.

Curl, R.L., 1968, Solution kinetics of calcite: Proceedings of 4th International Congress of Speleology, Ljubljana, Slovenia, v. 3, p. 61–66.

Curl, R.L., 1972, Minimum diameter stalactites: National Speleological Society Bulletin, v. 34, no. 4, p. 129–136.

Curl, R.L., 1973, Minimum diameter stalagmites: National Speleological Society Bulletin, v. 35, no. 1, p. 1–9.

Curl, R.L., 1974, Deducing flow velocity in cave conduits from scallops: National Speleological Society Bulletin, v. 36, no. 2, p. 1–5.

Curl, R.L., 1986, Fractal dimensions and geometries of caves: Mathematical Geology, v. 18, no. 8, p. 765–783.

Cvijić, J., 1893, Das Karstphänomen [The phenomenon of karst]: Vienna, Geographische Abhandlungen herausgegeben von a. Penck, v. 5, no. 3.

Daly, D., D. Drew, J. Deakin, D. Ball, M. Parkes, and G. Wright (eds.), 2000, The karst of Ireland: Dublin, Karst Working Group, Geological Survey of Ireland, 37 p.

Dasher, G. R., 1994, On station: Huntsville, Ala., National Speleological Society, 240 p.

Davies, W.E., 1951, Mechanics of cavern breakdown: National Speleological Society Bulletin, v. 13, p. 36–43.

Davies, W.E., 1957, Erosion levels in the Potomac drainage system and their relation to cavern development: National Speleological Society, 1957 Speleo-Digest, p. 2:32–2:36.

Davies, W.E., 1960, Origin of caves in folded limestone: National Speleological Society Bulletin, v. 22, no. 1, p. 5–18.

Davis, D.G., 1980, Cave development in the Guadalupe Mountains: A critical review of recent hypotheses: National Speleological Society Bulletin, v. 42, no. 3, p. 42–48.

Davis, D.G., 1989, Helictite bushes: A subaqueous speleothem? National Speleological Society Bulletin, v. 51, p. 120–124.

Davis, D.G., 1995, Rims, rills, and rafts: Shaping of cave features by atmospheric water exchange: GEO², National Speleological Society, Section on Cave Geology and Geography, v. 22, no. 2, p. 23–29.

Davis, D.G., 1999, The Anvil Points Claystone Caves: The Explorer (Southern California Grotto, National Speleological Society), June issue, p. 98–103.

Davis, D.G., 2005, Speleothems: Helictites and related forms, in D.C. Culver and W.B. White (eds.), Encyclopedia of caves: San Diego, Elsevier / Academic Press, p. 549–554.

Davis, D.G., M.V. Palmer, and A.N. Palmer, 1990, Extraordinary subaqueous speleothems in Lechuguilla Cave, New Mexico: National Speleological Society Bulletin, v. 52, no. 2, p. 70–86.

Davis, J.C., 2002, Statistics and data analysis in geology (3rd ed.): Hoboken, N.J., Wiley, 638 p.

Davis, S.N., and G.W. Moore, 1965, Semidiurnal movement along a bedrock joint in Wool Hollow Cave, California: National Speleological Society Bulletin, v. 27, no. 4, p. 133–142.

Davis, W.M., 1922, Peneplains and the geographical cycle: Geological Society of America Bulletin, v. 33, p. 587–598.

Davis, W.M., 1930, Origin of limestone caverns: Geological Society of America Bulletin, v. 41, p. 475–628.

Day, M.J., 2004, Karstic problems in the construction of Milwaukee's deep tunnels: Environmental Geology, v. 45, no. 6, p. 859–863.

Deal, D.E., 1968, Origin and secondary mineralization of caves in the Black Hills of South Dakota: Proceedings of 4th International Congress of Speleology, Ljubljana, Slovenia, p. 67–70.

Debevec, V., 2004, Speleotherapy, in J. Gunn.(ed.), Encyclopedia of caves and karst science: New York, Fitzroy Dearborn, p. 697–698.

Decker, R.W., T.L. Wright, and P.H. Stauffer, 1987 (eds.), Volcanism in Hawaii: U.S. Geological Survey Professional Paper 1350, 1667 p. (2 volumes).

de Freitas, C.R., and R.N. Littlejohn, 1987, Cave climate: Assessment of heat and moisture exchange: Journal of Climatology, v. 7, p. 553–569.

Deike, G.H., and W.B. White, 1969, Sinuosity in limestone solution conduits: American Journal of Science, v. 267, p. 230–241.

Delannoy, J.-J., and S. Caillault, 1998, Les apports de l'endokarst dans la reconstitution morphogénique d'un karst: Exemple de l'Antre de Vénus (Vercors, France) [Use of underground alluvial deposits to reconstruct karst landscapes: An example from the Antre de Vénus, Vercors, France]: Karstologia, v. 31, p. 27–41.

Dennis, P.F., P.J. Rowe, and T. C. Atkinson, 2001, The recovery and isotopic measurement of water from fluid inclusions in speleothems: Geochimica et Cosmochimica Acta, v. 65, p. 871–884.

Despain, J.D., 2003, Hidden beneath the mountains: Caves of Sequoia and Kings Canyon National Parks: Dayton, Ohio, Cave Books, 128 p.

Despain, J.D., and G.M. Stock, 2005, Geomorphic history of Crystal Cave, southern Sierra Nevada, California: Journal of Cave and Karst Studies, v. 67, no. 2, p. 92–102.

De Waele, J., 2004, Geomorphologic evolution of a coastal karst: The Gulf of Orosei (central-east Sardinia, Italy): Acta Carsologica, v. 33, no. 2, p. 37–54.

Dewers, T.A., 1997, Dedolomitization as a driving mechanism for karst generation in Permian Blaine Formation, southwestern Oklahoma, U.S.A.: Carbonates and Evaporites, v. 12, p. 24–31.

Dewars, T., and M. Raines, 1997, Mixed transport/reaction control of gypsum dissolution kinetics in aqueous solutions and initiation of gypsum karst: Chemical Geology, v. 140, p. 29–48. [see also discussion by W. Dreybrodt and F. Gabrovšek, 2000, Chemical Geology, v. 168, no. 1–2, p. 169–172; and reply by T. Dewars and M. Raines, 2000, Chemical Geology, v. 168, no. 3–4, p. 275–278.]

Dobrin, M.B., and C.H. Savit, 1988, Introduction to geophysical prospecting (4th ed.): New York, McGraw-Hill, 867 p.

Doerfliger, N., 1996, Advances in karst groundwater protection strategy using artificial tracer tests analysis and multi-attribute vulnerability mapping (EPIK method): Ph.D. thesis, University of Neuchâtel, Switzerland, 308 p.

Dogwiler, T., 1998, Analysis of bell hole morphology and distribution: A tool for evaluating formational processes: M.S. thesis, Mississippi State University, Starkville, Miss., 106 p.

Dom, J.E., and C. Wicks, 2003, Morphology of the caves of Missouri: Journal of Cave and Karst Studies, v. 65, no. 3, p. 155–159.

Domenico, P. A., and F.W. Schwartz, 1990, Physical and chemical hydrogeology: New York, Wiley, 824 p.

Dorale, J.A., R.L. Edwards, I. Ito, and L.A. González, 1998, Climate and vegetation history of the midcontinent from 75 to 25 ka: A speleothem record from Crevice Cave, Missouri, U.S.A.: Science, v. 282, p. 1871–1874.

Dorale, J.A., L.A. González, M.K. Reagan, D.A. Pickett, M.T. Murrell, and R.G. Baker, 1992, A high-resolution record of Holocene climate change in speleothem calcite from Coldwater Cave, northeast Iowa: Science, v. 258, p. 1626–1630.

Douglas, H.H., 1964, Caves of Virginia: Falls Church, Va., National Speleological Society, Virginia Cave Survey, 761 p.

Drake, J.J., 1983, The effects of geomorphology and seasonality on the chemistry of carbonate groundwater: Journal of Hydrology, v. 61, p. 223–236.

Dreiss, S.J., 1982, Linear kernels for karst aquifers: Water Resources Research, v. 18, no. 4, p. 865–876.

Drever, J.I., 1997, The geochemistry of natural waters (3rd ed.): Upper Saddle River, N.J., Prentice-Hall, 436 p.

Dreybrodt, W., 1988, Processes in karst systems: Physics, chemistry and geology: Berlin, Germany, Springer-Verlag, 288 p.

Dreybrodt, W., 1990, The role of dissolution kinetics in the development of karst aquifers in limestone: A model simulation of karst evolution: Journal of Geology, v. 98, no. 5, p. 639–655.

Dreybrodt, W., 1996, Principles of early development of karst conduits under natural and man-made conditions revealed by mathematical analysis of numerical models: Water Resources Research, v. 32, p. 2923–2935.

Dreybrodt, W., 1999, Chemical kinetics, speleothem growth, and climate: Boreas, v. 28, p. 347–356.

Dreybrodt, W., 2003, Viewpoints and comments on feasibility of condensation processes in caves: Web site *Speleogenesis and Evolution of Karst Aquifers*, v. 1, no. 2, www.speleogenesis.info.

Dreybrodt, W., 2005, Speleothem deposition, *in* D.C. Culver and W.B. White (eds.), Encyclopedia of caves. San Diego, Elsevier / Academic Press, p. 543–549.

Dreybrodt, W., and L. Eisenlohr, 2000, Limestone dissolution rates in karst environments, *in* A. Klimchouk, D. Ford, A. Palmer, and W. Dreybrodt (eds.), Speleogenesis: Evolution of karst aquifers: Huntsville, Ala., National Speleological Society, p. 136–148.

Dreybrodt, W., and F. Gabrovšek, 2002, Basic processes and mechanisms governing the evolution of karst, *in* F. Gabrovšek (ed.), Evolution of karst: From prekarst to cessation: Institute for Karst Research, ZRC SAZU, Postojna-Ljubljana, Slovenia, p. 115–154.

Dreybrodt, W, F. Gabrovšek, and M. Perne, 2005, Condensation corrosion: A theoretical approach: Acta Carsologica, v. 34, no. 2, p. 317–348.

Dreybrodt, W., F. Gabrovšek, and D. Romanov, 2005, Processes of speleogenesis: A modeling approach (with guest contributions by S. Bauer, S. Birk, R. Liedl, M. Sauter, and G. Kaufmann): Carsologica, Ljubljana, Slovenia, ZRC Publishing, 376 p + CD.

Dreybrodt, W., and J. Siemers, 2000, Cave evolution in two-dimensional networks of primary fractures in limestones, *in* A. Klimchouk, D. Ford, A. Palmer, and W. Dreybrodt (eds.), Speleogenesis: Evolution of karst aquifers: Huntsville, Ala., National Speleological Society, p. 201–211.

Droppa, A., 1966, Untersuchungen der parallelität von Flussterrassen mit horizontalen Höhlen [*Correlation between river terraces and horizontal caves*]: Proceedings of 3rd International Congress of Speleology, Vienna, v. 5, p. 79–81.

Dublyansky, V.N., 1980, Hydrothermal karst in the alpine folded belt of southern parts of the U.S.S.R.: Kras I Speleologia, v. 3, no. 12, p. 18–36.

Dublyansky, V.N., 2000, A giant hydrothermal cavity in the Rhodope Mountains, Bulgaria, *in* A. Klimchouk, D. Ford, A. Palmer, and W. Dreybrodt (eds.), Speleogenesis: Evolution of karst aquifers: Huntsville, Ala., National Speleological Society, p. 317–318.

Dublyansky, V.N., and Y.V. Dublyansky, 2000, The role of condensation in karst hydrogeology and speleogenesis, *in* A. Klimchouk, D. Ford, A. Palmer, and W. Dreybrodt (eds.), Speleogenesis: Evolution of karst aquifers: Huntsville, Ala., National Speleological Society, p. 100–112.

Dublyansky, Y.V., 2000, Hydrothermal speleogenesis—its settings and peculiar features, *in* A. Klimchouk, D. Ford, A. Palmer, and W. Dreybrodt (eds.), Speleogenesis: Evolution of karst aquifers: Huntsville, Ala., National Speleological Society, p. 292–297.

Dublyansky, Y.V., and S.Z. Smirnov, 2005, Cavity–based secondary mineralization in volcanic tuffs of Yucca Mountain, Nevada: A new type of the polymineral vadose speleothem, or a hydrothermal deposit? International Journal of Speleology, v. 34, no. 1–2, p. 25–44.

DuBois, P., P. Sorriaux, and H.J. Soudet, 1993, Rospo Mare (Adriatique): Un paléokarst pétrolier du domaine méditerranéen [*Rospo Mare: A Mediterranean petroleum field in paleokarst*]: Karstologia, v. 21, no. 1, p. 31–42.

DuChene, H.R., and K.I. Cunningham, 2006, Tectonic influences on speleogenesis in the Guadalupe Mountains, New Mexico and Texas: New Mexico Geological Society, Guidebook to 57th Annual Field Conference, p. 211–218.

DuChene, H.R., and C.A. Hill (eds.), 2000, The caves of the Guadalupe Mountains: Research Symposium: Journal of Cave and Karst Studies, v. 62, no. 2, 107 p.

Dumont, K.A., 1995, Karst hydrology and geomorphology of the Barrack Zourie Cave System, Schoharie County, New York: New York Cave Survey, Bulletin 5, 70 p.

Dunham, R.J., 1962, Classification of carbonate rocks according to depositional texture: American Association of Petroleum Geologists, Memoir 1, p. 108–121.

Durov, S.A., 1956, On the question about the origin of the salt composition of karst water: Ukrainian Chemical Journal, v. 22, p. 106–111. Reprinted in English in Cave Geology (National Speleological Society, Section on Cave Geology and Geography), v. 1, no. 6, June 1979, p. 186–190.

Eavis, A.J., 1981, Caves of Mulu '80: London, Royal Geographical Society, 52 p.

Egemeier, S.J., 1973, Cavern development by thermal waters with a possible bearing on ore deposition: Ph.D. thesis, Stanford University, Stanford, California, 88 p.

Egemeier, S.J., 1981, Cavern development by thermal waters: National Speleological Society Bulletin, v. 43, no. 2, p. 31–51.

Egemeier, S.J., 1987, A theory for the origin of Carlsbad Caverns: National Speleological Society Bulletin, v. 49, no. 2, p. 73–76.

Ehrlich, H.L., 1996, Geomicrobiology (3rd ed.): New York, Marcel Dekker, 719 p.

Eisenlohr, L., K. Meteva, F. Gabrovšek, and W. Dreybrodt, 1999, The inhibiting action of intrinsic impurities in natural calcium carbonate minerals to their dissolution kinetics in aqueous H_2O-CO_2 solutions: Geochimica et Cosmochimica Acta, v. 63, p. 989–1002.

Ek, C., 1961, Conduits souterraines en relation avec les terraces fluviales: Annales Soc. Geol. Belgique, v. 84, p. 314–340.

Elliot, W.K., 2005, Protecting caves and cave life, *in* D.C. Culver and W.B. White (eds.), Encyclopedia of caves: San Diego, Elsevier / Academic Press, p. 458–467.

Engel, A.S, L.A. Stern, and P.C. Bennett, 2004, Microbial contributions to cave formation: New insight into sulfuric acid speleogenesis: Geology, v. 32, p. 269–273.

Eraso, A., and M. Pulina, 1992, Cuevas en hielo y ríos bajo los glaciares [*Ice caves and sub-glacial streams*]: Madrid, Spain, Serie McGraw-Hill de Divulgación Científica, 242 p.

Etheridge, D.M., L.P. Steele, R.L. Langenfelds and R.J. Francey, 1996, Natural and anthropogenic changes in atmospheric CO_2 over the last 1000 years from air in Arctic ice and firn: Journal of Geophysical Research, v. 101, p. 4115–4128.

Evans, J., P. Quick, and B. Sloane, 1979, An introduction to caves of the Northeast: Guidebook for the 1979 National Speleological Society convention, 76 p.

Ewers, R.O., 1966, Bedding-plane anastomoses and their relation to cavern passages: National Speleological Society Bulletin, v. 28, no. 3, p. 133–140.

Ewers, R.O., 1982, Cavern development in the dimensions of length and breadth: Ph.D. thesis, McMaster University, Hamilton, Ontario, Canada, 398 p.

Ewers, R.O., 1985, Patterns of cavern development along the Cumberland Escarpment, *in* P.H. Dougherty, Caves and karst of Kentucky: Kentucky Geological Survey, Special Publication 12, Series IX, p. 63–77.

Ewers, R.O., 2006, Karst aquifers and the role of assumptions and authority in science, *in* R.S. Harmon and C.M. Wicks (eds.), Perspectives on karst geomorphology, hydrology, and geochemistry—A tribute volume to Derek C. Ford and William B. White: Geological Society of America, Special Paper 404, p. 235–242.

Exley, S., 1994a, World's largest underwater cave discovered: Underwater Speleology, v. 21, p. 8–13.

Exley, S., 1994b, Caverns measureless to man: St. Louis, Cave Books, 326 p.

Farrant, A., 2004, Paragenesis, *in* J. Gunn (ed.), Encyclopedia of caves and karst science: New York, Fitzroy Dearborn, p. 569–571.

Farrant, A., P. Smart, F. Whitaker, and D. Tarling, 1995, Long-term Quaternary uplift rates inferred from limestone caves in Sarawak, Malaysia: Geology, v. 23, p. 357–360.

Faulkner, T.L., 2005, Cave inception and development in Caledonide metacarbonate rocks: Ph.D. thesis, University of Huddersfield, U.K., 330 p. + 306 p. of appendices.

Faulkner, T.L., 2006, Tectonic inception in Caledonide marbles: Acta Carsologica, v. 35, no. 1, p. 7–21.

Faure, G., 1998, Principles and applications of geochemistry (2nd ed.): Upper Saddle River, N.J., Prentice-Hall, 600 p.

Faure, G., and T.M. Mensing, 2005, Isotopes: Principles and applications (3rd ed.): New York, Wiley, 897 p.

Faust, B., 1947, An unusual phenomenon: National Speleological Society Bulletin, v. 9, p. 52–56.

Fawley, J.P., and K.M. Long, 1997, Harlansburg Cave: The longest cave in Pennsylvania: Journal of Cave and Karst Studies, v. 59, no. 3, p. 106–111.

Fernández-Gibert, E., J.M. Calaforra, and C. Rossi, 2000, Speleogenesis in the Picos de Europa Massif, northern Spain, in A. Klimchouk, D. Ford, A. Palmer, and W. Dreybrodt (eds.), Speleogenesis: Evolution of karst aquifers: Huntsville, Ala., National Speleological Society, p. 352–357.

Fetter, C.W., 2001, Applied hydrogeology (4th ed.): New York, Macmillan, 598 p. + CD ROM.

Field, M.S., 2002a, The QTRACER2 program for tracer-breakthrough curve analysis for tracer tests in karstic aquifers and other hydrologic systems: U.S. Environmental Protection Agency, Publication EPA/600/R-02/001, 179 p. + CD ROM.

Field, M.S., 2002b, A lexicon of cave and karst terminology with special reference to environmental karst hydrology: U.S. Environmental Protection Agency, Publication EPA/600/R-02/003, 214 p. + CD ROM.

Filippov, A.G., 2000, Speleogenesis of Botovskaya Cave, eastern Siberia, Russia in A.B. Klimchouk, D.C. Ford, A.N. Palmer and W. Dreybrodt (eds.), Speleogenesis: Evolution of karst aquifers: Huntsville, Alabama, National Speleological Society, p. 282–286.

Filippov, A.G., 2004, Siberia, Russia, in J. Gunn (ed.), Encyclopedia of caves and karst science: New York, Fitzroy Dearborn, p. 645–647.

Fischer, J.A., R.W. Greene, and J.J. Fischer, 2003, Roadway design in karst, in B.F. Beck, Applied karst geology: Proceedings of fourth conference on engineering and environmental impacts of karst, Lisse, Netherlands, A.A. Balkema, p. 219–223.

Fish, J.E., 1977, Karst hydrology of the Sierra de El Abra and the Valles - San Luis Potosí region, Mexico: Ph.D. thesis, McMaster University, Hamilton, Ontario, Canada, 620 p. Reprinted in 2004 as Karst hydrology of the Sierra de El Abra, Mexico: Association of Mexican Cave Studies Bulletin 14, 186 p.

Fitts, C.R., 2002, Groundwater science: San Diego, Academic Press, 450 p.

Florea, L.J., 2005, Using state-wide GIS data to identify the coincidence between sinkholes and geologic structure: Journal of Cave and Karst Studies, v. 67, no. 2, p. 120–124.

Florea, L.J., 2006, Architecture of air-filled caves within the karst of the Brooksville Ridge, west-central Florida: Journal of Cave and Karst Studies, v. 68, no. 2, p. 64–75.

Florea, L.J., and H.L. Vacher, 2004, Morphology and classification of conduits in the unconfined Floridan Aquifer system of west-central Florida [abstract]: National Speleological Society, Program of 2004 annual convention, Marquette, MI, p. 44–45.

Folk, R.L., 1962, Spectral subdivision of limestone types: American Association of Petroleum Geologists, Memoir 1, p. 62–84.

Folk, R.L., 1974, The natural history of crystalline calcium carbonates: Effect of magnesium content and salinity: Journal of Sedimentary Petrology, v. 44, p. 40–53.

Folk, R.L., 1993, SEM imaging of bacteria and nannobacteria in carbonate sediments and rocks: Journal of Sedimentary Petrology, v. 63, p. 990–999.

Folk, R.L., H.H. Roberts, and C.M. Moore, 1973, Black phytokarst from Hell, Cayman Islands, West Indies: Geological Society of America Bulletin, v. 84, p. 2351–2360.

Forbes, J.R., 2000, Geochemistry of Carlsbad Cavern pool waters, Guadalupe Mountains, New Mexico: Journal of Cave and Karst Studies, v. 62, no. 2, p. 127–134.

Ford, D.C., 1965a, Stream potholes as indicators of erosion phases in caves: National Speleological Society Bulletin, v. 27, no. 1, p. 27–32.

Ford, D.C., 1965b, The origin of limestone caverns: A model from the central Mendip Hills, England: National Speleological Society Bulletin, v. 27, no. 1, p. 109–132.

Ford, D.C., 1971, Geologic structure and a new explanation of limestone cavern genesis: Transactions of the Cave Research Group of Great Britain, v. 13, no. 2, p. 81–94.

Ford, D.C., 1983, Effects of glaciations upon karst aquifers in Canada: Journal of Hydrology, v. 61, p. 149–158.

Ford, D.C., 1986, Genesis of paleokarst and strata-bound zinc-lead sulfide deposits in a Proterozoic dolostone, northern Baffin Island, Canada: A discussion: Economic Geology, v. 81, no. 6, p. 1562–1563.

Ford, D.C., 1987, Effects of glaciations and permafrost upon the development of karst in Canada: Earth Surface Processes and Landforms, v. 12, no. 5, p. 507–521.

Ford, D.C., 1988, Characteristics of dissolutional cave systems in carbonate rocks, in N.P. James and P.W. Choquette (eds.), Paleokarst: New York, Springer-Verlag, p. 25–57.

Ford, D.C., 1989a, Paleokarst of Canada, in P. Bosák, D. Ford, J. Glazek, and I. Horáček (eds.), Paleokarst: Prague and Amsterdam, Academia and Elsevier, p. 313–336.

Ford, D.C., 1989b, Features of the genesis of Jewel Cave and Wind Cave, Black Hills, South Dakota: National Speleological Society Bulletin, v. 51, no. 2, p. 100–110.

Ford, D.C., 1995, Paleokarst as a target for modern karstification: Carbonates and Evaporites, v. 10, no. 2, p. 138–147.

Ford, D.C., 1997, Dating and paleo-environmental studies of speleothems, in C.A. Hill and P. Forti, 1997, Cave minerals of the world (2nd ed.): Huntsville, Ala., National Speleological Society, p. 273–284.

Ford, D.C., 2004, Canada, in J. Gunn (ed.), Encyclopedia of caves and karst science: New York, Fitzroy Dearborn, p. 175–178.

Ford, D.C., and R.O. Ewers, 1978, The development of limestone cave systems in the dimensions of length and depth: Canadian Journal of Earth Sciences, v. 15, p. 1783–1798.

Ford, D.C., and J. Lundberg, 1987, A review of dissolutional rills in limestone and other soluble rocks: Catena, Supl. 8, p. 119–140.

Ford, D.C., J. Lundberg, A.N. Palmer, M.V. Palmer, H.P. Schwarcz, and W. Dreybrodt, 1993, Uranium-series dating of the draining of an aquifer: The example of Wind Cave, Black Hills, South Dakota: Geological Society of America Bulletin, v. 105, p. 241–250.

Ford, D., J.-N. Salomon, and P. Williams, 1996, Les "forêts de Pierre" ou "Stone forests" de Lunan: Karstologia, v. 28, p. 25–40.

Ford, D.C., P.L. Smart, and R.O. Ewers, 1983, The physiography and speleogenesis of Castleguard Cave, Columbia Icefields, Alberta, Canada: Arctic and Alpine Research, v. 15, no. 4, p. 437–450.

Ford, D.C., and P.W. Williams, 1989, Karst geomorphology and hydrology: London, Unwin Hyman, 601 p.

Ford, D.C., and P.W. Williams, 2007, Karst hydrogeology and geomorphology: Chichester, U.K., John Wiley and Sons, Ltd., 562 p.

Ford, T.D., 2000, Vein cavities: An early stage in the evolution of the Castleton Caves, Derbyshire, U.K.: Cave and Karst Science, v. 27, no. 1, p. 5–14.

Ford, T.D., and C.H.D. Cullingford (eds.), 1976, The science of speleology: London, Academic Press, 593 p.

Fornós, J.J., B. Gelabert, A. Ginés, J. Ginés, P. Tuccimei, and P. Vesica, 2002, Phreatic overgrowths on speleothems: A useful tool in structural geology in littoral karstic landscapes; the example of eastern Mallorca (Balearic Islands): Geodinamica Acta, v. 15, p. 113–125.

Forti, P., 2001, Biogenic speleothems: An overview: International Journal of Speleology, v. 30A, no. 1/4, p. 39–56.

Forti, P., 2005, Genetic processes of cave minerals in volcanic environments: An overview: Journal of Cave and Karst Studies, v. 67, no. 1, p. 3–13.

Forti, P., E. Galli, A. Rossi, J. Pint, and S. Pint, 2004, Ghar Al Hibashi lava tube: The richest site in Saudi Arabia for cave minerals: Acta Carsologica, v. 33, no. 2, p. 189–205.

Forti, P., G. Giudice, A. Marino, and A. Rossi, 1994, La Grotta Cutrona (MC1) sul Monte Etna e i suoi speleotemi metastabili [Cutrona Cave, Mt. Etna, and its metastable speleothems]: Atti Congresso Regionale de Speleologia, Catania, Italy, p. 125–151.

Forti, P., M. Panzicala Manna, and A. Rossi, 1996, The peculiar mineralogic site of the Alum Cave (Vulcano, Sicily): Proceedings of 7th International Symposium on Vulcanospeleology, Canary Islands, p. 34–44.

Fountain, A.G., 2005, Glacier caves, *in* D.C. Culver and W.B. White (eds.), Encyclopedia of caves: San Diego, Elsevier / Academic Press, p. 271–275.

Frank, E.F., J. Mylroie, J. Troester, E.C. Alexander, and J.L. Carew, 1998, Karst development and speleogenesis, Isla de Mona, Puerto Rico: Journal of Cave and Karst Studies, v. 60, no. 2, p. 73–83.

Franke, H.W., and M.A. Geyh, 1970, Zur Wachstumgeschwindigkeit der Stalagmiten [*On the growth rate of stalagmites*]: Atompraxis, v. 16, no. 1, p. 46–48.

Freeze, R.A., and J.A. Cherry, 1979, Groundwater: Englewood Cliffs, N.J., Prentice-Hall, 604 p.

Friedman, G.M., and B. Radke, 1979, Evidence for sabkha overprint and conditions of intermittent emergence in Cambrian-Ordovician carbonates of northeastern North America and Queensland, Australia: Northeastern Geology, v. 1, p. 18–42.

Fritz, R.D., J.L. Wilson, and D.A. Yurewicz, (eds.), 1993, Paleokarst related hydrocarbon reservoirs: Society for Sedimentary Geology, SEPM Core Workshop no. 18, Tulsa, Okla., 275 p.

Fryer, S., 2005, Halite caves of the Atacama: National Speleological Society, NSS News, v. 63, no. 11, p. 4–19.

Frumkin, A., 1994, Morphology and development of salt caves: National Speleological Society Bulletin, v. 56, no. 2, p. 82–95.

Furman, F.C., 1993, Formation of east Tennessee Knox MVT bodies by hypogenetic-interstratal-evaporite-TSR-sulfuric acid karstification, *in* K.L. Shelton and R.D. Hagni, (eds.), Geology and geochemistry of Mississippi Valley-type ore deposits: University of Missouri, Rolla, Missouri, p. 133–148.

Gabrovšek, F., 2000, Evolution of early karst aquifers: From simple principles to complex models: Postojna, Slovenia, Inštitut za razusjivanje krasa ZRC SAZU, 150 p.

Gabrovšek, F. (ed.), 2002, Evolution of karst, from prekarst to cessation: Postojna, Slovenia, Inštitut za razusjivanje krasa ZRC SAZU, 448 p.

Gádoros, M., and F. Cser, 1986, Aerosols in caves—theoretical considerations: Proceedings of 9th International Congress of Speleology, Barcelona, v. 2, p. 90–92.

Galdenzi, S., 2001, L'azione morfogenetica delle acque sulfuree nelle grotte di Frasassi, Acquasanta Terme (Appennino Marchigiano - Italia) e de Movile (Dobrogea - Romania) [*Morphological effects of sulfide-rich water on the caves of Frasassi, Acquasanta Terme, and Movile*]: Le Grotte d'Italia, series 5, v. 2, p. 49–61.

Galdenzi, S., and T. Maruoka, 2003, Gypsum deposits in the Frasassi Caves, central Italy: Journal of Cave and Karst Studies, v. 65, no. 2, p. 111–125.

Galdenzi, S., and M. Menichetti, 1995, Occurrence of hypogenic caves in a karst region: Examples from central Italy: Environmental Geology, v. 26, p. 39–47.

Galdenzi, S., M. Menichetti, S. Sarbu, and A. Rossi, 1999, Frasassi Caves: A biogenic hypogean karst system? Karst 99, Études de Géographie physique, travaux, Supplement 28, Université de Provence, France, p. 101–106.

Gale, S.J., 1984, The hydraulics of conduit flow in carbonate aquifers: Journal of Hydrology, v. 70, p. 309–324.

Gams, I., 1965, Types of accelerated corrosion, *in* O. Štelcl (ed.), Problems of the speleological research: International Congress of Speleology, Brno, Czechoslovakia, p. 133–139.

Gams, I., 1974, Kras [*Karst*]: Ljubljana, Izdala Slovenska matica, 359 p.

Gams, I., 1981, Comparative research of limestone solution by means of standard tablets: Proceedings of 8th International Congress of Speleology, Bowling Green, Ky., v. 1, p. 273–275.

García-Ruiz, J., R. Villasuso, C. Ayora, A. Canals, and F. Otálora, 2007, Formation of natural gypsum megacrystals in Naica, Mexico: Geology, v. 35, no. 4, p. 327–330.

Gardner, J.H., 1935, Origin and development of limestone caverns: Geological Society of America Bulletin, v. 46, no. 8, p. 1255–1274.

Garrels, R.M., and C.L. Christ, 1965, Solutions, minerals, and equilibria: New York, Harper and Row, 450 p.

Gary, M. 2002, Understanding Zacatón: Exploration and initial interpretation of the world's deepest known phreatic sinkhole and related karst features, southern Tamaulipas, Mexico, *in* J.B. Martin, C.M. Wicks, and I.D. Sasowsky (eds.), Hydrogeology and biology of post-Paleozoic carbonate aquifers: Charles Town, W.Va., Karst Waters Institute Special Publication 7, p. 141–145.

Gary, M.O., and J.M. Sharp, 2006, Volcanogenic karstification of Sistema Zacatón, Mexico, *in* R.S. Harmon and C.M. Wicks (eds.), Perspectives on karst geomorphology, hydrology, and geochemistry — A tribute volume to Derek C. Ford and William B. White: Geological Society of America, Special Paper 404, p. 79–89.

Gascoyne, M.G., 1992, Paleoclimate determinations from cave calcite deposits: Quaternary Science Reviews, v. 11, p. 609–632.

Gascoyne, M., D.C. Ford, and H.P. Schwarcz, 1981, Late Pleistocene chronology and paleoclimate of Vancouver Island determined from cave deposits: Canadian Journal of Earth Science, v. 18, p. 1643–1652.

Genty, D., and Y. Quinif, 1996, Annually laminated sequences in the internal structure of some Belgian stalagmites — importance for paleoclimatology: Journal of Sedimentary Research, v. 66, p. 275–288.

George, A.I., 1984, Cave passage modification changes in relation to lineaments, Mammoth Cave National Park, Kentucky: Cave Research Foundation Annual Report, p. 19–24.

George, A.I., and G.A. O'Dell, 1992, The saltpeter works at Mammoth Cave and the New Madrid earthquake: The Filson Club History Quarterly, v. 66, no. 1, 18 p.

Gibson, D., 2004, Radiolocation, *in* J. Gunn (ed.), Encyclopedia of caves and karst science: New York, Fitzroy Dearborn, p. 615–617.

Gibson, P.J., P. Lyle, and D.M. George, 2004, Application of resistivity and magnetometry geophysical techniques for near-surface investigations in karstic terranes in Ireland: Journal of Cave and Karst Studies, v. 66, no. 2, p. 35–38.

Gilli, E., 1993, Les grands volumes souterrains du massif de Mulu (Bornéo, Sarawak, Malasie) [*Large cave rooms in Mulu, Borneo*]: Karstologia, v. 22, p. 1–14.

Gillieson, D., 1986, Cave sedimentation in the New Guinea Highlands: Earth Surface Processes and Landforms, v. 11, p. 533–543.

Gillieson, D., 1996, Caves: Processes, development, and management: Oxford, U.K., Blackwell Publishers, 324 p.

Gillett, S.L., 2006, A nanotechnology revolution for the geosciences: Geotimes, v. 51, no. 6, p. 18–21.

Ginés, A., 1995, Speleochronological aspects of Majorcan caves: Endins, v. 20, p. 99–112.

Ginsberg, M., and A. Palmer, 2002, Delineation of source-water protection areas in karst aquifers in the Ridge and Valley and Appalachian Plateaus physiographic provinces: Rules of thumb for estimating the capture zones of springs and wells: U.S. Environmental Protection Agency, Publication EPA 816-R-02-015, 41 p.

Glazek, J., J. Rudnicki, and A. Szynkiewicz, 1977, Proglacial caves: A special genetic type of cave in glaciated areas: Proceedings of 7th International Congress of Speleology, Sheffield, U.K., p. 215–217.

Gonzáles, L.A., and K.C. Lohmann, 1988, Controls on mineralogy and composition of spelean carbonates: Carlsbad Caverns, New Mexico, *in* N.P. James and P.W. Choquette (eds.), Paleokarst: New York, Springer-Verlag, 416 p.

Goodman, L.R., 1964, Planes of repose in Höllern, Germany: Cave Notes, v. 6, no. 3, p. 17–19.

Goodman, L.R., 1965, Formation of solution bevels at intersections of joints and bedding planes: Cave Notes, v. 7, no. 4, p. 25–31.

Gonzáles, L.A., and K.C. Lohmann, 1988, Controls on mineralogy and composition of spelean carbonates, Carlsbad Caverns, New Mexico, *in* N. James and P. Choquette (eds.), Paleokarst: New York, Springer-Verlag, p. 81–101.

Gospodarič, R., and P. Habič (eds.), 1976, Underground water tracing: Investigations in Slovenia, 1972–1975: Postojna, Slovenia, Institute for Karst Research SAZU, 309 p.

Gradzinski, M., J. Szulc, and B. Smyk, 1997, Microbial agents of moonmilk calcification: Proceedings of 12th International Congress of Speleology, La Chaux-de-Fonds, Switzerland, v. 1, p. 275–278.

Graf, W.H., 1971, Hydraulics of sediment transport: New York, McGraw-Hill, 509 p.

Graff, J., 2006, The battle to save the cave: TIME, v. 167, no. 20, p. 44–48.

Granger, D.E., D. Fabel, and A.N. Palmer, 2001, Pliocene-Pleistocene incision of the Green River, Kentucky, determined from radioactive decay of cosmogenic ^{26}Al and ^{10}Be in Mammoth Cave sediments: Geological Society of America Bulletin, v. 113, no. 7, p. 825–836.

Granger, D.E., and Fabel, D., 2005, Cosmogenic isotope dating, *in* D.C. Culver and W.B. White (eds.), Encyclopedia of caves: San Diego, Elsevier / Academic Press, p. 137–141.

Granger, D.E., J.W. Kirchner, and R.C. Finkel, 1997, Quaternary downcutting rate of the New River, Virginia, measured from differential decay of cosmogenic ^{26}Al and ^{10}Be in cave-deposited alluvium: Geology, v. 25, p. 107–110.

Greeley, R., 1992, Lava tubes in the Solar System: Huntsville, Ala., National Speleological Society, Proceedings of 6th International Symposium on Vulcanospeleology, Hilo, Hawaii (1991), p. 223–230.

Green, D.J., 1991, On the origin of folia and rims: National Speleological Society, Salt Lake Grotto Technical Note 88, p. 182–196.

Green, D.J., 1997, Is it condensation corrosion or something else? [abstract]: Journal of Cave and Karst Studies, v. 59, no. 1, p. 60.

Green, D.J., 2003, The effects of lava on compass readings: Salt Lake City, Salt Lake Grotto, National Speleological Society, Technical Note 99, p. 75–84.

Greene, F.C., 1909, Caves and cave formations of the Mitchell Limestone: Indiana Academy of Science Proceedings, v. 18, p. 175–184.

Grimes, K.G., 1998, Redefining the boundary between karst and pseudokarst: A discussion: Cave and Karst Science, v. 24, no. 2, p. 87–90.

Grimes, K.G., 2003, Syngenetic karst in Australia: A review: Proceedings of 24th Biennial Speleological Conference, Northern Australian Speleological Federation, p. 138–148.

Groves, C.G., 1993, Early development of karst systems: Ph.D. thesis, University of Virginia, Charlottesville, Va., 253 p.

Groves, C.G., and A.D. Howard, 1994, Early development of karst systems, 1. Preferential flow path enlargement under laminar flow: Water Resources Research, v. 30, no. 10, p. 2837–2846.

Groves C.G., and J. Meiman, 1996, Speleogenesis of Mammoth Cave: What are we learning at Hawkins River? Proceedings of 5th Mammoth Cave Science Conference, Mammoth Cave, Ky., p. 131–136.

Groves, C., and J. Meiman, 2005, Weathering, geomorphic work, and karst landscape evolution in the Cave City groundwater basin, Mammoth Cave, Kentucky: Geomorphology, v. 67, p. 115–126.

Grow, S.R., 1986, Water quality in the Forestville Creek karst basin of southeastern Minnesota: M.S. thesis, Univ. of Minnesota, St. Paul, Minn., 228 p.

Grund, A., 1903, Die Karsthydrographie: Geographisches Abhandlung herausgegeben von A. Penck [*Karst hydrology: Geographic proceedings edited by A. Penck*], v. 7, no. 3, 200 p.

Gulley, J., 2006, Matanuska Glacier cave research expedition: National Speleological Society, NSS News, v. 64, no. 12, p. 13–16, 19.

Gunn, J., 1983, Point recharge of limestone aquifers — a model from New Zealand karst: Journal of Hydrology, v. 61, p. 19–29.

Gunn, J. (ed.), 2004a, Encyclopedia of caves and karst science: New York, Fitzroy Dearborn, 902 p.

Gunn, J., 2004b, Radon in caves, *in* J. Gunn (ed.), Encyclopedia of caves and karst science: New York, Fitzroy Dearborn, p. 617–619.

Gunn, J., 2004c, Erosion rates: Field measurements, *in* J. Gunn (ed.), Encyclopedia of caves and karst science: New York, Fitzroy Dearborn, p. 321–323.

Gunn, J., S. Fletcher, and D. Prime, 1991, Research on radon in British limestone caves and mines, 1970–1990: Cave Science, v. 18, p. 63–65.

Gurnee, R., and J. Gurnee, 1990, Gurnee guide to American caves: Closter, N.J., R.H. Gurnee, Inc., 288 p.

Gustafson, G., and J. Krasny, 1994, Crystalline rock aquifers: Their occurrence, use, and importance: Applied Hydrogeology, v. 94, no. 2, p. 64–75.

Hack, J.T., 1960, Interpretation of erosional topography in humid temperate regions: American Journal of Science, v. 258-A, p. 80–97.

Halliday, W.R., 1954, Ice caves of the United States: National Speleological Society Bulletin, v. 16, p. 3–28.

Halliday, W.R., 1960a, Pseudokarst in the United States: National Speleological Society Bulletin, v. 22, no. 2, p. 109–113.

Halliday, W.R., 1960b, Changing concepts of speleogenesis: National Speleological Society Bulletin, v. 22, no. 1, p. 23–29.

Halliday, W.R., 1963, Caves of Washington: Washington Dept. of Conservation, Division of Mines and Geology, Information Circular No. 40, 132 p.

Halliday, W.R., 1982, Mount St. Helens update: National Speleological Society, Guidebook to 1982 annual convention, Bend, Oregon, p. 1–2.

Halliday, W.R., 1995, A record year in Hawaii: National Speleological Society, NSS News, v. 53, no. 11, p. 292–299.

Halliday, W.R., 2004a, Piping caves and badlands pseudokarst, *in* J. Gunn (ed.), Encyclopedia of caves and karst science: New York, Fitzroy Dearborn, p. 589–593.

Halliday, W.R., 2004b, Crevice caves, *in* J. Gunn (ed.), Encyclopedia of caves and karst science: New York, Fitzroy Dearborn, p. 249–252.

Halliday, W.R., 2004c, Pseudokarst, *in* J. Gunn (ed.), Encyclopedia of caves and karst science: New York, Fitzroy Dearborn, p. 604–608.

Halliday, W.R., 2004d, Volcanic caves, *in* J. Gunn (ed.), Encyclopedia of caves and karst science: New York, Fitzroy Dearborn, p. 760–764.

Halliday, W.R., 2004e, Disease, *in* J. Gunn (ed.), Encyclopedia of caves and karst science: New York, Fitzroy Dearborn, p. 293–295.

Han, B., 1993, Study of mechanisms of oilfield karst: Proceedings of 11th International Congress of Speleology, Beijing, China, p.104–106.

Hanna, R.B., and H. Rajaram, 1998, Influence of aperture variability on dissolutional growth of fissures in karst formations: Water Resources Research, v. 34, no. 11, p. 2843–2853.

Hanor, J.S., 1996, Controls on the solubilization of lead and zinc in basinal brines, *in* D.F. Sangster (ed.), Carbonate-hosted lead-zinc deposits: Society of Economic Geologists, Special Publication 4, p. 483–500.

Hardisty, P.E., and E.Özdemiroğlu, 2004, The economics of groundwater remediation and protection: Boca Raton, Florida, CRC Press, 368 p.

Harmon, R.S., H.P. Schwarcz, D.C. Ford, and D.L. Koch, 1979, An isotopic paleotemperature record for late Wisconsinan time: Geology, v. 7, p. 430–433.

Harmon, R.S., P. Thompson, H.P. Schwarcz, and D.C. Ford, 1975, Uranium-series dating of speleothems: National Speleological Society Bulletin, v. 37, no. 2, p. 21–33.

Harmon, R.S., P. Thompson, H.P. Schwarcz, and D.C. Ford, 1978, Late Pleistocene paleoclimates of North America as inferred from stable isotope studies of speleothems: Quaternary Research, v. 9, p. 54–70.

Harmon, R.S., and C.M. Wicks (eds.), 2006, Perspectives on karst geomorphology, hydrology, and geochemistry — A tribute volume to Derek C. Ford and William B. White: Geological Society of America, Special Paper 404, 366 p.

Häuselmann, P., 2002, Cave genesis and its relationship to surface processes: Investigations in the Siebenhengste region (BE, Switzerland): Ph.D. thesis, University of Bern, Switzerland, reprinted by Höhlenforschergemeinschaft Region Hohgant, Bern, Switzerland, 168 p.

Häuselmann, P., 2005, Cross-formational flow, diffluence and transfluence observed in St. Beatus Cave and Sieben Hengste (Switzerland): International Journal of Speleology, v. 34, no. 1–2, p. 65–70.

Häuselmann, P., and D.E. Granger, 2005, Dating of caves by cosmogenic nuclides: Method, possibilities, and the Siebenhengste example (Switzerland): Acta Carsologica, v. 34, no. 1, p. 43–50.

Häuselmann, P., and P. Tognini, 2005, Kaltbach Cave (Siebenhengste, Switzerland): Phantom of the sandstone? Acta Carsologica, v. 34, no. 2, p. 383–396.

Hendy, C.H., 1971, The isotopic geochemistry of speleothems, I. The calculation of the effects of different modes of formation on the isotope composition of speleothems and their applicability as palaeoclimatic indicators: Geochimica et Cosmochimica, v. 35, p. 801–824.

Hendy, C.H., and A.T. Wilson, 1968, Paleoclimatic data from speleothems: Nature, v. 216, p. 48–51.

Herman, J.S., and D.A. Hubbard, 2002, Microbial mediation of dissolved sulfide oxidation and its role in speleogenesis, *in* J.B. Martin, C.M. Wicks, and I.D. Sasowsky (eds.), Hydrogeology and biology of post-Paleozoic carbonate aquifers: Charles Town, W. Va., Karst Waters Institute, Special Publication 7, p. 87–88.

Herman, J.S., and W.B. White, 1985, Dissolution kinetics of dolomite: Effects of lithology and fluid flow velocity: Geochimica and Cosmochimica Acta, v. 49, p. 2017–2026.

Herron, D.A., 1998, Origin and geologic history of the Timpanogos Cave System, Timpanogos Cave National Monument, Utah County, Utah: M.S. thesis, Brigham Young University, Provo, Utah, 75 p.

Hess, J.W., and W.B. White, 1993, Groundwater geochemistry of the carbonate aquifer, south-central Kentucky, U.S.A.: Applied Geochemistry, vol. 8, p. 189–204.

High, C.J., 1970, Aspects of the solutional erosion of limestone, with special consideration of lithological factors: Ph.D. thesis, University of Bristol, Bristol, U.K., 228 p.

High, C.J., and G.K. Hanna, 1970, A method for the direct measurement of erosion of rock surfaces: British Geomorphological Research Group, Technical Publication 5, 24 p.

Higham, S., 2002, Caves of New Hampshire, *in* M. Nardacci (ed.), A guide to the caves of the Acadian coast: National Speleological Society, Huntsville, AL, 2002 Convention guidebook, p. 28–31.

Hildreth-Werker, V., and J.C. Werker (eds.), 2006, Cave conservation and restoration: Huntsville, Ala., National Speleological Society, 616 p.

Hill, C.A., 1978, Mineralogy of Ogle Cave: National Speleological Society bulletin, v. 40, no. 1, p. 19–24.

Hill, C.A., 1981a, Speleogenesis of Carlsbad Caverns and other caves of the Guadalupe Mountains: Proceedings of 8th International Congress of Speleology, Bowling Green, Ky., p. 143–144.

Hill, C.A. (ed.), 1981b, Saltpeter: A symposium: National Speleological Society Bulletin, v. 43, no. 4, p. 83–131.

Hill, C.A., 1982, Origin of black deposits in caves: National Speleological Society Bulletin, v. 44, no. 1, p. 15–19.

Hill, C.A., 1987, Geology of Carlsbad Cavern and other caves in the Guadalupe Mountains, New Mexico and Texas: New Mexico Bureau of Mines and Mineral Resources, Bulletin 117, 150 p.

Hill, C.A., 2000, Overview of the geologic history of cave development in the Guadalupe Mountains, New Mexico: Journal of Cave and Karst Studies, v. 62, no. 2, p. 60–71.

Hill, C.A., 2003, Intrastratal karst at the Waste Isolation Pilot Plant site, southeastern New Mexico, *in* K.S. Johnson and J.T. Neal (eds.), Evaporite karst and engineering/environmental problems in the United States: Oklahoma Geological Survey, Circular 109, p. 197–209.

Hill, C.A., and P. Forti, 1997, Cave minerals of the world (2nd ed.): Huntsville, Ala., National Speleological Society, 463 p.

Hill, C.A., V.J. Polyak, W.C. McIntosh, and P.P. Provencio, 2004, Preliminary evidence from Grand Canyon caves and mines for the evolution of the Grand Canyon and Colorado River System, *in* R.A. Young and E.E. Spamer (eds.), The Colorado River: Origin and evolution: Grand Canyon Association, Monograph 12, p. 141–145.

Hjulström, F., 1935, The morphological activity of rivers as illustrated by River Fyris: Geological Institute of Upsala Bulletin, v. 25, p. 221–527.

Hoke, J.A., and C.M. Wicks, 1997, Contaminant transport in karst terranes, *in* B.F. Beck, J.B. Stephenson, and J.G. Herring (eds.), The engineering geology and hydrogeology of karst terranes: Boston, Massachusetts, A.A. Balkema, p. 189–192.

Holland, H.D., T. Kirsipu, J. Huebner, and U. Oxburgh, 1964, On some aspects of the chemical evolution of cave waters: Journal of Geology, v. 72, p. 36–67.

Holsinger, J.R., 2000, Ecological derivation, colonization, and speciation, *in* H. Wilkens, D. Culver, and W. Humphreys (eds.), Subterranean ecosystems – Ecosystems of the world (Volume 30), p. 399–415.

Horáček, I., and L. Kordos, 1989, Biostratigraphic investigations in paleokarst, *in* P. Bosák, D. Ford, J. Glazek, and I. Horáček (eds.), Paleokarst: Prague and Amsterdam, Academia and Elsevier, p. 599–612.

Horn, G., 1947, Karsthuler in Nordland [*Limestone caves of Nordland*]: Norges Geologiske Undersøkelse, v. 165, 77 p. Partial text in English in Cave Science, v. 3, no. 5, p. 123–128.

Hose, L.D., 2000, Speleogenesis of Sistema Cheve, Oaxaca, Mexico, *in* A. Klimchouk, D. Ford, A. Palmer, and W. Dreybrodt (eds.), Speleogenesis: Evolution of karst aquifers: Huntsville, Ala., National Speleological Society, p. 358–361.

Hose, L.D., 2005, ICS pre-Congress field trip: H₂S caves in central Italy: National Speleological Society, NSS News, v. 53, no. 12, p. 10–11.

Hose, L.D., A.N. Palmer, M.V. Palmer, D.E. Northup, P.J. Boston, and H.R. DuChene, 2000, Microbiology and geochemistry in a hydrogen-sulphide-rich karst environment: Chemical Geology, v. 169, p. 399–423.

Hovey, H.C., 1882, Celebrated American caverns; especially Mammoth, Wyandot, and Luray, together with historical, scientific, and descriptive notice of caves and grottoes in other lands: Cincinnati, Robert Clarke and Company, 228 p.

Howard, A.D., 1964a, Processes of limestone cave development: International Journal of Speleology, v. 1, p. 47–60.

Howard, A. D., 1964b, Model for cavern development under artesian ground water flow, with special reference to the Black Hills: National Speleological Society Bulletin, v. 26, no. 1, p. 7–16.

Howard, A.D., 1971, Quantitative measures of cave patterns: Caves and Karst, v. 13, p. 1–7.

Howard, A.D., and C.G. Groves, 1995, Early development of karst systems, 2. Turbulent flow: Water Resources Research, v. 31, no. 1, p. 19–26.

Howes, C., 1997, Images below: A manual of underground and flash photography: Cardiff, U.K., Wild Places Publishing, 268 p.

Hubbard, D.A., and J.S. Herman, 1991, Travertine-marl: The "doughnut-hole" of karst, *in* E.H. Kastning and K.M. Kastning (eds.), Appalachian karst: Proceedings of Appalachian Karst Symposium, Radford, Virginia, p. 59–64.

Hubbert, M.K., 1940, The theory of groundwater motion: Journal of Geology, v. 48, no. 8, p. 785–944.

Huff, L.C., 1940, Artificial helictites and gypsum flowers: Journal of Geology, v. 48, no. 6, p. 641–659.

Huizing, T., M. Jarnot, G. Neumeier, R.P. Richards and G. Staebler (eds.), 2003, Calcite — the mineral with the most forms: East Hampton, Conn., Lapis International, extraLapis English No. 4, 114 p.

Huntoon, P.W., 1996, Large-basin ground water circulation and paleoreconstruction of circulation leading to uranium mineralization in Grand Canyon breccia pipes, Arizona: The Mountain Geologist, v. 33, p. 71–84.

Hutton, J., 1795, Theory of the Earth, with proofs and illustrations: Edinburgh, Cadell, 2 vols.

Ikeya, M., 1975, Dating of a stalactite by electron paramagnetic resonance: Nature, v. 255, p. 48–50.

Imbrie, J., J. Hays, D. Martinson, A. McIntyre, A. Mix, J. Morley, N. Pisias, W. Prell, and N. Shackleton, 1984, The orbital theory of Pleistocene climate: Support from a revised chronology of the marine δ¹⁸O record, *in* A.L. Burger and others (eds.), Milankovitch and climate, Part I: Dordrecht, Netherlands, Reidel, p. 269–305.

Jacobson, R.L., and D. Langmuir, 1972, An accurate method for calculating saturation levels of ground waters with respect to calcite and dolomite: Transactions of Cave Research Group of Great Britain, v. 14, p. 104–108.

Jagnow, D.H., 1979, Cavern development in the Guadalupe Mountains: Cave Research Foundation, Columbus, Ohio, 55 p.

Jakucs, L., 1977, Morphogenetics of karst regions: New York, Wiley, 284 p.

James, A.N., and I.M. Kirkpatrick, 1980, Design of foundations of dams containing soluble rocks and soils: Quarterly Journal of Engineering Geology, v. 13, p. 189–198.

James, J.M., 1977, Carbon dioxide in the cave atmosphere: Transactions of British Cave Research Association, v. 4, p. 417–429.

James, J.M., A.J. Peavey, and A.F. Rogers, 1975, Foul air and the resulting hazards to cavers: Transactions of British Cave Research Association, v. 2, p. 79–88.

James, N.P., and P.W. Choquette (eds.), 1988, Paleokarst: New York, Springer-Verlag, 416 p.

Jameson, R.A., 1985, Structural segments and the analysis of flow paths in the North Canyon of Snedegar Cave, Friars Hole Cave System, West Virginia: M.S. thesis, West Virginia University, Morgantown, W. Va., 421 p.

Jameson, R., 1991, Concept and classification of cave breakdown: An analysis of patterns of collapse in Friars Hole Cave System, West Virginia, *in* E.H. Kastning and K.M. Kastning (eds.), Appalachian karst: Huntsville, Ala., National Speleological Society, Proceedings of Appalachian Karst Symposium, Radford, Va., p. 35–44.

Jameson, R.A., 1995, Condensation, condensation corrosion, and associated features in Snedegars and Greenville Saltpeter Caves, *in* C. Zokaites (ed.), Underground in the Appalachians: Huntsville, Alabama, Guidebook to 1995 National Speleological Society Convention, p. 122–125.

Jameson, R.A., 2006, Identification and analysis of early flow paths in branchwork caves in West Virginia, USA, *in* R.S. Harmon and C.M. Wicks (eds.), Perspectives on karst geomorphology, hydrology, and geochemistry — A tribute volume to Derek C. Ford and William B. White: Geological Society of America, Special Paper 404, p. 23–30.

Jancin, M., and D.D. Clark, 1993, Subsidence-sinkhole development in light of mud infiltrate structures within interstratal karst of the Coastal Plain, southeast United States, *in* B.F. Beck, Applied karst geology: Proceedings of 4th conference on engineering and environmental impacts of karst, Lisse, Netherlands, A.A. Balkema, p. 29–36.

Jarvis, T., 2003, The Money Pit: Karst failure of Anchor Dam, Wyoming, *in* K. Johnson and J. Neal (eds.), Evaporite karst and engineering/environmental problems in the United States: Oklahoma Geological Survey, Circular 109, p. 271–278.

Jeannin, P.-Y., 1990, Neotectonique dans le Karst du Nord du Lac de Thoune (Suisse) [*Neotectonics in the karst north of Lake Thun, Switzerland*]: Karstologia, v. 15, no. 1, p. 41–54.

Jeannin, P.-Y., 1996, Structure et comportement hydraulique des aquifères karstiques [*Structure and hydraulic behavior of karst aquifers*]: Ph.D. thesis, Université de Neuchâtel, Institut de Géologie, Centre d'Hydrogéologie, 237 p. + 2 appendices.

Jeannin, P.-Y., T. Bitterli, and P. Häuselmann, 2000, Genesis of a large cave system: The case study of the North of Lake Thun system (Canton Bern, Switzerland), *in* A. Klimchouk, D.C. Ford, A.N. Palmer, and W. Dreybrodt (eds.), Speleogenesis: Evolution of karst aquifers: Huntsville, Ala., National Speleological Society, p. 338–347.

Jeannin, P.-Y., F. Zwahlen, and N. Doerfliger, 1999, From a conceptual model of karst hydrological systems to water-vulnerability mapping, *in* A.N. Palmer, M.V. Palmer, and I.D. Sasowsky (eds.), Karst modeling: Charles Town, W. Va., Karst Waters Institute, Special Publication 5, p. 65–69.

Jennings, J.N., 1963, Geomorphology of Dip Cave, Wee Jasper, New South Wales: Helictite, v. 1, p. 43–58.

Jennings, J.N., 1968, Syngenetic karst in Australia: Australian National University, Canberra, Department of Geography Publication G/5, p. 41–110.

Jennings, J.N., 1983, The disregarded karst of the arid and semiarid domain: Karstologia, v. 1, no. 1, p. 61–73.

Jennings, J.N., 1985, Karst geomorphology: Oxford, U.K., Basil Blackwell, 293 p.

Jenson, J.W., T.M. Keel, J.R. Mylroie, J.E. Mylroie, K.W. Stafford, D. Taboroši, and C. Wexel, 2006, Karst of the Mariana Islands: The interaction of tectonics, glacio-eustasy, and freshwater/seawater mixing in island carbonates, *in* R.S. Harmon and C.M. Wicks (eds.), Perspectives on karst geomorphology, hydrology, and geochemistry — A tribute volume to Derek C. Ford and William B. White: Geological Society of America, Special Paper 404, p. 129–138.

Jeschke, A.A., K. Vosbeck, and W. Dreybrodt, 2001, Surface controlled dissolution rates in aqueous solutions exhibit nonlinear dissolution kinetics: Geochimica et Cosmochimica Acta, v. 65, p. 13–20.

Johnson, D.E., and J. Meiman, 1994, Investigation of changes in stage and the effects on a conduit-adjacent karst aquifer, Mill Hole, Mammoth Cave, Kentucky: Proceedings of Third Science Conference, Mammoth Cave National Park, p. 215–247.

Johnson, K.S., and J.T. Neal (eds.), 2003, Evaporite karst and engineering/environmental problems in the United States: Oklahoma Geological Survey, Circular 109, 353 p.

Johnson, P.A., and B. Gomez, 1994, Cave levels and cave development in the Mitchell Plain following base-level lowering: Earth Surface Processes and Landforms, v. 19, p. 517–524.

Jones, W.K., 1997, Karst hydrology atlas of West Virginia: Charles Town, W. Va., Karst Waters Institute, Special Publication 4, 111 p.

Jones, W.K., 2005, Karst water tracing, *in* D.C. Culver and W.B. White (eds.), Encyclopedia of caves: San Diego, Elsevier / Academic Press, p. 321–329.

Jones, W.K., D.C. Culver and J.S. Herman (eds.), 2004, Epikarst: Charles Town, W. Va., Karst Waters Institute, Special Publication 9, 160 p.

Jones, W.K., H.H. Hobbs, C.M. Wicks, R.R. Currie, L.D. Hose, R.C. Kerbo, J.R. Goodbar, and J. Trout, 2003, Recommendations and guidelines for managing caves on protected lands: Charles Town, W. Va., Karst Waters Institute, Special Publication 8, 95 p.

Kambesis, P., 2004, Encantado, Sistema del Río, *in* J. Gunn (ed.), Encyclopedia of caves and karst science: New York, Fitzroy Dearborn, p. 316–318.

Kantor, B.Z., 2003, Crystal growth and development, interpreted from a mineral's present form: Mineralogical Almanac, v. 6, 128 p.

Käss, W., 1998, Tracing technique in geohydrology: Rotterdam, Netherlands, A.A. Balkema, 581 p.

Kastning, E.H., 1977, Faults as positive and negative influences on groundwater flow and conduit enlargement, *in* R.R. Dilamarter, and S.C. Csallany (eds.), Hydrologic problems in karst regions: Western Kentucky University, Bowling Green, Ky., p. 193–201.

Kastning, K., D.A. Hubbard, E.H. Kastning, and K.M. Kastning, 1995, Origin of caves and karst in the Shenandoah Valley, Rockingham and Augusta Counties, Virginia: Guidebook for geologic field trip, National Speleological Society Annual Convention, Blacksburg, Virginia, 50 p.

Katz, D.A., G.P. Eberli, P.K. Swart, and L.B. Smith, 2006, Tectonic-hydrothermal brecciation associated with calcite precipitation and permeability destruction in Mississippian carbonate reservoirs, Montana and Wyoming: American Association of Petroleum Geologists Bulletin, v. 90, p. 1803–1841.

Katzer, F., 1909, Karst und Karsthydrographie [*Karst and karst hydrology*]: Zur Kunde der Balkanhalbinsel, no. 8, 94 p.

Kauahikaua, J., K. Cashman, T. Mattox, C. Heliker, K. Hon, M. Mangan, and C. Thornber, 1998, Observations in basaltic lava streams from Kilauea Volcano, island of Hawai'i: Journal of Geophysical Research, v. 103, no. B11, p. 303–327.

Kaufmann, G., and J. Braun, 1999, Karst aquifer evolution in fractured rocks: Water Resources Research, v. 35, no. 11, p. 3223–3238.

Kaufmann, G., and W. Dreybrodt, 2007, Calcite dissolution kinetics in the system CO_2-H_2O-$CaCO_3$ at high undersaturation: Geochimica et Cosmochimica Acta, in press.

Kaye, C.A., 1957, The effect of solvent motion on limestone solution: Journal of Geology, v. 65, p. 35–46.

Kehew, A.E., 2001, Applied chemical hydrogeology: Upper Saddle River, N.J., Prentice-Hall, 368 p.

Kemmerly, P., 1981, The need for recognition and implementation of a sinkhole-floodplain hazard designation in urban karst terrains: Environmental Geology, v. 3, p. 281–292.

Kempe, S., 1972, Cave genesis in gypsum, with particular reference to underwater conditions: Cave Science, v. 49, p. 1–6.

Kempe, S., 1982, Höhlen in Deutschland [*Caves of Germany*]: Hamburg, HB Verlags- und Vertriebs-Gesellschaft, 114 p.

Kempe, S., 1987, Welt voller Geheimnisse: Höhlen [*World of secrets: Caves*]: Hamburg, Germany, HB Verlags- und Vertriebs-Gesellschaft, 114 p.

Kempe, S., A. Brandt, M. Seeger, and G. Vladi, 1975, "Facetten" and "Laugdecken": Typical morphological elements of caves developed in standing water [*German equivalents: Facetten ("facets") = inclined, planar portions of cave walls; Laugdecken ("solutional ceilings") = ceilings flattened by exposure to standing water*]: Annales de Spéléologie, v. 30, no. 4, p. 705–708.

Kempe, S., and M.S. Werner, 2003, The Kuka'iau Cave, Mauna Kea, Hawaii, created by water erosion: A new Hawaiian cave type: Journal of Cave and Karst Studies, v. 65, p. 53–67.

Kerans, C., 1988, Karst-controlled reservoir heterogeneity in Ellenburger Group carbonates of West Texas: American Association of Petroleum Geologists Bulletin, v. 72, p. 1160–1183.

Kesler, S.E., 1996, Appalachian Mississippi Valley-type deposits: Paleoaquifers and brine provinces, *in* D.F. Sangster (ed.), Carbonate-hosted lead-zinc deposits: Society of Economic Geologists, Special Publication 4, p. 29–57.

Kharaka, Y., L. Law, W. Carothers, and D. Goerlitz, 1986, Role of organic species dissolved in formation waters from sedimentary basins in mineral diagenesis, *in* D.L. Gautier (ed.), Roles of organic matter in sediment diagenesis: Society of Economic Paleontologists and Mineralogists, Special Publication 38, p. 111–122.

Kilpatrick, F.A., and E.D. Cobb, 1985, Measurement of discharge using tracers: Techniques of Water-Resources Investigations of the U.S. Geological Survey, Book 3, Chapter A16, 52 p.

Kincaid, T.R., 1998, River water intrusion to the unconfined Floridan aquifer: Environmental and Engineering Geoscience, v. 4, p. 361–374.

Kindler, P., and P. Hearty, 1997, Geology of the Bahamas: Architecture of Bahamian islands, *in* H. Vacher and T. Quinn (eds.), Geology and hydrogeology of carbonate islands: Developments in Sedimentology 54, Amsterdam, Elsevier, p. 141–160.

Kiraly, L., 1975, Rapport sur l'état actuel des connaissances dans le domaine des charactères physiques des roches karstiques [*Current understanding of the physical character of karstic rocks*], *in* A. Burger and L. Dubertret (eds.), Hydrogeology of karstic terrains: International Union of Geological Sciences, series B, no. 3, p. 53–67.

Kiraly, L., 2002, Karstification and groundwater flow, *in* F. Gabrovšek, Evolution of early karst aquifers: From simple principles to complex models: Postojna, Slovenia, Inštitut za razusjivanje krasa ZRC SAZU, p. 155–190.

Kirk, K.G., and E. Werner, 1981, Handbook of geophysical cavity-locating techniques: U.S. Department of Transportation, Implementation Package FHWA-IP-81-3.

Kirkland, D.W., and R. Evans, 1976, Origin of limestone buttes, gypsum plain, Culberson County, Texas: American Association of Petroleum Geologists Bulletin, v. 60, p. 2005–2018.

Klappacher, W., and H. Knapczyk (eds.), 1976, Salzburger Höhlenbuch, Band 2 [*Salzburg caves, v. 2*]: Salzburg, Austria, Landesverein für Höhlenkunde in Salzburg, 348 p.

Klimchouk, A.B., 1991, Large maze caves in gypsum in the Western Ukraine: Speleogenesis under artesian conditions: National Speleological Society Bulletin, v. 53, no. 2, p. 71–82.

Klimchouk, A.B., 1992, Large gypsum caves in the western Ukraine and their genesis: Cave Science, v. 19, p. 3–11.

Klimchouk, A.B., 1996a, The typology of gypsum karst according to its geological and geomorphological evolution, *in* A. Klimchouk, D. Lowe, A. Cooper, and U. Sauro (eds.), Gypsum karst of the world: International Journal of Speleology, v. 25, nos. 3–4, p. 49–60.

Klimchouk, A.B., 1996b, Speleogenesis in gypsum, *in* A. Klimchouk, D. Lowe, A. Cooper, and U. Sauro (eds.), Gypsum karst of the world: International Journal of Speleology, v. 25, nos. 3–4, p. 61–82.

Klimchouk, A.B., 1997, Artesian speleogenetic setting: Proceedings of 12th International Speleological Congress, La Chaux-de-Fonds, Switzerland, v. 1, p. 157–160.

Klimchouk, A.B., 2000, The formation of epikarst and its role in vadose speleogenesis, *in* A. Klimchouk, D. Ford, A. Palmer, and W. Dreybrodt (eds.), Speleogenesis: Evolution of karst aquifers: Huntsville, Ala., National Speleological Society, p. 91–99.

Klimchouk, A., 2005a, Krubera (Voronja) Cave, *in* D.C. Culver and W.B. White (eds.), Encyclopedia of caves: San Diego, Elsevier / Academic Press, p. 335–338.

Klimchouk, A., 2005b, Conceptualization of speleogenesis in multistory artesian systems: A model of transverse speleogenesis: International Journal of Speleology, v. 34, no. 1–2, p. 45–64.

Klimchouk, A., 2006, Unconfined versus confined speleogenetic settings: Variations of solution porosity: International Journal of Speleology, v. 35, no. 1, p. 19–24.

Klimchouk, A.B., and S.D. Aksem, 2005, Hydrochemistry and solution rates in gypsum karst: case study from the Western Ukraine: Environmental Geology, v. 48, p. 307–319.

Klimchouk, A.B., D.C. Ford, A.N. Palmer, and W. Dreybrodt (eds.), 2000, Speleogenesis: Evolution of karst aquifers: Huntsville, Ala., National Speleological Society, 527 p.

Klimchouk, A.B., and D. Lowe (eds.), 2002, Implication of speleological studies for karst subsidence hazard assessment: International Journal of Speleology, v. 31, no. 1/4, 199 p.

Klimchouk, A.B., D. Lowe, A. Cooper, and U. Sauro (eds.), 1996, Gypsum karst of the world: International Journal of Speleology, v. 25, no. 3–4, 307 p.

Klimchouk, A.B., V.M. Nasedkin, and K.I.Cunningham, 1995, Speleothems of aerosol origin: National Speleological Society Bulletin, v. 57, no. 1, p. 31–42.

Klimchouk, A.B., U. Sauro, and M. Lazzarotto, 1996, "Hidden" shafts at the base of the epikarstic zone: A case study from the Sette Communi plateau, Venetian Pre-Alps, Italy: Cave and Karst Science, v. 23, p. 101–107.

Knez, M., and T. Slabe, 2004, Karstology and the opening of caves during motorway construction in the Karst region of Slovenia: International Journal of Speleology, theme issue on Implication of Speleological Studies for Karst Subsidence Hazard Assessment, v. 31, no. 1/4, p. 159–168.

Kolesar, P.T., and A.C. Riggs, 2004, Influence of depositional environment on Devils Hole calcite morphology and petrology, *in* I.D. Sasowsky and J.E. Mylroie (eds.), Studies of cave sediments: Physical and chemical records of paleoclimate: New York, Kluwer Academic / Plenum Publishers, 322 p.

Kolev, B., and Y. Shopov, 1992, Volcanic caves in Bulgaria: Huntsville, Ala., National Speleological Society, Proceedings of 6th International Symposium on Vulcanospeleology, p. 171–175.

Komac, B., 2001, The karst springs of the Kanin Massif: Acta Geographica, v. 41, p. 7–45.

Koša, E., and D.W. Hunt, 2006, Heterogeneity in fill and properties of karst-modified syndepositional faults and fractures: Upper Permian Capitan platform, New Mexico, U.S.A.: Journal of Sedimentary Research, v. 76, p. 131–151.

Kowalski, K., 2005, Paleontology of caves: Pleistocene mammals, *in* D.C. Culver and W.B. White (eds.), Encyclopedia of caves: San Diego, Elsevier / Academic Press, p. 431–435.

Kranjc, A. (ed.), 2002, Monitoring of karst caves: Acta Carsologica, v. 31, no. 1, 183 p.

Kranjc, A., 2004, From "rock desert" to forest — an example from Kras: Proceedings of conference on Natural and Cultural Lanscapes — the Geological Foundation (2002), Royal Irish Academy, Dublin Castle, Ireland, p. 201–204.

Krothe, N.C., and R.D. Libra, 1983, Sulfur isotopes and hydrochemical variations in spring waters of southern Indiana, U.S.A.: Journal of Hydrology, v. 61, p. 267–283.

Kuehn, K.W., C.G. Groves, N.C. Crawford, and J. Meiman, 1994, Geomorphology and environmental problems of the Central Kentucky karst, Annual Field Conference of the Geological Society of Kentucky: Geological Society of Kentucky 50 p.

Kyle, J.R., 1983, Economic aspects of subaerial carbonates, *in* P.A. Scholle, D.G. Bebout, and C.H. Moore (eds.), Carbonate depositional environments: American Association of Petroleum Geologists, Memoir 33, p. 73–92.

LaMoreaux, P.E., and W.J. Powell, 1963, Stratigraphic and structural guides to the development of water wells and well fields in a limestone terrane: International Association of Scientific Hydrology, Publ. 52, p. 363–375.

Land, L., and D. Love, 2006, Gypsum karst processes in the Seven Rivers Formation, *in* L. Land, V. Lueth, W. Raatz, P. Boston, and D. Love (eds.), Caves and karst of southeastern New Mexico: New Mexico Geological Survey, 57th Annual Field Conference, p. 85–93.

Lange, A.L., 1963, Planes of repose in caves: Cave Notes, v. 5, no. 6, p. 41–48.

Lange, A.L., 1964, Solution bevels in limestone caves: Cave Notes, v. 6, no. 5, p. 33–39.

Lange, A.L., 1999, Geophysical studies at Kartchner Caverns State Park, Arizona: Journal of Cave and Karst Studies, v. 61, p. 68–72.

Langmuir, D., 1971, The geochemistry of some carbonate ground waters in Central Pennsylvania: Geochimica et Cosmochimica Acta, v. 35, p. 1023–1045.

Langmuir, D., 1997, Aqueous environmental geochemistry: Upper Saddle River, N.J., Prentice-Hall, 600 p.

Laptev, F.F., 1939, Aggressive action of water on carbonate rocks, gypsum, and concrete: Trudy Spetsgeo, v. 1, Moscow-Leningrad, State Science-Technical Publishing, 104 p. (in Russian).

LaRock, E.J., and K.I. Cunningham, 1995, Helictite bush formation and aquifer cooling in Wind Cave, Wind Cave National Park, South Dakota: The National Speleological Society Bulletin, v. 57, no. 1, p. 43–51.

Larson, C.V., 1993, An illustrated glossary of lava tube features: Vancouver, Washington, Western Speleological Survey, 56 p.

Latham, A.G., H.P. Schwarcz, D.C. Ford, and W.G. Pearce, 1979, Paleomagnetism of stalagmite deposits: Nature, v. 280, p. 383–385.

Lattman, L.H., and R.R. Parizek, 1964, Relationship between fracture traces and the occurrence of ground water in carbonate rocks: Journal of Hydrology, v. 2, p. 73–91.

Lauritzen, S.-E., 1986, CO_2 content of glacial environments and the likelihood of sub-glacial karstification: Proceedings of 9th International Congress of Speleology, Barcelona, Spain, Part 1, p. 127–130.

Lauritzen, S.-E. (ed.), 1996, Climate change: The karst record: Charles Town, W.Va., Karst Waters Institute, Special Publication 2, 195 p.

Lauritzen, S.-E., 2001, Marble stripe karst of the Scandinavian Caledonides: An end-member in the contact karst spectrum: Acta Carsologica, v. 30, no. 2, p. 47–79.

Lauritzen, S.-E., J. Abbott, R. Arnesen, G. Crossley, D. Grepperud, A. Ive, and S. Johnson, 1985, Morphology and hydraulics of an active phreatic conduit: British Cave Research Association Transactions, v. 12, no. 4, p. 139–146.

Lauritzen, S.-E., and A. Lauritsen, 1995, Differential diagnosis of paragenetic and vadose canyons: Cave and Karst Science, v. 21, no. 2, p. 55–59.

Lauritzen, S.-E., and J. Lundberg, 2000, Solutional and erosional morphology of caves, *in* A. Klimchouk, D. Ford, A. Palmer, and W. Dreybrodt (eds.), Speleogenesis: Evolution of karst aquifers: Huntsville, Ala., National Speleological Society, p. 408–426.

Lauritzen, S.-E., and J.E. Mylroie, 1996, Late Quaternary climatic history of the Helderberg Plateau, New York, U.S.A.: Preliminary results from U/Th dating of speleothems, *in* S.-E. Lauritzen (ed.), Climate change: The karst record: Charles Town, W.Va., Karst Waters Institute, Special Publication 2, p. 87–88.

Lauritzen, S.-E. & J.E. Mylroie, 2000, Results of a speleothem U/Th dating reconnaissance from the Helderberg Plateau, New York: Journal of Cave and Karst Studies, v. 62, no. 1, p. 20–26.

Lauritzen, S.-E., and B.-P. Onac, 1995, Uranium series dating of some speleothems from Romania: Theoretical and Applied Karstology, v. 8, p. 25–36.

Lazcano Sahagun, C., 2001, Naica's subterranean marvels: National Speleo-logical Society, NSS News, v. 59, no. 6, p. 166–169.

Leél-Össy, S., 2003, Effects of anthropogeneous activities on cave exploration in the Buda Mountains: Proceedings of workshop on Soil Effect on Karst Processes (2002), Budapest-Aggtelek, Hungary, p. 127–141.

Lehmann, E.L., 1997, Testing statistical hypotheses (2nd ed.): Berlin, Springer, 600 p.

Lehmann, H. (ed.), 1954, Das Karstphänomen in den verschiedenen Klimazonen [*Karst phenomena in various climatic zones*]: Erdkunde, v. 8, p. 112–139.

Lehmann, O., 1932, Die Hydrographie der Karstes [*Karst hydrology*]: Leipzig, Enzyklopädie der Erdkunde, v. 6, 212 p.

Lindsay, R.F., 1998, Meteoric recharge, displacement of oil columns, and the development of residual oil intervals in the Permian Basin, *in* W.D. DeMis and M.K. Nelis (eds.), The search continues into the 21st century: West Texas Geological Society, Publication 98-105, p. 271–273.

Lismonde, B. (ed.), 1997, La Dent de Crolles et son réseau souterrain [*The Dent de Crolles and its cave system*]: Grenoble, France, Comité Départemental de Spéléologie de l'Isère, 303 p.

Lismonde, B., 2000, Corrosion des cupoles de plafond par les fluctuations de pression de l'air emprisoné [*Dissolution of ceiling cupolas by pressure fluctuations in trapped air*]: Karstologia, v. 35, p. 39–46.

Liu, Z., and W. Dreybrodt, 1997, Dissolution kinetics of calcium carbonate minerals in H_2O-CO_2 solutions in turbulent flow: The role of the diffusion boundary layer and the slow reaction $H_2O + CO_2 <=> H^+ + HCO_3^-$: Geochimica et Cosmochimica Acta, v. 61, p. 2879–2889.

Liu Z. and W. Dreybrodt, 2001, Kinetics and rate-limiting mechanisms of dolomite dissolution at various CO_2 partial pressures: Science in China (Series B), v. 44, no. 5, p. 500–509.

Lively, R.S., and B. Krafthefer, 1994, Radon concentrations, radon decay product activity, meteorological conditions and ventilation in Mystery Cave: Unpublished report, Mystery Cave Resources Evaluation for Minnesota Department of Natural Resources, 39 p.

Lobeck, A.K., 1928, The geology and physiography of the Mammoth Cave National Park: Kentucky Geological Survey, Series 6, v. 31, p. 325–399.

Lohmann, K.C., 1988, Geochemical patterns of meteoric diagenetic systems and their application to studies of paleokarst, *in* N. James and P. Choquette (eds.), Paleokarst: New York, Springer-Verlag, p. 58–80.

Loop, C.M., 2005, Contamination of cave waters by nonaqueous phase liquids, *in* Culver, D.C., and W.B. White (eds.), Encyclopedia of caves: San Diego, Elsevier / Academic Press, p. 131–137.

Loucks, R.G., 1999, Paleocave carbonate reservoirs: Origins, burial-depth modifications, spatial complexity, and reservoir implications: American Association of Petroleum Geologists Bulletin, v. 83, no. 11, p. 1795–1834.

Loucks, R.G., 2007, A review of coalesced, collapsed-paleocave systems and associated suprastratal deformation: Acta Carsologica, v. 36, no. 1, p. 121–132.

Loucks, R.G., and J.H. Anderson, 1985, Depositional facies, diagenetic terranes, and porosity development in Lower Ordovician Ellenburger Dolomite, Puckett Field, west Texas *in* P.O. Roehl and P.W. Choquette (eds.), Carbonate petroleum reservoirs: New York, Springer-Verlag, p. 20–37.

Loucks, R.G., and C.R. Handford, 1992, Origin and recognition of fractures, breccias, and sediment fills in paleocave-reservoir networks, *in* M.P. Candelaria and C.L. Reed (eds.), Paleokarst, karst-related diagenesis, and reservoir development: Examples from Ordovician-Devonian age strata of west Texas and the mid-continent: Permian Basin Section, Society of Economic Paleontologists and Mineralogists, Publication 92-33, p. 31–44.

Lowe, D.J., 1992, The origin of limestone caverns: An inception horizon hypothesis: Ph.D. thesis, Manchester Polytechnic University, Manchester, U.K., 512 p.

Lowe, D.J., 2000, Development of speleogenetic ideas in the 20th century: The early modern approach, *in* A. Klimchouk, D.C. Ford, A.N. Palmer, and W. Dreybrodt (eds.), Speleogenesis: Evolution of karst aquifers: Huntsville, Ala., National Speleological Society, p. 30–38.

Lowe, D.J., and J. Gunn, 1997, Carbonate speleogenesis: An inception horizon hypothesis: Acta Carsologica, v. 26, no. 2, p. 457–488.

Lowe, D.J., and T. Waltham, 1995, A dictionary of karst and caves: A brief guide to the terminology and concepts of cave and karst science: London, British Cave Research Association, Cave Studies Series, no. 6, 40 p.

Lowry, D.C., and J.N. Jennings, 1974, The Nullarbor karst, Australia: Zeitschrift für Geomorphologie, v. 18, p. 35–81.

Ludwig, K., 1977, Effect of initial radioactive-daughter disequilibrium on U-Pb isotope apparent ages of young minerals: Journal of Research of the United States Geological Survey, v. 5, p. 663–667.

Luetscher, M., 2005, Processes in Ice Caves and their Significance for Paleoenvironmental Reconstructions: Swiss Institute for Speleology and Karst Studies, La Chaux-de-Fonds, Switzerland, 154 p.

Luiszer, F.G., 1994, Speleogenesis of Cave of the Winds, Manitou Springs, Colorado, in I.D. Sasowsky, and M.V. Palmer, (eds.), Breakthroughs in karst geomicrobiology and redox geochemistry: Charles Town, W. Va., Karst Waters Institute, Special Publication 1, p. 91–109.

Luiszer, F.G., and M. Frazier, 1997, Hurricane Cave geology: National Speleological Society, National Speleological Society News, v. 55, no. 1, p. 9.

Lundberg, J., 2005, Karren, in D. Culver and W. White (eds.), Encyclopedia of caves: San Diego, Elsevier / Academic Press, p. 315–321.

Lundberg, J., D.C. Ford, and C.A. Hill, 2000, A preliminary U-Pb date on cave spar, Big Canyon, Guadalupe Mountains, New Mexico, USA: Journal of Cave and Karst Studies, v. 62, no. 2, p. 144–146.

Lundberg, J., and D.A. McFarlane, 2006, Speleogenesis of the Mount Elgon elephant caves,, in R.S. Harmon and C.M. Wicks (eds.), Perspectives on karst geomorphology, hydrology, and geochemistry — A tribute volume to Derek C. Ford and William B. White: Geological Society of America, Special Paper 404, p. 51–64.

Lundegard, P., and L. Land, 1986, Carbon dioxide and organic acids: Their role in porosity enhancement and cementation, Paleogene of the Texas Gulf coast, in D.L. Gautier (ed.), Roles of organic matter in sediment diagenesis: Society of Economic Paleontologists and Mineralogists, Special Publication 38, p. 129–146.

Lundquist, C.A., and W.W. Varnedoe, 1991, Mud flow in a karst setting, in E.H. Kastning and K.M. Kastning (eds.), Appalachian karst: Huntsville, Ala., National Speleological Society, Proceedings of Appalachian Karst Symposium, Radford, Va., p. 45–50.

Lundquist, C.A., and W.W. Varnedoe, 2006, Salt ingestion caves: International Journal of Speleology, v. 35, no. 1, p. 13–18.

MacGowan, D.B., Z. Jiao, R. Surdam, and F. Miknis, 1994, Formation water chemistry of the Muddy Sandstone and organic geochemistry of the Mowry Shale, Powder River Basin, Wyoming: Evidence for mechanism of pressure compartment formation, in P.J. Ortoleva (ed.), Basin compartments and seals: American Association of Petroleum Geologists, Memoir 61, p. 321–331.

Machel, H.G., 2001, Bacterial and thermochemical sulfate reduction in diagenetic settings — old and new insights: Sedimentary Geology, v. 140, p. 143–175.

Maire, R., 1990, La haute montagne calcaire [Carbonate mountain regions]: La Ravoire, France, Editions GAP, Karstologia Mémoires no. 3, 731 p.

Maire, R., J.-P. Barbary, Zhang S., N. Vanara, and J. Bottazzi (eds.), 2004, Spéléo-karstologie et environnement en Chine (Guizhou, Yunnan, Liaoning) [Studies of caves, karst, and their environment in Guizhou, Yunnan, and Liaoning Provinces, China]: Karstologia Mémoires 9, 562 p.

Malott, C.A., 1922, A subterranean cut-off and other subterranean phenomena along Indian Creek, Lawrence County, Indiana: Proceedings of Indiana Academy of Science, v. 31, p. 203–210.

Malott, C.A., 1937, The invasion theory of cavern development [abstract]: Geological Society of America Proceedings, p. 323.

Malott, C.A., 1949, Hudelson Cavern, a storm-water route of underground Lost River, Orange County, Indiana: Proceedings of Indiana Academy of Science, v. 58, p. 236–243.

Maltsev, V.A., 1997, Speleothems of aerosol origin: Discussion: Journal of Cave and Karst Studies, v. 59, no. 1, p.43–44.

Maltsev, V.A., V.A. Korshunov, and A.A. Semikolennykh, 1997, Cave chemolithotrophic soils: Proceedings of 12th International Congress of Speleology, La Chaux-de-Fonds, Switzerland, p. 29–32.

Maltsev, V., and V. Korshunov, 1998, Geochemistry of fluorite and related features of the Kugitangtau Ridge caves, Turkmenistan: Journal of Cave and Karst Studies, v. 60, no. 3, p. 151–155.

Manga, M., and G. Ventura (eds.), 2005, Kinematics and dynamics of lava flows: Geological Society of America, Special Paper 396, 218 p.

Mangin, A., 1975, Contribution à l'étude hydrodynamique des aquifères karstiques [Contributions to the study of karst aquifer hydrodynamics]: Annales de Spéléologie, v. 29, p. 283–332, 495–601; v. 30, p. 21–124.

Marbach, G., and B. Tourte, 2002, Alpine caving techniques: Allschwil, Switzerland, Speleo Projects, 320 p. (English translation by M. Alspaugh.)

Martel, E.A., 1894, Les Abîmes [The depths]: Paris, Delagrave, 578 p.

Martel, E. A., 1921, Nouveau traité des eaux souterraines [A new treatise on groundwater]: Paris, Librairie Octave Doin, 838 p.

Martin, J.B., C.M. Wicks, and I.D. Sasowsky (eds.), 2002, Hydrogeology and biology of post-Paleozoic carbonate aquifers: Charles Town, W. Va., Karst Waters Institute, Special Publication 7, 232 p.

Martini, J., 1981, Early Proterozoic paleokarst of the Transvaal, South Africa: Proceedings of 8th International Speleological Congress, Bowling Green, Ky., Part 1, p. 4–5.

Martini, J., 1986, The trays: An example of evaporation-controlled speleothems: South African Speleological Association Bulletin, v. 27, no. 1, p. 46–51.

Martini, J., 2000, Dissolution of quartz and silicate minerals, in A. Klimchouk, D.C. Ford, A.N. Palmer, and W. Dreybrodt (eds.), Speleogenesis: Evolution of karst aquifers: Huntsville, Ala., National Speleological Society, p. 171–174.

Martini, J., and H. Moen, 1998, Blue Lagoon, Afrique du Sud, une grotte à remplissage paléokarstique permien et à concrétions d'aragonite [Blue Lagoon, South Africa, a cave with Permian paleokarst fill and aragonite speleothems]: Karstologia, v. 32, p. 27–38.

Maslin, M., X. Li, M.-F. Loutre, and A. Berger, 1998, The contribution of orbital forcing to the progressive intensification of northern hemisphere glaciation: Quaternary Science Reviews, v. 17, p. 411–426.

Maslyn, R.M., 1979, Cavern development via H2S dissolved in hot spring and natural gas field waters [abstract]: National Speleological Society Bulletin, v. 41, no. 4, p. 115.

Massen, F. (ed.), 1997, The Moestroff Cave: A study on the geology and climate of Luxembourg's largest maze cave: Centre de Recherche Public, Centre Universitaire, Luxemburg, 199 p.

Matchus, E.J., and T.S. Jones, 1984, East to west cross section through the Permian Basin, west Texas: West Texas Geological Society, Special Publication 84-79, one sheet.

Matson, G.C., 1909, Water resources in the Blue Grass Region, Kentucky: U.S. Geological Survey, Water-Supply Paper 233, p. 42–45.

Mazzullo, S.J., and P.M. Harris, 1991, An overview of dissolution porosity development in the deep-burial environment, with examples from carbonate reservoirs in the Permian Basin, in M.P. Candelaria (ed.), Permian Basin plays — tomorrow's technology today: Society of Economic Paleontologists and Mineralogists, West Texas Geological Society Symposium Publication no. 91-89, p. 125–138.

McClurg, D., 1996, Adventure of caving (2nd ed.): Carlsbad, New Mexico, D&J Press, 251p.

McFarlane, D.A., J. Lundberg, and F. Belton, 2004, An unusual lava cave from Ol Doinyo Lengai, Tanzania: Journal of Cave and Karst Studies, v. 66, no. 3, p. 98–101.

McLean, J., and B. Luke, 2006, Electrical resistivity surveys of karst features near Fort Stanton, Lincoln County, New Mexico: New Mexico Geological Society, Guidebook to 57th Annual Field Conference, p. 227–232.

Medville, D.M., 2001, The exploration and survey of Surprise Cave: National Speleological Society, National Speleological Society News, v. 59, no. 10, p. 288–289.

Medville, D.M., 2006, The Beall Caves: Hawai'i Speleological Society Newsletter, National Speleological Society, no. 19, p. 7–9.

Medville, D.M., and W.K. Storage, 1986, Structural and stratigraphic influences on the development of solution conduits in the upper Elk Creek River valley, West Virginia: National Speleological Society Bulletin, v. 48, no. 1, p. 8–25.

Meiman, J., and M.T. Ryan, 1999, The development of basin-scale conceptual models of the active-flow conduit system, *in* A.N. Palmer, M.V. Palmer, and I.D. Sasowsky (eds.), Karst modeling: Charles Town, W. Va., Karst Waters Institute, Special Publication 5, p. 203–212.

Meinzer, O.E., 1923, Outline of ground-water hydrology, with definitions: U.S. Geological Survey Water-Supply Paper 494, p. 1–71.

Menichetti, M., 1992, Grotta di Monte Cucco [hydrologic maps of the Monte Cucco Caves, Italy]: Costacciaro, Italy, Catasto Speleologico dell'Umbria, single large sheet.

Merriam, P., 1950, Ice caves: National Speleological Society, Bulletin 12, p. 32–37.

Meshri, I.D., 1986, On the reactivity of carbonic and organic acids and generation of secondary porosity, *in* D.L. Gautier (ed.), Roles of organic matter in sediment diagenesis: Society of Economic Paleontologists and Mineralogists, Special Publication 38, p. 123–128.

Michie, N.A., 1997, The threat to caves of the human dust source: Proceedings of 12th International Congress of Speleology, La Chaux-de-Fonds, Switzerland, v. 5, p 43–46.

Middleton, J., and T. Waltham, 1986, The underground atlas: A gazetteer of the world's cave regions: New York, St. Martin's Press, 239 p.

Milanović, P.T., 1981, Karst hydrogeology: Littleton, Colorado, Water Resources Publications, 434 p.

Milanović, P.T., 2000, Geological engineering in karst: Belgrade, Zebra, 350 p.

Milanović, P.T., 2004, Water resources engineering in karst: Boca Raton, Florida, CRC Press, 312 p.

Miller, T.E., 1990, Bellholes: Biogenic (bat) erosion features in tropical caves: GEO^2, National Speleological Society, Section on Cave Geology and Geography, v. 17, no. 2, p. 3.

Miller, T.E., 1996, Geologic and hydrologic controls on karst and cave development in Belize: Journal of Cave and Karst Studies, v. 58, no. 2, p. 100–120.

Miller, T.E., 2006, Integration of a large tropical cave network in brecciated limestone, *in* R.S. Harmon and C.M. Wicks (eds.), Perspectives on karst geomorphology, hydrology, and geochemistry—A tribute volume to Derek C. Ford and William B. White: Geological Society of America, Special Paper 404, p. 91–103.

Milske, J.A., E.C. Alexander, and R.S. Lively, 1983, Clastic sediments in Mystery Cave, southeastern Minnesota: National Speleological Society Bulletin, v. 45, no. 3, p. 55–75.

Minton, M., 2004, 1000-meter deep caves and world records: National Speleological Society, National Speleological Society News, v. 62, no. 12, p. 340–341.

Miotke, F.-D., and A.N. Palmer, 1972, Genetic relationship between caves and landforms in the Mammoth Cave National Park area: Würtzburg, Germany, Böhler Verlag, 69 p.

Mixon, W., 1966, Locating an underground transmitter by surface measurements: National Speleological Society, National Speleological Society News, v. 24, no. 4, p. 61, 74–75.

Mocochain, L., G. Clauzon, and J.-Y. Bigot, 2006, Réponses de l'endokarst ardéchois aux variations eustatiques générées par la cris de salinity messinienne [*Response of the Ardèche endokarst to eustatic variations generated by the Messinnian salinity crisis*]: Bulletin de la Societé Géologique de France, v. 177, no. 1, p. 27–36.

Moneymaker, B.C., 1941, Subriver solution cavities in the Tennessee Valley: Journal of Geology, v. 49, p. 74–86.

Monroe, W.H., 1968, The karst features of northern Puerto Rico: National Speleological Society Bulletin, v. 30, no. 3, p. 75–86.

Moore, C.H., 1989, Carbonate Diagenesis and porosity: Amsterdam, Netherlands, Elsevier, Developments in Sedimentology 46, 338 p.

Moore, G.W., 1952, Speleothem — a new cave term: National Speleological Society, NSS News, v. 10, no. 6, p. 2.

Moore, G.W., 1958, Role of earth tides in the formation of disc-shaped cave deposits: Proceedings of 2nd International Congress of Speleology, Bari, Italy, v. 1, p. 500–506.

Moore, G.W. (ed.), 1960, Origin of limestone caves: Bulletin of the National Speleological Society, v. 22, no.1, 84 p.

Moore, G.W., 1981, Manganese speleothems: Proceedings of 8th International Congress of Speleology, Bowling Green, Ky., p. 642–644.

Moore, G.W., and G.N. Sullivan, 1997, Speleology: Caves and the cave environment: St. Louis, Cave Books, 176 p.

Morehouse, D.F., 1968, Cave development via the sulfuric acid reaction: National Speleological Society Bulletin, v. 30, no. 1, p. 1–10.

Morrison, R.D., and B.L. Murphy, 2005, Environmental forensics: Contaminant specific guide: Burlington, Mass., Academic Press, 576 p.

Morse, J.W., 1978, Dissolution kinetics of calcium carbonate in sea water; VI. the near-equilibrium dissolution kinetics of calcium carbonate-rich deep sea sediments: American Journal of Science, v. 278, p. 344–353.

Morse, J.W., Q. Wang, and M.Y. Tsio, 1997, Influences of temperature and Mg:Ca ratio on $CaCO_3$ precipitates from seawater: Geology, v. 25, p. 85–97.

Moskal, E., A. Palmer, and T. Kraemer, 2005, Use of radium isotopes and water chemistry to determine patterns of groundwater recharge to Otsego Lake, Otsego County, NY [abstract]: Geological Society of America, Northeastern Section, annual meeting, abstracts with programs, v. 37, no. 1, p. 69.

Motycka, J., and M. Szuwarzynski, 1989, Growth of speleothems below the karst water table: Considerations on the genesis of sulfide stalactites from the Upper Silesian Zn-Pb ore bodies: Annals of the Geological Society of Poland, v. 59, p. 417–435.

Müller, P., 1974, A melegforrás-barlangok és a gömbfülkék kelet-kezéséről [*Origin of hydrothermal caves and cupolas*]: Karszt és Barlang, Hungarian Speleological Society Bulletin, v. 1, p. 7–10.

Müller, P., and I. Sárváry, 1977, Some aspects of developments in Hungarian speleology theories during the last 10 years: Karszt és Barlang, Hungarian Speleological Society Bulletin, Special issue, p. 53–60.

Murphy, P.J., A. Parr, K. Strange, G. Hunter, S. Allshorn, R. Halliwell, J. Helm, and R. Westerman, 2005, Investigating the nature and origins of Gaping Gill Main Chamber, North Yorkshire, UK, using ground penetrating radar and lidar: Cave and Karst Science, v. 32, no. 1, p. 25–38.

Mylroie, J.E., 1977, Speleogenesis and karst geomorphology of the Helderberg Plateau, Schoharie County, New York: New York Cave Survey, Bulletin 2, 336 p.

Mylroie, J.E., and J.L. Carew, 1987, Field evidence of the minimum time for speleogenesis: National Speleological Society Bulletin, v. 49, no. 2, p. 67–72.

Mylroie, J. E., and J.L. Carew, 1990, The flank margin model for dissolution cave development in carbonate platforms: Earth Surface Processes and Landforms, v. 15, p. 413–424.

Mylroie, J.E., and J.L. Carew, 1995, Karst development on carbonate islands, *in* D.A. Budd, A.H. Saller, and P. Harris (eds.), Unconformities and porosity in carbonate strata: American Association of Petroleum Geologists Memoir 63, p. 55–76.

Mylroie, J.E., and M. Dyas, 1985, Western Kentucky region, *in* P.H. Dougherty (ed.), Caves and karst of Kentucky: Kentucky Geological Survey, Special Publication 12, Series XI, p. 119–145.

Mylroie, J.E., J.W. Jenson, D. Taborosi, J.M.U. Jocson, D.T. Vann, C. and Wexel, 2001, Karst features of Guam in terms of a general model of carbonate island karst: Journal of Cave and Karst Studies, v. 63, p. 9–22.

Mylroie, J.E., and J.R. Mylroie, 2004, Glaciated karst: How the Helderberg Plateau revised the geologic perception: Northeastern Geology and Environmental Sciences, v. 26, nos. 1–2, p. 82–92.

Mylroie, J.E., and H.L. Vacher, 1999, A conceptual view of carbonate island karst, *in* A.N. Palmer, M.V. Palmer, and I.D. Sasowsky (eds.), Karst modeling: Charles Town, W. Va., Karst Waters Institute, Special Publication 5, p. 48–57.

Navas, A., 1990, The effect of hydrochemical factors on the dissolution rate of gypsiferous rocks in flowing water: Earth Surface Processes and landforms, v. 15, p. 709–715.

Neuendorf, K., J. Mehl, and J. Jackson, 2005, Glossary of geology (5th ed.): Alexandria, Va., American Geological Institute, 779 p.

Newell, D., L. Crossey, K. Karlstrom, T. Fischer, and D. Hilton, 2005, Continental-scale links between the mantle and groundwater systems of the western United States: Evidence from travertine springs and regional He isotope data: Geological Society of America, GSA Today, v. 15, no. 12, p. 4–10.

Newson, M.D., 1971, The role of abrasion in cavern development: Cave Research Group of Great Britain, Transactions, v. 13, p. 101–107.

Neill, R.H., J.K. Channell, L. Chaturvedi, M.S. Little, K. Rehfeldt, and P. Spiegler, 1983, Evaluation of the suitability of the WIPP site: Environmental Evaluation Group, Albuquerque, NM, Publication EEG-23, 157 p.

Northup, D.E., S. Barns, L. Yu, M. Spilde, R. Schelble, K. Dano, L. Crossey, C. Connolly, P. Boston, D. Natvig, and C. Dahm, 2003, Diverse microbial communities inhabiting ferromanganese deposits in Lechuguilla and Spider Caves: Environmental Microbiology, v. 5, no. 11, p. 1071–1086.

Northup, D.E., C. Dahm, L. Melim, M. Spilde, L. Crossey, K. Lavoie, L. Mallory, P. Boston, K. Cunningham, and S. Barns, 2000, Evidence for geomicrobiological interactions in Guadalupe caves: Journal of Cave and Karst Studies, v. 62, p. 149–160.

Northup, D.E., and K.H. Lavoie, 2001, Geomicrobiology of caves: a review: Geomicrobiology Journal, v. 18, p. 199–222.

Northup, D.E., E. D. Mobley, K.L. Ingham, and W.W. Mixon (eds.), 1998, A guide to the speleological literature of the English language, 1794–1996: St. Louis, Cave Books, 539 p.

Ogden, A.E., 1974, The relationship of cave passages to lineaments and stratigraphic strike in central Monroe County, West Virginia: Proceedings of 4th Conference on Karst Geology and Hydrology, Morgantown, W. Va., West Virginia Geological and Economic Survey, p. 29–32.

Ogden, A.E., 2003, The perched water table cave origin theory as applied to the Central Basin, Highland Rim, and Cumberland Plateau escarpment: National Speleological Society, Southeast Regional Association, Guidebook to 2003 SERA convention, p. 10–18, 56.

Ogden, A.E., and R.K. Redman, 1993, Methods for predicting the directions of contaminant transport in flat-lying and folded carbonate rocks, *in* B.F. Beck, Applied karst geology: Proceedings of 4th Conference on Engineering and Environmental Impacts of Karst, Lisse, Netherlands, A.A. Balkema, p. 175–179.

Ogden, A.E., A.T. Scott, S. Jacks, S. Barksdale, L. Bean, M. Alverson, and L. Thomas, 1998, Delineation of ground water spring basins in Rutherford County, Tennessee; a first step in understanding sinkhole flooding: Nashville, Proceedings of 8th Annual Tennessee Water Resources Symposium, v. 8, p. 2B.7–2B.17.

Ohle, E.R., 1985, Breccias in Mississippi Valley-type deposits: Economic Geology, v. 80, p. 1736–1752.

Olson, R.A., 1984, Genesis of paleokarst and strata-bound zinc-lead sulfide deposits in a Proterozoic dolostone, northern Baffin Island, Canada: Economic Geology, v. 79, p. 1056–1103.

Olson, R.A., and D.B. Thompson, 1988, Scanning electron microscopy and energy dispersive X-ray analysis of artificial and natural substrates from the Phantom flowstone of Sulphur river in Parker Cave, Kentucky: National Speleological Society Bulletin, v. 50, no. 2, p. 47–53.

Onac, B.P., 2000, Geologia regiunilor carstice [*Geology of karst terrains*]: Bucharest, Romania, Editura Didactică și Pedagogică, 399 p. (Includes extensive summaries in English.)

Onac, B.P., and L. Ghergari, 1993, Moonmilk mineralogy in some Romanian and Norwegian caves: Cave Science, v. 20, no. 3, p. 107–111.

Onac, B.P., J.E. Mylroie, E. White, and W.B. White, 2001, Mineralogy of cave deposits on San Salvador Island, Bahamas: Carbonates and Evaporites, v. 16, no. 1, p. 8–16.

Onac, B., T. Tamas, S. Constantin, and A. Persolu, 2006, Climate Change: The Karst Record IV: Charles Town, W.Va., Karst Waters Institute, Special Publication 10, 249 p.

Orndorff, R.C., D.J. Weary, and R.W. Harrison, 2006, The role of sandstone in the development of an Ozark karst system, south-central Missouri, *in* R.S. Harmon and C.M. Wicks (eds.), Perspectives on karst geomorphology, hydrology, and geochemistry — A tribute volume to Derek C. Ford and William B. White: Geological Society of America, Special Paper 404, p. 31–38.

Osborne, R.A.L., 1984, Lateral facies changes, unconformities, and stratigraphic reversals: Their significance for cave sediment stratigraphy: Cave Science, v. 11, no. 3, p. 175–184.

Osborne, R.A.L., 2001, Halls and narrows: Network caves in dipping limestones, examples from eastern Australia: Cave and Karst Science, v. 28, no. 1, p. 3–14.

Osborne, R.A.L., 2002, Cave breakdown by vadose weathering: International Journal of Speleology, v. 31 (1/4), p. 37–53.

Osborne, R.A.L., 2005a, Dating ancient caves and related paleokarsts: Acta Carsologica, v. 34, no. 1, p. 51–72.

Osborne, R. A. L., 2005b, Partitions, compartments and portals: Cave development in internally impounded karst masses: International Journal of Speleology, v. 34, no. 1–2, p. 71–81.

Osborne, R.A.L., H. Zwingmann, R.E. Pogson, and D.M. Colchester, 2006, Carboniferous clay deposits from Jenolan Caves, New South Wales: Implications for timing of speleogenesis and regional geology: Australian Journal of Earth Science, v. 53, p. 377–406.

Padgett, A., and B. Smith, 1987, On Rope: Huntsville, Ala., National Speleological Society, 341 p.

Padilla, A., A. Pulido-Bosch, and A. Mangin, 1994, Relative importance of baseflow and quickflow from hydrographs of karst springs: Ground Water, v. 32, no. 2, p. 267–277.

Palmer, A.N., 1969, A hydrologic study of the Indiana karst: Ph.D. thesis, Indiana University, Bloomington, Ind., 181 p.

Palmer, A.N., 1972, Dynamics of a sinking stream system: Onesquethaw Cave, New York: National Speleological Society Bulletin, v. 34, no 3., p. 89–110.

Palmer, A.N., 1974, Geologic influence upon cave-passage orientation in Ludington Cave, Greenbrier County, West Virginia: Proceedings of 4th Conference on Karst Geology and Hydrology, Morgantown, W. Va., West Virginia Geological and Economic Survey, p. 33–40.

Palmer, A.N., 1975, The origin of maze caves: National Speleological Society Bulletin, v. 37, no. 3, p. 56–76.

Palmer, A.N., 1977, Influence of geologic structure on groundwater flow and cave development in Mammoth Cave National Park, Kentucky, U.S.A.: International Association of Hydrogeologists, 12th Memoirs, p. 405–414.

Palmer, A.N., 1981a, A geological guide to Mammoth Cave National Park: Teaneck, N.J., Zephyrus Press, 210 p.

Palmer, A.N., 1981b, Hydrochemical controls in the origin of limestone caves: Proceedings of 8th International Congress of Speleology, Bowling Green, Kentucky, p. 120–122.

Palmer, A.N., 1981c, The geology of Wind Cave: Hot Springs, S.D., Wind Cave Natural History Association, 44 p.

Palmer, A.N., 1984a, Recent trends in karst geomorphology: Journal of Geological Education, v. 32, p. 247–253.

Palmer, A.N., 1984b, Geomorphic interpretation of karst features, *in* R.G. LaFleur, Groundwater as a geomorphic agent: Boston, Massachusetts, Allen and Unwin, p. 173–209.

Palmer, A.N., 1986, Prediction of contaminant paths in karst aquifers: Proceedings of First Conference on Environmental Problems in Karst Terranes and Their Solutions, Dublin, Ohio, National Water Well Association, p. 32–53.

Palmer, A.N., 1987, Cave levels and their interpretation: National Speleological Society Bulletin, v. 49, no. 2, p. 50–66.

Palmer, A.N., 1988, Solutional enlargement of openings in the vicinity of hydraulic structures in karst regions: Dublin, Ohio, Proceedings of 2nd Conference on Environmental Problems in Karst Terranes, Association of Ground Water Scientists and Engineers, p. 3–13.

Palmer, A.N., 1989a, Stratigraphic and structural control of cave development and groundwater flow in the Mammoth Cave region, *in* W. White and E. White (eds.), Karst Hydrology: Concepts from the Mammoth Cave area: New York, Van Nostrand Reinhold, p. 293–316.

Palmer, A.N., 1989b, Geomorphic history of the Mammoth Cave System, *in* W.B. White and E.L. White (eds.), Karst Hydrology: Concepts from the Mammoth Cave area: New York, Van Nostrand Reinhold, p. 317–363.

Palmer, A.N., 1991, Origin and morphology of limestone caves: Geological Society of America Bulletin, v. 103, no. 1, p. 1–21.

Palmer, A.N., 1996, Rates of limestone dissolution and calcite precipitation in cave streams of east-central New York State [abstract]: Northeast Section, Geological Society of America, v. 28, no. 3, p. 89.

Palmer, A.N., 1999, A statistical evaluation of the structural influence on solution-conduit patterns, *in* A.N. Palmer, M.V. Palmer, and I.D. Sasowsky (eds.), Karst Modeling: Charles Town, W.Va., Karst Waters Institute Special Publication 5, p. 187–195.

Palmer, A.N., 2000a, Digital modeling of individual solution conduits, *in* A. Klimchouk, D. Ford, A.Palmer, and W. Dreybrodt (eds.), Speleogenesis: Evolution of karst aquifers: Huntsville, Ala., National Speleological Society, p. 194–200.

Palmer, A.N., 2000b, Maze origin by diffuse recharge through overlying formations, *in* A. Klimchouk, D. Ford, A. Palmer, and W. Dreybrodt (eds.), Speleogenesis: Evolution of karst aquifers: Huntsville, Ala., National Speleological Society, p. 387–390.

Palmer, A.N., 2001, Dynamics of cave development by allogenic water: Acta Carsologica, v. 31, no. 2, p. 13–32.

Palmer, A.N., 2002, Speleogenesis in carbonate rocks, in F. Gabrovšek, Evolution of karst from prekarst to cessation: Karst Research Institute, Postojna, Slovenia, p. 43–59.

Palmer, A.N., 2006, Digital modeling of karst aquifers — Successes, failures, and promises, *in* R.S. Harmon and C.M. Wicks (eds.), Perspectives on karst geomorphology, hydrology, and geochemistry — A tribute volume to Derek C. Ford and William B. White: Geological Society of America, Special Paper 404, p. 243–250.

Palmer, A.N., 2007, Variation in rates of karst processes: Acta Carsologica, v. 36, no. 1, p. 15–24.

Palmer, A.N., and M.V. Palmer, 1989, Geologic history of the Black Hills caves, South Dakota: National Speleological Society Bulletin, v. 51, no. 2, p. 72–99.

Palmer, A.N., and M.V. Palmer, 1995a, The Kaskaskia paleokarst of the Northern Rocky Mountains and Black Hills, northwestern U.S.A.: Carbonates and Evaporites, v. 10, no. 2, p.148–160.

Palmer, A.N., and M.V. Palmer, 1995b, Geochemistry of capillary seepage in Mammoth Cave: Mammoth Cave National Park, 4th Science Conference, p. 119–133.

Palmer, A.N., and M.V. Palmer, 2000, Hydrochemical interpretation of cave patterns in the Guadalupe Mountains, New Mexico: Journal of Cave and Karst Studies, v. 62, no. 2, p. 91–108.

Palmer, A.N., and M.V. Palmer, 2004, Sulfate-carbonate interactions in the development of karst: Northeastern Geology and Environmental Sciences, v. 26, no. 1-2, p. 93-106.

Palmer, A.N., M.V. Palmer, and J.M. Queen, 1977, Geology and origin of the caves of Bermuda: Proceedings of 7th International Congress of Speleology, Sheffield, U.K., p. 336–339.

Palmer, A.N., M.V. Palmer, and I.D. Sasowsky (eds.), 1999, Karst modeling: Charles Town, W. Va., Karst Waters Institute, Special Publication 5, 265 p.

Palmer, M.V., 1976, Ground-water flow patterns in limestone solution conduits: M.A. thesis, State University of New York, Oneonta, N.Y., 150 p.

Palmer, M.V., and A.N. Palmer, 1975, Landform development in the Mitchell Plain of southern Indiana: Origin of a partially karsted plain: Zeitschrift für Geomorphologie, v. 19, p. 1–39.

Palmer, M.V., and A.N. Palmer, 1989, Paleokarst of the U.S.A., *in* P. Bosák, D. Ford, J. Glazek, and I. Horáček (eds.), Paleokarst: Prague and Amsterdam, Academia and Elsevier, p. 337–363.

Parizek, R.R., 1976, On the nature and significance of fracture traces and lineaments in carbonate and other terranes, *in* V. Yevjevich (ed.), Karst hydrology and water resources: Fort Collins, Colo., Water Resources Publications, p. 47–108.

Pashenko, S.E., and Y.V. Dublyansky, 1997, Generation of cave aerosols by alpha particles: Critical evaluation of the hypothesis: Journal of Cave and Karst Studies, v. 59, no. 3, p. 103–105.

Passerby, M., 2005, Illustrated Walls: Descent (U.K.), v. 183, p. 26–27.

Peachey, W.D., 1993, Cave development in the structural domain of a metamorphic core complex: Arkenstone Cave, Pima County, Arizona: Midland, Texas, National Speleological Society, Southwestern Regional Organization, proceedings of winter regional meeting, 2 p.

Pease, B., 1997, Determining depth by radiolocation: An extreme case: Cave Radio and Electronics Group Journal, v. 27, p. 22–25.

Pease, P.P., B. Gomez, and V.A. Schmidt, 1994, Magnetostratigraphy of cave sediments, Wyandotte Ridge, Crawford County, Indiana: Towards a regional correlation: Geomorphology, v. 11, p. 75–81.

Peck, S.B., 1986, Bacterial deposition of iron and manganese oxides in North American caves: National Speleological Society Bulletin, v. 48, no. 1, p. 26–30.

Perrone, M.L., 2005, Experimental determination of the biogenicity of moonmilk, and the characterization of moonmilk and its depositional environment in Spider Cave, Carlsbad Caverns National Park, New Mexico: M.S. thesis, New Mexico State Univ., Las Cruces, 193 p.

Peterson, D.W., R.T. Holcomb, R.I. Tilling, and R.L. Christiansen, 1994, Development of lava tubes in the light of observations of Mauna Ulu, Kilauea Volcano, Hawaii: Bulletin of Volcanology, v. 56, p. 343–360.

Peterson, D.W., and B.A. Swanson, 1974, Observed formation of lava tubes during 1970–1971 at Kilauea Volcano, Hawaii: Studies in Speleology, v. 2, no. 6, p. 209–224.

Pezdič, J., F. Šušteršič, and M. Mišič, 1998, On the role of clay-carbonate reactions in speleo-inception: A contribution to the understanding of the earliest stage of karst channel formation: Acta Carsologica, v. 27, no. 12, p. 187–200.

Piccini, L., R. Drysdale, and H. Heijnis, 2003, Karst morphology and cave sediments as indicators of the uplift history in the Alpi Apuane (Tuscany, Italy): Quaternary International, v. 101–102, p. 219–227.

Pint, J., and S. Pint, 2005, The lava tubes of Harrat Kishb, Saudi Arabia [abstract]: National Speleological Society, 2005 Convention Program Guide, p. 98.

Piper, A.M., 1932, Ground water in north-central Tennessee: U.S. Geological Survey Water-Supply Paper 640, 238 p.

Pitty, A.F., 1966, An approach to the study of karst water: University of Hull, U.K., Occasional Papers in Geography, no. 5, 70 p.

Plummer, L.N., 1975, Mixing of sea water with calcium carbonate ground water: Geological Society of America Memoir 142, p. 219–236.

Plummer, L.N., and T.M.L. Wigley, 1976, The dissolution of calcite in CO_2-saturated solutions at 25°C and 1 atmosphere total pressure: Geochimica et Cosmochimica Acta, v. 40, p. 191–202.

Plummer, L.N., T.M.L. Wigley, and D.L. Parkhurst, 1978, The kinetics of calcite dissolution in CO_2-water systems at 5° to 60°C and 0.0 to 1.0 atm CO_2: American Journal of Science, v. 278, p. 179–216. Experimental data in National Auxiliary Publication Service Document 03209.

Pohl, E.R., and W.B. White, 1965, Sulfate minerals — their origin in the central Kentucky karst: American Mineralogist, v. 50, p. 1461–1465.

Polyak, V.J., and N. Güven, 1996, Alunite, natroalunite, and hydrated halloysite in Carlsbad Cavern and Lechuguilla Cave, New Mexico: Clays and Clay Minerals, v. 44, no. 6, p. 843–850.

Polyak, V.J., W.C. McIntosh, N. Güven, and P. Provencio, 1998, Age and origin of Carlsbad Cavern and related caves from $^{40}Ar/^{39}Ar$ of alunite: Science, v. 279, p. 1919–1922.

Polyak, V.J., and C.J. Mosch, 1995, Metatyuyamunite from Spider Cave, Carlsbad Caverns National Park, New Mexico: National Speleological Society Bulletin, v. 57, no. 2, p. 85–90.

Polyak, V.J., and P. Provencio, 2001, By-product materials related to H_2S-

H₂SO₄ influenced speleogenesis of Carlsbad, Lechuguilla, and other caves of the Guadalupe Mountains, New Mexico: Journal of Cave and Karst Studies, v. 63, no. 1, p. 23–32.

Polyak, V.J., and P. Provencio, 2005, Comet cones: A variety of cave cone from Fort Stanton Cave, New Mexico: Journal of Cave and Karst Studies, v. 67, no. 2, p. 125–126.

Porter, A., 2000, The initial exploration of Lower Laeʻapuki Cave System, Hawaiʻi Volcanoes National Park: National Speleological Society, National Speleological Society News, v. 58, no. 1, p. 10–17.

Porter Nuñez, R., 2002, The Cave of the Marbles: National Speleological Society, National Speleological Society News, v. 60, no. 4, p.100–103.

Powell, R.L., 1970, Base-level, lithologic, and climatic controls of karst groundwater zones in south-central Indiana: Proceedings of Indiana Academy of Science, v. 79, p. 281–291.

Powell, R.L., 1977, Lateral unloading of isotropic rock as a process of solution channel enlargement: International Association of Hydrogeologists, Memoirs, v. 12, p. 433–441.

Principi, P., 1931, Fenomeni di idrologia sotteranea nei dintorni a Triponzo [*Underground hydrologic phenomena in the vicinity of Trionzo (Umbria, Italy)*]: Le Grotte d'Italia, series 1, no. 5, p. 45–47; reprinted in Le Grotte d'Italia, series 5, no. 4, p. 3–5 (2003).

Prosser, J., and H.V. Gray (eds.), 1992, National Speleological Society cave diving manual: Branford, Florida, National Speleological Society, Cave Diving Section, 377 p.

Proudlove, G.S. (ed.), 2006, Essential sources in cave science: A guide to the literature of cave science: British Cave Research Association, Cave Studies Series 16, 56 p.

Pruitt, B., 1997, The Archer caves: National Speleological Society, National Speleological Society News, v. 55, no. 11, p.336–343.

Qing, H., and E.W. Mountjoy, 1994, Origin of dissolution vugs, caverns, and breccias in the Middle Devonian Presqu'ile Barrier, host of Pine Point Mississippi Valley-Type deposits: Economic Geology, v. 89, p. 858–876.

Queen, J.M., 1973, Large-scale replacement of carbonate by gypsum in some New Mexico caves [abstract]: National Speleological Society, abstracts of national convention, Bloomington, Indiana, p. 12.

Queen, J.M., 1994a, Speleogenesis in the Guadalupes: The unsettled question of the role of mixing, phreatic or vadose sulfide oxidation, *in* I.D. Sasowsky and M.V. Palmer (eds.), Breakthroughs in karst geomicrobiology and redox geochemistry: Charles Town, W. Va., Karst Waters Institute, Special Publication 1, p. 64–65.

Queen, J.M., 1994b, Influence of thermal atmospheric convection upon the nature and distribution of microbiota in cave environments, *in* I.D. Sasowsky and M.V. Palmer (eds.), Breakthroughs in karst geomicrobiology and redox geochemistry: Charles Town, W. Va., Karst Waters Institute, Special Publication 1, p. 62–63.

Queen, J.M., and L.A. Melim, 2006, Biothems: Biologically influenced speleothems in caves of the Guadalupe Mountains, New Mexico, USA: New Mexico Geological Society, Guidebook to 57th Annual Field Conference, p. 167–173.

Quinif, Y., 1989, Paleokarst of Belgium, *in* P. Bosák, D. Ford, J. Glazek, and I. Horáček (eds.), Paleokarst: Prague and Amsterdam, Academia and Elsevier, p. 35–50.

Quinif, Y., 1999, Fantômisation, cryptoaltération et altération sur roche nue, le triptyque de la karstification [*Phantomization, cryptoalteration, and alteration of bare bedrock, three-fold aspect of karstification*]: Études de géographie physique, supplement 28, p. 159–164.

Quinlan, J.F., 1974, Origin, distribution, and detection of development of two types of sinkholes in an anthropogenic karst, South Africa [abstract]: Proceedings of 4th Conference on Karst Geology and Hydrology, Morgantown, W. Va., West Virginia Geological and Economic Survey, p. 161.

Quinlan, J.F., and E.C. Alexander, 1987, How often should samples be taken at relevant locations for reliable monitoring of pollutants from an agricultural, waste disposal, or spill site in a karst terrane? Proceedings of 2nd Multidis-ciplinary Conference on Sinkholes and Environmental Impacts of Karst, Florida Sinkhole Research Institute, Orlando, Florida, p. 277–286.

Quinlan, J.F., and J.A. Ray, 1981, Groundwater basins in the Mammoth Cave region, Kentucky: Mammoth Cave, Ky., Friends of Karst, Occasional Publication 1 (map).

Quinlan, J.F., J.A. Ray, and G.M. Schindel, 1995, Intrinsic limitations of standard criteria and methods for delineation of ground water-source protection areas (springhead and wellhead protection areas) in carbonate terrains: Critical review, technically-sound resolution of limitations, and case study in a Kentucky karst, *in* B.F. Beck (ed.), Karst geohazards: Engineering and environmental problems in karst terrain: Proceedings of 5th conference on Engineering and Environmental Impacts of Karst, Rotterdam, Netherlands, A.A. Balkema, p. 525–537.

Quinlan, J. F., and D.R. Rowe, 1978, Hydrology and water quality in the Central Kentucky Karst: Phase II, Part A: Preliminary summary of the hydrogeology of the Mill Hole sub-basin of the Turnhole Springs groundwater basin: Water Resources Research Institute, Report 109, University of Kentucky, Lexington, 42 p.

Raines, T. (ed.), 1968, Sótano de las Golondrinas: Association for Mexican Cave Studies, AMCS Bulletin 2, 20 p.

Ranney, W., 2004, Carving Grand Canyon: Evidence, theories, and mystery: Grand Canyon, Ariz., Grand Canyon Association, 160 p.

Rauch, H.W., and W.B. White, 1970, Lithologic controls on the development of solution porosity in carbonate aquifers: Water Resources Research, v. 6, p. 1175–1192.

Rauch, H.W., and W.B. White, 1977, Dissolution kinetics of carbonate rocks. 1. Effects of lithology on dissolution rate: Water Resources Research, v. 13, p. 381–394.

Ravbar, N., 2003, The earliest Chinese karstologist Xu Xiake: Acta Carsologica, v. 32, no. 1, p. 243–254.

Ray, J.A., 2005, Sinking streams and losing systems, *in* D.C. Culver and W.B. White (eds.), Encyclopedia of caves: San Diego, Elsevier / Academic Press, p. 509–514.

Ray, J.A., and P.W. O'Dell, 1993, Dispersion/velocity-related groundwater sensitivity, *in* B.F. Beck, Applied karst geology: Proceedings of 4th conference on engineering and environmental impacts of karst, Lisse, Netherlands, A.A. Balkema, p. 189–198.

Rea, G. T. (ed.), 1992, Caving basics (3rd ed.): Huntsville, Ala., National Speleological Society, 187 p.

Renault, P., 1970, La formation des cavernes [*Cave origin*]: Paris, Presses Universitaires de France, 127 p.

Rhoades, R., and M. Sinacori, 1941, Pattern of ground-water flow and solution: Journal of Geology, v. 49, p. 785–794.

Rhodes, D., E. Lantos, J. Lantos, R. Webb, and D. Owens, 1984, Pine Point orebodies and their relationship to the stratigraphy, structure, dolomitization, and karstification of the Middle Devonian barrier complex: Economic Geology, v. 79, p. 991–1055.

Richards, D.A., S.H. Bottrell, R.A. Cliff, and K.D. Stoehle, 1996, U-Pb dating of Quaternary age speleothems, *in* S.-E. Lauritzen (ed.), Climate change; the karst record: Charles Town, W.Va., Karst Waters Institute Special Publication 2 , p. 136–137.

Richardson, K., and P. Carling, 2005, A typology of sculpted forms in open bedrock channels: Geological Society of America, Special Paper 392, 108 p.

Riggs, A.C., W.J. Carr, P.T. Kolesar, and R.J. Hoffman, 1994, Tectonic speleogenesis of Devils Hole, Nevada, and implications for hydrogeology and the development of long, continuous paleoenvironmental records: Quaternary Research, v. 42, p. 241–254.

Roehl, P.O., and P.W. Choquette (eds.), 1985, Carbonate petroleum reservoirs: New York, Springer-Verlag, 622 p.

Rogers, B.W., 1981, Soil pipe caves in the Death Valley Region, California: Proceedings of 8th International Congress of Speleology, Bowling Green, Kentucky, p. 547–548.

Rogers, B.W., and P.H. Rice, 1992, Geology and mineralogy of lava tube caves in Medicine Lake Volcano, California: National Speleological Society, Proceedings of 6th International Symposium of Vulcanospeleology, 1991, Hilo, Hawai'i, p. 45–49.

Roques, H., 1962, Considérations théoretiques sur la chimie des carbonates [*Theoretical aspects of carbonate chemistry*]: Annales de Spéléologie, v. 7, p. 1–41, 241–284, 463–467.

Roques, H., 1964, Contributions a l'étude statique et cinétique des systèmes gaz carbonique-eau-carbonate [*Static and kinetic CO_2-water-carbonate systems*]: Annales de Spéléologie, v. 19, p. 255–484.

Rossi, G., and R. Zorzin, 1986, Underlining an interesting paleokarstic phenomenon in the Lessini (Prealpi Venete - Northern Italy): Proceedings of 9th International Congress of Speleology, Barcelona, Spain, v. 1, p. 290–293.

Rowling, J., 2003, Underwater helictites from the Nullarbor: Proceedings of 24th Biennial Speleological Conference, Northern Australian Speleological Federation, p. 86–93.

Roy, W.R., 1988, Preliminary assessment of the solution equilibria of Sulphur River, Parker Cave, Kentucky: National Speleological Society Bulletin, v. 50, no. 2, p. 37–41.

Rubin, P.A., 1991, Modification of preglacial caves by glacial meltwater invasion in east-central New York, *in* E.H. Kastning and K.M. Kastning (eds.), Appalachian karst: Proceedings of Appalachian Karst Symposium, Radford, Virginia, p. 91–99.

Rudnicki, J., 1989, Relation between natural convection and cave formation in hydrothermal karst: Proceedings of 10th International Congress of Speleology, Budapest, Hungary, p. 14–16.

Runnells, D.D., 1969, Diagenesis, chemical sediments, and the mixing of natural waters: Journal of Sedimentary Petrology, v. 39, p. 1188–1201.

Sando, W.J., 1988, Madison Limestone (Mississippian) paleokarst: A geologic synthesis, *in* N.P. James and P.W. Choquette (eds.), Paleokarst: New York, Springer-Verlag, p. 256–277.

Sangster, D.F. (ed.), 1996, Carbonate-hosted lead-zinc deposits: Society of Economic Geologists, Special Publication 4, 664 p.

Sarbu, S.M., T.C. Kane, and B.K. Kinkle, 1996, A chemoautotrophically based groundwater ecosystem: Science, v. 272, p. 1953–1955.

Sarbu, S., and C. Lascu, 1997, Condensation corrosion in Movile Cave, Romania: Journal of Cave and Karst Studies, v. 59, p. 99–102.

Sasowsky, I.D., 1998, Determining the age of what is not there: Science, v. 279, p. 1874.

Sasowsky, I.D., 2005, Paleomagnetic record in cave sediments, *in* D.C. Culver and W.B. White (eds.), Encyclopedia of caves: San Diego, Elsevier / Academic Press, p. 427–431.

Sasowsky, I.D., and C.T. Dalton, 2005, Measurement of pH for field studies in karst areas: Journal of Cave and Karst Studies, v. 67, no. 2, p. 127–132.

Sasowsky, I.D., and J.E. Mylroie (eds.), 2004, Studies of cave sediments: Physical and chemical records of paleoclimate: New York, Kluwer Academic / Plenum Publishers, 322 p.

Sasowsky, I.D., and M.V. Palmer (eds.), 1994, Breakthroughs in karst geomicrobiology and redox geochemistry: Charles Town, W.Va., Karst Waters Institute Special Publication 1, 111 p.

Sasowsky, I.D., and W.B. White, 1994, The role of stress release fracturing in the development of cavernous porosity in carbonate aquifers: Water Resources Research, v. 30, no. 12, p. 3523–3530.

Sasowsky, I.D., W.B. White, and V.A. Schmidt, 1995, Determination of stream-incision rate in the Appalachian plateaus by using cave-sediment magnetostratigraphy: Geology, v. 23, p. 415–418.

Sasowsky, I.D., and C.W. Wicks (eds.), 2000, Groundwater flow and contaminant transport in carbonate aquifers: Rotterdam, A.A. Balkema, 193 p.

Sass-Gustkiewicz, M., 1996, Internal sediments as a key to understanding the hydrothermal karst origin of the Upper Silesian Zn-Pb ore deposits: Society of Economic Geologists, Special Publication 4, p. 171–181.

Sass-Gustkiewicz, M., S. Dzulynski, and J. Ridge, 1982, The emplacement of zinc-lead sulfide ores in the Upper Silesian district — a contribution to the understanding of Mississippi Valley-Type deposits: Economic Geology, v. 77, p. 1057–1068.

Sauro, U., 2005, Closed depressions, *in* D.C. Culver and W.B. White (eds.), Encyclopedia of caves: San Diego, Elsevier / Academic Press, p. 108–122.

Sauter, M., 1992, Quantification and forecasting of regional groundwater flow and transport in a karst aquifer (Gallusquelle, Malm, SW Germany): University of Tübingen, Germany, Tübinger Geowissenschaftliche Arbeiten (TGA), 151 p.

Schindel, G.M., and S. Johnson, 2005, Tracer tests in the Edwards Aquifer recharge zone [abstract]: Geological Society of America, annual meeting, Abstracts with Programs, v. 37, p. 216.

Schindel, G. M., J.F. Quinlan, G. Davies, and J.A. Ray, 1997, Guidelines for wellhead and springhead protection area delineation in carbonate rocks: U.S. Environmental Protection Agency, Technical Report EPA/904/B-97/003.

Schmidt, V.A., 1974, The paleohydrology of Laurel Caverns, Pennsylvania: Proceedings of 4th Conference on Karst Geology and Hydrology, Morgantown, W. Va., West Virginia Geological and Economic Survey, p. 123–128.

Schmidt, V.A., 1982, Magnetostratigraphy of sediments in Mammoth Cave, Kentucky: Science, v. 217, p. 827–829.

Schoeller, H., 1962, Les eaux souterraines [*Underground water*]: Paris, Masson and Cie, 642 p.

Scholle, P.A., D.G. Bebout, and C.H. Moore (eds.), 1983, Carbonate depositional environments: Tulsa, Okla., American Association of Petroleum Geologists, Memoir 33, 708 p.

Scholle, P.A., and D.S. Ulmer-Scholle, 2003, A color guide to the petrography of carbonate rocks: Grains, textures, porosity, diagenesis: American Association of Petroleum Geologists, Memoir 77, 474 p.

Schwarcz, H.P., 1986, Geochronology and isotope geochemistry of speleothem, *in* J. Fontes and P. Fritz (eds.), Handbook of environmental isotope geochemistry: Amsterdam, Netherlands, Elsevier, p. 271–303.

Schwarcz, H.P., R.S. Harmon, P. Thompson, and D.C. Ford, 1976, Stable isotope studies of fluid inclusions in speleothems and their paleoclimatic significance: Geochimica et Cosmochimica Acta, v. 40, p. 657–665.

Šebela, S., 1998, Tectonic structure of Postojnska jama Cave System: Postjna, Slovenia, Inštitut za razusjivanje krasa ZRC SAZU, 112 p.

Self, C.A., and C.A. Hill, 2003, How speleothems grow: An introduction to the ontogeny of cave minerals: Journal of Cave and Karst Studies, v. 65, no. 2, p. 130–151.

Shaler, N.S., 1898, The work of underground water: Chapter 7 of Outlines of Earth's history: New York, D. Appleton, 417 p. (Available on line at *www.gutenberg.org*.)

Shaw, T.R., 1992, History of cave science: The exploration and study of limestone caves, to 1900 (2nd ed.): Sydney Speleological Society, Broadway, New South Wales, Australia, 338 p.

Shaw, T.R., 2000, Views on cave formation before 1900, *in* A. Klimchouk, D. Ford, A. Palmer, and W. Dreybrodt (eds.), Speleogenesis —evolution of karst aquifers: Huntsville, Ala., National Speleological Society, p. 21–29.

Shopov, Y.Y., 1997, Luminescence of cave minerals, *in* C.A. Hill and P. Forti, 1997, Cave minerals of the world (2nd ed.): Huntsville, Ala., National Speleological Society, p. 244–248.

Shopov, Y.Y. (ed.), 2004, Cave climate and paleoclimate, best record of the global change: Proceedings of International Workshop of IGCP 448 and the International Union of Speleology, International Journal of Speleology, v. 33, no. 1/4, 127 p.

Shopov, Y.Y., 2006, Speleothem luminescence—The past twenty years, *in* R.S. Harmon and C.M. Wicks (eds.), Perspectives on karst geomorphology, hydrology, and geochemistry—A tribute volume to Derek C. Ford and William B. White: Geological Society of America, Special Paper 404, p. 319–330.

Shopov, Y.Y., D.C. Ford, and H.P. Schwarcz, 1994, Luminescent microbanding in speleothems: High-resolution chronology and paleoclimate: Geology, v. 22, p. 407–410.

Short, M.B., J.C. Baygents, J.W. Beck, D.A. Stone, R.S. Toomey, and R.E. Goldstein, 2005, Stalactite growth as a free-boundary problem: A geometric law and its potential ideal: Physical Review Letters, v. 94, paper no. 018501, 4 p.

Shuster, E.T., and W.B. White, 1971, Seasonal fluctuations in the chemistry of limestone springs: A possible means for characterizing carbonate aquifers: Journal of Hydrology, v. 14, p. 93−128.

Shuster, D.L., T.A. Ehlers, M.E. Rusmoren, and K.A. Farley, 2005, Rapid glacial erosion at 1.8 Ma revealed by $^4He/^3He$ thermochronometry: Science, v. 310, p. 1668−1670.

Sides, S.D., and H. Meloy, 1971, The pursuit of health in the Mammoth Cave: Bulletin of the History of Medicine, v. 45, no. 4, p. 367−379.

Siemers, J., and W. Dreybrodt, 1998, Early development of karst aquifers in percolation networks of fractures in limestone: Water Resources Research, v. 34, p. 409−419.

Siemion, J., A. Palmer, and T. Kraemer, 2005, Use of quantitative dye tracing and water chemistry to characterize karst springs in the Helderberg Plateau, east-central New York [abstract]: Geological Society of America, Northeastern Section, annual meeting, abstracts with programs, v. 37, no. 1, p. 68.

Siemion, J., 2006, Use of isotopes, tracer tests, and dissolved solids to characterize a karst aquifer: M.A. thesis, State University of New York, Oneonta, N.Y., 49 p.

Silvestru, E., 1999, Perennial ice in caves in temperate climate and its significance: Theoretical and Applied Karstology (Romania), v. 11−12, p. 83−93.

Sippal, R.F., and E.D. Glover, 1964, The solution alteration of carbonate rocks: The effects of temperature and pressure: Geochimica et Cosmochimica Acta, v. 28, p. 1401−1417.

Sjöberg, E.L., and D.T. Rickard, 1984, Temperature dependence of calcite dissolution kinetics between 1 and 62°C at pH 2.7 to 8.4 in aqueous solutions: Geochimica et Cosmochimica Acta, v. 48, p. 485−493.

Sket, B., 2002, The evolution of the karst versus the distribution and diversity of the hypogean fauna, in F. Gabrovšek (ed.), Evolution of karst: From prekarst to cessation: Institute for Karst Research, ZRC SAZU, Postojna-Ljubljana, Slovenia, p. 225−232.

Skinner, C., 1983, Open vertical volcanic conduits: The structure and speleogenesis of an unusual volcanic cave form with examples from the Oregon High Cascades [abstract]: National Speleological Society Bulletin, v. 45, no. 1, insert.

Slabe, T., 1995, Cave rocky relief and its speleological significance: Ljubljana, Slovenia, Inštitut za razusjivanje krasa ZRC SAZU, 128 p.

Smart, C.C., 1981, Glacier-groundwater interaction: Proceedings of 8th International Congress of Speleology, Bowling Green, Ky., p. 720−723.

Smart, C.C., 1983, Hydrology of a glacierized alpine karst: Ph.D. thesis, McMaster University, Hamilton, Ontario, 343 p.

Smart, C.C., 1988, Artificial tracer techniques for the determination of the structure of conduit aquifers: Ground Water, v. 26, p. 445−453.

Smart, C.C., 1999, Subsidiary conduit systems: A hiatus in aquifer monitoring and modeling, in A.N. Palmer, M.V. Palmer, and I.D. Sasowsky (eds.), Karst Modeling: Charles Town, W.Va., Karst Waters Institute Special Publication 5, p. 146−157.

Smart, C.C., and W. Campbell, 2005, Speleogenesis in the Cumberland Plateau of northeastern Alabama [abstract]: National Speleological Society, Program of 2005 annual convention, Huntsville, Ala., p. 91.

Smart, C.C., and B. Simpson, 2001, An evaluation of the performance of activated charcoal in detection of fluorescent compounds in the environment, in B.F. Beck and J.G. Herring (eds.), Geotechnical and Environmental Applications of Karst Geology and Hydrology: Proceedings of 8th Multidisciplinary Conference on Sinkholes and the Engineering and Environmental Impacts of Karst, Lisse, Netherlands, A.A. Balkema, p. 265−270.

Smart, C.C., and S.R.H. Worthington, 2004, Springs, in J. Gunn (ed.), Encyclopedia of caves and karst science: New York, Fitzroy Dearborn, p. 699−703.

Smart, P.L., P.A. Beddows, J. Coke, S. Doerr, S. Smith, and F.F. Whitaker, 2006, Cave development on the Caribbean coast of the Yucatan Peninsula, Quintana Roo, Mexico, in R.S. Harmon and C.M. Wicks (eds.), Perspectives on karst geomorphology, hydrology, and geochemistry − A tribute volume to Derek C. Ford and William B. White: Geological Society of America,

Special Paper 404, p. 105−128.

Smart, P.L., P. Beddows, S. Doerr, S. Smith, and F. Whitaker, 2002, Hydrochemical processes and cave development, Caribbean coast, Yucatan Peninsula, Mexico, in J. Martin, C. Wicks, and I. Sasowsky, eds., Hydrogeology and biology of post-Paleozoic carbonate aquifers: Charles Town, W.Va., Karst Waters Institute, Special Publication 7, p. 70−83.

Smart, P.L., J.M. Dawans, and F. Whitaker, 1988, Carbonate dissolution in a modern mixing zone: Nature, v. 335, p. 811−813.

Smart, P.L., and H. Friederich, 1986, Water movement and storage in the unsaturated zone of a maturely karstified carbonate aquifer, Mendip Hills, England: Proceedings of First Conference on Environmental Problems in Karst Terranes and Their Solutions, Dublin, Ohio, National Water Well Association, p. 59−87.

Smart, P.L., and I.M.S. Laidlaw, 1977, An evaluation of some fluorescent dyes for water tracing: Water Resources Research, v. 13, p. 15−33.

Smith, D.I., and M.D. Newson, 1974, The dynamics of solutional and mechanical erosion in limestone catchments on the Mendip Hills, Somerset, in K.J. Gregory and D.E. Walling (eds.), Fluvial processes in instrumented watersheds: Institute of British Geographers, Special Publication 6, p. 155−167.

Smith, D.I., F.H. Nicholson, and C.J. High, 1969, Limestone solution and the caves, in E.K. Tratman (ed.), The caves of north-west Clare, Ireland: Newton Abbot, U.K., David and Charles, p. 96−123.

Smith, J.H., 1994, Hydrogeology of the Sistema Huautla karst groundwater basin, Sierra Mazateca, Oaxaca, Mexico: M.S. thesis, Western Kentucky University, Bowling Green, Ky., 338 p.

Smith, L.B. C.M. Lugert, and R.E. Nyahay, 2003, Integrated characterization of hydrothermal dolomite reservoirs in Trenton-Black River carbonates of New York [abstract]: Northeastern Science Foundation, Silver Jubilee Anniversary Symposium program with abstracts, p. 20−21.

Southam, G., and J.A. Saunders, 2005, The geomicrobiology of ore deposits: Economic Geology, v. 100, no. 6, p. 1067−1084.

Spangler, L.E., 1999, Delineation of source-protection zones for carbonate springs in the Bear River Range, northeastern Utah, in A.N. Palmer, M.V. Palmer, and I.D. Sasowsky (eds.), Karst modeling: Charles Town, W. Va., Karst Waters Institute, Special Publication 5, p. 230−232.

Sparrow, A., 1997, The complete caving manual: Ramsbury, U.K., Crowood Press, 192 p.

Spate, A.P., J.N. Jennings, D.I. Smith, and M.A. Greenaway, 1985, The micro-erosion meter: Use and limitations: Earth Surface Processes and Landforms, v. 10, p. 427−440.

Spilde, M.N., L. Crossey, T.P. Fischer, H.J. Turin, and P. J. Boston, 2005, Possible source of hydrogen sulfide gas in Cueva de Villa Luz, Tabasco, Mexico [abstract]: National Speleological Society, Program of 2005 annual convention, Huntsville, Ala., p. 80.

Spirakis, C.S., and A.V. Heyl, 1988, Possible effects of thermal degradation of organic matter on carbonate paragenesis and fluorite precipitation in Mississippi Valley-type deposits: Geology, v. 16, p. 1117−1120.

Spirakis, C.S., and A.V. Heyl, 1995, Interaction between thermally convecting basinal brines and organic matter in genesis of Upper Mississippi Valley zinc-lead district: Transactions of the Institution of Mining and Metallurgy, v. 104, p. B37−B45.

Springer, G.S., and J.S. Kite, 1997, River-derived slackwater sediments in caves along Cheat River, West Virginia: Geomorphology, v. 18, p. 91−100.

Springer, G.S., J.S. Kite, and V.A. Schmidt, 1997, Cave sedimentation, genesis, and erosional history in the Cheat River Canyon, West Virginia: Geological Society of America Bulletin, v. 109, no. 5, p. 524−532.

Springer, G.S., and E.E. Wohl, 2002, Empirical and theoretical investigation of sculpted forms in Buckeye Creek Cave, West Virginia: Journal of Geology, v. 110, p. 469−481.

Stanton, R.J., 1966, The solution brecciation process: Geological Society of America Bulletin, v. 77, p. 843−848.

Steele, C.W., and J.H. Smith, 2005, Sistema Huautla, Mexico, in D.C. Culver and W.B. White (eds.), Encyclopedia of caves: San Diego, Elsevier / Academic Press, p. 514–521.

Stefánsson, Á.B., 1992, Þríhnúkargígur: National Speleological Society, Proceedings of 6th International Symposium of Vulcanospeleology, 1991, Hilo, Hawai'i, p. 197–203.

Stern, L., A. Summers-Engel, P. Bennett, and M. Porter, 2002, Subaqueous and subaerial speleogenesis in a sulfidic cave, *in* J.B. Martin, C.M. Wicks, and I.D. Sasowsky (eds.), Hydrogeology and biology of post-Paleozoic carbonate aquifers: Charles Town, W. Va., Karst Waters Institute, Special Publication 7, p. 89–91.

Stierman, D.J., 2004, Geophysical detection of caves and karstic voids, *in* J. Gunn (ed.), Encyclopedia of caves and karst science: New York, Fitzroy Dearborn, p. 377–380.

Stock, G.M. (ed.), 2003, Tectonics, climate change, and landscape evolution in the southern Sierra Nevada, California: Friends of the Pleistocene, Pacific Cell, 2003 Field Trip Guidebook, Sequoia and Kings Canyon, 139 p.

Stock, G.M., C.A. Riihimaki, and R.S. Anderson, 2006, Age constraints on cave development and landscape evolution in the Bighorn Basin of Wyoming, USA: Journal of Cave and Karst Studies, v. 69, no. 2, p. 76–84.

Stone, R.W., 1953, Caves of Pennsylvania: National Speleological Society Bulletin, v. 15, 143 p.

Stone, W., 1995, History of Huautla exploration: Association for Mexican Cave Studies, AMCS Activities Newsletter 21, p. 17–30.

Stone, W., and B. am Ende, 1995, The 1994 San Agustín Expedition: Association for Mexican Cave Studies, AMCS Activities Newsletter 21, p. 44–64.

Stone, W., and B. am Ende, 2002, Beyond the deep: New York, Warner Books, 351 p.

Strahler, A.N., 1971, The earth sciences: New York, Harper and Row, 824 p.

Surdam, R., S. Boese, and L. Crossey, 1984, The chemistry of secondary porosity: American Association of Petroleum Geologists, Memoir 37, p. 127–149.

Surdam, R.C., Z.X. Jiao, and D.B. MacGowan, 1993, Redox reactions involving hydrocarbons and mineral oxidants: A mechanism for significant porosity enhancement in sandstones: American Association of Petroleum Geologists Bulletin, v. 77, no. 9, p. 1509–1518.

Šušteršič, F., 1984, A simple model of the collapse doline transformation: Acta Carsologica, v. 12, p. 107–138.

Šušteršič, F., 2000, Speleogenesis in the Ljubljanica River drainage basin, Slovenia, *in* A. Klimchouk, D. Ford, A. Palmer, and W. Dreybrodt (eds.), Speleogenesis –evolution of karst aquifers: Huntsville, Ala., National Speleological Society, p. 397–406.

Šušteršič, F., 2006, Relationships between deflector faults, collapse dolines and collector channel formation: Some examples from Slovenia: International Journal of Speleology, v. 35, no. 1, p. 1–12.

Svensson, U., and W. Dreybrodt, 1992, Dissolution kinetics of natural calcite minerals in CO_2-water systems approaching calcite equilibrium: Chemical Geology, v. 100, p. 129–145.

Sweeting, M.M., 1950, Erosion cycles and limestone caverns in the Ingleborough District of Yorkshire: Geographical Journal, v. 124, p. 63–78.

Sweeting, M.M., 1995, Karst in China: Its geomorphology and environment: Berlin, Springer Verlag, 265 p.

Swinnerton, A.C., 1932, Origin of limestone caverns: Geological Society of America Bulletin, v. 43, p. 662–693.

Szabo, B.J., P.T. Kolesar, A.C. Riggs, I.J. Winograd, and K.R. Ludwig, 1994, Paleoclimatic influences from a 120,000-yr calcite record of water-table fluctuation in Browns Room of Devils Hole, Nevada: Quaternary Research, v. 41, p. 59–69.

Szukalski, B.W. (ed.), 2002, Cave and karst GIS: Journal of Cave and Karst Studies, v. 64, no. 3, 91 p.

Taboroši, D., and K. Hirakawa, 2003, Microclimate controls of vadose carbonate precipitation: Evidence from stalactite morphology: Theoretical and Applied Karstology (Romania), v. 16, p. 25–40.

Taboroši, D., K. Hirakawa, and T. Sawagaki, 2005, Carbonate precipitation along a microclimatic gradient in a Thailand cave — continuum of calcareous tufa and speleothems: Journal of Cave and Karst Studies, v. 67, no. 1, p. 69–87.

Takácsné Bolner, K.,, 1989, Regional and special genetic marks on the Pál-völgy Cave, the largest cave of thermal water origin in Hungary: Proceedings of 10th International Congress of Speleology, Budapest, Hungary, p. 819–822.

Takácsné Bolner, K., and S. Kraus, 1989, The results of research into caves of thermal water origin: Karszt és Barlang, Hungarian Speleological Society Bulletin, special issue for 10th International Congress of Speleology, p. 31–38.

Tarhule-Lips, R., and D.C. Ford, 1998, Bell hole development on Cayman Brac based on morphology: Cave and Karst Science, v. 25, no. 3, p. 119–130.

Tásler, R., V. Cílek, and H. Hercman, 2001, Speleothem decoration of giant domes in Bohemia Cave (New Zealand: Cave and Karst Science, v. 28, no. 3, p. 113–120.

Taylor, M.R., 1999, Dark Life: New York, Scribner, 287 p.

Taylor, M.R., and U. Widmer (eds.), 1991, Lechuguilla — Jewel of the Underground: Basel, Switzerland, Speleo Projects, 144 p.

Taylor, P.M., 2000, Calcite deposition from high-sulfate springs, Van Hornesville, New York: M.A. thesis, State University of New York, Oneonta, N.Y., 121 p.

Terjesen, S., O. Erga, and A. Ve, 1961, Phase boundary processes as rate determining steps in reactions between solids and liquids: Chemical Engineering Science, v. 74, p. 277–288.

Terrell, L., A. Palmer, and T. Kraemer, 2005, Chemistry of sulfide-rich karst springs in Otsego and Schoharie Counties, New York [abstract]: Geological Society of America, Northeastern Section, annual meeting, abstracts with programs, v. 37, no. 1, p. 69.

Ţenu, A., and F. Davidescu, 1995, Environmental isotopic studies in karstic calcareous areas of Romania: Theoretical and Applied Karstology (Romania), v. 8, p. 9–24.

Teutsch, G., and M. Sauter, 1991, Groundwater modeling in karst terranes: Scale effects, data acquisition and field observations: Proceedings of Third Conference on Hydrogeology, Ecology, Monitoring, and Management of Ground Water in Karst Terranes, Nashville, Tennessee, National Ground Water Association, p. 17–34.

Thayer, C.W., 1967, Mud stalagmites and the conulite: National Speleological Society Bulletin, v. 29, no. 3, p. 91–95.

Thompson, D.B., and R.A. Olson, 1988, A preliminary survey of the protozoa and bacteria from Sulphur River, in Parkers Cave, Kentucky: National Speleological Society Bulletin, v. 50, no. 2, p. 42–46.

Thompson, J., and M. Marvin, 2005, Experimental research on the use of thermography to locate heat signatures from caves: Huntsville, Ala., National Speleological Society, Proceedings of 17th National Cave and Karst Management Symposium, Albany, NY, p. 102–115.

Thompson, N., and J. Van Swearingen (eds.), 2005, On caves and cameras: Huntsville, AL, National Speleological Society, 336 p.

Thompson, P., 1976, Cave exploration in Canada: Edmonton, Alberta, special issue of Canadian Caver, 183 p.

Thompson, P., H.P. Schwarcz, and D.C. Ford, 1976, Stable isotope geochemistry, geothermometry, and geochronology of speleothems from West Virginia: Geological Society of America Bulletin, v. 87, p. 1730–1738.

Thornbury, W.D., 1965, Regional Geomorphology of the United States: New York, Wiley, 609 p.

Thrailkill, J.V., 1968, Chemical and hydrologic factors in the excavation of limestone caves: Geological Society of America Bulletin, v. 79, p. 19–46.

Thrailkill, J.V., 1971, Carbonate deposition in Carlsbad Caverns: Journal of Geology, v. 79, p. 683–695.

Thrailkill, J.V., and T.L. Robl, 1981, Carbonate geochemistry of vadose water recharging limestone aquifers: Journal of Hydrology, v. 54, p. 195–208.

Trombe, F., 1952, Traité de Spéléologie [*A treatise on speleology*]: Paris, Payot, 376 p.

Troutman, T., 2004, Reservoir characterization, paleogeomorphology, and genesis of the Mississippian Redwall Limestone paleokarst, Hualapai Indian Reservation, Grand Canyon area, Arizona, U.S.A.: M.S. thesis, University of Texas, Austin, Texas, 221 p.

Trudgill, S., 1976, Limestone erosion under soil: Proceedings of 6th International Congress of Speleology, Prague, Academia Press, p. 409–422.

Trudgill, S., 1985, Limestone geomorphology: New York, Longman Group, Ltd., 196 p.

Tsykin, R.A., 1989, Paleokarst of the U.S.S.R., *in* P. Bosák, D. Ford, J. Glazek, and I. Horáček (eds.), Paleokarst: Prague and Amsterdam, Academia and Elsevier, p 253–295.

Tucker, M.E., and V.P. Wright, 1990, Carbonate Sedimentology: London, Blackwell, 482 p.

Tullis, E.L., and J.P. Gries, 1938, Black Hills caves: Black Hills Engineer, v. 24, p. 233–271.

Turcotte, D.L., and G. Schubert, 1982, Geodynamics: New York, Wiley, 450 p.

Turin, H.J., and M.A. Plummer, 1995, Tritium in Lechuguilla Cave pool water: Implications for recharge processes [abstract]: Geological Society of America Abstracts with Programs, v. 27, no. 6, p. 95.

Urbani, F., 2005, Quartzite caves: The Venezuelan perspective: National Speleological Society, National Speleological Society News, v. 63, no. 7, p. 20–21.

Vacher, H.L., 1988, Depuit-Ghyben-Herzberg analysis of strip-island lenses: Geological Society of America Bulletin, v. 100, p. 580–591.

Vacher, H.L., and T.M. Quinn (eds.), 1997, Geology and hydrogeology of carbonate islands: Amsterdam, Elsevier, 948 p.

Vacher, H.L., and J.E. Mylroie, 2002, Eogenetic karst from the perspective of an equivalent porous medium: Carbonates and Evaporites, v. 17, no. 2, p. 182–196.

Valvasor, J.W., 1689, Die Ehre dess Hertzogthums Crain [*The glory of the Duchy of Carniola (formerly of Austria, now Slovenia)*]: Endter, Laibach (Ljubljana), 2872 folio pages in 4 vols.

Van Beynen, P.E., H.P. Schwarcz, and D.C. Ford, 2004, Holocene climatic variation recorded in a speleothem from McFail's Cave, New York: Journal of Cave and Karst Studies, v. 66, no. 1, p. 20–27.

Varnedoe, W.W., 1964, The formation of an extensive maze cave in Alabama: Alabama Academy of Science Journal, v. 35, no. 4, p. 143–148.

Varnedoe, W.W., 1973, Alabama caves and caverns: Huntsville, Alabama, National Speleological Society, 1375 p.

Vaughan, K., 1998, A quantitative analysis of interstitial fluid chemistry and limestone dissolution rates within the clastic sediment of a karst aquifer conduit, Mammoth Cave, KY: M.S. thesis, Western Kentucky University, Bowling Green, Ky., 128 p.

Vearncombe, J., A. Chisnall, M. Dentith, S. Dörling, M. Rayner, and P. Holyland, 1996, Structural controls on Mississippi Valley-Type mineralization, the southeast Lennard Shelf, western Australia, *in* D.F. Sangster (ed.), Carbonate-hosted lead-zinc deposits: Society of Economic Geologists, Special Publication 4, p. 74–95.

Veni, G., 2004, Environmental impacts assessments, *in* J. Gunn (ed.), Encyclopedia of caves and karst science: New York, Fitzroy Dearborn, p. 319–321.

Veni, G., and N.C. Crawford, 1986, Origins of water-spouts in karst regions: National Speleological Society Bulletin, v. 48, no. 2, p. 43–53.

Veni, G., H. DuChene, N. Crawford, C. Groves, G. Huppert, E. Kastning, R. Olson, and B. Wheeler, 2001, Living with karst: Alexandria, Va., American Geological Institute, Environmental Awareness Series, no. 4, 65 p.

Verrecchia, E., and K. Verrecchia (1994), Needle-fiber calcite: a critical review and a proposed classification: Journal of Sedimentary Research, v. A64, p. 650–664.

Vesica, P.L., P. Tuccimei, B. Turi, J.J. Fornós, A. Ginés, and J. Ginés, 2000, Late Pleistocene paleoclimates and sea-level change in the Mediterranean as inferred from stable isotope and U-series studies of overgrowths on speleothems, Mallorca, Spain: Quaternary Science Reviews, v. 19, p. 685–679.

Vesper, D.J., 2005, Contamination of cave waters by heavy metals, *in* D.C. Culver, and W.B. White (eds.), Encyclopedia of caves: San Diego, Elsevier / Academic Press, p. 127–131.

Vesper, D.J., and W.B. White, 2006, Comparative storm response of contaminants

in a carbonate aquifer, Fort Campbell, Kentucky-Tennessee, *in* R.S. Harmon and C.M. Wicks (eds.), Perspectives on karst geomorphology, hydrology, and geochemistry — A tribute volume to Derek C. Ford and William B. White: Geological Society of America, Special Paper 404, p. 267–274.

Viles, H.A., 1984, Biokarst: Review and prospect: Progress in Physical Geography, v. 8, no. 4, p. 523–542.

Vlasceanu, L., S.M. Sarbu, A.S. Engel, and B.K. Kinkle, 2000, Acidic cave-wall biofilms located in the Frasassi Gorge, Italy: Geomicrobiology Journal, v. 17, p. 125–139.

Von Knebel, W., 1906, Cave Science with consideration of karst phenomena: Sammlung Naturwissenschaftlicher und Mathematischer Monographien, Heft 15: Druck und Verlag von Friedrich Vieweg und Sohn, Braunschweig. Partial translation in Cave Geology, National Speleological Society Section on Cave Geology and Geography, v. 1, p. 139–162.

Walck, C., 2005, Observations on halite cave geomorphology: National Speleological Society, NSS News, v. 63, no. 11, p. 20–21.

Walker, R.T., 1928, Deposition of ore in pre-existing limestone caves: American Institute of Mining and Metallurgy Engineering, Technical Publication 154, 43 p.

Waltham, A.C., 1970, Cave development in limestone of the Ingleborough District: Geographical Journal, v. 136, p. 19–46.

Waltham, A.C., 1974a, Caves: New York, Crown Publishers, 240 p.

Waltham, A.C. (ed.), 1974b, The limestones and caves of north-west England: Newton Abbot, U.K., David and Charles, 477 p.

Waltham, A.C., 2005, Tiankengs of the world, outside China: Cave and Karst Science, v. 32, no. 2–3, p. 67–74.

Waltham, A.C., F. Bell, and M. Culshaw, 2005, Sinkholes and subsidence: Karst and cavernous rocks in engineering and construction: Chichester, U.K., Springer-Praxis, 382 p.

Warild, A., 1994, Vertical (3rd ed.): Broadway, Australia, Speleological Research Council, Ltd., 128 p.

Warwick, G.T., 1968, Some primitive features in British caves: Proceedings of 4th International Congress of Speleology, Ljubljana, Slovenia, p. 239–252.

Watson, P.J. (ed.), 1998, Archeology of the Mammoth Cave area: Dayton, Ohio, Cave Books, 255 p

Watson, R.A., and W.B. White, 1985, The history of American theories of cave origin: Geological Society of America Centennial, Special Volume 1, p. 109–123.

Webb, J.A., 1997, Skipton Lava Cave, Victoria, Australia, *in* C.A. Hill and P. Forti, 1997, Cave minerals of the world (2nd ed.): Huntsville, Ala., National Speleological Society, p. 331–335.

Weller, J.M., 1927, Geology of Edmonson County [Kentucky]: Kentucky Geological Survey, Series 6, v. 28, 246 p.

Wells, J., and J. Borden, 2005, Perching layers, vadose tubes, and exploration in Mammoth Cave, Kentucky [abstract]: National Speleological Society, Program of 2005 annual convention, Huntsville, Ala., p. 90.

Wenrich, K.J., 1985, Mineralization of breccia pipes in northern Arizona: Economic Geology, v. 80, p. 1722–1735.

Wentworth, C.K., and G.A. MacDonald, 1953, Structures and forms of basaltic rocks in Hawaii: U.S. Geological Survey Bulletin, v. 994, 98 p.

Werner, E., 1972, Effects of small thrusts on cave passage cross section: National Speleological Society Bulletin, v. 34, no. 4, p. 143–147.

Werner, M.S., and C. Werner, 1992, Impact of Richter 6.1 temblor upon Malama Cave, Puna District, Hawaii: An insider's view: Huntsville, Ala., National Speleological Society, Proceedings of 6th International Symposium on Vulcanospeleology, Hilo, Hawaii (1991), p. 27–28.

Weyl, P.K., 1958, The solution kinetics of calcite: Journal of Geology, v. 66, p. 163–176.

Whitaker, F.F., and P.L. Smart, 1994, Bacterially-mediated oxidation of organic matter: A major control on groundwater geochemistry and porosity generation in oceanic carbonate terrains, *in* I.D. Sasowsky and M.V. Palmer (eds.), Breakthroughs in karst geomicrobiology and redox geochemistry: Charles

Town, W. Va., Karst Waters Institute, Special Publication 1, p. 72–74.

White, E.L., and W.B. White, 1968, Dynamics of sediment transport in limestone caves: National Speleological Society Bulletin, v. 30, no. 4, p. 115–129.

White, E.L., and W.B White, 1969, Processes of cavern breakdown: National Speleological Society Bulletin, v. 31, no. 4, p. 83–96.

White, S., 1994, Speleogenesis in eolian calcarenite: A case study in western Victoria: Environmental Geology, v. 23, p. 248–255.

White, W.B., 1960, Terminations of passages in Appalachian caves as evidence for a shallow phreatic origin: National Speleological Society Bulletin, v. 22, no. 1, p. 43–53.

White, W.B., 1969, Conceptual models of carbonate aquifers: Ground Water, v. 7, no. 3, p. 15–21.

White, W.B., 1976, The caves of western Pennsylvania: Pennsylvania Geological Survey, General Geology Report 67, 98 p.

White, W.B., 1977a, Role of solution kinetics in the development of karst aquifers, *in* J.S. Tolson and F.L. Doyle (eds.), Karst hydrogeology: International Association of Hydrogeologists, 12th Memoirs, p. 503–517.

White, W.B., 1977b, Conceptual models of carbonate aquifers, revisited, *in* R.R. Dilamarter and S.C. Csallany (eds.), Hydrologic problems in karst regions: Bowling Green, Ky., Western Kentucky University, p. 176–187.

White, W.B., 1981, Reflectance spectra and color in speleothems: National Speleological Society Bulletin, v. 43, p. 20–26.

White, W.B., 1984, Rate processes: Chemical kinetics and karst landform development, *in* R.G. LaFleur (ed.), Groundwater as a geomorphic agent: Boston, Allen and Unwin, p. 227–248.

White, W.B., 1988, Geomorphology and hydrology of karst terrains: New York, Oxford University Press, 464 p.

White, W.B., 1994, The anthodites from Skyline Caverns, Virginia: the type locality: National Speleological Society Bulletin, v. 56, no. 1, p. 23–26.

White, W.B., 1997, Thermodynamic equilibrium, kinetics, activation barriers, and reaction mechanisms for chemical reactions in karst terrains: Environmental Geology, v. 30, p. 46–58.

White, W.B., 2000, Development of speleogenetic ideas in the 20th century: The modern period, 1957 to the present, *in* A. Klimchouk, D.C. Ford, A.N. Palmer, and W. Dreybrodt (eds.), Speleogenesis: Evolution of karst aquifers: Huntsville, Ala., National Speleological Society, p. 39–43.

White, W.B., 2004a, Paleoclimate records from speleothems in limestone caves, *in* I.D. Sasowsky and J.E. Mylroie (eds.), Studies of cave sediments: Physical and chemical records of paleoclimate: New York, Kluwer Academic / Plenum Publishers, p. 135–175.

White W.B., 2004b, Manganese oxide minerals in caves; microbially driven heavy metal scavengers [abstract]: Geological Society of America annual meeting, abstracts with programs, v. 36, no. 5, p. 258.

White, W.B., 2006, Identification of cave minerals by Raman spectroscopy: New technology for non-destructive analysis: International Journal of Speleology, v. 35, no. 2, p. 103–107.

White, W.B., and G.H. Deike, 1989, Hydraulic geometry of cave passages, *in* W.B. White and E.L. White (eds.), Karst hydrology: Concepts from the Mammoth Cave region: New York, Van Nostrand Reinhold, p. 223–258.

White, W.B., and J.W. Hess, 1982, Geomorphology of Burnsville Cove and the geology of the Butler Cave - Sinking Creek System: National Speleological Society Bulletin, v. 44, no. 3, p. 67–77.

White, W.B., and J. Longyear, 1962, Some limitations on speleogenetic speculation imposed by the hydraulics of groundwater flow in limestone: National Speleological Society, Nittany Grotto Newsletter, vol. 10, no 9, p. 155–167.

White, W.B., and E.L. White, 1974, Base-level control of underground drainage in the Potomac River Basin: Proceedings of 4th Conference on Karst Geology and Hydrology, Morgantown, W. Va., West Virginia Geological and Economic Survey, p. 41–53.

White, W.B., and E.L. White (eds.), 1989, Karst hydrology: Concepts from the Mammoth Cave region: New York, Van Nostrand Reinhold, 346 p.

White, W.B., and E.L. White, 1995, Correlation of contemporary karst landforms with paleokarst landforms: The problem of scale: Carbonates and

Evaporites, v. 10, no. 2, p. 131–137.

White, W.B., and E.L. White, 2001, Conduit fragmentation, cave patterns, and the localization of karst groundwater basins: The Appalachians as a test case: Theoretical and Applied Karstology, v. 13–14, p. 9–23.

White, W.B., and E.L. White, 2003, Gypsum wedging and cavern breakdown: Studies in the Mammoth Cave System, Kentucky: Journal of Cave and Karst Science, v. 65, no. 1, p. 43–52.

Wicks, C.M., 2005, Modeling karst aquifers, *in* D.C. Culver and W.B. White (eds.), Encyclopedia of caves: San Diego, Elsevier / Academic Press, p. 378–382.

Wigley, T.M.L., 1975, Speleogenesis: A fundamental approach: Proceedings of 6th International Congress of Speleology, Oloumec, Czech Republic, v. 3, p. 317–324.

Wigley, T.M.L., and M.C. Brown, 1976, The physics of caves, *in* T.D. Ford and C.H.D. Cullingford (eds.), The science of speleology: London, Academic Press, p. 329–358.

Wigley, T.M.L., and L.N. , 1976, Mixing of carbonate waters: Geochimica et Cosmochimica Acta, v. 40, p. 989–995.

Wilcock, J.D., 2002, The science of dowsing for caves: British Cave Research Association, Caves and Caving, v. 92, p. 33–37.

Williams, P.W., 1977, Hydrology of the Waikoropupu Springs: A major tidal karst resurgence in northwest Nelson (New Zealand): Journal of Hydrology, v. 35, p. 73–92.

Williams, P.W., 1983, The role of the subcutaneous zone in karst hydrology: Journal of Hydrology, v. 61, p. 45–67.

Williams, P.W., 1985, Subcutaneous hydrology and the development of doline and cockpit karst: Zeitschrift für Geomorphologie, v. 29, p. 463–482.

Williams, P.W. (ed.), 1997, Tropical and subtropical karst: Essays dedicated to the memory of Dr. Marjorie Sweeting: Zeitschrift für Geomorphologie, supplementary volume, 107 p.

Wilson, W.L., 1995, Sinkhole and buried sinkhole densities and new sinkhole frequencies in karsts of northwest peninsular Florida: Proceedings of 5th Multidisciplinary Conference on Sinkholes and the Engineering and Environmental Impacts of Karst, Rotterdam, A,.A. Balkema, 16 p.

Wilson, W.L., 2002, Conduit morphology and hydrodynamics of the Floridan Aquifer: Moving to the next level — conduit modeling, *in* J.B. Martin, C.M. Wicks, and I.D. Sasowsky (eds.), Hydrogeology and biology of post-Paleozoic carbonate aquifers: Charles Town, W. Va., Karst Waters Institute, Special Publication 7, p. 5–8.

Winograd, I.J., T.B. Coplen, J.M. Landwehr, A.C. Riggs, K.R. Ludwig, B.J. Szabo, P.T. Kolesar, and K.M. Revesz, 1992, Continuous 500,000-year climate record from vein calcite in Devil's Hole, Nevada: Science, v. 258, p. 255–260.

Winograd, I.J., and F.N. Robertson, 1982, Deep oxygenated ground water: Anomaly or common occurrence? Science, v. 216, p. 1227–1230.

Winograd, I.J., and B.J. Szabo, 1988, Water-table decline in the south-central Great Basin during the Quaternary: Implications for toxic waste disposal, *in* M.D. Carr and J.C. Younts (eds.), Geologic and hydrologic investigations of a potential nuclear waste disposal site at Yucca Mountain, southern Nevada: U.S. Geological Survey Bulletin 1790, p. 147–152.

Wood, C., 1974, The genesis and classification of lava tube caves: Transactions of British Cave Research Association, v. 1, p. 15–28.

Wood, C., 1976, Caves in rocks of volcanic origin, *in* T.D. Ford and C.H.D. Cullingford (eds.), The science of speleology: London, Academic Press, p. 127–150.

Wood, C., 1981, Exploration and geology of some lava tube caves on the Hawaiian volcanoes: Transactions of British Cave Research Association, v. 8, no. 3, p. 111–129.

Wood, J.R., 1986, Thermal mass transfer in systems containing quartz and calcite, *in* D.L. Gautier (ed.), Roles of organic matter in sediment diagenesis: Society of Economic Paleontologists and Mineralogists, Special Publication 38, p. 169–180.

Wood, W.W., and M.J. Petraitis, 1984, Origin and distribution of carbon dioxide in the unsaturated zone of the southern High Plains: Water Resources

Research, v. 20, p. 1193–1208.

Woodell, P.A., 2004, Hydraulic interpretation of limestone solution conduits from dye tracing and flow analysis, Schoharie County, New York: M.A. thesis, State University of New York, Oneonta, N.Y., 74 p.

Woods, J.C., 2004, On three! An introduction to digital photography for cavers: CD-ROM available through Descent Magazine, *www.caving.uk.com*.

Woodward, H.P., 1961, A stream piracy theory of cave formation: National Speleological Society Bulletin, v. 23, p. 39–58.

Worthington, S.R.H., 1984, The paleodrainage of an Appalachian fluviokarst: Friars Hole, West Virginia: M.S. thesis, McMaster University, Hamilton, Ontario, Canada, 218 p.

Worthington, S.R.H., 1991, Karst hydrogeology of the Canadian Rocky Mountains: Ph.D. thesis, McMaster University, Hamilton, Ontario, Canada, 227 p.

Worthington, S.R.H., 1994, The possible importance of sulfur minerals in initiating epigenic caves [abstract], *in* I.D. Sasowsky and M.V. Palmer (eds.), Breakthroughs in karst geomicrobiology and redox geochemistry: Charles Town, W. Va., Karst Waters Institute, Special Publication 1, p. 80–82.

Worthington, S.R.H., 1999, A comprehensive strategy for understanding flow in carbonate rocks, *in* A.N. Palmer, M.V. Palmer, and I.D. Sasowsky (eds.), Karst Modeling: Charles Town, W. Va., Karst Waters Institute, Special Publication 5, p. 30–37.

Worthington, S.R.H., 2001, Depth of conduit flow in unconfined carbonate aquifers: Geology, v. 29, p.335–338.

Worthington, S.R.H., 2004, Hydraulic and geological factors influencing conduit flow depth: Cave and Karst Science, v. 31, no. 3, p. 123–134.

Worthington, S.R.H., 2005, Evolution of caves in response to base-level lowering: Cave and Karst Science, v. 32, no. 1, p. 3–12.

Worthington, S.R.H., and D.M. Medville, 2005, Friars Hole Cave System, West Virginia, *in* D.C. Culver and W.B. White (eds.), Encyclopedia of caves: San Diego, Elsevier / Academic Press, p. 264–270.

Worthington, S.R.H., G.M. Schindel, and E.C. Alexander, 2002, Techniques for investigating the extent of karstification in the Edwards Aquifer, Texas, *in* J.B. Martin, C.M. Wicks, and I.D. Sasowsky (eds.), Hydrogeology and biology of post-Paleozoic carbonate aquifers: Charles Town, W.Va., Karst Waters Institute, Special Publication 7, p. 173–175.

Worthington, S.R.H., and C.C. Smart, 2003, Empirical determination of tracer mass for sink to spring tests in karst, *in* B.F. Beck (ed.), Sinkholes and the Engineering and Environmental Impacts of Karst: American Society of Civil Engineers, Geotechnical Special Publication No. 122, p. 287–295.

Worthington, S.R.H., and C.C. Smart, 2004, Groundwater in karst: Mathematical models, *in* J. Gunn (ed.), Encyclopedia of caves and karst science: New York, Fitzroy Dearborn, p. 401–403.

Worthington, S.R.H., Smart, C.C., and Ruland, W.W., 2003, Assessment of groundwater velocities to the municipal wells at Walkerton, Proceedings of the 2002 Joint annual conference of the Canadian Geotechnical Society and the Canadian chapter of the International Association of Hydrogeologists, Niagara Falls, Ontario, p. 1081–1086.

Wray, R.A.L., 1997, Quartzite dissolution: Karst or pseudokarst? Cave and Karst Science, v. 24, no. 2, p. 81–86.

Wright, H.E., 1989, The Quaternary, *in* A.W. Bally and A.R. Palmer (eds.), The geology of North America; an overview: Boulder, Colorado, Geological Society of America, The geology of North America, volume A, p. 513–536.

Wright, T.L., and R.T. Okamura, 1977, Cooling and crystallization of tholeiitic basalt, 1965, Makopuhi Lava Lake, Hawaii: U.S. Geological Survey Professional Paper 1004, 78 p.

Wright V.P., M. Esteban, and P.L. Smart (eds.), 1991, Palaeokarsts and palaeokarstic reservoirs: University of Reading, U.K., Postgraduate Research Institute for Sedimentology, Occasional Publication Series 2, 158 p.

Yonge, C.J., 1981, Fluid inclusions in speleothem as paleoclimate indicators: Proceedings of 8th International Congress of Speleology, Bowling Green, Kentucky, v. 1, p. 301–304.

Yonge, C.J., 2004, Ice in caves, *in* J. Gunn (ed.), Encyclopedia of caves and karst science: New York, Fitzroy Dearborn, p. 435–437.

Yuan D. (ed.), 1991, Karst of China: Beijing, Geological Publishing House, 224 p.

Zhang Z., 1980, Karst types in China: Geographical Journal, v. 4.6, p. 541–570.

Zhu X. and Chen W., 2005, Tiankengs in the karst of China: Cave and Karst Science, v. 32, no. 2–3, p. 55–66.

Zhu X. and Zhang Y., 1995, The world's largest dolines and Great Crack Gorge in southern Sichuan: Carsologica Sinica, v. 14 (supplement), p. 1–11.

Zötl, J.G., 1961, Die Hydrographie des nordostalpinen Karstes [*Karst hydrology of the northeastern Alps*]: Steirisches Beitrag zur Hydrogeologie, 1960–1961, p. 54–183.

Zupan-Hajna, N., 2003, Incomplete solution: Weathering of cave walls and the production, transport, and deposition of carbonate fines: Postojna, Slovenia, Inštitut za razusjivanje krasa ZRC SAZU, 167 p.

Index

Bold = major reference to the subject, or illustrated with a figure.

Conversion of units

Nearly all scientific measurements are made in metric units (International System). The United States is the only major country that has not adopted the metric system as its national standard.

Unit conversions:

to convert	into	multiply by	to convert	into	multiply by
feet	meters	0.3048	meters	feet	3.281
inches	centimeters	2.540	centmeters	inches	0.3937
miles	kilometers	1.609	kilometers	miles	0.6214
cubic feet	liters	28.32	liters	cubic feet	0.03531
cubic feet/sec	cubic meters/sec	0.02832	cubic meters/sec	cubic feet/sec	35.31
gallons	liters	3.785	liters	gallons	0.2642
gallons/min	liters/sec	0.06308	liters/sec	gallons/min	15.85
grams	ounces	0.3215	ounces	grams	28.35
pounds (mass)	kilograms	0.4535	kilograms	pounds	2.205
pounds (force)	dynes	4.448×10^5	dynes	pounds	2.248×10^{-6}

1 meter = 100 centimeters = 1000 millimeters   1 millimeter = 1000 micrometers (microns), μm

Exact lengths:

1 inch

1 cm

Visual comparisons:

Golden Gate Bridge

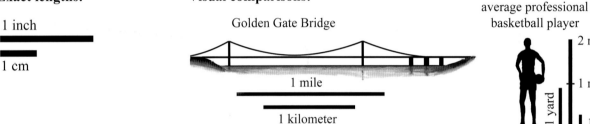

1 mile

1 kilometer

average professional
basketball player

2 meters

1 meter

1 yard

1 foot

Quick length conversions (only 1.6% error):

To convert **feet** to **meters**, multiply feet by 3 and move the decimal point one digit to left.
    Example: 150 ft x 3 = 450 ⟶ 45 m (actually 45.7 m)
To convert **meters** to **feet**, divide by 3 and move the decimal point one digit to right.
    Example: 12 m / 3 = 4 ⟶ 40 ft (actually 39.4 ft)

Volume and mass:

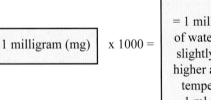

1 milligram (mg)   x 1000 =

1 gram

= 1 milliliter (ml) of water (at 4°C; slightly more at higher and lower temperatures)
1 ml = 1 cm³

x 1000 =

1 kilogram (kg)

= 1 liter of water at 4°C
= 1000 cm³

x 1000 =

1 metric ton (1000 kg) of water

= 1 cubic meter (10^6 cm³)

Temperature:

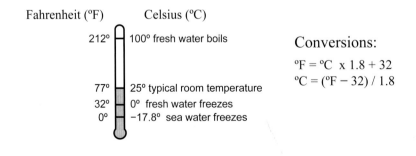

Fahrenheit (°F)   Celsius (°C)

212°   100° fresh water boils

77°   25° typical room temperature
32°   0° fresh water freezes
0°   −17.8° sea water freezes

Conversions:

°F = °C x 1.8 + 32
°C = (°F − 32) / 1.8